S0-BEB-785

Education Resource Center
University of Delaware
Newark, DE 19716-2940

Orlando • Austin • New York • San Diego • Toronto • London

Visit *The Learning Site!*
www.harcourtschool.com

T 41682

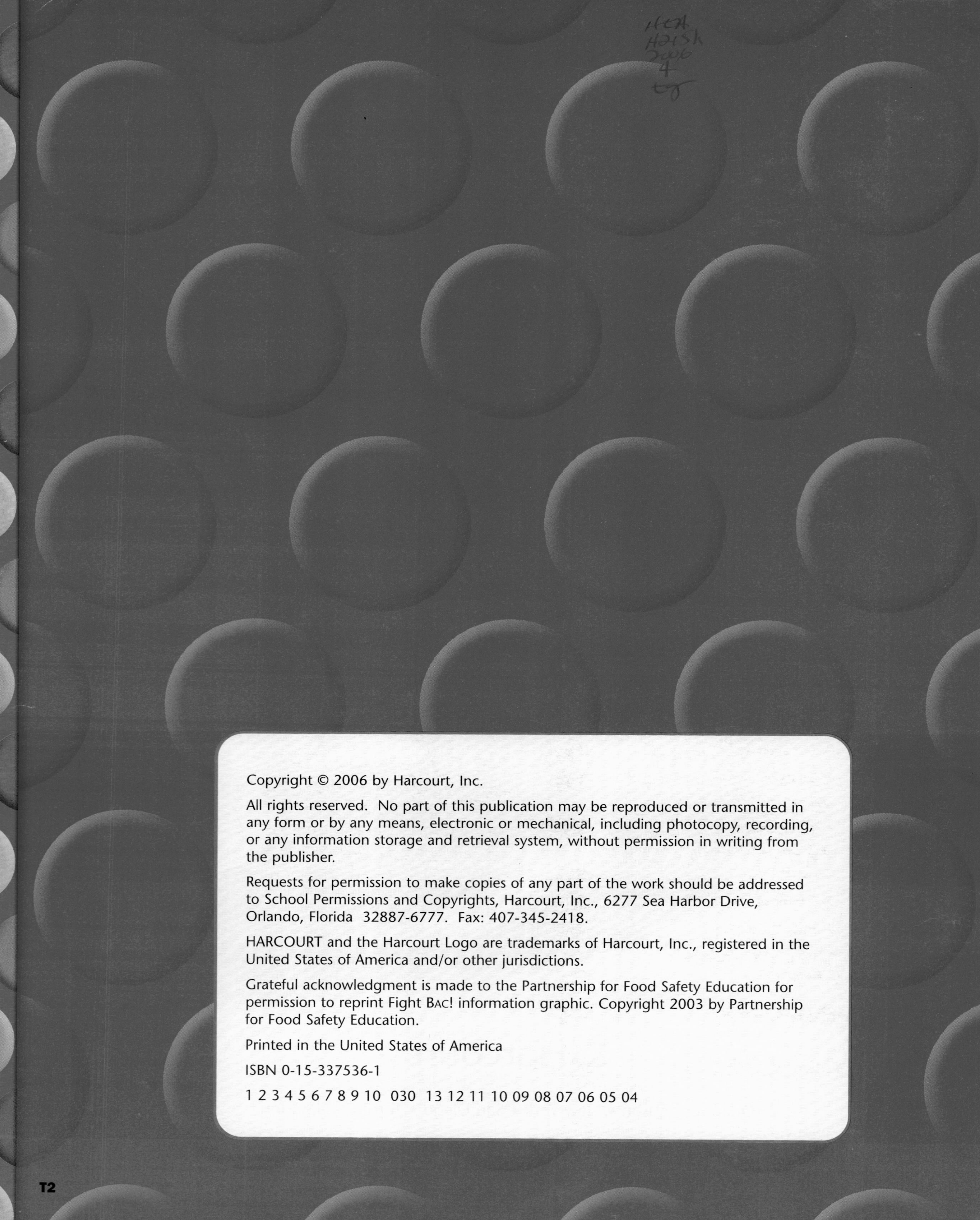

Copyright © 2006 by Harcourt, Inc.

All rights reserved. No part of this publication may be reproduced or transmitted in any form or by any means, electronic or mechanical, including photocopy, recording, or any information storage and retrieval system, without permission in writing from the publisher.

Requests for permission to make copies of any part of the work should be addressed to School Permissions and Copyrights, Harcourt, Inc., 6277 Sea Harbor Drive, Orlando, Florida 32887-6777. Fax: 407-345-2418.

HARCOURT and the Harcourt Logo are trademarks of Harcourt, Inc., registered in the United States of America and/or other jurisdictions.

Grateful acknowledgment is made to the Partnership for Food Safety Education for permission to reprint Fight BAC! information graphic. Copyright 2003 by Partnership for Food Safety Education.

Printed in the United States of America

ISBN 0-15-337536-1

1 2 3 4 5 6 7 8 9 10 030 13 12 11 10 09 08 07 06 05 04

Teacher Edition Contents

About This Program

Student Edition

Read-Aloud Anthology

Teacher Reference Section **TR-1**

Professional Development

Organization and Correlations

CONSULTING AUTHORS

Lisa Bunting, M.Ed., has over 25 years of experience as a coach and physical education teacher in middle and elementary schools in the Houston, Texas area. Her broad-based experience and background in athletics, health, and physical education is evidenced by her extensive professional involvement at the local, state, and national levels. A member of both the American and Texas Associations for Health, Physical Education, Recreation, and Dance (AAHPERD and TAHPERD) and the Texas Classroom Teachers Association, Ms Bunting has served on many TAHPERD committees and state initiatives. Ms Bunting is currently teaching elementary physical education in the Katy Independent School District and is involved with writing and implementing curriculum and training teachers in many aspects of coordinated school health.

Thomas M. Fleming, Ph.D., recently retired as Director of Health and Physical Education at the Texas Education Agency (TEA) in Austin, Texas. As Director, Dr. Fleming oversaw many state initiatives and served on many committees such as the Governor's Council for Physical Fitness, The Texas Diabetes Council, and the Texas School Health Advisory Council. Prior to his work at the TEA, Dr. Fleming was an instructor in the Department of Health and Kinesiology at Stephen F. Austin State University in Nacogdoches, Texas and at the University of Montevallo in Montevallo, Alabama where he was also the university baseball coach. Dr. Fleming recently received a Distinguished Service Citation Award from TAHPERD in recognition of his years of leadership and contributions to the education and health of Texas children.

Charlie Gibbons, Ed.D., recently retired after 30 years of university teaching experience at Alabama State University, Auburn University at Montgomery, and Georgia Southern College. He is presently Director of Youth and School Age Programs at Maxwell Air Force Base, Montgomery, Alabama and serving as an adjunct professor at Alabama State University Department of Health, Physical Education and Dance. Dr. Gibbons is a past president of the Alabama AHPERD and a past vice-president of the Health Division of Southern District AAHPERD. He continues to serve his professional organizations on state and district committees. He has served on numerous public service committees providing inservice workshops and presentations on various areas of school health curricula including such topics as HIV/AIDS prevention, physical fitness for children, and weight control. Dr. Gibbons was presented with the Alabama State and Southern District Honor Awards.

Jan Ozias, Ph.D., R.N., has extensive experience in school health services and health education from a nursing perspective. She worked as Nursing Supervisor and Administrator of Health Services in the Austin Independent School District, Austin, Texas. Dr. Ozias holds adjunct faculty appointments in both the School of Nursing and the College of Education at the University of Texas at Austin from which she also earned an M.A. in Special Education and a Ph.D. in Health Education. Dr. Ozias has worked as Director of Medical Underwriting, Texas Healthy Kids Corporation and presently serves as Director, Texas Diabetes Council/Program at the Texas Department of Health. She is co-chief editor of School Health Alert, a national newsletter for school nurses and educators.

Carl Anthony Stockton, Ph.D., is Dean of the School of Education at the University of Texas at Brownsville and Texas Southmost College. Previously, he served as Department Chair and Professor of Health Education in the Department of Health and Applied Human Sciences at the University of North Carolina in Wilmington. Throughout his professional career, Dr. Stockton has taught health education classes focusing on a wide variety of health topics. His curricula have included such diverse health topics as health programs in the elementary schools, nutrition, national and international health, accident and safety education, public health administration, and the use of technology in health promotion.

Dear Educator,

Harcourt Health and Fitness is a comprehensive program designed to help your students develop positive behaviors and attitudes that will lead to a lifetime of good health. In order to achieve that goal, students need knowledge, life skills, good character, and consumer skills.

Knowledge includes current information, facts, and concepts in the following content areas:

- Human Body, Growth and Development
- Consumer/Personal Health
- Nutrition
- Physical Activity and Fitness
- Injury Prevention
- Disease Prevention and Control
- Drug Use Prevention
- Emotional, Intellectual, and Social Health
- Family Life
- Community and Environmental Health

Life Skills are health-enhancing behaviors that help children reduce risks to their health. *Harcourt Health and Fitness* provides opportunities for children to learn and practice life skills through lessons that use real-life situations. These important skills are:

- Make responsible decisions
- Manage stress
- Set goals
- Resolve conflicts
- Communicate
- Refuse risky behaviors

Building Good Character is also an important part of having good health. When students develop good character traits, they have positive relationships with others and can make responsible decisions about their health and fitness. The character traits emphasized in *Harcourt Health and Fitness* include:

- Caring
- Citizenship
- Fairness
- Respect
- Responsibility
- Honesty (Trustworthiness)

Consumer Skills are important for helping students evaluate the enormous amount of information that is transmitted to them via print, electronic, and broadcast media. These skills include:

- Analyze advertisements and media messages
- Make buying decisions
- Access valid health information

We are confident that Harcourt Health and Fitness provides you with the tools you need to motivate your students to take an active role in maintaining and improving their health.

Sincerely,
The Authors

CONSULTING HEALTH SPECIALISTS

Sharon A. Braun, M.S., R.D., C.D.E.
Clinical Dietitian
Childrens Hospital Los Angeles
Los Angeles, California

Martha Gwendolyn Roberts Camp, Ph.D.
Educational Consultant
Asheville, North Carolina

Barry Conrad, M.P.H., R.D., C.D.E.
Clinical Dietitian
Childrens Hospital Los Angeles
Los Angeles, California

Elisabeth K. Constandy, M.S., C.H.E.S.
Health Promotion Coordinator
New Hanover County Health Department
Adjunct Faculty
Department of Health and Applied Human Sciences
University of North Carolina, Wilmington
Wilmington, North Carolina

Brian O. Coleman, D.D.S.
President, Omega Dental Group
Orlando, Florida

Jim DeLine, M.Ed.
CATCH Program Physical Education Coordinator
University of Texas Houston Health Science Center
Austin, Texas

Pam Ernest, M.S.
Department Chair, Girl's Athletics
Physical Education Coordinator
Belton Independent School District
Belton, Texas

Michael Hammes, Ph.D.
Associate Professor
University of New Mexico
Program of Health Education
Albuquerque, New Mexico

Francine R, Kaufman, M.D.
Division of Endocrinology and Metabolism
Childrens Hospital Los Angeles
Los Angeles, California

Mark J. Kittleson, Ph.D., F.A.A.H.B.
Professor, Health Education
Southern Illinois University
Carbondale, Illinois

Mary Kathleen Klier, R.D.
Clinical Dietitian
Childrens Hospital Los Angeles
Los Angeles, California

Melody Kyzer, Ph.D., R.D., L.D.N.
Assistant Professor
Department of Health & Applied Human Sciences
University of North Carolina, Wilmington
Wilmington, North Carolina

Jaime Orejan, Ph.D.
Assistant Professor
Leisure and Sport Management
Elon University
Elon, North Carolina

Howard Taras, M.D.
Department of Pediatrics
University of California, San Diego
La Jolla, California

Pam Tollefsen, R.N.
Med Program Supervisor
Health/Fitness Education and HIV/STD Prevention
Office of Superintendent of Public Instruction
Olympia, Washington

KEY

C.D.E.	Certified Diabetes Educator
C.H.E.S.	Certified Health Education Specialist
D.D.S.	Doctor of Dental Surgery
F.A.A.H.B.	Fellow, American Academy of Health Behavior
L.D.N.	Licensed Dietitian/Nutritionist
M.Ed.	Master of Education
M.D.	Medical Doctor
M.P.H.	Master of Public Health
M.S.	Master of Science
Ph.D.	Doctor of Philosophy
R.D.	Registered Dietician
R.N.	Registered Nurse

REVIEWERS AND FIELD TEST TEACHERS

Janet Ahmed
Grand Oaks Elementary
Citrus Heights, California

Teresa Battle
Orangeburg Consolidated District 5
Orangeburg, South Carolina

Susan J. Bergman
Tarkington Intermediate School
Cleveland, Texas

Jodi Booher
Harrison Elementary
Hamilton, Ohio

Betsy Bowles
DeZavala Elementary
Fort Worth, Texas

Dee Carter
Holmes Elementary
Wilmington, Ohio

Diana Cassels
Charlestown Elementary
Malvern, Pennsylvania

Dr. Bob Cockburn
Syracuse Elementary
Syracuse, Indiana

Terry Condrasky
Great Oaks Elementary
Round Rock, Texas

Emiko Davis
Campbell Elementary
Austin, Texas

Birdia DeShazer
Woods Academy
Chicago, Illinois

Dora Fernandez
Palm Lakes Elementary
Hialeah, Florida

Ana M. Gallo
Bent Tree Elementary
Miami, Florida

Nancy Garman
Jefferson Elementary
Charleston, Illinois

Susan Harkabus
Ready Elementary
Griffin, Indiana

Debra Horton
Alice Drive Elementary
Sumter, South Carolina

Scott Hudson
Covedale Elementary
Cincinnati, Ohio

Julie Huff
Jefferson Elementary
South Bend, Indiana

Roz Husband
Greene Elementary
South Bend, Indiana

Jan Kirk
Needmore Elementary
Bedford, Indiana

Sherry Knickerbocker
Shugart Elementary
Garland, Texas

Lisa Krienke
Mission CISD
Mission, Texas

Kathy Kruthoff
Washington Elementary
Stevens Point, Wisconsin

Theresa Lunsford
Rocklin Academy
Rocklin, California

Daniel Manseau
Boland Elementary
Springfield, Massachusetts

Dana Moore
Cypress Elementary
Leander ISD
Cedar Park, Texas

Christine Moyer
West Pottsgrove Elementary
Stowe, Pennsylvania

Karla Cacho Negrete
Bowen Elementary
Bryan, Texas

Cindy Noyes
Carmichael Elementary
Carmichael, California

Vicki J. Peters
Flower Mound Elementary
Flower Mound, Texas

Clementine Pitts
Van E. Blanton Elementary
Miami, Florida

Danny Poarch
Woodridge Elementary
San Antonio, Texas

Cindy Rau
Burton Hill Elementary
Ft. Worth, Texas

Stayci Roznovak
Johnson Elementary
Irving, Texas

Kathy Seidel
Sam Houston Elementary
Corpus Christi, Texas

Marilyn Spiegel
Greer Elementary
Sacramento, California

Sally Stricklin
PS 182
Bronx, New York

Cindy Terry
Chapel Lakes Elementary
Lee Summit, Missouri

Brenda Thomas
Kyger Elementary
Frankfort, Indiana

Victoria Thompson
Anderson Mill Elementary
Moore, South Carolina

Wendy Wear
Gray Elementary
Balch Springs, Texas

Patti Weid
DeLeon Elementary
Victoria, Texas

Tricia Wong
Commodore Sloat School
San Francisco, California

THE NATIONAL HEALTH EDUCATION STANDARDS

The National Health Education Standards were developed by representatives of various health organizations, including the American School Health Association, the Association for the Advancement of Health Education, and the American Cancer Society. The standards describe what students should know and be able to do in order to be health literate. A health-literate person obtains, interprets, and understands basic health information and services and uses that information and those services in ways that are health-enhancing.

Harcourt Health and Fitness promotes health literacy in the following ways:

- provides all students with the **knowledge** and **behaviors** they need to make informed decisions about their health.
- provides students with opportunities to learn and practice **life skills** and develop **character traits** for positive health behaviors.
- encourages students to **solve problems** and **think critically**.

Every lesson in ***Harcourt Health and Fitness*** was developed to help students meet the Standards. A correlation to the Standards and their performance indicators is provided beginning on page TR-50 in this Teacher Edition.

National Health Education Standards

1. Students will comprehend concepts related to health promotion and disease prevention.
2. Students will demonstrate the ability to access valid health information and health-promoting products and services.
3. Students will demonstrate the ability to practice health-enhancing behaviors and reduce health risks.
4. Students will analyze the influence of culture, media, technology, and other factors on health.
5. Students will demonstrate the ability to use interpersonal communication skills to enhance health.
6. Students will demonstrate the ability to use goal-setting and decision-making skills to enhance health.
7. Students will demonstrate the ability to advocate for personal, family, and community health.

COORDINATED SCHOOL HEALTH

The development of knowledge and skills alone is not enough to ensure that children achieve health literacy. A collaborative approach that coordinates the efforts of the families, schools, and the community is the most effective way to promote health literacy for all children.

A Coordinated School Health Program involves eight components that work together to develop and reinforce health knowledge, skills, attitudes, and behaviors. Each of these eight components is vital to the overall goal of promoting health literacy. The components are most effective when they are planned and implemented in a consistent and supportive manner.

How Harcourt Health and Fitness Supports Coordinated School Health

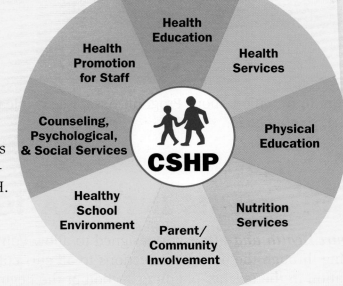

- The program provides a comprehensive approach to teaching health, with content that addresses all the major strands of health.
- Where appropriate, the program suggests resources that teachers and other school personnel may consult for making the links to all components of CSH. See the Resources page for each chapter in the Teacher Editions. See also the References for Coordinated School Health in the *Teaching Resources* book.
- The content and teaching strategies address the physical, emotional, and social needs of children.
- ***Harcourt Health and Fitness*** goes beyond the teaching of health content by focusing on healthful skills and behaviors. For example, the Life Skills and Building Good Character features teach life-enhancing behaviors that will contribute to a lifetime of good health.
- Together with ***Be Active! Resources for Physical Education***, the program provides a comprehensive and coordinated approach to teaching physical education.
- Specific features of the ***Harcourt Health and Fitness Teacher Editions*** that support CSH include the following:

 **School-Home Connection**

 **Daily Physical Activity**

 **Daily Fitness Tip**

 **Activities for Home and Community**

Health Background: Webliography

For more information about Coordinated School Health, please see pages TR18–21.

PROGRAM ASSESSMENT

Harcourt Health and Fitness provides a variety of assessment strategies and tools for assessing student health literacy. The assessment is based on the following model:

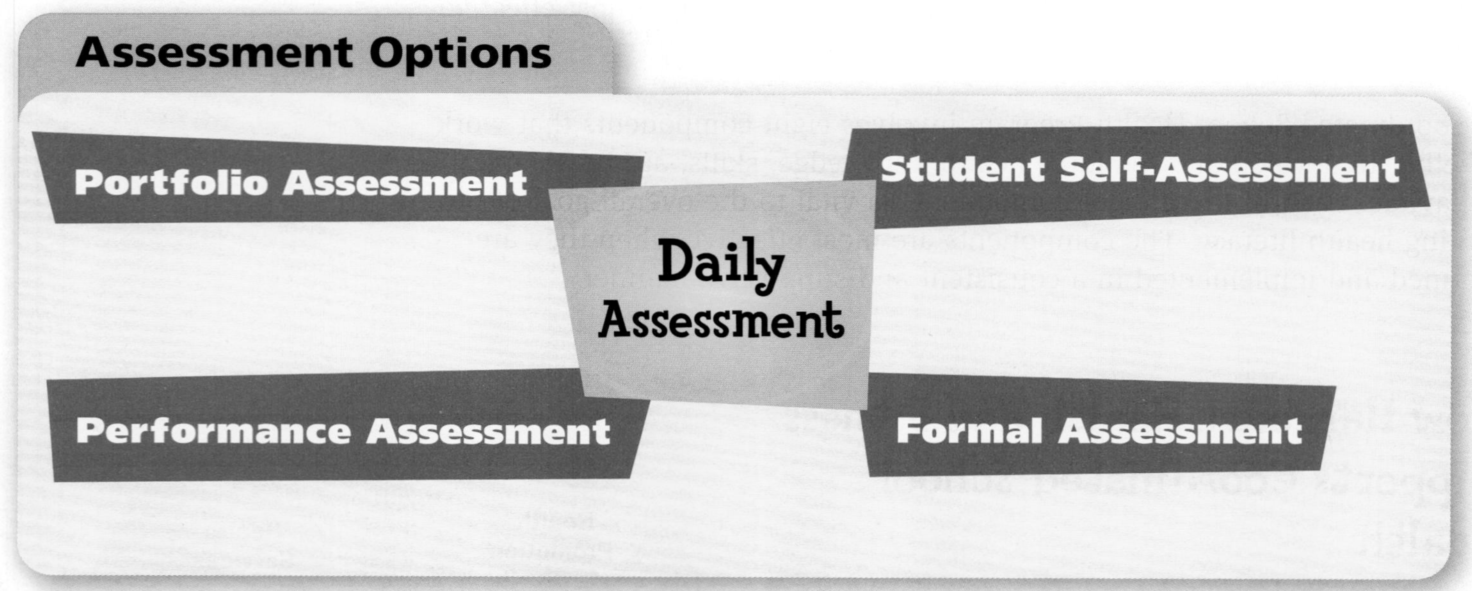

For more information about Program Assessment, please refer to pages 2–3 in the *Assessment Guide*.

CURRICULUM INTEGRATION

Harcourt Health and Fitness is designed to allow you to integrate health into your daily planning through the use of connections to all curriculum areas. Look for Curriculum Integration in the teacher planning section at the beginning of each chapter.

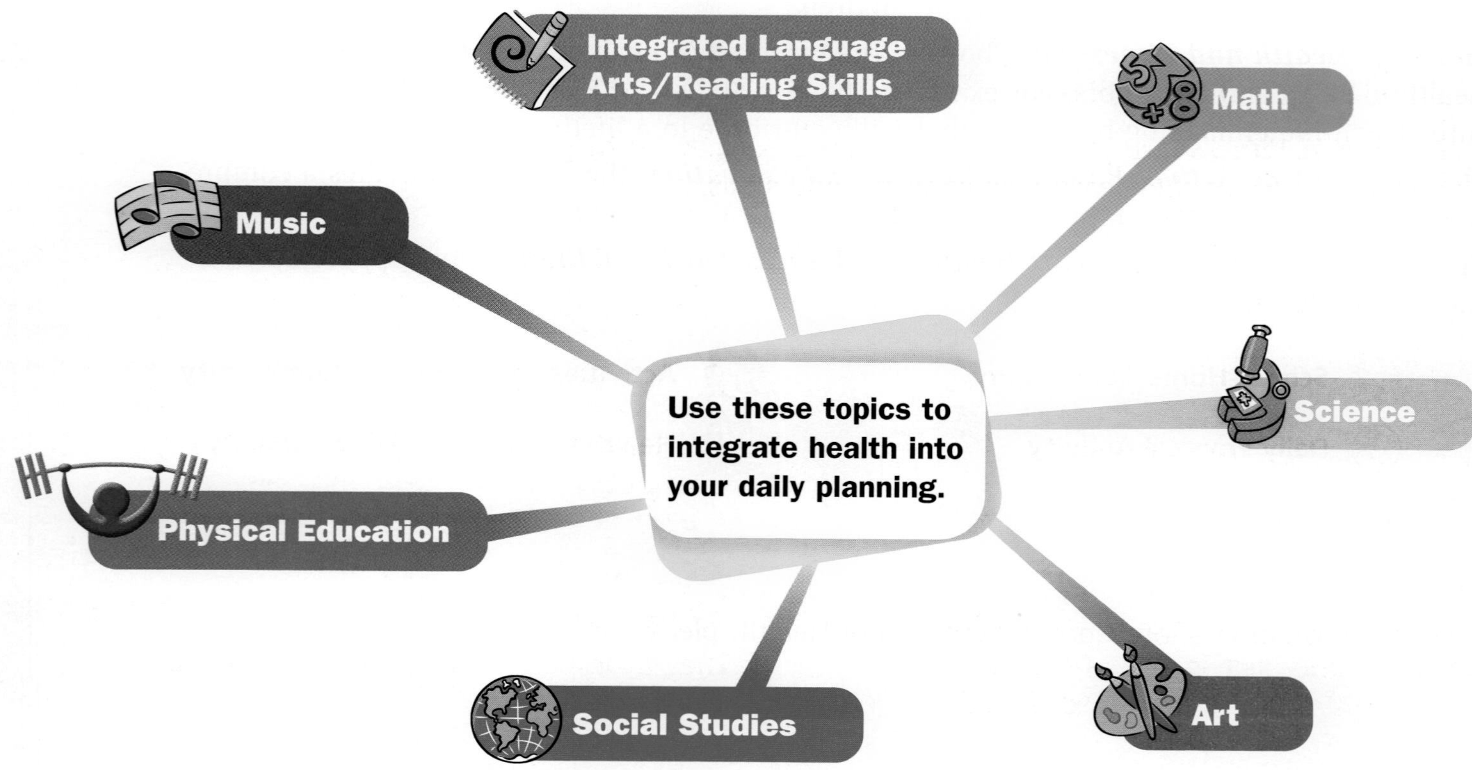

Reading in Health

Reading underlies everything students do in school, and many of the skills taught in reading programs can be reinforced during health instruction. A Reading Focus Skill is introduced at the beginning of each chapter in ***Harcourt Health and Fitness***. Throughout the chapter, the Focus Skill logo alerts the student to each opportunity for practicing and applying the skill.

Grades 1–2	Grades 3–6
1. Find Cause and Effect	**1.** Compare and Contrast
2. Find the Main Idea	**2.** Draw Conclusions
3. Make Predictions	**3.** Identify Cause and Effect
4. Recall and Retell	**4.** Identify Main Idea and Details
5. Sequence	**5.** Sequence
6. Use Context Clues	**6.** Summarize

Reading is also reinforced in *Harcourt Health and Fitness* in the following ways:

- A reading comprehension question appears after every "chunk" of text in the student edition. The question helps students check their comprehension of the text and also reinforces the Focus Skills, which are listed above.
- In the Teacher Edition, a Reading Mini-lesson appears with the first lesson in every chapter and can be used to provide focused instruction on each skill.
- The Reading in Health Handbook in the back of each Student Edition provides detailed, student-friendly information about each skill.
- Teaching Transparencies with Graphic Organizers provide visual support and can be used to record student's answers to Focus Skill questions. The Teaching Transparencies are also provided on CD-ROM in interactive format.
- Strategies for Content-Area Reading Support appear throughout the Teacher Edition and include skills such as Using Respellings, Using Signal Words, Using Text Patterns, and Using Charts and Graphics.

TEACHING ALL LEARNERS

Harcourt Health and Fitness also provides point-of-use strategies for helping all students be successful as they learn new concepts and skills.

ESL/ELL Support

These features address language issues in three critical areas:

- Comprehensible Input
- Language and Vocabulary
- Background and Experience

They also provide language strategies for students at varied levels of proficiency: Beginning, Intermediate, and Advanced.

Meeting Individual Needs Leveled Activities

These strategies reinforce key lesson concepts via activities at three instructional levels:

- Below-level
- On-level
- Challenge

They promote hands-on learning in every lesson.

PROGRAM COMPONENTS

Harcourt Health and Fitness provides components that meet a variety of instructional needs.

For Pre K

- Teacher's Guide
- Big Books, Little Books, and Fold-Out Books
- Posters
- Activity Book
- Hand Puppet

For Kindergarten

- Big Book
- Teacher Edition
- Activity Book
- Teaching Resources (includes School-Home Connection letters, Take-Home Booklets, Assessment Options, and Patterns)
- Teaching Transparencies with Accompanying Copying Masters

For Grades 1 through 2

- Student Editions
- Big Book version of the Student Edition
- Teacher Edition
- Activity Book
- Assessment Guide
- Teaching Resources (includes School-Home Connection letters, Take-Home Booklets, and reproducible copies of the Health and Safety Handbook)
- Posters
- Teaching Transparencies with Accompanying Copying Masters
- Teaching Transparencies in Interactive Format (CD-ROM)
- Be Active! Music for Daily Physical Activity

For Grades 3 through 6

- Student Editions
- Teacher Edition
- Activity Book
- Assessment Guide
- Teaching Resources (includes School-Home Connection letters, Take-Home Booklets, and reproducible copies of the Health and Safety Handbook)
- Posters
- Teaching Transparencies with Accompanying Copying Masters
- Teaching Transparencies in Interactive Format (CD-ROM)
- Be Active! Music for Daily Physical Activity
- Growth, Development, and Reproduction (an optional resource)

The Learning Site

Visit Harcourt's growing Learning Site for a variety of teacher resources and student activities, including:

- The Health Webliography for Teachers (carefully chosen links to health background and teaching resources)
- Student games and activities

www.harcourtschool.com/health

For Physical Education

Be Active! Resources for Physical Education

Primary and Intermediate Levels

This program provides a wealth of lessons, activities, games, and ideas for health-related fitness. Promotes a lifetime of physical activity for all students.

Chapters

Contents

v

VI

CHAPTER 8 Medicines, Drugs, and Your Health

CHAPTER 9 Harmful Effects of Tobacco and Alcohol

VII

VIII

Living in a Healthful Community . . 302

Reading in Health Handbook 330

Health and Safety Handbook 342

Glossary 359

Index 369

IX

Why should you learn about health?

You can do many things to help yourself stay healthy and fit. Just as importantly, you can avoid doing things that will harm you. If you know ways to stay safe and healthy and do these things, you can help yourself have good health throughout your life.

x

Having good relationships with family and friends
Avoiding alcohol, tobacco, and other drugs
Dealing with emotions in positive ways

Why should you learn about life skills?

Being healthy and fit doesn't come from just knowing facts. You also have to think about these facts and know how to use them every day.

These are some important life skills for you to have:

Communicating

Sharing ideas, needs, and feelings with others

Making Responsible Decisions

Deciding the most responsible thing to do to avoid taking risks

Managing Stress

Finding ways to avoid and relieve negative feelings and emotions

Refusing

Saying *no* to doing things that are risky and dangerous

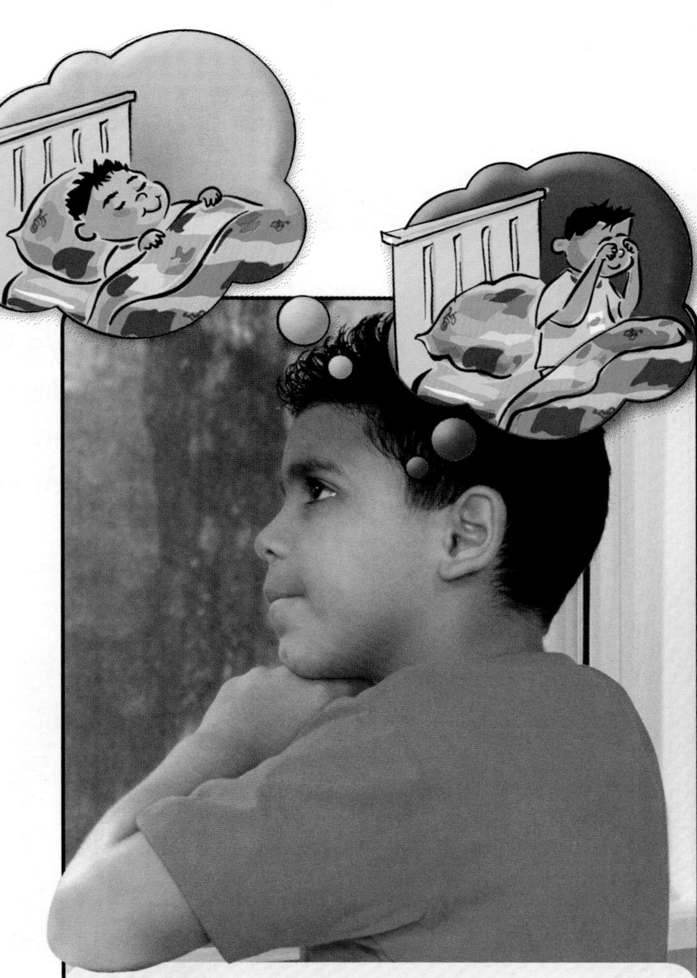

Setting Goals

Deciding on specific ways to make improvements to your health and fitness

Resolving Conflicts

Finding solutions to problems in ways that let both sides win

Whenever you see [LIFE SKILLS icon] in this book, you can learn more about using life skills.

XIII

Why should you learn about good character?

Having good character is also an important part of having good health. When you have good character, you have good relationships with others and can make responsible decisions about your health and fitness.

These are some important character traits:

Caring

Showing kindness and concern for friends, family, and others

Citizenship

Having pride in your school and community and obeying rules and laws

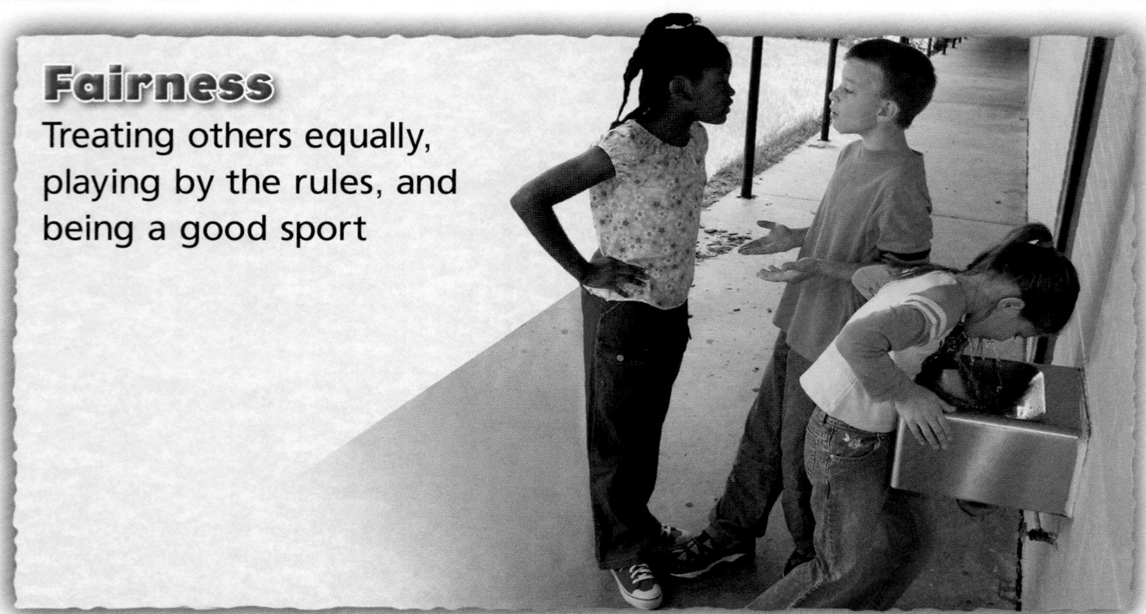

Fairness

Treating others equally, playing by the rules, and being a good sport

xiv

Respect

Showing consideration for yourself and others

Responsibility

Doing what you are supposed to do, practicing self-control, and completing tasks

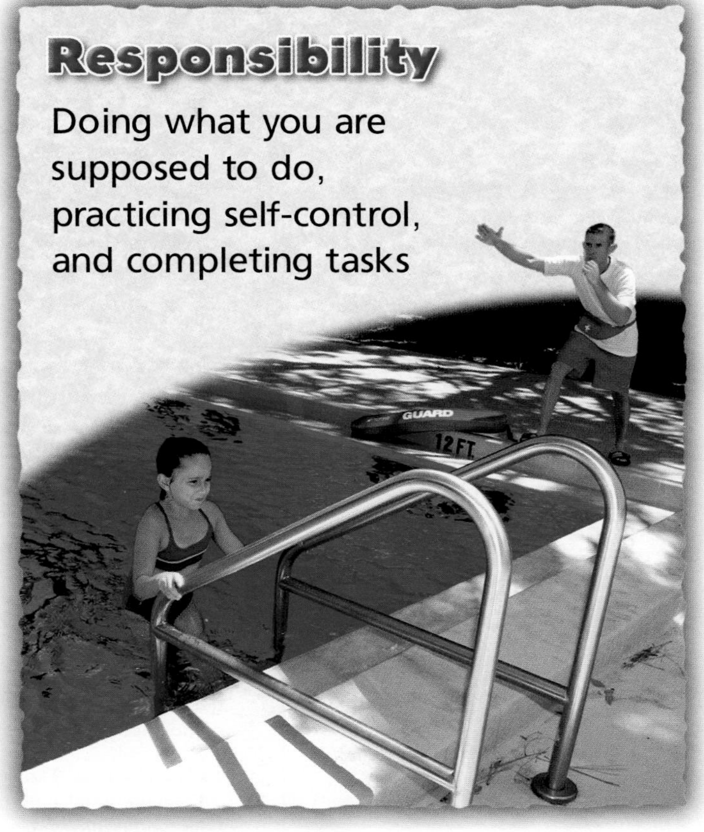

Trustworthiness

Being honest, dependable, and loyal

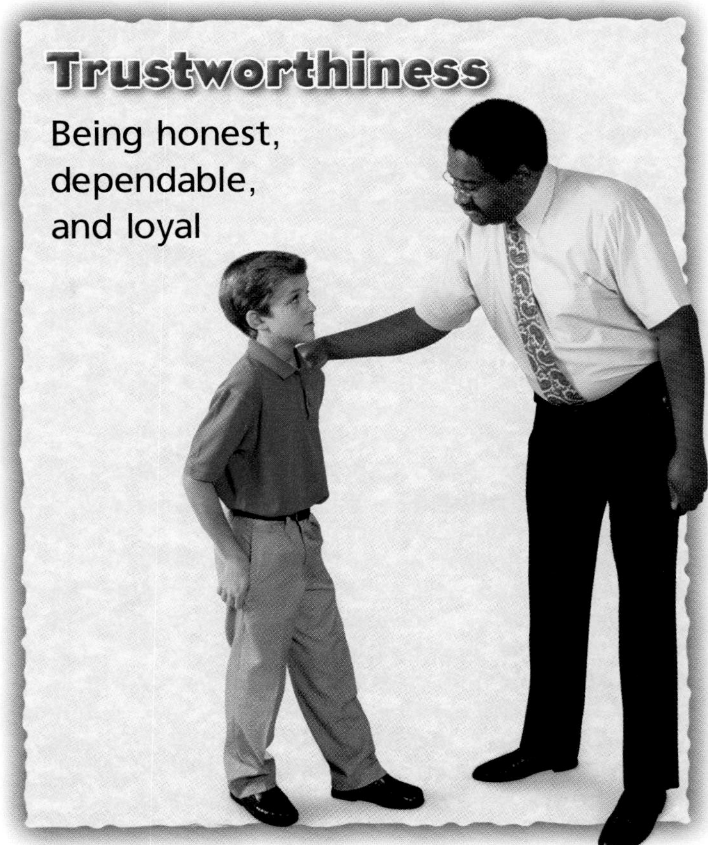

Whenever you see Building Good Character in this book, you can learn more about building good character.

xv

What are ways to be a successful reader?

Students need good reading skills to do well in school. Here are some tips to help you understand, remember, and use information you read.

Reading Tip

These sections can help you know what to look for as you read.

Reading Tip

Vocabulary words are listed at the beginning of the lesson so you can preview them. They are also highlighted and defined when they are first used.

LESSON 3

Staying Safe in a Conflict

Lesson Focus
You can resolve conflicts without fighting. You can learn skills to avoid getting hurt as a result of violence.

Why Learn This?
When you practice these skills, you reduce your risk of injury.

Vocabulary
bully
gang
weapon

Resolving Conflict

Conflict among people is normal. There are ways to resolve conflicts without fighting. Here are some suggestions:

- Stay calm. Keep your voice even and quiet.
- Speak respectfully. Do not call the other person names. Say "Please," "Thank you," and "I'm sorry."
- Agree that there is a problem. Listen to the other side. Try to see things the way others see them.
- Identify choices to end the conflict. Each person should compromise, or give a little.
- Leave if another person threatens you.

Focus Skill **DRAW CONCLUSIONS** **Why is it important to resolve conflicts peacefully?**

Resolving a Problem
Look at the picture. Write how you would go about resolving the conflict these students are having.

148

Reading Tip

Check your understanding by answering these questions at the end of each section. These questions also help you practice reading skills. You will see six reading focus skills:

- Compare and Contrast
- Draw Conclusions
- Identify Cause and Effect
- Identify Main Idea and Details
- Sequence
- Summarize

Whenever you see Focus Skill in this book, you can learn more about using reading skills.

Reading Tip

Use this section to summarize what you have read, review vocabulary and concepts, and practice writing skills.

What will you say if someone tries to get you to use drugs? Having a plan can help you say *no* with confidence. One way to avoid being tempted is to have friends who don't abuse drugs. Another way is to go to places where drugs are not used. Getting involved with activities you enjoy will help you find friends who don't use drugs.

Organizations in your community may offer activities for people your age. Check out a community center, your school, or a religious center for fun things to do. You might join a sports team, a club, or a musical group.

If you have a problem, don't turn to drugs. Instead, talk with a parent or another trusted adult about your problem.

Focus Skill SUMMARIZE **Identify ways to cope with or seek assistance when confronted with situations involving drugs.**

▼ If you have a problem, talk with your parents or other trusted adults.

Lesson 4 Summary and Review

1. **Summarize with Vocabulary**
   Use vocabulary and other terms from this lesson to complete the statements.
   If you know the ways that drugs can harm you, it is easier to resist _____. Planning ways to say *no* can make it easier to _____. Refusing drugs will help you like yourself and feel proud of your actions and will help build _____.
2. **Critical Thinking** Why is it important to talk to a trusted adult to get help with your problems?
3. What are three healthful alternatives to drug use?
4. Focus Skill **SUMMARIZE** Draw and complete this graphic organizer to show ways to refuse drugs.

Main Idea:	+	Details:	=	Summary:
There are many ways to say no to drugs.				

5. **Write to Express—Solution to a Problem**
   Write about how you would respond if you are ever offered drugs.

209

Throughout **Harcourt Health and Fitness**, you will have many opportunities to learn new ideas and skills that will lead to good health.

CHAPTER 1 Body Systems at Work

Lesson	Pacing	Objectives	Reading Skills
Introduce the Chapter pp. 2–3		• Preview chapter concepts.	**Sequence** pp. 3, 338–339
1 **You Are Growing** pp. 4–9	3 class periods	• Explain how inherited and acquired traits make an individual unique. • Describe how the body is organized from cells to body systems. • Compare growth from infancy to adulthood.	**Sequence** pp. 5, 9 • Compare and Contrast, p. 7 • Cause and Effect, p. 9
Life Skills pp. 10–11	1 class period	• Identify steps for managing stress. • Use stress-management steps to deal with stress in a healthful way.	
2 **The Brain and Nervous System** pp. 12–14	1 class period	• Explain the functions of the brain and nervous system. • Describe behaviors that keep the nervous system healthy.	**Sequence** p. 14 • Summarize, p. 13 • Draw Conclusions, p. 14
Building Good Character p. 15		• Identify ways to show respect for others by accepting individual differences.	
3 **The Digestive System** pp. 16–19	1 class period	• Identify the parts and functions of the digestive system. • Describe behaviors that keep the digestive system healthy.	**Sequence** pp. 17, 19 • Summarize, p. 19
4 **The Respiratory and Circulatory Systems** pp. 20–23	1 class period	• Identify the parts and functions of the respiratory and circulatory systems. • Describe healthful behaviors to take care of the respiratory and circulatory systems.	**Sequence** pp. 21, 23 • Main Idea and Details, p. 23
5 **The Skeletal and Muscular System** pp. 24–26	1 class period	• Explain the functions of the skeletal and muscular systems. • Describe behaviors that keep the skeletal and muscular systems healthy.	**Sequence** pp. 24, 26 • Compare and Contrast, p. 26
Activities p. 27		• Extend chapter concepts.	
Chapter Review pp. 28–29	1 class period	• Assess chapter objectives.	

Vocabulary	Program Resources
	Music CD Teaching Resources, p. 23
trait **cell** **nucleus** **tissue** **organs** **system**	Transparencies 5, 7, 8 Activity Book, pp. 1–3 Growth, Development, and Reproduction, pp. 2–25
	Activity Book, p. 4 Poster 9
nervous system **brain** **nerves**	Transparencies 5, 9, 10 Activity Book, pp. 1–2
	Poster 4
esophagus **stomach** **small intestine** **large intestine** **nutrients**	Transparencies 5, 11 Activity Book, pp. 1–2
trachea **bronchi** **lungs** **diaphragm** **heart** **arteries** **capillaries** **veins**	Transparencies 5, 12, 13 Activity Book, pp. 1–2
skull **skeletal system** **spine** **muscle** **muscular system**	Transparencies 5, 10, 14, 15 Activity Book, pp. 1–2, 5 Growth, Development, and Reproduction, pp. 34–43
	The Learning Site www.harcourtschool.com
	Assessment Guide, pp. 19–21

Interactive Transparencies available on CD-ROM.

Reading Skill

These reading skills are reinforced throughout this chapter and one skill is emphasized as the Focus Skill.

- **Sequence**
- Draw Conclusions
- Identify Cause and Effect
- Identify Main Idea and Details
- Compare and Contrast
- Summarize

KEY READING SKILLS TRANSPARENCY 5

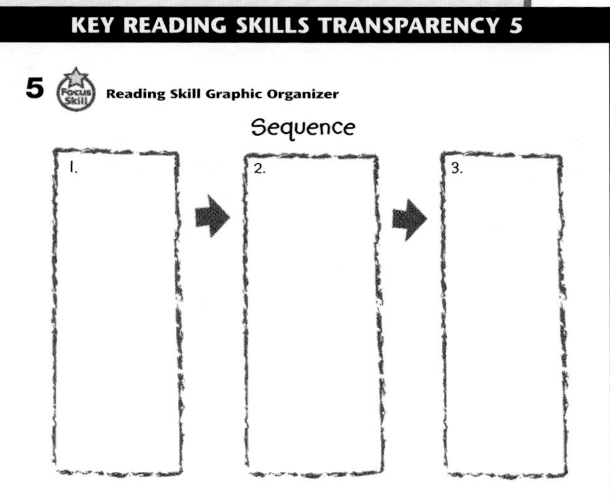

Life Skills

Life Skills are health-enhancing behaviors that can help students reduce risks to their health and safety.

Six Life Skills are reinforced throughout *Harcourt Health and Fitness*. The skill emphasized in this chapter is Manage Stress.

POSTER 9 MANAGE STRESS

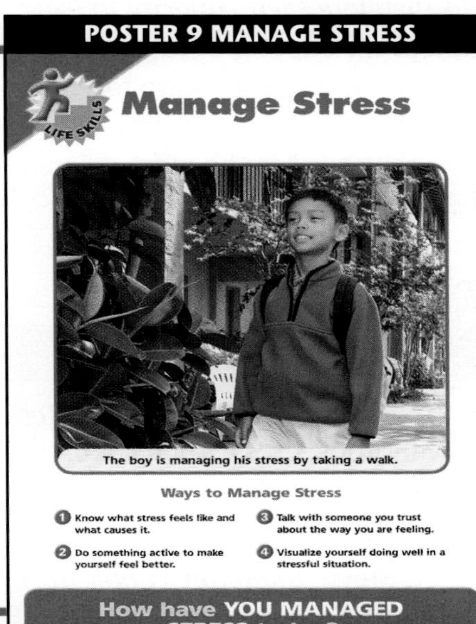

Manage Stress
The boy is managing his stress by taking a walk.
Ways to Manage Stress
1 Know what stress feels like and what causes it.
2 Do something active to make yourself feel better.
3 Talk with someone you trust about the way you are feeling.
4 Visualize yourself doing well in a stressful situation.
How have YOU MANAGED STRESS today?

Building Good Character

Character education is an important aspect of health education. When children behave in ways that show good character, they promote the health and safety of themselves and others.

Six character traits are reinforced throughout *Harcourt Health and Fitness*. The trait emphasized in this chapter is Respect.

POSTER 4 RESPECT

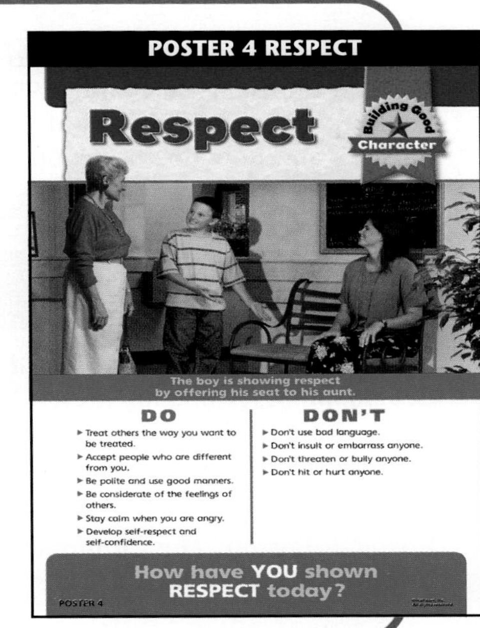

Respect
Building Good Character
The boy is showing respect by offering his seat to his aunt.
DO
Treat others the way you want to be treated.
Accept people who are different from you.
Be polite and use good manners.
Be considerate of the feelings of others.
Stay calm when you are angry.
Develop self-respect and self-confidence.
DON'T
Don't use bad language.
Don't insult or embarrass anyone.
Don't threaten or bully anyone.
Don't hit or hurt anyone.
How have YOU shown RESPECT today?

Resources

Coordinated School Health Program

Health Education
Health Services
Physical Education
Nutrition Services
Parent/ Community Involvement
Healthy School Environment
Counseling, Psychological, & Social Services
Health Promotion for Staff
CSHP

A Coordinated School Health Program endeavors to improve children's health and therefore their capacity to learn through the support of families, schools, and communities working together. The following information is provided to help classroom teachers be more aware of these resources.

The National Center for Chronic Disease and Health Promotion, part of the **CDC,** funds the Coordinated School Health Program. Visit its website for information about the eight components that make up this program. **www.cdc.gov/nccdphp/dash**

Thirteen percent of children and adolescents are now overweight or obese, which represents more than a doubling in the last thirty years. The National Governor's Association **(NGA)** Center for Best Practices, endorses the Coordinated School Health Program and offers information on the obesity epidemic. **www.nga.org/center/divisions/**

The **American Heart Association** instructs children on the function of the heart through the song "Everybody Needs a Heart." Older students can be challenged to write their own verses. **www.americanheart.org/**

The **Texas Comprehensive School Health Network** and the **School Nurse Consultancy** implement the Coordinated School Health Program in the mandatory screening of students for abnormal spine curvature. **www.tdh.state.tx.us/oshp/pop/school.pdf**

Other resources that support a Coordinated School Health Program:
- School-Home Connection
- Daily Physical Activity
- Daily Fitness Tips
- Activities: Home & Community
- Health Background: Webliography
- *Be Active! Resources for Physical Edcucation*

Media Resources

Books for Students

Cobb, Vicki. ***Your Tongue Can Tell.*** Millbrook Press, 2000. Explains the sense of taste and includes simple activities. EASY

Parker, Steve. ***Skeleton (Look at Your Body)***. Copper Beech Books, 1996. Explains the workings of the human skeletal system. AVERAGE

Parker, Steve. ***Muscles (Look at Your Body)***. Copper Beech Books, 1997. Looks at the different types of muscles and how they function. ADVANCED

Books for Teachers and Families

Cameron, Noel. ***Human Growth and Development***. Academic Press, 2002. Deals with a wide range of subjects on growth and maturation.

Woolf, Alan D., Ed., Children's Hospital, Boston. ***The Children's Hospital Guide to Your Child's Health and Development***. Perseus Books, 2001. Explains every aspect of child development.

Free and Inexpensive Materials

Federal Citizen Information Center
Request a copy of *Kids and Their Bones: A Parents' Guide* which deals with the health of children's bones.

Social Studies School Service
Will send a free copy of *Health Education*, containing topics such as "The Human Body."

National Institute of Child Health
Will provide pamphlets, posters, and stickers on growth and development topics such as "Exercise to Build Healthy Bones."

The American Heart Association
Receive up to five free copies of select AHA-printed materials, such as #65-9016, *The Circulatory System*.

To access free and inexpensive resources on the Web, visit **www.harcourtschool.com/health/free**

Videos

All About the Senses. Schlessinger Media, 2001.

Body Systems. Discovery Channel School, 2001.

My Amazing Human Body. DK Interactive Learning, 2001. (CD-ROM)

These resources have been selected to meet a variety of individual needs. Please review all materials and websites prior to sharing them with students to ensure the content is appropriate for your class. Note that information, while correct at time of publication, is subject to change.

Visit **The Learning Site** for related links, activities, resources, and the health **Webliography.**

www.harcourtschool.com/health

Meeting Individual Needs

Below-Level

Display a copy of a paragraph from the text. Help students identify the main idea and the important details that tell *who*, *where*, *when*, and *what happens*. Have students draw a picture of the main idea and tell how the details of the paragraph are important in knowing the main idea.

Activities

- Illustrated Healthful Behaviors, p. 8
- Trace a Diagram, p. 14
- Show Good Posture, p. 25

On-Level

Understanding new words is easier when students use context to confirm the word's meaning. Have partners determine a new word's meaning from context clues. Then have them substitute a word for the new word and read the sentence to see if it still makes sense.

Activities

- Draw a System, p. 8
- Make a Concept Map, p. 14
- Take a Stretch Break, p. 25

Challenge

Have small groups of students choose a topic related to a healthful lifestyle. Have each group make a visual advertisement persuading others of the benefits of that healthful choice. Students may use computers or video cameras, if available, to present their ads.

Activities

- Make a Chart, p. 8
- Investigate the Role of Sleep, p. 14
- Make a Chart, p. 25

ESL/ELL

Vocabulary Workshop

Build background with students through frequent use of concrete contextual referents, such as visuals, props, and graphics. Being able to touch a prop or see a picture of a new word makes the experience more meaningful and the concept more understandable.

Activities

- Language and Vocabulary, pp. 6, 22
- Comprehensible Input, p. 18

Curriculum Integration

Use these topics to integrate health into your daily planning.

Integrated Language Arts/Reading Skills

- Heart Healthy Behaviors, p. 23

Math

- Speed of Nerve Messages, p. 12
- Length of Intestines, p. 17

Physical Education

- Daily Fitness Tip, pp. 4, 12, 16, 20, 24
- Daily Physical Activity, p. 3
- Advocate for Safety, p. 12

Science

- Discovery of Cells, p. 7
- Analyze Breath, p. 21
- Muscle Cells, p. 26

Social Studies

- Air Pollution in Cities, p. 21
- Bone Tools, p. 24

Art

- Digestive System Models, p. 19

CHAPTER

1

Pages 2–29

CHAPTER SUMMARY

In this chapter, students

- examine the basic parts and functions of major body systems.
- learn how health behaviors affect body systems.

Life Skills
Students *manage stress* related to their growing and changing bodies.

Building Good Character
Students show *respect* for individual differences.

Consumer Health
Students *access valid health information* about bones.

Literature Springboard

Use the poem "Mark's Fingers" to spark interest in the chapter topic. See the Read-Aloud Anthology on page RA-2 of this *Teacher Edition*.

Prereading Strategies

SCAN THE CHAPTER Have students preview the chapter content by scanning the titles, headings, pictures, tables, and graphs. Ask volunteers to predict what they will learn. Use their predictions to determine their prior knowledge.

PREVIEW VOCABULARY Provide small groups of students with handouts of each body system studied in this chapter and a list of vocabulary terms of body systems and parts. Have students identify as many body systems and parts as they can.

Words I Know	Words I've Seen or Heard	New Words

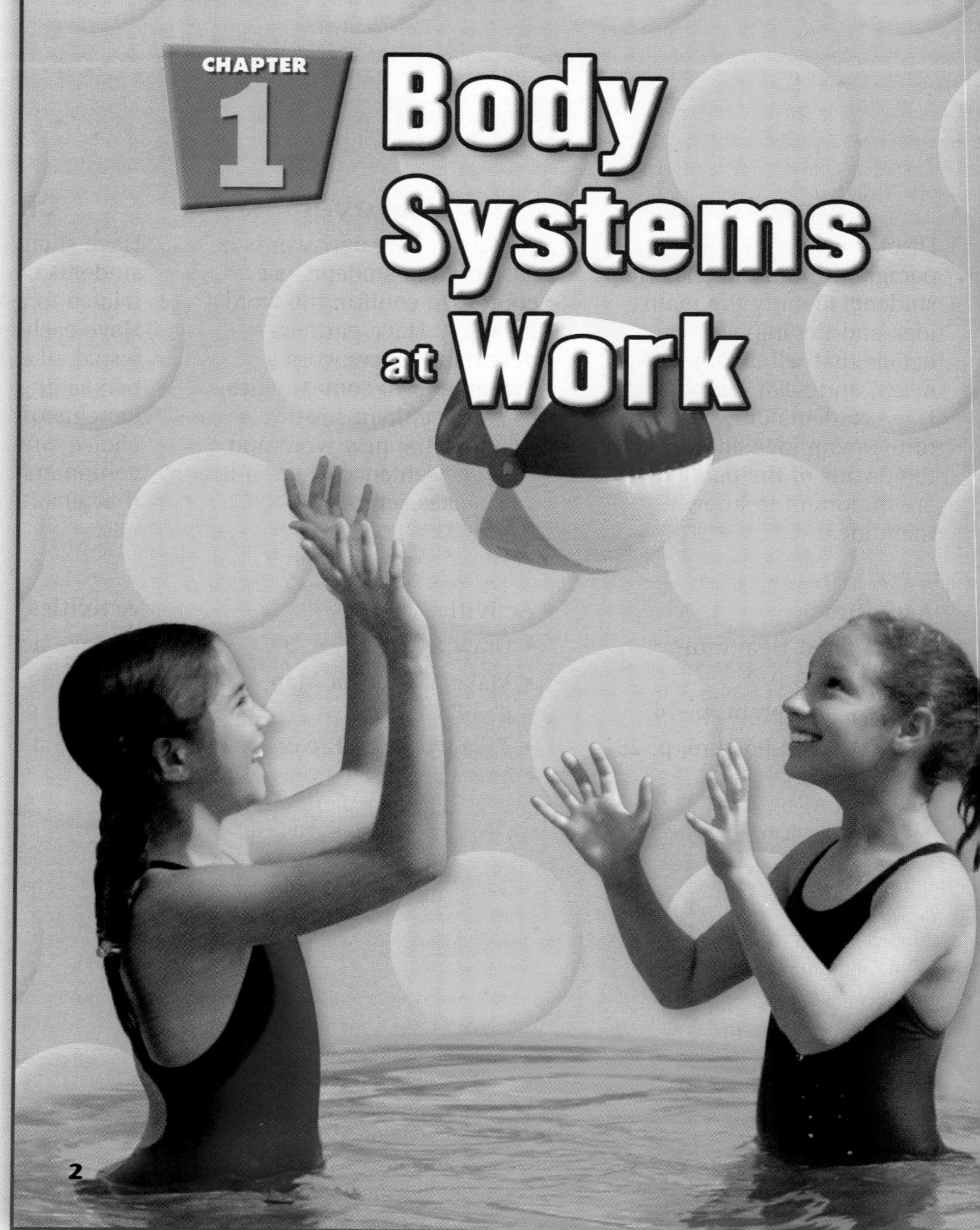

2

Reading Skill

SEQUENCE To introduce or review this skill, have students use the Reading in Health Handbook pp. 338–339. Teaching strategies and additional activities are also provided.

Students will have opportunities to practice and apply this skill throughout this chapter.

- Focus Skill Reading Mini-Lesson, p. 4
- Reading comprehension questions identified with the 
- *Activity Book* p. 3 (shown on p. 9)
- Lesson Summary and Review, pp. 9, 14, 19, 23, 26
- Chapter Review and Test Preparation, pp. 28–29

Reading Skill

SEQUENCE When you sequence, you show the order in which things occur. Use the Reading in Health Handbook on pages 338–339 and this graphic organizer to help you read the health facts in this chapter.

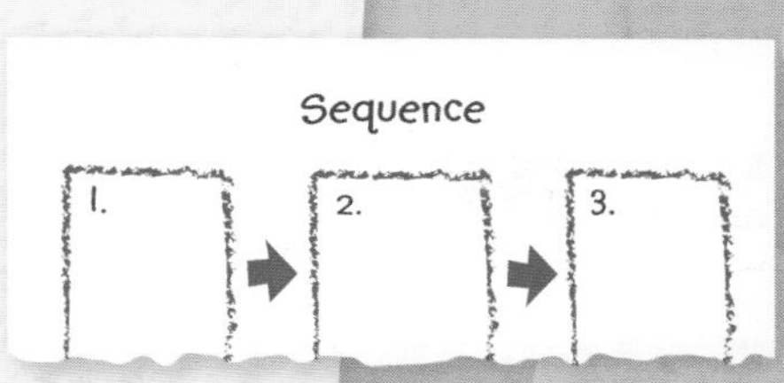

Health Graph

INTERPRET DATA The human body is about two-thirds water. Muscles are three-fourths water, and bones are about one-fourth water. In a 150-pound man, about how much more do the muscles weigh than the bones?

Weight of Organs
(150-Pound Man)

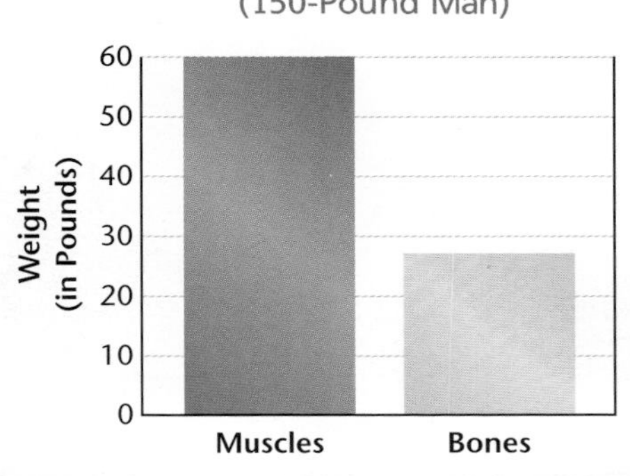

Daily Physical Activity

You should exercise to keep all of your body systems healthy.

 ***Be Active!***

Use the selection Track 1, **Saucy Salsa**, to get your whole body moving.

School-Home Connection

Distribute copies of the School-Home Connection (in English or Spanish). Have students take the page home to share with their families as you begin this chapter.

Follow Up Have volunteers share the results of their activities.

 **Supports the Coordinated School Health Program**

TEACHING RESOURCES P. 23

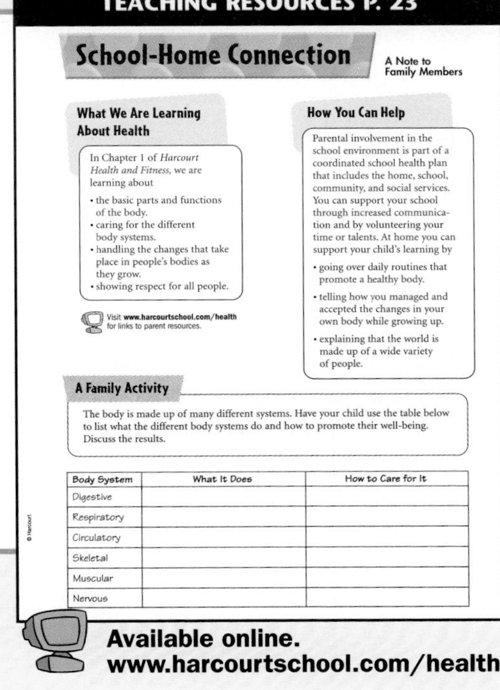

School-Home Connection

A Note to Family Members

What We Are Learning About Health

In Chapter 1 of *Harcourt Health and Fitness,* we are learning about

- the basic parts and functions of the body.
- caring for the different body systems.
- handling the changes that take place in people's bodies as they grow.
- showing respect for all people.

Visit **www.harcourtschool.com/health** for links to parent resources.

How You Can Help

Parental involvement in the school environment is part of a coordinated school health plan that includes the home, school, community, and social services. You can support your school through increased communication and by volunteering your time or talents. At home you can support your child's learning by

- going over daily routines that promote a healthy body.
- telling how you managed and accepted the changes in your own body while growing up.
- explaining that the world is made up of a wide variety of people.

A Family Activity

The body is made up of many different systems. Have your child use the table below to list what the different body systems do and how to promote their well-being. Discuss the results.

Body System	What It Does	How to Care for It
Digestive		
Respiratory		
Circulatory		
Skeletal		
Muscular		
Nervous		

© Harcourt

Available online.
www.harcourtschool.com/health

INTRODUCE THE CHAPTER

Health Graph

Interpret Data

Ask a volunteer to explain what the *x*-axis and the *y*-axis show.

About how much more do muscles weigh than bones? about twice as much

How much more water do muscles contain than bones? about three times as much

Daily Physical Activity

Use *Be Active! Music for Daily Physical Activity* with the Instant Activity Cards to provide students with movement activities that can be done in limited space. Options for using these components are provided beginning on page TR2 in this *Teacher Edition.*

Chapter Project

Fact or Fiction? (*Assessment Guide* p. 56)

ASSESS PRIOR KNOWLEDGE Use students' initial ideas for the project as a baseline assessment of their understanding of chapter concepts. Have students complete the project as they work through the chapter.

PERFORMANCE ASSESSMENT The project can be used for performance assessment. Use the Project Evaluation Sheet (rubric), *Assessment Guide* p. 62.

LESSON 1

Pages 4–9

Objectives

- Explain how inherited and acquired traits make an individual unique.
- Describe how the body is organized, from cells to body systems.
- Compare growth from infancy to adulthood.

When Minutes Count . . .

Assign the Quick Study, Lesson 1, Activity Book pp. 1–2 (shown on p. 5).

Program Resources

- Activity Book pp. 1–3
- Transparencies 5, 7, 8
- Growth, Development, and Reproduction pp. 2–25

Vocabulary

trait p. 4, **cell** p. 4, **nucleus** p. 6, **tissue** p. 7, **organs** p. 7, **system** p. 7

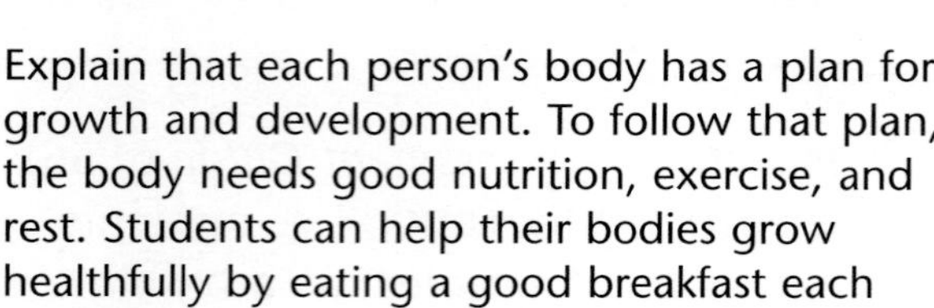

Daily Fitness Tip

Explain that each person's body has a plan for growth and development. To follow that plan, the body needs good nutrition, exercise, and rest. Students can help their bodies grow healthfully by eating a good breakfast each morning.

For more about choosing appropriate physical activities, see *Be Active! Resources for Physical Education* p. 135.

1. MOTIVATE

Optional Activity Materials picture of a model car, airplane, or ship

Show the model, and ask students if they have ever built a model.

How did you know how to put the model together? It had instructions.

What might happen if you tried putting pieces together at random? The model wouldn't look or work right.

Explain that instructions help us put things together in a proper sequence, or order, so that whatever we are making works.

LESSON 1 You Are Growing

Lesson Focus
As you grow, your body will change.

Why Learn This?
As you learn what causes growth, you will understand the changes in your own body.

Vocabulary
trait
cell
nucleus
tissue
organs
system

Traits

Think of some physical qualities that describe you. You may have red hair like your mother's. Your nose may look like your father's. These qualities are examples of traits. A **trait** (TRAYT) is a characteristic, or quality, that you have. You may also have blue eyes like your grandmother's. She may have passed that trait on to your father, who passed it on to you. Characteristics passed on to you from your parents in this way are called *inherited* (in•HEHR•uh•tuhd) *traits*.

The instructions for your inherited traits are contained within each of your body cells. A **cell** is the smallest working part of your body. Some inherited traits affect the way your body works. Other traits affect how you look.

▲ What physical traits did this mother and father pass on to their daughter?

4

Focus Skill Reading Skill

Mini-Lesson

SEQUENCE Remind students that sequence shows the order in which things happen. Have them practice this skill by responding to the Focus Skill question on page 5. Have students draw and complete the graphic organizer as you model it on the transparency.

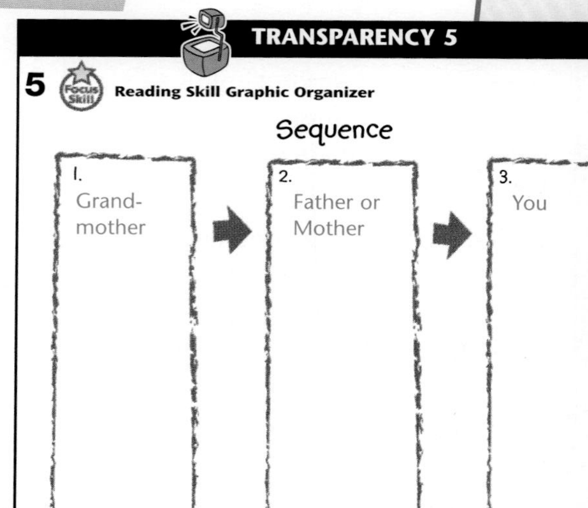

Interactive Transparencies available on CD-ROM.

Some traits are not inherited. Your *acquired* (uh•KWYRD) *traits* are characteristics you develop as a result of your life experiences. For example, you might like to take care of dogs. Your parents might like dogs, too. But this trait was not passed to you through your parents' cells. You developed an interest in dogs after you were born. You might enjoy skateboarding, reading, or belonging to a club. Acquired traits may change as your interests change. Inherited traits do not change simply because your interests change.

Some traits may be both inherited and acquired. For example, you might be good at playing a musical instrument. You inherited a musical ability. You have become a skilled player because you have practiced. You practiced because you acquired the interest.

No two people are exactly alike. Together, your interests, skills, and talents make you a unique person.

Did You Know?

Identical twins have the same inherited traits. They look exactly alike and are either both boys or both girls. Fraternal twins do not have the same inherited traits. They do not look exactly alike. They can both be boys, both be girls, or a boy and a girl.

Focus Skill **SEQUENCE Describe how you might have ended up with an inherited trait from your grandmother.**

Traits are passed from each parent to their children and can be illustrated showing a box with an arrow leading to a second box with an arrow leading from it to a third box, each labeled *grandmother, father or mother, you*.

▼ **How do inherited traits and acquired traits work together as this boy shapes the clay?**

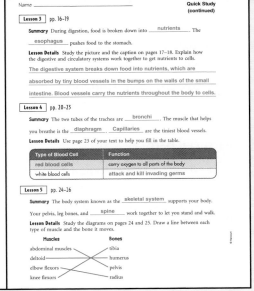

5

2. TEACH

Discuss

Explain that just as a model kit has instructions, a person's cells contain instructions that determine an individual's growth and development. These instructions also determine a person's inherited traits. A person inherits traits from each parent.

Critical Thinking Why might children of the same parents look different? They may have inherited different traits from each parent.

Problem Solving Why might identical twins look the same but have different interests? Their appearance is inherited. Their interests are acquired traits.

Content-Area Reading Support

Using Titles and Headings Direct attention to the lesson title in blue. Explain that the title tells what the lesson is about—it gives the "big idea." Ask a volunteer to read the title and then to make a prediction about what the lesson will prove to be about. Then have students read the first subhead in red. **How does the head *Traits* help you organize your reading?** It gives readers a clue about what they will read. Tell students that paying attention to lesson titles and subheads can help them organize information as they read. Point out that making an outline is one good way to use titles and subheads.

QUICK STUDY, ACTIVITY BOOK PP. 1–2

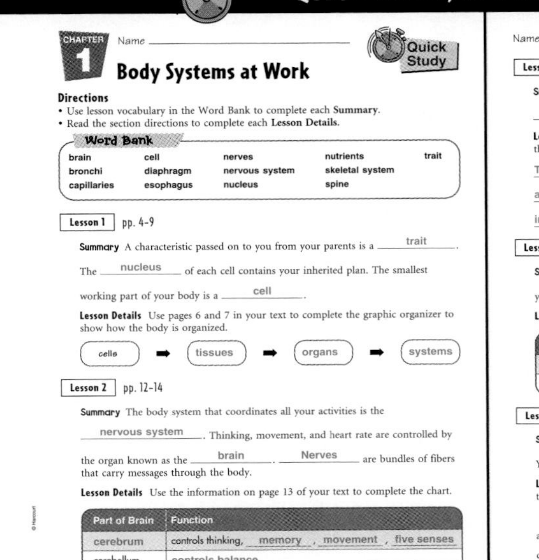

CHAPTER 1 Name ______________ Quick Study

Body Systems at Work

Directions
- Use lesson vocabulary in the Word Bank to complete each **Summary**.
- Read the section directions to complete each **Lesson Details**.

Word Bank

brain	cell	nerves	nutrients	trait
bronchi	diaphragm	nervous system	skeletal system	
capillaries	esophagus	nucleus	spine	

Lesson 1 pp. 4-9

Summary A characteristic passed on to you from your parents is a trait. The nucleus of each cell contains your inherited plan. The smallest working part of your body is a cell.

Lesson Details Use pages 6 and 7 in your text to complete the graphic organizer to show how the body is organized.

cells ➡ tissues ➡ organs ➡ systems

Lesson 2 pp. 12-14

Summary The body system that coordinates all your activities is the nervous system. Thinking, movement, and heart rate are controlled by the organ known as the brain. Nerves are bundles of fibers that carry messages through the body.

Lesson Details Use the information on page 13 of your text to complete the chart.

Part of Brain	Function
cerebrum	controls thinking, memory, movement, five senses
cerebellum	controls balance
brain stem	controls breathing, heart rate, growth

© Harcourt

Name ______________ Quick Study (continued)

Lesson 3 pp. 16-19

Summary During digestion, food is broken down into nutrients. The esophagus pushes food to the stomach.

Lesson Details Study the picture and the caption on pages 17–18. Explain how the digestive and circulatory systems work together to get nutrients to cells.

The digestive system breaks down food into nutrients, which are absorbed by tiny blood vessels in the bumps on the walls of the small intestine. Blood vessels carry the nutrients throughout the body to cells.

Lesson 4 pp. 20-23

Summary The two tubes of the trachea are bronchi. The muscle that helps you breathe is the diaphragm. Capillaries are the tiniest blood vessels.

Lesson Details Use page 23 of your text to help you fill in the table.

Type of Blood Cell	Function
red blood cells	carry oxygen to all parts of the body
white blood cells	attack and kill invading germs

Lesson 5 pp. 24-26

Summary The body system known as the skeletal system supports your body. Your pelvis, leg bones, and spine work together to let you stand and walk.

Lesson Details Study the diagrams on pages 24 and 25. Draw a line between each type of muscle and the bone it moves.

Muscles	Bones
abdominal muscles	tibia
deltoid	humerus
elbow flexors	pelvis
knee flexors	radius

© Harcourt

Available online.
www.harcourtschool.com/health

TEACH *continued*

Interpret Visuals—Pictures

Direct attention to the diagram of the cell. Explain that this is a simplified view of a cell under a microscope. Tell students that most cells are too small to be seen without a microscope. Have students read the labels for the cell parts. Help students understand the functions of cell parts by comparing the organization and structure of the classroom to a cell: The teacher is the control (nucleus), and students are the many parts contained within the classroom space (cytoplasm).

What part of the cell could be compared to the classroom walls? cell membrane

What is the job of the cell membrane? It holds the cell together and controls what enters and leaves the cell.

Discuss

Be sure students do not confuse the meanings of the terms *multiply* and *divide* with their mathematical definitions. When a cell divides, each new cell is complete and exactly like the original. It is not one-half of the original.

Tell students that cells use energy to divide and to carry out other functions. They get energy from certain nutrients in food you eat.

Critical Thinking Why is it important to eat a nutritious, balanced diet? so that cells get the energy and nutrients they need to do their jobs

When Minutes Count . . .

Transparency 7: Types of Body Cells can be used to present material in this lesson. *Interactive Transparencies available on CD-ROM.*

Activities of Cells

All living things are made up of cells. Cells take in food and get rid of waste. They grow, multiply, and die. The cells that make up your body come in many different shapes and sizes.

You grew from a single cell, which divided to make two cells. This process has continued, and now your body has trillions of cells. Your body's cells will continue to divide, making you grow and replacing worn-out cells. You can see some parts of a cell in the diagram below.

Different types of cells do different types of work. Red blood cells carry oxygen to all parts of the body. Nerve cells carry messages.

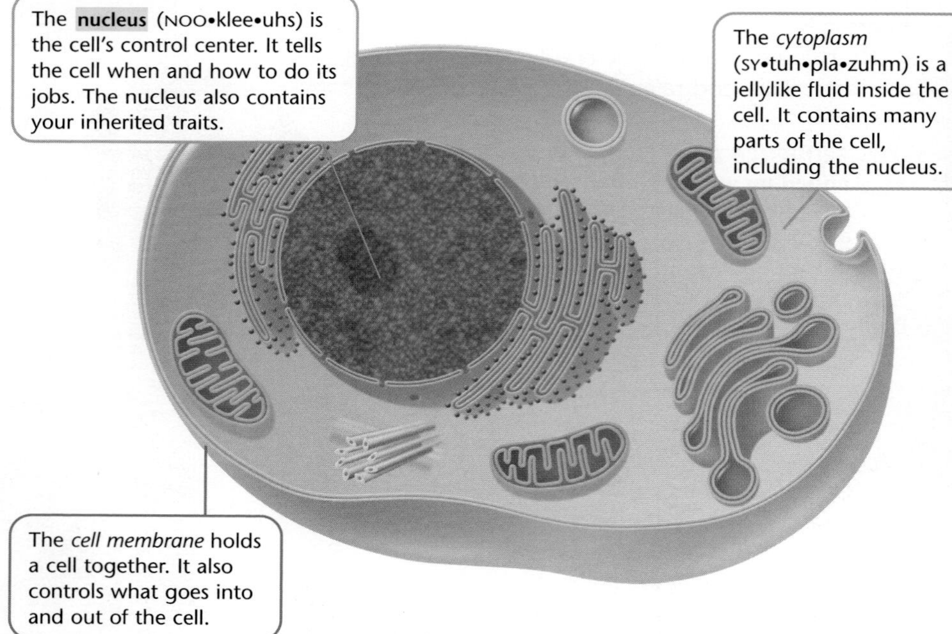

The **nucleus** (NOO•klee•uhs) is the cell's control center. It tells the cell when and how to do its jobs. The nucleus also contains your inherited traits.

The *cytoplasm* (SY•tuh•pla•zuhm) is a jellylike fluid inside the cell. It contains many parts of the cell, including the nucleus.

The *cell membrane* holds a cell together. It also controls what goes into and out of the cell.

▲ **Most cells are so small that you can see them only through a microscope.**

ESL/ELL Support

LANGUAGE AND VOCABULARY Familiarize students with the parts of a cell.

Beginning Have students use clay blocks or other items to visually express the terms *multiply* and *divide*.

Intermediate Have students explain in their own words the definition of each cell part.

Advanced Ask students to look up the names of the cell parts in a dictionary and break the words into their parts. Have them find the meaning of each part (for example, *cyto* means "cell") and relate the meaning to the definition.

Types of Tissue

Tissue	Function
Muscle Tissue	Muscle cells are long and narrow. Muscle tissue contracts and relaxes to make your body parts move.
Epithelial Tissue	Epithelial cells are wide and flat. These tissues line surfaces inside your body and make up the outer layer of your skin.
Connective Tissue	Connective tissue holds up your body and connects all its parts. Bone is one kind of connective tissue.
Nerve Tissue	Nerve cells are long, and they branch through your body. Nerve tissue carries messages.

A group of cells that work together to do a job in the body is called **tissue**. Groups of tissues join together to form **organs**. Each organ has a job to do. For example, your heart is an organ made mostly of muscle tissue. It pumps blood through your body. Other organs include your stomach, lungs, and brain.

Sometimes several organs work together to do a job. Groups of organs that work together are called a **system**. Your brain, nerves, and spinal cord make up your nervous system. Together, they send and receive messages throughout your body.

COMPARE AND CONTRAST Tell how organs are alike and different.
Alike: organs are made of tissues. Each organ has a job to do. Different: not all organs have exactly the same tissues. Each organ performs a unique job.

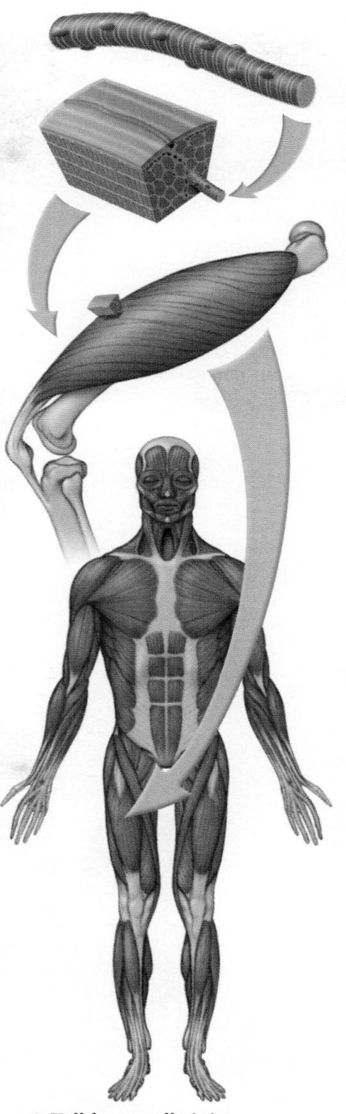

▲ **Tell how cells join together to make up the muscular system.**

7

Content-Area Reading Support

Using Tables and Charts Direct attention to the Types of Tissues chart. Point out that some charts, such as this one, contain information that isn't in the paragraph text. The text in charts is presented in different ways, depending on what's important for the reader to notice. This chart highlights the differences among the types of tissues. Lead students to observe that the function of each type of tissue is presented in a separate box. Tell students to look for charts as they read the lessons, because charts give important information.

Discuss

Draw attention to the definition of *organ*.

What are the names of some other body organs? Possible answers: liver, kidney, esophagus, skin, spleen, intestines

What characteristics do these organs have in common? They're made of tissues that join together to do a job.

Trace the sequence of cells to body systems by looking at the picture of the muscular system. The muscular system begins with muscle cells. The cells join to make muscle tissue. Tissues join to make an organ, such as this leg muscle. The various muscles combine to make your entire muscular system.

When Minutes Count . . .

Transparency 8: From Cells to Systems can be used to present material in this lesson. *Interactive Transparencies available on CD-ROM.*

Teacher Tip

View Cell Parts Set up some microscopes with prepared slides of cells that clearly show the cell parts discussed in this lesson. To help students understand the concept of microscopic objects, allow them to examine their skin with a hand lens. They'll discover that their skin looks different when enlarged. Then have them look at a cell under a microscope. Explain that the microscope makes the object they're looking at appear many times larger than the hand lens does.

Science

Discovery of Cells In 1665 Robert Hooke, a British scientist, became the first person to observe cells under a microscope. What he saw were the cell walls of cork cells that were left behind when the cells died. A few years later, Dutch merchant Anton van Leeuwenhoek used his own handmade microscope to observe microscopic creatures in pond scum. Have students find out more about the discoveries of these two men.

TEACH *continued*

Personal Health Plan

Plans should not be used to evaluate or assess students, nor should they be shared among students.

Plans should include:

- personality traits, behaviors, and talents.
- qualities to continue or improve upon.

Discuss

Discuss the term "trusted adult" with students. Explain that sometimes their parents or guardians may not be nearby when they need help. Students should be encouraged to identify other adults whom they can trust in the absence of their parents or legal guardians. Such "trusted adults" should be individuals well known to the child and MAY include grandparents, teachers, counselors, nurses, doctors, fire fighters, police officers, and neighbors.

Critical Thinking If girls start their growth spurt earlier than boys, why aren't the girls a lot taller than the boys? The girls' growth spurt won't begin until they're about ten or eleven.

Consumer Activity

Students should conclude that babies have about 300 bones. Adults have 206 bones. Some bones fuse together during growth. So as we grow, the number of bones in our bodies decreases from the number of bones we are born with. Calcium and phosphorus are the minerals found in bones. Students should cite the sources they used to find their information.

Growth, Development, and Reproduction An optional lesson about growth and changes in puberty is provided in this supplement on pp. 2–25. Use this component in compliance with state and local guidelines.

Personal Health Plan

Real-Life Situation
Suppose you are concerned about the growth changes your body is going through.

Real-Life Plan
Write how you can go about discussing this concern or other critical issues with your parents or other trusted adults.

Growing and Changing

When you get ready for school every year, do you notice that your old clothes no longer fit? That is because your body is growing. Between the ages of two and eleven, you grow about 2 or 3 inches each year. After age ten, girls have a growth spurt. They grow faster than boys for about two years. Then boys have a growth spurt.

This period of rapid growth is called *adolescence* (a•duhl•EH•suhnts). The physical changes you experience during adolescence are called *puberty*. Ask your parents or another trusted adult about these growth changes.

Everyone grows at his or her own rate. As a teenager, you will grow rapidly. Your looks will change in many ways. The different parts of your body will grow at different times and rates. For a time, it may be awkward for you to move or perform well in sports. This is normal. You will grow at your own rate until you reach adulthood.

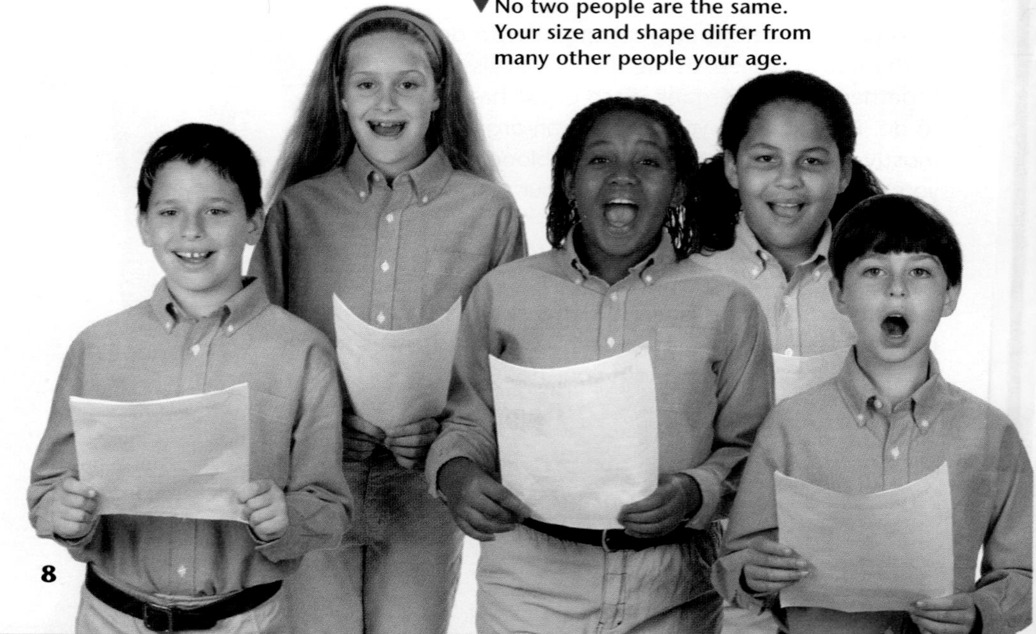

▼ No two people are the same. Your size and shape differ from many other people your age.

8

Meeting Individual Needs
Leveled Activities

BELOW-LEVEL Illustrate Healthful Behaviors Have students draw pictures to illustrate the healthful behaviors described on page 9. Have them write sentences telling how each behavior helps maintain a healthy body.

ON-LEVEL Draw a System Have students examine the diagram of the muscular system on page 7. Tell them to choose another system and draw a similar diagram of it.

CHALLENGE Make a Chart Ask students to research which vitamins and minerals people their age need to grow healthfully and to make a table showing the results.

Taking care of your body will help you reach your full height and size. Here are some healthful behaviors that can help:

- Eat healthfully. Choose fruits, vegetables, and low-fat meat and poultry. Limit sugary and high-fat snacks. Cells need the right nutrients to work best.
- Get enough physical activity—about one hour every day. Go for a walk, play on a sports team, or ride a bike. Being active helps deliver oxygen and nutrients to your cells and can also strengthen your heart.
- Get enough sleep. If you are tired, rest. People your age need about nine hours of sleep every night.

CAUSE AND EFFECT Why does your body change during adolescence?

during adolescence your body goes through growth spurts

Consumer Activity

Access Valid Health Information Find out more about how bones grow. Do adults and children have the same number of bones? What minerals are found in bones? Use the guidelines on pages 52–54. Write down the information you find.

Lesson 1 Summary and Review

1. **Summarize with Vocabulary**
   Use vocabulary and other terms from this lesson to complete these statements.
   A trait passed on to you from your parents is an _____. The _____ is the control center of a _____. Groups of _____ join together to form _____, which work together as a _____.
2. How are inherited traits and acquired traits alike? How are they different?
3. **Critical Thinking** Describe how the activities and functions of a cell are like a house with a fence around it.
4. **SEQUENCE** Fill in this graphic organizer to show the sequence of growth from child to adult.

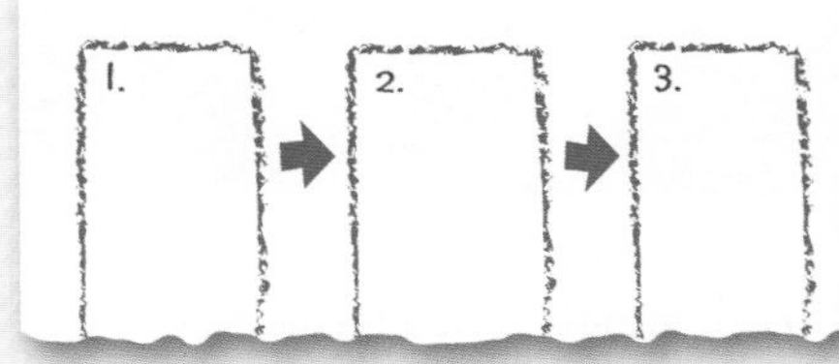

5. **Write to Inform—Description**
   Write a paragraph describing how you have grown since first grade.

9

3. WRAP UP

Lesson 1 Summary and Review

1. inherited trait; nucleus, cell; tissue, organs, system
2. Alike—everyone has some. Different—obtained differently: inherited traits passed from parents to child; acquired traits based on life experiences
3. Descriptions may include how the fence is like the cell membrane; how the sidewalk allows things to go into and out of the house; how the inside of the house works like the nucleus; how the different rooms inside the house are like other cell parts inside the cytoplasm
4. Answers may vary:

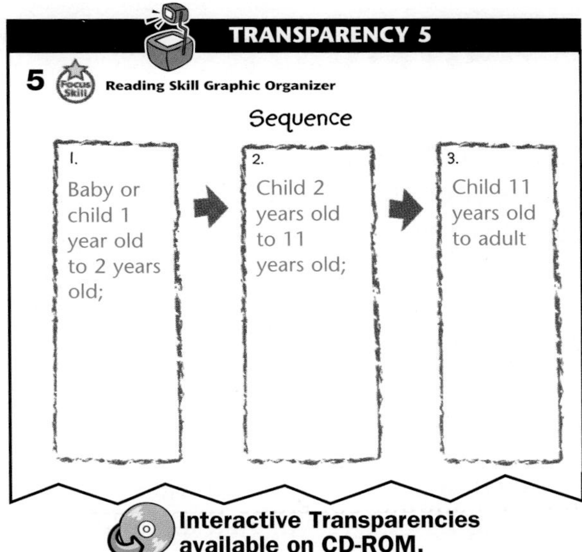

Interactive Transparencies available on CD-ROM.

5. Students will likely note that they grew a few inches each year. They might point out how their sizes and shapes have changed.

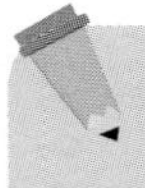

For **writing models** with examples, see *Teaching Resources* pp. 47–61. Rubrics are also provided.

Quick Study Students can use *Activity Book* pages 1–2 (shown on p. 5) as they complete each lesson in this chapter.

Teacher Tip

Growth Worries Some students may be uncomfortable discussing growth, especially those who see themselves as too tall or too short. Be sensitive to their concerns. Help students realize that almost everyone worries about how and when he or she will grow. Assure students that it's OK for a person to wonder how tall he or she will be. Encourage students to talk with their parents or other trusted adults about any concerns they have about how they are growing.

ACTIVITY BOOK P. 3

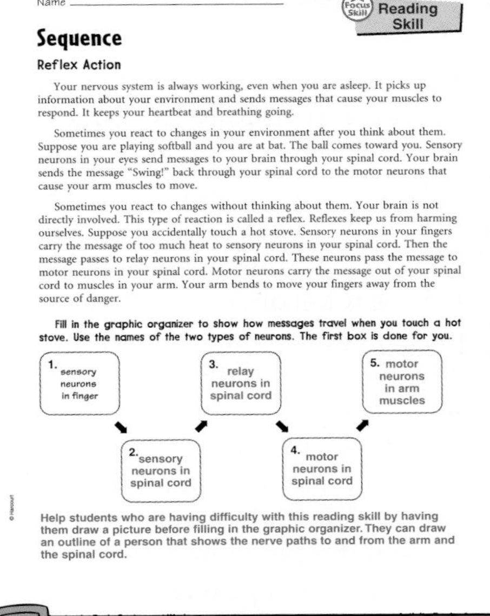

Name ____________

Focus Skill Reading Skill

Sequence

Reflex Action

Your nervous system is always working, even when you are asleep. It picks up information about your environment and sends messages that cause your muscles to respond. It keeps your heartbeat and breathing going.

Sometimes you react to changes in your environment after you think about them. Suppose you are playing softball and you are at bat. The ball comes toward you. Sensory neurons in your eyes send messages to your brain through your spinal cord. Your brain sends the message "Swing!" back through your spinal cord to the motor neurons that cause your arm muscles to move.

Sometimes you react to changes without thinking about them. Your brain is not directly involved. This type of reaction is called a reflex. Reflexes keep us from harming ourselves. Suppose you accidentally touch a hot stove. Sensory neurons in your fingers carry the message of too much heat to sensory neurons in your spinal cord. Then the message passes to relay neurons in your spinal cord. These neurons pass the message to motor neurons in your spinal cord. Motor neurons carry the message out of your spinal cord to muscles in your arm. Your arm bends to move your fingers away from the source of danger.

Fill in the graphic organizer to show how messages travel when you touch a hot stove. Use the names of the two types of neurons. The first box is done for you.

1. sensory neurons in finger
2. sensory neurons in spinal cord
3. relay neurons in spinal cord
4. motor neurons in spinal cord
5. motor neurons in arm muscles

Help students who are having difficulty with this reading skill by having them draw a picture before filling in the graphic organizer. They can draw an outline of a person that shows the nerve paths to and from the arm and the spinal cord.

© Harcourt

Available online. www.harcourtschool.com/health

Life Skills

Communicate
Make Responsible Decisions
Manage Stress
Refuse
Resolve Conflicts
Set Goals

Objectives

- ► Identify the steps for managing stress.
- ► Use the stress-management steps to deal with stress in a healthful way.

Program Resources

- ► Activity Book p. 4
- ► Poster 9

1. MOTIVATE

Ask students if they've ever heard the phrase "butterflies in your stomach." Having your stomach feel "jumpy" is a sign of stress. Ask volunteers for other signs of stress, such as a faster heartbeat, and give examples of situations in which people might feel stress.

2. TEACH

Direct students' attention to the photographs of LaToya. Ask a student volunteer to read the lead-in paragraph.

Step 1

How does stress feel to LaToya? She gets a headache and sweaty palms.

In what situation does LaToya feel stress? when she plays softball

Step 2

Why is LaToya feeling stress? She's afraid she won't perform well and will let her team down or be made fun of.

Manage Stress

As You Grow

It can be hard to deal with changes in your body as you grow. Sometimes you might feel clumsy. You might trip over your own feet or drop a ball. Use the steps for **Managing Stress** to help you handle the stress of your changing body.

Lately, LaToya has grown taller and thinner. She is having a hard time coordinating her hands and arms. How can LaToya handle the stress she feels when she plays softball?

1 Know what stress feels like and what causes it.

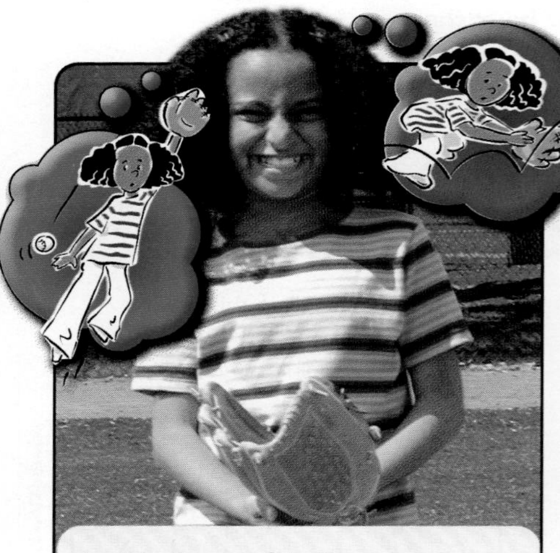

Just before softball games, LaToya gets a headache and sweaty palms.

2 Try to determine the cause of the stress.

LaToya feels stressed because she doesn't want to let the team down or be made fun of.

10

Teacher Tip

Sources of Stress Point out that stress can be positive or negative; much depends on how a person handles it. For example, LaToya is managing her stress by practicing. The stress is positive because LaToya is becoming a better player. LaToya's stress could be negative if she did nothing. If she didn't practice, her poor performance could let down the team and have a negative effect on her. Ask student volunteers to tell about a time when they dealt with stress in a positive way.

ACTIVITY BOOK P. 4

Name ____________

Problem Solving

Life Skill

Manage Stress

Steps for Managing Stress

1. Know what stress feels like and what causes it.
2. Try to determine the cause of the stress.
3. Prepare to handle a stressful situation.
4. Think positively rather than negatively.

Use the steps to help these students manage stress.

A. Devon is on a soccer team. Devon has not grown as much as his teammates, who are stronger and able to kick the ball farther. Although Devon is a fast runner, he is worried that he will be dropped from the team. He has trouble sleeping the night before every soccer game.

- Explain how Devon can manage his feelings of stress.

Possible answer: Devon can talk to his parents. He can also talk to his coach about his performance. The coach will help Devon become a better player and will point out his strengths. Devon can focus on doing his best and being a good team member.

B. Anya has grown taller in the past few months. She feels clumsy around her classmates. Whenever she has to give an oral report or perform in a skit, Anya's heart pounds and her face turns red. Anya has decided not to give oral reports or perform in skits anymore.

- Is Anya managing her stress in a healthful way? What would you say to Anya to help her manage her stress?

Possible answer: Avoiding activities is not a healthful response to stress. I would tell Anya that people grow at different rates and in different ways; remind her of her positive qualities; tell her to talk to her parents about the stress she is feeling.

© Harcourt

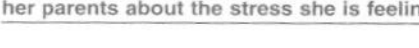

Available online.
www.harcourtschool.com/health

3 **Prepare to handle a stressful situation.**

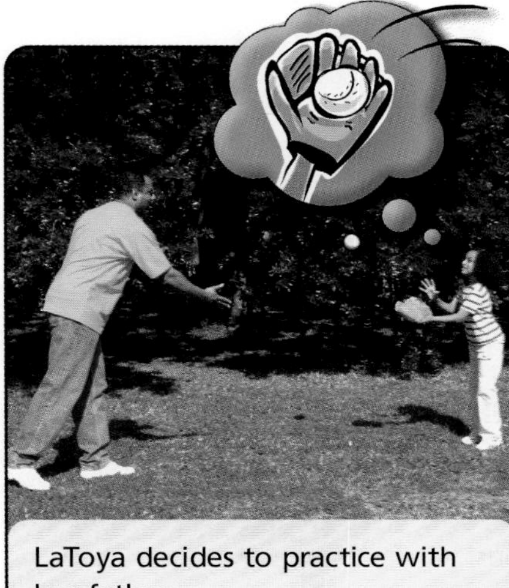

LaToya decides to practice with her father.

4 **Think positively rather than negatively.**

LaToya imagines herself catching the ball. She gives her full attention to what she is doing and tries her best.

Problem Solving

Miguel is getting ready to go to a party. He puts on his favorite jacket, but it doesn't fit. The sleeves are too short. Miguel is upset that he can't wear the jacket. Miguel has outgrown a lot of his clothes lately. Use the steps for **Managing Stress** to help Miguel manage his feelings about outgrowing his clothes. If you were Miguel's friend, what might you do to show caring in helping him to deal with his feelings?

Step 3

How does LaToya handle the stress she is feeling? She decides to practice with her father.

Critical Thinking What are other ways to handle stress? Possible answers: talk to a friend, talk to my parents, get physical activity, write in a journal or diary

Building Good Character

Tell students that personal responsibility means that a person takes care of his or her health. A responsible person doesn't blame others when a stressful situation arises. The person takes action to deal with the stress.

Step 4

How does LaToya think positively? She imagines herself catching the ball. She pays attention and tries her best.

3. WRAP UP

Problem Solving

Students might respond that they can share with Miguel their own experiences of outgrowing their clothes; people often feel better knowing that others understand what they are feeling. They might also point out to him the positive aspects about growing and suggest that Miguel share his feelings with his parents.

Using the Poster

Activity Hold a class discussion in which students describe techniques they have found to be effective for dealing with stress. Using the poster as a springboard, students can make their own posters informing others of ways to manage stress.

Display the poster to remind students of the steps for managing stress.

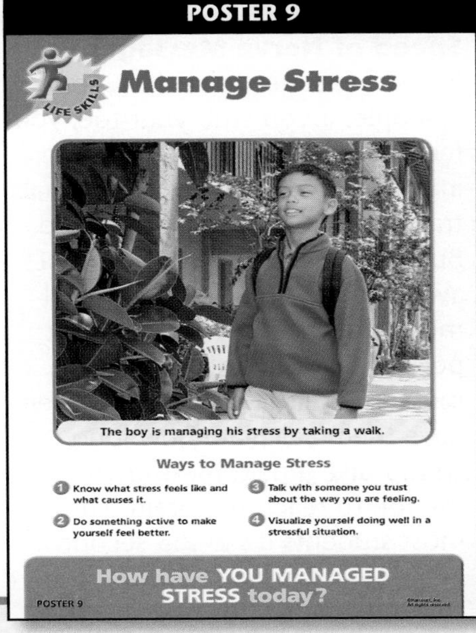

POSTER 9
Manage Stress
LIFE SKILLS
The boy is managing his stress by taking a walk.
Ways to Manage Stress
1 Know what stress feels like and what causes it.
2 Do something active to make yourself feel better.
3 Talk with someone you trust about the way you are feeling.
4 Visualize yourself doing well in a stressful situation.
How have YOU MANAGED STRESS today?
POSTER 9

LESSON 2

Pages 12–14

Objectives

- ► Explain the functions of the brain and nervous system.
- ► Describe behaviors that keep the nervous system healthy.

When Minutes Count . . .

Assign the Quick Study, Lesson 2, Activity Book pp. 1–2 (shown on p. 5).

Program Resources

- ► Activity Book pp. 1–2
- ► Transparencies 5, 9, 10

Vocabulary

nervous system p. 12, **brain** p. 12, **nerves** p. 12

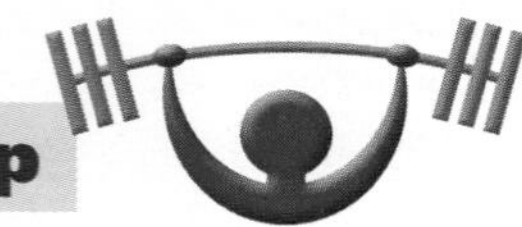

Daily Fitness Tip

The brain is protected by the skull. However, impacts to the head can still cause injury. Explain to students that they should wear helmets. Encourage students to identify activities in which a helmet should be worn.

For more about choosing appropriate safety equipment, see *Be Active! Resources for Physical Education* p. 183.

1. MOTIVATE

Ask students how they communicate with other people. Write their answers on the board. Possible answers: talk face to face; call or leave a message on the phone; use pagers; write letters and notes; send e-mail; sign; use hand signals; use facial expressions Tell students that in this lesson they will learn how the nervous system communicates and coordinates all the body's activities through a communication network.

When Minutes Count . . .

Transparencies 9, 10: The Nervous System; The Brain and the Skull can be used to present material in this lesson. *Interactive Transparencies available on CD-ROM.*

LESSON 2

The Brain and Nervous System

Lesson Focus

Your nervous system controls all your body systems, your emotions, your memory, and your learning.

Why Learn This?

When you know what your nervous system does, you understand why it's important to take care of it.

Vocabulary

nervous system
brain
nerves

Your Nervous System

Your **nervous system** coordinates all your body's activities. You might think of the nervous system as a communications system.

The nervous system has two main parts. One part is the central nervous system, made up of the brain and the spinal cord. The **brain** is an organ that controls the nervous system. The spinal cord is a long column of nerve tissue. It links the brain with other parts of your body and helps send and receive messages. The other part of the nervous system is made up of nerves. **Nerves** are bundles of fibers that carry messages.

Identify the parts of the nervous system. What messages are being communicated in this person's body?▲

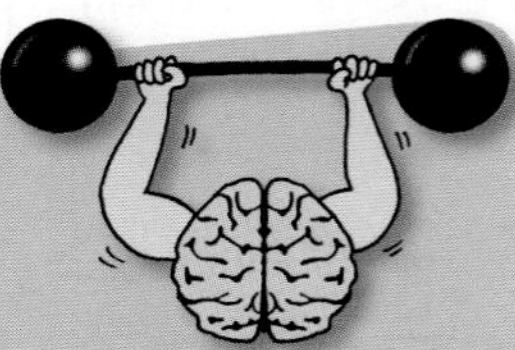

Myth and Fact

Myth: We use only 10 percent of our brain.

Fact: That figure was made up in the 1930s as part of an advertising campaign. Modern brain scans show that 100 percent of your brain is active.

12

Math

Speed of Nerve Messages
Nerve messages travel fast. For example, if you stub your toe, you feel the pressure almost immediately because touch signals travel about 250 feet per second. But you won't feel the pain right away because pain signals travel much slower—only about 2 feet per second. Have students measure their height in feet. Then have them calculate how long it would take a pain message from the toe to reach the brain. For most students it's 2–2.5 seconds.

Physical Education

Advocate for Safety Encourage students to identify different types of helmets for different activities. Have them make posters that illustrate students wearing the proper helmets while they are performing the activities. The posters should include a safety slogan encouraging others to wear helmets.

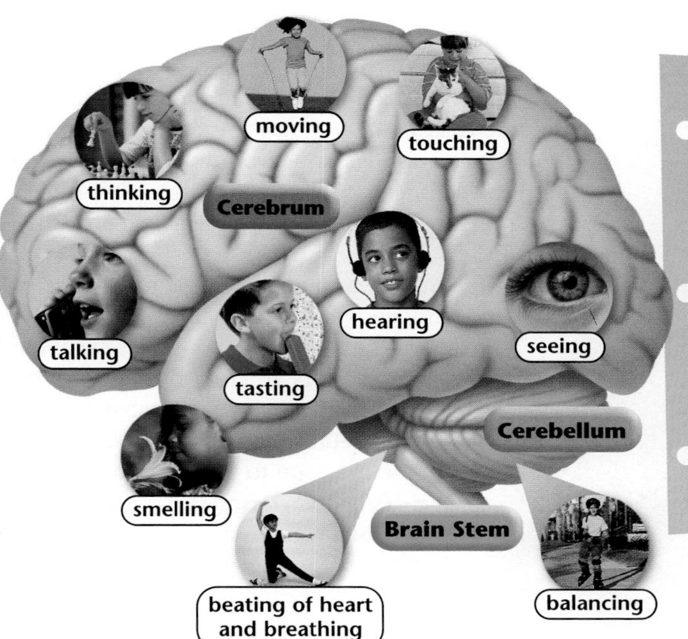

Personal Health Plan

Real-Life Situation
Your brain sends messages to parts of your body to help it function correctly. Suppose you want to help your brain do its job.

Real-Life Plan
Using the tips below, pick two behaviors that can help you take care of your brain. Write how you will plan to practice these behaviors.

The brain has three main parts. Each part has different jobs. Locate the parts in the diagram above.

The *cerebrum* (suh•REE•bruhm) controls thinking, memories, movement, and the five senses.

The *cerebellum* (sehr•uh•BEH•luhm) helps you keep your balance.

The *brain stem* controls your breathing and your heart rate.

SUMMARIZE How do the parts of the nervous system work together?
The brain is linked to all parts of the body and sends and receives messages through the nerves of the nervous system.

Caring for Your Nervous System

- Get enough sleep.
- Eat healthfully. Your brain needs protein and energy from foods.
- Avoid using tobacco, alcohol, and other harmful drugs.
- Wear a safety belt in vehicles.
- Wear a helmet for certain sports and physical activities.

13

2. TEACH

Interpret Visuals—Diagrams

Direct attention to the diagram of the brain. Help students orient its position relative to the body. Have students work with a partner to list five activities they did in the past five minutes and write which part of the brain controlled each activity.

Discuss

Instruct students to use their fingers to trace the sequence of messages from the body to the brain and back, using the picture on page 12.

Critical Thinking What is an example of the kind of quick communication that occurs between the brain and nerves throughout the body? Possible answer: catching a ball

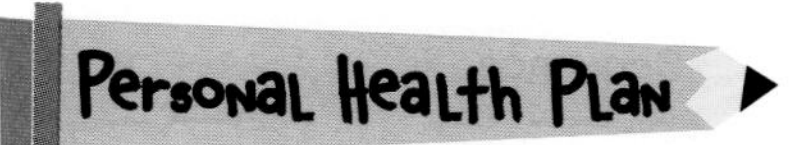

Plans should
- list two healthful behaviors.
- determine a goal.
- state specific actions to meet the goal.

Teacher Tip

Memory Power Tell students that one way to build memory is through connecting something you want to remember with something else that is interesting. Examples are a song to recall the alphabet or a sentence to recall the nine planets in order. Ask students to create a memory device to help them learn unfamiliar terms in this lesson.

Health Background

Human Brain The brain is divided into three main parts: the brainstem, the cerebellum, and the cerebrum. (1) The brainstem consists of the medulla, pons, midbrain, hypothalamus, and thalamus. The medulla regulates vital functions like heartbeat and breathing. The hypothalamus is the primary link between the nervous system and the endocrine system, while the thalamus relays sensory messages to the cerebral cortex. (2) The cerebellum maintains posture and balance, and helps coordinate voluntary movement. (3) The cerebrum is the source of intellectual activities. It holds memories and allows you to recognize people, read books, and play games. A layer of tissue about the thickness of a stack of three dimes covers the cerebrum and the cerebellum. This layer, the cortex, is where most information in the brain is processed. It's gray in color and is the reason the brain is sometimes called a person's gray matter.

Source: *National Institutes of Health*

3. WRAP UP

Lesson 2 Summary and Review

1. nervous system; brain; Nerves; brain stem; neurons
2. Answers may vary but should address how messages travel between the central nervous system (brain and spinal cord) and other parts of the body.
3. Answers may vary but should include helping your nervous system stay healthy; protecting it from injury or harm; and helping with such things as thinking, movement, the five senses, balance, breathing, heart rate, and growth.
4. Responses may include:

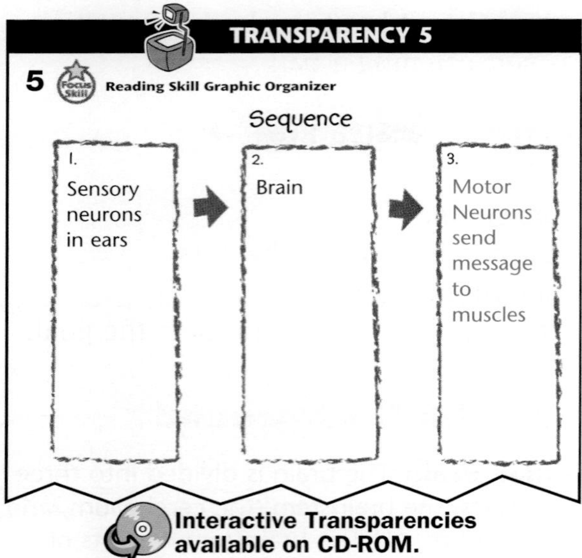

5. Narratives should include some of the common functions of the nervous system.

For **writing models** with examples, see *Teaching Resources* pp. 47–61. Rubrics are also provided.

When Minutes Count . . .

Quick Study Students can use *Activity Book* pages 1–2 (shown on p. 5) as they complete each lesson in this chapter.

Explain how this person's eyes, nerves, brain, and muscles work together to let her know when it is safe to cross the street. ▼

Messages to and from Your Brain

The brain and spinal cord respond to your body's needs through the messages carried by millions of nerve cells, or *neurons* (NOO•rahnz). Sensory neurons pick up messages from the body and send them to the brain or spinal cord. Motor neurons carry messages from the brain or spinal cord to muscles.

Suppose you are walking home and a stranger in a car pulls up beside you. Sensory neurons from your eyes carry the image to your brain. Your brain interprets the image and sends the message "Run!" to motor neurons in your spinal cord, which send the message to your leg muscles.

DRAW CONCLUSIONS Use what you read about neurons to describe what might happen when someone tosses you a ball.

Lesson 2 Summary and Review

1. **Summarize with Vocabulary**
   Use vocabulary and other terms from this lesson to complete these statements.
   Your _____ is made up of the brain, spinal cord, and nerves. The _____ controls the nervous system. _____ carry messages. The part of the brain that controls breathing is the _____. Another name for nerve cells is _____.
2. Explain how the nervous system is like a communications system.
3. **Critical Thinking** How might the tips on page 13 help your nervous system?
4. **SEQUENCE** Suppose you hear a strange noise in the middle of the night. Describe how messages move through your nervous system.

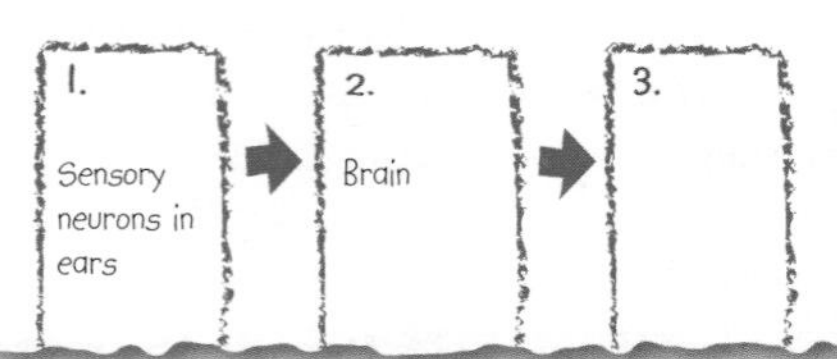

5. **Write to Inform—Narration**
   Write about a day in the life of your brain. Tell all the ways that your brain took care of your body and why its work was important.

14 Sensory neurons carry messages to the brain or spinal cord. Motor neurons carry messages from the brain or spinal cord. Your hand moves because the neurons send the messages of what has happened and instructions for what the body is to do, and so you might try to catch the ball.

Meeting Individual Needs
Leveled Activities

BELOW-LEVEL Trace a Diagram Ask students to trace the diagram of the brain shown on page 13. Have them list the various functions in the correct locations.

ON-LEVEL Make a Concept Map Have students find each boldfaced and italicized term in the lesson and make a concept map to show the relationships that exist among the parts of the brain and the rest of the nervous system.

CHALLENGE Investigate the Role of Sleep Ask students to use print or online sources to find out why the brain needs sleep. Students can prepare a brief report summarizing their findings and including tips for getting a good night's sleep.

Respect

Building Good Character

Accepting Individual Differences

People have different shapes and are different sizes. They also have different physical and mental abilities. Every person, regardless of ability, deserves to be treated with respect. Here are ways to show respect for individual differences:

- **Avoid using put-downs. Don't call someone names.**
- **Think about how the other person feels. Put yourself in that person's place.**
- **Apologize if you hurt someone's feelings.**
- **Avoid talking unkindly about someone just because of his or her looks.**
- **Encourage others to try their best, regardless of their abilities.**
- **Try not to exclude others from your clubs or games. Give everyone a fair chance.**
- **If you see a person bullying someone else, tell your teacher or another trusted adult.**
- **Appreciate what is special about yourself and others.**

Activity

During physical education or one of your other classes, encourage one of your classmates to do his or her best. Make a list of the ways that you can show respect toward others. Share your list with your classmates.

15

Building Good Character

Caring
Citizenship
Fairness
Respect
Responsibility
Trustworthiness

Objective

► Identify ways to show respect for others by accepting individual differences.

Program Resource

► Poster 4

BEFORE READING

Ask students to think about their best friend.

Is your best friend exactly like you? Students will most likely respond *no*. Point out that best friends accept the differences in each other. This is one way they show respect.

DISCUSS

After reading the list of ways to show respect, remind students that it's important to value people for who they are on the inside, not how they look or perform in school or sports. Point out that everyone is different from someone else. Ask volunteers for additional suggestions to show respect for differences.

ACTIVITY

Advise students that people who show respect for others usually receive respect back. As students keep their lists, ask them to also note in what ways other people seem more respectful to them. Have students relate their experiences when they share their lists with the class.

Using the Poster

Activity Have students work in small groups to discuss the poster and make a list of ways they can apply the poster's message to their relationships with friends, classmates, and family members.

Display Poster 4 to remind students of ways to show respect. The poster can be displayed in the classroom, the school cafeteria, or another common area.

POSTER 4
Respect
Building Good Character
The boy is showing respect by offering his seat to his aunt.
DO
► Treat others the way you want to be treated.
► Accept people who are different from you.
► Be polite and use good manners.
► Be considerate of the feelings of others.
► Stay calm when you are angry.
► Develop self-respect and self-confidence.
DON'T
► Don't use bad language.
► Don't insult or embarrass anyone.
► Don't threaten or bully anyone.
► Don't hit or hurt anyone.
How have YOU shown RESPECT today?
POSTER 4

LESSON 3

Pages 16–19

Objectives

- ► Identify the parts and functions of the digestive system.
- ► Describe behaviors that keep the digestive system healthy.

When Minutes Count . . .

Assign the Quick Study, Lesson 3, Activity Book pp. 1–2 (shown on p. 5).

Program Resources

- ► Activity Book pp. 1–2
- ► Transparencies 5, 11

Vocabulary

esophagus p. 16, **stomach** p. 16, **small intestine** p. 17, **large intestine** p. 17, **nutrients** p. 18

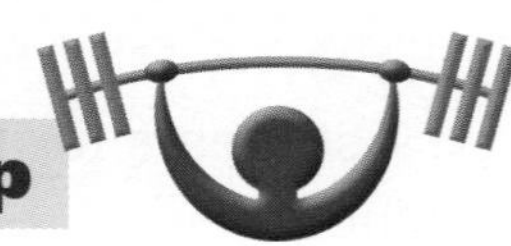

Daily Fitness Tip

Explain that digestion is the process of breaking down food into usable nutrients. Teeth are important to digestion because they break food up into tiny pieces when a person chews. Tell students they should brush their teeth twice daily with a fluoride toothpaste. Recommend that they see a dentist on a regular basis.

For more about food's effect on your body, see *Be Active! Resources for Physical Education* p. 143.

1. MOTIVATE

Optional Activity Materials soda crackers

Caution: Check for food allergies before giving any food to students.

Provide each student with a cracker. Ask students to bite off about half and hold it in their mouth.

What is happening to the cracker? It's becoming soft and breaking down.

Explain that saliva moistens food and contains chemicals that break it down. Ask students to chew the other half and notice the actions of their teeth and tongue.

The Digestive System

Lesson Focus
Your digestive system helps your body get energy from food.

Why Learn This?
Learning about your digestive system will help you take better care of it.

Vocabulary
esophagus
stomach
small intestine
large intestine
nutrients

Your Digestive System

Your body needs food. Food gives you energy to think, move, and grow. Your body needs energy for everything it does. The system that breaks down food is the digestive system.

The diagram shows your digestive system. It has several different parts. The mouth contains teeth, which break down food into smaller pieces. The **esophagus** (ih•SAH•fuh•guhs) is a tubelike organ that pushes food from your mouth to your stomach. The **stomach** is an organ that churns and mixes digestive juices with food.

The **small intestine** is another tubelike organ. It is just below your stomach. Food goes from the stomach to the small intestine. Another organ involved with digestion is the *liver*. The liver sends bile to the small intestine. Bile is a substance that breaks down fats into smaller particles that can be digested more easily.

The walls of the small intestine are lined with many small, finger-shaped bumps. Tiny blood vessels here absorb nutrients from digested food. From the small intestine, food goes to the **large intestine**, the last major organ of the digestive system. This tubelike organ handles solid wastes.

Did You Know?
The small intestine is about 22 feet long. That's the length of twenty-two notebooks laid end to end.

16

Cultural Connection

Breakfast in Different Cultures Cultural, religious, and genetic factors influence dietary customs. As an example, many people of Asian, African, and Native American descent lack an enzyme necessary to digest dairy products. Have groups of students choose a country or an ethnicity within the United States and research typical breakfast foods. For example, breakfast pizza is popular in Italy, sweet potato in New Guinea, and dried seaweed in Japan.

Teacher Tip

Type 2 Diabetes The number of children diagnosed with Type 2 diabetes is increasing. Eighty-five percent of those diagnosed were considered obese. Most children diagnosed with Type 2 diabetes are in middle to late puberty. The increase of overweight and less active children has doctors predicting that Type 2 diabetes will be seen in even younger children. For information on the importance of healthy eating and diabetes, see Chapters 3 and 7.

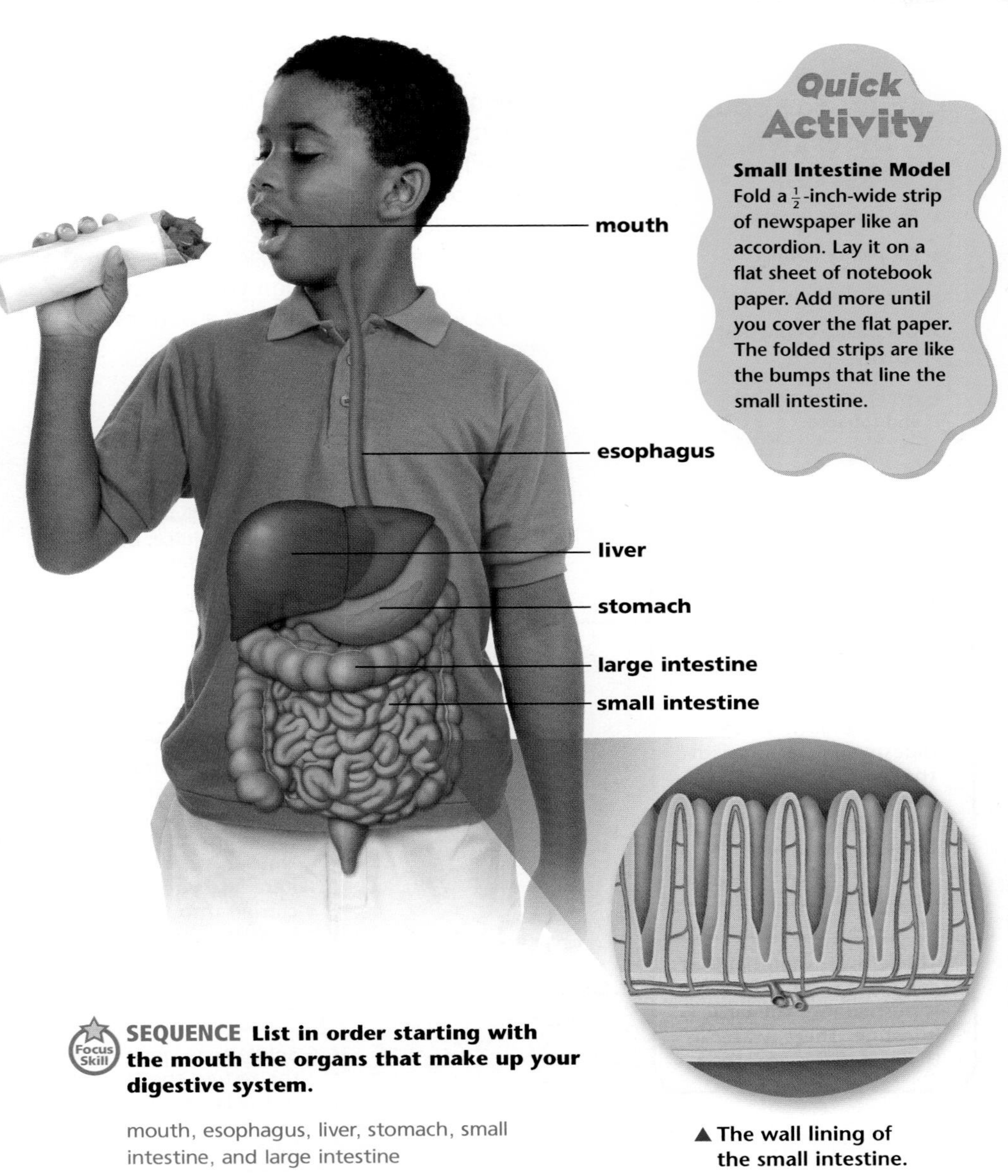

Quick Activity

Small Intestine Model Fold a $\frac{1}{2}$-inch-wide strip of newspaper like an accordion. Lay it on a flat sheet of notebook paper. Add more until you cover the flat paper. The folded strips are like the bumps that line the small intestine.

▲ The wall lining of the small intestine.

SEQUENCE List in order starting with the mouth the organs that make up your digestive system.

mouth, esophagus, liver, stomach, small intestine, and large intestine

17

2. TEACH

Interpret Visuals—Pictures

Ask students to point to each organ shown in the picture of the digestive system as you or a volunteer reads the caption and the passage on these two pages. The gall bladder is located behind the liver and the pancreas is located behind the stomach. Explain that food does not pass through the liver.

Why is the liver considered an organ of the digestive system? It produces a substance that breaks down fats in foods.

Direct attention to the close-up of bumps in the small intestine. These are villi, fingerlike projections that increase the surface area of the small intestine so that more nutrients can be absorbed. The large intestine does not contain villi.

Quick Activity

Lead students to recognize that the total surface area of the folded newspaper is greater than the area of the notebook paper. Point out that this is a flat model of how the tubular small intestine has a large surface area squeezed into a small space. Tell students that the inner surface area of an adult's small intestine could cover an area the size of a baseball diamond.

Teacher Tip

Fuel as Energy Explain that the body and a car are similar in one important way—they each need energy to work. A car gets its energy from gasoline. The body gets its energy from foods. Good-quality gas helps a car run well. Likewise, healthful food choices provide the energy and other materials the body needs to grow and function well.

Math

Length of Intestines Point out that the longest part of the path through the digestive system is the small intestine (about 22 feet) and the large intestine (about 5 feet). Have students measure, cut, and label different colors of yarn to represent the correct lengths of the small and large intestines. As an extension, students can research the time it takes for different types of food to pass through each part of the digestive system.

Health Background

Digestive System The human digestive tract is made up of a continuous tube consisting of the mouth, esophagus, stomach, small intestine, and large intestine. Accessory digestive organs—salivary glands, gall bladder, liver, and pancreas—produce substances that help digest foods. These secretions enter the digestive tube through ducts or tubes.

Source: *World Book Online Reference Center*

When Minutes Count . . .

Transparency 11: The Digestive System can be used to present material in this lesson. *Interactive Transparencies available on CD-ROM.*

TEACH *continued*

Discuss

Tell students that muscles in the mouth, esophagus, stomach, small intestine, and large intestine move without your having to think of moving them.

Critical Thinking Which body system controls the movement of muscles in the digestive system? nervous system

Problem Solving The nervous system and the digestive system work together to digest food. What might happen if nerve messages couldn't get to organs of the digestive system? Muscles wouldn't work and food wouldn't be digested.

Have students read the points listed under Caring for Your Digestive System. Ask them to describe how health behaviors affect their digestive system.

Content-Area Reading Support

Using Signal Words Direct attention to the first paragraph on page 19. Have a volunteer read the paragraph. Explain that the word *however* in the last sentence signals a contrast. **When we contrast two things, we examine how they are different. The *however* here emphasizes that body cells do not need fiber but that the digestive system does.**

Health Background

Health Benefits of Fiber Soluble fiber (dissolves in liquid) helps lower cholesterol levels and may help people with diabetes reduce their risk of heart disease. Oatmeal, beans, and citrus fruits have this type of fiber. Insoluble fiber (does not dissolve in liquid) helps with digestive function (prevention of constipation) and is found in most grains, fruits, and vegetables.

Source: *The Merck Manual of Medical Information Website*

For more background, visit the **Webliography** in Teacher Resources at **www.harcourtschool.com/health**
Keyword nutrition

Caring for Your Digestive System

- Eat healthful foods.
- Eat plenty of fiber.
- Drink plenty of water.
- Get plenty of physical activity.
- Avoid use of alcohol and tobacco.

Digestion of Food

Your body can't use food in the form that you eat it. Food must be broken down into **nutrients** (NOO•tree•uhnts), or substances the body can use. This process of breaking down food into nutrients is called *digestion*.

In the diagram below, you can see the path that food takes as it travels through your digestive system. Use your finger to trace the path as you read about each step.

1 Your teeth break food down into smaller pieces. Saliva, a digestive juice, begins breaking down starches.

2 Muscles in the esophagus push food from the mouth to the stomach.

3 In the stomach, more digestive juices mix with the food. The food gets churned, broken down into nutrients, and pushed out of your stomach as a thick liquid.

4 Most digestion takes place in the small intestine, where digestive juices finish breaking down food. Nutrients are absorbed here into your blood and carried throughout your body to your cells. Your cells use the nutrients for energy and growth.

5 The leftover material that can't be used by the body is pushed into the large intestine. There, water in the material is absorbed.

6 Solid wastes pass into the *rectum*, the last part of the large intestine, and then out of the body.

18

ESL/ELL Support

COMPREHENSIBLE INPUT Familiarize students with the parts and functions of the digestive system.

Beginning Have students trace the digestive system shown on page 17 and then label and describe the function of each organ.

Intermediate Provide a list of short, simple questions to which each answer is the name of an organ of the digestive system. Students list their answers. Ask students to also describe the function of the digestive system.

Advanced Assist students in writing the names of digestive organs and their definitions separately on index cards. Students mix up the cards, place them face down, and match the organ names with their definitions. Also ask them to describe the function of the digestive system.

Many foods contain an important substance called fiber. *Fiber* comes from plants. Your body cells don't need fiber. However, your digestive system needs it to help move food and wastes through the system. Oatmeal, brown rice, and beans are good sources of fiber. So are fruits such as oranges, apples, and pears. Vegetables such as broccoli, corn, and peas have a lot of fiber, too.

Drinking plenty of water and doing physical activity also help move food and wastes through your digestive system. A good way to protect your digestive system is to avoid tobacco and alcohol. These substances can cause diseases in digestive organs.

SUMMARIZE Why does your body need fiber?

Your body needs fiber to move food and wastes through your digestive system.

▼ **Which of these high-fiber foods are a part of your diet?**

Lesson 3 Summary and Review

1 Summarize with Vocabulary

Use vocabulary and other terms from this lesson to complete these statements.

The ____ pushes food from your mouth to your _____. Food spends time in the ____ before going to the _____, where water and solid wastes are removed. The _____ makes bile to help digest fats.

2 In what organ of the digestive system does most digestion of food take place?

3 Critical Thinking How can being ill affect your digestive process?

4 **SEQUENCE** Draw and complete this graphic organizer to show how food moves through the digestive system.

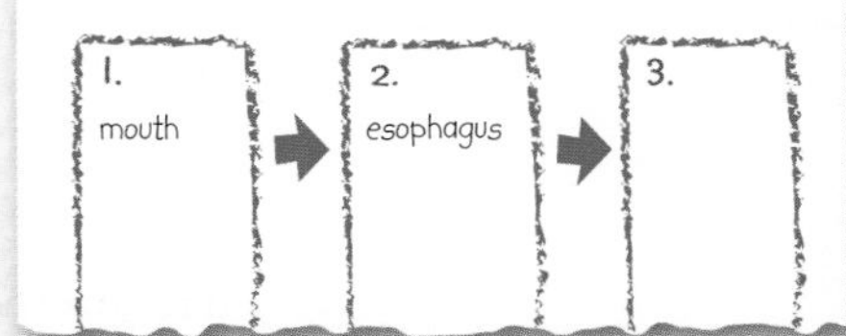

5 Write to Inform—Explanation

Write a paragraph explaining how to take care of your digestive system. How can your behavior help?

Art

Digestive System Models

Arrange students in small groups, and allow them to make small models of the digestive system. Provide materials such as highlighters, cardboard, colored paper, plastic foam, foam packing peanuts, plastic tubing, and yarn. Students can glue materials onto a sturdy backing. Encourage students to add text to their display, describing each part and providing tips to take care of the digestive system.

3. WRAP UP

Lesson 3 Summary and Review

1. esophagus; stomach; small intestine; large intestine; liver
2. the small intestine
3. Possible answers: Digestion may be slowed or stopped; food may be thrown up.
4. Responses may vary:

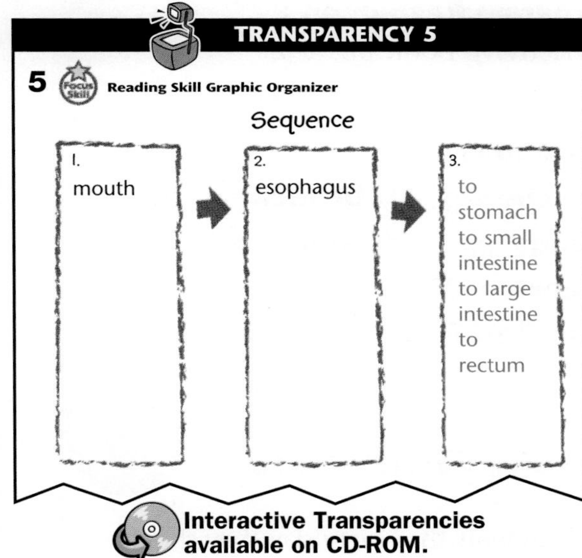

Interactive Transparencies available on CD-ROM.

5. Paragraphs should include that healthful foods help cells get nutrients they need; fiber, water, and exercise help move food and wastes; avoiding tobacco and alcohol helps prevent diseases.

For **writing models** with examples, see *Teaching Resources* pp. 47–61. Rubrics are also provided.

When Minutes Count . . .

Quick Study Students can use *Activity Book* pages 1–2 (shown on p. 5) as they complete each lesson in this chapter.

LESSON 4
Pages 20–23

Objectives
- ► Identify the parts and functions of the respiratory and circulatory systems.
- ► Describe healthful behaviors to take care of the respiratory and circulatory systems.

When Minutes Count . . .
Assign the Quick Study, Lesson 4, Activity Book pp. 1–2 (shown on p. 5).

Program Resources
- ► Activity Book pp. 1–2
- ► Transparencies 5, 12, 13

Vocabulary
trachea p. 20, **bronchi** p. 20, **lungs** p. 21, **diaphragm** p. 21, **heart** p. 22, **arteries** p. 22, **capillaries** p. 22, **veins** p. 22

Daily Fitness Tip
Tell students that every day they should engage in physical activity that causes an increase in their heartbeat and breathing. This helps the heart and lungs work at their best. Examples of vigorous physical activity are running, jumping rope, swimming, and skating.

For more about exercises that benefit the heart and lungs, see *Be Active! Resources for Physical Education* p. 139.

1. MOTIVATE
Have students place their hands on either side of their rib cage. Tell students to breathe in slowly as you describe what is happening: **As you breathe in, you can feel air pass through your nose into your trachea. Your ribs are being pulled up and out, making your chest larger. Now breathe out slowly. Feel your ribs move back to their original position and your chest become smaller.**

LESSON 4

The Respiratory and Circulatory Systems

Lesson Focus
Your respiratory and circulatory systems work together to carry oxygen and nutrients to body cells.

Why Learn This?
When you know how your respiratory and circulatory systems work, you understand why it's important to care for them.

Vocabulary
trachea
bronchi
lungs
diaphragm
heart
arteries
capillaries
veins

Your Respiratory System
You've probably seen someone choke because food "went down the wrong way." Instead of going into the digestive system, the food went into the respiratory system.

Your respiratory system moves air into and out of the body. All your body's cells need oxygen from the air to live. When you breathe in, air from your mouth or nose goes into your **trachea** (TRAY•kee•uh), an organ that carries air into the lungs. The trachea branches into two smaller tubes called **bronchi** (BRAHNG•ky).

The trachea and bronchi are coated with mucus. Mucus is a sticky substance that traps germs and dust. Tiny hairs line the trachea and bronchi. These hairs constantly sweep the mucus up and out. This keeps dirt and germs out of your lungs. Smoking and breathing in tobacco smoke harm these small hairs. Tobacco smoke destroys lung tissue. It also decreases the amount of oxygen that can get into blood cells.

The **lungs** are organs that allow oxygen to pass into your body. Inside the lungs, oxygen passes through the thin walls of tiny air sacs. There, the oxygen moves into the blood and is carried to all parts of the body. Carbon dioxide from all parts of the body is carried by your blood into the lungs. Carbon dioxide is a waste gas. It goes out of your body when you exhale.

20

Teacher Tip
Speech The respiratory system helps people speak. Have students place a hand lightly on the front of their neck. Tell them to first say "Ah" and then to blow as if they were blowing out a candle. Ask what difference they feel. The neck vibrates when saying "Ah." Tell students that when they create speech sounds, air passes between their vocal cords and makes them vibrate. The vibrations travel through the air, and we hear these vibrations as sound.

Breathing is made possible by the **diaphragm** (DY•uh•fram), a muscle beneath your lungs. When this muscle moves, air is moved into or out of your lungs.

SEQUENCE Follow the path of oxygen from your mouth or nose into your blood vessels.

Air enters through the nose or mouth and travels down the trachea and through bronchi into the lungs. In the lungs, the air moves into tiny air sacs where oxygen in the air passes into blood vessels.

Quick Activity

Graph Your Breathing Record the number of breaths you take while sitting, walking, and running at different speeds. Then graph and interpret the data you collect.

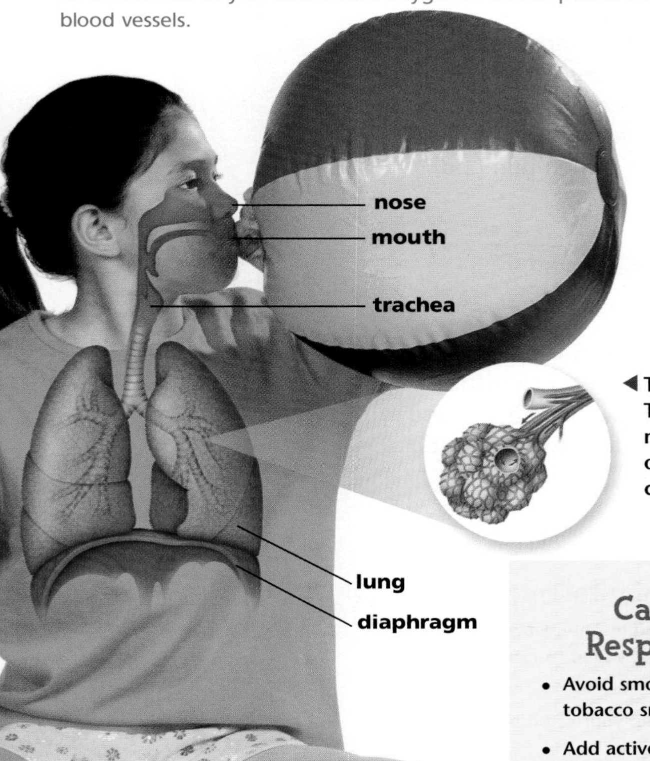

◀ The lungs contain tiny air sacs. The walls of these air sacs have many blood vessels, where oxygen enters the blood and carbon dioxide leaves it.

Caring for Your Respiratory System

- Avoid smoking and breathing in tobacco smoke.
- Add active exercise to your daily activity.
- If you have asthma, a breathing disorder, follow your doctor's directions and take your medicines.
- Exercise indoors on days of high air pollution.

21

Science

Analyze Breath You'll need drinking straws and limewater (calcium hydroxide solution). Have students blow gently through the straw into the limewater and record their observations. **Caution:** Tell students not to draw up or suck up the limewater.

The limewater should turn cloudy. Calcium carbonate, a chalky solid, forms as carbon dioxide in breath reacts chemically with the limewater to produce the cloudy liquid.

Social Studies

Air Pollution in Cities Air pollutants, such as toxic gases and very small particles, can cause serious health concerns, including throat irritation, difficulty breathing, and even cancer. Many daily newspapers list the level and types of air pollution in their city each day. Have students locate this indicator for their city or a large city near them in their newspaper or in a newspaper online.

2. TEACH

When Minutes Count . . .

Transparency 12: The Respiratory System can be used to present material in this lesson. *Interactive Transparencies available on CD-ROM.*

Discuss

Explain that cells need oxygen in order to get energy from nutrients. Explain that the more muscle cells work, the more energy they need.

Problem Solving What're some physical activities that make you breathe harder and deeper? Possible answers: running, jumping, dancing

Quick Activity

Discuss the purpose of the graph to compare the number of breaths among activities and the best type of graph to present the data. bar graph Point out that the length of time while recording the number of breaths for each activity must stay constant.

Health Background

Choking Normally when a person swallows, a flap of tissue called the epiglottis closes over the opening of the larynx (the glottis) to prevent food and fluids from entering the trachea. During inhalation the glottis is open to allow air to enter the trachea. If a person inhales while trying to swallow, the glottis doesn't close properly. Common causes of choking are eating while laughing; eating too fast; and walking, playing, or running with food or objects in the mouth.

Sources: *Textbook of Medical Physiology and American Red Cross*

For more background, visit the **Webliography** in Teacher Resources at **www.harcourtschool.com/health** **Keyword** first aid

TEACH *continued*

When Minutes Count . . .

Transparency 13: The Circulatory System can be used to present material in this lesson. *Interactive Transparencies available on CD-ROM.*

Interpret Visuals—Pictures

Direct attention to the picture of the circulatory system. Point out that the blood in the veins isn't really blue. It's actually a slightly darker red than the bright red blood in the arteries. Diagrams of the circulatory system usually show veins in blue to help distinguish the two types of vessels.

Tell students that capillaries are so narrow that red blood cells must pass through them in single file. Thirty red blood cells lined up take up only the space of a period at the end of a sentence.

Discuss

Ask students to describe the function of the circulatory system. Ask volunteers to read aloud the tips for Caring for Your Circulatory System. Explain that some diseases can be spread through getting someone else's blood in a cut or scratch you may have. People can carry diseases in their blood, but in many cases, you can't tell just by looking at a person if he or she is carrying a disease. For this reason caution should be used when injuries involve bleeding. For example, medical workers such as doctors, nurses, dentists, and EMTs wear gloves and safety glasses or face shields.

Tell students that when a person gets a cut, platelets clump together to trap red blood cells and form a blood clot. The blood clot hardens to make a scab that seals the cut.

Critical Thinking Why shouldn't you pick at a scab? You might make the cut bleed, and the clotting process would have to begin again.

Your Circulatory System

How are nutrients and oxygen carried all through your body? That's the job of the circulatory system. Your circulatory system is made up of your heart, blood, and *blood vessels*, which are tubes through which blood flows. Think of the blood as a train and blood vessels as tracks. The blood delivers oxygen and nutrients to cells like a train dropping off passengers at different stations.

The **heart** is an organ that pumps blood. From the heart, blood goes through vessels to the lungs, where it gives up carbon dioxide and picks up oxygen. Next, the blood moves through vessels back to the heart. The blood is then pumped into other vessels that go all through the body. **Arteries** are blood vessels that carry blood away from the heart. Arteries branch into **capillaries**, tiny blood vessels that deliver blood to tissues. From the capillaries, blood flows to **veins**, blood vessels that carry blood back toward the heart.

▼ Trace the flow of blood from the heart to one of the feet and back to the heart.

Caring for Your Circulatory System

- Eat foods low in fat and high in fiber. Fiber can help take away substances that may lead to fatty buildup in blood vessels.
- Eat foods high in iron to help your red blood cells carry oxygen.
- Avoid contact with another person's blood.
- Get plenty of physical activity to make your heart strong.
- Avoid tobacco use and tobacco smoke.

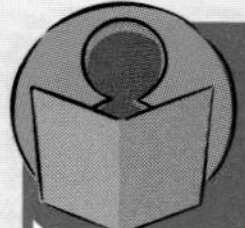

ESL/ELL Support

LANGUAGE AND VOCABULARY Clarify directional terms with students.

Beginning Ask students to trace the circulatory system and then use colored pencils to indicate veins and arteries. Have them write *toward* and *back* and draw arrows to show how blood flows relative to the heart.

Intermediate Have students identify directional terms, such as *into, away,* and *flows to* in the second paragraph on this page. Then have them describe in words and gestures what these words mean.

Advanced Have students use directional terms to write a paragraph telling how oxygen moves through the respiratory and circulatory systems.

Blood is made up of several parts. Over half of your blood is a liquid called *plasma*. The rest is made of cells. Red blood cells carry oxygen to all parts of your body. White blood cells attack and kill invading germs. Platelets help clot your blood and stop the bleeding from a cut or a wound.

MAIN IDEA AND DETAILS
List the three types of blood vessels, and tell what each type does.

Arteries carry blood away from the heart. Capillaries carry blood from arteries to veins. Veins carry blood back to the heart.

Heartbeats

Beats per minute: 0, 20, 40, 60, 80, 100, 120, 140
whale, human adult, dog, human child, cat

The hearts of some living things beat faster than others. For example, the heart of a hummingbird beats 700 times per minute. How much faster is that than a human child?

Lesson 4 Summary and Review

1. **Summarize with Vocabulary** Use vocabulary from this lesson to complete these statements.

   Air moves from your nose or mouth to the _____. When you breathe, your _____ moves air in and out of your lungs. Blood flows from your heart through _____ and returns through _____.

2. **Critical Thinking** What behaviors can harm your lungs and heart? What behaviors can help them?

3. How do your respiratory and circulatory systems work together?

4. **SEQUENCE** Draw and complete this graphic organizer to show how air moves through the respiratory system.

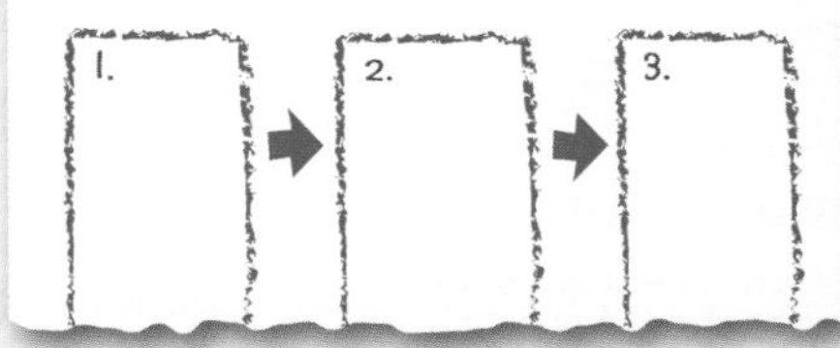

5. **Write to Entertain—Short Story** Imagine you are a red blood cell. Write a story that describes your journey through the circulatory system.

23

Interpret Visuals—Graphs

Hummingbird's 700 beats per minute minus a human child's 100 beats per minute equals 600 beats per minute. Ask students to find the difference between the number of heartbeats of some living things.

3. WRAP UP

Lesson 4 Summary and Review

1. lungs; diaphragm; arteries, veins
2. Possible answers: being around tobacco smoke; getting plenty of physical activity and eating healthfully
3. The respiratory system moves oxygen into the body. When blood flows into the lungs, blood cells pick up oxygen and take it to body cells.
4. Responses may vary:

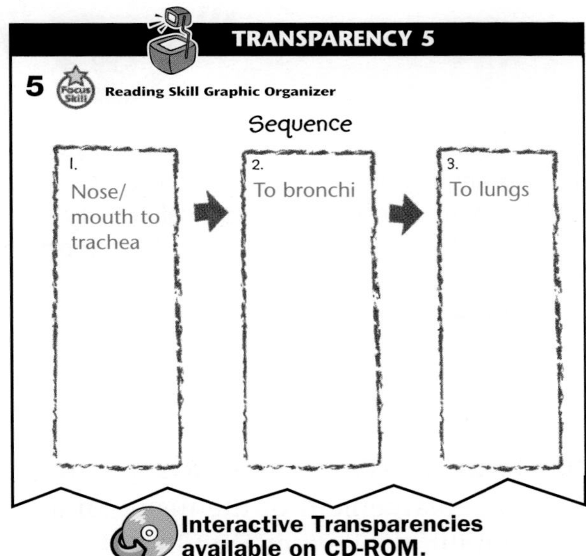

TRANSPARENCY 5
5 Reading Skill Graphic Organizer
Sequence
1. Nose/ mouth to trachea
2. To bronchi
3. To lungs
Interactive Transparencies available on CD-ROM.

5. Students should include the correct sequence of the flow of blood through the body.

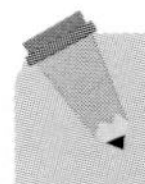

For **writing models** with examples, see *Teaching Resources* pp. 47–61. Rubrics are also provided.

Teacher Tip

Listen to the Beat Have small groups of students make a stethoscope-like instrument by slipping a 1-foot length of rubber tube over the small opening of a funnel. Demonstrate placing the wide end of the funnel over the heart while holding the other end of the tubing to your ear. Have group members listen to their own heartbeat. Explain that the "lubb dup" sound of a heartbeat is produced by the closing of valves in the heart.

Language Arts

Heart Healthy Behaviors Allow students to work in small groups to devise a slogan to help them remember tips for caring for their circulatory system. Then have them use their textbook and other references to identify at least one way they can follow each guideline. For example, one group might choose to demonstrate how to ask someone politely not to smoke around them.

When Minutes Count . . .

Quick Study Students can use *Activity Book* pages 1–2 (shown on p. 5) as they complete each lesson in this chapter.

LESSON 5
Pages 24–26

Objectives
- Explain the functions of the skeletal and muscular systems.
- Describe behaviors that keep the skeletal and muscular systems healthy.

When Minutes Count . . .
Assign the Quick Study, Lesson 5, Activity Book pp. 1–2 (shown on p. 5).

Program Resources
- Activity Book pp. 1–2, 5
- Transparencies 5, 14, 15
- Growth, Development, and Reproduction pp. 34–43

Vocabulary
skull p. 24, **skeletal system** p. 24, **spine** p. 24, **muscle** p. 25, **muscular system** p. 25

Daily Fitness Tip
Tell students that before doing any vigorous physical activity, they should stretch their muscles. Stretching before physical activity helps protect muscles from injury. Stretching after exercise when muscles are warm improves range of motion.

1. MOTIVATE
Optional Activity Materials picture showing enlargement of the inside of a long bone in the arm or leg

Ask students if they believe that bone is solid. Pass around the picture and point out that bone is living tissue through which nerves and blood vessels flow. The inside of the bone resembles a honeycomb. Nevertheless, bones are very strong. In fact, for its weight, bone is five times stronger than steel!

When Minutes Count . . .
Transparency 14: The Skeletal System can be used to present material in this lesson. *Interactive Transparencies available on CD-ROM.*

The Skeletal and Muscular Systems

Lesson Focus
Your skeletal and muscular systems support your body, protect your organs, and help you move.

Why Learn This?
When you know how your skeletal and muscular systems work, you will understand why it's important to take care of them.

Vocabulary
skull
skeletal system
spine
muscle
muscular system

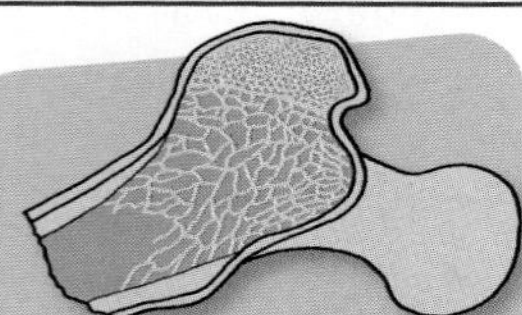

Myth and Fact
Myth: Bones are solid.
Fact: The outsides of bones have canals through which blood vessels pass. The insides of bones look like honeycombs and contain bone marrow, fat cells, and blood vessels.

Your Skeletal System
The bones in your head, called the **skull**, protect your brain. Bones make up the **skeletal system**, a body system that supports your body, protects your organs, and helps you move.

Your **spine**, or backbone, is made up of small bones that protect your spinal cord. Each of these bones has a hole in the center, as in a tire. These bones fit together, one on top of the other. Your spinal cord runs from your brain down your back inside your spine.

Your spine, pelvis, and leg bones work together to let you stand up straight, twist, turn, bend, and walk.

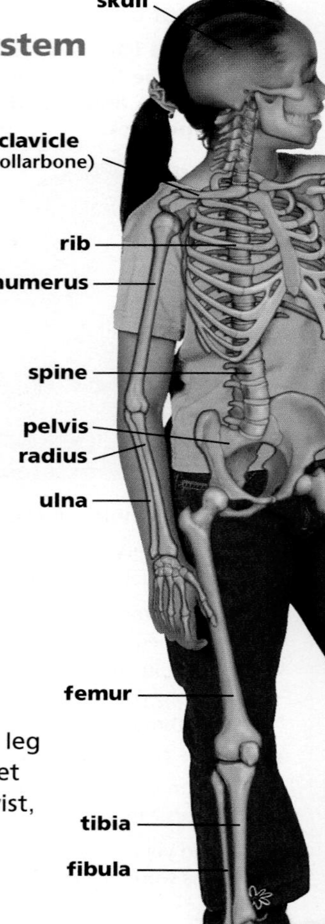

SEQUENCE List the order of bones from the skull to the hips.

skull, clavicle (collarbone), rib cage, humerus, spine, pelvis

24

Social Studies
Bone Tools Tell students that because bone tissue is so hard, prehistoric cultures used animal bones to make tools and weapons. Have students investigate the types of tools and weapons that were created from bone and find out how prehistoric civilizations made the tools.

Teacher Tip
Muscle Contraction Have a volunteer stand in a doorway with his or her arms at the side, palms facing toward the body. Tell the student to push against the sides of the door frame with the backs of the hands for about 30 seconds. Then ask the volunteer to relax his or her hands and move from the doorway. Have the class observe what happens. (The student's arms will slowly rise without effort from the student.) Tell students that the reason the arms move is because the muscles are still contracted.

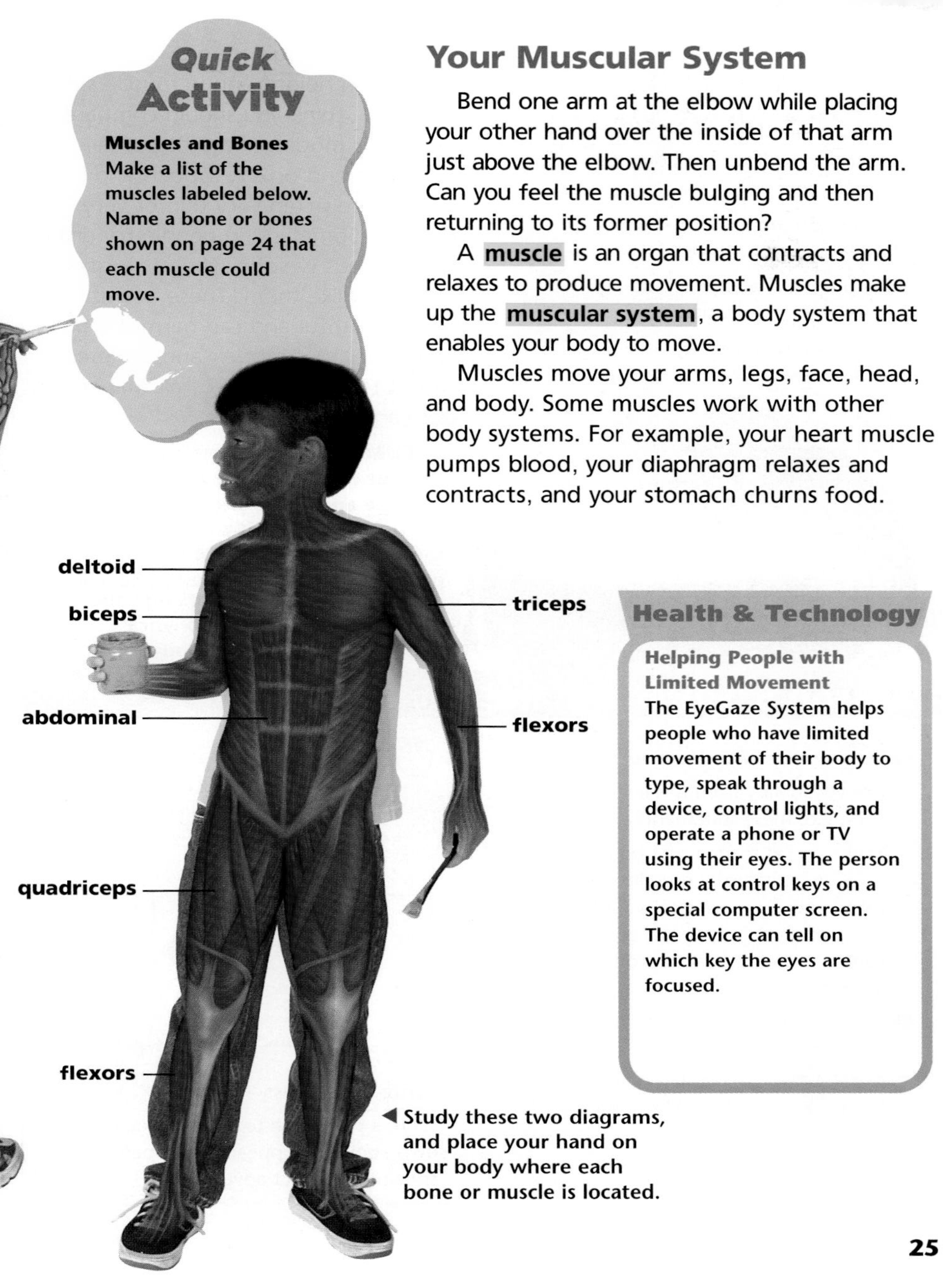
Quick Activity
Muscles and Bones
Make a list of the muscles labeled below. Name a bone or bones shown on page 24 that each muscle could move.
deltoid
biceps
abdominal
quadriceps
flexors
triceps
flexors

Your Muscular System

Bend one arm at the elbow while placing your other hand over the inside of that arm just above the elbow. Then unbend the arm. Can you feel the muscle bulging and then returning to its former position?

A **muscle** is an organ that contracts and relaxes to produce movement. Muscles make up the **muscular system**, a body system that enables your body to move.

Muscles move your arms, legs, face, head, and body. Some muscles work with other body systems. For example, your heart muscle pumps blood, your diaphragm relaxes and contracts, and your stomach churns food.

Health & Technology

Helping People with Limited Movement
The EyeGaze System helps people who have limited movement of their body to type, speak through a device, control lights, and operate a phone or TV using their eyes. The person looks at control keys on a special computer screen. The device can tell on which key the eyes are focused.

◀ Study these two diagrams, and place your hand on your body where each bone or muscle is located.

25

Meeting Individual Needs
Leveled Activities

BELOW-LEVEL Show Good Posture Have students practice standing and sitting using good posture. Explain that this helps take care of muscles around the spine.

ON-LEVEL Take a Stretch Break Encourage students to ask the physical education teacher to teach them stretches to perform after sitting for a while. Have students perform the stretches throughout the day.

CHALLENGE Make a Table Calcium is needed for strong bones and is involved in muscle contraction. Ask students to use references to identify foods that are good sources of calcium and then to prepare a table showing the foods, the amount of calcium per serving, and the daily requirement of calcium for children their age. Have students include an explanation of why calcium is important.

2. TEACH

When Minutes Count . . .

Transparency 15: The Muscular System can be used to present material in this lesson. *Interactive Transparencies available on CD-ROM.*

Content-Area Reading Support

Use Signal Words Point out that the second sentence of the second paragraph states a main idea: *Some muscles work with other body systems.* Have a volunteer read the next sentence aloud. Explain that the phrase *for example* signals that there are details that support the idea. Tell students to pay attention to signal words to better understand how ideas are connected.

Interpret Visuals—Diagrams

As you read the name of each bone or muscle aloud from the diagrams on these two pages, ask students to name the bone or muscle that it moves with.

Quick Activity

Students should discover that the eyes will eventually blink and that blinking is both voluntary and involuntary. Students can cause their eyelids to blink. Eyelids also blink involuntarily to moisten the eyes or to protect them when an object suddenly comes close.

Health Background

Remodeling of Bone Bones are continuously breaking down and reforming, a process called remodeling. Bones grow in width and length while people are growing. They sometimes grow in width in later life. Bones increase in density until about the age of 30. After that, bones break down faster than they form.

Source: *The Merck Manual of Medical Information*

GO
ONLINE

For more background, visit the **Webliography** in Teacher Resources at **www.harcourtschool.com/health**
Keyword human body

3. WRAP UP

Lesson 5 Summary and Review

1. skeletal system; muscular system; skull; spine; muscle
2. When voluntary muscles contract, they pull on bones.
3. Possible answers: get physical activity and plenty of calcium; live a healthful lifestyle and eat healthful foods
4. Responses may vary:

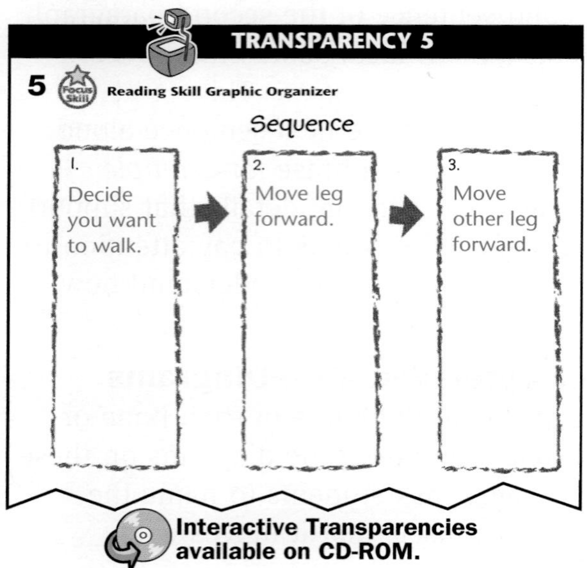

TRANSPARENCY 5
5 Focus Skill Reading Skill Graphic Organizer
Sequence
1. Decide you want to walk.
2. Move leg forward.
3. Move other leg forward.
Interactive Transparencies available on CD-ROM.

5. Paragraphs may vary but should include that unhealthful practices can harm the body.

For **writing models** with examples, see *Teaching Resources* pp. 47–61. Rubrics are also provided.

When Minutes Count . . .

Quick Study Students can use *Activity Book* pages 1–2 (shown on p. 5) as they complete each lesson in this chapter.

Growth, Development, and Reproduction An optional lesson about the reproductive system is provided in this supplement on pp. 34–43. Use this component in compliance with state and local guidelines.

Caring for Your Skeletal and Muscular Systems

- Eat food with plenty of calcium for strong bones.
- Get plenty of physical activity for strong bones and muscles.
- Wear protective equipment during certain physical activities.
- Warm up your muscles by stretching before strenuous physical activity.

People your age are growing and changing in height and in muscle size. You might think you should compare yourself to models and athletes in magazines and on TV. Models and athletes are often very thin or very muscular. Some young people try drugs or dangerous weight-lifting exercises to try to look like them. These activities are unhealthful and can harm the body. Remember that models and athletes are not typical. People of all shapes and sizes can be healthy.

COMPARE AND CONTRAST How are your muscular and skeletal systems alike and different? Alike: both systems hel body to move, and they work with other systems. Different: the skeletal system gives support and protects organs. The muscular system helps you m

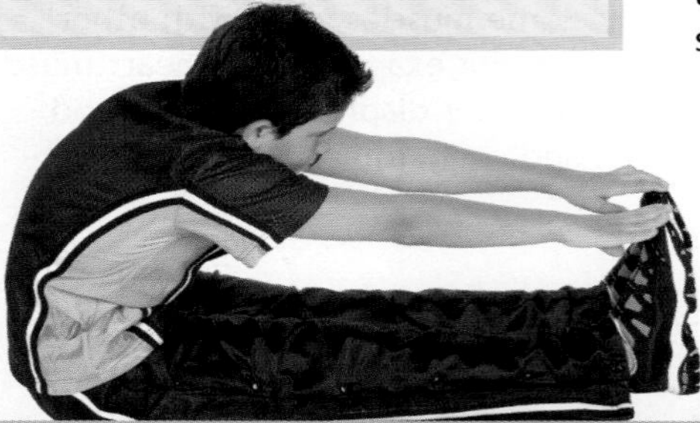

◀ **Stretching and working your muscles are good physical activities for your body.**

Lesson 5 Summary and Review

1. **Summarize with Vocabulary**
   Use vocabulary from this lesson to complete these statements.
   Your _____ is made up of bones, and your _____ is made up of muscles. The bones called your _____ protect your brain. Your _____ protects your spinal cord. A _____ contracts and relaxes to produce movement.
2. How do muscles work with bones to allow you to move?
3. **Critical Thinking** What behaviors help you have strong bones and muscles?
4. **SEQUENCE** Draw and complete this graphic organizer to show how muscle movements enable you to walk.

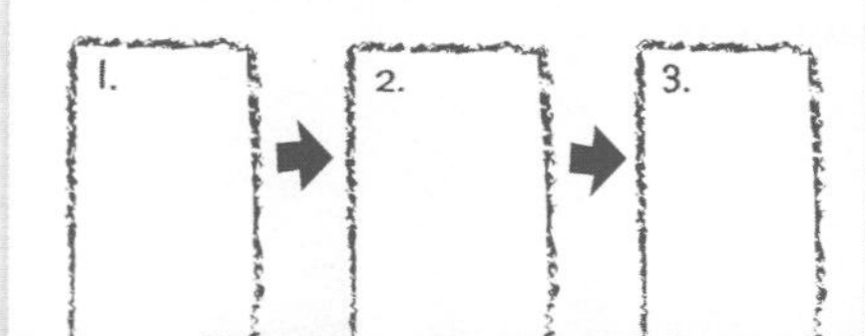

5. **Write to Express—Idea**

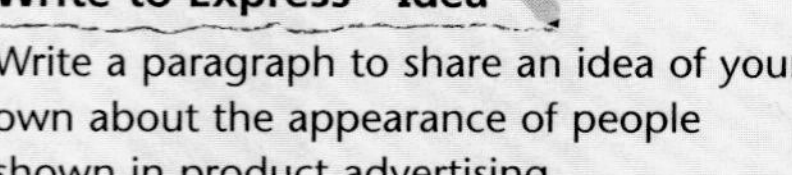

Write a paragraph to share an idea of your own about the appearance of people shown in product advertising.

26

ACTIVITY BOOK P. 5

Name ____________

Vocabulary Reinforcement

Multiple Choice

A. Circle the letter of the correct answer.

1. Messages are carried through the body by ____.
   A arteries (C) nerves
   B the brain D veins
2. Air moves first from the nose to the ____.
   F bronchi H diaphragm
   (G) trachea J esophagus
3. ____ carry blood away from the heart.
   A Capillaries C Muscles
   (B) Arteries D Veins
4. Food is NOT broken down in the ____.
   (F) esophagus H small intestine
   G mouth J stomach
5. The ____ protects the brain from injury.
   A muscular system C spine
   B nerves (D) skull
6. The movement of your ____ moves air in and out of your lungs.
   F esophagus (H) diaphragm
   G heart J stomach

B. Explain your answer to question 6.

Possible answer: The movement of the diaphragm makes breathing possible. The diaphragm is a muscle beneath your lungs. When the diaphragm moves, air is moved into or out of your lungs.

© Harcourt

Available online. www.harcourtschool.com/health

Science

Muscle Cells The three types of muscle cells—skeletal, smooth, and cardiac—are easy to tell apart under a microscope. If possible, show students prepared slides of these three types. Have students compare and contrast what they see. Skeletal muscle cells have a long shape, many nuclei, and light and dark bands. Smooth muscle cells taper, have one nucleus, and no bands. Cardiac muscle cells have a branched shape, one or more nuclei, and bands.

ACTIVITIES

Physical Education

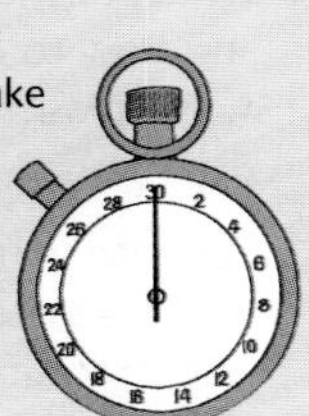
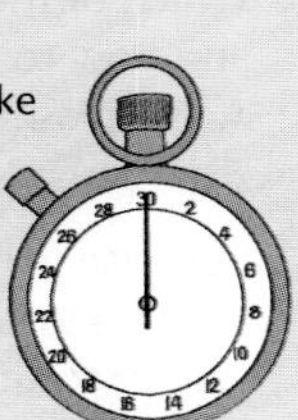

Check Your Pulse Learn from your teacher how to take your pulse. Run in place for a minute, and then retake your pulse. Explain the increase in your pulse rate.

Home & Community

Appreciating Family Members Tell family members what you learned about the importance of appreciating individual differences. Let each person in your family know what you appreciate about him or her. Give each family member a chance to do the same thing.

Science

Compare Blood Cells Use reference materials to find pictures and descriptions of blood cells. Draw a picture of what a drop of blood might look like under a microscope.

Career Link

Medical Doctor A medical doctor is a physician who can treat a number of body system problems. Suppose you are a medical doctor. You have a patient who broke her arm because she was skateboarding too fast and went out of control. What would you tell your patient about following safety rules? What other ways would you tell her to protect her nervous, skeletal, and muscular systems?

Technology Project

Review the chapter and list the main ideas of each lesson. Make an outline of ways to take care of your body systems. Use a computer to make a presentation. If a computer is not available, make a colorful poster or some slides to display your outline.

For more activities, visit The Learning Site. www.harcourtschool.com/health

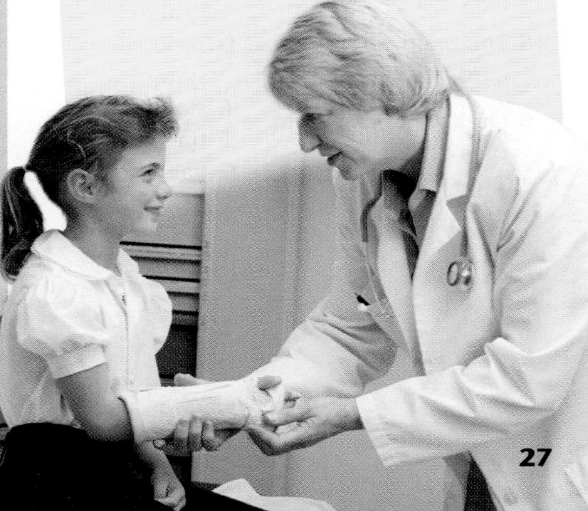

27

Career Link

Medical Doctor Invite students to share their ideas for following safety rules and protecting body systems as you write them on the board. Have students work in small groups to develop and present a brief skit based on the given scenario.

Encourage interested students to identify medical specialties related to the body systems studied in this chapter (for example, cardiology, neurology, orthopedics). Students who are interested in a medical career may want to find out more about the education and training needed to become a medical doctor.

For more information on health careers, visit the **Webliography** in Teacher Resources at **www.harcourtschool.com/health**
Keyword health careers

Activities

Physical Education

Instruct students to turn their left palm up and then place the first two fingers of the right hand on their left wrist just beneath the thumb. Advise students that they may have to move their fingers around a little to feel the pulse. Tell them not to press too hard or they will not feel the pulse.

Science

Remind students that blood is made up of a liquid and individual cells. Their drawings should show the cells. Blood cells are present in roughly these ratios: red blood cells 500: platelets 25: white blood cells 1.

Home & Community

Before students do this activity at home, remind them that there are many ways to appreciate someone. For example, you can appreciate people for what they do for you (teach you, care for you, encourage you), for qualities you admire, or for their affection and friendship. Encourage students to share with their families all the ways in which students appreciate them.

Supports the Coordinated School Health Program

Technology Project

Suggest several options for computer-generated presentations. Students may choose to create a slide presentation or use a word processing program to make diagrams or tables.

Chapter Review and Test Preparation

Pages 28–29

Reading Skill 5 pts. each

1. Students should indicate that food travels down the esophagus to the stomach and then to the small intestine, where nutrients are absorbed into the blood and then are carried through the body via the circulatory system to body cells.
2. Students should indicate that veins return blood to the heart. From the heart, arteries carry the blood to the lungs and then through veins back to the heart, where the blood is again pumped away from the heart through arteries, this time to the arm.

Use Vocabulary 5 pts. each

3. G, trait
4. A, cell
5. C, nervous system
6. E, stomach
7. F, trachea
8. B, heart
9. D, skeletal system

Check Understanding 5 pts. each

10. B, nucleus
11. J, muscular
12. A, pituitary gland
13. H, clavicle
14. C, Body Systems
15. H, move messages to the brain

Think Critically 5 pts. each

16. The person would probably lose weight because body cells cannot divide and grow without nutrients.
17. Smoking damages the small hairs in the trachea and bronchi. The hairs cannot do their job as well, so people who smoke must cough to get rid of mucus and dust.

Chapter Review and Test Preparation

Reading Skill

SEQUENCE

Draw and then use this graphic organizer to answer questions 1 and 2.

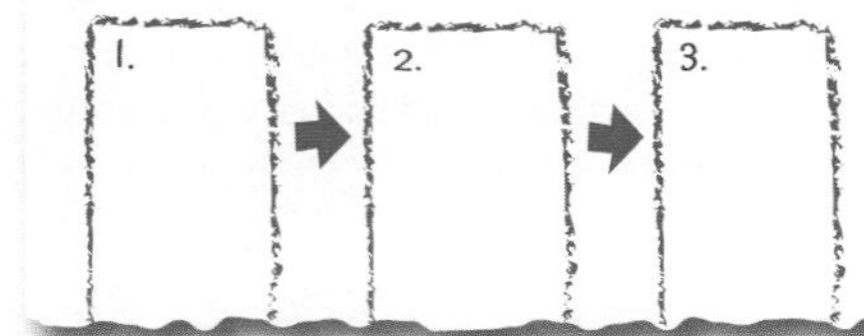

1 Show the path of nutrients from the mouth to body cells.

2 Show how blood flows from a vein in the leg to an artery in the arm.

Use Vocabulary

Match each term in Column B with its meaning in Column A.

Column A	Column B
3 Characteristic	**A** cell
4 The smallest working part of your body	**B** heart
5 The brain, spinal cord, and nerves	**C** nervous system
6 Organ that churns to break down food	**D** skeletal system
7 Organ that carries air into the lungs	**E** stomach
8 Organ that pumps blood	**F** trachea
9 Body system that protects organs	**G** trait

Check Understanding

10 Which of the following tells cells when and how to do their job? (p. 6)

A cytoplasm **C** tissue
B nucleus **D** cell membrane

11 Suppose you touch a hot stove. Your nervous system works with your _____ system to make your hand draw back. (p. 25)

F circulatory **H** digestive
G respiratory **J** muscular

12 The _____ at the base of your brain controls your breathing and heart rate. (p. 13)

A heart
B cerebrum
C brain stem
D cerebellum

13 Which belongs in the skeletal system? (p. 24)

F heart

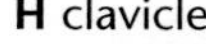
H clavicle

G biceps
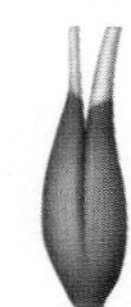

J stomach

28

Formal Assessment

ASSESSMENT GUIDE P. 19

Name _______________

1 Chapter Test

Body Systems at Work

Match the words below to the sentences. Write the correct letter on the line to the left of the sentence.

a trachea	**d** bronchi	**g** lungs	**j** diaphragm
b heart	**e** arteries	**h** capillaries	
c veins	**f** brain	**i** nerves	

_i_ **1.** These bundles of fibers carry messages to and from the brain or spinal cord.
_a_ **2.** This organ carries air from your nose and mouth to your lungs.
_h_ **3.** These tiny blood vessels deliver blood to your body's tissues.
_g_ **4.** These organs allow oxygen to pass into your body.
_d_ **5.** These two tubes, found at the end of the trachea, bring air to the lungs.
_e_ **6.** These blood vessels carry blood away from the heart.
_f_ **7.** This organ controls the nervous system.
_b_ **8.** This organ is responsible for pumping blood throughout your body.
_c_ **9.** These blood vessels carry blood toward the heart.
_j_ **10.** This muscle, located below your lungs, makes breathing possible.

© Harcourt

ASSESSMENT GUIDE P. 20

Name _______________

Write the letter of the best answer on the line at the left.

_C_ **11.** Your parents passed this characteristic, or quality, down to you.
A cell **C** trait
B tissue **D** nucleus

_G_ **12.** This tubelike organ pushes food from your mouth to your stomach.
F diaphragm **H** trachea
G esophagus **J** small intestine

_B_ **13.** Digestion breaks food into these substances, which the body can use.
A capillaries **C** organs
B nutrients **D** nucleus

_F_ **14.** This is the smallest working part of your body.
F cell **H** tissue
G stomach **J** trait

_B_ **15.** This organ churns and mixes digestive juices with food.
A esophagus **C** trachea
B stomach **D** diaphragm

Write *T* or *F* to show whether the sentence is true or false.

_F_ **16.** A group of cells that work together to do a job is an organ.
_T_ **17.** Your skeletal system includes your skull, your spine, and your other bones.
_F_ **18.** The system that enables your body to move is your circulatory system.
_F_ **19.** Your nervous system includes your brain, nerves, and spine.
_F_ **20.** Your small and large intestines are part of your respiratory system.

© Harcourt

14 Which of the following is the missing term needed to complete the graphic organizer? (p. 7)
A Tissue Systems
B Communication Systems
C Body Systems
D Cell Systems

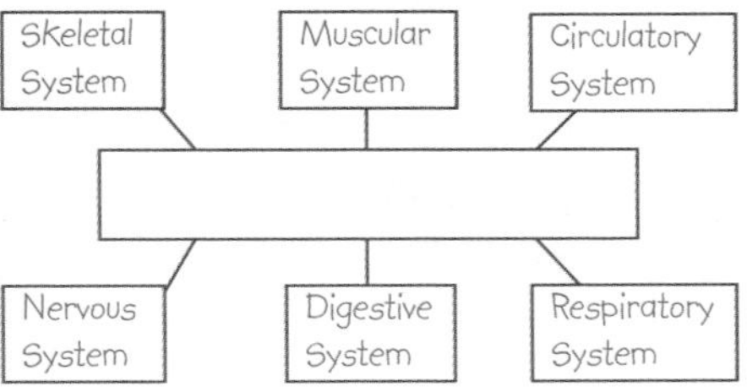

15 Which of the following does the skeletal system NOT do? (p. 24)
F protect your organs
G support your body
H move messages to the brain
J help you move

Think Critically

16 A person has a disease in which the small intestine does not absorb nutrients well. What might be the effects of that disease? Explain your answer.

17 Many people who smoke get lung infections and cough more than people who do not smoke. Why do you think this is true?

Apply Skills

18 **BUILDING GOOD CHARACTER**
Responsibility When you ride in a car with your older sister, she never puts on her safety belt. Applying what you know about taking care of the nervous system, what could you do to be a positive role model for your sister?

19 **LIFE SKILLS**
Set Goals You want to make your heart and muscles stronger through physical activity. List five activities that you enjoy, such as skateboarding or jumping rope. Set a goal to fit at least one of those activities from your list into your schedule every day.

Write About Health

20 **Write to Inform—Explanation** Explain how getting plenty of physical activity helps all of your body systems.

29

ASSESSMENT GUIDE P. 21

Name ______

When you are hungry and you eat, your body uses all the major organ systems. Tell how each system below is used when you eat a snack because you are hungry.

21. nervous system Possible answer: Nerves carry the hunger message from the stomach to the brain. Then the brain sends messages to the muscles to produce eating movements.

22. muscular system Possible answer: The muscular system receives messages from the brain to produce eating movements.

23. digestive system Possible answer: As you eat the snack, the digestive system breaks down the food into nutrients your body can use.

24. circulatory system Possible answer: The nutrients from the food are carried by the circulatory system to cells in all parts of the body. As cells process the nutrients, they produce carbon dioxide, which the circulatory system carries to your lungs.

25. respiratory system Possible answer: When carbon dioxide reaches your lungs, it is exchanged for oxygen, which the respiratory system has brought to the lungs.

Apply Skills 5 pts. each

18. Answers should include that the student will always wear a safety belt when riding with the sister. Students may respond that they would tell the sister about the importance of wearing safety belts.

19. Answers will vary but should include five physical activities and when the student will do them. For example: I will jump rope after school every other day.

Write About Health 5 pts.

20. Answers may include making bones, muscles, heart, and lungs stronger; helping body cells in all the systems get oxygen and nutrients; helping the digestive system move food and wastes.

Performance Assessment

Use the Chapter Project and the rubric provided on the Project Evaluation Sheet. See *Assessment Guide* pp. 18, 56, 62.

Portfolio Assessment

Have students select their best work from the following suggestions:

- Leveled Activities, p. 8
- Quick Activity, p. 21
- Write to Inform, p. 19
- Activities, p. 27

See *Assessment Guide* pp. 12–16.

CHAPTER 2 Personal Health

Lesson	Pacing	Objectives	Reading Skills
Introduce the Chapter pp. 30–31		• Preview chapter concepts.	**Main Idea and Details** pp. 31, 336–337
1 **Your Skin and Its Care** pp. 32–35	1 class period	• Describe the structure and function of skin. Explain how to take care of skin, including the use of sunscreen. • Demonstrate the ability to identify personal health needs.	**Main Idea and Details** pp. 33, 35 • Cause and Effect, p. 35
2 **Your Teeth and Their Care** pp. 36–41	3 class periods	• Describe tooth and gum problems and explain how to prevent them. • Describe and demonstrate how to brush and floss correctly.	**Main Idea and Details** p. 41 • Sequence, p. 37 • Draw Conclusions, pp. 39, 41
3 **Your Vision and Hearing** pp. 42–45	1 class period	• Identify and explain the causes of common vision and hearing problems. • Describe and demonstrate how to take good care of eyes and ears.	**Main Idea and Details** p. 45 • Cause and Effect, p. 43
Life Skills pp. 46–47	1 class period	• Identify communication skills. • Use communication skills to make one's health needs known.	
4 **Being a Health Consumer** pp. 48–50	1 class period	• Describe how advertisements can be analyzed to choose products that best meet your needs. • Explain how the usefulness and value of health products and services can be determined by comparison. • Explain the importance of refusal skills that are helpful in resisting negative peer pressure and media influences.	**Main Idea and Details** p. 50 • Summarize, p. 49 • Sequence, p. 50
Building Good Character p. 51		• Recognize the importance of trustworthiness and truthfulness with family members about personal care.	
5 **Getting Health Information** pp. 52–54	1 class period	• Identify factual sources, including media and technology, for obtaining health information. • Explain how information resources can be used to recognize and determine the usefulness of products and services. • Describe a variety of ways to convey accurate health information and ideas.	**Main Idea and Details** p. 54 • Draw Conclusions p. 53 • Summarize, p. 54
Activities p. 55		• Extend chapter concepts.	
Chapter Review pp. 56–57	1 class period	• Assess chapter objectives.	

Vocabulary	Program Resources
	Music CD Teaching Resources, p. 25
epidermis **dermis**	Transparencies 4, 16 Activity Book, pp. 6–8
plaque **cavities**	Transparencies 4, 17 Activity Book, pp. 6–7
pupil **lens** **retina**	Transparencies 4, 18, 19 Activity Book, pp. 6–7
	Poster 7 Activity Book, p. 9
advertising **consumer**	Transparency 4 Activity Book, pp. 6–7
	Poster 6
	Transparency 4 Activity Book, pp. 6–7, 10
	The Learning Site www.harcourtschool.com
	Assessment Guide, pp. 22–24

Interactive Transparencies available on CD-ROM.

Reading Skill

These reading skills are reinforced throughout this chapter and one skill is emphasized as the Focus Skill.

Identify Main Idea and Details

- Draw Conclusions
- Identify Cause and Effect
- Compare and Contrast
- Sequence
- Summarize

KEY READING SKILLS TRANSPARENCY 4

4 Reading Skill Graphic Organizer

Identify Main Idea and Details

Main Idea:

Detail: | Detail: | Detail:

Life Skills

Life Skills are health-enhancing behaviors that can help students reduce risks to their health and safety.

Six Life Skills are reinforced throughout *Harcourt Health and Fitness*. The skill emphasized in this chapter is Communicate.

POSTER 7 COMMUNICATE

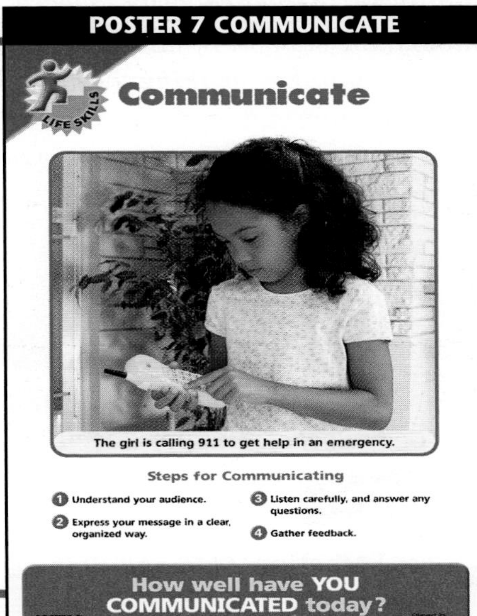

Communicate
Life Skills
The girl is calling 911 to get help in an emergency.
Steps for Communicating
1 Understand your audience.
2 Express your message in a clear, organized way.
3 Listen carefully, and answer any questions.
4 Gather feedback.
How well have YOU COMMUNICATED today?
POSTER 7

Building Good Character

Character education is an important aspect of health education. When children behave in ways that show good character, they promote the health and safety of themselves and others.

Six character traits are reinforced throughout *Harcourt Health and Fitness*. The trait emphasized in this chapter is Trustworthiness.

POSTER 6 TRUSTWORTHINESS

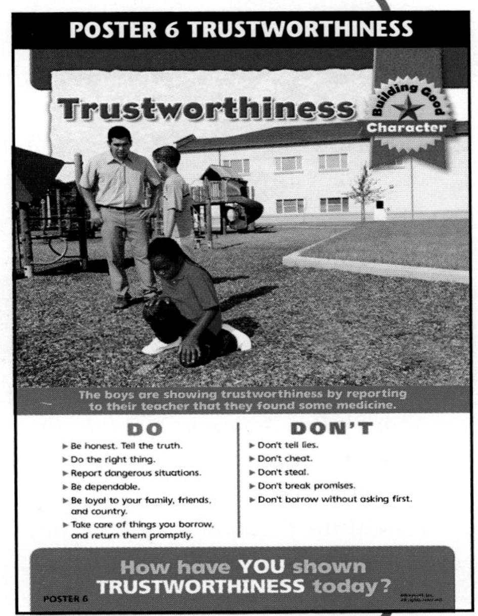

Trustworthiness
Building Good Character
The boys are showing trustworthiness by reporting to their teacher that they found some medicine.
DO
Be honest. Tell the truth.
Do the right thing.
Report dangerous situations.
Be dependable.
Be loyal to your family, friends, and country.
Take care of things you borrow, and return them promptly.
DON'T
Don't tell lies.
Don't cheat.
Don't steal.
Don't break promises.
Don't borrow without asking first.
How have YOU shown TRUSTWORTHINESS today?
POSTER 6

Resources

Coordinated School Health Program

Health Education
Health Services
Physical Education
Nutrition Services
Parent/ Community Involvement
Healthy School Environment
Counseling, Psychological, & Social Services
Health Promotion for Staff
CSHP

A Coordinated School Health Program endeavors to improve children's health and therefore their capacity to learn through the support of families, schools, and communities working together. The following information is provided to help classroom teachers be more aware of these resources.

The National Center for Chronic Disease and Health Promotion, part of the **CDC**, funds the Coordinated School Health Program. Visit its website for information about the eight components that make up this program.
www.cdc.gov/nccdphp/dash/

The **CDC's** website, BAM! (Body and Mind), instructs students on various health topics. *Survival Skills* explains how the body reacts when it is overheated; the importance of sunscreen, sunglasses, and skin protection; and similar topics.
www.bam.gov/

A Coordinated School Health Program must include the involvement of parents and community members to ensure healthy children today and in the future. The **American Cancer Society** uses the program to encourage students to practice healthful living habits to prevent disease.
www.cancer.org/docroot/home/index.asp

Other resources that support a Coordinated School Health Program:

- School-Home Connection
- Daily Physical Activity
- Daily Fitness Tips
- Activities: Home & Community
- Health Background: Webliography
- *Be Active! Resources for Physical Education*

Media Resources

Books for Students

Sandeman, Anna. ***Skin, Teeth & Hair (Body Books).*** Copper Beech Books, 1996. Looks at skin, teeth, and hair care. **EASY**

Goode, Katherine. ***Skin and Hair.*** Blackbirch Marketing, 2000. Describes the functions, characteristics, disorders, and care of skin and hair. **AVERAGE**

Silverstein, Dr. Alvin. ***Tooth Decay and Cavities.*** Franklin Watts, 1999. Describes the function of teeth and discusses how cavities form and how to prevent them. **ADVANCED**

Books for Teachers and Families

Pantell, Robert H., M.D. ***Taking Care of Your Child: A Parent's Guide to Complete Medical Care.*** Perseus Books, 2002. Good advice on nutrition, discipline, medicines, and other aspects of child care.

Forness, Larry M. ***Don't Get Duped!: A Consumer's Guide to Health and Fitness.*** Prometheus Books, 2002. Evaluates the health care and fitness services/products available.

Free and Inexpensive Materials

American Academy of Pediatric Dentistry
Has brochures such as fluoride use, X-ray safety, and calming the anxious child.

Purell
Download "Healthy Hands. Healthy Kids,"™ free curriculum lesson plans.

P&G Companies
Will send free hygiene product samples.

American Dental Association
Has word games and coloring sheets to download.

To access free and inexpensive resources on the Web, visit
www.harcourtschool.com/health/free

Videos

Skeletal and Muscular Systems. Schlessinger Media, 2001.

Human Body: The Inside Scoop (Bill Nye, the Science Guy Series). Walt Disney Home Video, 1995.

Come See About Nutrition and Exercise. ETR Associates, 1996.

These resources have been selected to meet a variety of individual needs. Please review all materials and websites prior to sharing them with students to ensure the content is appropriate for your class. Note that information, while correct at time of publication, is subject to change.

Visit **The Learning Site** for related links, activities, resources, and the health **Webliography.**

www.harcourtschool.com/health

Meeting Individual Needs

Below-Level

Have students write a new word on an index card and cut it into parts based on its syllables or word parts. Have them identify the strategy, such as context clues or spelling patterns, that helped them identify the word. Students can tape the parts back together to make the word.

Activities

- Illustrate Brushing, p. 38
- Investigate Pupil Reaction, p. 42
- Ad Tricks Display, p. 48

On-Level

Using text structure and format can help students understand new words and information. Have them look at the chapter headings for clues on how the author organized information. If students have trouble, tell them to think about how the words and pictures go together.

Activities

- Describe Brushing, p. 38
- Research Differences, p. 42
- Consumer Challenge, p. 48

Challenge

Have students work together to create a class newsletter relating to topics discussed in health class. Have students conduct interviews of school personnel or other students to get opinions, perspectives, and information on health issues discussed in the classroom.

Activities

- Describe Brushing and Flossing, p. 38
- Research Rods and Cones, p. 42
- Analyze Ad Language, p. 48

ESL/ELL

Language Workshop

After reading a paragraph aloud, encourage students to develop language skills through paraphrasing. Select one student to retell ideas presented by the text. Have other students check the retelling for accuracy and add any other information that should be included.

Activities

- Language and Vocabulary, p. 40
- Background and Experience p. 44
- Comprehensible Input, p. 52

Curriculum Integration

Use these topics to integrate health into your daily planning.

Integrated Language Arts/Reading Skills

- Tooth Story, p. 37
- List Health Agencies, p. 53

Math

- Measure and Add Floss, p. 39
- Unit Prices, p. 49

Music

- Sound Rhythms, p. 45
- Ad Jingle, p. 49

Science

- Bacteria Exploration, p. 36
- Fluoride Protection, p. 41
- Research Optical Illusions, p. 43
- Advertising Color, p. 50

Physical Education

- Daily Fitness Tip, pp. 32, 36, 42, 48, 52
- Daily Physical Activity, p. 31
- Protective Gear, p. 45

Social Studies

- History of the Toothbrush, p. 39

Art

- Health Slogans and Posters, p. 54

CHAPTER

2

Pages 30–57

CHAPTER SUMMARY

In this chapter, students

- ► examine the role of hygiene in health.
- ► identify the structure and function of skin, teeth, gums, eyes, and ears and explain how to care for them.
- ► analyze ways to make wise consumer decisions about health-care products.

Life Skills

Students *communicate* about health needs.

Building Good Character

Students show *trustworthiness* by being truthful about personal care.

Consumer Health

Students *analyze media messages* in advertising for products.

Literature Springboard

Use the poem "A Pig Is Never Blamed" to spark interest in the chapter topic. See the Read-Aloud Anthology on page RA-3 of this *Teacher Edition.*

Prereading Strategies

SCAN THE CHAPTER Have students preview the chapter content by scanning the titles, headings, pictures, and tables. Assess prior knowledge by asking volunteers to predict what they will learn.

PREVIEW VOCABULARY As students preview the vocabulary in each lesson, ask them to consider how they could illustrate the meaning of each term. Have students choose one term to write and illustrate to explain its meaning.

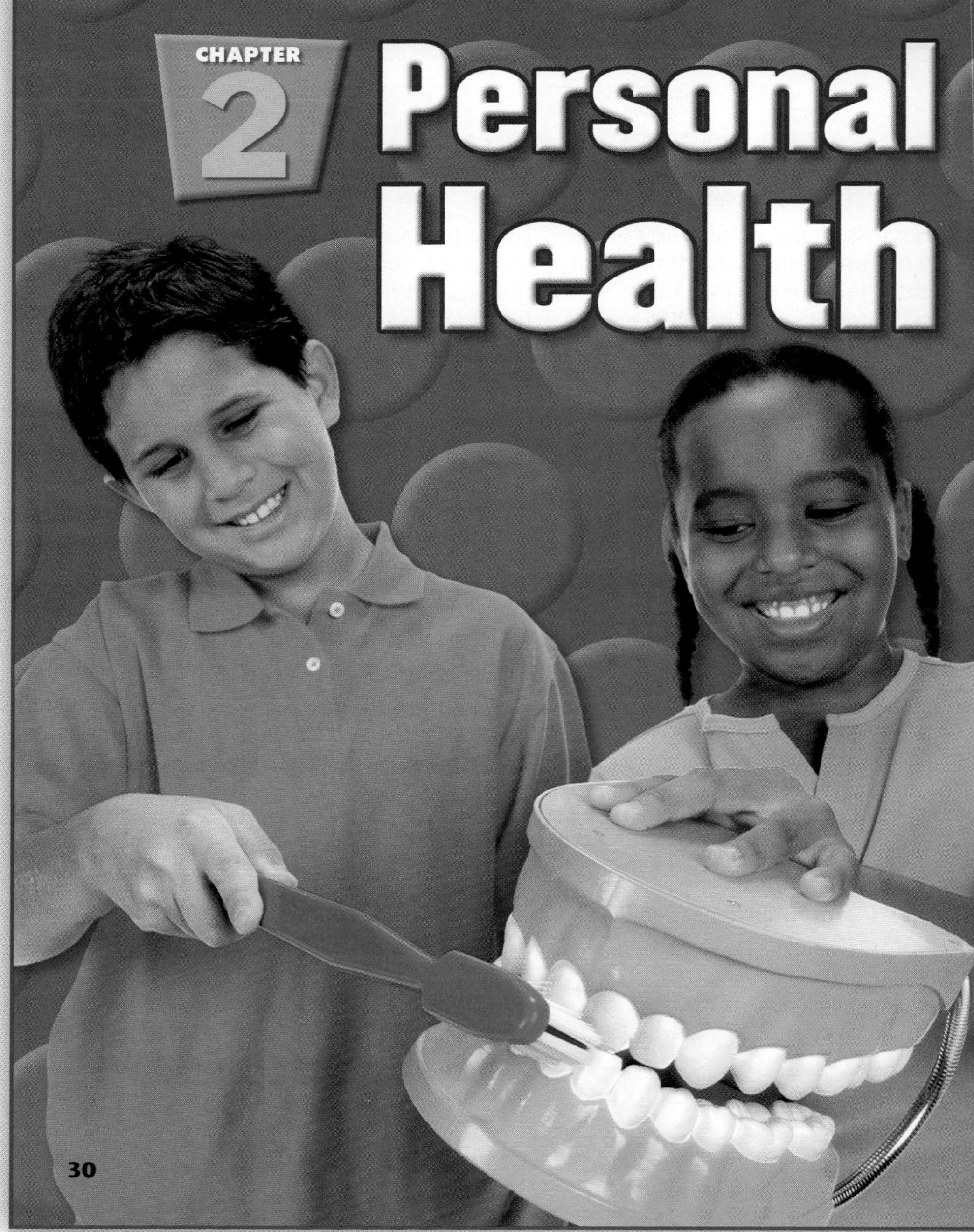

Reading Skill

IDENTIFY MAIN IDEA AND DETAILS To introduce or review this skill, have students use the Reading in Health Handbook, pp. 336–337. Teaching strategies and additional activities are also provided.

Students will have opportunities to practice and apply this skill throughout this chapter.

- Focus Skill Reading Mini-Lesson, p. 32
- Reading comprehension questions identified with the 
- *Activity Book* p. 8 (shown on p. 35)
- Lesson Summary and Review, pp. 35, 41, 45, 50, 54
- Chapter Review and Test Preparation, pp. 56–57

Reading Skill

IDENTIFY MAIN IDEA AND DETAILS The main idea is the most important thought in a passage. Details tell about the main idea and help you understand it. Use the Reading in Health Handbook on pages 336–337 and this graphic organizer to help you read the health facts in this chapter.

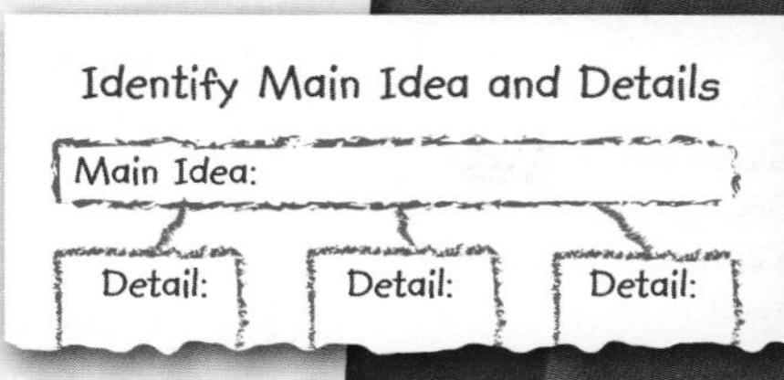

Health Graph

INTERPRET DATA The United States Department of Health and Human Services' Healthy People 2010 program has set some goals for cavity prevention. Compare the two graphs. How are they alike, and how are they different? How many more children without cavities per 100 is the goal?

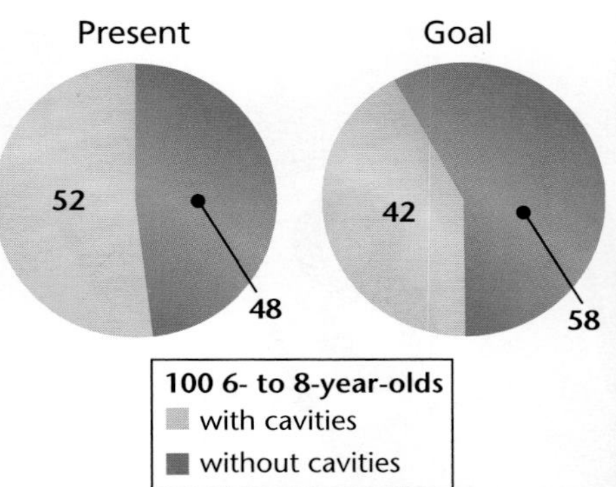

Daily Physical Activity

Take an active role maintaining your personal health. Exercise for you health.

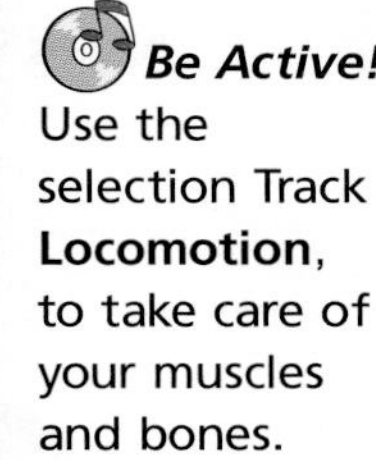

Be Active! Use the selection Track 2, **Locomotion**, to take care of your muscles and bones.

31

INTRODUCE THE CHAPTER

Health Graph

Interpret Data

Ask for volunteers to explain the information shown on the graph.

Does the shaded part of the circle show the percentage of people with cavities or without cavities? people with cavities

Which graph shows that the percentage of people with cavities is less than the percentage of people without cavities? the graph labeled Healthy People 2010 Goal

How many more people on the first graph have cavities than on the second graph? ten more

Daily Physical Activity

Use *Be Active! Music for Daily Physical Activity* with the Instant Activity Cards to provide students with movement activities that can be done in limited space. Options for using these components are provided beginning on page TR2 in this *Teacher Edition.*

Chapter Project

For Your Information (*Assessment Guide* p. 56)

ASSESS PRIOR KNOWLEDGE Use students' initial ideas for the project as a baseline assessment of their understanding of chapter concepts. Have students complete the project as they work through the chapter.

PERFORMANCE ASSESSMENT The project can be used for performance assessment. Use the Project Evaluation Sheet (rubric), *Assessment Guide* p. 63.

School-Home Connection

Distribute copies of the School-Home Connection (in English or Spanish). Have students take the page home to share with their families as you begin this chapter.

Follow Up Have volunteers share the results of their activities.

Supports the Coordinated School Health Program

TEACHING RESOURCES P. 25

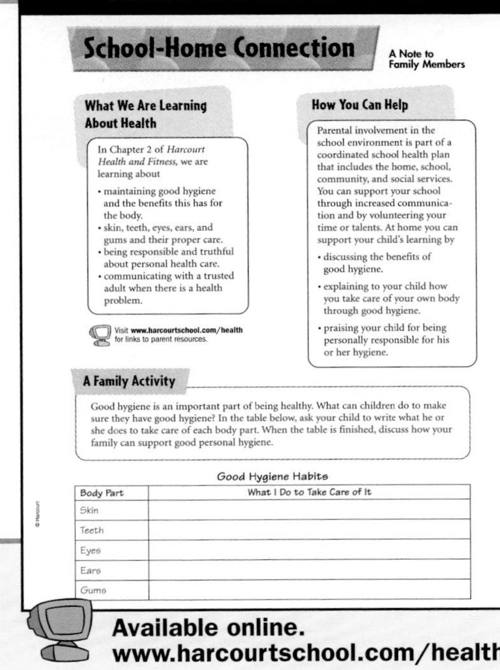

School-Home Connection

A Note to Family Members

What We Are Learning About Health

In Chapter 2 of *Harcourt Health and Fitness,* we are learning about

- maintaining good hygiene and the benefits this has for the body.
- skin, teeth, eyes, ears, and gums and their proper care.
- being responsible and truthful about personal health care.
- communicating with a trusted adult when there is a health problem.

Visit **www.harcourtschool.com/health** for links to parent resources.

How You Can Help

Parental involvement in the school environment is part of a coordinated school health plan that includes the home, school, community, and social services. You can support your school through increased communication and by volunteering your time or talents. At home you can support your child's learning by

- discussing the benefits of good hygiene.
- explaining to your child how you take care of your own body through good hygiene.
- praising your child for being personally responsible for his or her hygiene.

A Family Activity

Good hygiene is an important part of being healthy. What can children do to make sure they have good hygiene? In the table below, ask your child to write what he or she does to take care of each body part. When the table is finished, discuss how your family can support good personal hygiene.

Good Hygiene Habits

Body Part	What I Do to Take Care of It
Skin	
Teeth	
Eyes	
Ears	
Gums	

© Harcourt

Available online. www.harcourtschool.com/health

LESSON 1
Pages 32–35

Objectives
- ► Describe the structure and function of skin. Explain how to take care of skin, including the use of sunscreen.
- ► Demonstrate the ability to identify personal health needs.

When Minutes Count . . .
Assign the Quick Study, Lesson 1, Activity Book pp. 6–7 (shown on p. 33).

Program Resources
- ► Activity Book pp. 6–8
- ► Transparencies 4, 16

Vocabulary
epidermis p. 32, **dermis** p. 33

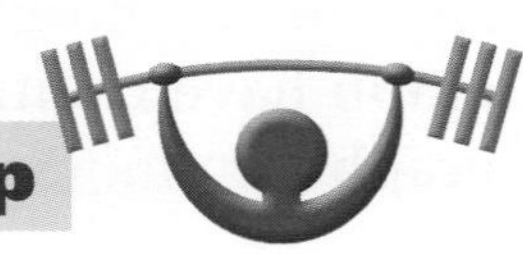

Daily Fitness Tip
In spite of warnings about the harm of exposure to the sun, some young people think a tan makes a person look healthy. A tan is really damaged skin. To protect cells from the damaging effects of sunlight, the skin darkens to shield lower layers from being burned.

For more guidelines about selecting the proper gear for activities, see *Be Active! Resources for Physical Education* p. 185.

1. MOTIVATE
Optional Activity Materials red tempera paint, soap, warm and cold water, hand lens

Have students rub a small drop of water-based paint on the palm of one hand, using a finger of the same hand. After the paint dries, have students rinse their hands in cold water and examine them with a hand lens. (Some paint should remain.) Then have students wash their hands in warm, soapy water and examine them.

When Minutes Count . . .
Transparency 16: The Skin can be used to present material in this lesson. *Interactive Transparencies available on CD-ROM.*

Lesson Focus
Taking care of your skin is important for your health.

Why Learn This?
Understanding how your skin protects you can help you make good choices about caring for it.

Vocabulary
epidermis
dermis

Your Skin
Look at your skin. Do you know what an important organ it is? Throughout your life, your skin protects you in many ways. Taking care of your skin helps it take care of you.

Your skin has two main layers—the epidermis and the dermis. You can see both layers and their parts in the picture on the next page.

The top layer of your skin is the **epidermis** (ep•uh•DER•mis). Its outermost part is made of dead skin cells. These cells keep moisture in your body and keep germs out. If the epidermis is broken, germs can enter the body. That's why washing cuts and keeping them clean until they heal is important.

Did You Know?
A three-quarter-inch square patch of skin that is about one-twentieth of an inch thick contains
- 9 feet of blood vessels
- 13 yards of nerves
- 600 pain receptors
- 300 sweat glands
- 4 oil glands
- 30 hairs

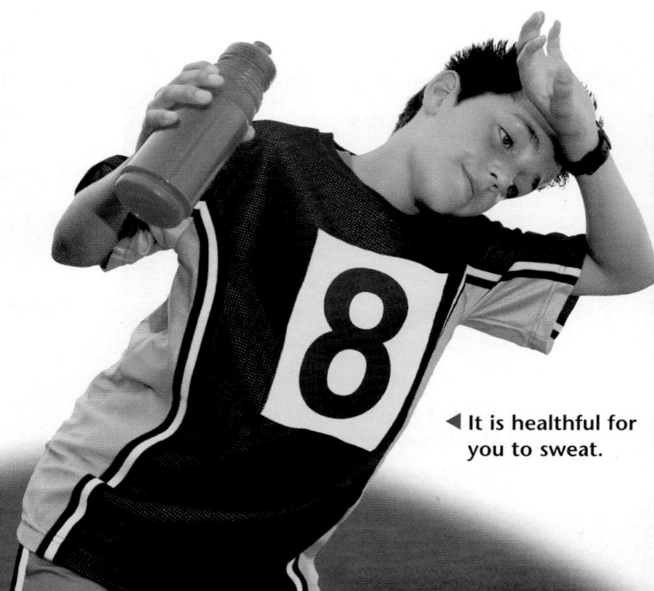

◄ It is healthful for you to sweat.

32

Reading Skill

Mini-Lesson
MAIN IDEA AND DETAILS
The main idea is the most important part of what is read. Details explain the main idea. Have students practice this skill by responding to the Focus Skill question on page 33. Have them draw and complete the graphic organizer as you model it on the transparency.

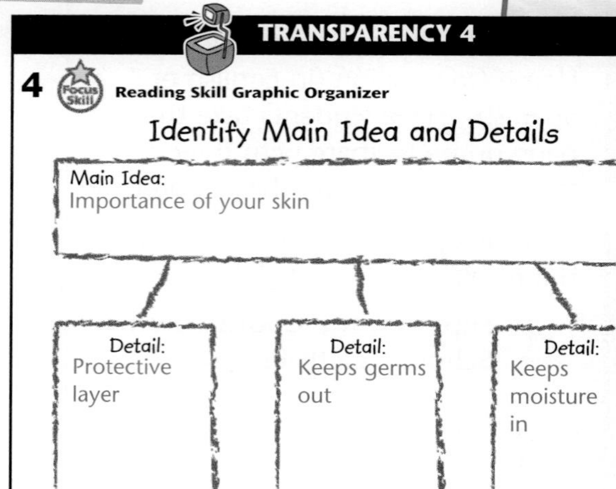
TRANSPARENCY 4

4 Reading Skill Graphic Organizer

Identify Main Idea and Details

Main Idea: Importance of your skin

Detail: Protective layer

Detail: Keeps germs out

Detail: Keeps moisture in

Interactive Transparencies available on CD-ROM.

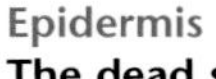

Epidermis
The dead skin cells that make up the top layer of the epidermis are constantly flaking off. New cells grow to replace them.

Pores are openings in the skin's surface, from which sweat is released.

Hair is a long, narrow stack of dead skin cells piled one on top of the other.

Each year up to nine pounds of your skin wear away as dead cells flake off. Cells in the bottom part of the epidermis make new cells to replace the dead ones.▶

Sweat glands
Sweat produced in the sweat glands helps rid your body of wastes and helps keep you cool.

Dermis The thick bottom layer of skin, the dermis contains blood vessels and nerves.

Oil glands make oil that helps soften your skin.

Your skin has another important job. It keeps your body at the right temperature. It does this by producing sweat. Sweat is the salty liquid that forms on your skin when you are hot. Sweat is made by *sweat glands* in your skin. When your body gets hot, sweat glands become more active. Sweat helps cool your body.

Sweat reaches the skin's surface through *pores*. There, sweat changes from a liquid to a gas. This process is called *evaporation*. During evaporation, your body uses its heat energy to change the liquid sweat into a gas. As a result, your body loses heat and cools down.

MAIN IDEA AND DETAILS What is the importance of your skin?
It is a protective layer for your body that keeps germs out and moisture in.

Information Alert

Artificial Skin
Scientists are learning how to make skin that can be used to treat people who have been seriously burned.

GO ONLINE **For the most up-to-date information, visit The Learning Site. www.harcourtschool.com/health**

33

2. TEACH

Discuss

Problem Solving Suppose you fell on the sidewalk and scraped your hand. The skin was scraped but didn't bleed. Which layer of skin did you likely damage when you fell? Explain. The epidermis; it's the outer layer of dead cells.

Critical Thinking How is evaporation important in preventing your body from overheating? The evaporation of sweat on the skin's surface helps cool the body.

Interpret Visuals—Illustrations

Direct students' attention to the illustration of skin on this page. Ask volunteers to read the captions that tell about the parts of skin. Have students brainstorm reasons each part of the skin is important and how it helps protect the body.

Problem Solving Why doesn't getting a haircut hurt? Hair is made of dead skin cells, and there are no nerves in the dead cells.

Health Background

Skin As each new skin cell is produced at the base of the epidermis, it moves toward the skin's surface. As it does so, its cytoplasm, the jellylike material that fills the cell, is changed into a tough protein known as keratin, and the cell dies. This process protects the body because invading germs have difficulty penetrating keratin. The outer dead cells fall continuously from the skin's surface. In fact, a large part of household dust is dead skin cells.

Sweat glands are found on all surfaces of the body that grow hair. The oily secretion they produce results from the breakdown of cells. The oil coats the skin's surface and the hair, discouraging the attachment of germs. Sweat also provides nutrients for beneficial bacteria that live on the skin's surface. These bacteria produce waste products that make living on the skin difficult for harmful germs.

Source: *The Human Body Explained website*

QUICK STUDY, ACTIVITY BOOK PP. 6–7

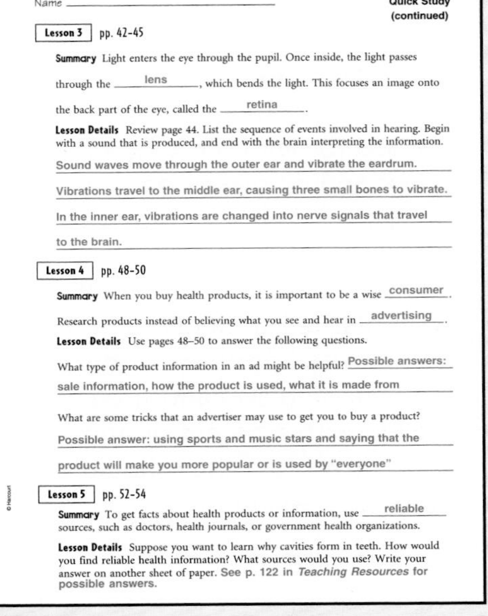

CHAPTER 2 Name ______ Quick Study

Personal Health

Directions
- Use lesson vocabulary in the Word Bank to complete each **Summary**.
- Read the section directions to complete each **Lesson Details**.

Word Bank

consumer	plaque	retina
lens	reliable	epidermis
dermis	advertising	cavities

Lesson 1 pp. 32–35

Summary Caring for your skin is important to your health. This includes protecting the top layer of skin, called the epidermis, and the bottom layer, called the dermis.

Lesson Details Use the information on pages 32–33 to complete the table. The first line has been completed for you.

Feature	Description and Function
epidermis	the top layer of skin, which keeps moisture in and germs out
dermis	the bottom layer of skin, which contains blood vessels and nerves
sweat gland	produces sweat to rid your body of wastes and help keep you cool
oil gland	makes oil that helps keep skin soft
pore	opening in the skin from which sweat is released
hair	a stack of dead skin cells

Lesson 2 pp. 36–41

Summary Caring for your teeth includes removing sticky plaque from them to prevent holes called cavities from forming.

Lesson Details On a separate sheet of paper, write a list of habits you can use to keep your teeth and gums healthy. Draw a picture for each habit to help you remember to do the activity. Check students' lists and drawings.

© Harcourt

Name ______ **Quick Study (continued)**

Lesson 3 pp. 42–45

Summary Light enters the eye through the pupil. Once inside, the light passes through the lens, which bends the light. This focuses an image onto the back part of the eye, called the retina.

Lesson Details Review page 44. List the sequence of events involved in hearing. Begin with a sound that is produced, and end with the brain interpreting the information.

Sound waves move through the outer ear and vibrate the eardrum. Vibrations travel to the middle ear, causing three small bones to vibrate. In the inner ear, vibrations are changed into nerve signals that travel to the brain.

Lesson 4 pp. 48–50

Summary When you buy health products, it is important to be a wise consumer. Research products instead of believing what you see and hear in advertising.

Lesson Details Use pages 48–50 to answer the following questions.

What type of product information in an ad might be helpful? Possible answers: sale information, how the product is used, what it is made from

What are some tricks that an advertiser may use to get you to buy a product? Possible answer: using sports and music stars and saying that the product will make you more popular or is used by "everyone"

Lesson 5 pp. 52–54

Summary To get facts about health products or information, use reliable sources, such as doctors, health journals, or government health organizations.

Lesson Details Suppose you want to learn why cavities form in teeth. How would you find reliable health information? What sources would you use? Write your answer on another sheet of paper. See p. 122 in *Teaching Resources* for possible answers.

© Harcourt

Available online. www.harcourtschool.com/health

TEACH *continued*

Interpret Visuals—Table

Direct students' attention to the Wash Your Hands table. Have students read each item in the list and explain why hand washing is important before and after each action.

Discuss

Have students mime the movements they use to wash their hands as you count out 30 seconds.

Did the time seem long or short to you? Answers will vary.

Critical Thinking Why can germs that can't enter your body through the skin enter your body if you touch your eyes, nose, or mouth? These body parts tend to be moist, dark places where germs can grow.

Health Background

Sunscreens Sunlight contains ultraviolet (UV) rays, which can damage the DNA of cells when they strike the skin. A sunscreen acts as a "bulletproof vest" that stops UV rays before they can damage the skin. Effective sunscreens contain organic molecules that absorb UV rays. They also contain pigments that absorb, scatter, and reflect UV rays. Sunscreen products that contain significant levels of zinc oxide, avobenzone, or titanium dioxide offer good protection from the damaging effects of sunlight.

Source: *Scientific American website*

For more background, visit the **Webliography** in Teacher Resources at **www.harcourtschool.com/health** **Keyword** personal care

Myth and Fact

Myth: Antibacterial soap is the best soap for everyday use.

Fact: Regular soap is fine for everyday use. Scientists say that using too much antibacterial soap has made some bacteria more resistant to the antibiotics that are used to kill them.

Care of Your Skin

If your hands or face are dirty, germs can enter the body when you touch your eyes, nose, or mouth. Wash your face at least twice a day. Use soap, warm water, and a clean washcloth. When you wash your hands, rub them all over with soap and warm water. Squeeze the suds between your fingers. Scrub your knuckles and fingernails carefully. Germs often collect there. Rinse your hands well and dry them. Apply lotion if your skin feels tight or rough.

If you are very active, take a bath or shower every day. Wash your hair with shampoo when it begins to look or feel dirty.

Wash Your Hands

After
- blowing your nose
- sneezing or coughing
- going to the bathroom
- handling anything dirty
- touching an animal

Before
- handling food
- eating

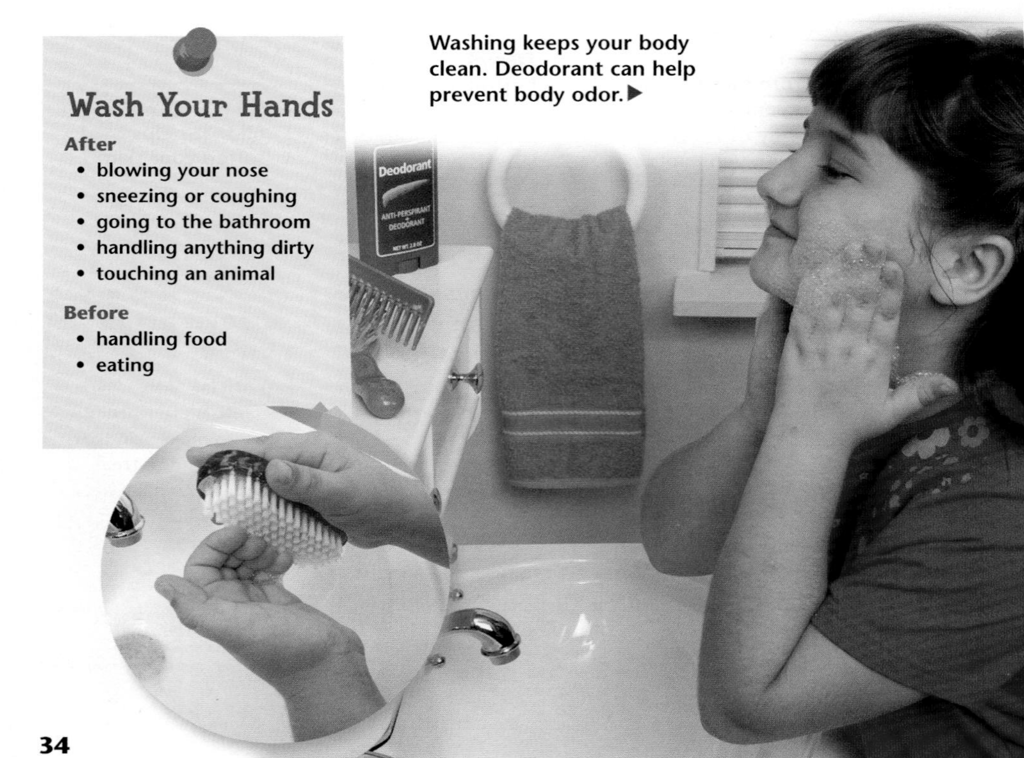

Washing keeps your body clean. Deodorant can help prevent body odor. ▶

34

Teacher Tip

Daily Showers Fourth graders are less likely than fifth and sixth graders to be in puberty, when sweat and oil glands become overactive. Therefore, fourth graders may not need to shower daily, as is recommended for older students. Tell students to evaluate the oiliness or dryness of their own hair and skin and then discuss with a parent or another adult how often they should bathe and shampoo.

Cultural Connection

Hot Weather Clothing In the United States, most people tend to wear less clothing—short-sleeve clothing, for example—during warm summer seasons. However, the people of some cultures in areas of the world where the climate is very hot and dry tend to cover the body with clothing such as long sleeves, long pants, and robes. Have students research this custom to determine why people of some cultures dress this way.

Too much sunlight can harm your skin. It can cause the skin to burn, dry out, and wrinkle. Over time, too much sun can also cause a serious disease called *skin cancer*.

You can protect your skin from the sun in several ways. If possible, stay out of the sun when it is strongest—between 10:00 A.M. and 4:00 P.M. Whenever you are in the sun, use sunscreen. *Sunscreen* is lotion that helps block some of the sun's harmful rays. Read the sunscreen label to see its sun protection factor (SPF). The higher the number, the more protection you get. Use a sunscreen that has an SPF of 30 or more. For additional protection, wear a hat and cover your skin with loose, light-colored clothes that are lightweight.

CAUSE AND EFFECT What is the effect of too much sun exposure?

sunburn; dry and wrinkled skin; cancer

▼ You can get sunburn in winter. When in the sun, be sure to use sunscreen. Also, wear a hat and cover your skin with clothing.

Lesson 1 Summary and Review

1 Summarize with Vocabulary

Use vocabulary and other terms from this lesson to complete these statements.

The top layer of skin is the _____. Under it lies the _____. _____ helps keep your skin soft. _____ helps keep your body cool. Oil and sweat reach the top layer of your skin through _____. To help protect your skin from sunlight, you should use _____.

2 What SPF should you use to protect your skin from the sun?

3 Critical Thinking Why is your skin important to your health?

4 MAIN IDEA AND DETAILS Draw and complete this graphic organizer to show the parts that make up the dermis.

Main Idea:

Detail: | Detail: | Detail:

5 Write to Inform—How-To

Write the steps you should use to thoroughly wash your hands.

35

ACTIVITY BOOK P. 8

Name ____________

Focus Skill Reading Skill

Identify Main Idea and Details

Sunny Solutions

The sun is shining and it's a beautiful summer day. You're ready to grab your swimsuit or basketball and head outside for some fun in the sun. Before you go, don't forget to also grab some sunscreen. One of the most important health decisions you can make is choosing to protect your body's largest organ—your skin.

Wearing sunscreen is an important part of caring for your skin. Sunlight can cause skin damage, including wrinkles and skin cancer. That's where quality sunscreen can help. Sunscreens reduce or block the damaging effects of the sun's rays. The chemicals that make up a sunscreen protect your skin from the sun. A good-quality sunscreen will absorb, scatter, and reflect sunlight before it reaches your skin. A sunscreen with SPF 30 will allow you to stay in the sun 30 times longer without burning than if you didn't wear sunscreen. So before heading outside, be sure to save your skin by taking along the sunscreen.

Use the graphic organizer. Fill in the main idea and supporting details of the passage.

Main Idea: Using sunscreen is important to protect your skin from the sun's damaging rays.

Detail: Sunlight can cause damage to the skin, including wrinkles and cancer.

Detail: Sunscreens absorb, scatter, and reflect sunlight before it reaches the skin.

Detail: Sunscreen with SPF 30 allows you to stay in the sun 30 times longer without burning than if you didn't wear sunscreen.

Available online.
www.harcourtschool.com/health

3. WRAP UP

Lesson 1 Summary and Review

1. epidermis; dermis; Oil; Sweat; pores; sunscreen
2. It holds in moisture, keeps out germs, helps cool the body, and removes some wastes from the body.
3. SPF 30 or higher
4. Responses may include:

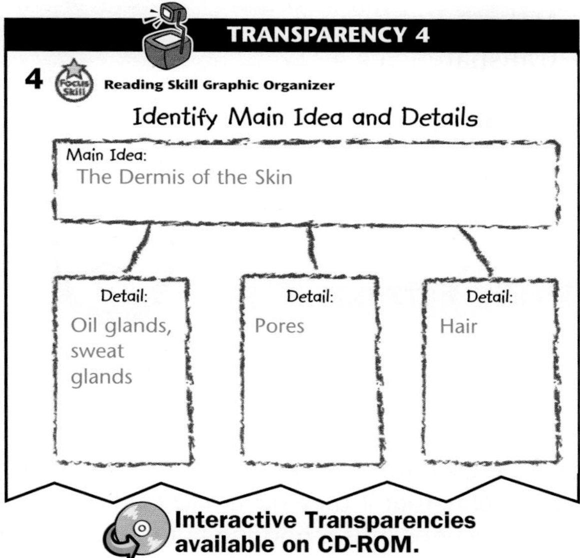

TRANSPARENCY 4
4 Reading Skill Graphic Organizer
Identify Main Idea and Details
Main Idea:
The Dermis of the Skin
Detail:
Oil glands, sweat glands
Detail:
Pores
Detail:
Hair
Interactive Transparencies available on CD-ROM.

5. Rub the hands all over with soap and warm water. Squeeze the suds between your fingers. Scrub your knuckles and fingernails carefully. Rinse your hands well. Then dry them.

For **writing models** with examples, see *Teaching Resources* pp. 47–61. Rubrics are also provided.

When Minutes Count . . .

Quick Study Students can use *Activity Book* pages 6–7 (shown on p. 33) as they complete each lesson in this chapter.

LESSON 2
Pages 36–41

Objectives
- ► Describe tooth and gum problems and explain how to prevent them.
- ► Describe and demonstrate how to brush and floss correctly.

When Minutes Count . . .
Assign the Quick Study, Lesson 2, Activity Book pp. 6–7 (shown on p. 33).

Program Resources
- ► Activity Book pp. 6–7
- ► Transparencies 4, 17

Vocabulary
plaque p. 36, **cavities** p. 36

Daily Fitness Tip
Students may not think about the cleanliness of their toothbrushes. Remind students that toothbrushes should never be shared and never be used for cleaning anything but teeth. Tell students that if they have had colds or other infections, it is a good idea to replace their toothbrushes. Otherwise, most dentists recommend replacing a toothbrush every three to four months.

1. MOTIVATE
Ask students to describe a tooth they have lost. If students describe baby teeth that they lost, explain that by the time the baby tooth falls out, the root of the tooth has completely dissolved in the gum. Tell them that the root is usually about twice as long as the part of the tooth that can be seen above the gum. **What advantage is the dissolving of the root before a tooth falls out?** The tooth comes out of the gum easier.

When Minutes Count . . .
Transparency 17: The Teeth can be used to present material in this lesson. *Interactive Transparencies available on CD-ROM.*

LESSON 2 Your Teeth and Their Care

Lesson Focus
Taking care of your teeth and gums is important for your health.

Why Learn This?
Knowing about your teeth and gums will help you make good choices about caring for them.

Vocabulary
plaque
cavities

Your Teeth
Your teeth do more than chew your food. They make your smile look nice. They also help you talk. They even help shape your face. Teeth are most important, though, for chewing. Your teeth grind the food you eat into smaller pieces. Your digestive system can more easily digest smaller pieces of food.

As you eat, however, leftover bits of food and bacteria can stick to your teeth. The bacteria are part of a sticky, natural film on the teeth called **plaque** (PLAK). Bacteria in plaque break down sugars in food to form acids. The acids can make holes, called **cavities** (KAV•uh•teez), in the outer layers of your teeth.

ACTIVITY

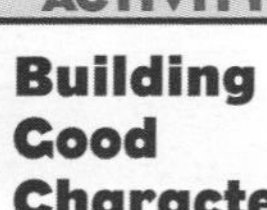

Building Good Character
Responsibility Josh is going on a weekend camping trip with a friend's family. As he is leaving, his mother reminds him to continue caring for his teeth while he is away. What are two ways that Josh can show responsible behavior for his teeth?

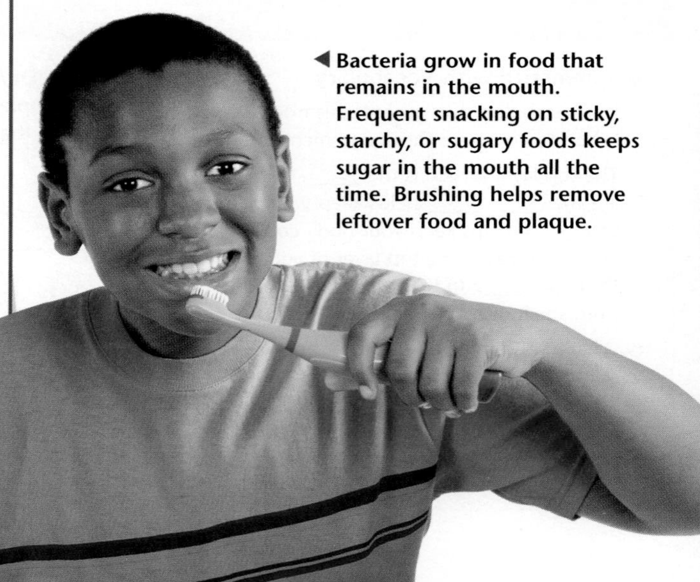

◄ Bacteria grow in food that remains in the mouth. Frequent snacking on sticky, starchy, or sugary foods keeps sugar in the mouth all the time. Brushing helps remove leftover food and plaque.

36

Science
Bacteria Exploration Have students investigate bacteria. Provide images or have students view websites that show greatly magnified bacteria so that students can visualize these microscopic organisms that can cause problems with teeth. Explain that the bacteria in the pictures can live within a person's mouth. After students view the bacteria, ask them why brushing their teeth is important.

Teacher Tip
Tooth Care at Home Some students may live in homes where tooth care is not a well-established habit. Also, many families are unable to afford dental insurance, so you may have students whose family circumstances prohibit regular dental visits. Be sensitive to these issues as you discuss the lesson.

Cavities can get larger and larger until they reach deep inside a tooth. The process of forming cavities is called tooth decay. *Decay* means "to rot." If the cavity reaches the dentin layer, bacteria can travel through it into the tooth's pulp. Nerves in the pulp may swell with infection, causing pain. If the tooth is not treated in time, it can die.

Plaque can cause problems for your gums, too. If plaque is left on teeth, it hardens and becomes tartar. Tartar rubs against gums and can make them bleed. This can lead to infection that destroys the bone that holds teeth in place. Serious gum disease can cause even healthy teeth to fall out.

Myth and Fact

Myth: All cavities are caused by eating sugar.
Fact: Bacteria also act on starches, such as bread, crackers, and cereal, to form acid, which can result in tooth decay.

SEQUENCE List in order the events that can result in the loss of a healthy tooth.

Crown
Enamel
Gum
Pulp
Dentin
Root

▲ Although your teeth have different shapes, they all have these same parts.

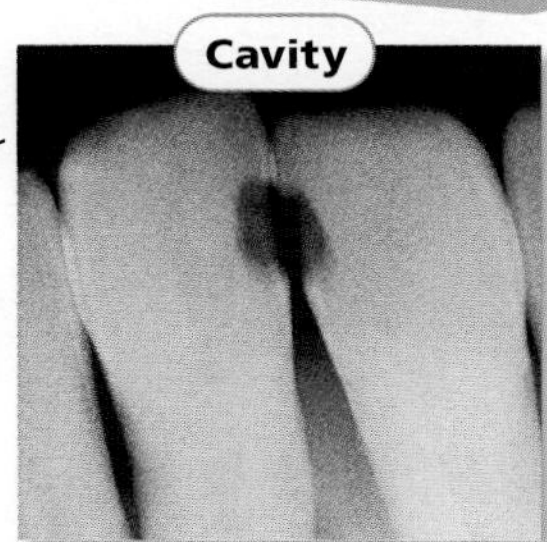

▲ A cavity first forms on a tooth's enamel. At first, you can't feel a cavity because tooth enamel has no nerves.

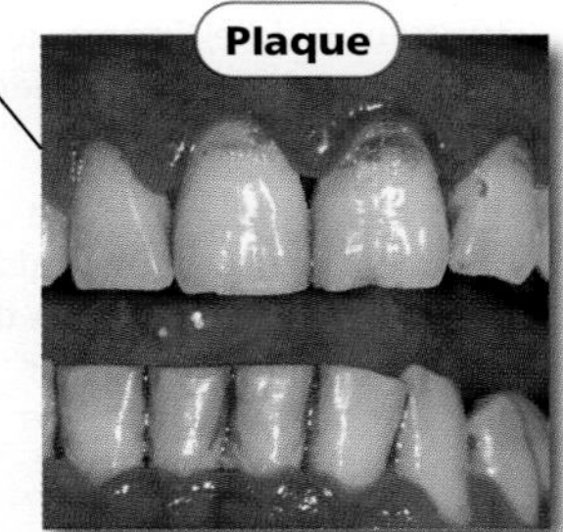

▲ Without daily care, plaque can build up on your teeth and along the gum line.

Possible response: 1. Plaque builds up. 2. Tartar forms. 3. Gums bleed/cavity forms. 4. Infection destroys bone which holds tooth; bacteria infects pulp and kills tooth. 5. Tooth falls out.

37

Language Arts

Tooth Story Have students write a story about a child who loses a tooth. Stories can be whimsical or serious or written as poems. Remind students to use descriptive adjectives and active verbs that give the reader a true picture of what the character is seeing, hearing, tasting, feeling, or doing. Allow time for volunteers to read their stories to the rest of the class. You might consider putting the stories in a class "Tooth Book."

2. TEACH

Interpret Visuals—Diagrams

Direct attention to the diagram of the tooth. Explain that the enamel is the hard outer covering, the dentin is the bonelike layer underneath, and the pulp is the soft core. Have students describe what is happening in the two smaller pictures.

On what part of the tooth does tooth decay begin? Tooth decay begins as cavities that first form on the tooth's enamel.

If a cavity is untreated, what tooth layers will it affect? enamel, dentin, pulp

Activity

Responsibility Discuss how Josh can brush his teeth and floss to show responsibility.

Health Background

Tooth Anatomy Each tooth is made up of two basic parts: the crown and the root. The crown is the part that sits above the gum line. The root is the part below the gum line. The root takes up about two-thirds of the tooth's total length. Four kinds of material make up the tooth. (1) The enamel, which covers the crown of the tooth, is the hardest tissue in the body. It is thickest near the biting surface of the tooth. The enamel has no nerves and therefore no feeling. (2) The dentin is a bonelike material that surrounds the pulp. It makes up most of the tooth. (3) The pulp is a soft tissue that contains many blood vessels and nerves. The blood vessels nourish the tooth and the nerves transmit sensations such as pain and temperature. (4) Cementum, which covers most of the root of the tooth, helps attach the tooth to the jawbone. Connective tissue called periodontal ligament surrounds the root of the tooth and holds the root in the jaw.

Source: *Summa Health System website*

For more background, visit the **Webliography** in Teacher Resources at **www.harcourtschool.com/health**
Keyword human body

TEACH *continued*

Discuss

Refer students to page 348 of the Health and Safety Handbook for information on what to do for some dental emergencies. Explain to students that experts recommend that people visit a dentist every six months.

Why should you visit a dentist regularly if you aren't having any dental problems? The dentist can remove tartar that can lead to cavities and also check for other problems.

Interpret Visuals—Pictures

Direct students' attention to the pictures of the child flossing. Provide pieces of floss or string, and have students demonstrate the correct way to hold floss. Then have them tell how to floss correctly.

Critical Thinking **Why is it important to unwind and use a clean section of floss for each pair of teeth?** Floss that has been used might introduce plaque between the next pair of teeth.

Discuss

Critical Thinking **Why should you rinse your mouth with water after meals when you can't brush?** The water will help wash sugars and starches off your teeth after the meal.

Content-Area Reading Support

Using Text Format Direct attention to the bulleted text on this page. Have students describe how this text differs from that of the first paragraph. All bulleted text is indented and there are no paragraph indents. Have students read the bulleted text. Then ask them what the text is about. healthful habits to keep teeth and gums healthy Point out that each bullet describes a different habit; it's like a list. Tell students to pay attention to bulleted text when they read because it often presents important information.

Did You Know?

Bottled drinking water is often advertised as "pure" or as containing only small amounts of minerals. Because the mineral fluoride is so important to dental health, some bottled-water companies are now adding fluoride to their water.

Preventing Tooth Problems

With proper care, your teeth can last a lifetime. Keep your teeth and gums healthy by practicing these healthful habits.

- Avoid sugary and sticky snacks. Milk products and fruits help build strong teeth. These foods are a good choice if you can brush soon after eating. Crunchy vegetables are the best choice if you can't brush right away.
- Floss once a day. Brush your teeth at least twice a day. Rinse your mouth with water after meals when you can't brush.
- Visit a dentist often. The dentist or dental hygienist will remove any tartar and check for problems. He or she may also apply sealants to protect the teeth or fluoride to strengthen them. *Flouride* (FLAWR•yd) is a mineral that helps prevent cavities.

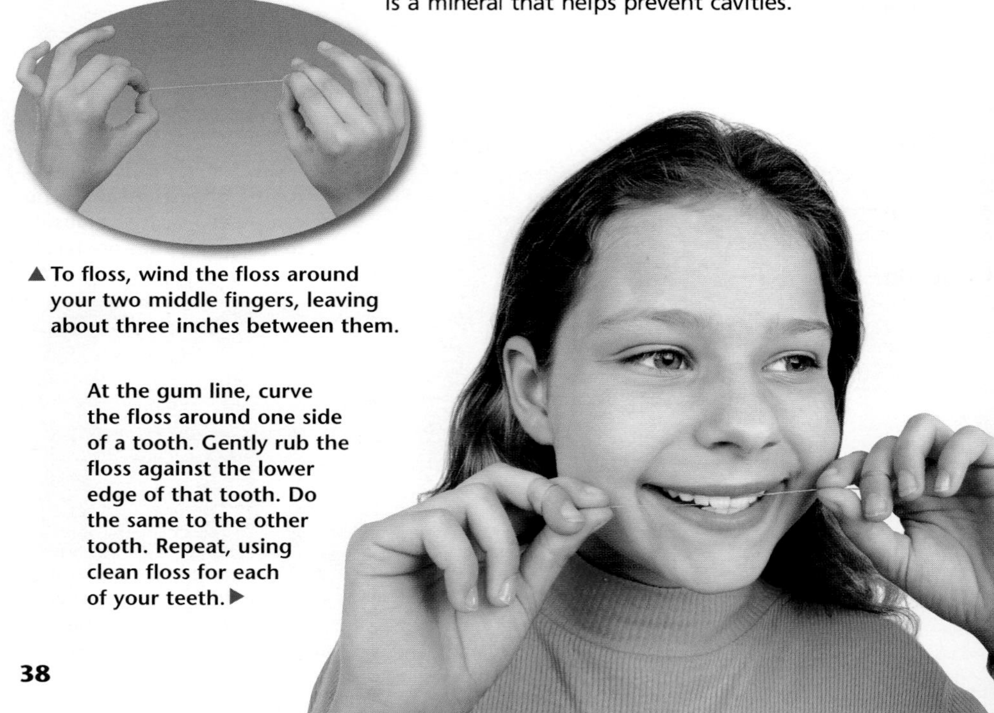

▲ To floss, wind the floss around your two middle fingers, leaving about three inches between them.

At the gum line, curve the floss around one side of a tooth. Gently rub the floss against the lower edge of that tooth. Do the same to the other tooth. Repeat, using clean floss for each of your teeth. ▶

Meeting Individual Needs
Leveled Activities

BELOW-LEVEL **Illustrate Brushing** Have groups of students make pictures to illustrate each of the Tips for Proper Brushing.

ON-LEVEL **Describe Brushing** Have groups of students make pictures to illustrate each of the Tips for Proper Brushing. Have them write a caption for each picture.

CHALLENGE **Describe Brushing and Flossing** Have pairs of students write a video script describing to younger students how to properly brush and floss.

You can help prevent tooth decay and gum disease. Remember to floss and brush. Your toothbrush will remove plaque and bits of food scattered by flossing. When you brush, use a toothpaste that contains fluoride.

It's important to floss and brush properly. You can find out about the proper way to floss and brush by looking at the photos and reading the captions on these two pages.

DRAW CONCLUSIONS Why is tooth care important, and how should you take care of your teeth?

to prevent tooth decay and gum disease; by proper flossing and brushing after meals to remove plaque and bits of food scattered by flossing

Tips for Proper Brushing

1. Place the toothbrush at a 45° angle against the gums.
2. Move the brush gently back and forth in short strokes.
3. Brush the outer, inner, and chewing surfaces of the teeth.
4. Use the end of the brush to clean the inside surfaces of front teeth.
5. Brush your tongue to remove bacteria and freshen your breath.

Your dentist can work with you to keep your teeth and gums healthy. ▼

39

Discuss

Direct students' attention to the Tips for Proper Brushing. On the board, draw a horizontal line and a line illustrating a 45-degree angle. Over the 45-degree-angle line, sketch the outline of a toothbrush. Over the horizontal line, sketch the outline of a tooth and the gum line. Discuss why holding a toothbrush at this angle would be important in preventing tooth decay.

Critical Thinking Some dentists recommend that the gums also be brushed. What is the advantage of brushing your gums? Bacteria and food might be on your gums, and they can be pushed onto the teeth. Brushing the gums will remove the bacteria and food and help prevent cavities.

Problem Solving Your friend tells you that you need to brush only the chewing surfaces of your teeth. Do you agree or disagree? Explain your reasoning. Possible answer: disagree because harmful bacteria are found on all surfaces of a tooth

Why should you also floss your teeth? When you floss your teeth, you remove the bits of food and plaque that are stuck between your teeth.

Math

Measure and Add Floss Have students use string to measure an 18-inch length. Have them calculate how much floss isn't stretched between the fingers when they are using the length (15–16 inches). Have them calculate how much floss they would use in a week. (Note: students multiply 18 x 7 days per week.)

Social Studies

History of the Toothbrush Today there are about 3,000 patents for toothbrushes. The earliest toothbrushes were small twigs. One end of the twig was mashed to flatten it. Have students research other devices used to clean the teeth throughout history. They might also look at how other cultures practice dental hygiene.

TEACH *continued*

Consumer Activity

Students should list considerations such as whether the product has fluoride or the ADA seal as well as the price of the toothpaste product. After students complete the activity, ask them to describe the importance of accessing health information through a variety of health sources.

Discuss

Brainstorm with students a list of different types of dental products, including toothbrushes, toothpaste, and dental floss. Encourage students to describe the types of products they use and tell why they buy the products they do.

Critical Thinking You are at the store to buy toothpaste. Your parents want you to use only toothpaste with fluoride. As you are looking over your choices, you see one package that has the ADA seal. Would your parents approve of this product? yes, because toothpaste with the ADA seal contains fluoride

Problem Solving Suppose your teeth are very close together. When it's time to floss your teeth, you can choose between waxed and unwaxed dental floss. Which choice might be better for your teeth and why? The waxed floss might be better for teeth that are very close together because the wax helps the floss slide between teeth without shredding or breaking.

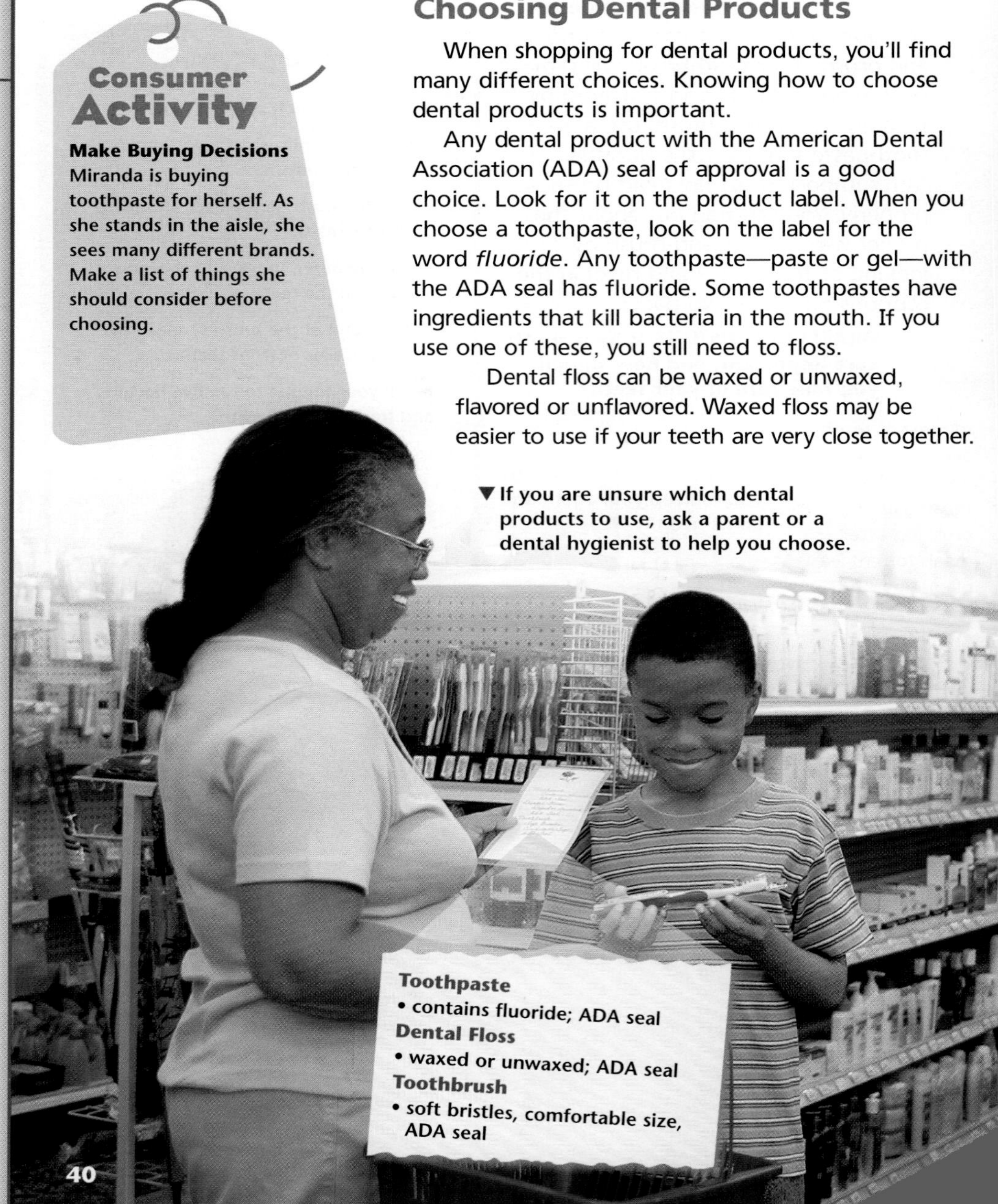

Toothpaste
• contains fluoride; ADA seal
Dental Floss
• waxed or unwaxed; ADA seal
Toothbrush
• soft bristles, comfortable size, ADA seal

Consumer Activity

Make Buying Decisions Miranda is buying toothpaste for herself. As she stands in the aisle, she sees many different brands. Make a list of things she should consider before choosing.

Choosing Dental Products

When shopping for dental products, you'll find many different choices. Knowing how to choose dental products is important.

Any dental product with the American Dental Association (ADA) seal of approval is a good choice. Look for it on the product label. When you choose a toothpaste, look on the label for the word *fluoride*. Any toothpaste—paste or gel—with the ADA seal has fluoride. Some toothpastes have ingredients that kill bacteria in the mouth. If you use one of these, you still need to floss.

Dental floss can be waxed or unwaxed, flavored or unflavored. Waxed floss may be easier to use if your teeth are very close together.

▼ **If you are unsure which dental products to use, ask a parent or a dental hygienist to help you choose.**

40

ESL/ELL Support

LANGUAGE AND VOCABULARY Help students understand the use of the prefix *un-*.

Beginning Allow students to feel waxed and unwaxed dental floss, pointing out the words on the product label. Explain that *un-* tells that the floss has no wax.

Intermediate Have students compare waxed, unwaxed, flavored, and unflavored dental flosses and write definitions of *waxed, unwaxed, flavored,* and *unflavored.*

Advanced Provide students with a list of adjectives, such as *flavored, happy, fair,* and *healthy*. Have students add the prefix *un-* to each word in the list and then use the new words in sentences.

Choose a toothbrush with soft bristles. Soft bristles will remove plaque without hurting your gums. The toothbrush should fit comfortably in your mouth. It should have a shape that will help you get to hard-to-reach teeth. Your toothbrush can be manual or battery powered. Replace your toothbrush every three months and after an illness.

DRAW CONCLUSIONS **What should you look for on the label of any dental product?** ADA seal of approval

Quick Activity

Choosing Dental Products Which of the products pictured on this page would you use? Write a sentence explaining your reasoning for each of your choices.

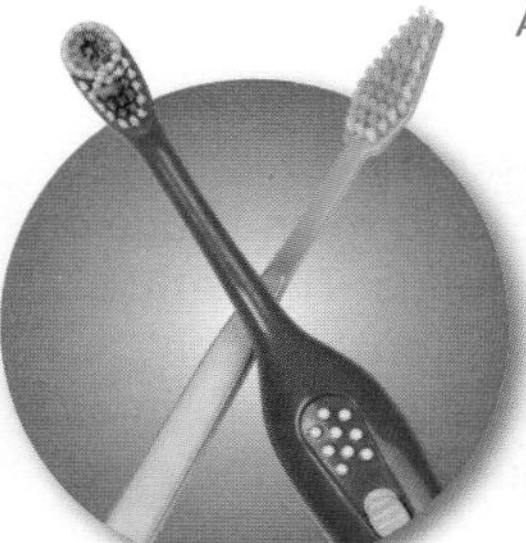

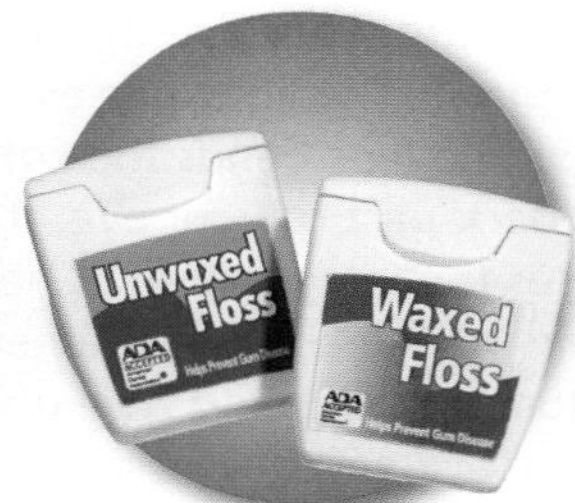

▲ **Many good dental-care products are available. Often your choices will depend on your own likes or dislikes, such as a favorite color or flavor.**

Lesson 2 Summary and Review

1. **Summarize with Vocabulary** Use vocabulary and other terms from this lesson to complete these statements.

   Bacteria in _____ form acid that can cause tooth _____. This can result in holes in the teeth called _____. Using toothpaste with _____ can help prevent dental problems.

2. What is tartar, and what problem can result from its buildup?
3. **Critical Thinking** If you are unable to brush after a meal, what is the next-best thing you can do?
4. **MAIN IDEA AND DETAILS** Draw and complete this graphic organizer to show ways to care for your teeth.

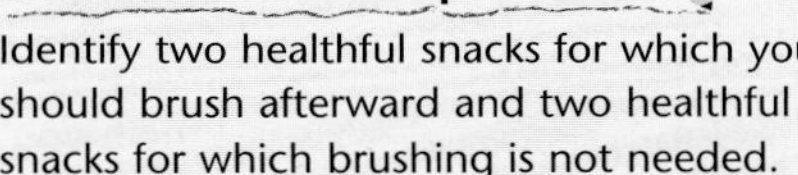

5. **Write to Inform—Explanation** Identify two healthful snacks for which you should brush afterward and two healthful snacks for which brushing is not needed.

41

Science

Fluoride Protection Tell students that tooth decay has been reduced by 40 to 60 percent in cities that add fluoride to drinking water. Ask students to research whether fluoride is added to bottled water. If fluoride has been added, they should check to see if the amount of fluoride is sufficient to protect teeth against decay.

Quick Activity

Student sentences should state the student's choice and support the choice with convincing facts and details.

3. WRAP UP

Lesson 2 Summary and Review

1. plaque; decay; cavities; fluoride
2. hardened plaque; gum disease
3. Rinse your mouth with water.
4. Responses may include:

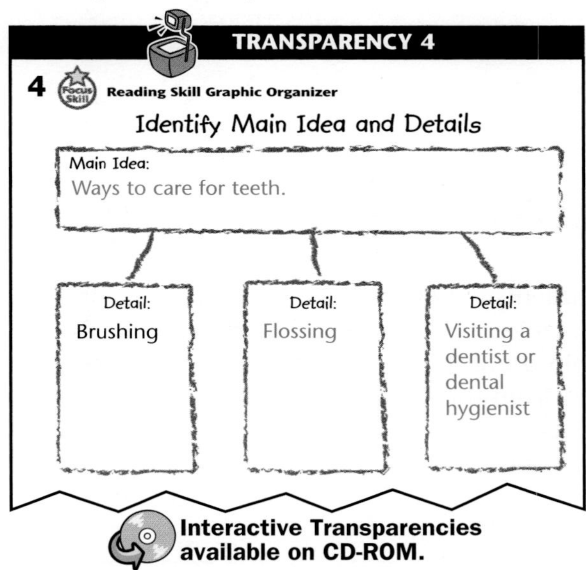

TRANSPARENCY 4
4 Reading Skill Graphic Organizer
Identify Main Idea and Details
Main Idea:
Ways to care for teeth.
Detail:
Brushing
Detail:
Flossing
Detail:
Visiting a dentist or dental hygienist

Interactive Transparencies available on CD-ROM.

5. Students should provide examples of starches, milk products, or fruit for the first category and crunchy vegetables for the second category.

For **writing models** with examples, see *Teaching Resources* pp. 47–61. Rubrics are also provided.

When Minutes Count . . .

Quick Study Students can use *Activity Book* pages 6–7 (shown on p. 33) as they complete each lesson in this chapter.

LESSON 3
Pages 42–45

Objectives
- ► Identify and explain the causes of common vision and hearing problems.
- ► Describe and demonstrate how to take good care of eyes and ears.

When Minutes Count . . .
Assign the Quick Study, Lesson 3, Activity Book pp. 6–7 (shown on p. 33).

Program Resources
- ► Activity Book pp. 6–7
- ► Transparencies 4, 18, and 19

Vocabulary
pupil p. 42, **lens** p. 42, **retina** p. 42

Daily Fitness Tip
Students may not know that red, itchy, or watery eyes could be a sign of infection. To help prevent infection, students should keep dirt from their eyes. They should avoid touching their eyes, especially when they are sick. If they must touch their eyes for any reason, they should first wash their hands with soap and warm water.

1. MOTIVATE
Have students work in pairs. Have one student hold his or her arm to the side with the thumb extended upward. Then have the partner observe the student's eyes as he or she focuses on the thumb and slowly moves the thumb toward the nose.

What does the observer see? The pupils of the partner's eyes move inward as the thumb comes closer to the nose.

What does the person watching his or her thumb feel? The person may feel an odd sensation as the eyes aim inward.

How is this different from normal vision? The eyes usually move in the same direction, parallel to each other.

Explain that the muscles around the eyes control the direction in which the eyes look.

LESSON 3

Your Vision and Hearing

Lesson Focus
Taking care of your vision and hearing is important for your health.

Why Learn This?
Learning about your eyes and ears helps you make good choices about caring for them.

Vocabulary
pupil
lens
retina

How the Eye Works
The parts of your eye work together to help you gather information about the world around you. Light enters your eye through an opening called the **pupil**. The light passes through a clear, curved **lens**. The lens bends the light to form an image on the back part of your eye, the retina. The **retina** passes the image through nerve signals to the brain. Your brain uses the nerve signals to form a picture in your mind. The diagram shows the parts of the eye and how they work together.

For people with normal vision, the lens focuses images clearly on the retina. But not everyone has normal vision. Sometimes images do not focus correctly on the retina. As you can see from the diagram, a person may be nearsighted or farsighted. Both problems can be corrected by using corrective lenses—glasses or contact lenses. These lenses focus images correctly on the retinas.

CAUSE AND EFFECT **What causes many people to need corrective lenses?**

Your eyes adjust to the light. Your pupils get bigger to let in more light when it is dark. Your lenses change shape to help you focus on objects both near and far.▶

Their eyes do not focus correctly on the retina.

Information Alert!
Braces for Your Eyes
Special contact lenses can be used to correct vision while you sleep. As you wear the lenses, the eye is reshaped. In the morning, you remove the lenses, and you can see without glasses or contacts.

For the most up-to-date information, visit The Learning Site. www.harcourtschool.com/health

42

Meeting Individual Needs
Leveled Activities

BELOW-LEVEL **Investigate Pupil Reaction** Pair students to study how the pupil reacts to light. Have them look at each other's eyes in a darkened room and then shine a small flashlight toward but not into their partner's eyes. Have them explain what happens to the eyes.

ON-LEVEL **Research Differences** Have students find out the differences between an optician (makes glasses), optometrist (prescribes lenses to correct vision), and ophthalmologist (treats diseases and injuries of the eye).

CHALLENGE **Research Rods and Cones** Have groups of students research the purpose of rods and cones in the retina. Have them prepare a class presentation to inform other class members about what they learn. If possible, have them use a computer to create a slide presentation.

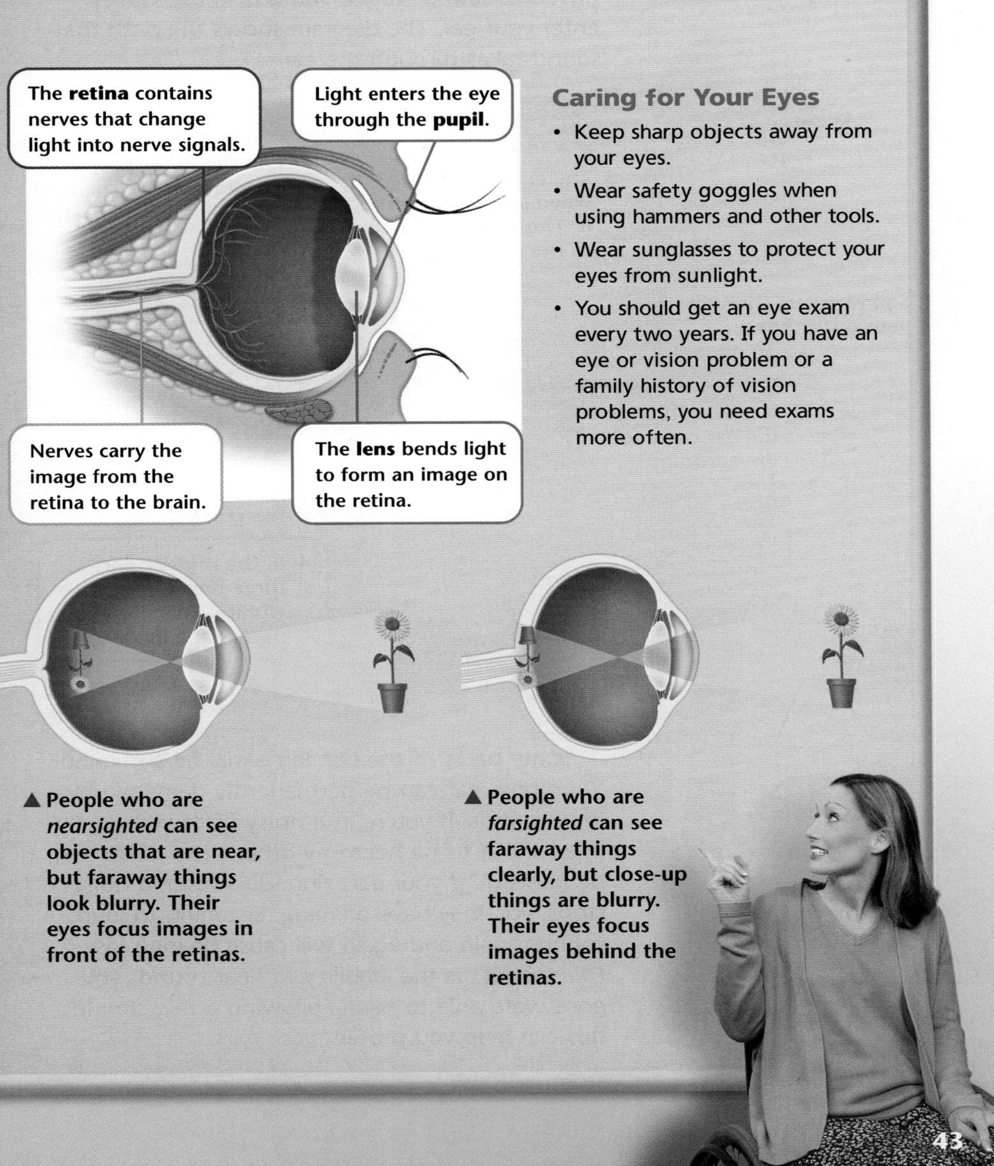

The **retina** contains nerves that change light into nerve signals.
Light enters the eye through the **pupil**.
Nerves carry the image from the retina to the brain.
The **lens** bends light to form an image on the retina.

Caring for Your Eyes

- Keep sharp objects away from your eyes.
- Wear safety goggles when using hammers and other tools.
- Wear sunglasses to protect your eyes from sunlight.
- You should get an eye exam every two years. If you have an eye or vision problem or a family history of vision problems, you need exams more often.

▲ People who are *nearsighted* can see objects that are near, but faraway things look blurry. Their eyes focus images in front of the retinas.

▲ People who are *farsighted* can see faraway things clearly, but close-up things are blurry. Their eyes focus images behind the retinas.

43

2. TEACH

Interpret Visuals—Pictures

Direct students' attention to the pictures on this page. Have students point to the retina in the diagram. Explain that the image must focus on the retina in order to be seen clearly. Have students compare where the images focus in the illustrations showing nearsighted and farsighted eyes.

Critical Thinking If someone's eye focuses images in front of the retina, would that person be able to see clearly without corrective lenses? No, the image needs to focus on the retina in order for a person to see clearly.

When Minutes Count . . .

Transparency 18: The Eye can be used to present material in this lesson. *Interactive Transparencies available on CD-ROM.*

Health Background

Inside the Eye The adult eyeball is about 1 inch wide. The outermost covering is called the sclera. You see the sclera as the "whites of the eyes." Beneath the sclera is a thin layer called the choroid, which has many blood vessels that nourish the eye. The retina is the layer below the choroid. The retina contains many light-sensitive cells that detect light and change it into nerve signals. Most of the eye is filled with a jellylike substance called the vitreous humor. Light that enters the eye through the cornea and lens travels through the vitreous humor to the retina.

Source: *Gray's Anatomy website*

For more background, visit the **Webliography** in Teacher Resources at **www.harcourtschool.com/health** **Keyword** human body

Science

Research Optical Illusions Have students research and copy some examples of optical illusions. Have students present their illusions to the class. If possible, have students explain their illusions and describe why the eye responds to the illusion in the way it does.

Teacher Tip

Eye First Aid Share with students these eye first-aid tips:

- If something gets in your eye, wash it with plain water.
- If your eye's hit by an object, put cold cloths on it for 15 minutes. If it swells, see a doctor.
- If an object gets stuck in the eye, don't pull it out. Go see a doctor.
- If a chemical gets in your eyes, wash them with water for at least 10 minutes. Then see a doctor.

TEACH *continued*

Content-Area Reading Support

Using Paragraph Structure Have students read the first sentence of the second paragraph on this page. Point out that the sentence states the main idea of the paragraph: *Some parts of the ear can be easily damaged.*

Explain that paragraphs in textbooks often begin with a main-idea sentence that tells what the other sentences in the paragraph are about. Call on volunteers to read the remaining sentences aloud. Help students recognize that the sentences form an informational and structural pattern, with each sentence stating ways that hearing can be damaged. Suggest that students look for main ideas and the details that follow whenever they read. Tell them that doing so can help them better understand and recall what they read.

Discuss

Critical Thinking Earplugs help protect the ears from sound by plugging the end of the ear canal. Why would this help block the damaging effects of loud sounds? The earplugs prevent damaging sound waves from entering the ears.

When Minutes Count . . .

Transparency 19: The Ear can be used to present material in this lesson. *Interactive Transparencies available on CD-ROM.*

Interpret Visuals—Illustrations

Have students study the shape of the outer ear in the diagram.

Critical Thinking How does the shape of the outer ear aid hearing? The outer ear acts like a funnel to gather sound waves.

Critical Thinking Why is the inner ear located so far into the skull? to protect it

How the Ear Works

When an object makes a sound, the sound travels as sound waves. Some of these waves enter your ear. The diagram shows the path that sound takes through the ear.

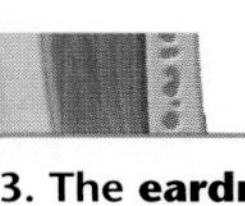

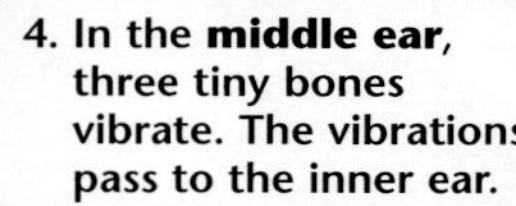

1. Sound enters through your **outer ear**.
2. It moves through the ear canal to the eardrum.
3. The **eardrum** vibrates when sound waves hit it. The vibrations pass to the middle ear.
4. In the **middle ear**, three tiny bones vibrate. The vibrations pass to the inner ear.
5. In the **inner ear**, vibrations are changed into nerve signals that move to the brain.

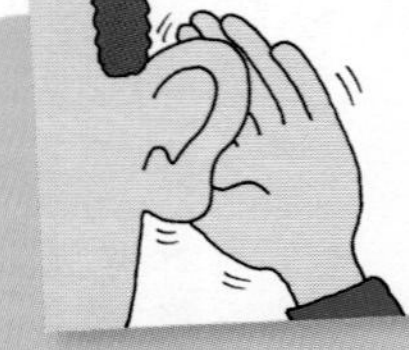

Did You Know?

A person with hearing loss in one ear often has a hard time knowing where certain sounds come from. That is because the brain needs information from both ears to tell the direction of sound.

Some parts of the ear can easily be damaged. Your inner ear can be permanently damaged by loud sounds. If you're in a noisy place where you must shout to be heard by others, the noise may be harmful. If your ears ring when a loud noise stops, you may have damage. Listening to loud sounds again and again will cause hearing loss. *Hearing loss* is the inability to hear sounds you once were able to hear. Following a few simple tips can help you protect your ears.

44

ESL/ELL Support

BACKGROUND EXPERIENCE Encourage students to share prior experiences they have had with loud noises.

Beginning Have students draw a picture of a time when they heard a very loud sound, such as a fire truck's siren or a concert. Help students write a caption for their picture.

Intermediate Have students write a sentence about a very loud sound they have heard. Encourage students to share how the loud sound made them feel.

Advanced Have students form teams and make lists of situations that could cause damage to their ears. Have each team circle the situations they think are most dangerous to healthy hearing.

Avoid loud sounds. Keep the volume down when using a stereo or headphones. Stay away from noisy places or wear earplugs. Keep objects, including cotton swabs, out of your ears. Wear a helmet with ear protection when you play sports. See a doctor if you develop a problem with your ears or hearing.

MAIN IDEA AND DETAILS **List some ways that you can protect your ears from harm.**

ACTIVITY

Life Skills

Manage Stress

Your friend is playing his stereo so loudly that the sound is stressing you. How can you deal with this situation and manage your stress? Use the steps to Manage Stress on pp.10–11 to write a paragraph that describes how you might deal with your stress.

Sound Levels

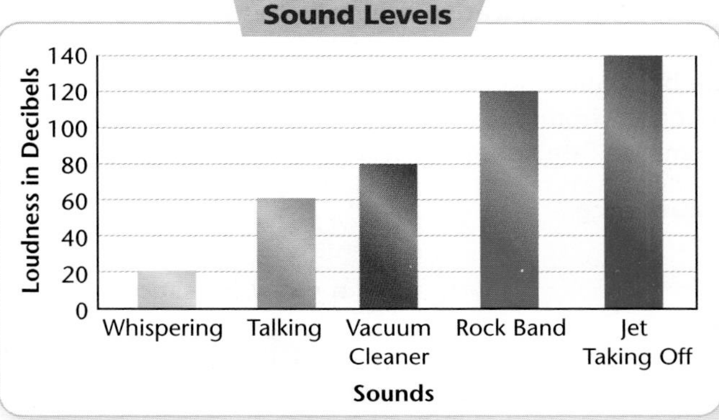

◀ Sounds are measured in decibels (DES•uh•belz). The louder the sound, the greater the number in decibels. Your hearing can be damaged after just one hour of listening to noise of 100 decibels. How can you prevent injury from these noises?

Lesson 3 Summary and Review

❶ **Summarize with Vocabulary**

Use vocabulary and other terms from this lesson to complete these statements.

Light enters the eye through the _____. The _____ then bends the light and focuses it on the _____. For people who are _____, faraway objects appear blurry. For people who are _____, close-up objects are blurry.

❷ List three ways to protect your vision.

❸ **Critical Thinking** Your friends say that you don't hear them sometimes when they talk to you. What can you do?

❹ **MAIN IDEA AND DETAILS** Draw and complete this graphic organizer to show what the parts of the ear do.

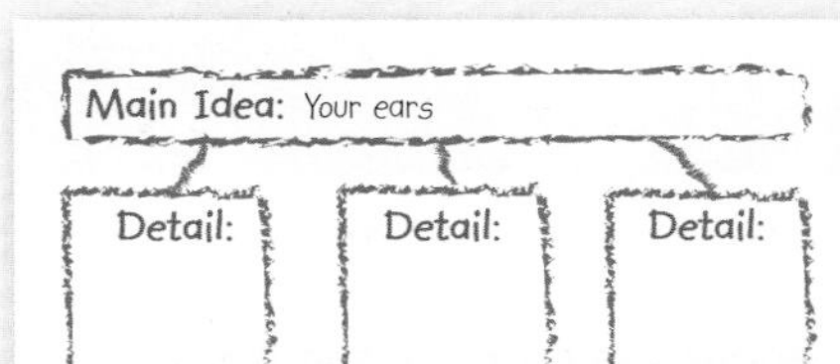

❺ **Write to Inform—Explanation**

Explain how decibels and hearing loss are related.

Avoid loud sounds, keep earphones and stereo volumes low, wear earplugs, stay away from noisy places, keep objects out of ears, wear a helmet with ear protection for sports, and see a doctor for ear or hearing problems.

Music

Sound Rhythms Provide students with a variety of classroom or household objects, such as erasers, pencils, spoons, or books. Challenge each student to compose a rhythm using the object, such as rhythmically tapping a pencil on a tabletop. Have each student share his or her rhythm with the rest of the class. Then discuss how each object produced the sound.

Physical Education

Protective Gear Have students describe headgear that is used to protect the eyes and ears, such as baseball batting helmets with ear guards. Direct students to choose one type of eye or ear protection and tell how it protects the body, in what sports the gear is used, and why wearing the gear is important to a player's safety.

Activity

Manage Stress Students' paragraphs should show an understanding of the actions they can take to manage stress.

3. WRAP UP

Lesson 3 Summary and Review

1. pupil; lens, retina; nearsighted; farsighted
2. Possible answers: Keep sharp objects away from the eyes; wear safety goggles when working with tools; wear sunglasses
3. Possible answers: Mention this to a parent; talk about it and consider consulting a doctor
4. Responses may include:

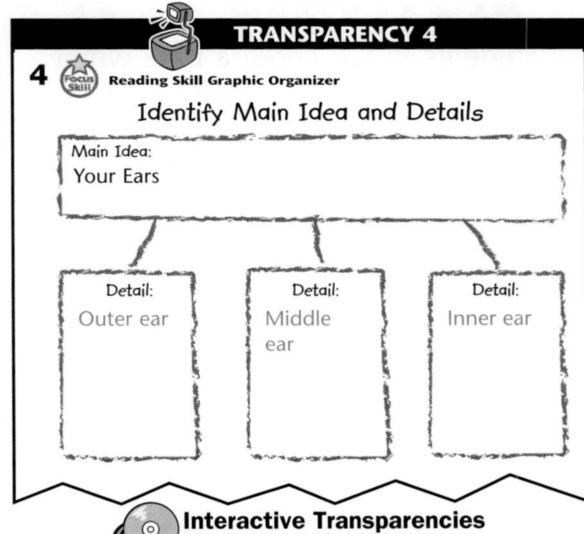

Interactive Transparencies available on CD-ROM.

5. Decibels measure sound. The louder the sound, the greater the number of decibels. Loud sounds can damage hearing.

For **writing models** with examples, see *Teaching Resources* pp. 47–61. Rubrics are also provided.

When Minutes Count . . .

Quick Study Students can use *Activity Book* pages 6–7 (shown on p. 33) as they complete each lesson in this chapter.

Life Skills

Communicate
Make Responsible Decisions
Manage Stress
Refuse
Resolve Conflicts
Set Goals

Objectives

- Identify communication skills.
- Use communication skills to make one's health needs known.

Program Resources

- Activity Book p. 9
- Poster 7

1. MOTIVATE

Ask students to tell about a time when they hurt themselves or needed medical attention. Have them explain the importance of seeking guidance from parents and other trusted adults in making healthy decisions and solving problems.

2. TEACH

Direct students' attention to the pictures of Tonya on these pages.

Step 1

How does Tonya know that she needs to talk with a parent or teacher? What might happen if she doesn't tell someone? She knows that she needs to tell a parent or teacher because she needs good vision to do her school work. If she doesn't tell someone, her school work may suffer.

Step 2

Critical Thinking How does Tonya's description of her vision help her parents better understand her health need? By hearing her explanation, her parents can determine that she needs to see an eye doctor.

Communicate
About a Health Need

Communication is important to your health. Sharing your feelings with your parents or other health providers and talking about any problems you are experiencing enables them to help. Using the steps for **Communicating** can make this task easier.

Tonya has noticed that she has difficulty seeing the chalkboard from her seat in class. How can Tonya communicate about her vision problem?

1 Understand your audience.

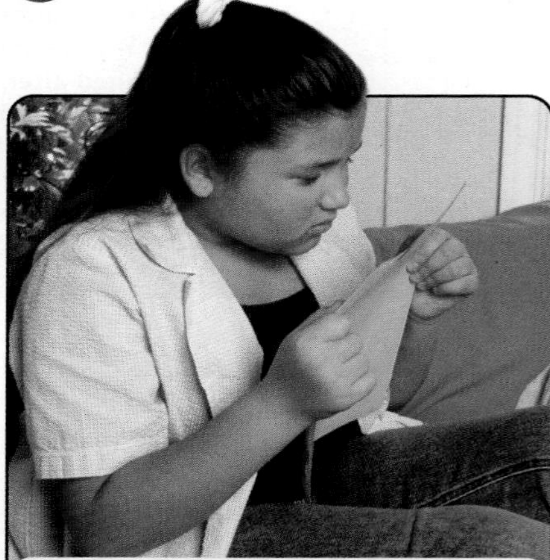

Tonya knows that she needs to talk to her parents or her teacher about the problem she has seeing things clearly.

2 Give a clear message.

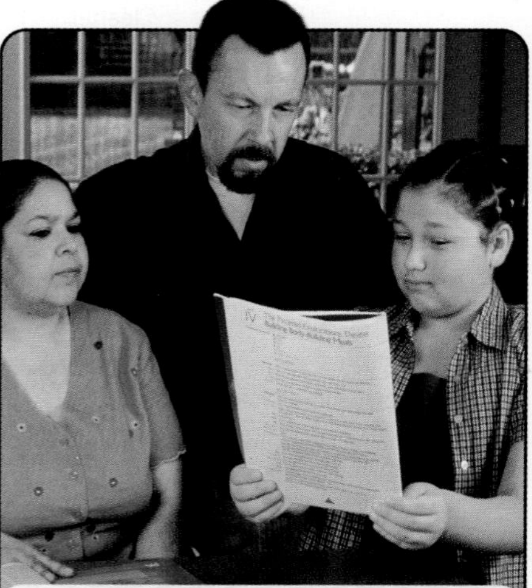

Tonya tells her parents that faraway things look blurry.

Teacher Tip

Emotional Needs Students should know that health needs include both physical and emotional needs. Students are much more apt to seek help when they have suffered a bodily injury than if they have been emotionally wounded. Emotional health is as important to students' well-being as physical health, and students should be encouraged to exercise their communication skills for both their physical and emotional needs.

ACTIVITY BOOK P. 9

Name ______

Problem Solving

Life Skill
Communicate

Steps for Making Responsible Decisions

1. Understand your audience.
2. Give a clear message.
3. Listen carefully and answer any questions.
4. Gather feedback.

Use the steps to tell how these students should communicate their health needs.

A. Marissa was practicing softball with her friends, Latoya and Lina. Marissa was talking with Latoya when Lina threw her the ball. Not knowing the ball was coming, Marissa didn't turn to catch it, and it hit the side of her ear. Marissa felt okay then, but a few hours later her ear started to hurt and make a ringing sound.

- Should Marissa tell anyone about her ear? If so, how should she communicate the information?

Possible answer: Marissa should tell a parent, guardian, or trusted adult about the injury and the sensations she is feeling in her ear. The injury may not be serious, but Marissa may need to have her ear examined by a doctor.

B. A month ago, Tony got contact lenses for his birthday. Getting the contacts into his eyes has been tricky, and he still has difficulty with the task. After he gets the contacts in, his eyes are very red from his struggle. He had wanted contacts for two years and was afraid that if he told his parents about his trouble, he would have to wear his glasses again. When Tony's father asked about his red eyes one morning, Tony said that he was just feeling really tired.

- Will the way Tony communicated help solve his problem? Did it show that he was trustworthy? How should Tony communicate about the problem he is having with his eyes?

Possible answer: Tony's communication will not help solve his problem. It won't show that he is trustworthy. Tony should explain his problem to his parents. Then his doctor can help him make sure that he does not damage his eyes and vision.

© Harcourt

Available online. www.harcourtschool.com/health

3 Listen carefully and answer any questions.

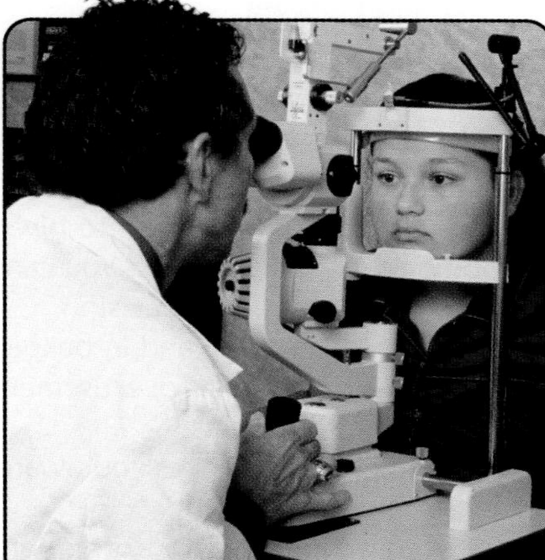

At the eye doctor's office, Tonya follows the instructions given her. She tells the doctor when things appear clear.

4 Gather feedback.

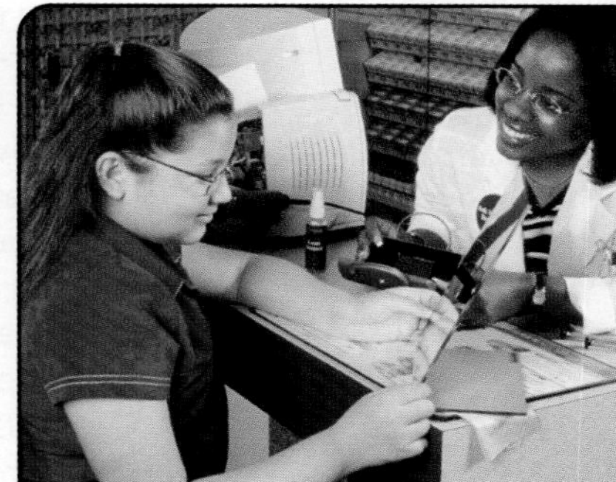

After talking with the doctor, Tonya realizes that using corrective lenses can solve her vision problem.

Problem Solving

Alex fell from a swing while on the playground. He landed awkwardly and hit his mouth. It hurt, but he didn't think much about it and continued to play. Once in class, however, he found that he had loosened a tooth. Use the steps for **Communicating** to explain how Alex can get help for his injury. Also explain how Alex's going to someone about his problem shows that he is responsible.

Using the Poster

Display Poster 7 to remind students of the steps for communicating.

Ask for volunteers to role-play situations that require communication skills to make a need known. Have students pantomime their role-play so that others need to pay close attention. Use the poster for a reference.

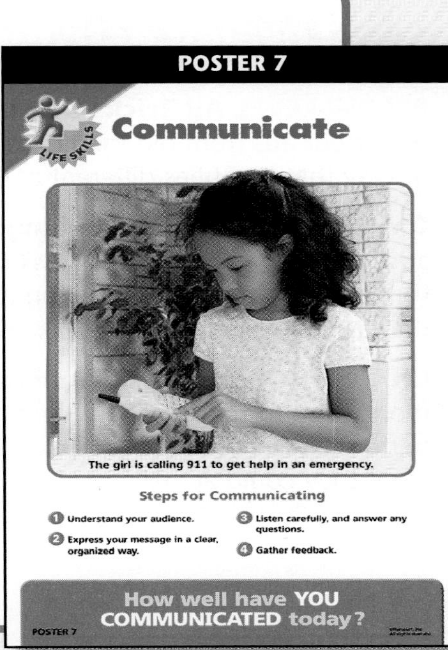

POSTER 7
Communicate
LIFE SKILLS
The girl is calling 911 to get help in an emergency.
Steps for Communicating
1 Understand your audience.
2 Express your message in a clear, organized way.
3 Listen carefully, and answer any questions.
4 Gather feedback.
How well have YOU COMMUNICATED today?
POSTER 7

Step 3

Critical Thinking Why is it important for Tonya to communicate during her eye examination? The only way that the doctor will know how best to treat Tonya's vision problem is through her descriptions of when things appear clear.

Building Good Character

By communicating and following the instructions of her eye doctor, Tonya is showing good character by being responsible. Remind students that when communicating information, they should consider how what they say can show good character. They can ask themselves these questions: Am I being trustworthy and responsible? Am I showing consideration for others by listening carefully after I communicate?

Step 4

What did Tonya learn by listening to what the eye doctor had to say? that her vision problem could be solved with corrective lenses

Critical Thinking Why is listening an important part of communicating? If you don't listen carefully, you may misunderstand what is said or you may communicate inaccurate information.

3. WRAP UP

Problem Solving

Answers should reflect the steps for communicating. Students should provide their ideas about how Alex could best communicate his injury, including talking with his teacher and school nurse. Students should also provide details that explain how Alex's action shows that he is responsible.

LESSON 4

Pages 48–50

Objectives

- ► Describe how advertisements can be analyzed to choose products that best meet your needs.
- ► Explain how the usefulness and value of health products and services can be determined by comparison.
- ► Explain the importance of refusal skills that are helpful in resisting negative peer pressure and media influences.

When Minutes Count . . .

Assign the Quick Study, Lesson 4, Activity Book pp. 6–7 (shown on p. 33).

Program Resources

- ► Activity Book pp. 6–7
- ► Transparency 4

Vocabulary

advertising p. 48, **consumer** p. 48

Daily Fitness Tip

Some health-care products contain chemicals that can harm the body if they aren't used properly. Tell students that knowing how to read labels and being informed about health-care products can help them avoid problems.

1. MOTIVATE

Optional Activity Materials a variety of magazines

Have students identify characteristics of health information. Ask them to look through magazines for advertisements. Discuss what the ads are trying to sell and how they are trying to get people to buy the products or services shown.

Is everything in the ad true? Answers will vary.

How could you find out? Answers will vary. Tell students that in this lesson they will learn about advertising tricks.

LESSON 4 Being a Health Consumer

Lesson Focus
Being a wise consumer can be important to your health.

Why Learn This?
Learning about the tricks used in some ads can help you become an informed consumer.

Vocabulary
advertising
consumer

Personal Health Plan

Real-Life Situation
Knowing the truth behind advertisements can provide you with a better understanding of a product.

Real-Life Plan
Write two things you could do to find out the truth about advertising messages you read.

Analyze Media Messages

You don't have to look far to see **advertising** (AD•ver•tyz•ing), a method businesses use to give people information about their products. You can find advertising along roadsides, on television, radio, and computers, in magazines, and in ballparks and stadiums. Businesses hope their advertisements will get people to buy their products.

Advertising can be helpful. It makes you aware that a product is for sale.

It also may offer some important information about how a product is used or what it is made from. A **consumer** (kuhn•SOOM•er) is someone who buys products. As a consumer you should be aware that some ads use tricks to get you to buy the product.

Advertisements are also called ads. ▶

48

Meeting Individual Needs
Leveled Activities

BELOW-LEVEL Ad Tricks Display Have students work in small groups to cut out ads from old magazines. Have them arrange the ads in a display that identifies different advertising tricks.

ON-LEVEL Consumer Challenge Have students find several magazine ads for health-care products. Ask students to circle the parts of the ads that offer important information about the product and underline parts that are solely intended to make people want to buy the product.

CHALLENGE Analyze Ad Language Have students examine ten or more ads and make a list of terms commonly used, such as "superior performance." Then have students look up the meanings of the words to see if they could actually apply to the product.

Have you ever seen an ad that only said bad things about another product? If so, did the ad give any useful information about its own product? Often, companies that advertise in this way do not want you to know the truth—that the other product may be just as good as or better than their own! When you see ads, form your own opinions about the product. Look at the product label to learn facts about it. You can see some other ways of advertising here and on page 48.

SUMMARIZE Why is it important to form your own opinions about products and not just believe everything that is advertised?
Ads may not really provide you with important information you need to decide whether you need or want the product.

Quick Activity

Analyze Ads The boy in the picture is trying to decide on a pair of sunglasses. He's read the advertisements on page 48. Help him make a decision by writing a reply to each advertisement.

THE REAL YOU
Trick: People who use this product become more popular.
Truth: A product can't make someone more popular.
FEEL THE QUALITY
Trick: Your favorite sports or music star tells you to buy the product.
Truth: The star cannot know whether the product is right for you. Something else may be better.
THE LATEST RAGE
Trick: Everyone is using this product, and you'll be left out if you don't.
Truth: Everyone cannot be using the same product. Buy only things that you need.

49

Math

Unit Prices Provide students with real or made-up prices for health-care products. Tell them they have a certain amount of money to spend to buy products on a list, such as soap, toothpaste, shampoo, and conditioner. Have them compare unit prices of similar products and then make buying decisions without going over their budget.

Music

Ad Jingle Ask students to write a jingle, or advertising song, for their favorite toothpaste. Explain that their advertisement song will be played on the radio in a 30-second time slot. Ask students to make up the music and lyrics to a catchy song that promotes the toothpaste. Encourage students to perform their jingles for the rest of the class.

2. TEACH

Interpret Visuals—Pictures

Have volunteers read the ads on page 48. Point out that each ad gives a message to the consumer. Have students state in their own words the message each ad gives. Ask how they would respond to each message. Then have students read the information in the picture on this page. Ask them to explain how the media can influence health behaviors. Help students compare their responses to the information in the picture.

Discuss

Why would an ad say bad things about another product in an advertisement? The ad is trying to make one product appear better than other products, even though it may be of equal or lesser quality.

Problem Solving Imagine that you work in an advertising company, and you're asked to create a TV ad for dental floss. How would you get people to buy the product? Answers will vary but should reflect the understanding that the main goal of advertisers is to sell products, not provide detailed information about the product.

Quick Activity

Students' answers should apply the steps for making responsible decisions to explain why they chose a particular pair of sunglasses.

Personal Health Plan

Point out to students that not every source of information about health products is reliable. Have them describe the importance of accessing health information through a variety of health resources. Tell students to consider their ideas carefully before deciding how to find out the truth about advertising. Possible answers: do research, ask a parent, ask a doctor or pharmacist

3. WRAP UP

Lesson 4 Summary and Review

1. Advertising; consumer; brands
2. Students should list three of the four tips: find out who's giving the message and why; watch for tricks to make consumers notice or agree with the ad; notice the values and points of view shown; learn whether important information has been left out
3. An ad can make you aware that a product is for sale and offer important information.
4. Responses may include:

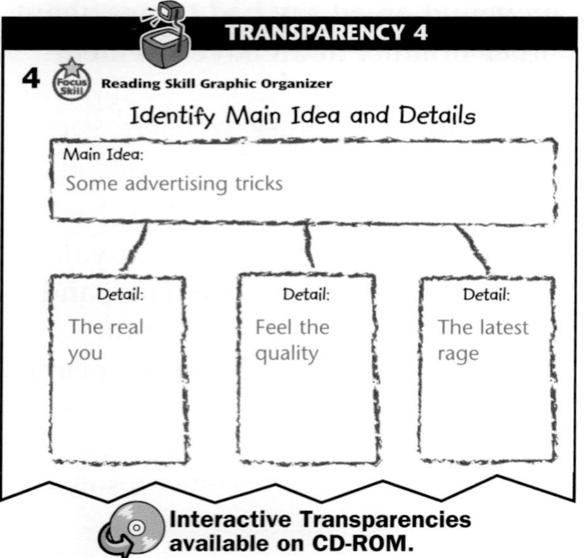

TRANSPARENCY 4
4 Reading Skill Graphic Organizer
Identify Main Idea and Details
Main Idea:
Some advertising tricks
Detail:
The real you
Detail:
Feel the quality
Detail:
The latest rage

Interactive Transparencies available on CD-ROM.

5. Students' signs should include information about analyzing ads and about making good buying decisions.

For **writing models** with examples, see *Teaching Resources* pp. 47–61. Rubrics are also provided.

When Minutes Count . . .

Quick Study Students can use *Activity Book* pages 6–7 (shown on p. 33) as they complete each lesson in this chapter.

Tips for Analyzing Ads and Media Messages

- Find out who is giving the message and why.
- Watch for tricks to make you notice or agree with the ad.
- Notice the values and points of view shown.
- Learn whether important information has been left out.

Make Wise Buying Decisions

Advertisements shouldn't be the only information you use to make buying decisions. Here are some other steps to help you.

1. Decide whether your choice is based on a true need for the item or a want for the item.
2. Compare several brands of the same item.
3. Choose the best item for the lowest price.
4. Think about the result of your decision.

SEQUENCE What should you do before you buy a product?

Decide whether you need it or only want it; compare products; choose the best for the lowest price; think about the results.

Lesson 4 Summary and Review

1. **Summarize with Vocabulary**
   Use vocabulary and other terms from this lesson to complete these statements.
   _____ is a method businesses use to tell people about a product. A person who buys a product is a _____. When making a buying decision, compare several _____ of the same item.
2. **Critical Thinking** In what two ways can an ad be helpful in your buying decisions?
3. List three tips for analyzing ads.
4. **MAIN IDEA AND DETAILS** Draw and complete this graphic organizer to show the types of tricks used in advertising.

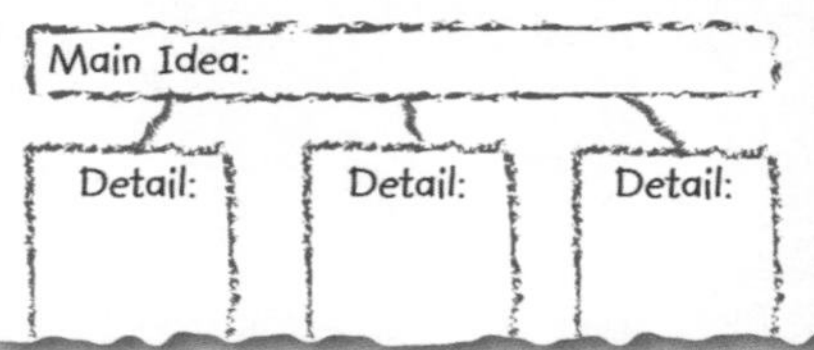

5. **Write to Inform—How-To**
   Write a sign that tells consumers how to make good buying decisions. Use your own words.

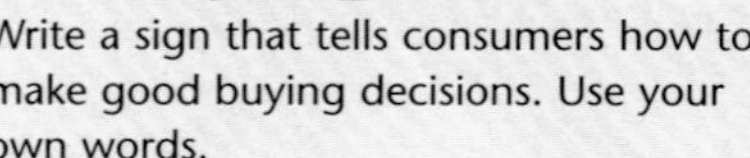

50

Science

Advertising Color Certain colors, such as red, tend to attract consumers better than other colors. Have groups of students create a simple ad and make several copies of it. Tell them to color each copy differently. Then have each group present the ads to the rest of the class, who can vote on which ads they like best and least. Complete the activity by having students analyze the data and draw a conclusion about advertising colors.

Teacher Tip

Consumer Reports Give groups of students practice in finding valid health information by having them choose a health-care product, such as toothpaste, shampoo, or sunscreen. Have them find consumer information about the type of product they have chosen and about the particular product. Help students analyze the information and write a summary about what to look for when buying that type of product.

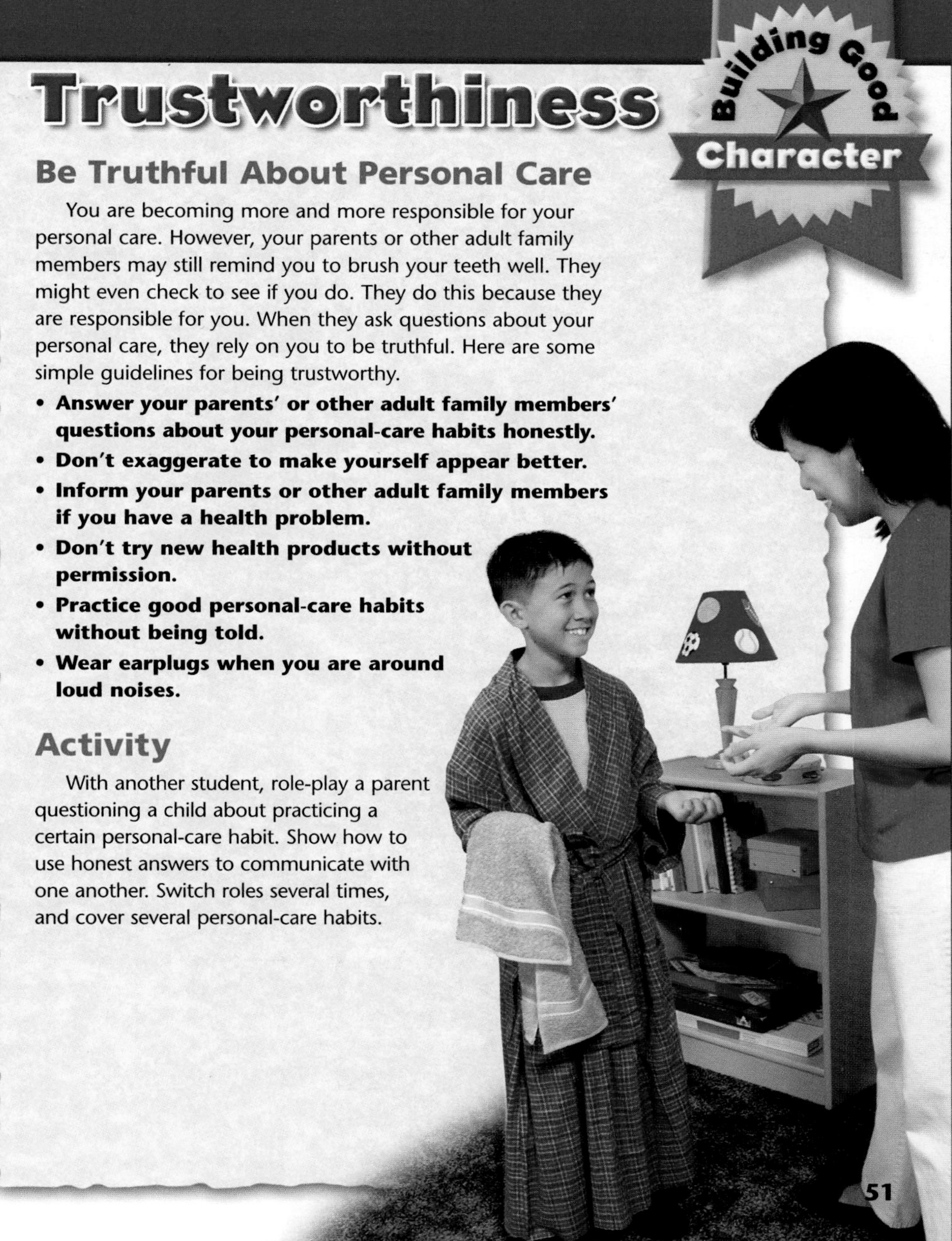

Trustworthiness

Be Truthful About Personal Care

You are becoming more and more responsible for your personal care. However, your parents or other adult family members may still remind you to brush your teeth well. They might even check to see if you do. They do this because they are responsible for you. When they ask questions about your personal care, they rely on you to be truthful. Here are some simple guidelines for being trustworthy.

- **Answer your parents' or other adult family members' questions about your personal-care habits honestly.**
- **Don't exaggerate to make yourself appear better.**
- **Inform your parents or other adult family members if you have a health problem.**
- **Don't try new health products without permission.**
- **Practice good personal-care habits without being told.**
- **Wear earplugs when you are around loud noises.**

Activity

With another student, role-play a parent questioning a child about practicing a certain personal-care habit. Show how to use honest answers to communicate with one another. Switch roles several times, and cover several personal-care habits.

51

Building Good Character

Caring
Citizenship
Fairness
Respect
Responsibility
Trustworthiness

Objective

► Recognize the importance of trustworthiness and truthfulness with family members about personal care.

Program Resource

► Poster 6

BEFORE READING

Discuss with students some ways that they show trustworthiness. After a discussion of various situations in which people can demonstrate trustworthiness, ask students to share their ideas about why it's important to be truthful about personal care and health matters. List students' ideas on the board.

DISCUSS

After students have read the page, have students explain how each bulleted statement shows trustworthiness. Ask why each statement promotes good health.

ACTIVITY

Be sure students understand that when students role-play, they pretend to be a certain person or type of person. Before students role-play, you may want to brainstorm some questions that parents may ask their child about personal-care habits, such as whether the child has brushed his or her teeth, flossed, and taken a bath or shower. Discuss reasons a parent might ask these questions and why the child should be honest.

Using the Poster

Activity Have students design a poster that illustrates how being truthful about personal care shows trustworthiness.

Display Poster 6 to remind students of ways to show trustworthiness. Students' posters can be displayed in the classroom, school cafeteria, or other common areas.

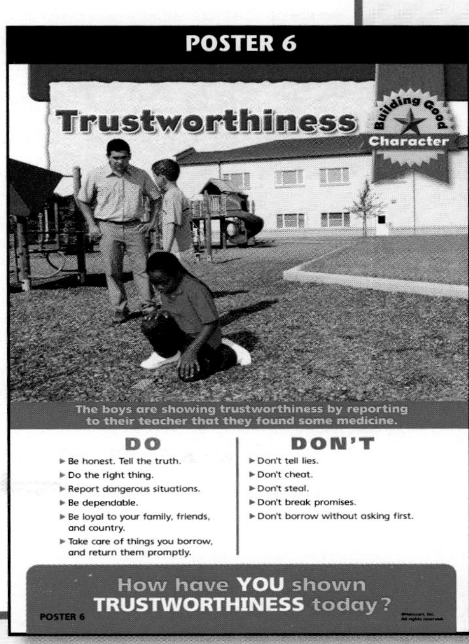

POSTER 6
Trustworthiness
Building Good Character
The boys are showing trustworthiness by reporting to their teacher that they found some medicine.
DO
► Be honest. Tell the truth.
► Do the right thing.
► Report dangerous situations.
► Be dependable.
► Be loyal to your family, friends, and country.
► Take care of things you borrow, and return them promptly.
DON'T
► Don't tell lies.
► Don't cheat.
► Don't steal.
► Don't break promises.
► Don't borrow without asking first.
How have YOU shown TRUSTWORTHINESS today?
POSTER 6

LESSON 5

Pages 52–54

Objectives

- Identify factual sources, including media and technology, for obtaining health information.
- Explain how information resources can be used to recognize and determine the usefulness of products and services.
- Describe a variety of ways to convey accurate health information and ideas.

When Minutes Count . . .

Assign the Quick Study, Lesson 5, Activity Book pp. 6–7, (shown on p. 33).

Program Resources

- Activity Book pp. 6–7, 10
- Transparency 4

Daily Fitness Tip

Some students may think that friends are trustworthy sources for health information. Although friends may not intend to provide inaccurate information, students should know that friends don't have the knowledge and experience of health experts and shouldn't be used as sources for health information. Encourage students to discuss their health concerns with their parents and rely on health experts, such as doctors or pharmacists, for information about health care.

1. MOTIVATE

Optional Activity Materials a variety of informational sources, such as a newspaper, a teen magazine, an advertisement, an encyclopedia, or a medical journal

Display the print materials, and have students scan the pages of each. Ask students to describe the importance of accessing health information through a variety of health resources.

Which materials have the best information about health care and products? Answers should reflect that popular magazines and ads may or may not contain facts.

Getting Health Information

Lesson Focus
Getting reliable health information can be important to your health.

Why Learn This?
Learning about where to find reliable health information will be helpful when you have health questions or problems.

Using Reliable Sources

If you want health information, where do you go? Television, newspapers, magazines, and books are just a few sources of health information. You can also find a lot of health information on the Internet.

Not everything you see and read about health is true, however. Some information is based on opinions, not facts. Some information is meant to get you to buy a product. Other information is wrong because the person who wrote it just didn't know the facts. Knowing where you can find reliable health facts is important.

▼ Have a parent or teacher help you look for information on the Internet.

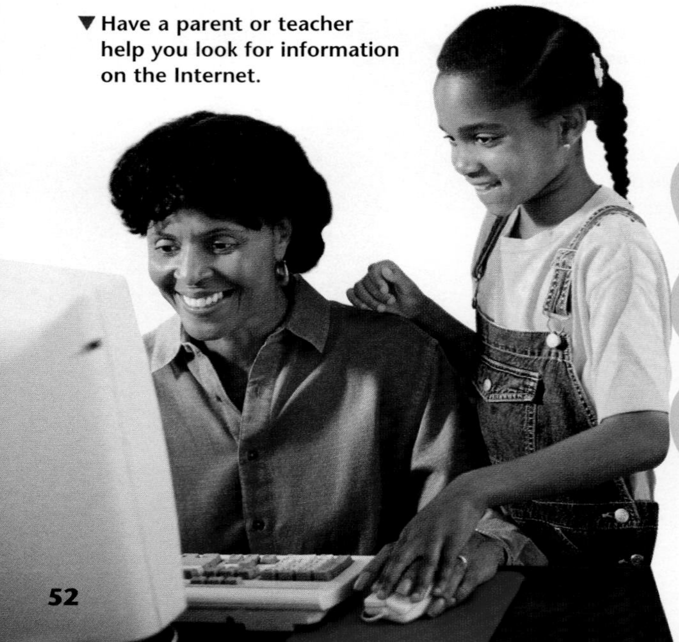

Quick Activity

Accessing Information The sources listed on page 53 are not the only places to find good health information. List at least three other reliable sources of health information.

52

ESL/ELL Support

COMPREHENSIBLE INPUT Some students may not comprehend the difference between factual information and biased information.

Beginning Give students a variety of factual statements and opinions, and ask students to say *yes* if the statement is a fact and *no* if the statement isn't factual. Discuss what clues in the sentence help tell if it's factual or not.

Intermediate Have students write a sentence that states a health fact and a sentence that states an opinion about the same health information.

Advanced Have students review an advertisement for a health product. Have them identify the information in the ad that's factual and the information that isn't.

Suppose you had a problem with your bike. You probably would ask a bike expert, not a baker, how to fix it. The same is true for health information. The best information comes from people who are health experts.

Among the best sources of health information are health professionals. Nurses, doctors, and pharmacists are good examples. Such people are more likely to give you trustworthy information. They have studied health and deal with health problems every day.

For most other sources, especially the Internet, you should think about which person or group has given out the information. If the source is not one of the kinds mentioned in this lesson, it may not be one you should trust.

DRAW CONCLUSIONS For health information, why is a doctor a more reliable source than what you already know?

A doctor is a health expert; he or she would know a great deal more than you about health matters simply because they have spent a greater number of years of study and practice than you have.

Reliable Sources

- College and university websites, which end in .edu
- Science and health journals
- Major national newspapers
- National health magazines
- National health organizations and their websites, which end in .org
- Government health organizations and their websites, which end in .gov

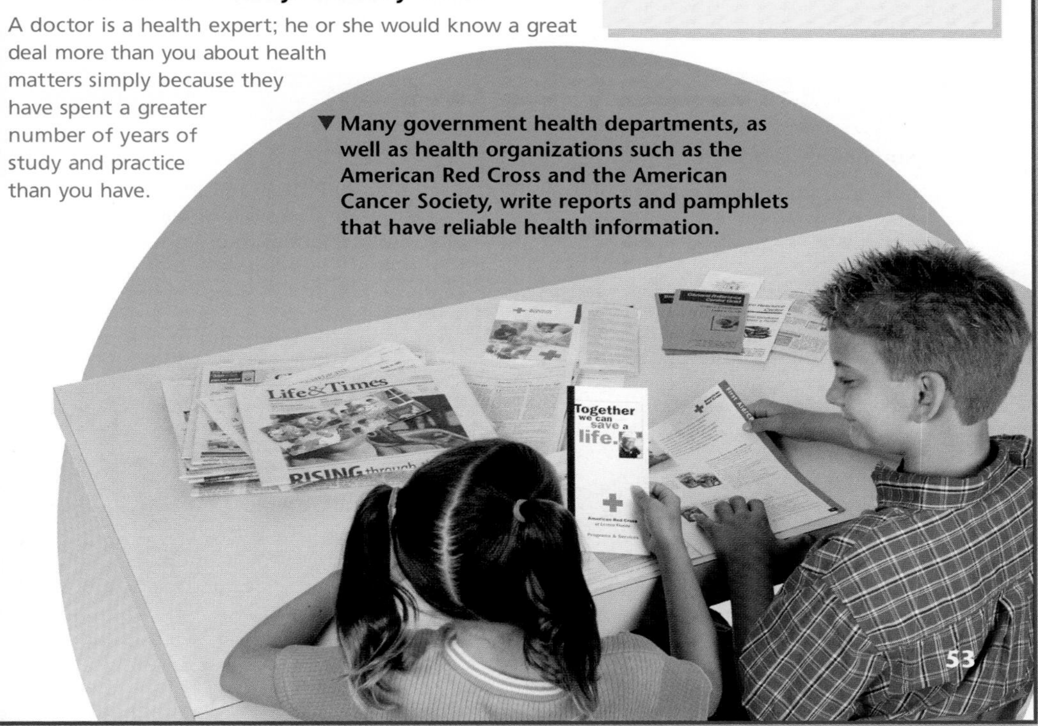

▼ Many government health departments, as well as health organizations such as the American Red Cross and the American Cancer Society, write reports and pamphlets that have reliable health information.

53

2. TEACH

Content-Area Reading Support

Using Lists Direct attention to the boxed text on this page. Point out that the box gives important information about the topic—reliable sources. Tell students to look for similar features throughout the book. Explain that they should read the copy in the box carefully to learn important health information.

Quick Activity

Students need to take care to use reliable sources of information. In particular, they should avoid websites that sell products. Students' responses should include websites that end in .org and .gov.

Discuss

Ask students if they have ever seen posters or slogans with health information. An example might be "Just say *no.*"

Can posters and slogans provide reliable sources of health information? Explain your answer. Yes; as with other sources of health information, it's important to look for the source. Point out that health organizations, such as the American Heart Association or the American Cancer Society, often use posters and slogans to give reliable information.

Problem Solving When researching soap, you find one website posted by an individual, one by a soap-making company, and one by a health organization. Which website probably has the most reliable information? The health organization website is probably the most reliable.

Language Arts

List Health Agencies Have groups of students find the names and contact information for a variety of health organizations. Have each group contact an agency to find out what types of consumer information it provides. Have students from all groups enter the information in a class database that students can access when they want to find a source for a certain kind of health information.

Teacher Tip

Internet Safety The Children's Online Privacy Protection Act requires website operators to get a parent's permission before collecting personal information from children under the age of thirteen. Students should not give out personal information, such as their last name, address, or telephone number. Students should never agree to meet with someone or send pictures of themselves without first checking with their parents.

3. WRAP UP

Lesson 5 Summary and Review

1. reliable; experts; sources
2. Students should list three of the following five points: Be sure the website is reliable; look for initials of a college degree after the writer's name; find out if the website is selling something; look for websites with evidence of health research; and always check with more than one source.
3. Some information is based on opinion or personal experience.
4. Responses may include:

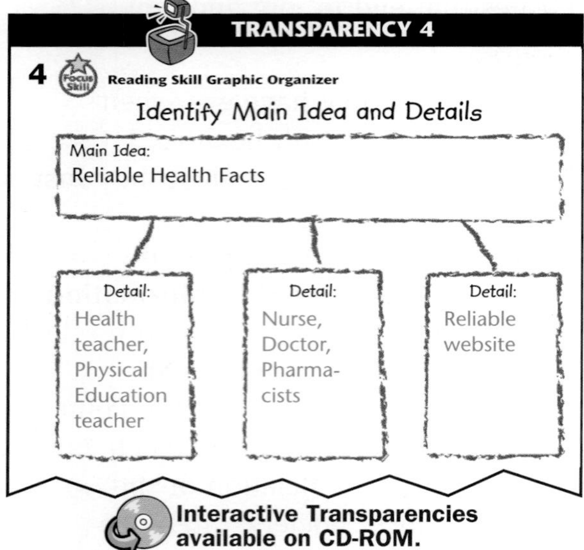

TRANSPARENCY 4
4 Reading Skill Graphic Organizer
Identify Main Idea and Details
Main Idea:
Reliable Health Facts
Detail:
Health teacher, Physical Education teacher
Detail:
Nurse, Doctor, Pharma-cists
Detail:
Reliable website

Interactive Transparencies available on CD-ROM.

5. Students should address one or more of the questions regarding the reliability of websites.

For **writing models** with examples, see *Teaching Resources* pp. 47–61. Rubrics are also provided.

When Minutes Count . . .

Quick Study Students can use *Activity Book* pages 6–7 (shown on p. 33) as they complete each lesson in this chapter.

Access Valid Health Information

- Find out who is responsible for the information.
- Decide if the information is reasonable.
- Check the information against other reliable sources. Keep a questioning attitude.
- Discuss the information with a parent or a health expert.

Evaluate Health Websites

It's important to remember that almost anyone can put information on the Internet. Follow these guidelines when you are looking at health websites.

- ► Be sure the website is a reliable source, such as a college or a government agency.
- ► Look for initials of a college degree after the writer's name.
- ► Find out if the website is selling anything. Websites that sell something may tell you only what sounds good.
- ► Look for sites that show evidence from health research.
- ► Always check with more than one source.

SUMMARIZE Why would a website selling a product probably not be a good source of reliable information?

Lesson 5 Summary and Review

1. **Summarize with Vocabulary**
   Use terms from this lesson to complete these statements.
   It is very important for health information to be trustworthy, or _____. Nurses and doctors can give good information because they are health _____. Science journals and health magazines usually are reliable _____.
2. **Critical Thinking** Why isn't all health information reliable?
3. What are three things you should consider when evaluating health websites?
4. **MAIN IDEA AND DETAILS** Draw and complete this graphic organizer to show three reliable sources of health information.

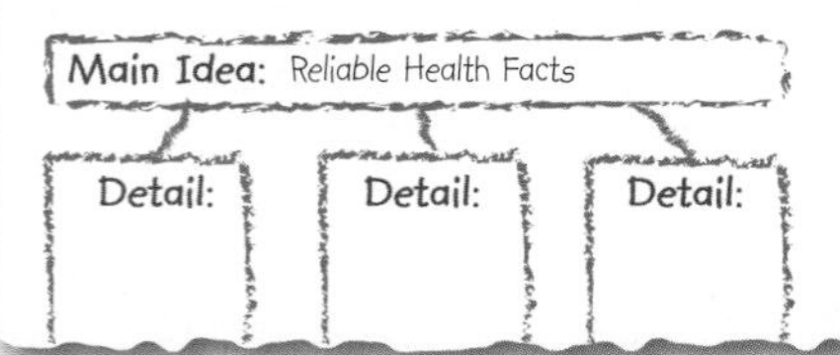

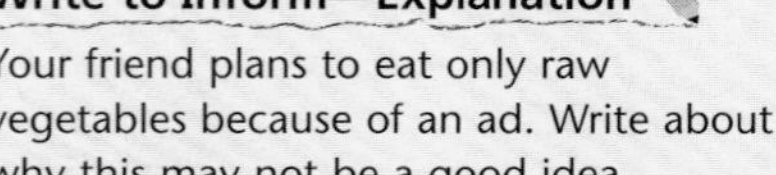

5. **Write to Inform—Explanation**
   Your friend plans to eat only raw vegetables because of an ad. Write about why this may not be a good idea.

A site selling something may present only information that supports what they are selling and not all the facts from good research.

Art

Health Slogans and Posters
Have each student write a health slogan and design a poster that convey accurate health information. Students may choose to create a slogan and poster for topics such as dental hygiene, caring for the skin, eye care, or ear care. Encourage students to use color, text, and pictures to communicate information on their posters.

ACTIVITY BOOK P. 10

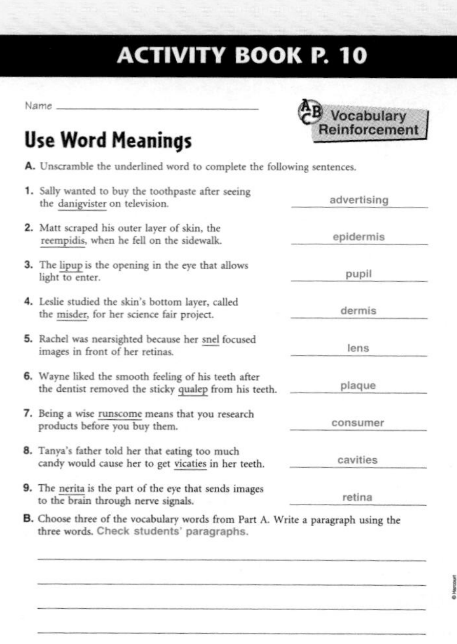

Name ________

Vocabulary Reinforcement

Use Word Meanings

A. Unscramble the underlined word to complete the following sentences.

1. Sally wanted to buy the toothpaste after seeing the danigvister on television. advertising
2. Matt scraped his outer layer of skin, the reempidis, when he fell on the sidewalk. epidermis
3. The lipup is the opening in the eye that allows light to enter. pupil
4. Leslie studied the skin's bottom layer, called the misder, for her science fair project. dermis
5. Rachel was nearsighted because her snel focused images in front of her retinas. lens
6. Wayne liked the smooth feeling of his teeth after the dentist removed the sticky qualep from his teeth. plaque
7. Being a wise runscome means that you research products before you buy them. consumer
8. Tanya's father told her that eating too much candy would cause her to get vicaties in her teeth. cavities
9. The nerita is the part of the eye that sends images to the brain through nerve signals. retina

B. Choose three of the vocabulary words from Part A. Write a paragraph using the three words. Check students' paragraphs.

Available online. www.harcourtschool.com/health

ACTIVITIES

Math

Count Hairs Cut a one-inch-square hole in a sheet of paper. Hold the sheet of paper on top of your forearm. Use a hand lens to count the hairs on your arm that are visible inside the square. Then measure your whole arm. Use the count to estimate how many hairs are on your arm.

Home & Community

Communicate Create an advertisement for a health product, using one or more of the techniques discussed in this chapter. Include some important information about the product. Apply labels to your ad that identify advertising techniques and useful information. Show your ad to your family to help them become more alert to advertising tricks.

Art

Protection Poster With a partner, make a poster that shows ways to protect the eyes or ears. Draw pictures, and write one or more slogans. Share your poster with younger students.

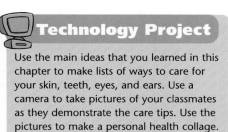

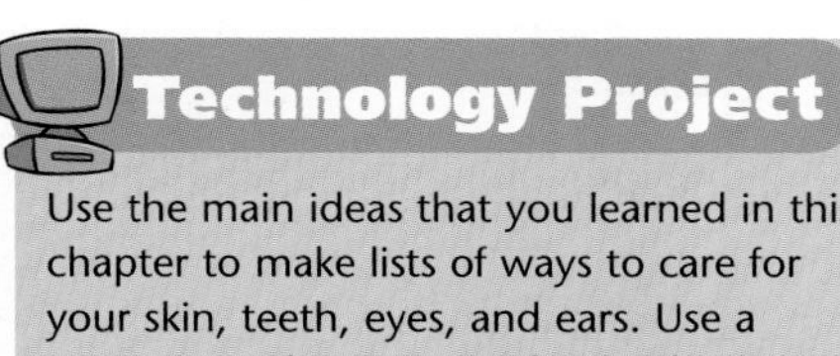

Career Link

Dental Hygienist A dental hygienist cares for the basic dental needs of patients, such as dental cleaning and X rays. Suppose you are a dental hygienist. A new patient arrives for her first visit. Describe what you would tell your patient about what to expect during her visit. Explain the importance of each step in her treatment.

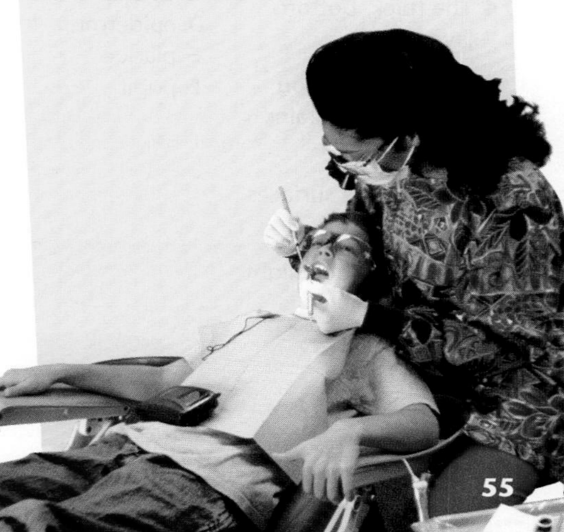

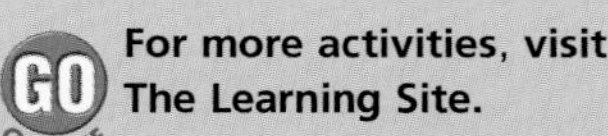

Technology Project

Use the main ideas that you learned in this chapter to make lists of ways to care for your skin, teeth, eyes, and ears. Use a camera to take pictures of your classmates as they demonstrate the care tips. Use the pictures to make a personal health collage.

For more activities, visit The Learning Site. www.harcourtschool.com/health

55

Career Link

Dental Hygienist Students may wish to research what happens during a visit to a dentist's office. Encourage students to make an outline of the activities that take place during a dental checkup. Have students use their outlines to describe the events during a visit to the dental office and provide explanations of the purpose of each event.

For more information on health careers, visit the **Webliography** in Teacher Resources at **www.harcourtschool.com/health**
Keyword health careers

Activities

Math

Have students work in groups to perform this activity. Provide each group with a hand lens, and ask students to record their own information. Once students have counted and made their estimates, have students compare their results with those collected by other members of the group.

Art

Before students create their posters, brainstorm a list of scenarios in which eye and ear protection would be needed. Encourage students to focus on two or three ways to protect the eyes or ears, and discourage them from attempting to show all the possible forms of protection on one poster. Provide students with a variety of art supplies, and remind them that their posters should clearly convey the health information.

Home & Community

Ads should reflect students' understanding that advertisements try to get people to buy a product. Encourage students to use words and color to make their ads capture people's attention and make the information interesting.

Supports the Coordinated School Health Program

Technology Project

Ask students to write a caption for each picture on their collages, telling what the picture shows and why that activity is important to personal care. Post student collages in the classroom. Then, as a class activity, have students classify the collages by types of health care, such as those about skin care and those for teeth, for eyes, and for ears.

Chapter Review and Test Preparation

Pages 56–57

Reading Skill 5 pts. each

1. reliable information
2. Possible answers: health experts, Internet, college and university websites, science and health journals, major national newspapers, national health magazines, national health organizations, and government health organizations

Use Vocabulary 5 pts. each

3. D, epidermis
4. C, dermis
5. E, plaque
6. A, cavities
7. F, pupil
8. B, consumer

Check Understanding 5 pts. each

9. D, pores
10. H, fluoride
11. C, farsighted
12. H, cotton swab
13. D, eardrum
14. J, information
15. C, is reliable

Chapter Review and Test Preparation

Reading Skill

MAIN IDEA AND DETAILS

Draw and then use this graphic organizer to answer questions 1 and 2.

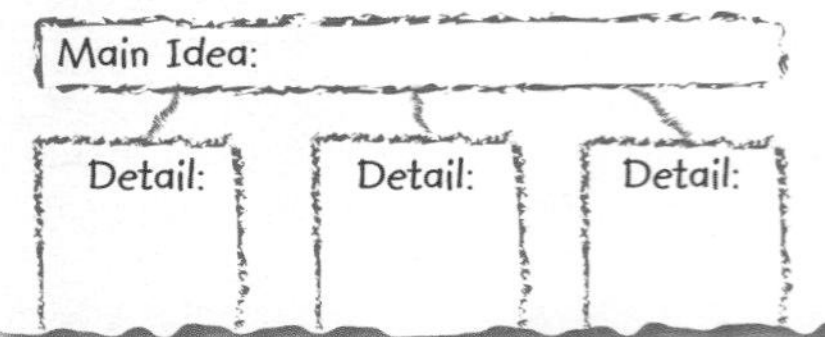

1 What is most important when getting health information?

2 Name three sources for health information.

Use Vocabulary

Match each term in Column B with its meaning in Column A.

Column A	Column B
3 The top, thinner layer of skin	A cavities
4 The thick, bottom layer of skin	B consumer
5 Sticky material on teeth that contains bacteria	C dermis
6 Holes in the surfaces of teeth	D epidermis
7 The hole where light enters the eye	E plaque
8 Someone who buys products	F pupil

Check Understanding

9 Sweat reaches the surface of skin through _____. (p. 33)
A evaporation **C** oil glands
B sweat glands **D** pores

10 Toothpaste containing _____ helps strengthen teeth and prevent decay. (pp. 38–39)
F milk **H** fluoride
G mint flavoring **J** gel

11 If nearby objects appear blurry but faraway objects are clear, you are _____. (p. 43)
A normal **C** farsighted
B blind **D** nearsighted

12 Which of these does **NOT** help prevent hearing loss? (p. 45)

F
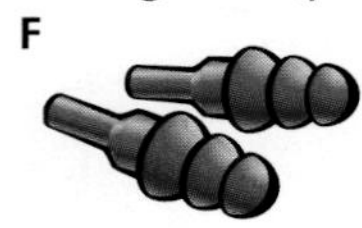

H

G
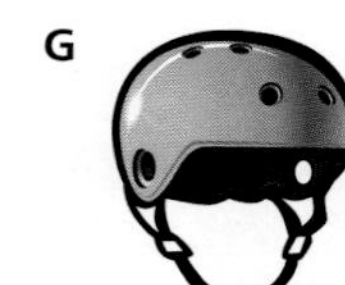

J
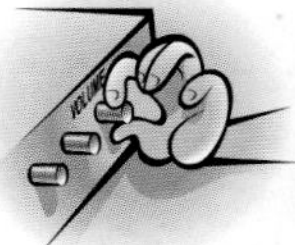

56

Formal Assessment

ASSESSMENT GUIDE P. 22

2 Name ______________ Chapter Test

Personal Health

Write the letter of the best answer on the line at the left.

C 1. The _____ is the top layer of your skin.
A dermis **B** pores **C** epidermis **D** sweat glands

J 2. The sticky, natural film that clings to your teeth is _____.
F dermis **G** cavities **H** decay **J** plaque

C 3. The acids in foods can make holes called _____ in your teeth.
A plaque **B** floss **C** cavities **D** pores

F 4. The _____ is the thick bottom layer of your skin.
F dermis **G** epidermis **H** lens **J** pores

D 5. The opening in your eye that lets light in is the _____.
A lens **B** dermis **C** retina **D** pupil

H 6. A _____ is a person who buys products.
F bully **G** passenger **H** consumer **J** advertiser

A 7. Information about products is contained in _____.
A advertising **B** consumer **C** messages **D** passenger

G 8. After light enters your eye, it is bent by the clear, curved _____.
F pupil **G** lens **H** retina **J** dermis

C 9. The _____ receives the image from the lens and sends nerve signals about the image to the brain.
A lens **B** pupil **C** retina **D** plaque

F 10. When plaque is left on the teeth, it hardens and becomes _____.
F tartar **G** decay **H** dermis **J** fluoride

© Harcourt

ASSESSMENT GUIDE P. 23

Name ______________

Match each phrase in Column A with a sentence part in Column B to make a true statement.

Column A	Column B
c 11. Dead skin cells	**a** can harm your skin.
e 12. As sweat evaporates,	**b** that helps prevent cavities.
a 13. Too much sunlight	**c** keep moisture in your body.
b 14. Fluoride is a mineral	**d** can permanently damage your hearing.
d 15. Loud sounds	**e** your body loses heat and gets cooler.

Underline the term that makes each statement false. Then choose the correct term from the box, and write it in the blank following the statement.

ear canal	cavities	decay	sweat	epidermis

16. The top layer of the dermis is made of dead skin cells. epidermis

17. Oil glands produce sweat, which helps rid your body of wastes and helps keep you cool. sweat

18. The process of forming pores in teeth is called tooth decay. cavities

19. Sound enters through your outer ear and moves through the middle ear to the eardrum. ear canal

20. Plaque means "to rot." decay

© Harcourt

13 What part of the ear is missing from the graphic organizer? (p. 44)

A pupil
B lens
C tartar
D eardrum

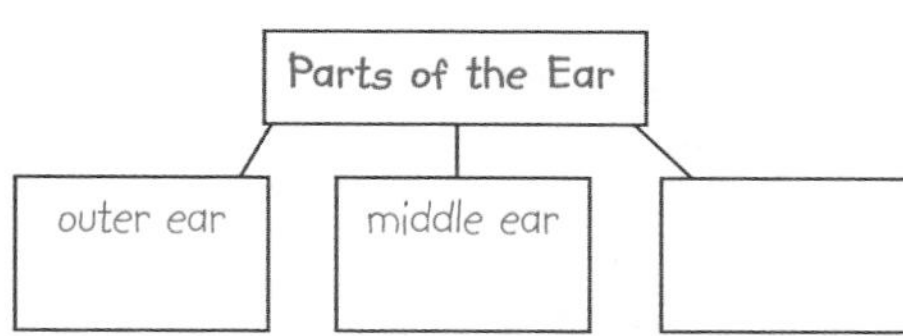

14 Advertising offers some important _____. (p. 48)

F sales
G tips
H notes
J information

15 Before believing information about health, you should make sure it _____. (pp. 52–54)

A is well written
B is funny
C is reliable
D is written by someone you know

Think Critically

16 You are spending the day at the pool. What should you do to help protect your skin from sunlight each time you get out of the pool?

17 You have found information about dental floss from two different sources that disagree. What should you do?

Apply Skills

18 **BUILDING GOOD CHARACTER**
Trustworthiness You need to start finding information for a report that is due tomorrow. Your parents, who are at a neighbor's house, have told you not to use the computer unless they are home. What could you do to show that you are trustworthy?

19 **LIFE SKILLS**
Communication You are at school, and an earache is really bothering you. Use the steps for Communicating to explain your problem to the school nurse.

Write About Health

20 **Write to Inform—Explanation** Explain why learning to analyze advertising helps you to be a wise consumer.

57

ASSESSMENT GUIDE P. 24

Name ____________________

Complete the table below by explaining how each item listed can help prevent tooth and gum problems.

Possible answers:

Ways to Help Prevent Tooth and Gum Problems	Why They Help
21. flossing	Flossing helps remove the plaque that can build up on teeth.
22. brushing	Brushing helps remove the left-over food, bacteria, and plaque that can build up on teeth and along the gum line.
23. using fluoride	Fluoride helps strengthen teeth and prevent cavities.
24. choosing healthful snacks	Snacks such as milk and fruit help to strengthen teeth. Crunchy vegetable snacks do not leave behind the food for bacteria that sugary and starchy foods do.
25. visiting the dentist often	The dentist can remove any tartar on teeth. He or she can apply fluoride or other products to help make teeth stronger.

© Harcourt

Think Critically 5 pts. each

16. Possible answers: put on more sunscreen, stay in a shaded area, put on more clothes to cover your skin

17. Possible answers: check to see that each source is reliable, look for other reliable sources to see what they say, talk with a health expert

Apply Skills 5 pts. each

18. Wait for your parents, call them to explain the situation, or find information from another source.

19. Answers should address each of the four steps for communicating: understand your audience, give a clear message, listen carefully and answer questions, and gather feedback.

Write About Health 5 pts.

20. Students' writings should reflect that it helps them recognize helpful information in ads and helps them avoid being tricked into buying products.

Performance Assessment

Use the Chapter Project and the rubric provided on the Project Evaluation Sheet. See *Assessment Guide* pp. 18, 56, 63.

Portfolio Assessment

Have students select their best work from the following suggestions:

- Leveled Activities, p. 38
- Quick Activity, p. 41
- Write to Inform, p. 50
- Activities, p. 55

See *Assessment Guide* pp. 12–16.

CHAPTER 3 Food and Your Health

Lesson	Pacing	Objectives	Reading Skills
Introduce the Chapter pp. 58–59		• Preview chapter concepts.	**Compare and Contrast** pp. 59, 330–331
1 **Nutrients for Your Body** pp. 60–64	3 class periods	• Identify the six major nutrients, their sources, and their functions in the body. • Explain why mealtimes are important.	**Compare and Contrast** pp. 61, 64 • Cause and Effect, p. 63 • Draw Conclusions, p. 64
Building Good Character p. 65		• Identify ways to show self-respect and respect for others during meals.	
2 **Food and the Nutrients It Contains** pp. 66–71	3 class periods	• Identify the food groups and explain why they are important. • Explain what a balanced diet is and why it is important.	**Compare and Contrast** p. 71 • Summarize, p. 67 • Sequence, p. 69 • Draw Conclusions, p. 71
3 **Using a Food Guide Pyramid** pp. 72–75	1 class period	• Use nutrition information from a food guide pyramid to make healthful food choices. • Demonstrate healthful eating practices by making healthful food choices.	**Compare and Contrast** p. 75 • Summarize, p. 75 • Draw Conclusions, p. 73
Life Skills pp. 76–77	1 class period	• Identify the steps for decision-making. • Use the decision-making steps to make healthful food choices.	
4 **Food Guidelines and Labels** pp. 78–83	3 class periods	• Learn how to make wise choices when shopping for food. • Gather data to make informed health choices. • Learn how to read and compare food labels.	**Compare and Contrast** p. 83 • Main Idea and Details, p. 79 • Draw Conclusions, p. 81 • Summarize, p. 83
5 **Keeping Foods Safe** pp. 84–86	1 class period	• Describe how food poisoning occurs. • Explain how to handle food safely to prevent food poisoning.	**Compare and Contrast** p. 86 • Summarize, p. 84 • Cause and Effect, p. 86
Activities p. 87		• Extend chapter concepts.	
Chapter Review pp. 88–89	1 class period	• Assess chapter objectives.	

Vocabulary	Program Resources
	Music CD Teaching Resources, p. 27
carbohydrates **fats** **proteins** **vitamins** **minerals** **water**	Transparency 1 Activity Book, pp. 11–13
	Poster 4
food guide pyramid **serving** **balanced diet** **portion**	Transparencies 1, 21 Activity Book, pp. 11–12
habit	Transparency 1 Activity Book, pp. 11–12
	Activity Book, p. 14 Poster 8
nutritious **ingredients**	Transparencies 1, 22 Activity Book, pp. 11–12
food poisoning	Transparencies 1, 23 Activity Book, pp. 11–12, 15
	The Learning Site www.harcourtschool.com
	Assessment Guide, pp. 25–27

Interactive Transparencies available on CD-ROM.

Reading Skill

These reading skills are reinforced throughout this chapter and one skill is emphasized as the Focus Skill.

Compare and Contrast

- Draw Conclusions
- Identify Cause and Effect
- Identify Main Idea and Details
- Sequence
- Summarize

KEY READING SKILLS TRANSPARENCY 1

1 Reading Skill Graphic Organizer

Compare and Contrast

Topic: Carbohydrates and Fats

Alike	Different

Life Skills

Life Skills are health-enhancing behaviors that can help students reduce risks to their health and safety.

Six Life Skills are reinforced throughout *Harcourt Health and Fitness*. The skill emphasized in this chapter is Make Responsible Decisions.

POSTER 8
MAKE RESPONSIBLE DECISIONS

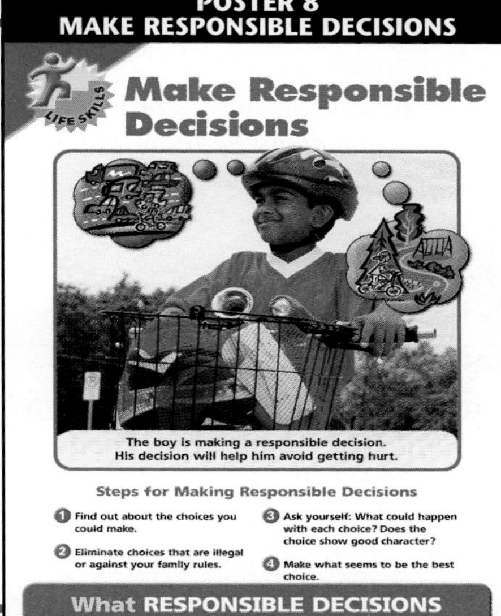

Make Responsible Decisions
LIFE SKILLS
The boy is making a responsible decision. His decision will help him avoid getting hurt.
Steps for Making Responsible Decisions
1 Find out about the choices you could make.
2 Eliminate choices that are illegal or against your family rules.
3 Ask yourself: What could happen with each choice? Does the choice show good character?
4 Make what seems to be the best choice.
What RESPONSIBLE DECISIONS have YOU MADE today?

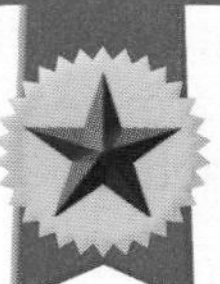

Building Good Character

Character education is an important aspect of health education. When children behave in ways that show good character, they promote the health and safety of themselves and others.

Six character traits are reinforced throughout *Harcourt Health and Fitness*. The trait emphasized in this chapter is Respect.

POSTER 4 RESPECT

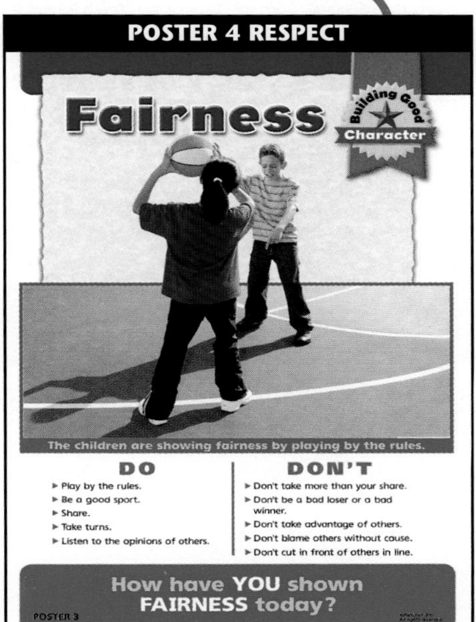

Fairness
Building Good Character
The children are showing fairness by playing by the rules.
DO
Play by the rules.
Be a good sport.
Share.
Take turns.
Listen to the opinions of others.
DON'T
Don't take more than your share.
Don't be a bad loser or a bad winner.
Don't take advantage of others.
Don't blame others without cause.
Don't cut in front of others in line.
How have YOU shown FAIRNESS today?

Resources

Coordinated School Health Program

Health Education
Health Services
Physical Education
Nutrition Services
Parent/ Community Involvement
Healthy School Environment
Counseling, Psychological, & Social Services
Health Promotion for Staff
CSHP

A Coordinated School Health Program endeavors to improve children's health and therefore their capacity to learn through the support of families, schools, and communities working together. The following information is provided to help classroom teachers be more aware of these resources.

The National Center for Chronic Disease and Health Promotion, part of the **CDC**, funds the Coordinated School Health Program. Visit its website for information about the eight components that make up this program. **www.cdc.gov/nccdphp/dash/**

California Healthy Kids provides reviewed health educational, instructional materials for free loan to California residents. The materials include such topics as nutrition education and food safety. **www.californiahealthykids.org**

The U.S. surgeon general has declared childhood obesity an epidemic in the United States. For photocopies of journal articles on this and related topics, visit the **Texas Medical Association** website. **www.texmed.org**

The goals of the Coordinated Approach to Child Health (**CATCH**) are to help schools, children, and families adopt positive changes in eating and physical activity habits to improve long-term health. CATCH has four components, one of which is *Eat Smart. Play Hard™.* **www.fns.usda.gov/FNS/**

Other resources that support a Coordinated School Health Program:
- School-Home Connection
- Daily Physical Activity
- Daily Fitness Tips
- Activities: Home & Community
- Health Background: Webliography
- *Be Active! Resources for Physical Education*

Media Resources

Books for Students

Lambourne, Mike. ***Down the Hatch—Find Out About Your Food***. Millbrook Press, 1992. Good information, activities, and child-friendly format. **EASY**

Powell, Jillian. ***Vegetables (Everyone Eats)***. Raintree/Steck-Vaughn, 1997. Many details on history, nutrients, and food processing. **AVERAGE**

Erlbach, Arlene. ***Peanut Butter***. Lerner Publications Co., 1995. History, recipes, charts, glossary, and index make it a great report book. **ADVANCED**

Books for Teachers and Families

Balch, Phyllis A. and James F. Balch,. ***Prescription for Nutritional Healing.*** Avery Penguin Putnam, 2000. A comprehensive children's nutritional guide.

Byrd-Bredbenner, Carol. ***Adventures in Food and Nutrition.*** Goodheart-Willcox Company, 2001. An annotated resource on foods and nutrition.

Free and Inexpensive Materials

Dairy Council of California
Classroom health education materials on nutrition are free of charge to California teachers.

Leafy Greens Council
Will send free book covers, trading cards, brochures, and posters.

Fleischmann's Yeast
Has free three-pack sampler of bread activity booklets and Teacher's Guides.

Eden Foods
Will send a free T-shirt to students submitting Eden-themed drawings and photos.

To access free and inexpensive resources on the Web, visit **www.harcourtschool.com/health/free**

Videos

Nutrition Facts—The New Food Label. Family Experiences Productions, Inc., 1994.

The Magic School Bus for Lunch. Warner Vision Entertainment, 1995.

Basic Food Safety. Educational Video Network, 1996.

These resources have been selected to meet a variety of individual needs. Please review all materials and websites prior to sharing them with students to ensure the content is appropriate for your class. Note that information, while correct at time of publication, is subject to change.

Visit **The Learning Site** for related links, activities, resources, and the health **Webliography.**

www.harcourtschool.com/health

Meeting Individual Needs

Below-Level

Recalling facts is easier when students have visual aids. Have students take turns telling one fact they learned from reading the selection. Write that fact on an index card and have the student hang the card on a classroom clothesline.

Activities

- Food Group Match, p. 68
- Junk Food Labels, p. 80
- Make Your Points, p. 84

On-Level

Understanding nonfiction is easier when students picture in their minds what they are reading about. After students read a descriptive passage, for example, on ways to stay safe at home, have them draw a cartoon strip depicting those ways. Combine the strips into a class book.

Activities

- Biggest Crop Producers, p. 68
- That Much More, p. 80
- In Summary, p. 84

Challenge

Write vocabulary words on cards and place them face down. Have students take turns choosing a card and pantomiming or illustrating the word without speaking or writing. The other students must try to guess the word.

Activities

- Balanced Meals, p. 68
- More Vitamins and Minerals, p. 80
- Details, p. 84

ESL/ELL

Language Workshop

After students have read the text, have them present the information in another form. Encourage students to share their new knowledge in pictures, diagrams, charts, posters, dramatizations, songs, or stories in oral or written form.

Activities

- Comprehensible Input, pp. 62, 82
- Background and Experience, p. 66

Curriculum Integration

Integrated Language Arts/Reading Skills

- Correct Cuisine Café, p. 75
- Guideline Jingle, p. 78

Math

- Food Math, p. 69
- Snack Sense, p. 83

Physical Education

- Daily Fitness Tip, pp. 60, 66, 72, 78, 84
- Daily Physical Activity, p. 59

Use these topics to integrate health into your daily planning.

Science

- Testing Foods for Fats, p. 63

Social Studies

- Sharing Food Customs, p. 70

Art

- Food Collage, p. 67
- Junk Art, p. 81
- Safe Food Art, p. 85

CHAPTER 3

Pages 58–89

CHAPTER SUMMARY

In this chapter, students

- learn about the basic nutrients and their functions in the body.
- find out how a food guide pyramid can be used to plan balanced meals.
- learn the basics of handling and preparing foods safely.

Life Skills
Students practice *making responsible decisions* about food.

Building Good Character
Students show *respect* by learning proper table manners.

Consumer Health
Students *analyze* advertisements.

Literature Springboard

Use the poem "Greedy Mable" to spark interest in the chapter topic. See the Read-Aloud Anthology on page RA-5 of this *Teacher Edition*.

Prereading Strategies

SCAN THE CHAPTER Have students preview the chapter content by scanning the titles, headings, pictures, tables, and graphs. Ask volunteers to predict what they will learn. Use their predictions to assess prior knowledge.

PREVIEW VOCABULARY As students scan the chapter, ask them to sort the vocabulary words. Have students look up unfamiliar words in the Glossary.

Words I Know	Words I've Seen or Heard	New Words

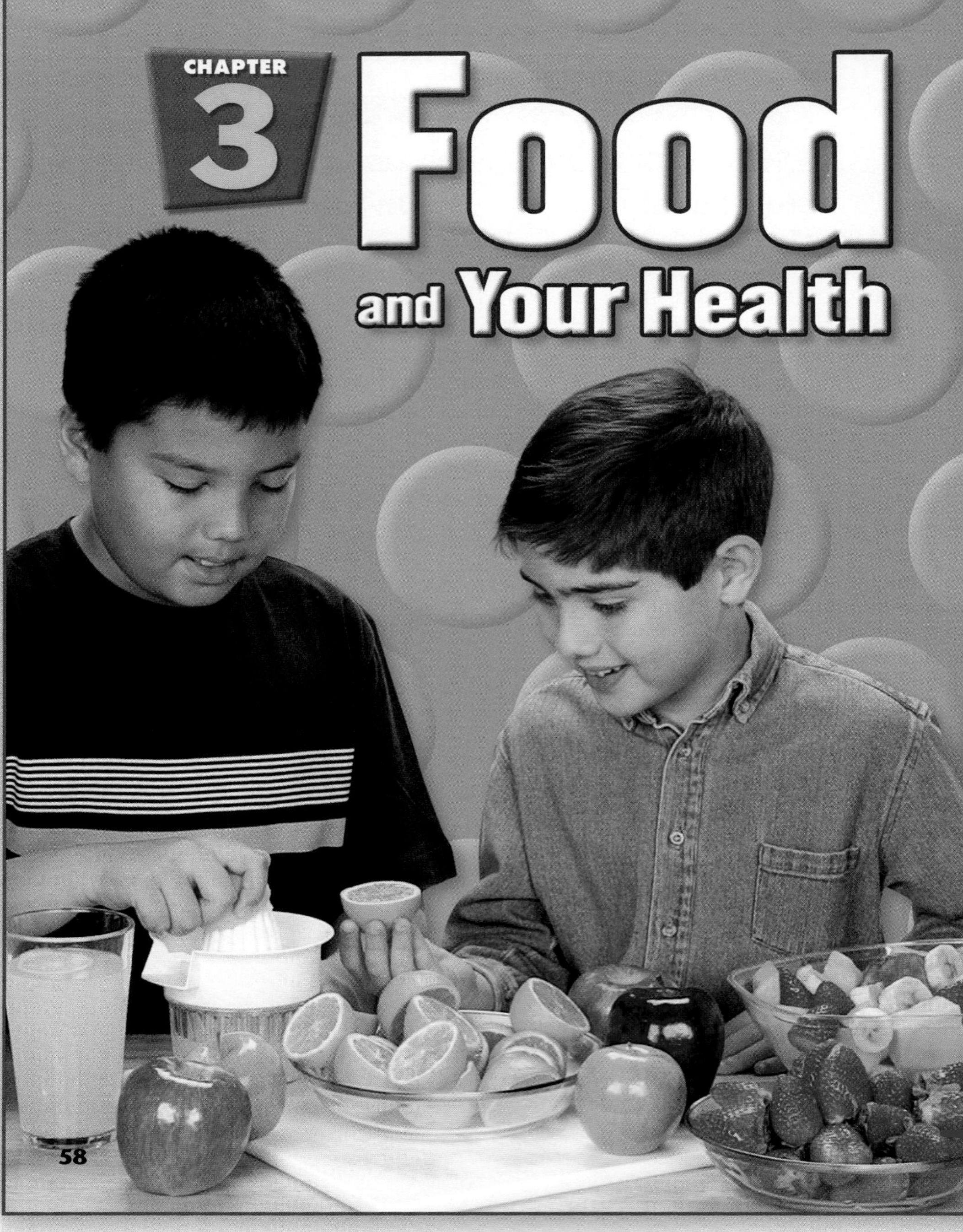

Reading Skill

COMPARE AND CONTRAST To introduce or review this skill, have students use the Reading in Health Handbook, pp. 330–331. Teaching strategies and additional activities are also provided.

Students will have opportunities to practice and apply this skill throughout this chapter.

- Focus Skill Reading Mini-Lesson, p. 60
- Reading comprehension questions identified with the 
- *Activity Book* p. 13 (shown on p. 64)
- Lesson Summary and Review, pp. 64, 71, 75, 83, 86
- Chapter Review and Test Preparation, pp. 88–89

Reading Skill

COMPARE AND CONTRAST When you compare, you tell how two or more things are alike. When you contrast, you tell how they are different. Use the Reading in Health Handbook on pages 330–331 and this graphic organizer to help you read the health facts in this chapter.

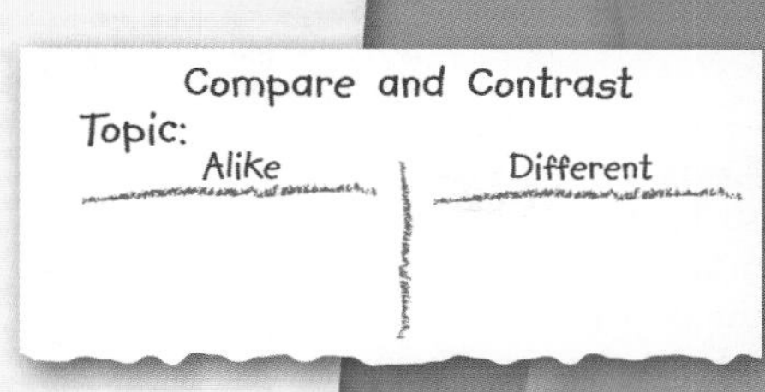

Health Graph

INTERPRET DATA Some food products have added sugar. If you are a person trying to limit the amount of sugar in the foods you eat, which of the following foods would you pick?

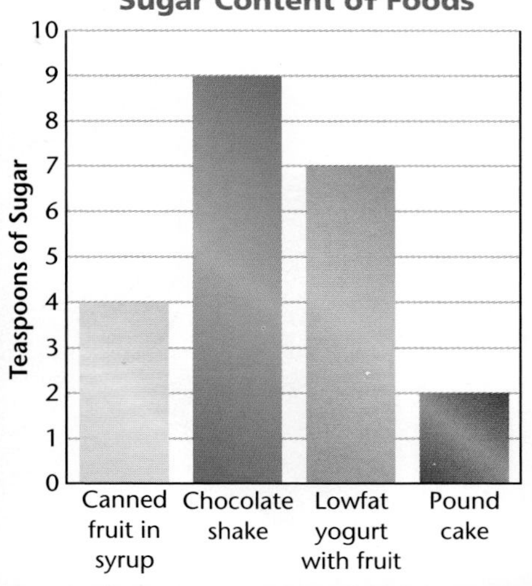

Daily Physical Activity

You should eat the right amounts of healthful foods every day. Exercise should also be a part of your day.

Be Active! Use the selection Track 3, **Late for Supper** to use some food energy.

INTRODUCE THE CHAPTER

Health Graph

Interpret Data

Have students look at the graph. Ask for volunteers to explain what information the graph is presenting.

About how many teaspoons of sugar would be in two lowfat yogurts with fruit? If the student estimates one lowfat yogurt with fruit to equal 7 teaspoons, two lowfat yogurts with fruit would be about 14.

Which food on the graph has about twice as much sugar by volume as the pound cake? canned fruit in syrup

Daily Physical Activity

Use *Be Active! Music for Daily Physical Activity* with the Instant Activity Cards to provide students with movement activities that can be done in limited space. Options for using these components are provided beginning on page TR2 in this *Teacher Edition.*

Chapter Project

You're the Chef! (*Assessment Guide* p. 57)

ASSESS PRIOR KNOWLEDGE Use students' initial ideas for the project as a baseline assessment of their understanding of chapter concepts. Have students complete the project as they work through the chapter.

PERFORMANCE ASSESSMENT The project can be used for performance assessment. Use the Project Evaluation Sheet (rubric), *Assessment Guide* p. 64.

School-Home Connection

Distribute copies of the School-Home Connection (in English or Spanish). Have students take the page home to share with their families as you begin this chapter.

Follow Up Have volunteers share the results of their activities.

Supports the Coordinated School Health Program

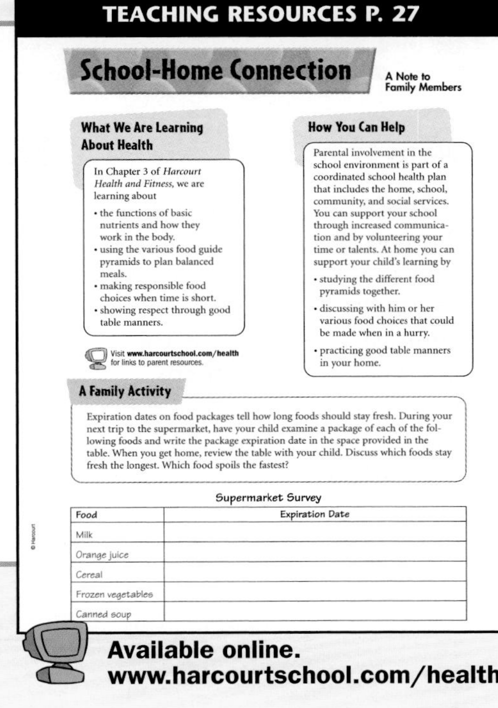

TEACHING RESOURCES P. 27

School-Home Connection

A Note to Family Members

What We Are Learning About Health

In Chapter 3 of *Harcourt Health and Fitness,* we are learning about

- the functions of basic nutrients and how they work in the body.
- using the various food guide pyramids to plan balanced meals.
- making responsible food choices when time is short.
- showing respect through good table manners.

Visit **www.harcourtschool.com/health** for links to parent resources.

How You Can Help

Parental involvement in the school environment is part of a coordinated school health plan that includes the home, school, community, and social services. You can support your school through increased communication and by volunteering your time or talents. At home you can support your child's learning by

- studying the different food pyramids together.
- discussing with him or her various food choices that could be made when in a hurry.
- practicing good table manners in your home.

A Family Activity

Expiration dates on food packages tell how long foods should stay fresh. During your next trip to the supermarket, have your child examine a package of each of the following foods and write the package expiration date in the space provided in the table. When you get home, review the table with your child. Discuss which foods stay fresh the longest. Which food spoils the fastest?

Supermarket Survey

Food	Expiration Date
Milk	
Orange juice	
Cereal	
Frozen vegetables	
Canned soup	

© Harcourt

Available online.
www.harcourtschool.com/health

LESSON 1
Pages 60–64

Objectives
- ► Identify the six major nutrients, their sources, and their functions in the body.
- ► Explain why mealtimes are important.

When Minutes Count . . .
Assign the Quick Study, Lesson 1, Activity Book pp. 11–12 (shown on p. 61).

Program Resources
- ► Activity Book pp. 11–13
- ► Transparency 1

Vocabulary
carbohydrates p. 60, **fats** p. 61, **proteins** p. 61, **vitamins** p. 62, **minerals** p. 62, **water** p. 63

Daily Fitness Tip
Practice healthful habits to ensure that the foods you eat will not make you ill. Raw fresh fruits and vegetables are important parts of a healthful diet. Remind students to wash fruits and vegetables thoroughly before eating them. Bacteria or pesticides that can cause illness may be on these foods.

For more about nutrition and health, see *Be Active! Resources for Physical Education,* p. 165.

1. MOTIVATE
Have students get up and move about energetically. Then have them move as if they were out of energy. Discuss how their movements in each example differed.

What gives you the energy to move?
The foods you eat give you energy.
Explain that a healthful diet provides the substances the body needs for energy to move and work. A healthful diet also helps the body grow and heal. Some starches are stored by the body for later use.

Nutrients for Your Body

Lesson Focus
Six kinds of nutrients provide your body with the energy and materials it needs for growth and repair.

Why Learn This?
What you learn can be used to help you choose healthful foods.

Vocabulary
carbohydrates
fats
proteins
vitamins
minerals
water

Energy Nutrients
In Chapter 1, you learned that nutrients are the substances in food that you need for growth, energy, and good health. Foods contain six important kinds of nutrients: carbohydrates, fats, proteins, vitamins, minerals, and water. You must eat a variety of foods to get all the nutrients you need to stay healthy.

Carbohydrates (karb•oh•HY•drayts) are starches and sugars. They are your body's main source of energy. Most carbohydrates come from plants.

You can get starches from breads, potatoes, cereals, beans, carrots, peas, and corn. Sugars are found in fruits and sweets such as cookies and pies. Sugars are used quickly by the body. Starches are used more slowly.

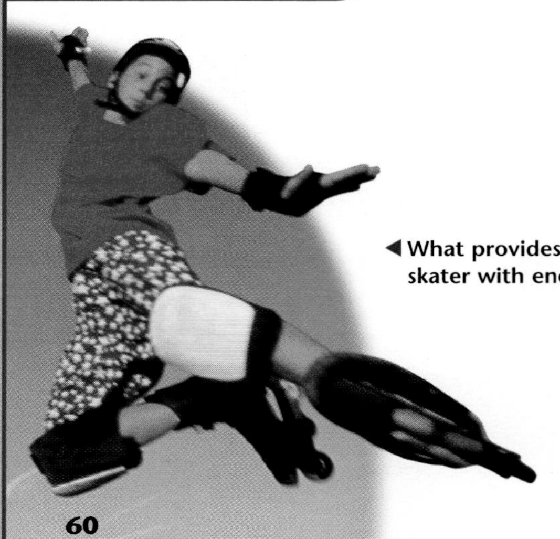

◄ What provides this skater with energy?

60

Reading Skill

Mini-Lesson
COMPARE AND CONTRAST
Remind students that, when they compare, they tell how things are alike. When they contrast, they tell how they are different. Have them practice this skill by answering the Focus Skill question on page 61. Have students draw and complete the graphic organizer as you model it on the transparency.

TRANSPARENCY 1

1 Reading Skill Graphic Organizer

Compare and Contrast

Topic: Carbohydrates and Fats

Alike	Different
• Both are nutrients. • Both are sources of energy.	• Carbohydrates come mostly from plants, and fats come from both plants and animals. • Carbohydrates are use quickly for energy, and fats are used for energ when carbohydrates aren't available.

Interactive Transparencies available on CD-ROM.

Fats give your body more energy than any other kind of nutrient. Fats come from some plant and animal products. Your body stores extra fat when you don't use all the food you take in. You use this energy from stored fats when you don't get enough energy from carbohydrates. Oils, butter, meat, cheese, milk, and nuts all have fats. Many fast foods are high in fat.

Proteins (PROH•teenz) are another kind of nutrient that give you energy. They help build and repair your cells. Without protein your body would not grow or get better if you were ill. You can get protein by eating eggs, meat, poultry, fish, and peanut butter. Some vegetables, seeds, grains, and beans also have some protein.

Focus Skill **COMPARE AND CONTRAST How are carbohydrates and fats alike and different?**

Alike: all major sources of energy; different: carbohydrates come mostly from plants and are used quickly by body. Fats come from both plants and animals and are sometimes stored by the body.

Quick Activity

Identify Energy Nutrients Look at the foods shown on these pages. Name three foods for each of the energy nutrients.

61

2. TEACH

Interpret Visuals—Pictures

Before reading, students will likely cite food as providing the skater with energy. After reading, students should be able to list specific energy nutrients: carbohydrates, fats, and proteins.

Quick Activity

Possible answers: carbohydrates—bread, nuts, beans, potatoes; fats—oil, butter, milk, meat; proteins—eggs, meat, poultry, fish; vitamins—any; minerals—any; water—oranges, carrots, tomatoes, milk

Content-Area Reading Support

Using Respellings Direct attention to the phonetic respelling: PROH•teenz. Explain that respellings show how words are pronounced. Point out that the dot in the middle of the respelling divides the word into syllables and the small capital letters indicate the stressed, or accented, syllable.

Discuss

Though milk has fat in it, not all milk has the same amount of fat. It is recommended that children of this age should be drinking 1 or 2 percent milk.

Problem Solving Why would wheat bread be a better choice than cake for getting carbohydrates? Eating wheat bread instead of cake would provide more nutrients and less sugar and fat in the diet, so wheat bread is a more healthful choice for getting carbohydrates.

QUICK STUDY, ACTIVITY BOOK PP. 11–12

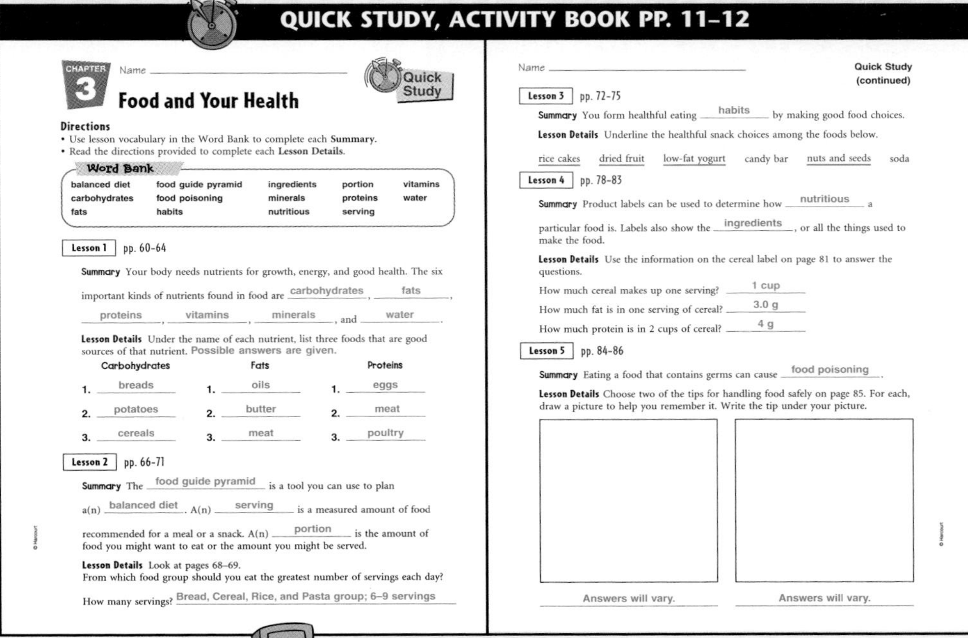

CHAPTER 3 Name ______

Food and Your Health

Quick Study

Directions
- Use lesson vocabulary in the Word Bank to complete each **Summary**.
- Read the directions provided to complete each **Lesson Details**.

Word Bank

balanced diet	food guide pyramid	ingredients	portion	vitamins
carbohydrates	food poisoning	minerals	proteins	water
fats	habits	nutritious	serving	

Lesson 1 pp. 60–64

Summary Your body needs nutrients for growth, energy, and good health. The six important kinds of nutrients found in food are carbohydrates, fats, proteins, vitamins, minerals, and water.

Lesson Details Under the name of each nutrient, list three foods that are good sources of that nutrient. Possible answers are given.

Carbohydrates	Fats	Proteins
1. breads	1. oils	1. eggs
2. potatoes	2. butter	2. meat
3. cereals	3. meat	3. poultry

Lesson 2 pp. 66–71

Summary The food guide pyramid is a tool you can use to plan a(n) balanced diet. A(n) serving is a measured amount of food recommended for a meal or a snack. A(n) portion is the amount of food you might want to eat or the amount you might be served.

Lesson Details Look at pages 68–69.
From which food group should you eat the greatest number of servings each day?
How many servings? Bread, Cereal, Rice, and Pasta group; 6–9 servings

© Harcourt

Name ______ Quick Study (continued)

Lesson 3 pp. 72–75

Summary You form healthful eating habits by making good food choices.

Lesson Details Underline the healthful snack choices among the foods below.

rice cakes dried fruit low-fat yogurt candy bar nuts and seeds soda

Lesson 4 pp. 78–83

Summary Product labels can be used to determine how nutritious a particular food is. Labels also show the ingredients, or all the things used to make the food.

Lesson Details Use the information on the cereal label on page 81 to answer the questions.

How much cereal makes up one serving? 1 cup
How much fat is in one serving of cereal? 3.0 g
How much protein is in 2 cups of cereal? 4 g

Lesson 5 pp. 84–86

Summary Eating a food that contains germs can cause food poisoning.

Lesson Details Choose two of the tips for handling food safely on page 85. For each, draw a picture to help you remember it. Write the tip under your picture.

Answers will vary. Answers will vary.

© Harcourt

Available online.
www.harcourtschool.com/health

Health Background

Macronutrients Nutritionists, dietitians, and doctors agree that people need to eat a variety of foods to meet their daily needs. There are three types of foods, or *macronutrients*—proteins, fats, and carbohydrates. These are broken down in the digestive system, enter the bloodstream, and provide body cells with energy.

Source: *Scientific American Frontiers*

TEACH *continued*

Interpret Visuals—Tables

Explain that the vitamins shown in the table are just a few of the many vitamins available in foods.

Have students find patterns in the vitamin content of different foods. **Which foods have more than one of the vitamins shown?** fish, D, E; tomatoes, A, C; asparagus, A, E; broccoli, C, K; spinach, A, E, K

Which of the vitamins shown is found only in fruits and vegetables? vitamin C

Continue the discussion by having students locate patterns in meats. Stress that the students do not have to memorize the vitamins and where they are found.

Discuss

Vitamins are easily destroyed by heat. After fresh peas are cooked, they have one-half of the original amount of vitamin C. Frozen peas have about one-fifth of the original amount of vitamin C, and canned peas have about one-twentieth.

Problem Solving How can you get more vitamins from vegetables? Eat fresh vegetables raw or slightly cooked.

Health Background

Vitamin A This vitamin occurs naturally in certain animal products. The body can also make vitamin A from beta-carotene.

Beta-carotene Beta-carotene gives plants such as carrots and apricots their red, orange, or yellow color. It is also present in dark-green, leafy vegetables. Because the body makes vitamin A from beta-carotene only when it needs to, there is little danger of getting too much vitamin A from eating foods with beta-carotene.

Source: *National Institutes of Health*

For more background, visit the **Webliography** in Teacher Resources at **www.harcourtschool.com/health**
Keyword nutrition

Myth and Fact

Myth: Eating a lot of carrots improves your vision.

Fact: Carrots, tomatoes, and sweet potatoes all have vitamin A, which helps keep your eyes healthy. But eating a lot of foods with vitamin A will not improve normal vision.

Vitamins, Minerals, and Water

Not all nutrients give you energy. **Vitamins** (VYT•uh•minz) are nutrients that help your body do certain jobs. You need only small amounts of each vitamin. Vitamins can be made by living things, like plants and animals.

Each vitamin does one or more jobs in the body. Vitamin A keeps your skin and eyes healthy. You need vitamin C for healthy gums and teeth. Vitamin D keeps bones and teeth strong. Vitamin E slows down cell damage. Your body uses vitamin K to control blood clotting.

Minerals (MIN•er•uhlz) are nutrients that help your body grow and work. Like vitamins, minerals are needed in only small amounts. However, minerals are not made by living things. One way we can get minerals is from plants. The plants take in minerals from the soil. When we eat certain plants we take in minerals.

▼ Some vitamins are found in many foods.

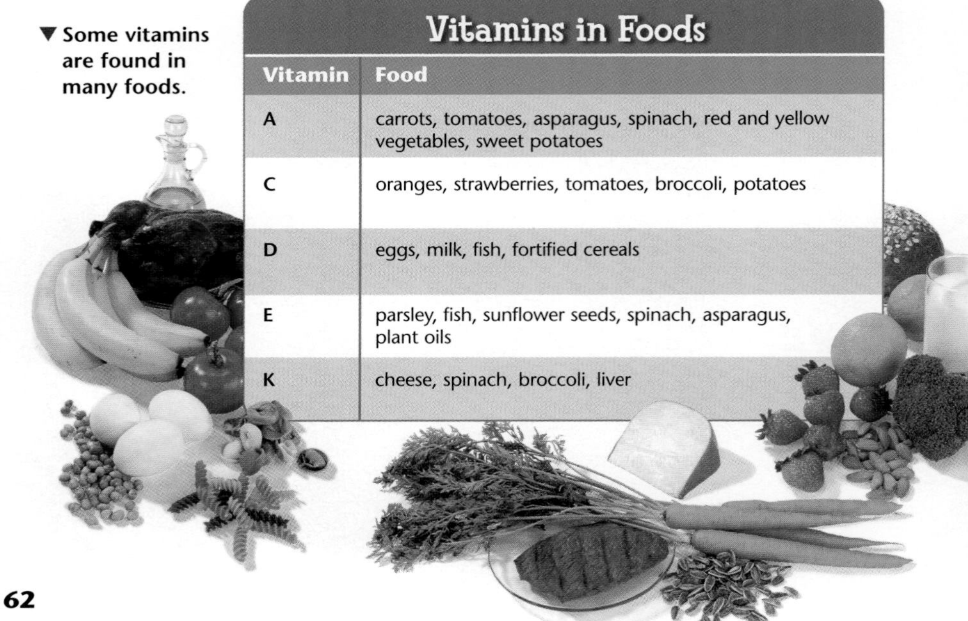

Vitamins in Foods

Vitamin	Food
A	carrots, tomatoes, asparagus, spinach, red and yellow vegetables, sweet potatoes
C	oranges, strawberries, tomatoes, broccoli, potatoes
D	eggs, milk, fish, fortified cereals
E	parsley, fish, sunflower seeds, spinach, asparagus, plant oils
K	cheese, spinach, broccoli, liver

ESL/ELL Support

COMPREHENSIBLE INPUT Familiarize students with the six basic nutrients.

Beginning Write the names of the six nutrients, and have students draw a food to show an example of each one—for example, a slice of bread for carbohydrate, an egg for protein, and a glass of water. Students should refer to the pictures in the *Student Edition*.

Intermediate Draw a six-column table with the six nutrients as column heads. For each nutrient, have students list foods that contain that nutrient.

Advanced Have students list the names of the six nutrients, followed by a few words that describe what each nutrient provides for the body. Students can also list at least one food that provides each nutrient.

Minerals for Good Health

Mineral	Source	Role in the Body
Calcium	milk, cheese, yogurt, dark green leafy vegetables	Builds strong bones and teeth, helps muscles and nerves work, helps blood clot
Iron	dark green leafy vegetables, peas, beans, meat, enriched grain products	Helps blood carry oxygen, helps cells use energy, protects against infection
Phosphorus	meat, peas, beans, whole grains, dairy products	Builds strong bones and teeth, helps cells function
Potassium	potatoes, lima beans, oranges, bananas	Helps nerves and muscles work, helps cells use energy
Zinc	eggs, seafood, grains, nuts, beef, liver, whole grains	Helps the body grow, helps heal wounds, maintains the senses of smell and taste

Did You Know?
Water makes up more than half of your body. Your body needs 48 to 64 ounces of water every day. That's equal to six to eight 8-ounce glasses.

Some minerals are added to prepared foods. For example, sodium is part of table salt. Salt is added to many foods as a preservative or for flavor. Since many foods contain added salt, eating too much salt can become a problem.

Water is a nutrient necessary for life. You could live only a few days without water. Foods such as lettuce, melons, apples, celery, and raw carrots have a lot of water. But actually drinking water is the best way to get the water your body needs. Water helps the body use vitamins and minerals. It carries digested nutrients to your cells. It also carries away wastes.

CAUSE AND EFFECT **What is the effect of eating the right amount of vitamins and minerals?**

Your body gets the nutrients it needs to grow and work properly.

Water in Foods

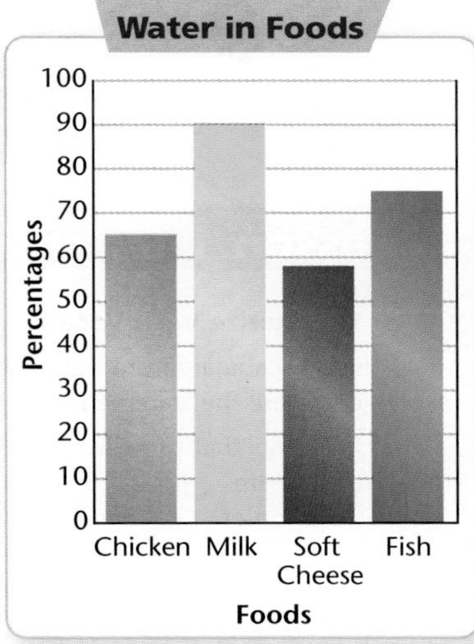

Some foods contain more water than others. Which of these foods contains the most water? Which vitamins and minerals are also in these foods?

Discuss

Some of the minerals required by the body are calcium, chromium, copper, fluoride, iodine, iron, magnesium, manganese, molybdenum, phosphorus, potassium, selenium, and zinc.

Interpret Visuals—Tables

Point out the table of minerals. To help students read the table, ask them questions such as the following: **What might happen to your bones if you don't get enough calcium?** They could become weak. **What mineral do you need to make cuts heal?** zinc

Content-Area Reading Support

Using Signal Words Direct students' attention to the first paragraph on this page. Point out the first sentence, which states the main idea of the paragraph. The second sentence begins with the phrase *for example*. Information that follows provides details for the main idea. Remind students that signal words like *for example* are clues to the way information in a paragraph is organized. They help readers understand how ideas are connected.

Interpret Visuals—Graphs

most water—milk; vitamins—D and K; minerals—calcium and possibly phosphorus

Teacher Tip

Food Allergies Keep in mind as you discuss foods that some students may have allergies that make normally healthful foods unhealthful for them. Remind class members that students with allergies to foods such as peanut butter or milk have many healthful alternatives to choose from—such as sesame butter and soy milk—to get needed nutrients. Help prevent children with allergies from feeling singled out or deprived because of their allergies.

Science

Testing Foods for Fats Students can conduct a simple test to see if certain foods contain fats. Have students place small pieces of food (such as potato chips, celery, and ham) onto labeled sections of a brown paper bag. After about an hour, have students remove the the foods and hold the bag up to a light source to check if any of the foods have left a greasy, translucent mark on the bag.

Health Background

Micronutrients In addition to macronutrients, two *micronutrients*—vitamins and minerals—are essential for good health. Some scientists argue as to whether these should come only from foods or if dietary supplements should be taken for those micronutrients missing in our diets today.

Source: *The Linus Pauling Institute and Oregon State University websites*

For more background, visit the **Webliography** in Teacher Resources at **www.harcourtschool.com/health** **Keyword** nutrition

3. WRAP UP

Lesson 1 Summary and Review

1. carbohydrates, fats, proteins; vitamins, minerals; water
2. Your body needs healthful foods to grow and work in healthy ways.
3. Possible answer: It can give you time to talk with your friends and to make new friends.
4. Graphics may include:

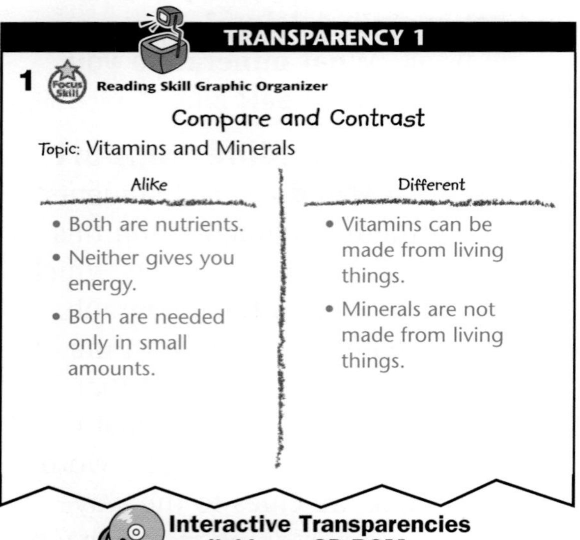
TRANSPARENCY 1

1 Reading Skill Graphic Organizer

Compare and Contrast

Topic: Vitamins and Minerals

Alike	Different
• Both are nutrients. • Neither gives you energy. • Both are needed only in small amounts.	• Vitamins can be made from living things. • Minerals are not made from living things.

Interactive Transparencies available on CD-ROM.

5. Carbohydrates—your main energy source; fats—stored energy; proteins—provide energy and also help build and repair cells; vitamins—help the body perform special functions; minerals—help the body grow and work; water—helps break down foods, helps the body use vitamins and minerals, and carries nutrients and wastes.

For **writing models** with examples, see *Teaching Resources* pp. 47–61. Rubrics are also provided.

When Minutes Count . . .

Quick Study Students can use *Activity Book* pages 11–12 (shown on p. 61) as they complete each lesson in this chapter.

Did You Know?

The fork you use at meals is a fairly new arrival to America. Until the introduction of forks from Europe and acceptance of their use in the mid-1700s, most people used only a knife and spoon for most of their eating.

Mealtime Is Important

People often come together for meals. Families try to meet for breakfast and dinner. Many people eat lunch at work or at school.

Families and friends also use mealtime as a time to communicate. During meals people often talk with and listen to one another. Children may talk about their day at school. Adults may talk about how their day has been. Mealtime can be a time of sharing that allows family members to talk about their feelings and thoughts.

Meals can also be shared for special occasions. People use meals as a way to celebrate birthdays, anniversaries, and holidays. Families sometimes use mealtimes to celebrate customs or traditions.

DRAW CONCLUSIONS Why is it important for people to have mealtimes?

to share, talk, and celebrate important days and cultural traditions

Lesson 1 Summary and Review

1. **Summarize with Vocabulary**
   Use vocabulary from this lesson to complete the statements.
   Nutrients that provide your body with energy are _____, _____, and _____. The main job of _____ and _____ is to help your body grow and work. Breaking down foods and helping the body use vitamins and minerals is a job for _____.
2. Identify the benefits of the six major nutrients contained in foods.
3. **Critical Thinking** How can mealtime affect your relationships at school?
4. **COMPARE AND CONTRAST** Draw and complete this graphic organizer to show how vitamins and minerals are alike and different.

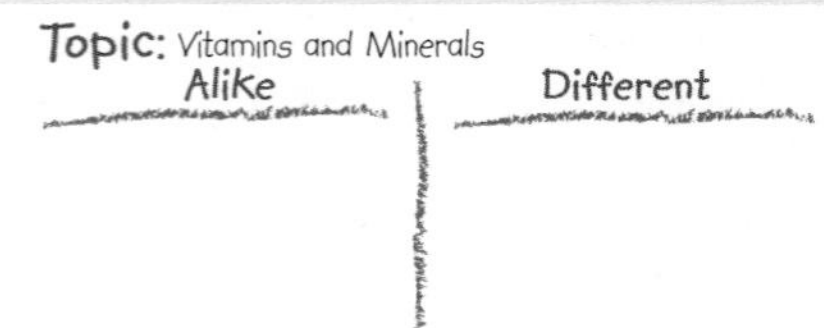

5. **Write to Inform—Explanation** 
   Explain why good nutrition is important for good health.

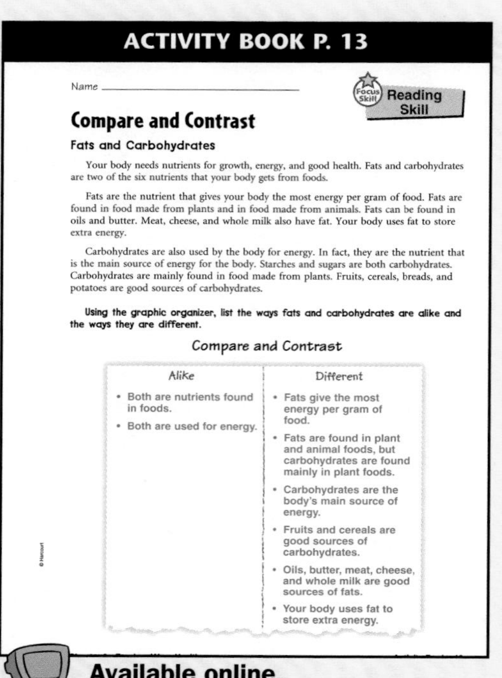
ACTIVITY BOOK P. 13

Name ____________

Reading Skill

Compare and Contrast

Fats and Carbohydrates

Your body needs nutrients for growth, energy, and good health. Fats and carbohydrates are two of the six nutrients that your body gets from foods.

Fats are the nutrient that gives your body the most energy per gram of food. Fats are found in food made from plants and in food made from animals. Fats can be found in oils and butter. Meat, cheese, and whole milk also have fat. Your body uses fat to store extra energy.

Carbohydrates are also used by the body for energy. In fact, they are the nutrient that is the main source of energy for the body. Starches and sugars are both carbohydrates. Carbohydrates are mainly found in food made from plants. Fruits, cereals, breads, and potatoes are good sources of carbohydrates.

Using the graphic organizer, list the ways fats and carbohydrates are alike and the ways they are different.

Compare and Contrast

Alike	Different
• Both are nutrients found in foods. • Both are used for energy.	• Fats give the most energy per gram of food. • Fats are found in plant and animal foods, but carbohydrates are found mainly in plant foods. • Carbohydrates are the body's main source of energy. • Fruits and cereals are good sources of carbohydrates. • Oils, butter, meat, cheese, and whole milk are good sources of fats. • Your body uses fat to store extra energy.

Available online. www.harcourtschool.com/health

Respect

Using Good Table Manners

Good table manners are ways to act that help make mealtimes enjoyable for everyone. Using good table manners shows the people you eat with that you have respect for them. Here are some simple rules for good table manners.

- **Wait to start eating until everyone is served.**
- **Ask for food to be passed to you instead of reaching for it.**
- **Cut food into small pieces.**
- **Chew with your mouth closed.**
- **Swallow your food before you talk.**
- **Eat with your fingers only if the food was meant to be eaten that way. Follow the example of adults at the table.**
- **Use a napkin during your meal.**
- **At a friend's house, eat the way your hosts do.**
- **If you don't like the food, don't complain or make a face. Just leave it on the plate.**
- **Remember to say "Please" and "Thank you."**

Activity

Play a good-manners game with your family. Make a chart that shows each person's name. At mealtime, watch and listen for examples of good manners. Each time you notice one, give the person who used good manners a point. At the end of the meal, the person with the most points wins the game. Be sure to take turns keeping score!

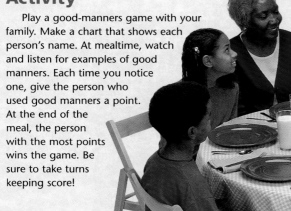

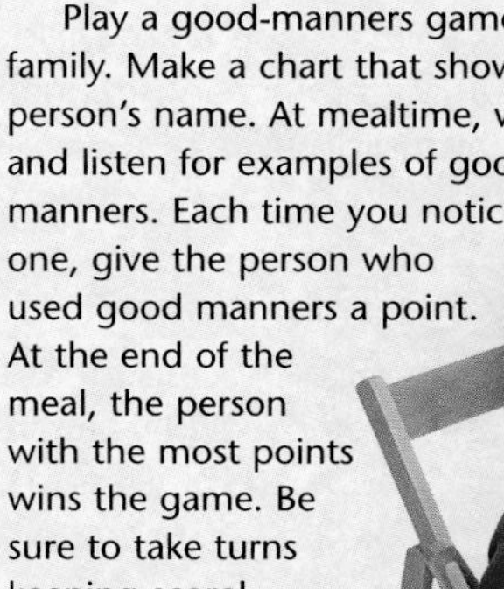

65

Building Good Character

Caring
Citizenship
Fairness
Respect
Responsibility
Trustworthiness

Objective

► Identify ways to show self-respect and respect for others during meals.

Program Resource

► Poster 4

BEFORE READING

Use this as an opportunity to ask students to analyze strengths and weaknesses in personal skills. Brainstorm with students some ways to show self-respect and respect for others. After a discussion about showing respect in various situations, lead students to discuss ways to show respect during meals. List some ideas on the board.

DISCUSS

After students have read the page, have them close their books. Have volunteers restate the points of good table manners. Add on the board any that were not in the original list.

ACTIVITY

Be sure students understand the directions for the good manners game. Small groups of students may like to use this game in school. Be sure your cafeteria—or other place where students eat—is conducive to the activity. Warn students that they should praise but not criticize.

Using the Poster

Activity Suggest that students design and display their own posters about respect.

Display Poster 4 to remind students of ways to show respect. The poster can be displayed in the classroom, the school cafeteria, or in other common areas.

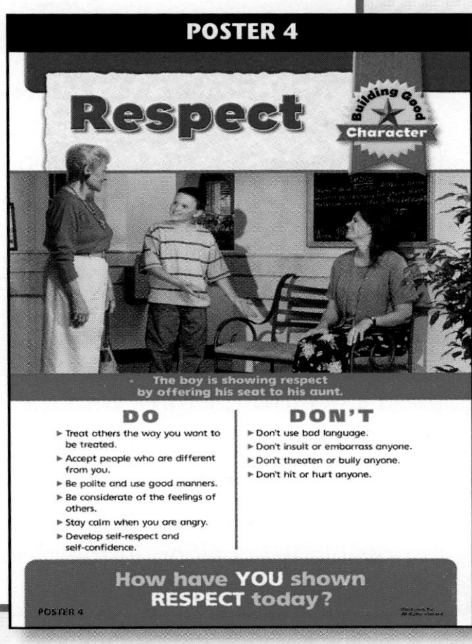

POSTER 4
Respect
Building Good Character
The boy is showing respect by offering his seat to his aunt.
DO
Treat others the way you want to be treated.
Accept people who are different from you.
Be polite and use good manners.
Be considerate of the feelings of others.
Stay calm when you are angry.
Develop self-respect and self-confidence.
DON'T
Don't use bad language.
Don't insult or embarrass anyone.
Don't threaten or bully anyone.
Don't hit or hurt anyone.
How have YOU shown RESPECT today?
POSTER 4

LESSON 2
Pages 66–71

Objectives
- ► Identify the food groups and explain why they are important.
- ► Explain what a balanced diet is and why it is important.

When Minutes Count . . .
Assign the Quick Study, Lesson 2, Activity Book pp. 11–12 (shown on p. 61).

Program Resources
- ► Activity Book pp. 11–12
- ► Transparencies 1, 21

Vocabulary
food guide pyramid p. 69, **serving** p. 69, **balanced diet** p. 69, **portion** p. 70

Daily Fitness Tip
Eating a healthful diet is one way to keep the body healthy, but the body needs other things as well. Point out that, in addition to eating right, it is important for students to get plenty of rest and exercise.

For more about nutrition and your physical fitness, see *Be Active! Resources for Physical Education*, p. 159.

1. MOTIVATE
Read the following poem. Then discuss things the students may already know about the USDA Food Guide Pyramid.

On the Food Guide Pyramid you start low,
With bread, cereal, pasta, and rice, you know.
These carbohydrates form the base
Of a diet that helps you win the race.
Then move up to fresh, sweet fruits
And vegetables, such as leaves and roots.
For minerals, vitamins, and carbohydrates,
Eat broccoli, green beans, spinach, and squash.
Next up are meat, poultry, eggs, beans, and nuts,
With protein for cells and for healing cuts.
Remember the dairy group; eat it up, please,
Milk, yogurt, milk products, and all kinds of cheese.
At the tip of the top are the fats, oils, and sweets.
The point is to eat very few of these treats!

Food and the Nutrients It Contains

Lesson Focus
Foods are divided into six groups based on the nutrients they contain.

Why Learn This?
A food guide pyramid can help you achieve a balanced diet.

Vocabulary
food guide pyramid
serving
balanced diet
portion

Food Groups
A healthful diet includes a variety of healthful foods in the right amounts. Foods are divided into six groups based on the nutrients they contain. The most healthful diet includes foods from several groups at each meal or snack.

Fats, Oils, and Sweets
Doughnuts, chocolate bars, cookies, cakes, butter, oil, and chips are just a few of the foods in this group. These foods give you very few nutrients. They may also contain large amounts of salt, fat, and sugar.

Milk, Yogurt, and Cheese
Cottage cheese, yogurt, and hard cheeses are made from milk. Milk and foods made from milk are good sources of protein, vitamins, and minerals. Some of these foods are also high in fat.

Meats, Poultry, Fish, Dry Beans, Eggs, and Nuts
Nuts, dry beans, eggs, fish, poultry, and meat are all good protein sources. They contain vitamins and minerals. Many of these foods are high in fat.

66

ESL/ELL Support
BACKGROUND AND EXPERIENCE Help students name the foods shown in the food groups. Then encourage them to talk about foods they like and foods that are popular in their cultures. Have them discuss the food group to which each belongs.

Beginning Give each student six sheets of drawing paper. Have them title each sheet with the name of one of the six food groups. Then have students draw on each sheet some foods that belong to that group.

Intermediate Have students do the same Beginning activity, but have them label their pictures with the names of the foods. You may want to pair students and have them write the labels together.

Advanced Have students form six teams, and let each team choose one of the food groups. Challenge the teams to write a list of as many foods as possible that belong in their food group.

Vegetables

Broccoli, cauliflower, carrots, corn, lettuce, and celery are in this group. Vegetables are rich in minerals, vitamins, and fiber. Many have small amounts of protein and very little or no fat.

Fruits

Fruits include peaches, strawberries, bananas, apples, oranges, and pineapples. These foods are rich in minerals, vitamins, carbohydrates, and fiber. They have little or no fat and protein.

Breads, Cereals, Rice, and Pasta

Foods in this group are grains or are made from grain. They include tortillas, cereals, rice, breads, pasta, and crackers. These foods contain carbohydrates, proteins, fiber, minerals, and vitamins. Most are low in fat.

To have a healthful, balanced diet, eat a combination of foods every day. Don't choose too many foods from only one group. Choose very few foods from the Fats, Oils, and Sweets Group. You get plenty of these nutrients from foods in the other groups.

SUMMARIZE **Name the six food groups and at least two foods found in each group.**
Fats, Oils, Sweets; Milk, Yogurt, Cheese; Meats, Poultry, Fish, Dry Beans, Eggs, Nuts; Vegetables; Fruits; Breads, Cereals, Rice, Pasta; answers will vary.

67

Teacher Tip

Dietary Differences Be sensitive to the variety of cultures represented by your students and the variety of foods and eating practices common in their homes. You may wish to discuss food practices represented in your classroom or in a larger community. If possible, you might want to have a tasting party. **CAUTION:** Check for food allergies before allowing students to eat any foods.

Art

Food Collage Have students choose one or more of the food groups. Have them cut from a magazine some pictures of foods that are in the groups and then paste the pictures onto the poster board.

2. TEACH

Interpret Visuals—Pictures

Point out the pictures of the foods on these pages. Ask students to use the pictures to suggest what other foods might belong in each food group. Accept any reasonable answers.

Content-Area Reading Support

Using Titles and Headings Direct attention to the headings on these pages. Point out that the first heading is in red and is a larger size than the other headings. This heading identifies the overall topic. The other headings identify subtopics. Explain that the placement, size, and sometimes the color of headings are clues to the topic and organization of information in a text passage.

Health Background

Complete Proteins Proteins that occur in foods from animal sources—such as meat, poultry, eggs, milk, and fish—are considered complete proteins. They have all the essential amino acids, or building blocks, the body needs.

Incomplete Proteins Proteins from vegetables and cereals—such as lentils, peas, and wheat—are sometimes called incomplete proteins because they lack one or more of the essential amino acids. To make up a complete protein, these food items need to be combined. For example, red beans or lentils and rice, hummus (sesame and garbanzos), or wheat bread and nuts result in complete proteins. The only plant that is a source of complete proteins is soy.

Source: *National Institutes of Health*

For more background, visit the **Webliography** in Teacher Resources at **www.harcourtschool.com/health**
Keyword nutrition

TEACH *continued*

Interpret Visuals—Pictures

Have students study the picture of the USDA Food Guide Pyramid. Help them recognize that the size of each section of the pyramid roughly corresponds to the number of servings recommended for that food group each day. For example, the smallest section is at the top and contains fats, oils, and sweets—foods to be eaten in the smallest amounts.

Why is the box for the vegetable group slightly larger than the box for the fruit group? Possible responses: The size suggests that more vegetables are to be eaten than fruits; one includes more servings than the other.

Discuss

Many foods that fit at the very top of the USDA Food Guide Pyramid are called "junk foods." Ask some students to identify some kinds of foods that might be considered junk foods. soft drinks, candy, chips

Critical Thinking **Why do you think foods such as these are called "junk foods"?** They contain a lot of calories but are not very nutritious, or useful for the body to function.

When Minutes Count . . .

Transparency 21: Food Guide Pyramid can be used to present material in this lesson. *Interactive Transparencies available on CD-ROM.*

The USDA Food Guide Pyramid

Fats, Oils, and Sweets Group
Use sparingly; not every day.

Milk, Yogurt, and Cheese Group
You need 3 SERVINGS. One serving equals 8 ounces of milk or yogurt or $1\frac{1}{2}$ ounces of cheese.

Vegetable Group
You need 3–5 SERVINGS. One serving equals $\frac{1}{2}$ cup cooked vegetable or 1 cup salad.

Bread, Cereal, Rice, and Pasta Group
You need 6–9 SERVINGS. One serving equals 1 slice of bread, 1 corn tortilla, $\frac{1}{2}$ cup cooked cereal, 1 cup dry cereal, $\frac{1}{2}$ cup cooked pasta.

68

Meeting Individual Needs
Leveled Activities

BELOW-LEVEL **Food Group Match** Ask each student to fold a sheet of paper in half lengthwise. On the left side, have them list the foods they usually eat. On the right side, have them list the food groups. Then have them match up each food with the correct food group.

ON-LEVEL **Biggest Crop Producers** Invite students to use reference materials, such as a world almanac or the Internet, to find out which countries grow and sell the most wheat, rice, and corn.

CHALLENGE **Balanced Meals** Have students write down what they ate for their last three meals. Ask them to evaluate whether or not these meals were balanced and to explain why or why not. Students need not share information about their meals.

Information Alert!

The USDA Food Guide Pyramid As scientists learn more about nutrition and health, the USDA Food Guide Pyramid may change.

GO ONLINE For the most up-to-date information, visit The Learning Site. www.harcourtschool.com/health

Meat, Poultry, Fish, Dry Beans, Eggs, and Nuts Group
You need 2–3 SERVINGS. A serving size is 2–3 ounces of cooked meat, chicken, or fish, $\frac{1}{2}$ cup cooked dry beans, 1 egg, or $\frac{1}{3}$ cup nuts.

Fruit Group
You need 2–4 SERVINGS. One serving equals 1 apple, 1 banana, 4 ounces of fruit juice, or 15 grapes.

The number of servings from each food group are suggested for children ages 7–12.

Getting the Nutrients You Need

The United States Department of Agriculture (USDA) is an agency involved with food production and safety. The USDA has developed a **food guide pyramid**, a tool to help you choose foods for a healthful diet. The USDA Food Guide Pyramid shows how many servings you should eat from each food group each day. A **serving** is the measured amount of a food recommended for a meal or snack.

The bottom of the pyramid is the largest part. This tells you that the foods from this group should form the largest part of your diet. These foods include pasta, rice, bread, and cereal. The foods from the top of the pyramid should be the smallest part of your diet. Eat these foods only in small amounts, and not every day.

The food guide pyramid shows you that no one food group gives you all the nutrients you need. It can help you choose a healthful variety of foods. It reminds you not to eat too many unhealthful foods. By using the USDA Food Guide Pyramid, you can be sure to get a balanced diet. A **balanced diet** is a diet made up of a healthful amount of foods from each of the food groups. Eating a balanced diet gives your body the nutrients it needs.

SEQUENCE **If you listed the foods on the food guide pyramid from the greatest number of servings to the least, which food group would follow the vegetable group?**

the fruit group

Discuss

The serving sizes indicated on the USDA Food Guide Pyramid pictured here are those recommended for children. These can vary, and young children especially may eat smaller servings at meals and as snacks.

Problem Solving If your servings are smaller than those described on the USDA Food Guide Pyramid, what could you do to get enough nutrients? Have more servings during the day.

Problem Solving Suppose you are the proper weight for your size and build according to your doctor. Why might achieving your healthful weight not necessarily mean that you are eating healthfully? Even though you appear to be the correct weight, you may not feel well or have enough energy because you aren't eating the right amount of each kind of food. You need to check your diet to see if you are getting the right balance of nutrients.

Teacher Tip

How Many a Day? The USDA suggests at least a total of five fruit or vegetable servings every day. Have students count the number of fruit and vegetable servings they had yesterday. Then have them look for "hidden" servings. For example, a salad may include two or three vegetable servings if it contains spinach, tomatoes, and green peppers. Some large apples and bananas equal two servings. Stir-fried dishes and many soups contain several vegetable servings.

Math

Food Math Have students decide on a menu for one day. Ask them to add the number of servings they planned to eat from each of the three bottom layers of the pyramid. Have they met the recommended number of servings in each group? Have they exceeded the recommendations? If so, by how much? Have they fallen short? If so, by how much? They may want to consider choosing higher or lower numbers of servings for their menus.

TEACH *continued*

Interpret Visuals—Pictures

The pictures on this page show what size a healthful recommended *serving* should be. These items were chosen because they are familiar. This makes it easier for people to determine whether the portion of food they are getting is larger or smaller than the recommended serving. **Which of the items shown might not always be the same in size?** Fist and thumb; the sizes of these might vary slightly from person to person in the same age group.

Activity

Make Responsible Decisions

Help students gain practice in using the steps of the decision-making model. You may wish to refer students to pages 66–69 for a reminder of how to decide on choices for menus. Ask volunteers to discuss their choices and identify why they think they have chosen foods for a balanced diet.

Health Background

Other Food Guide Pyramids The pyramid-shaped food guide was introduced in 1992 in the United States. There is also a vegetarian food guide pyramid. In an extensive survey, the shape was found to be most informative in conveying the message of moderation and proportionality. Puerto Rico and the Philippines also use the pyramid format. Still others have used the model but have adapted it to suit their individual cultures. For example, Canada uses a four-banded rainbow while China and South Korea rely on a pagoda. Most of the European countries have chosen a circular shape. Great Britain and Mexico use a round plate or dish shapes.

Source: *The American Dietetic Association*

For more background, visit the **Webliography** in Teacher Resources at **www.harcourtschool.com/health**
Keyword nutrition

ACTIVITY

Life Skills

Make Responsible Decisions

Make up a menu for a meal. Choose foods from the USDA Food Guide Pyramid. Then use what you have learned to decide how many servings each portion will contain. For more information, go to Estimating Serving Size on page 349 of the Health and Safety Handbook.

Use Serving Sizes to Control Portions

It is important to know the difference between servings and portions. You already know that a serving is the measured amount of a food you would probably eat during one meal or as a snack. A serving is not always the same as a portion.

A **portion** is the amount of food you want to eat or the amount you may be served. Sometimes you may be served one portion, but it might contain more than one serving. You can control your portions by using serving sizes. Some estimates of serving sizes are shown below.

Serving Size Estimates

▲ about the size of a 3-ounce serving of fish, chicken, or meat

▲ about equal to $1\frac{1}{2}$ ounces of cheese

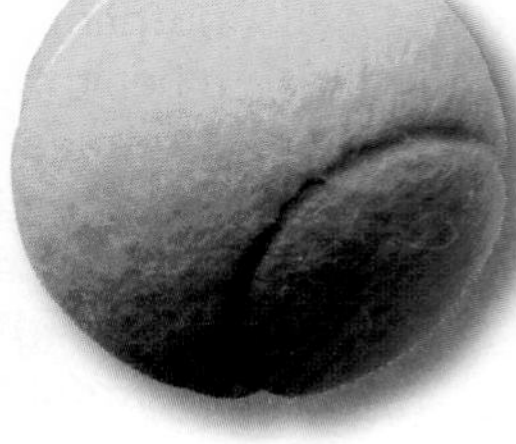

▲ about one medium-sized fruit

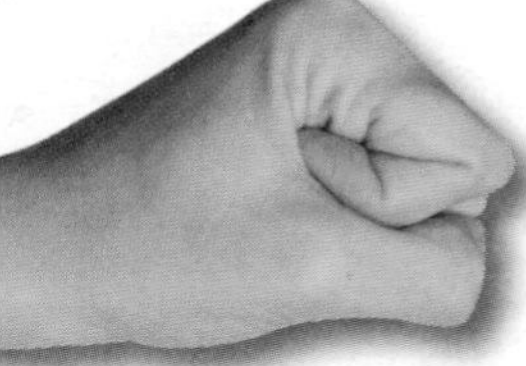

▲ about the size of $\frac{1}{2}$ cup of cooked pasta or cooked cereal

▲ about one teaspoon of oil or butter

Cultural Connection

Dietary Customs Cultural, religious, and genetic factors influence dietary customs. For example, many Jews and Muslims do not eat pork. Buddhists and Hindus may be strictly vegetarian. Many people of Asian, African, and Native American descent lack an enzyme necessary for digesting dairy products. Have students research and report on dietary customs of other cultures.

Social Studies

Sharing Food Customs Have students use a map or a globe to locate the countries that border the Mediterranean Sea. Have them locate the Asian countries. Ask them to speculate on why foods from these areas are popular in the United States. Discuss how the population of the United States is made up of people from many other countries and that ethnic foods have become popular in some parts of the country.

Do you choose the right portions for the foods you eat? If you eat portions that are too large, you may be overeating. This isn't healthful for you. When you are choosing foods to eat, remember the following:

- Use the USDA Food Guide Pyramid.
- Serving sizes are not always the same as a portion.
- Control the size of your food portions by using serving sizes.

In the next lesson, you will learn how to make good food choices from a menu and how to select healthful snacks.

DRAW CONCLUSIONS Why are food servings and portion amounts important when making meal choices?

choosing the right serving sizes helps you control the portions and keeps you from overeating

Consumer Activity

Accessing Valid Health Information Use a computer to learn more about food servings and portion sizes. Write a paragraph explaining what you learned. Use the information on pages 52–53 for accessing valid health information.

Lesson 2 Summary and Review

1. **Summarize with Vocabulary** Use vocabulary from this lesson to complete the statements.

   A food guide _____ can help you achieve a _____. The measured amount of food recommended for a meal or snack is a _____. A _____ is the amount of food you are served.

2. How are foods grouped?
3. **Critical Thinking** Explain how the shape of a pyramid is related to the amount of food servings you should eat daily.
4. **COMPARE AND CONTRAST** Draw and complete this graphic organizer to show how food servings and portion sizes are alike and different.

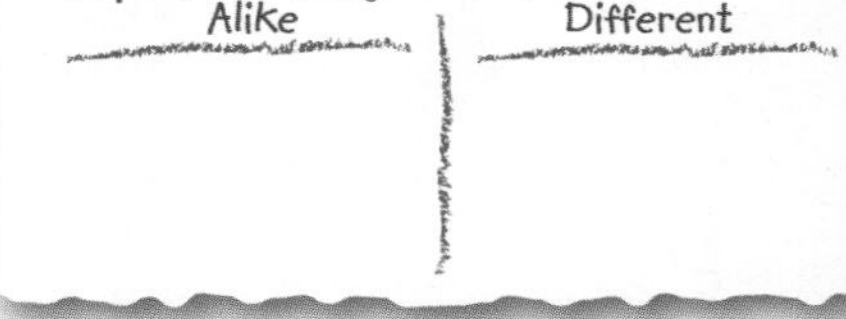

5. **Write to Inform—How-To** Write a plan on how to achieve a balanced diet.

Consumer Activity

Help students gain an understanding of the importance of using more than one reliable source of information. Refer students to websites that you have already confirmed as valid and reliable.

3. WRAP UP

Lesson 2 Summary and Review

1. pyramid, balanced diet; serving; portion
2. based on the nutrients they contain
3. You should eat the most servings of foods in the largest part of the pyramid. You should eat the fewest servings of foods in the smallest part of the pyramid.
4. Graphics may include:

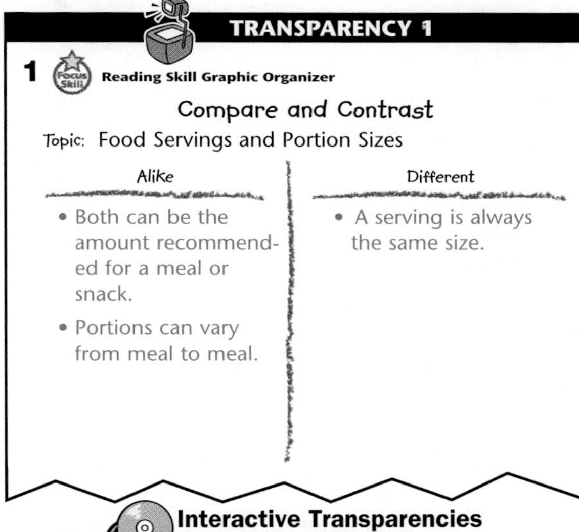

TRANSPARENCY 1
1 Reading Skill Graphic Organizer
Compare and Contrast
Topic: Food Servings and Portion Sizes
Alike
• Both can be the amount recommend-ed for a meal or snack.
• Portions can vary from meal to meal.
Different
• A serving is always the same size.

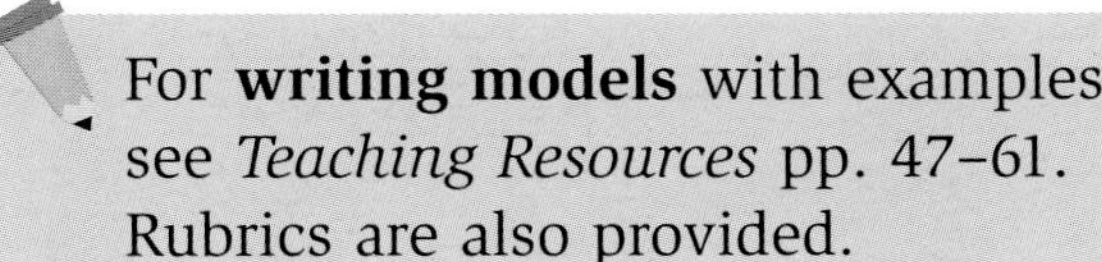

5. Students' responses will vary but should include: use the USDA Food Guide Pyramid; keep your portions under control; use serving size estimates.

For **writing models** with examples, see *Teaching Resources* pp. 47–61. Rubrics are also provided.

When Minutes Count . . .

Quick Study Students can use *Activity Book* pages 11–12 (shown on p. 61) as they complete each lesson in this chapter.

LESSON 3
Pages 72–75

Objectives
- ► Use nutrition information from a food guide pyramid to make healthful food choices.
- ► Demonstrate healthful eating practices by making healthful food choices.

When Minutes Count . . .
Assign the Quick Study, Lesson 3, Activity Book pp. 11–12 (shown on p. 61).

Program Resources
- ► Activity Book pp. 11–12
- ► Transparency 1

Vocabulary
habit p. 72

Daily Fitness Tip

Eating three balanced meals a day in sensible portions may not give your body all the servings needed from all the food groups. Point out that, in addition to breakfast, lunch, and dinner, it might also be important for students to enjoy healthful, tasty snacks to complete their balanced diet.

For more about the effects of food on your body, see *Be Active! Resources for Physical Education,* p. 143.

1. MOTIVATE

Ask students to identify information on menus. Invite several students to role-play ordering from a restaurant menu as the rest of the class, in the role of servers, writes down their orders. Have the servers analyze the ordered meals with regard to how balanced the meals are.

How can you tell a healthful, balanced meal from a nonhealthful one? A healthful, balanced meal provides servings in the recommended proportions from most of the food groups in a food guide pyramid.

Using a Food Guide Pyramid

Lesson Focus
A food guide pyramid can help you choose healthful meals and snacks.

Why Learn This?
Making wise food choices will help you develop healthful eating habits.

Vocabulary
habit

Choosing Foods from a Menu

Do you sometimes eat at a fast-food or another kind of restaurant? If so, you know that choosing a healthful meal is not always easy. A food guide pyramid can help you make a healthful choice.

Choosing foods wisely now will help you stay healthy all your life. It will help you form healthful eating habits. A **habit** is something you do so often that you don't even think about it.

The foods on the USDA Food Guide Pyramid are grouped according to type. But most of your meals contain more than one type of food. These are called *combination foods*. Some examples are stews, salads, pizza, sandwiches, and spaghetti with meatballs.

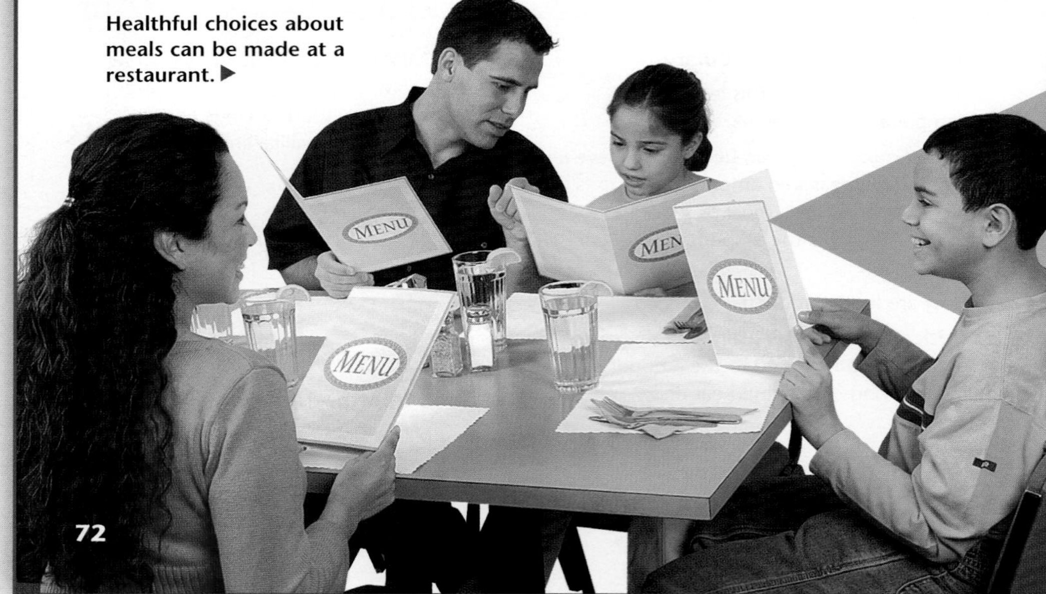

Healthful choices about meals can be made at a restaurant. ►

72

Teacher Tip

What's in It? Challenge students to identify the likely ingredients in the combination foods cited—stews: perhaps meat, poultry, fish, dry beans, vegetables, and pasta; salads: perhaps cheese, fruit, vegetables, and nuts; pizza: perhaps dough, cheese, meat, sauce; sandwiches: perhaps bread, meat, cheese, lettuce; spaghetti with meatballs: perhaps pasta, vegetables, meat, cheese.

The more often you choose healthful foods, the easier making healthful choices will become. You don't want to make a habit of eating too many foods from just one group. Eating this way wouldn't be a healthful habit.

Ramón is at a restaurant. He reads the menu. He wants to make choosing healthier foods a habit. He thinks about the food groups found in each of the menu choices. He asks himself, "Will I have a balanced diet if I choose that food? How many servings are in each portion?" Ramón wants to choose the food that will provide him with the nutrients he needs.

DRAW CONCLUSIONS Use the USDA Food Guide Pyramid to determine food groups in Ramón's menu choices.
Students should use the USDA Food Guide Pyramid to determine food groups mentioned in each menu choice.

Personal Health Plan

Real-Life Situation
Suppose you are ordering lunch from a restaurant menu.
Real-Life Plan
Write a step-by-step plan for ordering a healthful, balanced meal.

Combination Pizza
Deep-dish delicacy topped with pepperoni, sausage, ground beef, and double-layered cheeses. Comes with buttered breadsticks.

Cheeseburger
Mouth-watering all-beef patty topped with cheese, lettuce, and tomato on a whole-wheat bun. Accompanied by your choice of French fries or salad.

Taco Salad
Mix of ground beef, shredded lettuce, chopped tomato, onions, and shredded cheese, topped with sour cream, nestled in a deep-fried shell.

Quick Activity

Analyze Menu Choices Look at Ramón's menu choices. Decide for yourself which is the healthiest meal. Compare and contrast the amounts and balance of food groups represented in each selection.

Cultural Connection

My Culture's Cuisine Invite students to write a day's menu typical of their own or another culture. The menu should include a paragraph or two about the geographical area in which that food is most often served. Have students list the food groups the items on their menus belong to.

2. TEACH

Interpret Visuals—Pictures

Ask students if the portions shown on this page are like those they might find in a restaurant. Ask whether these and other portions offered in restaurants are healthful servings of food.

Discuss

Critical Thinking What habits, like nightly toothbrushing, do you have? Answers will vary. **How can people form good habits?** Students should recognize that repeatedly doing the same thing can lead to those behaviors becoming habits.

Personal Health Plan

Plans should include:

- Make menu choices.
- Determine if the selected foods are, or contain, foods from different groups.
- If needed, revise menu choices to include foods from a variety of food groups.

Ask students to identify the importance of taking personal responsibility for maintaining a personal health plan for nutrition.

Quick Activity

The cheeseburger with a salad is the most healthful choice. It has foods from all the major food groups: bun (breads group), salad (vegetables group), tomato (fruits group), hamburger (meats group), milk and cheese (milk and cheese group). Other choices have less variety and more fats. To extend this activity ask students **How will a beverage affect the overall healthfulness of the meals?**

Content-Area Reading Support

Using Reference Words Call attention to the third sentence in the third paragraph on page 72: *These are called combination foods*. Point out that the word *These* functions as a pronoun and refers to meals containing more than one type of food, in the previous sentence.

TEACH *continued*

Activity

Responsibility Amy can show responsibility in several ways. She can have a healthful snack and tell her mother when she gets home; she can choose not to eat but ask her mother when she gets home if it would be okay the next time she's hungry to have a healthful snack before dinner; or she could ask her mother for another suggestion.

Content-Area Reading Support

Unusual Sentence Structure Point out that the questions above Keisha's head are incomplete sentences (no subject and verb). They represent the food items in Keisha's thoughts. Each sentence fragment is understood to have the phrase "Should I have . . ." preceding it.

Discuss

Write on the board this recipe for soft corn tortillas. Have students find Mexico on a map. To make 20 small soft corn tortillas: Place in 5 bowls: 2 1/2 C shredded lettuce; 2 1/2 C chopped tomatoes; 1 1/2 C grated cheddar cheese; 3 1-lb. cans lowfat refried beans; and 1 C salsa. Mix 2 1/2 T salsa into beans. Spread bean mixture on a tortilla. Top with cheese, lettuce, tomatoes, and salsa. Makes 20 snack-size treats. CAUTION: Check for food allergies before allowing students to eat foods. Point out that the main ingredients, cornmeal and beans, are staples of the Mexican diet.

Problem Solving Where on the USDA Food Guide Pyramid would you place each ingredient of the combination food described above? Corn tortilla: breads, cereals, rice, pasta group; Lettuce: vegetables group; Tomatoes, salsa: fruits/vegetables groups; Cheese: milk, yogurt, cheese group; Beans: meats, poultry, fish, dry beans, eggs, nuts group

ACTIVITY

Building Good Character

Responsibility Amy gets home before the rest of her family. Amy is hungry. No one is supposed to eat before dinner, but Amy's mother has left some healthful snacks in the refrigerator. Name at least two ways Amy can show responsible behavior.

Choosing Healthful Snacks

You're hungry. It's not yet dinnertime. What do you choose for a snack? Should you choose cookies or fruit? A glass of milk or a doughnut?

When you choose a snack, think of the USDA Food Guide Pyramid. Limit the amount of sugar, fat, or salt that you eat. Foods high in these substances don't give you the nutrients you need. Think about the servings you have already had today and what you will have for dinner. Remember, don't overeat.

How you are feeling can also affect what you want to eat. Do you want something warm? Cold? Crunchy? Soft? Smooth? There's a healthful snack for every mood.

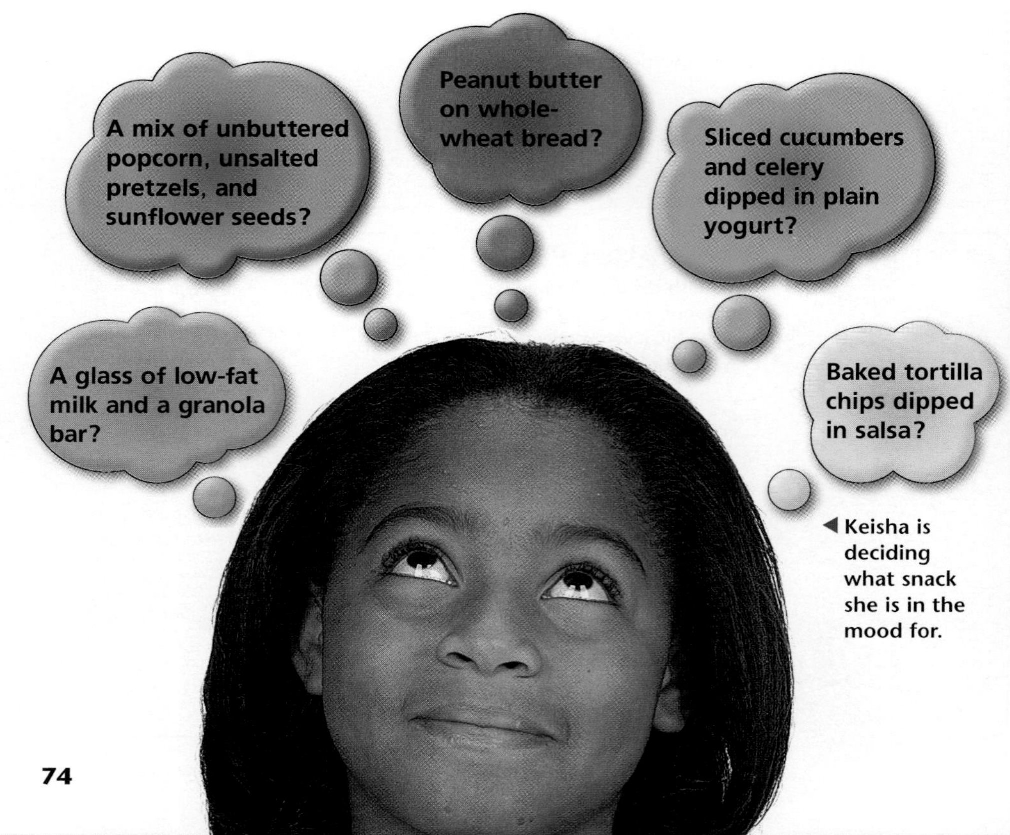

A mix of unbuttered popcorn, unsalted pretzels, and sunflower seeds?
Peanut butter on whole-wheat bread?
Sliced cucumbers and celery dipped in plain yogurt?
A glass of low-fat milk and a granola bar?
Baked tortilla chips dipped in salsa?

◀ Keisha is deciding what snack she is in the mood for.

Art

Use Your Head Invite your students to make their own versions of Keisha, on this page. Have them use their own heads (a drawing, photo, or collage of themselves) at the bottom of the page. Above their heads, have them place thought bubbles depicting (with magazine cutouts or drawings) healthful snack choices they are likely to consider.

You can eat tasty foods that are also healthful. Be daring! Be creative! Try something new! Be sure to make a healthful choice. Here are some ideas to help you:

▼ Which of these foods might you choose for your next snack?

- fresh fruit
- raw vegetables
- nuts and seeds
- whole-grain cereal
- rice cakes
- plain granola bars
- low-fat yogurt
- cheese
- unbuttered and unsalted popcorn
- dried fruit
- animal crackers
- peanut butter on whole-wheat crackers

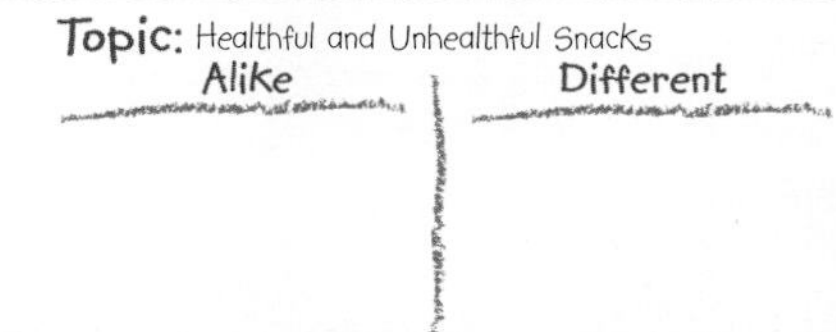

SUMMARIZE List some things to think about when you are choosing snacks.

The USDA Food Guide Pyramid; don't eat too much; limit sugar, fat, and salt; and so on.

Lesson 3 Summary and Review

❶ **Summarize with Vocabulary**
Use vocabulary and other terms from this lesson to complete the statements.

Choosing healthful foods can form healthful eating _____. With practice you can choose healthful combination _____, or foods that contain more than one food group. Eating a healthful _____ can give you the energy you need until your next meal.

❷ **Critical Thinking** How can you develop healthful eating habits?

❸ List at least four different healthful snacks you enjoy or would be willing to try. Then name the food groups in which they are found.

❹ **COMPARE AND CONTRAST** Draw and complete this graphic organizer to show how healthful and unhealthful snacks are alike and different.

Topic: Healthful and Unhealthful Snacks

Alike	Different

❺ **Write to Express—Idea**
Suppose you want to know the nutritional value of foods in a fast-food restaurant. Write what you might say in a letter requesting the information.

Language Arts

Correct Cuisine Café Invite students to create a menu consisting of three lunch specials. Each meal should provide servings from the bottom three levels of the USDA Food Guide Pyramid. Students may draw the foods or not, but they should describe them, incorporating catchy phrasing to entice customers. Provide a variety of art supplies, including construction paper. Then students may make the menu as eye-catching as possible.

3. WRAP UP

Lesson 3 Summary and Review

1. habits; foods; snack
2. by getting into the habit of making healthful food choices now
3. Answers will vary but might include the items in the list on this page.
4. Graphics may include:

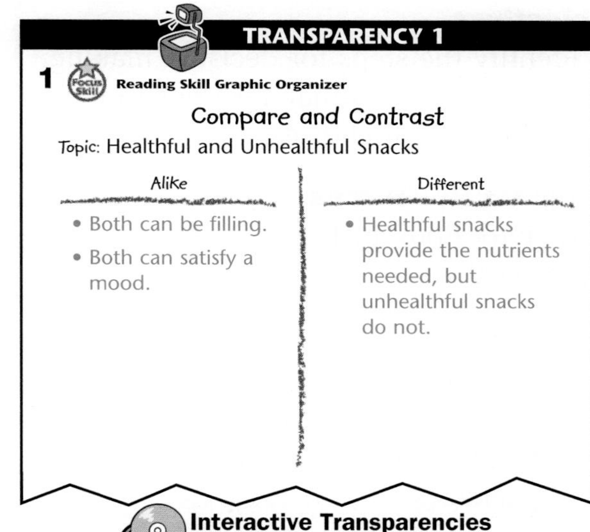

TRANSPARENCY 1

1 Reading Skill Graphic Organizer

Compare and Contrast

Topic: Healthful and Unhealthful Snacks

Alike	Different
• Both can be filling. • Both can satisfy a mood.	• Healthful snacks provide the nutrients needed, but unhealthful snacks do not.

Interactive Transparencies available on CD-ROM.

5. Letters will vary but should be carefully written and polite. The request should be about specific food items.

For **writing models** with examples, see *Teaching Resources* pp. 47–61. Rubrics are also provided.

When Minutes Count . . .

Quick Study Students can use *Activity Book* pages 11–12 (shown on p. 61) as they complete each lesson in this chapter.

Life Skills

Communicate
Make Responsible Decisions
Manage Stress
Refuse
Resolve Conflicts
Set Goals

Objectives

- Identify the steps for decision making.
- Use the decision-making steps to make healthful food choices.

Program Resources

- Activity Book p. 14
- Poster 8

1. MOTIVATE

Optional Activity Materials colorful food packages

Bring to class (or ask students to bring in) some colorful, empty food packages, such as cereal boxes. Ask students why these packages are so colorful. What images other than food do they see on the packages? How does packaging influence people's decisions about food? Some cereal boxes have pictures of famous athletes, suggesting that you can be a famous athlete if you eat that cereal. Be sure students understand that it takes more than just eating a certain brand of cereal to be a good athlete.

2. TEACH

Direct students' attention to the photos of Mai thinking about her breakfast choices.

Step 1

What are Mai's breakfast choices? skip breakfast, eat a candy bar, or prepare juice and toast with cheese.

Make Responsible Decisions

About Meals and Snacks

Every day you have to make decisions about meals and snacks. You must think through the decisions that you make. Using the steps for **Making Responsible Decisions** can help you make healthful choices.

Mai overslept this morning. She doesn't have time for her favorite breakfast of eggs, toast, and juice. What should Mai do?

1 Find out about the choices you could make.

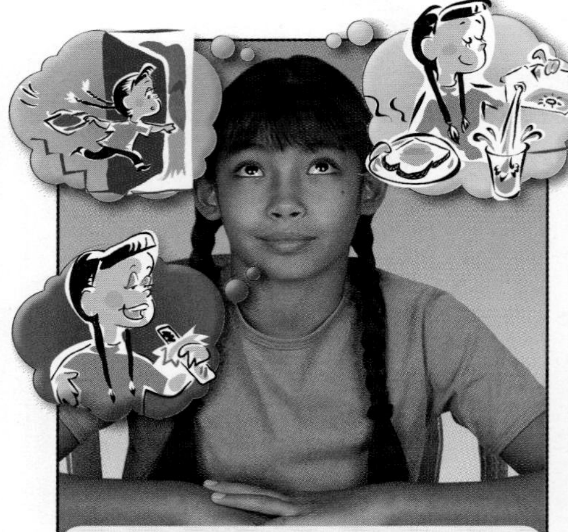

Mai can skip breakfast or eat a candy bar, or she can prepare juice and toast with cheese.

2 Eliminate choices that are against your family rules.

Mai knows her mother would not approve of the candy bar. She eliminates that choice.

76

Teacher Tip

Body Image Students see media messages about "perfect" body size and shape that often affect their decision-making processes. Students may skip meals or use fad diets to get a "perfect" body. These unhealthful behaviors and food choices can lead to eating disorders such as anorexia nervosa and bulimia. For these reasons, it is important that students learn refusal skills to resist the negative influences of peer pressure and the media.

ACTIVITY BOOK P. 14

Name ____________________

Problem Solving

Life Skill

Make Responsible Decisions

Steps for Responsible Decision Making

1. Find out about the choices you could make.
2. Eliminate choices that are against your family's rules.
3. Ask yourself: What could happen with each choice? Does the choice show good character?
4. Make what seems to be the best choice.

Use the steps to help students make responsible decisions.

A. Cory walks home from school with his friends. Lately his friends have been stopping at a fast-food restaurant to order French fries each day. Cory's family allows only healthful snacks after school. Cory decides it can't hurt to have French fries every day, so he goes with his friends.

- Did Cory make the best choice? Why or why not?

Possible answer: Cory did not follow his family's rules, so he did not make the best choice. Cory's family allows only healthful snacks after school, so he should not order French fries. Cory should look for a healthful choice on the fast-food restaurant menu so he can still hang out with his friends.

B. Maria and her cousin have just done several errands at the mall. Maria's mom gave Maria money for a healthful lunch at the mall. Maria sees a hair clip in a mall store that she would really like to have. If she skipped lunch and spent her lunch money on the clip, she could afford it.

- Use the steps for making responsible decisions to help Maria decide what to do.

Possible answer: Maria should buy a healthful lunch with the money her mom gave her. It is not healthful to skip meals. It would not be responsible or trustworthy for Maria to spend the money on a hair clip. Maybe Maria can plan to save some money to buy the clip later.

© Harcourt

Available online.
www.harcourtschool.com/health

3 **Ask yourself: What could happen with each choice? Does the choice show good character?**

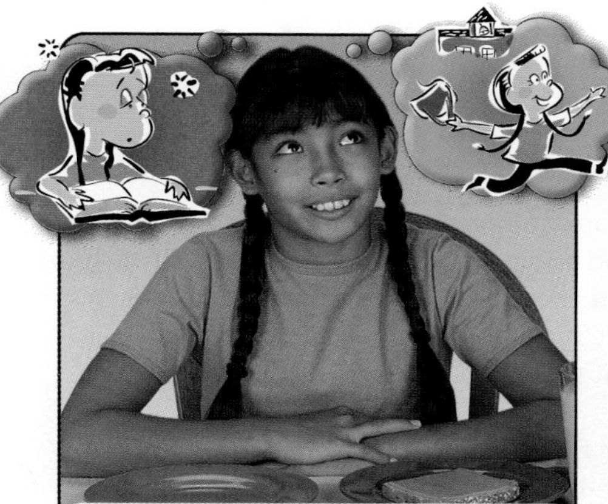

If Mai skips breakfast, she may be sleepy at school. If she eats breakfast, she may have more energy.

4 **Make what seems to be the best choice.**

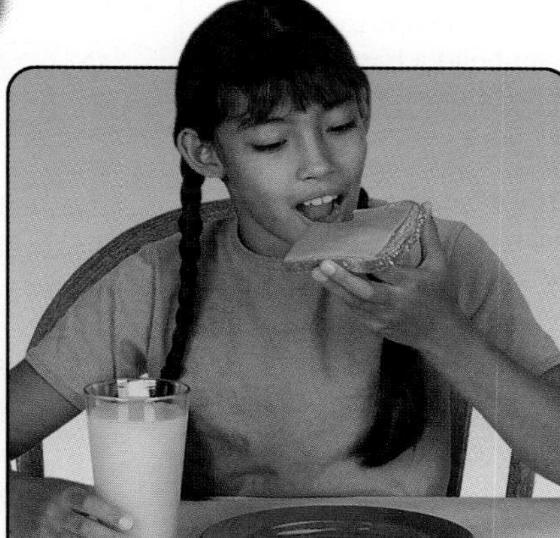

Mai decides to eat breakfast so she will have the energy she needs. Her decision shows she is being responsible.

Problem Solving

After school Madeline is allowed to have a snack before doing her homework. On the counter Madeline sees cupcakes her dad baked for her little brother's birthday. She knows there are 25 students in her brother's class. She counts 28 cupcakes.

Use the steps for **Making Responsible Decisions** to help Madeline make the best decision. Explain how Madeline's decision shows trustworthiness.

77

Using the Poster

Activity Have students write and perform skits showing situations in which children use the steps for Making Responsible Decisions in appropriate ways.

Display the poster to remind students of the steps for making responsible decisions.

POSTER 8
LIFE SKILLS
Make Responsible Decisions
The boy is making a responsible decision.
His decision will help him avoid getting hurt.
Steps for Making Responsible Decisions
1 Find out about the choices you could make.
2 Eliminate choices that are illegal or against your family rules.
3 Ask yourself: What could happen with each choice? Does the choice show good character?
4 Make what seems to be the best choice.
What RESPONSIBLE DECISIONS have YOU MADE today?

Critical Thinking **What other healthful choice could Mai prepare in a short time?** possibly cereal and milk

Step 2

Why is it important for Mai to eliminate a choice that's against family rules? Making a choice that she knows is wrong will only get her in trouble. Eliminating bad choices makes the decision-making process easier.

Step 3

What could happen with the first choice? If she skips breakfast, she may be sleepy at school and find it difficult to concentrate in class. **Would the first choice show Mai being responsible?** No. If she doesn't eat she'll probably not have enough energy and may be less alert in class.

Building Good Character

Remind students that when making any decision, they should consider how the decision shows good character. Here are questions they can ask: Am I being trustworthy and responsible? Am I showing consideration for others? Does my decision show that I'm being a good citizen? Am I respecting others?

Step 4

What is Mai's best choice? to eat breakfast **What do you think happened as a result of Mai's choice?** She had a successful day at school and was able to do her best.

3. WRAP UP

Problem Solving

Answers should reflect the steps for Making Responsible Decisions. Madeline should think about the choices she could make. She should make a decision based on her family's rules and what seems to be the best choice. Madeline would show she's trustworthy if she doesn't eat the cupcakes.

LESSON 4

Pages 78–83

Objectives

- Learn how to make wise choices when shopping for food.
- Gather data to make informed health choices.
- Learn how to read and compare food labels.

When Minutes Count . . .

Assign the Quick Study, Lesson 4, Activity Book pp. 11–12 (shown on p. 61).

Program Resources

- Activity Book pp. 11–12
- Transparencies 1, 22

Vocabulary

nutritious p. 80, **ingredients** p. 81

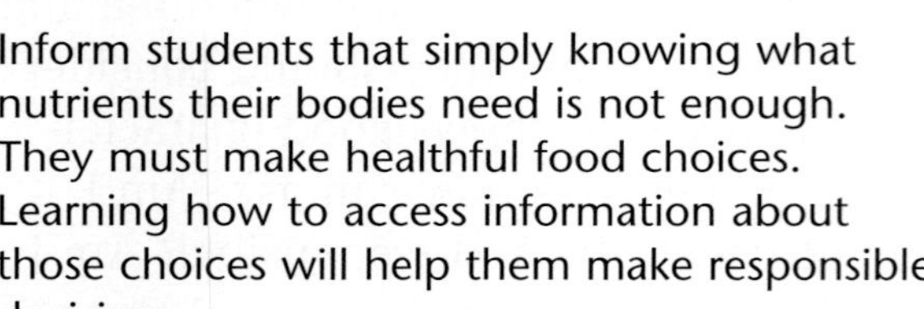

Daily Fitness Tip

Inform students that simply knowing what nutrients their bodies need is not enough. They must make healthful food choices. Learning how to access information about those choices will help them make responsible decisions.

For more about balancing your physical activity and food intake, see *Be Active! Resources for Physical Education,* p. 153.

1. MOTIVATE

Materials a variety of nutrition labels

Assess students' knowledge of and familiarity with food labels by asking them if they have ever read food labels. Have they ever read food labels out of curiosity or to help them make thoughtful purchases? What information do they think they can get from food package labels? Do they think the labels on packages might help them in some way, or do they think companies are simply required to supply that information? Tell students that this lesson will fill in some gaps in their knowledge and, perhaps, correct some misunderstandings about food labels.

LESSON 4 Food Guidelines and Labels

Lesson Focus
The Dietary Guidelines for Americans can help you build a base for healthful eating.

Why Learn This?
You can use what you learn to help you compare the nutritional values of foods.

Vocabulary
nutritious
ingredients

Dietary Guidelines for Americans

There are guidelines that can help you make good food choices. The USDA provides a nutrition plan called the Dietary Guidelines for Americans. This plan suggests ways for you to be physically active, eat well, and make good choices.

Aim for Fitness

- Aim for a weight that is good for you. Find out your recommended weight range from a health professional. If you need to, set goals to reach a good weight.
- Be physically active each day. Get enough exercise to help balance the types and amount of foods you eat. In the next chapter, you can discover how the Activity Pyramid can help you plan each week's activities.

Language Arts

Guideline Jingle Challenge students to write a song that teaches the ABC Dietary Guidelines for Americans. In addition to the words *aim, build,* and *choose*, encourage students to fit in words which address food groups that are healthful in moderation (e.g., *grains, fruits,* and *vegetables*) as well as food choices that are unhealthful in large quantities (e.g., *fats, sugars,* and *salt*).

Teacher Tip

Type 2 Diabetes The age most children are diagnosed with Type 2 diabetes is during middle to late puberty. However, the number of children with Type 2 diabetes has increased in recent years. Poor eating habits and less physical activity may be contributing factors to this rise. This has doctors predicting that even younger children will be diagnosed with Type 2 diabetes. For more on diabetes, see page 178 of Chapter 7.

Build a Healthy Base

- Use a food guide pyramid to guide your food choices.
- Each day, choose a variety of grains such as wheat, oats, rice, and corn. Choose whole grains when you can.
- Each day, choose a variety of fruits and vegetables.
- Keep food safe to eat. (Follow the tips in Lesson 5 for safe preparation and storage of food.)

Choose Sensibly

- Choose a diet that is moderate in total fat and low in saturated fat and cholesterol.
- Choose foods and drinks that are low in sugar. Lower the amount of sugars you eat.
- Choose foods that are low in salt. When you prepare foods, use very little salt.
- Choose reasonable food portions. Eat servings that meet your nutritional needs based on the recommendations of the USDA Food Guide Pyramid.

Following these guidelines will help you make good choices about your health.

MAIN IDEA AND DETAILS Write a sentence that states the main purpose of the Dietary Guidelines.

The Dietary Guidelines provide a nutrition plan that suggests ways for you to be physically active, eat well, and make good choices.

Consumer Activity

Analyze Advertisements and Media Messages
Junk food is a term used to describe foods high in calories, fat, sugar, or salt and low in nutritional value. Find an example of an ad for junk food. Write a paragraph describing how the ad might influence your choice of this food for a meal or snack.

Teacher Tip

Watching Weight It's important to be aware of students whose talk centers on weight concerns. Eating disorders can start at early ages, and fourth grade is an important time to help students become comfortable with maintaining a healthy weight rather than obsessing about thinness. As a counterpoint to ads that promote junk foods, you might have students look critically at ads that promote unreasonable expectations of low weight.

2. TEACH

Interpret Visuals—Pictures

Direct attention to the photo on page 78. Ask: **Why do you think there's a photo of a student being weighed? Do you think this lesson will be about dieting?** Tell students that maintaining a healthy weight is part of good health, and that a healthful diet means making thoughtful food choices, not eating less.

Content-Area Reading Support

Using Typographic Clues Direct attention to the letters A, B, and C, which begin the headings for the three guidelines. Tell students that the letters are mnemonic (nih•MAHN•ick) devices—or memory aids. Remembering *ABC* is easy, and associating words that begin with those letters—*Aim, Build,* and *Choose*—will help them remember the three Dietary Guidelines for Americans. Suggest that students take advantage of text memory aids, which are often in different types of print.

Discuss

Ask students to explain the advantages of setting short-term and long-term goals. Have them suggest a goal using the guidelines provided. Have volunteers read the four items under the heading *Choose Sensibly*.

Problem Solving How might you find out what foods are "moderate in total fat and low in saturated fat and cholesterol," or which foods and drinks are low in sugar or low in salt? from food labels

Consumer Activity

Help students see that junk foods may *appear* to provide healthful foods—for example, potatoes in potato chips, fruit in fruit drinks, grains in sugar-coated cereals, and wheat flour in cakes and cookies—but the nutritional benefits of these ingredients are overcome by unhealthy quantities of sugars, fats, salt, and/or artificial flavors, sweeteners, and/or colors.

TEACH *continued*

Critical Thinking **Suppose you saw a box of your favorite cereal that said "Low-fat" on the front. Do you think that information is all you need to know before deciding whether the cereal should be a healthful part of your regular breakfast diet? Why?** No. Often ads on the front of the box don't give all the information. The cereal might be low in fat content but might contain a lot of sugar and few other nutrients or fiber.

Discuss

Have students identify information on food labels. Direct students to study the minerals and vitamins listed on the nutrition label on page 81.

Problem Solving **What percent of the daily value of the mineral known for building strong bones and teeth does this cereal provide?** 0% **What percent of the daily value of the vitamin that builds healthy gums will you get from this cereal?** 0%

Critical Thinking **How could you get calcium and vitamin C as part of your breakfast if you eat this cereal?** Possible answer: by eating the cereal with milk and drinking orange juice

Personal Health Plan ▶

Plans might include:

- reading how much a serving size is on a package label.
- using self-control to stick to the single serving size.

When Minutes Count . . .

Transparency 22: Nutrition Facts Label can be used to present material in this lesson. *Interactive Transparencies available on CD-ROM.*

Did You Know?

In some parts of the world, insects are a major source of protein, vitamins, and minerals. The ancient Greeks and Romans ate insects such as locust and beetle larvae. Today ants, grasshoppers, water bugs, and crickets are just a few of the many insects that are eaten by people. A caterpillar called the mopane worm is even packaged as a food product.

Reading a Product Label

Trisha has been reading the label on a box of cereal. Product labels are provided on almost all packaged foods. The labels show how **nutritious** the food is, or how much nutritional value it has.

One part of a label tells how much protein, carbohydrate, and fat the food contains. It shows the amount of fiber. It also lists some vitamins and minerals in the food.

A product label also tells you the serving size. On Trisha's cereal box, a label states that a serving is one cup. The total calories, fats, proteins, and carbohydrates are given for one serving. What other things are listed?

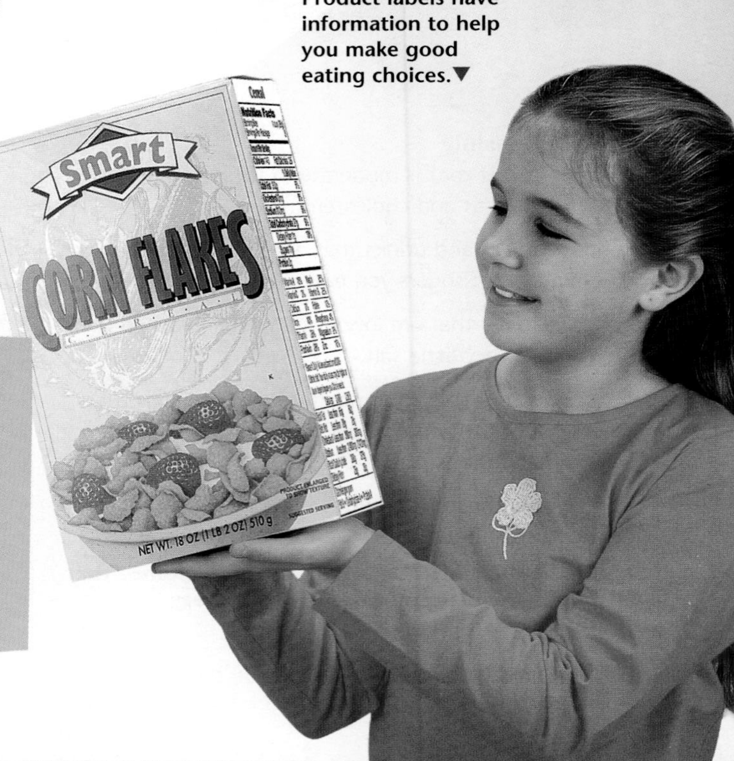

Product labels have information to help you make good eating choices.▼

Personal Health Plan ▶

Real-Life Situation
Suppose you want to control the portions in your daily diet better.
Real-Life Plan
Write a personal health goal listing ways you might use product labels to control better the amount of foods you eat.

80

Meeting Individual Needs
Leveled Activities

BELOW-LEVEL **Junk Food Labels** Have students choose one of their favorite junk foods, either in a store or at home, and read its product label. Have them write the name of the food items and copy the list of the first four ingredients. If necessary, provide samples of labels from some popular junk foods for them to use.

ON-LEVEL **That Much More** Have these students do the same as the students from the group above and copy the number of fat calories, the total calories, the grams of sugar, and the total grams of carbohydrates.

CHALLENGE **More Vitamins and Minerals** Ask students to research vitamins and minerals that have not been addressed in this lesson—for example, thiamin, riboflavin, niacin, magnesium, and vitamin E.

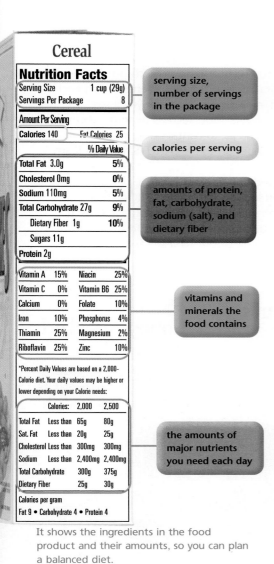

Cereal

Nutrition Facts

Serving Size	1 cup (29g)
Servings Per Package	8
Amount Per Serving	
Calories 140	Fat Calories 25
	% Daily Value
Total Fat 3.0g	5%
Cholesterol 0mg	0%
Sodium 110mg	5%
Total Carbohydrate 27g	9%
Dietary Fiber 1g	10%
Sugars 11g	
Protein 2g	

Vitamin A	15%	Niacin	25%
Vitamin C	0%	Vitamin B6	25%
Calcium	0%	Folate	10%
Iron	10%	Phosphorus	4%
Thiamin	25%	Magnesium	2%
Riboflavin	25%	Zinc	10%

*Percent Daily Values are based on a 2,000-Calorie diet. Your daily values may be higher or lower depending on your Calorie needs:

	Calories:	2,000	2,500
Total Fat	Less than	65g	80g
Sat. Fat	Less than	20g	25g
Cholesterol	Less than	300mg	300mg
Sodium	Less than	2,400mg	2,400mg
Total Carbohydrate		300g	375g
Dietary Fiber		25g	30g

Calories per gram
Fat 9 • Carbohydrate 4 • Protein 4

serving size, number of servings in the package

calories per serving

amounts of protein, fat, carbohydrate, sodium (salt), and dietary fiber

vitamins and minerals the food contains

the amounts of major nutrients you need each day

It shows the ingredients in the food product and their amounts, so you can plan a balanced diet.

If Trisha ate two cups of cereal, the total calories as well as amounts of nutrients would double. So you see, it is important to check the serving size before you eat packaged foods and snacks.

Another part of a food label is the ingredients list. The **ingredients** are all the things used to make a food product. The ingredients are listed in order from greatest amount to least amount.

Trisha is surprised when she reads the list of ingredients in her cereal. There are so many things in it!

DRAW CONCLUSIONS Explain how a product label can help you make food choices.

Quick Activity

Analyze a Label Read the ingredients list below. Find the four main ingredients. Think about what you know about the USDA Food Guide Pyramid. Is this food a good nutritional choice? Why or why not?

INGREDIENTS: Cornmeal, rice flour, oat flour, wheat flour, sugar, salt, corn syrup, malt flavoring, baking soda. **VITAMINS AND MINERALS:** Vitamin C, zinc, iron, Vitamin B_6, Vitamin B_2, Vitamin A, Vitamin B_1, Vitamin B_{12}, Vitamin D.

81

Quick Activity

The four main ingredients are cornmeal, rice flour, oat flour, and wheat flour. They are from the largest group of the USDA Food Guide Pyramid. The grains are not whole grains but flours, which provide less fiber than whole-grain cereals. The next three ingredients are sugars and salt, which are not healthful ingredients. Overall, the cereal is a nutritional choice, but probably not the most healthful.

Health Background

B Vitamins B vitamins are water soluble, so a daily source of them is needed because they are not stored in the body. The B-complex vitamins include eight vitamins: thiamine (B_1), riboflavin (B_2), niacin (B_3), pyridoxine (B_6), folic acid (B_9), cyanocobalamin (B_{12}), pantothenic acid, and biotin. These vitamins are essential for the breakdown of carbohydrates into glucose and the breakdown of fats and proteins. Muscle tone in the stomach and intestinal tract, and the health of hair, eyes, mouth, and liver, depend on the complex of B vitamins.

Source: *Encyclopaedia Britannica website*

For more background, visit the **Webliography** in Teacher Resources at **www.harcourtschool.com/health** **Keyword** nutrition

Art

Junk Art Invite students to invent a junk food and design a magazine advertisement to sell it. Encourage them to use some of the techniques they have seen in actual ads for junk foods.

Then have students design ads for a healthful snack using similar techniques.

TEACH *continued*

Discuss

After students have read this page, inform them that the sugars listed on *ingredients* labels—such as those listed at the end of the text section—are sugars that have been *added* to a product. Peanuts naturally have some sugar in them. Carbohydrates and sugars listed on *nutrition* labels include *both* natural and added sugars.

Remind students that the nutrition information is based on serving size. Ask them to keep this in mind when, for example, they determine how much fat, sugar, and oil they are getting in a serving.

Critical Thinking Why are junk foods tempting food choices? Possible answer: Junk foods are tempting because of their taste, which is due to their high fat and sugar contents.

Students should strive to choose foods whose calories from fat are less than half the total calories. A simpler way to determine a healthful snack is by choosing foods with less than 5 grams total fat per serving. They should also choose foods whose grams of sugar are less than half the total grams of carbohydrates per serving. In general, they should limit foods high in sugar, such as sugar-coated cereals, donuts, and candies, and foods high in oils, such as chips and fried foods.

Activity

Communicate Remind students to review the steps for good communicating. Since a parent would be interested in a child eating healthfully, responses should reflect the student's knowledge of good nutrition. Point out that while it is desirable for students to take responsibility for their food choices, it's also important that they confer with parents about health decisions.

ACTIVITY

Life Skills

Communicate

Suppose you are shopping for breakfast cereal. You make a choice after reading the food labels on the boxes. You believe you have made a wise choice. Tell how you can show your mother that it is a good choice.

Comparing Product Labels

Product labels give you information about a food. Reading a product label can help you decide if a food is healthful.

Suppose you want to buy peanuts. You find jars labeled "PEANUTS" and "HONEY ROASTED PEANUTS." You want to know which nuts to choose, so you look at the ingredients list on each jar. What differences do you think you'll see?

When you buy a food such as peanuts, you might expect the jar to contain only peanuts. As you read the label on the "PEANUTS" jar, you learn the food has no oil, no salt, and no sugar. It has just one ingredient—peanuts.

When you look at the "HONEY ROASTED PEANUTS" label, you find that peanuts are the first ingredient. But sugar is the second; then there's salt!

When you look closely, you see that most of the other ingredients are sugars. Honey, corn syrup, and fructose are all forms of sugar.

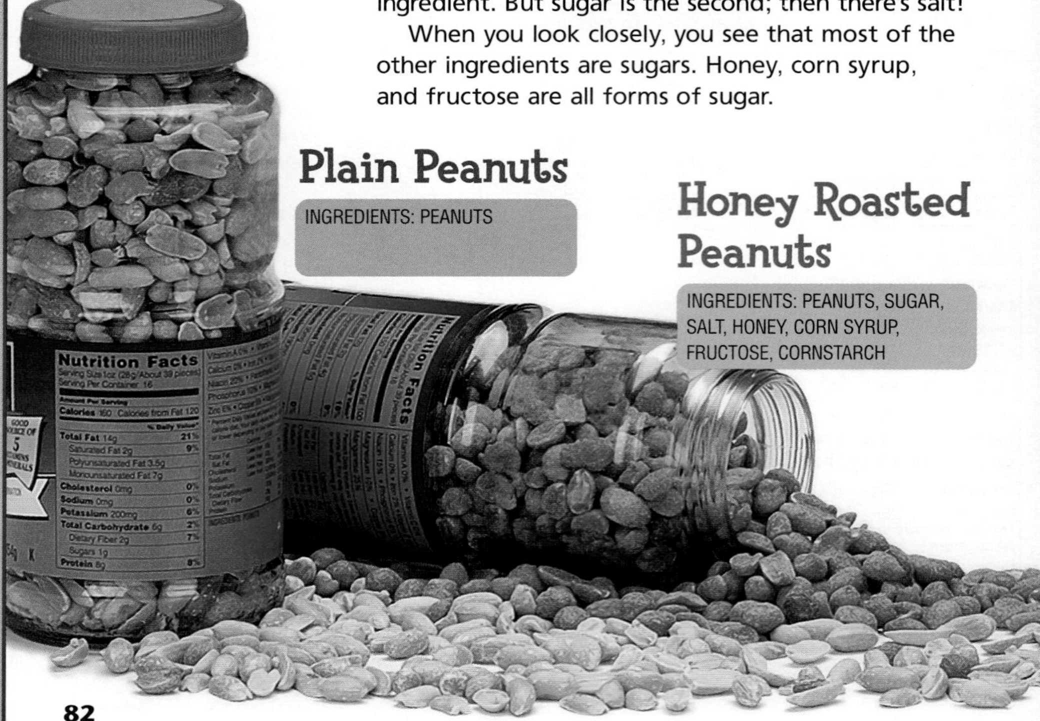

82

ESL/ELL Support

COMPREHENSIBLE INPUT Help students understand the concept of junk food. Explain that junk foods are foods that are usually sweet—sweeter than fruit—and greasy enough to leave a stain when laid on a napkin.

Beginning Give students a variety of preselected magazines. Have them cut out photos of foods that they think are junk foods. Have them glue their photos on a poster and label the individual foods.

Intermediate Have students work in small groups. Give each group a junk food label. Have the group compose a sentence explaining how the nutrition and ingredient labels on its product show that it is a junk food.

Advanced Follow the instructions for beginning students, and then talk to the students about how the presentation of these foods often makes them look more appealing. After the discussion, ask students to write a paragraph about how they feel advertising affects what people eat.

You might not know some of the words on an ingredients list. Some ingredients are used to keep the food from spoiling. Other ingredients may be food coloring. Coloring is usually added to make the food look better.

The Dietary Guidelines for Americans suggest choosing foods low in sugars, fats, and salt. You put back the honey roasted peanuts and take the plain peanuts. You munch happily, knowing you are eating a healthful snack, not a snack full of sugar!

SUMMARIZE What information does an ingredients list on a label tell you?

How much of what ingredients are found in the food and what ingredients have been added, such as sugar, salt and coloring

Health & Technology

Peanut Butter Alternative
Many people are allergic to peanuts and food products that contain peanuts. A sunflower seed producer and the USDA's Agricultural Research Service have developed a product called SunButter™, which is a spread similar to peanut butter. This spread is made from sunflower seeds. SunButter™ has vitamins, fat, and protein content like that of peanut butter. Since fewer people are allergic to sunflower seeds, SunButter™ makes a good alternative to peanut butter.

Lesson 4 Summary and Review

1. **Summarize with Vocabulary**
   Use vocabulary and other terms from this lesson to complete these statements.
   Using the Dietary _____ for_____ and product _____ can help you choose a healthful diet. Reading the _____ list on a product label can help you determine how _____ the food is.
2. List three things a food label can tell you.
3. **Critical Thinking** Which part of Dietary Guidelines for Americans is most important to you? Make sure to explain your choice.
4. **COMPARE AND CONTRAST** Draw and complete this graphic organizer to show how the two parts of a product label are alike and different.

Topic: Product Labels	
Alike	Different

5. **Write to Inform—Explanation**
   Write to someone to explain how following the Dietary Guidelines for Americans can benefit a person's health.

83

Math

Snack Sense Provide groups of students with the nutrition label from a snack food. Have groups answer the following per serving. Are the calories from fat less than half the total calories? Are the grams of sugar less than half the grams of total carbohydrates? For a snack to be healthful, the fat calories should be less than half the total calories, and the grams of sugar less than half the grams of total carbohydrates. Have students decide if the snack is a healthful choice.

3. WRAP UP

Lesson 4 Summary and Review

1. Guidelines, Americans, labels; ingredients, nutritious
2. A food label can tell you how much protein, fat, carbohydrates, vitamins, and minerals the food contains; the serving size; and the ingredients.
3. Answers will vary depending on student motivation. Students' responses should include a balance of choices from all three aspects of the Dietary Guidelines listed on pages 78 and 79.
4. Graphics may include:

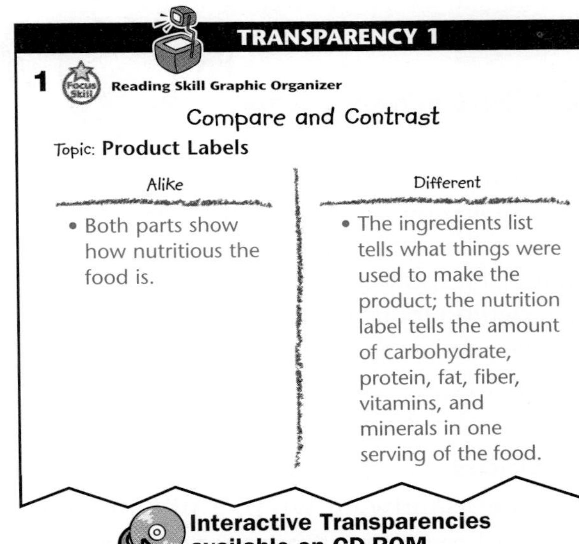

TRANSPARENCY 1

1 Reading Skill Graphic Organizer

Compare and Contrast

Topic: **Product Labels**

Alike	Different
• Both parts show how nutritious the food is.	• The ingredients list tells what things were used to make the product; the nutrition label tells the amount of carbohydrate, protein, fat, fiber, vitamins, and minerals in one serving of the food.

Interactive Transparencies available on CD-ROM.

5. Letters should follow a friendly letter format. They might include some of the specifics of the guidelines. Letters should tell how each guideline could be used to benefit someone's health. Answers should reflect how physical activity, eating well, and making good choices all benefit health.

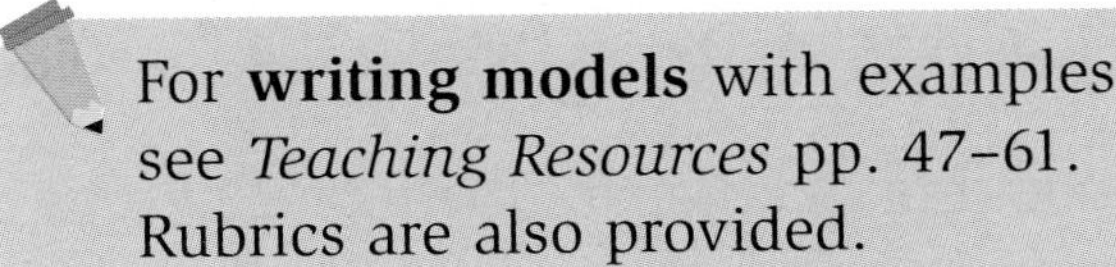

For **writing models** with examples, see *Teaching Resources* pp. 47–61. Rubrics are also provided.

When Minutes Count ...

Quick Study Students can use *Activity Book* pages 11–12 (shown on p. 61) as they complete each lesson in this chapter.

LESSON 5

Pages 84–86

Objectives

- ► Describe how food poisoning occurs.
- ► Explain how to handle food safely to prevent food poisoning.

When Minutes Count . . .

Assign the Quick Study, Lesson 5, Activity Book pp. 11–12 (shown on p. 61).

Program Resources

- ► Activity Book pp. 11–12, 15
- ► Transparency 1, 23

Vocabulary

food poisoning p. 84

Daily Fitness Tip

As students are being given increased responsibility for food preparation, they should be aware that safe food handling is an additional responsibility that can help them avoid getting food poisoning.

1. MOTIVATE

Materials knife, spoon, paper lunchbag, sandwich wrap, 2 unwrapped slices of bread, small amount of peanut butter, empty yogurt container

Invite volunteers to model for the class unsafe preparation of a lunch of yogurt and sandwich. Have the rest of the class identify unsafe practices. Alternatively, you might model such behavior and have the entire class identify your errors. Mistakes might include not washing the counter or your hands, using unclean utensils, sneezing on the food, not using cold packs for yogurt, and so on. Then model how to prepare the lunch safely.

When Minutes Count . . .

Transparency 23: Fight BAC can be used to present material in this lesson. *Interactive Transparencies available on CD-ROM.*

LESSON 5

Keeping Foods Safe

Lesson Focus
You must handle food carefully in order to avoid illness.

Why Learn This?
You can use what you learn to help you handle and prepare foods safely.

Vocabulary
food poisoning

Preparing Foods Safely

You may have seen moldy bread or rotten fruit. But foods don't have to look or smell spoiled to be dangerous. Germs can come from many places. Some fresh foods, including eggs, raw meat, and raw poultry, carry germs. Even when you are healthy, your body carries germs that can get onto food.

Food poisoning is an illness caused by eating food that contains germs. Some kinds of food poisoning are mild and do not last long. Other kinds can be very serious and can even cause death. To avoid food poisoning, you need to handle food safely.

SUMMARIZE **Explain what food poisoning is.**

illness caused by eating food that contains germs

84

Meeting Individual Needs
Leveled Activities

BELOW-LEVEL **Make Your Points** Have students make a list of four or more points about the safe preparation of school lunches at home, based on the Motivate activity.

ON-LEVEL **In Summary** Have students write a paragraph summarizing the observations they made during the Motivate activity. Then have them summarize safe food-preparation techniques for making school lunches at home.

CHALLENGE **Details** Ask students to research one of the primary causes of food poisoning in America—such as *Salmonella, E. coli* bacteria, and Norwalk-like viruses. Students should research one cause, its usual food source, and the ways to prevent getting ill from food contaminated by it.

How to Tell if Food Has Spoiled

Sometimes it's easy to tell that a food has spoiled. Breads, fruits, and vegetables may be covered with white or gray fuzzy mold. Spoiled meat or sour milk may smell strange. Sometimes spoiled food doesn't smell or look spoiled. It's always best to play it safe. If you think there's a problem, throw out the food.

You can help prevent food spoilage. When you return from shopping, put fresh foods in the refrigerator right away. After you eat, wrap leftovers and store them in the refrigerator.

Handling Food Safely

- ☐ Wash your hands with soap and warm water before and after handling food.
- ☐ Use a cutting board when cutting raw chicken or meat.
- ☐ Wash all work surfaces and utensils with hot water and soap.
- ☐ Don't eat foods that are made with raw eggs.
- ☐ Cook eggs until the yolks are hard.
- ☐ Cook meat and chicken until no red or pink shows.
- ☐ Wash all fresh fruits and vegetables.
- ☐ Don't handle food when you are ill.
- ☐ Thaw food in the refrigerator or microwave, not at room temperature.
- ☐ Keep pets away from food.

Quick Activity

Identify What's Wrong Study the picture of the boy and his mother in the kitchen. What unhealthful practices can you find? Discuss what they should do instead.

85

Teacher Tip

When to Call the Doctor
Many people with food poisoning don't seek medical attention. A health-care provider should be consulted for a diarrheal illness if it is accompanied by a high fever (over 101.5° F), blood in the stool, prolonged inability to keep liquids down, diarrhea that lasts more than 3 days, and signs of dehydration, including decrease in urination, dry mouth and throat, and dizziness when standing up.

Art

Safe Food Art Provide art materials. Invite each student to design an attractive small poster, showing the safe practices to use when handling food. Posters may include the preferred behaviors that students discussed when they observed the Motivate skit about making school lunches, or the general food-handling safety rules from this page. Students can then hang their posters on their refrigerator or some other central food-preparation area at home.

2. TEACH

Content-Area Reading Support

Using Text Format Direct attention to the Handling Food Safely checklist on this page. Point out that the information is presented in a checklist for easy comprehension. Encourage students to pay attention to such lists because they are usually easy-to-read summaries of important points of information.

Discuss

High sugar, salt, or acid levels prevent bacterial growth. This is why preserved foods such as jam, salted meats, and pickled vegetables don't spoil as quickly.

Tell students that knowledge of germs and the importance of cleanliness has helped improve food safety greatly. Modern technology has also helped.

Critical Thinking What technologies have made our store-bought foods safer in the last 200 years? canning, pasteurization, water purification

Inform students that certain types of food poisonings that occurred 200 years ago rarely occur now. Have them recall historical pictures or movies they've seen in which people bought food in markets with meats hung up in open-air stalls, and bought milk from a farmer down the road. Ask for comments on how they feel about it.

Interpret Visuals—Illustrations

Direct attention again to the Handling Food Safely checklist on this page. Ask students which of its items relates to an activity or situation in the kitchen scene on these pages.

Quick Activity

If necessary, encourage students to use the Handling Food Safely checklist to detect unhealthful practices in the picture and to choose alternative behaviors. Note that prepared meats and perishable foods left out over two hours should not be eaten. For more safety tips, see pages 350–3531 of the Health and Safety Handbook.

3. WRAP UP

Lesson 5 Summary and Review

1. food poisoning; washing, warm
2. Answers should include three of the following: washing hands, using a cutting board, washing work surfaces, cooking foods thoroughly, washing fruits and vegetables, not handling food when ill, thawing food properly, keeping pets away from food.
3. It is always better to be safe than to take the risk of food poisoning.
4. Graphics may include:

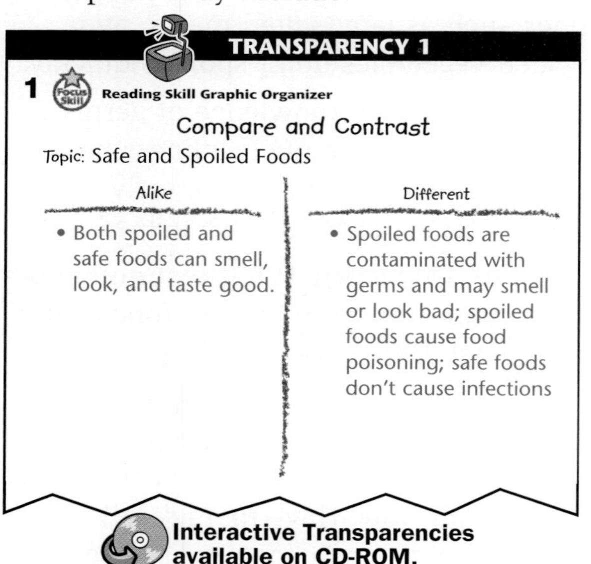

TRANSPARENCY 1
1 Reading Skill Graphic Organizer
Compare and Contrast
Topic: Safe and Spoiled Foods
Alike
Different
• Both spoiled and safe foods can smell, look, and taste good.
• Spoiled foods are contaminated with germs and may smell or look bad; spoiled foods cause food poisoning; safe foods don't cause infections

Interactive Transparencies available on CD-ROM.

5. Stories should tell what unsafe food-handling practices family members use, and what they need to do instead to handle food safely.

For **writing models** with examples, see *Teaching Resources* pp. 47–61. Rubrics are also provided.

When Minutes Count . . .

Quick Study Students can use *Activity Book* pages 11–12 (shown on p. 61) as they complete each lesson in this chapter.

Did You Know?
Many food containers must display expiration dates. These dates tell how long the product may be free from spoilage. Other food products provide instructions for safe storage after they have been opened.

Freeze bread and meat to keep them longer. Do not buy dented cans or cracked eggs. The dents or cracks may let germs get into the food. If the dents or the cracks happen at home later, throw the food away. The table below can help you store food safely.

Food Shelf Life

Food	Storage Life	Helpful Tips
Cereal	unopened 6–12 months; opened 2–3 months	Keep package free from air by tightly wrapping the liner.
Toaster Pastries	2–3 months	Keep in airtight container.
Ketchup	unopened 12 months; opened 1 month	Keep in refrigerator after opening.
Peanut Butter	unopened 6–9 months; opened 2 months	Will keep longer if refrigerated.
Lunch Meat	unopened 2 weeks; opened 3–5 days	Keep in refrigerator.

The dent may have let germs into the food, so people who eat the food might get sick.

CAUSE AND EFFECT What might be an effect of eating food from a dented can?

Lesson 5 Summary and Review

1. **Summarize with Vocabulary**
   Use vocabulary and other terms from this lesson to complete the statements.
   Preparing foods safely can help prevent an illness called _____. An important step in safe food preparation is _____ your hands with soap and _____ water.
2. Name three ways you can help keep the foods you prepare safe.
3. **Critical Thinking** Why is it a good idea to throw away any food that you might think is spoiled?
4. **COMPARE AND CONTRAST** Show how safe and spoiled foods are alike and different.

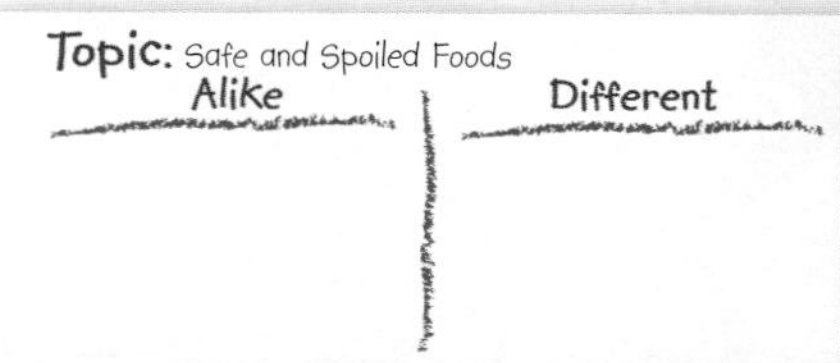

5. **Write to Inform—Narration**

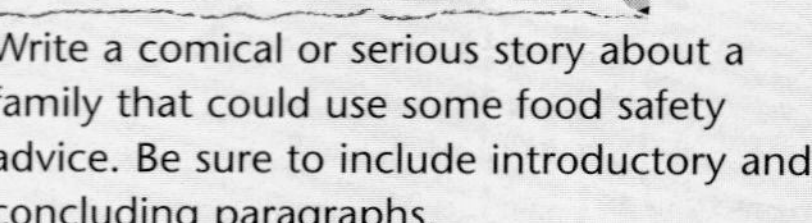

Write a comical or serious story about a family that could use some food safety advice. Be sure to include introductory and concluding paragraphs.

86

Teacher Tip

Cool It Generally, only food containing a large amount of bacteria can cause disease. If the conditions are right, if there are enough nutrients and warm, moist conditions, then one bacterium can reproduce to become 17 million within 12 hours. When food is refrigerated promptly, the bacteria (with a few exceptions) won't multiply. Use these facts to emphasize the importance of refrigerating certain foods.

ACTIVITY BOOK P. 15

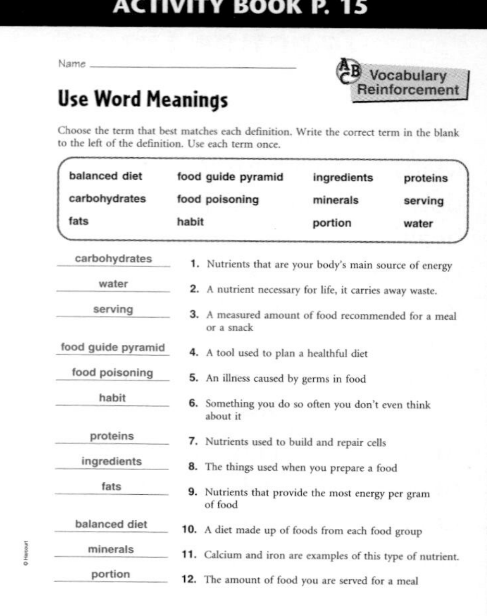

Name ______

Vocabulary Reinforcement

Use Word Meanings

Choose the term that best matches each definition. Write the correct term in the blank to the left of the definition. Use each term once.

balanced diet	food guide pyramid	ingredients	proteins
carbohydrates	food poisoning	minerals	serving
fats	habit	portion	water

carbohydrates 1. Nutrients that are your body's main source of energy
water 2. A nutrient necessary for life, it carries away waste.
serving 3. A measured amount of food recommended for a meal or a snack
food guide pyramid 4. A tool used to plan a healthful diet
food poisoning 5. An illness caused by germs in food
habit 6. Something you do so often you don't even think about it
proteins 7. Nutrients used to build and repair cells
ingredients 8. The things used when you prepare a food
fats 9. Nutrients that provide the most energy per gram of food
balanced diet 10. A diet made up of foods from each food group
minerals 11. Calcium and iron are examples of this type of nutrient.
portion 12. The amount of food you are served for a meal

Available online. www.harcourtschool.com/health

ACTIVITIES

Math

Calculate Servings With a partner, plan a menu for a family of four for one day. Calculate how much of each food you'll need so that everyone will get enough servings from each food group.

Home & Community

Communicating Make a poster encouraging people to use the USDA Food Guide Pyramid as a guideline. Display your poster in your classroom or cafeteria.

Science

Observe Bacterial Growth Put about half a cup of milk in each of two clear containers that can be sealed tight. Put one container in the refrigerator and the other in a warm, dark place. After one day, look at the containers of milk side by side. Describe the appearance of the milk in each container. Check both containers and write about your observations every day for a week.

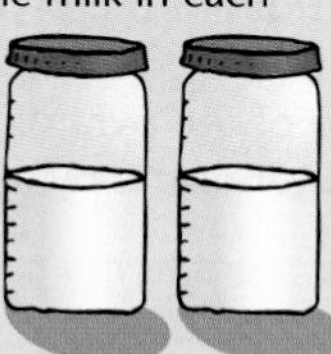

Your teacher will tell you how to dispose of the milk. ▲

Career Link

Restaurant Manager Suppose that you are the manager of a restaurant. Write a note to your employees in which you explain the importance of cleanliness. Make sure that you tell the employees why they need to wash their hands often and keep the kitchen and dining room areas clean.

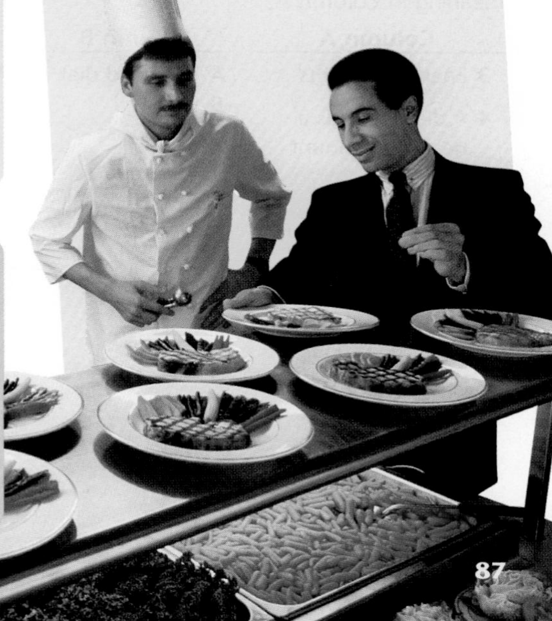

Technology Project

Use a computer to make a slide presentation of at least four tips for eating healthful meals. Present your slide show to your family or classmates.

For more activities, visit The Learning Site. www.harcourtschool.com/health

87

Career Link

Restaurant Manager Some students may not be aware of all the responsibilities a restaurant manager has. Not only must the manager oversee the healthful handling of food and operations at a restaurant, but he or she also must have critical thinking and problem solving skills. The manager must be able to work well with people. He or she may also be responsible for posting work schedules, doing inventory, overseeing maintenance, and handling public relations and customer service.

For more information on health careers, visit the **Webliography** in Teacher Resources at **www.harcourtschool.com/health**
Keyword health careers

Activities

Math

Remind students to include snacks as well as breakfast, lunch, and dinner in their menus. Have pairs share their menu plans and totals with the class.

Science

Students should observe that the milk in the container stored in the refrigerator should look the same as it did at the start of the investigation. Over the course of several days, the milk kept in a warm, dark place should show signs of spoilage. The milk may curdle or thicken. It may change color and thicken into clots. All these changes are due to the growth of bacteria. While no individual bacterium can be observed, the work of the bacteria as they multiply is observable as changes in the milk.

Pour the milk into a sink or other appropriate receptacle. Wash the containers with hot, soapy water. The spoiled milk may smell sour, but it should not otherwise be harmful. However, it is wise to avoid close contact with it.

Home & Community

Be sure to obtain necessary permission to display the posters in locations outside your classroom. When the study of this topic is complete, have students take their posters home to use as a reference for meal planning.

Supports the Coordinated School Health Program

Technology Project

Students can use Powerpoint™ or another presentation software for this project. For students without access to a computer, you might suggest that slides be made with construction paper.

Chapter Review and Test Preparation

Pages 88–89

Reading Skill 5 pts. each

1. Possible answer: Alike: Both contain six groups; using both food groups and nutrients as guidelines helps make a healthy diet. Different: Each is needed in different amounts.
2. Possible answer: Alike: Both nutrients found in foods; they have similar jobs in the body. Different: Vitamins are made by living things, minerals are not; minerals come from the soil by way of plants.

Use Vocabulary 5 pts. each

3. E, proteins
4. A, balanced diet
5. D, nutritious
6. C, ingredients
7. B, food poisoning

Check Understanding 5 pts. each

8. C, product label
9. G, 1 slice of bread
10. C, top of the pyramid
11. G, yogurt
12. A, carbohydrates
13. H, Use recommended serving sizes.
14. C, germs
15. G, how to be physically active

Think Critically 5 pts. each

16. Possible answer: Store chicken in the refrigerator. Use a wood or a plastic cutting board to cut it. Wash the cutting board with soap and hot water before using it for other foods. Wash your hands before and after handling the raw meat.

Chapter Review and Test Preparation

Reading Skill

COMPARE AND CONTRAST

Draw and then use this graphic organizer to answer questions 1 and 2.

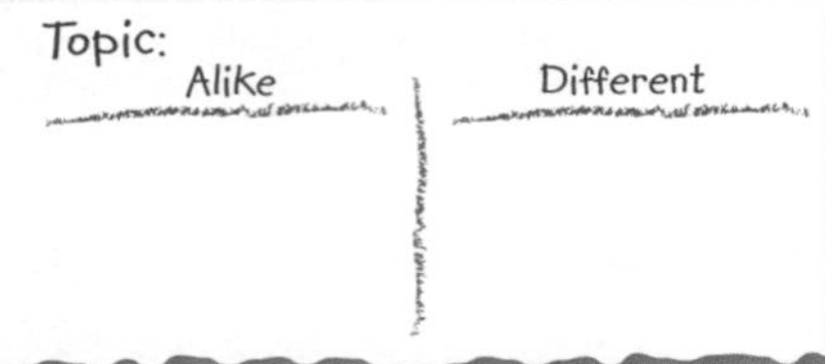

1 Write at least two ways nutrients and food groups are alike and different.

2 Write at least two ways vitamins and minerals are alike and different.

Use Vocabulary

Match each term in Column B with its meaning in Column A.

Column A	Column B
3 Energy nutrients	**A** balanced diet
4 A diet that has a healthful amount of foods from each group	**B** food poisoning
5 Food that has nutritional value	**C** ingredients
6 Things used to make a food product	**D** nutritious
7 An illness caused by eating food that has germs	**E** proteins

Check Understanding

Choose the letter of the correct answer.

8 If you want to know how much vitamin C is in a food, where would you look to find out? (p. 80)
A food guide pyramid
B Dietary Guidelines for Americans
C product label
D Food Shelf Life table

9 Which of these foods is considered one serving? (pp. 68–69)
F 1 cup of nuts **H** 2 eggs
G 1 slice of bread **J** 10 crackers

10 On a food guide pyramid, the foods you should eat the smallest amount of are located at the _____ (p. 69)
A bottom of the pyramid
B middle of the pyramid
C top of the pyramid
D center of the pyramid

11 If you were trying to add calcium to your diet, which of these foods would be the BEST to choose? (p. 63)

F

H

G

J

88

Formal Assessment

ASSESSMENT GUIDE P. 25

3 Name ____________ Chapter Test

Food and Your Health

Write the letter of the correct answer on the line at the left.

__A__ 1. Which of these is your body's main source of energy?
A carbohydrates **C** proteins
B vitamins **D** minerals

__J__ 2. From which food group should you have the largest number of servings each day?
F Meat, Poultry, Fish, Dried Beans, Eggs, and Nuts
G Fruits
H Vegetables
J Bread, Cereal, Rice, and Pasta

__C__ 3. _____ are the nutrients your body uses for growth.
A Carbohydrates **C** Proteins
B Fats **D** Vitamins

__J__ 4. Which part of a food label tells what is used to make the food product?
F serving size **H** total fat
G calories **J** ingredients

__B__ 5. The amount of food that comes on your plate at a restaurant is a _____.
A balanced diet **C** serving
B portion **D** nutrient

Write *T* or *F* to tell if the statements are true or false.

__T__ 6. Water is a nutrient that is necessary for life.

__T__ 7. Nutrients are substances in food that provide energy and other things the body needs.

__F__ 8. Proteins are the nutrients that are the body's main source of energy.

__T__ 9. Safe food handling can help you avoid food poisoning.

__F__ 10. The amount of food you are served is always one serving.

© Harcourt

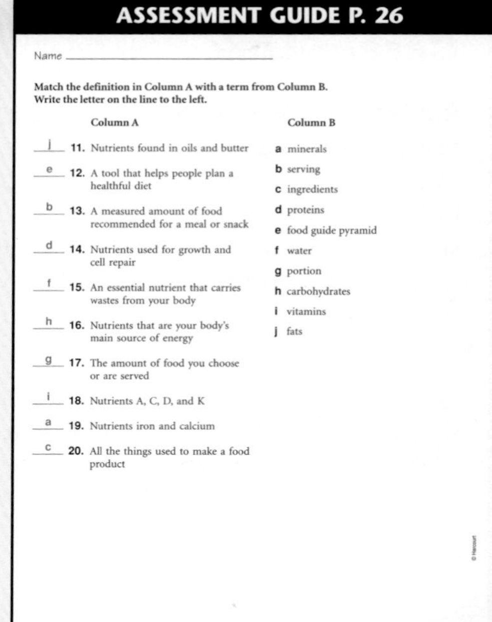

ASSESSMENT GUIDE P. 26

Name ____________

Match the definition in Column A with a term from Column B. Write the letter on the line to the left.

	Column A	Column B
__j__	11. Nutrients found in oils and butter	**a** minerals
__e__	12. A tool that helps people plan a healthful diet	**b** serving
__b__	13. A measured amount of food recommended for a meal or snack	**c** ingredients
__d__	14. Nutrients used for growth and cell repair	**d** proteins
__f__	15. An essential nutrient that carries wastes from your body	**e** food guide pyramid
__h__	16. Nutrients that are your body's main source of energy	**f** water
__g__	17. The amount of food you choose or are served	**g** portion
__i__	18. Nutrients A, C, D, and K	**h** carbohydrates
__a__	19. Nutrients iron and calcium	**i** vitamins
__c__	20. All the things used to make a food product	**j** fats

© Harcourt

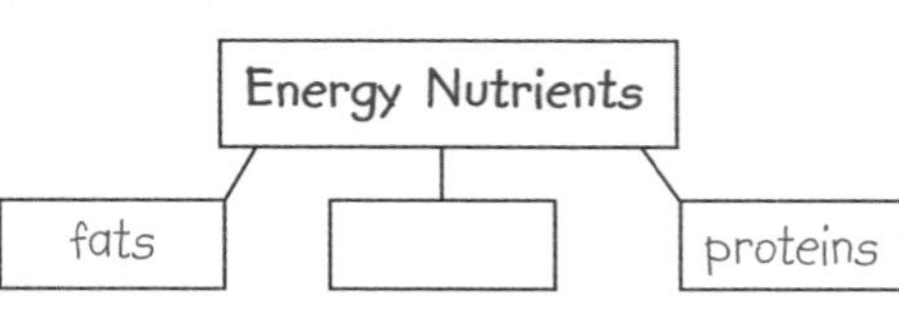

12 What nutrient is missing from the graphic organizer? (p. 60)
A carbohydrates **C** vitamins
B minerals **D** water

13 Which of these is a way to control portions? (p. 70)
F Eat everything on your plate.
G Eat three meals a day.
H Use recommended serving sizes.
J Wash your hands before eating.

14 Dents in cans or cracks in eggs are a way _____ can get into food. (p. 86)
A vitamins **C** germs
B minerals **D** proteins

15 The Dietary Guidelines for Americans suggest ways on how to eat well, make sensible choices, and _____. (p. 78)
F find the right amount of nutrients in a food
G be physically active
H read a product label
J figure out an expiration date

Think Critically

16 You buy raw chicken for tomorrow night's dinner. How would you safely store and handle the chicken before you cook it?

17 Study the ingredients list of the snack food label shown here. What does this information tell you about the healthfulness of the snack?

INGREDIENTS: flour, oats, molasses, corn syrup, vegetable oil, and salt

Apply Skills

18 **BUILDING GOOD CHARACTER**
Respect You have been invited to a friend's house for dinner. When the food is served, you notice a food that you don't like. Apply what you know about using good table manners to make a decision about what you should do.

19 **LIFE SKILLS**
Make Decisions You live in a cold area, and your family doesn't buy much fresh fruit. Make a healthful decision on how you might get the servings of food you need from the fruit group.

Write About Health

20 **Write to Inform—Explanation**
Explain why eating healthful foods now can help you when you are an adult.

89

ASSESSMENT GUIDE P. 27

Name ______________________

The USDA Food Guide Pyramid is a tool you can use to plan a healthful diet. There are six food groups in the Food Guide Pyramid. Complete the pyramid below by writing on the lines the name of each food group and the number of recommended daily servings for someone your age.

Fats, Oils, and Sweets Group: use sparingly; not every day

21. Milk, Yogurt, and Cheese Group: 3 servings per day

22. Vegetable Group: 3–5 servings per day

23. Meat, Poultry, Fish, Dried Beans, Eggs, and Nuts Group: 2–3 servings per day

25. Breads, Cereals, Rice, and Pasta Group: 6–9 servings per day

24. Fruit Group: 2–4 servings per day

© Harcourt

17. Possible answer: This food is not healthful because it contains ingredients in amounts that aren't nutritious. The food also contains sugar in two different forms. Too many ingredients are found at the top of the USDA Food Guide Pyramid.

Apply Skills 5 pts. each

18. Possible answer: If it's served on your plate, don't complain; just leave it on your plate and eat something else. If the food item is passed to you, pass it around the table without making a face. If someone asks you if you would like to have some of the food item, simply say, "No, thank you."

19. Possible answer: You could drink fruit juices such as apple or orange juice; you could eat dried, frozen, or canned fruit. You could eat foods with fruit in them, such as cereal with raisins or breakfast bars with strawberries.

Write About Health 5 pts.

20. Accept all reasonable answers. Eating healthful foods now helps the body grow and develop properly. This will help a person have a strong, healthy body as an adult. Choosing and eating healthful foods regularly also helps a person form healthful eating habits. These habits can carry on throughout life, providing the body with the nutrients it needs to grow, repair itself, and function properly.

Performance Assessment

Use the Chapter Project and the rubric provided on the Project Evaluation Sheet. See *Assessment Guide* pp. 18, 57, 64.

Portfolio Assessment

Have students select their best work from the following suggestions:
- Leveled Activities, p. 80
- Quick Activity, p. 61
- Write to Inform, p. 71
- Activities, p. 87

See *Assessment Guide* pp. 12–16.

CHAPTER 4

Fitness and Activity

Lesson	Pacing	Objectives	Reading Skills
Introduce the Chapter pp. 90–91		• Preview chapter concepts.	**Cause and Effect** pp. 91, 334–335
1 **Good Posture** pp. 92–96	3 class periods	• Describe how good posture can improve wellness and self-image. • Demonstrate good posture while sitting, standing, and moving.	**Cause and Effect** pp. 93, 96 • Summarize, p. 94 • Main Idea and Details, p. 96
Building Good Character p. 97		• Recognize the importance of fairness by being a good listener.	
2 **Physical Fitness** pp. 98–103	3 class periods	• Explain the benefits of regular physical activity. • Describe the differences between aerobic and anaerobic exercise. • Describe the importance of sleep and rest to overall fitness. • Describe proper balance of sleep, rest, and activity.	**Cause and Effect** pp. 99, 103 • Compare and Contrast, p. 101 • Draw Conclusions, p. 103
Life Skills p. 104–105	1 class period	• Identify goal-setting steps. • Practice goal setting for fitness.	
3 **Your Personal Fitness Plan** pp. 106–110	3 class periods	• Describe how to use the Activity Pyramid to improve physical fitness. • Describe the importance of developing a personal health plan for fitness. • Identify safety gear necessary for injury prevention.	**Cause and Effect** p. 110 • Sequence, p. 107 • Draw Conclusions, p. 108
Activities p. 111		• Extend chapter concepts.	
Chapter Review pp. 112–113	1 class period	• Assess chapter objectives.	

Vocabulary	Program Resources
	 Music CD Teaching Resources, p. 29
posture	Transparency 3 Activity Book, pp. 16–18
	Poster 3
aerobic exercise **anaerobic exercise** **rest**	Transparency 3 Activity Book, pp. 16–17
	Activity Book, p. 19 Poster 12
Activity Pyramid	Transparencies 3, 24 Activity Book, pp. 16–17, 20
	The Learning Site www.harcourtschool.com
	Assessment Guide, pp. 28–30

Interactive Transparencies available on CD-ROM.

Focus Skill Reading Skill

These reading skills are reinforced throughout this chapter and one skill is emphasized as the Focus Skill.

- **Identify Cause and Effect**
- Draw Conclusions
- Compare and Contrast
- Identify Main Idea and Details
- Sequence
- Summarize

KEY READING SKILLS TRANSPARENCY 3

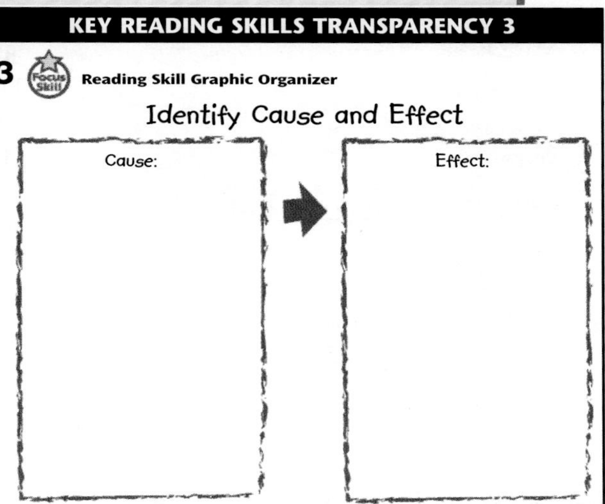

Life Skills

Life Skills are health-enhancing behaviors that can help students reduce risks to their health and safety.

Six Life Skills are reinforced throughout *Harcourt Health and Fitness*. The skill emphasized in this chapter is Set Goals.

POSTER 12 SET GOALS

Set Goals
The girl is setting a goal to recycle.
Steps for Setting Goals
1 Choose a goal.
2 Plan steps to reach that goal. Determine whether you will need help.
3 Check your progress as you work toward the goal.
4 Evaluate the results of your work.
What GOALS have YOU SET?

Building Good Character

Character education is an important aspect of health education. When children behave in ways that show good character, they promote the health and safety of themselves and others.

Six character traits are reinforced throughout *Harcourt Health and Fitness*. The trait emphasized in this chapter is Fairness.

POSTER 3 FAIRNESS

Resources

Coordinated School Health Program

Health Education
Health Services
Physical Education
Nutrition Services
Parent/ Community Involvement
Healthy School Environment
Counseling, Psychological, & Social Services
Health Promotion for Staff
CSHP

A Coordinated School Health Program endeavors to improve children's health and therefore their capacity to learn through the support of families, schools, and communities working together. The following information is provided to help classroom teachers be more aware of these resources.

The National Center for Chronic Disease and Health Promotion, part of the **CDC**, funds the Coordinated School Health Program. Visit its website for information about the eight components that make up this program.
www.cdc.gov/nccdphp/dash/

The **CDC**'s website, BAM! (Body and Mind), contains health topics for kids. Fit 4 Life instructs students on an exercise regime to get fit and stay fit.
www.bam.gov/

The "Walk Texas!" program from the **Texas Department of Health** encourages a united effort to help meet timely societal needs consistent with the Healthy People 2000 Goals and the Surgeon General's Report on Physical Activity.
www.tdh.state.tx.us/diabetes/walktx/index.html

The National Association for Sport and Physical Education (**NASPE**) commends the **California Department of Education** for its study that shows a distinct relationship between academic achievement and physical fitness of California's public school students.
www.aahperd.org/naspe/

Other resources that support a Coordinated School Health Program:

- School-Home Connection
- Daily Physical Activity
- Daily Fitness Tips
- Activities: Home & Community
- Health Background: Webliography
- *Be Active! Resources for Physical Education*

Media Resources

Books for Students

Roberts, Robin. ***Which Sport Is Right For You?*** Millbrook Press, 2001. Has useful information for beginners. **EASY**

McGinty, Alice B. ***Staying Healthy: Let's Exercise***. Rosen Publishing, 1997. Explains the benefits of exercise, and how to exercise safely. **AVERAGE**

Sadgrove, Judy. ***Exercise***. Raintree/Steck-Vaughn, 2000. Describes the benefits of exercise and how to choose an activity. **ADVANCED**

Books for Teachers and Families

Clayton, Lawrence. ***Everything You Need to Know About Sports Injuries***. Rosen Publishing, 1995. Describes basic medical concepts to prevent and treat sports injuries.

Schor, Edward L., Ed; American Academy of Pediatrics. ***Caring for Your School-Age Child: Ages 5–12***. Bantam, 1995. Offers guidance on many topics, including fitness.

Free and Inexpensive Materials

Magazine City
Offers a free trial subscription to *Bicycling* magazine.

The President's Council on Physical Fitness and Sports
Go on-line for easy exercises that will encourage kids to get up and get out.

United Health Foundation
Request their free book, *Be Happy, Be Healthy,* with simple health tips.

Fitness and Freebies
Will send a free health newsletter on fitness and resources.

To access free and inexpensive resources on the Web, visit
www.harcourtschool.com/health/free

Videos

Little Kicks: Dynamic Cardio-Fitness Workout. Bright Minds, 2001.

Exercise. Films for the Humanities and Sciences, 1994.

Fitness in a Box: Fit Kids Aerobic Workout. Vaac Digital, 1996.

These resources have been selected to meet a variety of individual needs. Please review all materials and websites prior to sharing them with students to ensure the content is appropriate for your class. Note that information, while correct at time of publication, is subject to change.

Visit **The Learning Site** for related links, activities, resources, and the health **Webliography.**

www.harcourtschool.com/health

Meeting Individual Needs

Below-Level

Read a vocabulary word or chapter concept aloud. Have one student give the meaning of the word or concept. If the meaning is correct, the player draws one part of a Word Bug's body on the board. Continue play until the Word Bug has six legs, a body, a head, and two antennas.

Activities

- Proper Lifting, p. 94
- Aerobic Pantomine, p. 100
- Bike Helmets, p. 109

On-Level

When students use strategies, they are thinking as a good reader thinks. Have students make predictions about the information that will be given in the selection. Then have them read to find out if they are right.

Activities

- Posture Interview, p. 94
- Aerobics in Sports, p. 100
- Safety Ads, p. 109

Challenge

Using chapter content as a springboard, work with students to brainstorm topics and people they would like to know more about. Organize their responses in a web. Students may use reference books and the Internet to begin inquiry projects related to the completed web.

Activities

- Posture for Health, p. 94
- Aerobic News, p. 100
- Sports Injuries, p. 109

ESL/ELL

Learning Log

After reading about a concept, students can use a Learning Log to think about what they have learned. In it they can reflect on new information, evaluate areas that are unclear to them, and write questions they want to discuss with the class.

Activities

- Comprehensible Input, pp. 95, 102
- Language and Vocabulary, p. 108

Curriculum Integration

Use these topics to integrate health into your daily planning.

Integrated Language Arts/Reading Skills

- Body Works, p. 98
- All Different Kinds, p. 101
- The Play's the Thing, p. 107

Science

- Pumping Heart, p. 98

Physical Education

- Daily Fitness Tip, pp. 92, 98, 106
- Daily Physical Activity, p. 91
- Eraser Relay Tag, p. 96
- Perfect Timing, p. 103

Art

- Successful Goals, p. 104
- Identifying Activities, p. 106
- Create a Bulletin Board, p. 110

Social Studies

- Cross-Cultural Activities, p. 99

CHAPTER 4

Pages 90–113

CHAPTER SUMMARY

In this chapter, students

- learn that good posture is important to overall health and self-image.
- identify exercise, rest, and sleep as important parts of overall fitness.
- describe a well-planned, safe exercise program to help make them healthier.

Life Skills
Students *set goals* for fitness.

Building Good Character
Students show *fairness* by learning to listen to others.

Consumer Health
Students access *valid health information* about rest and sleep.

Literature Springboard

Use the article "Making Fitness a Family Affair" to spark interest in the chapter topic. See the Read-Aloud Anthology on page RA-5 of this *Teacher Edition.*

Prereading Strategies

SCAN THE CHAPTER Have students preview the chapter content by scanning the titles, headings, graphs, and tables. Ask volunteers to predict what they will learn. Use their predictions to determine their prior knowledge.

PREVIEW VOCABULARY Have students preview the chapter vocabulary and sort the terms into familiar and unfamiliar terms. Have students look up unfamiliar terms in the Glossary.

Words I Know	Words I've Seen or Heard	New Words

Reading Skill

IDENTIFY CAUSE AND EFFECT To introduce or review this skill, have students use the Reading in Health Handbook, pp. 334–335. Teaching strategies and additional activities are also provided.

Students will have opportunities to practice and apply this skill throughout this chapter.

- Focus Skill Reading Mini-Lesson, p. 92
- Reading comprehension questions identified with the 
- *Activity Book* p. 18 (shown on p. 96)
- Lesson Summary and Review, pp. 96, 103, 110
- Chapter Review and Test Preparation, pp. 112–113

Reading Skill

IDENTIFY CAUSE AND EFFECT Effect is what happens. Cause is the reason, or why, it happens. Use the Reading in Health Handbook on pages 334–335 and this graphic organizer to help you read the health facts in this chapter.

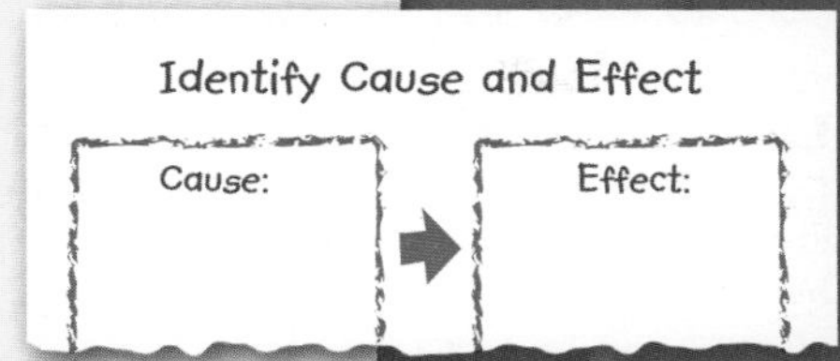

Health Graph

INTERPRET DATA Young people in the United States are becoming less fit and more overweight. One reason is that they spend more time watching television each week than they spend exercising. About how many hours per day do young people watch television?

Time Spent on Activities

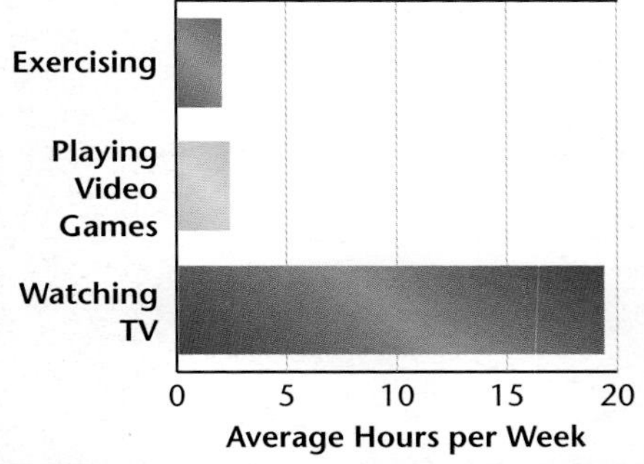

Daily Physical Activity

You need to be physically active. Stay active for your health.

Be Active!
Use the selection Track 4, **Jam Jive**, to give your heart a workout.

91

INTRODUCE THE CHAPTER

Health Graph

Interpret Data

Have students answer the Health Graph question. 2.76 hours per day

How many hours of exercise should young people get per week? at least three hours

What activities can you add to increase the amount of time you exercise each week? Possible answer: bike riding, walking to and from school, walking dog after dinner, doing sit-ups before going to bed

Daily Physical Activity

Use *Be Active! Music for Daily Physical Activity* with the Instant Activity Cards to provide students with movement activities that can be done in limited space. Options for using these components are provided beginning on page TR2 in this *Teacher Edition.*

Chapter Project

Get Active! (*Assessment Guide* p. 57)

ASSESS PRIOR KNOWLEDGE Use students' initial ideas for the project as a baseline assessment of their understanding of chapter concepts. Have students complete the project as they work through the chapter.

PERFORMANCE ASSESSMENT The project can be used for performance assessment. Use the Project Evaluation Sheet (rubric), *Assessment Guide* p. 65.

School-Home Connection

Distribute copies of the School-Home Connection (in English or Spanish). Have students take the page home to share with their families as you begin this chapter.

Follow Up Have volunteers share the results of their activities.

Supports the Coordinated School Health Program

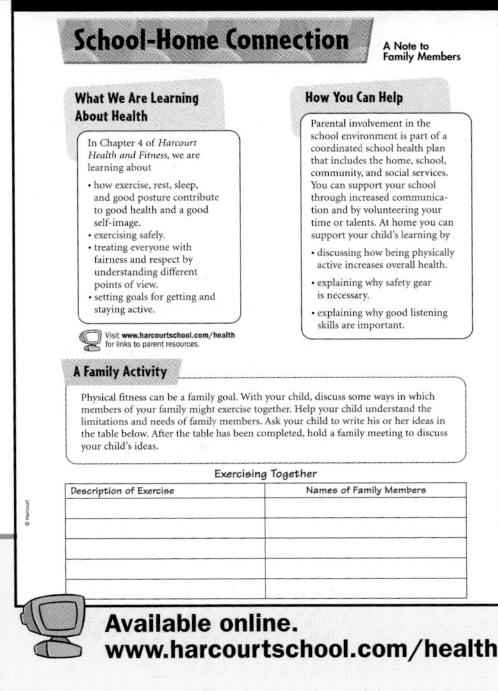

TEACHING RESOURCES P. 29

School-Home Connection

A Note to Family Members

What We Are Learning About Health

In Chapter 4 of *Harcourt Health and Fitness,* we are learning about

- how exercise, rest, sleep, and good posture contribute to good health and a good self-image.
- exercising safely.
- treating everyone with fairness and respect by understanding different points of view.
- setting goals for getting and staying active.

Visit **www.harcourtschool.com/health** for links to parent resources.

How You Can Help

Parental involvement in the school environment is part of a coordinated school health plan that includes the home, school, community, and social services. You can support your school through increased communication and by volunteering your time or talents. At home you can support your child's learning by

- discussing how being physically active increases overall health.
- explaining why safety gear is necessary.
- explaining why good listening skills are important.

A Family Activity

Physical fitness can be a family goal. With your child, discuss some ways in which members of your family might exercise together. Help your child understand the limitations and needs of family members. Ask your child to write his or her ideas in the table below. After the table has been completed, hold a family meeting to discuss your child's ideas.

Exercising Together

Description of Exercise	Names of Family Members

© Harcourt

Available online.
www.harcourtschool.com/health

LESSON 1
Pages 92–96

Objectives
- ► Describe how good posture can improve wellness and self-image.
- ► Demonstrate good posture while sitting, standing, and moving.

When Minutes Count . . .
Assign the Quick Study, Lesson 1, Activity Book pp. 16–17 (shown on p. 93).

Program Resources
- ► Activity Book pp. 16–18
- ► Transparency 3

Vocabulary
posture p. 92

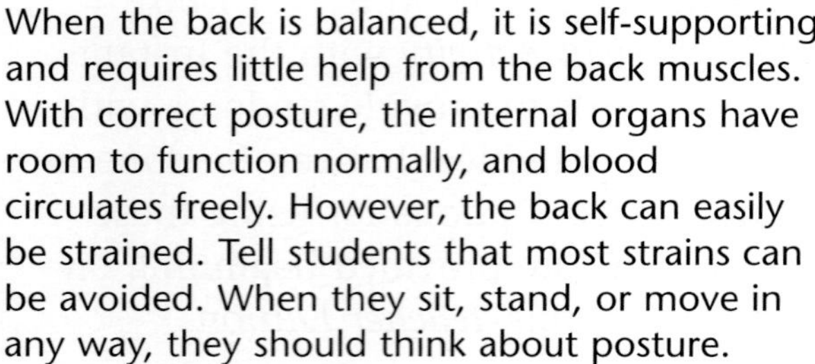

Daily Fitness Tip
When the back is balanced, it is self-supporting and requires little help from the back muscles. With correct posture, the internal organs have room to function normally, and blood circulates freely. However, the back can easily be strained. Tell students that most strains can be avoided. When they sit, stand, or move in any way, they should think about posture.

For more information about proper posture and care of the back, see *Be Active! Resources for Physical Education* p. 145.

1. MOTIVATE
Ask students to brainstorm words associated with the care of the back. Write the words on the board. Then have students group the words under the following headings: *General Fitness, Correct Posture, Lifting Safely, Carrying Items Properly.* Discuss how each area helps keep the back healthy.

How does good posture affect how you feel? Possible answer: It makes me feel taller, straighter, stronger, and at ease.

How does good posture affect the rest of your body? Possible answers: Organs have room to function; blood circulates freely; back muscles are not strained.

Good Posture

Lesson Focus
Good posture is important for your health and your self-image.

Why Learn This?
What you learn can help you have good posture, take pride in your appearance, and stay healthy.

Vocabulary
posture

Improve Your Form
Imagine that a string is gently pulling upward on the center of your head. Your ears, shoulders, and hips are in a straight line. Your chin is parallel to the floor. Your shoulders are level, and your knees are relaxed. This is good **posture** (PAHS•cher). It is holding your body in a balanced way when you stand, sit, and move. Good posture prevents problems with your bones, muscles, and joints. It also helps you feel good about yourself.

Many people suffer from aches and pains. You can help prevent pain by using good posture when you stand, when you sit, and when you lift and carry.

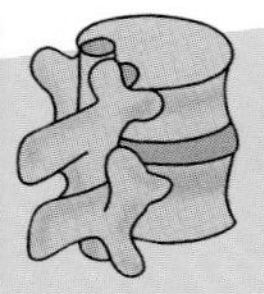

Did You Know?
In the morning, when you first get up, you are taller than when you went to bed. Overnight the discs that separate the bones in your spine swell with water so that you become taller. During the day, gravity and exercise squeeze out this liquid and your height is lessened.

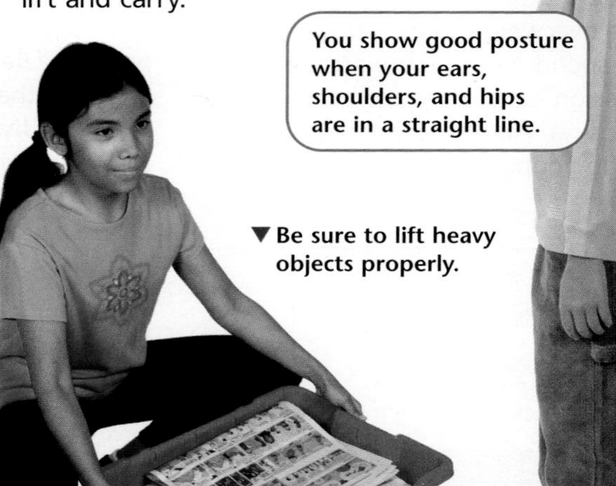

You show good posture when your ears, shoulders, and hips are in a straight line.

▼ Be sure to lift heavy objects properly.

92

Reading Skill

Mini-Lesson
CAUSE AND EFFECT Tell students that everything that happens has a cause and an effect. Have them practice this skill by responding to the Focus Skill question on page 93. Have students draw and complete the graphic organizer as you model it on the transparency.

TRANSPARENCY 3

3 Reading Skill Graphic Organizer

Identify Cause and Effect

Cause:		Effect:
Keep your knees straight when you bend over to lift a heavy object.	→	You might strain your back muscles because you are not letting your leg muscles do any of the work.

Interactive Transparencies available on CD-ROM.

Quick Activity

Identify What's Wrong List ways each student can improve his or her posture.

Practice good posture when you sit. Always sit with your back straight. When you sit at a desk, pull your chair close. Rest your feet on the floor to prevent backaches. Do not lean over your work. Sit up straight.

Use good posture when you lift heavy things. It is important to let your legs do most of the work. This is because your leg muscles are stronger than your back muscles. Never bend over to lift something heavy. Instead, bend your knees and keep your back as straight as possible. Stand behind the object. Hold it close to your body, and slowly lift it as you straighten your knees. The picture on page 92 shows how to lift objects by using good posture.

CAUSE AND EFFECT What might be the effect of keeping your knees straight when you bend over to lift a heavy object?

The effect might be that you would strain your back muscles because you are letting them, not your leg muscles, do most of the work.

Good Posture Tips

1. Keep your back straight.
2. Stand up straight.
3. Keep your chin up, with your head centered over your shoulders.
4. Keep your feet apart a little less than your shoulders are wide.
5. Keep your knees slightly bent.
6. Ears, shoulders, and hips should line up.

QUICK STUDY, ACTIVITY BOOK PP. 16–17

CHAPTER 4 Name ________ Quick Study

Fitness and Activity

Directions
- Use lesson vocabulary in the Word Bank to complete each **Summary**.
- Read the section directions to complete each **Lesson Details**.

Word Bank: posture, rest, Activity Pyramid, anaerobic, aerobic

Lesson 1 pp. 92–96

Summary You can prevent pain by using good posture when you stand, when you sit, and when you lift and carry.

Lesson Details Look at the Good Posture Tips on page 93. Rewrite the tips on a sheet of paper. Draw a picture for each tip to help you remember how to use good posture.

Check students' tips and drawings. Possible answers: keep your back straight; do not slouch; keep your chin up with your head centered over your shoulders; keep your feet apart a little less than your shoulders are wide; keep your knees slightly bent.

Lesson 2 pp. 98–103

Summary Aerobic exercise causes you to breathe deeply and makes your heart beat faster. Anaerobic exercise builds muscle strength. These exercises are short, intense activities. When you get enough rest, your mind and body feel at their best.

© Harcourt

Name ________ Quick Study (continued)

Lesson Details Use the information on the Three Basic Parts of Physical Fitness on pages 99–100 to complete the table.

Three Basic Parts of Physical Fitness	Example
Endurance	Running, swimming, bicycle riding
Muscle strength	Push-ups, pull-ups, sit-ups
Flexibility	Stretching

Lesson 3 pp. 106–110

Summary The Activity Pyramid can help you choose activities to include in your exercise program.

Lesson Details Look at pages 106–107. Explain why a pyramid shape is a better choice for the Activity Pyramid than a square.

Possible answer: The bottom of the pyramid shows the activities that you should do most often and in the greatest amount. This decreases as you move higher up the pyramid.

© Harcourt

Available online.
www.harcourtschool.com/health

2. TEACH

Discuss

Discuss the contribution that good posture makes to overall health. Tell students that the most common cause of back pain is poor posture. Signs of poor posture are an excessive curve in the lower back, an abdomen that sticks out, and shoulders that are slumped or rounded.

Critical Thinking Why is it better to keep your back straight when sitting than to slouch? Possible answer: Sitting straight protects your back from becoming strained.

Interpret Visuals—Pictures

Ask students to study the diagram that shows good posture while standing. Have students work in pairs to devise an eight-point list of the elements of good posture. Remind them to consider the head, chin, shoulders, natural curve of the back, stomach, hips, legs, and feet.

Content-Area Reading Support

Using Text Format Direct students' attention to the text in Did You Know? Have them explain how it connects to the lesson. The lesson is about the importance of posture, and the text describes information related to the spine.

Point out that side columns in many textbooks have high-interest facts related to the main text. Suggest that students read the primary text before reading the text in the side columns. That way, the flow of ideas and information will not be interrupted.

Quick Activity

Sample answer: The students are slouching, sitting far from a desk and leaning over their work, and bending from the waist to lift a box. Instead, they should sit straight in the chair, pull the chair close to the table, and keep their feet on the floor, and lift with bent knees, holding the object close to the body.

TEACH *continued*

Discuss

Tell students that hospital emergency rooms, doctors' offices, and clinics reported treating more than 13,620 injuries related to backpacks in 2000. Explain that the stress placed on the spine and shoulders by heavy backpacks can cause muscle fatigue and strain. Heavy backpacks can even cause some children to develop bad habits early in life, such as poor posture and slouching. Ask students to describe ways technology can influence health. Refer students to page 358 of the Health and Safety Handbook for more information and tips about backpack safety.

Critical Thinking Why is it important to wear both straps when carrying a backpack? Possible answer: Using only one strap could put too much weight on one side of your back, causing strain. Wearing both straps helps even out the weight.

Health Background

Backpacks and Backaches A person can carry more in a backpack than in his or her arms and hands alone. The risk, however, is overload, which can strain the back, neck, or shoulders. A heavy backpack can cause a person to lean forward, reducing balance and making it easier to fall. It can distort the natural curve of the back and cause rounding of the shoulders. Many organizations suggest that a child should not carry a backpack that weighs more than 20 percent of his or her body weight. The American Physical Therapy Association suggests that the backpack weight should be no more than 15 to 20 percent of body weight, and the American Chiropractic Association advises keeping backpack weight under 5 to 10 percent.

Source: *American Academy of Orthopaedic Surgeons website*

For more background, visit the **Webliography** in Teacher Resources at **www.harcourtschool.com/health** **Keyword** injury prevention

This girl is wearing a backpack correctly. The boy is not.▶

Health & Technology

Better Backpacks
Companies that make backpacks are now using much lighter materials. Some designs include support framing and padding. When worn properly, these backpacks can help reduce muscle strain and pain. This technology is also being used in the straps and design of utility bags, travel cases, and tote bags.

Wearing a Backpack

Your back and abdominal (ab•DAHM•uh•nuhl) muscles can support the weight of a backpack that is worn correctly. If your backpack is too heavy, or if you don't wear it correctly, you could harm your back. Carrying an overweight backpack can pull your body forward and force your spine to stretch or press together. That puts too much stress on your back. It can make your shoulders rounded and your upper back curved. This can cause shoulder, neck, and back pain.

SUMMARIZE What happens to your spine when you carry a backpack that is too heavy? A backpack that is too heavy can pull your body forward and force your spine to stretch or press together. That stresses your back. A heavy backpack can make your shoulders rounded and can make your upper back curved. It can cause shoulder, neck, and back pain.

94

Meeting Individual Needs
Leveled Activities

BELOW-LEVEL Proper Lifting Have students demonstrate how to lift a heavy object from the floor.

ON-LEVEL Posture Interview Have students ask a doctor these questions about posture and the skeletal system: What happens to posture as a person grows older? What preventive measures can be taken to avoid future back problems? Have students write a summary of the interview.

CHALLENGE Posture for Health Have students use library resources to locate information about the health benefits of good posture. Have students write short reports based on their findings.

Using a Computer

Good posture is important when you sit at a computer. It will help you work or play safely without getting tired. Your chair should support your shoulders and back. The seat should be high enough so that the monitor is at eye level. Your feet should rest comfortably flat on the floor. The keyboard should be at wrist level. You should be able to type without having to reach up or bend forward. Keep your wrists straight when you type. Hold the mouse loosely to prevent cramps in your hand.

Personal Health Plan

Real-Life Situation
When you have been sitting at a computer for a long time, you get tired.

Real-Life Plan
Write a step-by-step plan for using a computer in a way that is good for your body.

Your neck and shoulders should be relaxed.
Your shoulders should be in line with your ears and hips.
The top of your screen should be at or just below eye level.
Keep your wrists straight. Your arms need to be level with your keyboard, with your forearms horizontal.
Keep your feet flat on the floor.

95

Interpret Visuals—Pictures

Draw students' attention to the person sitting at the computer. Have students pretend that they are sitting at a computer. Ask them to read the captions and adjust their seating position to match the picture.

What stretching exercises could you do to help relax your back muscles while working at the computer? Possible answer: side bends, touch toes, stretches for hamstrings and quadriceps, forearm stretches

Personal Health Plan

Plans should include the following:

- Sit straight; do not lean over work.
- Relax neck and shoulders.
- Keep shoulders in line with ears and hips.
- Keep feet flat on floor.
- Keep wrists straight.
- Hold arms level with keyboard. Forearms should be parallel to the floor.
- Adjust chair so that top of screen is at or just below eye level.
- Pull chair close, and sit back in chair.
- Stand up and stretch often.
- Look away from screen every few minutes.
- Work in a well-lighted room.

ESL/ELL Support

COMPREHENSIBLE INPUT Help students understand that carrying their backpacks correctly can help keep their backs safe.

Beginning Invite student volunteers to demonstrate how to carry backpacks correctly. Encourage students to use the picture in this lesson as a guide.

Intermediate Have students weigh their loaded backpacks. Create a bar graph to show how much the backpacks weigh. Talk about how to make backpacks safer to carry.

Advanced Ask students to solve this math problem: Doctors say students shouldn't carry backpacks that weigh more than 20 percent of their body weight. If Cody weighs 80 pounds, what is the heaviest loaded backpack he should carry? (80 x 0.20 = 16 pounds)

3. WRAP UP

Lesson 1 Summary and Review

1. posture; bend; straight; computer
2. Possible answer: Carrying a heavy backpack can make you lean forward and force your spine to stretch or press together in ways that put too much stress on your back. It can make your shoulders rounded and your upper back curved. It can cause shoulder, neck, and back pain. These things could cause you to be unbalanced while riding a bike.
3. Blink your eyes often, look away from the screen every few minutes, and look into the distance to give eyes a chance to rest and refocus.
4. Responses may include:

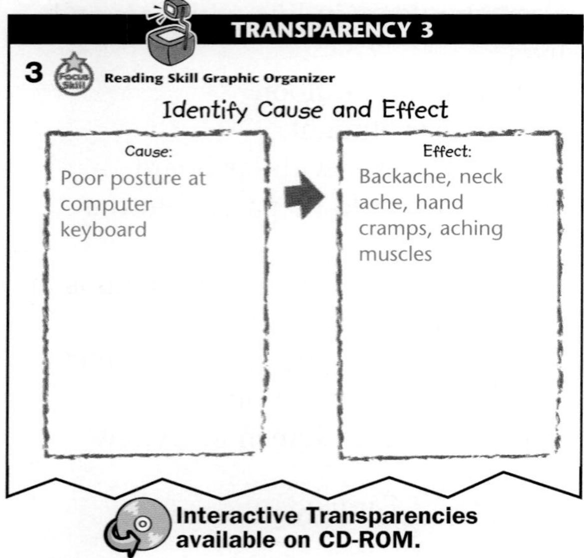
TRANSPARENCY 3

3 Reading Skill Graphic Organizer

Identify Cause and Effect

Cause:		Effect:
Poor posture at computer keyboard	→	Backache, neck ache, hand cramps, aching muscles

Interactive Transparencies available on CD-ROM.

5. Students' posters should include content from the graphic on p. 95.

For **writing models** with examples, see *Teaching Resources* pp. 47–61. Rubrics are also provided.

When Minutes Count . . .

Quick Study Students can use *Activity Book* pages 16–17 (shown on p. 93) as they complete each lesson in this chapter.

Sitting at a computer can make you as tired as playing your favorite sport can. Your muscles can feel tired from lack of movement. Your back may start to ache. It is important to stand up and stretch to help your muscles relax. Your eyes may also get tired. To help your eyes feel better, blink them often to moisten them.

Every few minutes, look away from the screen. Looking into the distance lets your eyes rest and adjust. Work in a room that is well lighted, away from the glare of windows.

MAIN IDEA AND DETAILS What is the main idea about computer use? What details support this main idea?

Myth and Fact

Myth: Using a computer in a room with low light will ruin your eyesight.

Fact: Bad lighting cannot ruin your eyesight. It can, however, make your eyes tired more quickly.

◀ Stretch at least once every half hour to help your muscles relax.

Lesson 1 Summary and Review

❶ **Summarize with Vocabulary**

Use vocabulary and other terms from this lesson to complete the statements.

Good _____ means holding your body in a balanced way. When you lift things, _____ your knees and keep your back as _____ as possible. Good posture is important when sitting and when working at a _____.

❷ **Critical Thinking** How could carrying a heavy backpack affect your riding a bike?

❸ What are three tips for preventing eyestrain when working at a computer?

❹ **CAUSE AND EFFECT** Complete this graphic organizer to show the effects of poor posture at a computer.

❺ **Write to Inform—Description**

Suppose you are going to make a poster about posture. You want to illustrate and describe five good posture tips and tell how each one helps your body. Write the tips for the poster.

Maintaining good computer posture is important; Getting good support from your chair, having the seat high enough for the monitor to be at eye level, being able to type without reaching or bending forward, keeping your wrists straight, and holding the mouse loosely.

Physical Education

Eraser Relay Divide the class into two lines. The first person in each line balances a clean eraser on his or her head and then moves around the room as fast as possible without letting the eraser fall off. Then the next person in each line gets a turn. If the eraser falls off, the student goes to the end of the line and tries again. Explain that if posture is correct, the eraser should not fall off.

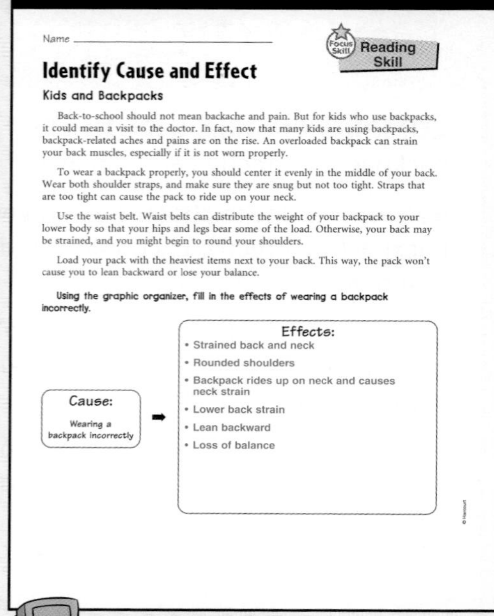
ACTIVITY BOOK P. 18

Name ______________________

Reading Skill

Identify Cause and Effect

Kids and Backpacks

Back-to-school should not mean backache and pain. But for kids who use backpacks, it could mean a visit to the doctor. In fact, now that many kids are using backpacks, backpack-related aches and pains are on the rise. An overloaded backpack can strain your back muscles, especially if it is not worn properly.

To wear a backpack properly, you should center it evenly in the middle of your back. Wear both shoulder straps, and make sure they are snug but not too tight. Straps that are too tight can cause the pack to ride up on your neck.

Use the waist belt. Waist belts can distribute the weight of your backpack to your lower body so that your hips and legs bear some of the load. Otherwise, your back may be strained, and you might begin to round your shoulders.

Load your pack with the heaviest items next to your back. This way, the pack won't cause you to lean backward or lose your balance.

Using the graphic organizer, fill in the effects of wearing a backpack incorrectly.

Cause:		Effects:
Wearing a backpack incorrectly	➡	• Strained back and neck • Rounded shoulders • Backpack rides up on neck and causes neck strain • Lower back strain • Lean backward • Loss of balance

© Harcourt

Available online. www.harcourtschool.com/health

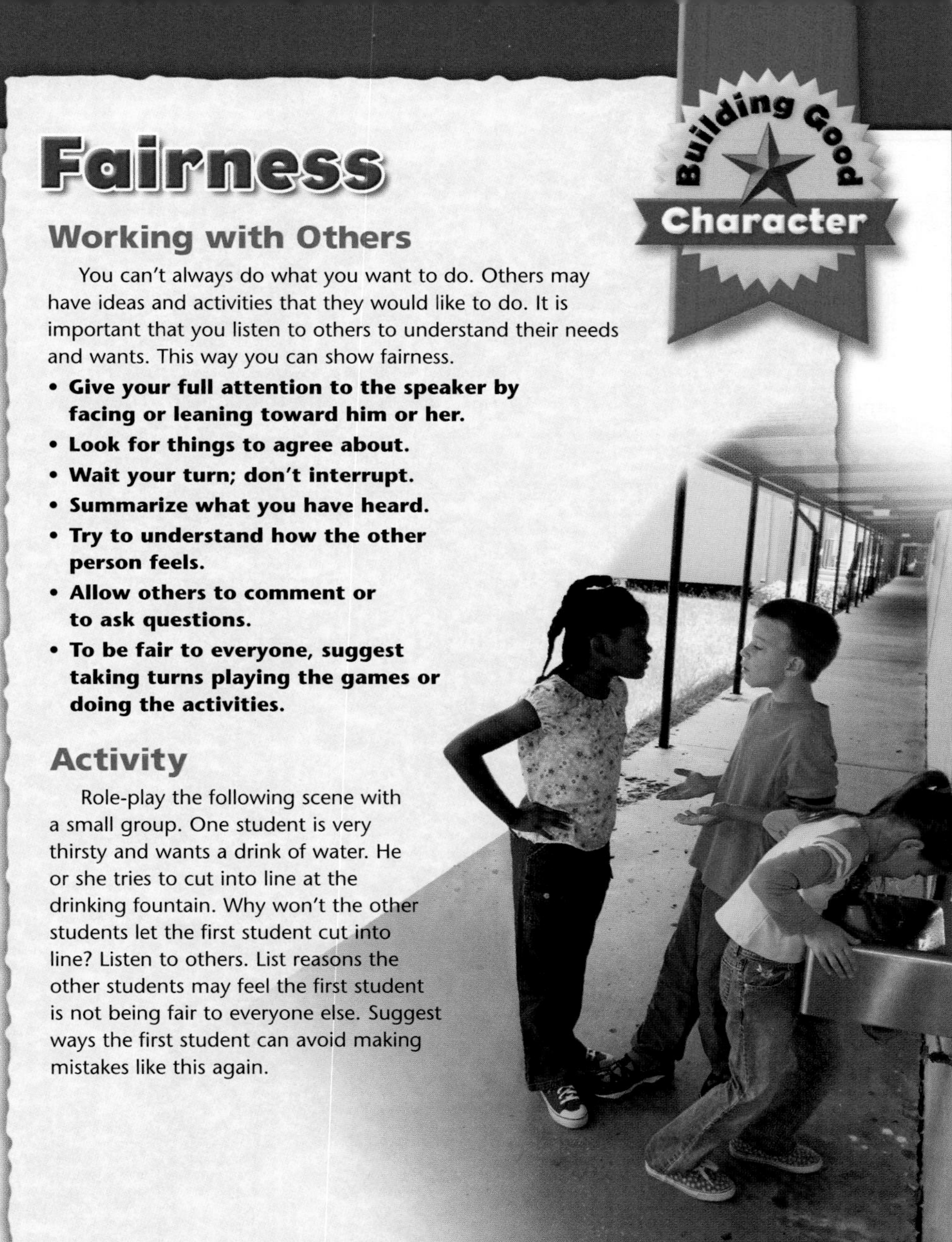

Fairness

Building Good Character

Working with Others

You can't always do what you want to do. Others may have ideas and activities that they would like to do. It is important that you listen to others to understand their needs and wants. This way you can show fairness.

- **Give your full attention to the speaker by facing or leaning toward him or her.**
- **Look for things to agree about.**
- **Wait your turn; don't interrupt.**
- **Summarize what you have heard.**
- **Try to understand how the other person feels.**
- **Allow others to comment or to ask questions.**
- **To be fair to everyone, suggest taking turns playing the games or doing the activities.**

Activity

Role-play the following scene with a small group. One student is very thirsty and wants a drink of water. He or she tries to cut into line at the drinking fountain. Why won't the other students let the first student cut into line? Listen to others. List reasons the other students may feel the first student is not being fair to everyone else. Suggest ways the first student can avoid making mistakes like this again.

97

Building Good Character

Caring
Citizenship
Fairness
Honesty
Respect
Responsibility

Objective

► Recognize the importance of fairness by being a good listener.

Program Resource

► Poster 3

BEFORE READING

Ask students to write a definition of *fairness*. Then have partners write a new definition, using ideas from their two individual definitions. Have one student from each pair write the combined definition on the board. The class can discuss the definitions and vote for one.

DISCUSS

How can not listening be unfair to the person who is speaking? It means that you are not considering the person's feelings. Not hearing him or her may cause misunderstanding. Everyone deserves to be heard.

Ask students to identify similarities in which healthy environments can be promoted in schools and communities.

ACTIVITY

After students role-play the scenario and discuss the questions, encourage them to observe the guidelines for being a good listener. Have them share what they've learned in a thoughtful way with family and friends. Tell students one of the best ways to teach someone is by example. When they listen carefully and practice fairness, they are encouraging others to do the same. You may wish to try different scenarios like playground activities or sharing roles in a game.

Using the Poster

Activity Suggest students design and display posters about being a good listener.

Display Poster 3 to remind students of ways to show fairness. Students' posters can be displayed in the classroom.

POSTER 3

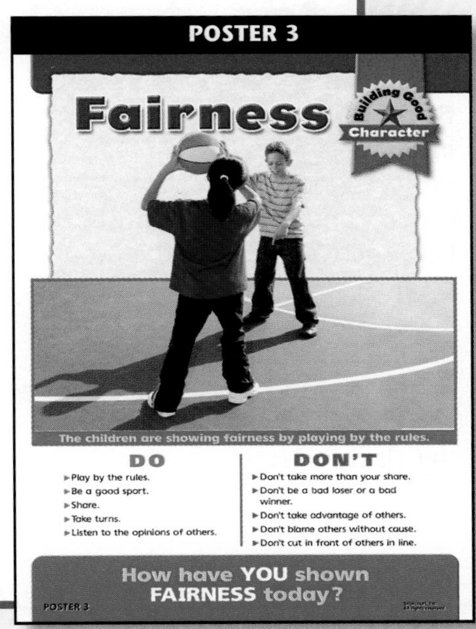

Fairness
Building Good Character
The children are showing fairness by playing by the rules.
DO
Play by the rules.
Be a good sport.
Share.
Take turns.
Listen to the opinions of others.
DON'T
Don't take more than your share.
Don't be a bad loser or a bad winner.
Don't take advantage of others.
Don't blame others without cause.
Don't cut in front of others in line.
How have YOU shown FAIRNESS today?
POSTER 3

LESSON 2
Pages 98–103

Objectives
- Explain the benefits of regular physical activity.
- Describe the difference between aerobic and anaerobic exercise.
- Describe the importance of sleep and rest to overall fitness.
- Describe a proper balance of sleep, rest, and activity.

When Minutes Count . . .
Assign the Quick Study, Lesson 2, Activity Book pp. 16–17 (shown on p. 93).

Program Resources
- Activity Book pp. 16–17
- Transparency 3

Vocabulary
aerobic exercise p. 100,
anaerobic exercise p. 100,
rest p. 102

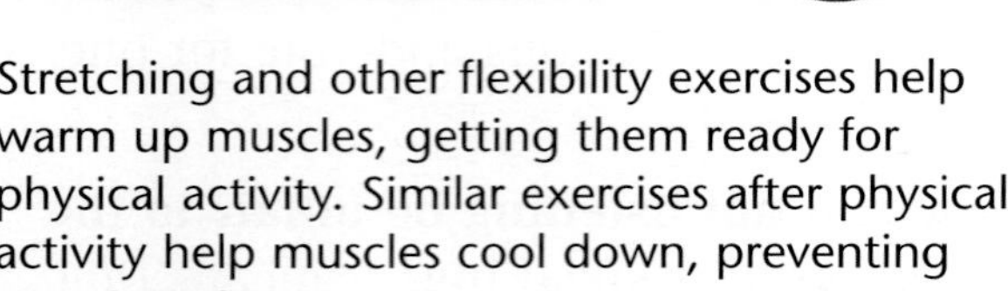

Daily Fitness Tip
Stretching and other flexibility exercises help warm up muscles, getting them ready for physical activity. Similar exercises after physical activity help muscles cool down, preventing muscle tightness.

For more about exercises, see *Be Active! Resources for Physical Education* p.141.

1. MOTIVATE
Write the following terms on strips of paper: *physical fitness*, *muscle strength*, *endurance*, *flexibility*, *aerobic exercise*, *anaerobic exercise*, *rest*. Write the definitions of the terms on the board. Divide the class into seven groups. Have each group choose a strip and match the term to the correct definition. Discuss each definition. Talk about the components of physical fitness and why each is important.

LESSON 2 Physical Fitness

Lesson Focus
Being physically fit involves endurance, muscle strength, and flexibility. Exercise and sleep play key roles in fitness.

Why Learn This?
What you learn can help you become physically fit, feel good, and stay healthy.

Vocabulary
aerobic exercise
anaerobic exercise
rest

What Your Body Needs
Do you like to jump rope, ride a bicycle, or swim? You might like these activities because they are fun. Physical activities such as these are what your body and mind need. They are forms of exercise. Exercise is any physical activity that makes your body work hard. Regular exercise can help you do better in school, sleep better, feel less tired, and be less stressed. Physical activities and team sports help you learn to interact and cooperate with others. You can meet new friends. Exercise can also help you feel good about yourself.

◀ Stretching is a good way to increase your flexibility.

Doing push-ups, sit-ups, and pull-ups can help your muscles get stronger. ▶

98

Language Arts
Body Works Divide the class into small groups. Assign each group a body part, and have the group name a sport that uses that body part. Then have the group create a script for the body part about its need to be stretched before and after exercising and how exercising makes it feel. Have each group present its script to the class.

Science
Pumping Heart Explain that the heart is a strong muscular organ that pumps blood through the body. Oxygen is carried by the blood. As the body works harder, more oxygen is needed. Have students squeeze their fists continuously for 60 seconds. Ask how tired their hands feel, and explain that the heart must be extremely strong in order to pump continuously every day.

Exercise is good for you. You need to work your muscles. Exercise makes them strong. Doing regular exercise can help build your body and keep it healthy. It helps you do better in sports. Regular exercise can also help reduce your chances of injury.

CAUSE AND EFFECT What is the effect of having strong muscles?

The more strength you have, the easier it is to do activities.

Did You Know?

You have 650 muscles in your body. They make up about one-half of your body weight. For example, if you weigh 80 pounds, about 40 pounds of you is muscle!

Three Basic Parts of Physical Fitness

1. **Endurance** (en•DUR•uhnts) Ability of your muscles to work hard for a long period of time without getting tired
2. **Muscle strength** Ability of your muscles to apply force. The more strength you have, the easier it is to do activities.
3. **Flexibility** (flek•suh•BIL•uh•tee) Ability to move joints and muscles through a full range of motion

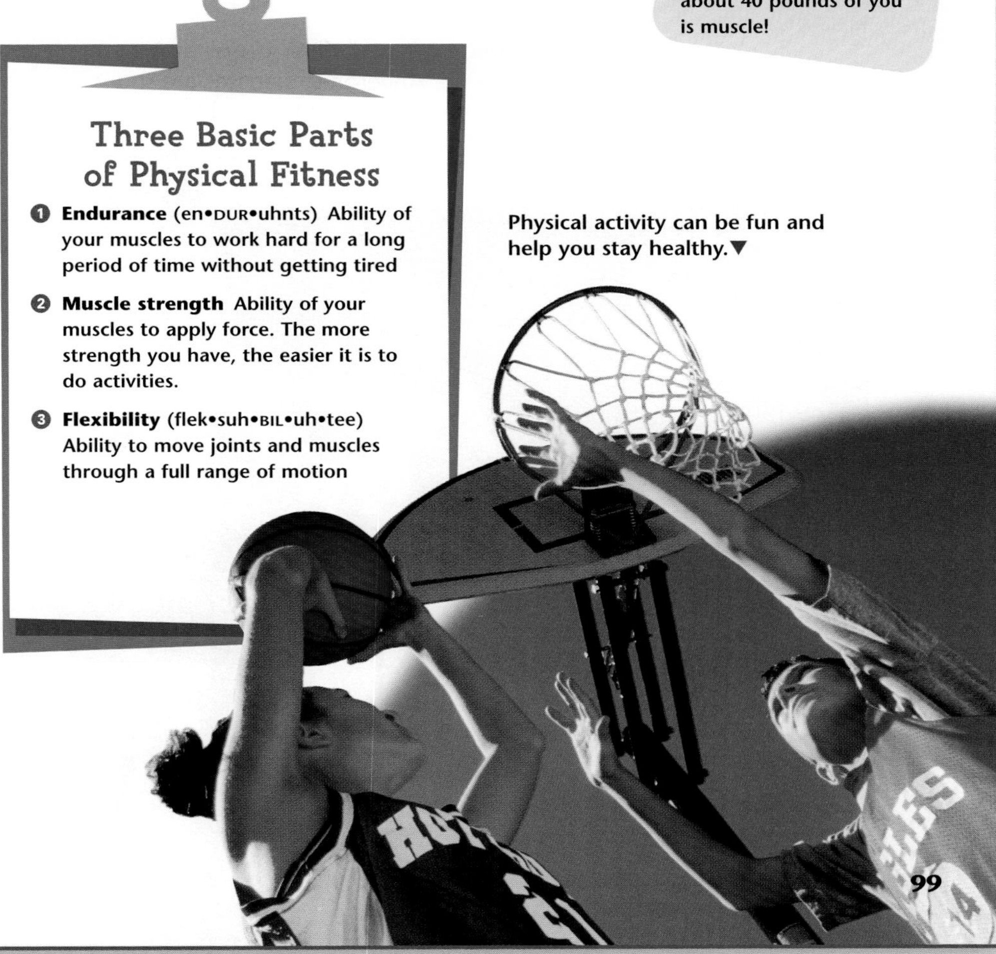

Physical activity can be fun and help you stay healthy.▼

2. TEACH

Discuss

Critical Thinking **Ask students to explain the physical benefits of fitness.** Possible answers: to look and feel good, to breathe easily, to improve blood circulation, to make the heart stronger, and to build firm muscles

Content-Area Reading

Support Using Respellings Direct attention to the phonetic respelling of *endurance* (en•DUR•uhns). Explain that respellings show how words are pronounced. Point out that the dots in the respelling divide the word into syllables and that capital letters indicate the stressed, or accented, syllable. Urge students to pay attention to respellings for help in pronouncing unfamiliar words and in recognizing words with unfamiliar spellings.

Discuss

Critical Thinking **When you participate in your favorite physical activity, are you thinking about making your heart stronger?** Possible answer: No; this is not something children usually think about.

Social Studies

Cross-Cultural Activities Divide the class into groups. Have each group research how children in another country typically spend their time. They should try to find information on the number of hours children spend in school and on homework as well as how much time they spend on sports and activities and whether the children are involved in organized activities. Have groups present their findings to the class, and then discuss differences among countries.

Teacher Tip

Cross-Cultural Activities When preparing the Cross-Cultural Activities exercise, you may want to visit your school's resource center first to determine what books and other materials are available. If materials are limited, it would be best to provide a list of countries from which the groups can choose so that you will be certain that appropriate information is available.

TEACH *continued*

Discuss

Ask students to differentiate between aerobic and anaerobic exercise.

What makes aerobic exercise especially good for your heart? Aerobic exercise makes the heart pump faster and harder, which makes it stronger.

How much aerobic exercise do you need to make your heart stronger? at least 30 minutes of moderate to vigorous activity on most, if not all, days

How can you get aerobic exercise? running, bicycling, and actively playing outdoors

How can you get anaerobic exercise? by doing push-ups, pull-ups, and sit-ups

Personal Health Plan

Plans might include the following:

- Reserve 10 minutes a day after school for the first week and 15 minutes for the second week.
- Spend a few minutes warming up before exercising and cooling down afterward.
- List several aerobic exercises for the first week, and add exercises for the second week.

The Personal Health Plan should not be used to evaluate or assess students, nor should the results be shared with the class. As a group, discuss barriers to performing personal plans and ways to overcome them.

Personal Health Plan

Real-Life Situation
Between school and after-school activities, you know you're not getting enough exercise.

Real-Life Plan
Make a plan to do ten minutes of aerobic exercise every day after school. Next week, increase your time to fifteen minutes.

Exercise Your Body

Different kinds of exercise are needed for strength, endurance, and flexibility. **Aerobic exercise** (air•OH•bik) is exercise that causes you to breathe deeply and makes your heart beat faster. You should do an aerobic exercise for at least 30 minutes. Aerobic exercise also improves your cardiovascular system (kar•dee•oh•VAS•kyuh•ler), which includes your heart and blood vessels. Skating, fast walking, bike riding, and cross-country running are examples of aerobic exercise.

Anaerobic exercise (an•air•OH•bik) builds muscle strength. Anaerobic exercises are short, intense activities such as curl-ups, pull-ups, sprinting, and push-ups.

▲ Aerobic exercise helps build endurance.

Aerobic Activities

Meeting Individual Needs
Leveled Activities

BELOW-LEVEL Aerobic Pantomime Ask students to draw or pantomime their favorite aerobic exercises.

ON-LEVEL Aerobics in Sports Ask students to draw pictures showing themselves participating in an aerobic sport or game. Have students label their drawings with short sentences on how each activity helps improve their fitness.

CHALLENGE Aerobic News Organize students into four groups, and have each group create a news story that focuses on the latest facts about aerobic exercise. Have students include five facts in their stories. The stories should be creative and informative.

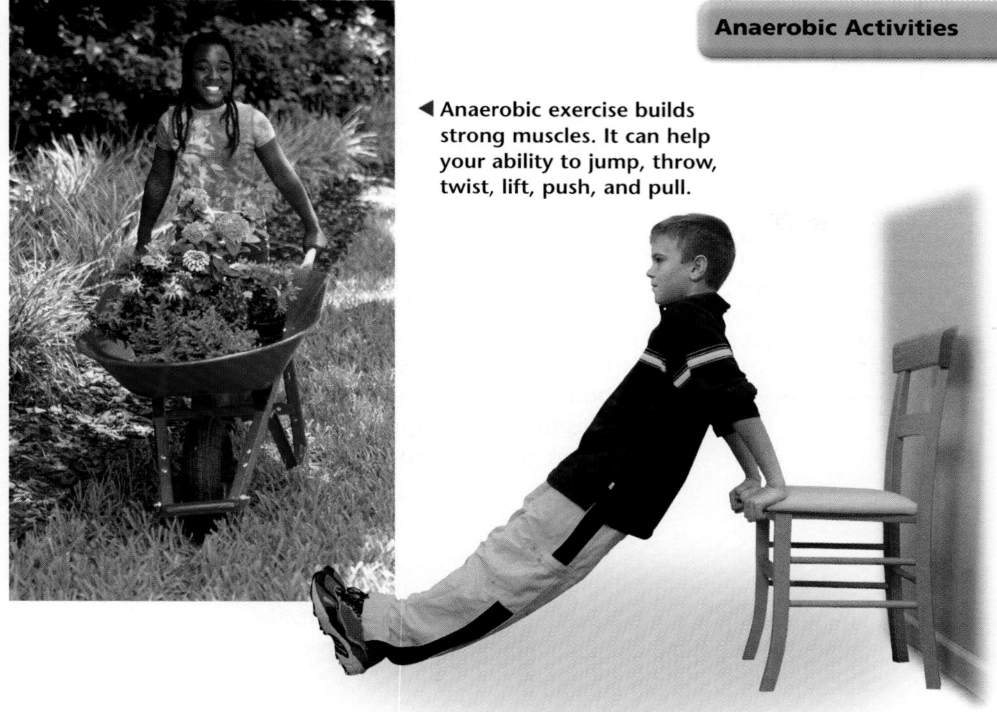

◀ Anaerobic exercise builds strong muscles. It can help your ability to jump, throw, twist, lift, push, and pull.

If doing your homework makes you tired and sleepy, take a quick activity break. Walk in place for a few minutes, or walk up and down stairs a few times. You'll feel better and be able to concentrate more. If you are having a bad day at school, go for a short walk during recess. Exercise helps take your mind off things that are bothering you and reduces stress. It also can help you let go of anger and other uncomfortable feelings. The physical activity of exercise can give you more energy and help you feel better.

Quick Activity

Evaluate Fitness Have a friend keep count while you do as many curl-ups as you can in one minute.

COMPARE AND CONTRAST How are aerobic and anaerobic exercise the same and different? Aerobic exercise causes you to breathe deeply and increases endurance. Anaerobic exercise increases muscle strength. Both kinds of exercise can make you feel better physically and emotionally.

Quick Activity

Before students begin, make sure they know the correct way to do curl-ups.

Discuss

Problem Solving Suppose you have just taken a long bike ride. How do you feel? Possible answer: tired, but good

Discuss

Talk about how everyone has bad feelings sometimes. Ask students if they have ever exercised when they felt angry or unhappy. Encourage volunteers to share their experiences.

How did you feel after doing physical activity? Many students will say that they felt better.

Point out that in addition to being good for our bodies, physical activity is also good for our emotional well-being.

Ask students to explain other social benefits of fitness, such as making new friends and providing encouragement for one another.

Health Background

FITT Method The FITT (frequency, intensity, time, type) method is used to guide physical activity. *Frequency* refers to the goal of participating in some sort of daily physical activity. Activities such as walking to school and walking the dog count as physical activity. *Intensity* relates to the goal of participating in activities that have at least moderate intensity; ideally, people also participate in several activities that are more vigorous. Vigorous activity is often defined as activity that makes a person breathe hard and sweat. *Time* requires activity to last between 30 and 60 minutes each day. *Type* refers to choosing a variety of activities that promote strength, flexibility, and endurance.

Source: *American Academy of Orthopaedic Surgeons website*

For more background, visit the **Webliography** in Teacher Resources at **www.harcourtschool.com/health**
Keyword physical fitness

Language Arts

All Different Kinds Have small groups of students look in magazines for pictures of people engaged in different physical activities. Remind students that physical activities involve moving the body and can include raking leaves, walking a dog, and flying a kite. Have students cut out one or two pictures. Ask them to write a caption for each picture, describing the benefits of the activity.

Teacher Tip

Showing Sensitivity Be sensitive to students in your class who may be physically challenged and whose fitness plans may be very different from those of classmates. These students need to decide what goals will help them be more active and what steps are needed to reach their goals.

TEACH *continued*

Consumer Activity

Students who do their research about sleep and rest on the Internet need to take care to use reliable sources of information. In particular, they should avoid websites that are selling products, such as pharmaceuticals that claim to improve sleep.

Activity

Manage Stress Have students apply the steps for managing stress to Mark's problem. Encourage them to use these steps in their explanations. For example:

- Mark can acknowledge that he is worried about doing well on the test.
- Mark can make a study plan.
- Mark can go for a run or walk his dog to feel more relaxed.
- Mark can plan to get at least 10 hours of sleep so he feels refreshed in the morning. He may have to go to bed earlier than usual.
- If Mark needs more study time, he could get up a little earlier in the morning to review for the test.

Remind students that developing an ongoing daily routine to reduce stress is a key part of mental and physical health. Ask students to explain the mental benefits of fitness.

Discuss

What effects does rest have on your body? Rest gives your heart and other muscles a chance to slow down and relax. Your heart rate and breathing rates slow down. Resting also relaxes the mind.

Problem Solving Suppose you did not get enough sleep last night. Explain how not getting enough sleep might affect your academic performance at school today. Possible answers: tired, sleepy, not able to concentrate, irritable, edgy

ACTIVITY

Life Skills

Manage Stress Mark is feeling stress because he has a big test tomorrow. He knows he needs to relax and get a good night's sleep. Use what you have learned to suggest some healthful ways that Mark can deal with his stress and get a good night's sleep.

Rest and Sleep

After a busy day of school and other activities, your body needs **rest**. Rest gives your heart and other muscles a chance to slow down. Resting is also good for your mind. Quiet activities such as reading, drawing, and listening to music help you rest.

Sleep is another way your body rests. When you sleep, your heart rate and breathing rate slow down. Your body's muscles relax. Even your brain rests. Sleep is important and necessary for everyone. While you sleep, your body repairs damaged cells and makes new cells to help you grow. During sleep, your body stores energy from the food you have eaten.

▼ Activities such as quiet games help your body rest.

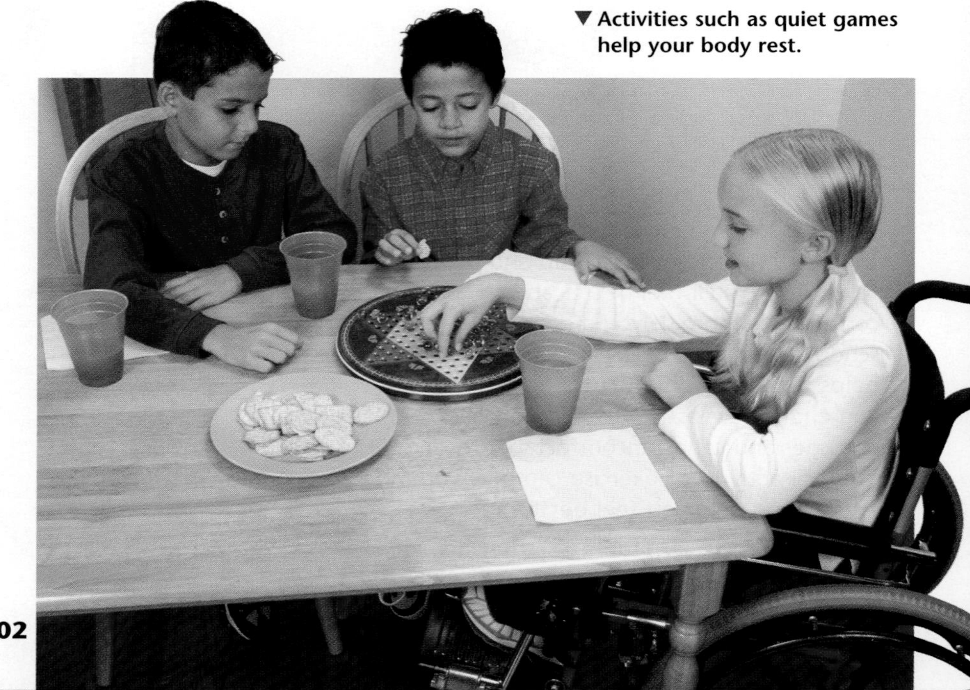

102

ESL/ELL Support

COMPREHENSIBLE INPUT Familiarize students with restful activities.

Beginning Have students develop a collage of restful activities.

Intermediate Have students write sentences about the benefits of sleep and rest.

Advanced Have students present an oral report on the benefits of sleep and rest.

Avoid hard exercise within two hours before bedtime. Instead, try an activity that will help you relax, such as reading or taking a bath.

Your body needs about ten hours of sleep every night. When you don't get enough sleep or rest, you can become ill. Without enough sleep, you may have a hard time paying attention or following directions in school. If you don't get enough sleep one night, try to go to bed earlier the next night.

DRAW CONCLUSIONS
Why is it important to get enough sleep?

Consumer Activity

Access Valid Health Information Find out more about the importance of rest and sleep. How can rest and sleep affect your school performance? Use the steps to Access Valid Health Information on pages 53–54. Write down the information you find.

◀ Reading is another quiet activity that is good for your body and mind.

Lesson 2 Summary and Review

1. **Summarize with Vocabulary** Use vocabulary and other terms from this lesson to complete the statements.

   The three parts of physical fitness are _____, _____, and _____. _____ *exercise* causes you to breathe deeply. _____ *exercise* builds muscle strength. The heart is part of your _____ system. You need _____ and at least ten hours of sleep each night.

2. **Critical Thinking** How can aerobic exercise improve your endurance?
3. Explain why you need anaerobic exercise.
4. **CAUSE AND EFFECT** Draw and complete this graphic organizer to show the effects of not getting enough sleep.

   Cause: | Effect:

5. **Write to Inform—Explanation** Explain the effects of exercise on your body and mind. Suggest a variety of enjoyable physical activities that you can do regularly.

Sleep allows your muscles to relax and your brain to rest. While you sleep, your body repairs damaged cells and makes new cells to help you grow. Your body also stores energy from food while you sleep. If you don't get enough sleep, you may have trouble paying attention in class, or you may become sick.

103

Physical Education

Perfect Timing When is the best time to exercise? Have students consult library resources and authoritative websites you've previewed to find reputable advice on the best time of day in which to engage in aerobic and anaerobic exercise. Students could make a poster illustrating their findings and discuss it with the class.

Teacher Tip

Activity Variety Some students may have difficulty thinking of activities that interest them, particularly if they are not interested in the sports played by their classmates. Be prepared to suggest alternative activities, including dancing, pilate exercises, Olympic walking, archery, horseback riding, and others.

3. WRAP UP

Lesson 2 Summary and Review

1. endurance, muscle strength, flexibility; Aerobic; Anaerobic; cardiovascular; rest
2. Possible answer: Aerobic exercises improve endurance because they use oxygen while you exercise. As your body takes in more oxygen, your heart and lungs become stronger, which helps you exercise longer.
3. Possible answer: to make your muscles stronger and bigger
4. Examples may include:

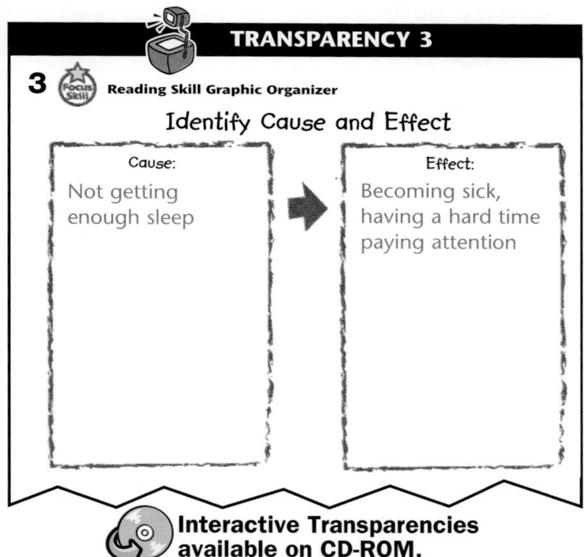

TRANSPARENCY 3
3 Reading Skill Graphic Organizer
Identify Cause and Effect
Cause:
Not getting enough sleep
Effect:
Becoming sick, having a hard time paying attention

Interactive Transparencies available on CD-ROM.

5. Answers should allude to beneficial effects such as those on pages 100–101 as well as to some of the activities pictured.

For **writing models** with examples, see *Teaching Resources* pp. 47–61. Rubrics are also provided.

When Minutes Count . . .

Quick Study Students can use *Activity Book* pp. 16–17 (shown on p. 93) as they complete each lesson in this chapter.

Life Skills

Communicate
Make Responsible Decisions
Manage Stress
Refuse
Resolve Conflicts
Set Goals

Objectives

- Identify goal-setting steps.
- Practice goal setting for fitness.

Program Resources

- Activity Book p. 19
- Poster 12

1. MOTIVATE

Ask students what a goal is. Ask how goals help us. give us purpose and direction Ask students to describe how goals give us confidence. When we achieve a goal, we feel good about ourselves. Ask students about goals they have set or achieved. Discuss why it is important to set short-term and long-term goals.

2. TEACH

Step 1

Direct students' attention to the photographs of Burt.

Step 2

How does Burt plan to meet his goal?

He lists the things he can do to relax. He plans his daily routine so he can go to bed earlier each night.

Set Goals

About Fitness

Exercise helps keep your body healthy, but you need to get enough rest to help your muscles rebuild after physical activity. Burt loves to play sports. Lately, he has not been getting enough rest. He feels tired a lot and has trouble staying awake in school. Use the steps for **Setting Goals** to help Burt get enough rest.

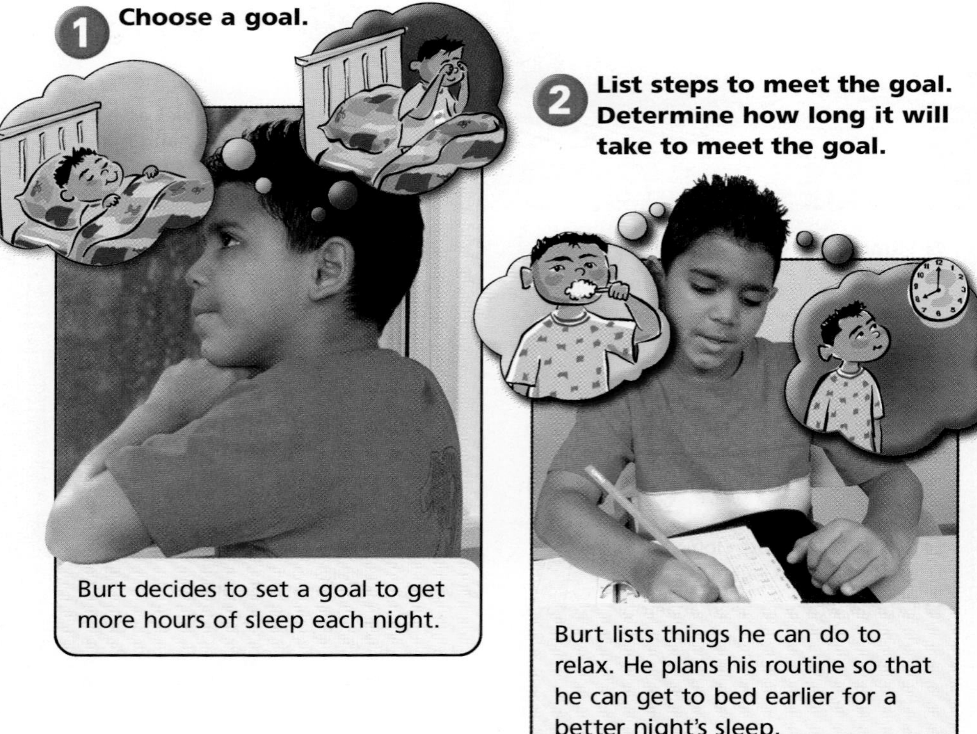

1 Choose a goal.

Burt decides to set a goal to get more hours of sleep each night.

2 List steps to meet the goal. Determine how long it will take to meet the goal.

Burt lists things he can do to relax. He plans his routine so that he can get to bed earlier for a better night's sleep.

Art

Successful Goals Ask students to think of a goal they would like to achieve. Have them answer the question *How would I look and feel if I achieved this goal?* by drawing a picture showing that they have achieved their goal. Encourage them to include some of the ways and things that helped them achieve the goal. Ask volunteers to share their drawings with the rest of the class.

ACTIVITY BOOK P. 19

Name ______________

Life Skill
Set Goals

Steps for Setting Goals

1. Choose a goal.
2. List steps to meet the goal. Determine how long it will take to meet the goal.
3. Check your progress as you work toward your goal.
4. Reflect on and evaluate your progress toward the goal.

Use the steps to help these students set fitness goals.

A. Trish wants to become stronger. She is a swimmer, and having strong arms could help her swim faster. She swims every day after school but doesn't do any other physical activity.

- Explain what steps Trish could take to achieve her goal.

Possible answer: Trish could start doing muscle-strengthening exercises before or after her swim practice. She might start off by doing push-ups two days a week. When that gets easy, she can increase the number of push-ups or begin doing other strengthening exercises such as pull-ups or sit-ups.

B. Larry wants to get in shape, so he decides to begin running five miles every day after school. He has never run before, but he feels that he could do it. Larry begins running, but after 15 minutes, he is gasping and has wobbly legs. Larry is in pain.

- Was Larry's goal responsible? Explain. Tell what a better goal would have been.

Possible answer: Larry's goal was not responsible because he had never run before. Larry should have set smaller goals that would have helped him get into shape faster and more safely. For instance, instead of running five miles, he could have started by walking one mile and seeing how that went. If it was too easy, he could have begun running.

© Harcourt

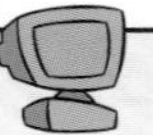

Available online.
www.harcourtschool.com/health

3 Check your progress as you work toward your goal.

Each night Burt checks the time he goes to bed.

4 Reflect on and evaluate your progress toward the goal.

Burt finds that he is now getting more sleep. He feels good and is awake and alert in school.

Problem Solving

Anne knows she should do aerobic exercise at least three times a week for thirty minutes each time. She likes to run, but during much of the winter, it's dark by the time she gets home from school. Use the four steps for **Setting Goals** to help Anne solve her problem. How can she use the goal-setting steps to help her take responsibility for getting the aerobic exercise she needs?

Using the Poster

Activity Suggest that students design and display posters about setting goals.

Display Poster 12 to remind students of the steps used to set goals.

Students' posters can be displayed in the classroom, school cafeteria, or other common areas.

POSTER 12
LIFE SKILLS
Set Goals
WASTE
The girl is setting a goal to recycle.
Steps for Setting Goals
1 Choose a goal.
2 Plan steps to reach that goal. Determine whether you will need help.
3 Check your progress as you work toward the goal.
4 Evaluate the results of your work.
What GOALS have YOU SET?
POSTER 12

Building Good Character

Ask students how setting the goal of getting more hours of sleep each night shows good character. It shows that Burt is responsible. He recognizes the importance to his wellness of getting a good night's sleep.

Step 3

Critical Thinking What could Burt do to help him get to bed earlier each night? Possible answers: He could finish his homework before playing with his friends after school; he might decide to reserve two hours after dinner as his homework time.

Step 4

Why is it important for Burt to evaluate his progress toward his goal? Evaluation lets him know how successful he is. It provides information he needs to set new goals.

3. WRAP UP

Problem Solving

Answers should reflect the Steps for Setting Goals. Anne needs to set a goal. She could set a goal to exercise three times a week, for 30 minutes each time. She needs to develop a plan. During the winter, she could run on a treadmill if one is available, or she could run up and down the stairs. She could decide to do jumping jacks and other aerobic exercises while she watches TV. Next, she needs to monitor her progress. She could keep a record of the types of exercises and the amounts of time she spends exercising. Finally, she should evaluate her progress. If she is not exercising three times a week for 30 minutes each time, she should revise her plan so that she can achieve her goal.

LESSON 3
Pages 106–110

Objectives
- Describe how to use the Activity Pyramid to improve physical fitness.
- Describe the importance of developing a personal health plan for fitness.
- Identify safety gear necessary for injury prevention.

When Minutes Count . . .
Assign the Quick Study, Lesson 3, Activity Book pp. 16–17 (shown on p. 93).

Program Resources
- Activity Book pp. 16–17, 20
- Transparencies 3, 24

Vocabulary
Activity Pyramid p. 106

Daily Fitness Tip
Explain that it's important to be aware of the intensity of exercise. The goal is to engage in moderate activity each day and to build to more vigorous activities. If students can sing while exercising, they are at a low intensity; if they can talk to a friend, they are exercising at a moderate intensity; and if they're breathing hard or sweating, they're exercising vigorously.

For more about physical activities, see *Be Active! Resources for Physical Education* p. 137.

1. MOTIVATE
Hold a physical activity contest. Have students number a sheet of paper from 1 to 30. Challenge students to list as many activities as possible in 60 seconds. Have the student with the most activities read his or her list to the rest of the class.

Where can you perform these exercises? Possible answer: pool, playground, back yard

When Minutes Count . . .
Transparency 24: Activity Pyramid can be used to present material in this lesson. *Interactive Transparencies available on CD-ROM.*

LESSON 3

Your Personal Fitness Plan

Lesson Focus
A personal fitness plan requires careful planning. It includes three parts: flexibility, aerobic fitness, and muscle strength and endurance.

Why Learn This?
What you learn can help you become more active physically and improve your health.

Vocabulary
Activity Pyramid

Be Physically Active
To improve your endurance, you need the exercise you get from doing activities. To help you choose activities that are right for you, use the **Activity Pyramid**, a guide to physical activity.

Sitting Still
Watching television, playing computer games
Small amounts of time

Light Exercise
Playtime, yardwork, softball
2–3 times a week

Regular Activities
Walking to school, taking the stairs, helping with housework
Every day

106

Art
Identifying Activities Have pairs of students draw a body outline on a large sheet of butcher paper. Have students label each part of the body with all the activities and exercises that use that body part. Students can use the Activity Pyramid as a guide. Ask volunteers to share their art and physical activities with the group.

Teacher Tip
Art Considerations You may want to provide students with a generic body outline rather than having them draw one for the Identifying Activities art project. This is particularly important if students are likely to embellish the drawing inappropriately or if some parents might find the activity offensive.

Like the USDA Food Guide Pyramid, you can use the Activity Pyramid when planning your personal fitness plan. Choose more activities from the base of the pyramid, fewer from the top.

A good fitness plan includes different kinds of exercise. Your plan should have exercises that help you develop aerobic fitness, muscle endurance, strength, and flexibility. Also include the three steps pictured here as part of your exercise program.

A warm-up of light activity, such as running in place, can help prepare your muscles for physical activity. Include slow gentle stretching, without bouncing. Doing stretches can help prevent muscle injury.

SEQUENCE List in order the steps for exercise: *workout, cool-down, warm-up*. Explain why they must occur in that order to avoid injury.

Warm-up, workout, and cool-down. They must occur in this order because warm-up means preparing for workout exercise and cool-down means getting your body back to a normal pace after exercise. Not following this order could result in physical injury.

Strength and Flexibility Exercises
Weight training, dancing, pull-ups
2–3 times a week

Aerobic Exercises
Biking, running, soccer, hiking
30-plus minutes, 2–3 times a week

If you warm up and cool down, you are less likely to injure yourself during exercise. ▶

▲ ***Warm up*** **for five to ten minutes to get your body ready for exercise. Good warm-up activities include jogging slowly, walking, and stretching.**

▲ ***Work out*** **after warming up, and exercise for at least thirty minutes.**

▲ ***Cool down*** **after exercise for five to ten minutes, ending with stretching. Walking is a good cool-down activity.**

107

Language Arts

The Play's the Thing Divide the class into groups. Have each group write a skit about two friends who are starting an exercise program. Skits should include some disagreement. One character could be resistant to the idea, the other could try to persuade him or her; or the two could disagree about the type or amount of exercise. The skits should use information from the chapter to resolve the disagreement.

Teacher Tip

Fitness Campaign The Centers for Disease Control and Prevention is sponsoring a national campaign called "VERB.™ It's what you do." The goal of the program is increased physical activity among young people between the ages of nine and thirteen. VERB includes educational materials for teachers, classrooms, principals, and parents. It can be accessed from the Centers for Disease Control and Prevention website.

2. TEACH

Discuss

Help students understand that the Activity Pyramid groups activities according to importance for fitness. The bottom of the pyramid contains the most important activities. The top names the least important.

Interpret Visuals—Pictures

How many different levels of activities are represented on the Activity Pyramid? five

Discuss

Critical Thinking If one level of the Activity Pyramid were removed, what might happen? What does that suggest about physical fitness? If you removed the bottom level, the pyramid would fall apart. If you removed the top level, the pyramid would still be strong. This suggests that if you don't get enough activity from the bottom level, your body won't be strong and healthy.

Discuss

Discuss goals that students could consider when creating a fitness plan, such as stronger muscles, increased endurance, and more flexibility. Talk about reasons for setting such goals. For example, a person who is interested in running a marathon might want to increase endurance. A swimmer might want to become stronger in order to move through the water faster.

What are the healthful effects of aerobic exercise? Possible answers: strengthens heart and lungs; increases endurance

What happens to your body when you do regular strength-training exercises? Possible answers: stronger muscles, better posture, weight loss

TEACH *continued*

Consumer Activity

Ads should make clear what sport the gear is intended for and what the gear protects against.

Content-Area Reading Support

Use Signal Words Direct attention to the second sentence in the third paragraph on this page. Point out that the first sentence states the main idea: *Do sets of exercises that strengthen your muscles*. Have a volunteer read the next sentence aloud. Explain that the phrase *for example* signals that the sentence contains details that support the main idea. Point out that signal words or phrases, such as *for example*, are clues to the way the information is organized. Recommend that students pay attention to signal words or phrases as a way to better understand how ideas are connected.

Discuss

Explain that the pulse rate indicates how quickly your heart is beating before, during, and after exercise. Show students how to take their pulse on the wrist by pressing the pointer and middle fingers of the right hand on the inside of the left wrist.

Discuss

Problem Solving Why is your pulse rate lower when you are fitter? The heart is stronger and can pump more blood with each beat. It needs to beat less often, so the pulse rates at rest and during exercise are lower.

Quick Activity

A stopwatch or a clock with a second hand is needed for this activity. Also try various other exercises and graph results. Students should see marked increases in pulse rate during aerobic exercise compared to during activities such as resting or stretching.

Consumer Activity

Make Buying Decisions Think about the safety gear you need to play one of your favorite sports. Design an advertisement for the safety gear for that sport. Highlight the benefits and importance of wearing each item. Share the ad with your class and with others who play the sport.

After-school activities can be fun and great exercise. ▶

Quick Activity

Monitor Pulse Rate Measure your pulse by counting the number of beats in ten seconds and then multiplying by six. Record your pulse rate while resting, and then after running in place. How do they compare?

Work Your Heart and Lungs

At least three days a week, the main part of your fitness plan should include aerobic exercise. It strengthens your heart and lungs.

If you are exercising hard enough, you will begin to breathe heavily. If you feel pain, you should stop and tell an adult. Over time you will be able to exercise harder.

Also, do sets of exercises that strengthen your muscles. For example, you might do three sets of ten push-ups, two days a week. Remember to warm up and cool down.

DRAW CONCLUSIONS Why should you do aerobic exercise for thirty minutes, three times a week?

It is important to do aerobic exercises for 30 minutes, three times a week, because the more you do these exercises, the more endurance you will build up.

ESL/ELL Support

LANGUAGE AND VOCABULARY Terms such as *endurance*, *muscular strength*, and *flexibility* may be new to students.

Beginner Have students act out or pantomime the meaning of each term.

Intermediate Have students work in pairs or small groups to illustrate the meaning of each term.

Advanced Challenge students to list as many activities as possible that help achieve endurance, muscular strength, or flexibility.

Keep Your Exercise Safe

Sometimes people hurt themselves when they exercise. You can lower your chances for injury by exercising safely. You can do this by wearing the proper safety gear and by using sports equipment correctly.

Safety gear is anything players wear to keep from getting hurt. Shin guards protect your legs from kicks while you play soccer. A helmet protects your head in case you fall off your bicycle. A mouth guard protects your mouth while you play hockey or volleyball. For skateboarding and inline skating, you need a helmet, wrist guards, elbow pads, and kneepads.

ACTIVITY

Building Good Character

Responsibility Donna wants to make the gymnastics team. To succeed in gymnastics, she needs to increase her flexibility. Donna must plan her daily activities so that she has time for gymnastics practice. List ways she can show responsibility and reach her goal.

Many activities require safety gear, such as helmets, to protect the body from injury. ▼

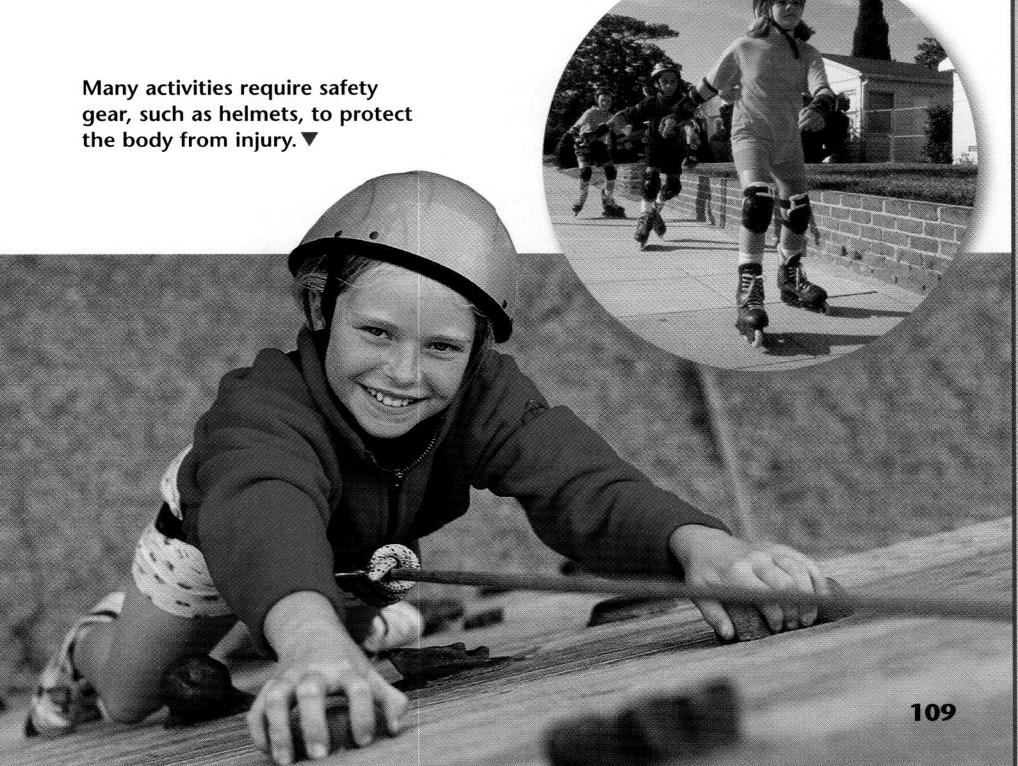

109

Activity

Responsibility Donna can show responsibility by making certain she can meet all her commitments in school and at home. She needs to get her homework and studying done on time. She will probably have to give up some activities, such as watching television, in order to practice gymnastics regularly.

Have students brainstorm ways that they can be more physically active and more responsible about following through on their own plans.

Discuss

Discuss the importance of wearing safety equipment while playing sports. Explain that about 3.2 million children ages five to fourteen suffer from sports and recreational injuries each year. Also mention that it's recommended that all youth involved in organized sports wear appropriate eye protection.

Interpret Visuals—Pictures

Point out the pictures and the caption on this page. Have students describe the safety equipment that is being used. Ask students to describe ways technology can influence health. Note that safety equipment can include shoes. Also consider proper injury prevention, such as a warm-up and a cool-down.

Meeting Individual Needs Leveled Activities

BELOW-LEVEL Bike Helmets Have students make posters encouraging the use of bike helmets and other safety gear.

ON-LEVEL Safety Ads Have students create radio advertisements for different pieces of safety gear for one of their favorite activities.

CHALLENGE Sports Injuries Have students research different types of sports-related injuries that occur when people do not wear safety equipment while being physically active. Suggest that they choose an injury and write a report on its treatment, how long recovery takes, and any aftereffects.

Health Background

Mouth Guards A mouth guard helps protect the teeth. It helps cushion blows that might otherwise cause broken teeth and injuries to the lips, tongue, face, or jaw. Mouth guards may also reduce the severity and incidence of concussion. New findings in sports dentistry show that even in noncontact sports, such as gymnastics, mouth guards protect participants. There are three types of mouth guards: ready-made, mouth-formed, and custom-made. Dentists can suggest the right type of mouth guard for each person.

Source: *American Dental Association website*

For more background, visit the **Webliography** in Teacher Resources at **www.harcourtschool.com/health**
Keyword injury prevention

3. WRAP UP

Lesson 3 Summary and Review

1. Activity Pyramid; workout, warm up; cool down; safety gear, rules
2. You are more likely to do the activity and stick with your plan if you like the activity.
3. Following rules can help make sure that no one does something that could hurt another player or put himself or herself or others at risk for an injury.
4. Responses may include:

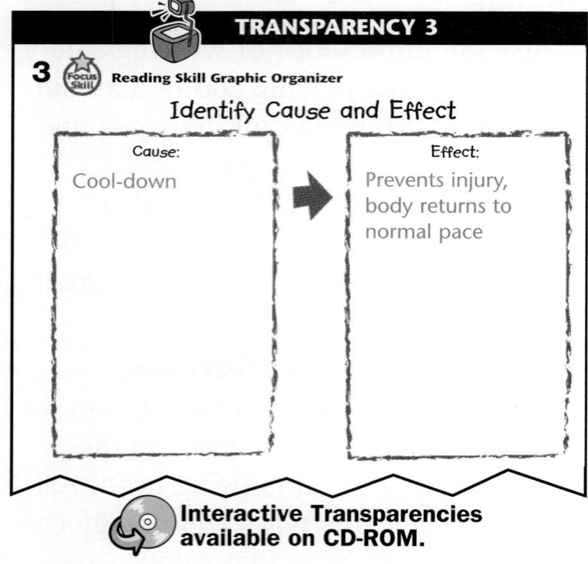

TRANSPARENCY 3
3 Reading Skill Graphic Organizer
Identify Cause and Effect
Cause:
Cool-down
Effect:
Prevents injury, body returns to normal pace

Interactive Transparencies available on CD-ROM.

5. Students should choose activities from at least three different levels of the Activity Pyramid.

For **writing models** with examples, see *Teaching Resources* pp. 47–61. Rubrics are also provided.

When Minutes Count . . .

Quick Study Students can use *Activity Book* pages 16–17 (shown on p. 93) as they complete each lesson in this chapter.

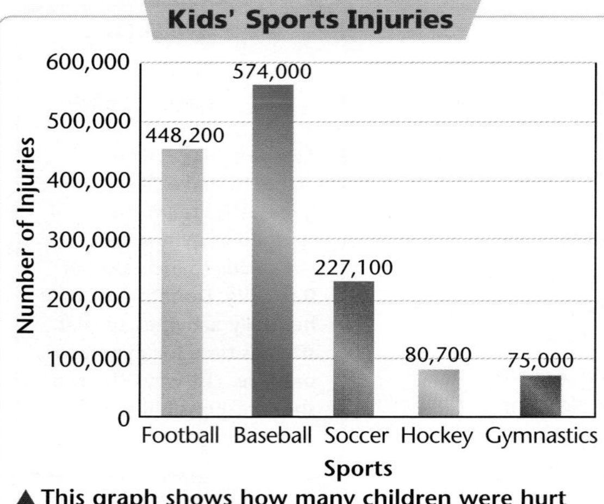

▲ This graph shows how many children were hurt playing five sports in one year. What kinds of safety gear might have helped avoid some of these injuries?

It is important to follow the rules of whatever sport or game you play. Rules help keep you safe and keep the game fair and fun for all. Following rules on the school playground and in PE class will keep you and your friends safer.

You can be physically active outside of school. You can enjoy public parks, playing fields, rinks, and pools. Wherever you exercise or play, be safe and have adult supervision.

CAUSE AND EFFECT What is the effect of wearing a helmet when you ride your bike? The effect is avoiding a head injury if you fall.

Lesson 3 Summary and Review

1. **Summarize with Vocabulary**
   Use vocabulary and other terms from this lesson to complete the statements.
   You can use the _____ to help you make a personal fitness plan. Before a _____, you need to _____. After you exercise, you need to _____. You should wear _____ and follow the _____ of the game.
2. Why is choosing an activity you like to do an important part of creating a personal fitness plan?
3. **Critical Thinking** How can following the rules of a game protect you and others from getting injured?
4. **CAUSE AND EFFECT** Draw and complete this graphic organizer to show the effect of cooling down after exercising.

5. **Write to Inform—Description**
   Write about three activities that you could do as part of your personal fitness plan. Use the Activity Pyramid to help you decide how long and how often you need to do each one.

110

Art

Create a Bulletin Board Have students create a bulletin board display showing activities and guidelines for the different levels of the Activity Pyramid. For each activity, students should indicate how often and for how long it should be performed. Students should also include information about staying safe while doing each activity.

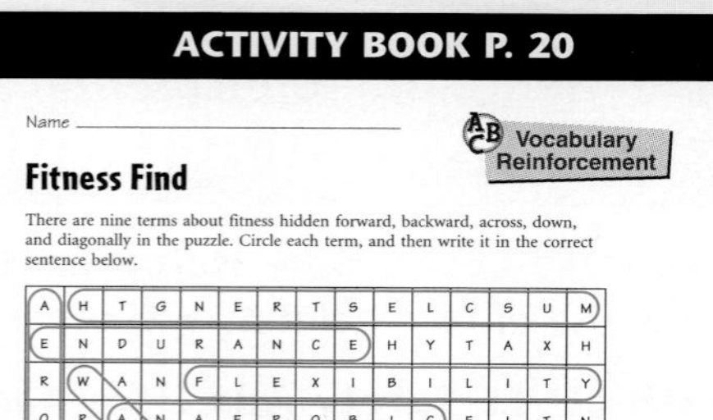

ACTIVITY BOOK P. 20

Name ________________

Vocabulary Reinforcement

Fitness Find

There are nine terms about fitness hidden forward, backward, across, down, and diagonally in the puzzle. Circle each term, and then write it in the correct sentence below.

A	H	T	G	N	E	R	T	S	E	L	C	S	U	M
E	N	D	U	R	A	N	C	E	H	Y	T	A	X	H
R	W	A	N	F	L	E	X	I	B	I	L	I	T	Y
O	R	A	N	A	E	R	O	B	I	C	F	I	T	N
B	C	I	R	B	O	R	E	A	N	D	R	R	T	W
I	G	H	S	M	U	Z	B	A	R	J	A	E	X	K
C	S	T	E	R	U	T	S	O	P	K	E	S	B	Z
D	I	M	A	R	Y	P	Y	T	I	V	I	T	C	A

1. Before exercising, it is important to warm up for five to ten minutes.
2. Running and swimming are examples of aerobic exercise.
3. Working muscles harder for longer periods without getting tired is endurance.
4. Push-ups and pull-ups help build muscle strength.
5. The Activity Pyramid lists activities that can help you plan a fitness program.
6. Sleep and rest help the body and mind relax.
7. Anaerobic exercises are short, intense activities.
8. Good posture is holding your body in a balanced way when you stand, sit, and move.
9. Stretching is a good exercise to help increase flexibility.

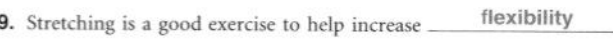

© Harcourt

Available online. www.harcourtschool.com/health

ACTIVITIES

Physical Education

Find a Fitness Role Model Choose a sport, and research a famous athlete from the United States or another country who has played that sport. Write a report that tells others about the athlete and the sport he or she plays and why he or she is fit.

Science

Exercise and Sleep Research shows that people who get regular exercise sleep better than those who don't. For one week, keep a record of how much exercise and sleep you get. Describe how you feel each morning when you get up. After one week, review your sleep and exercise patterns. How do you feel when you get enough exercise and sleep? How do you feel when you don't get enough?

Technology Project

List at least four tips for starting an activity plan. Use a computer to make a slide presentation of the tips. If a computer is not available, make colorful posters to display your tips.

For more activities, visit The Learning Site. www.harcourtschool.com/health

Home & Community

Communicating Make a poster encouraging others to use the Activity Pyramid to improve their fitness. Illustrate your poster with pictures of activities that are fun and healthful. Display your poster at home or in a hallway at school.

Career Link

Athletic Trainer An athletic trainer helps people exercise correctly. Suppose that you are an athletic trainer at a local gym. Your job is to get adults and children into better shape, or physically fit. Write a flier about the importance of creating a personal fitness plan. Tell people what to include in a personal fitness plan and why they need one. Decorate your flier with pictures of people exercising.

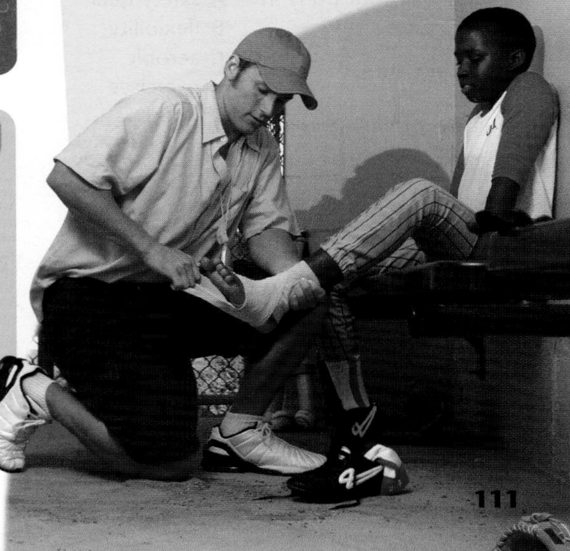

111

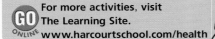

Career Link

Athletic Trainer Students might consider talking with the physical education teacher or a coach for ideas for their brochures. Plans should include warm-up activities, workout activities (both aerobic and anaerobic), and cool-downs. Students should also include frequency and duration information for each activity they include.

For more information on health careers, visit the **Webliography** in Teacher Resources at **www.harcourtschool.com/health**
Keyword health careers

Activities

Physical Education

Provide students with examples of your own fitness role models. Discuss what being a role model means and why you chose these particular people. If possible, invite a role model to talk with the class about his or her sport and achievements.

Science

Review results in general terms without requiring students to share personal information. Avoid discussing exercise patterns, as they may vary depending on student abilities. Note that some people need different amounts of sleep and rest than others, and also that people need different amounts of sleep and rest at different times in their lives. Students should conclude that people need adequate sleep and rest, and that people's bodies exhibit certain symptoms when adequate sleep and rest are not obtained. If the experiment doesn't go as expected, students could try to identify other factors that may have affected sleep.

Home & Community

Students' posters should address the physical, social, and emotional benefits of physical fitness.

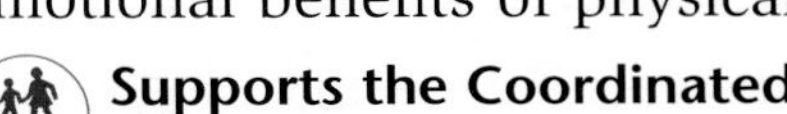

Supports the Coordinated School Health Program

Technology Project

Have students search for photographs or illustrations to complement their tips. Ask students to identify the importance of taking personal responsibility for maintaining a personal health plan for fitness. Instead of a computer slide show, students could use an overhead projector to project their tips.

Chapter Review and Test Preparation

Pages 112–113

Reading Skill 5 pts. each

1. Possible answer: increases endurance; improves cardiovascular system; strengthens heart and lungs
2. Possible answer: prevents injury; increases flexibility

Use Vocabulary 5 pts. each

3. D, good posture
4. F, endurance
5. B, flexibility
6. A, safety gear
7. C, aerobic exercises
8. E, rest

Check Understanding 5 pts. each

9. A, endurance
10. H, force
11. D, legs
12. F, work on computer
13. C, personal fitness plan
14. J, stretching
15. B, muscle strength
16. F, cells

Think Critically 5 pts. each

17. Possible answer: Take a light jog around the playing field for five minutes. Then perform some leg stretches and calf and back stretches.

Chapter Review and Test Preparation

Reading Skill

CAUSE AND EFFECT

Draw and then use these graphic organizers to answer questions 1 and 2.

1 Write at least two effects of aerobic exercise.

2 Write at least two effects of warming up before exercising.

Use Vocabulary

Match each term in Column B with its meaning in Column A.

Column A	Column B
3 Holding your body in a balanced way	**A** safety gear
4 What you have when your muscles can work for a long time without getting tired	**B** flexibility
5 The ability to move joints and muscles through a full range of motion	**C** aerobic exercises
6 Something you wear to help prevent injury	**D** good posture
7 Exercises that use fast walking	**E** endurance

Check Understanding

Choose the letter of the correct answer.

8 What does aerobic exercise mostly increase? (p. 100)
A endurance **C** strength
B energy **D** power

9 Muscle strength is the ability of your muscles to apply _____. (p. 99)
F flexibility **H** force
G endurance **J** motion

10 When you lift heavy objects, you should use your _____, not your back. (p. 93)
A arms **C** hands
B spine **D** legs

11 The Activity Pyramid suggests that you should do which activity least often? (p. 106)

F

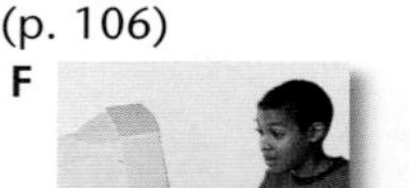

H

G

J

12 You can use the Activity Pyramid to create a _____. (pp. 106–107)
A work schedule
B sleep record
C personal fitness plan
D cardiovascular system

112

Formal Assessment

ASSESSMENT GUIDE P. 28

4

Name ______________________

Chapter Test

Fitness and Activity

Match the terms below to the sentences. Write the correct letter on the line to the left of each sentence.

a posture	**d** flexibility	**g** aerobic exercise	**j** rest
b anaerobic exercise	**e** warm-up	**h** Activity Pyramid	
c endurance	**f** cool-down	**i** muscle strength	

__a__ **1.** This is helped by exercises such as swimming, walking, and stretching.

__g__ **2.** This kind of activity is done for at least 30 minutes.

__b__ **3.** This is done in short, intense activities such as push-ups.

__c__ **4.** This is the ability to perform vigorous activity for a long time.

__i__ **5.** This is the ability of a muscle to apply force.

__j__ **6.** This gives your heart and other muscles a chance to slow down.

__d__ **7.** This is the ability to move muscles and joints through a full range of motion.

__e__ **8.** This is made up of slow movements that get the body ready to exercise.

__h__ **9.** This is a guide that identifies different types of physical activities and tells how long and how often each should be performed.

__f__ **10.** This is made up of exercises designed to help the body gradually return to normal levels.

© Harcourt

ASSESSMENT GUIDE P. 29

Name ______________________

Write the letter of the best answer on the line at the left.

__B__ **11.** Before beginning an exercise program, it is important to set realistic _____.
A decisions **C** limits
B goals **D** questions

__F__ **12.** When you are performing aerobic exercises, your _____.
F heart beats faster **H** sleep is easier
G heart beats slower **J** stomach growls

__D__ **13.** Aerobic exercise improves your cardiovascular system, which includes the heart and _____.
A intestines **C** lungs
B brain **D** blood vessels

__J__ **14.** Which of these is considered a benefit of physical fitness?
F long hair **H** improved speech
G long nails **J** improved sleep

__B__ **15.** Which of these will help you stay safe while playing team sports?
A thinking about other things
B following the rules
C paying attention to the spectators
D listening to a radio

Write *T* or *F* to show whether the statement is true or false.

__T__ **16.** The Activity Pyramid has five levels of physical activities.

__F__ **17.** Wearing safety gear while being physically active does not reduce your chance of injury.

__T__ **18.** You should get about 10 hours of sleep each night.

__T__ **19.** Taking an activity break will help you concentrate better.

__T__ **20.** Endurance, muscle strength, and flexibility are the three basic parts of physical fitness.

© Harcourt

13 _____ should be a part of both warm-ups and cool-downs. (p. 107)
F Endurance **H** Running
G Lifting weights **J** Stretching

14 The graphic organizer shows the three parts of physical fitness. What is missing? (p. 99)
A heart strength
B muscle strength
C cardiovascular fitness
D lung strength

15 When you sleep, your body repairs damaged _____. (p. 102)
F cells **H** blood
G energy **J** eyes

16 Which of the following do you need most after a busy day? (p. 102)
A workout **C** rest
B cool-down **D** endurance

Think Critically

17 You are going to play soccer with your friends. How would you safely warm up your body before playing?

Apply Skills

18 **BUILDING GOOD CHARACTER**
Fairness You and your friend Tony decide to start working out together. But every time you are supposed to get together, Tony makes excuses for not coming to your house. His house is one mile away from yours. Apply what you know about being fair and communicating with others to make a decision about what you should do.

19 **LIFE SKILLS**
Set Goals You would like to try out for your school's track team this spring. In order to make the team, you need to be able to run a mile in seven minutes. Use what you know to help you set a goal to make the team.

Write About Health

20 **Write to Inform—Explanation** Explain why exercising now can help you when you are an adult.

ASSESSMENT GUIDE P. 30

Name _______________

Exercise affects many parts of the body. Tell how exercise might affect each part of the body.

21. brain Possible answers: helps take your mind off things that are bothering you and reduces stress; helps you get rid of anger and other strong feelings

22. heart Possible answers: makes it stronger; increases amount of blood that the heart sends out to the body with each pump

23. lungs Possible answers: increases amount of air flowing in and out; makes the lungs stronger

Good posture prevents aches and pains. Tell how each part of the body should be held while sitting.

24. back should be straight

25. feet should be flat on the floor

© Harcourt

Apply Skills 5 pts. each

18. Possible answer: Explain to Tony that you do not feel it is fair that you always have to go to his home to exercise and that you would like him to come to your home sometimes. Decide to take turns going to each other's homes. If he can't come all the way to your house, maybe you could meet at a local park or school field that is between your homes.

19. Possible answer: Set a goal to begin running six weeks before tryouts. Run at least 15 minutes three days a week. Increase the amount of time you run by 10 minutes each week. Also plan some muscle-strengthening exercises to do on the days you do not run.

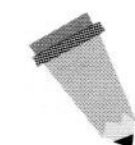

Write About Health 5 pts.

20. Possible answer: Exercising now can help me as an adult because it can strengthen my cardiovascular system, which can reduce my risk for heart disease. It can help me stay at a healthful weight. It can help prevent back injuries. It can also increase my flexibility, which can help prevent injuries as I get older.

Performance Assessment

Use the Chapter Project and the rubric provided on the Project Evaluation Sheet. See *Assessment Guide* pp. 18, 57, 65.

Portfolio Assessment

Have students select their best work from the following suggestions:
- Leveled Activities, p. 100
- Quick Activity, p. 108
- Write to Inform, p. 96
- Activities, p. 111

See *Assessment Guide* pp. 12–16.

CHAPTER 5
Safe at Home

Lesson	Pacing	Objectives	Reading Skills
Introduce the Chapter pp. 114–115		• Preview chapter concepts.	**Sequence** pp. 115, 300–301
1 **Responding to Emergencies** pp. 116–120	1 class period	• Recognize an emergency and know how to respond. • Explain how to develop a family emergency plan.	**Sequence** pp. 117, 120 • Main Idea and Details, p. 119 • Draw Conclusions, p. 120
Building Good Character p. 121		• Describe ways to demonstrate good citizenship during an emergency or practice drill.	
2 **Staying Safe at Home** pp. 122–125	1 class period	• Identify strategies for preventing injuries in the home. • Develop a fire safety plan.	**Sequence** p. 125 • Draw Conclusions, pp. 123, 124 • Main Idea and Details, p. 125
Life Skills p. 126–127	1 class period	• Identify the steps for decision-making. • Use the decision-making steps to stay safe.	
3 **Staying Safe Near Water** pp. 128–130	1 class period	• Identify safety rules for swimming, diving, and boating. • Describe how to respond to a water emergency.	**Sequence** pp. 129, 130 • Cause and Effect, p. 130
Activities p. 131		• Extend chapter concepts.	
Chapter Review pp. 132–133	1 class period	• Assess chapter objectives.	

Vocabulary	Program Resources
	Music CD Teaching Resources, p. 31
emergency family emergency plan	Transparencies 5, 25 Activity Book, pp. 21–22, 23
	Poster 2
hazard	Transparency 5 Activity Book, pp. 21–22
	Activity Book, p. 24 Poster 8
lifeguard	Transparency 5 Activity Book, pp. 21–22, 25
	The Learning Site www.harcourtschool.com
	Assessment Guide, pp. 31–33

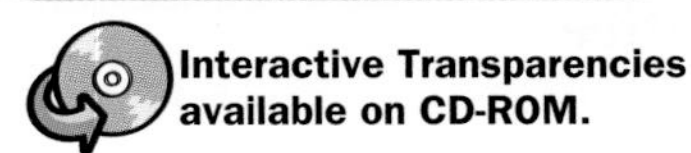
Interactive Transparencies available on CD-ROM.

Reading Skill

These reading skills are reinforced throughout this chapter and one skill is emphasized as the Focus Skill.

Sequence

- Draw Conclusions
- Identify Cause and Effect
- Identify Main Idea and Details
- Compare and Contrast
- Summarize

KEY READING SKILLS TRANSPARENCY 5

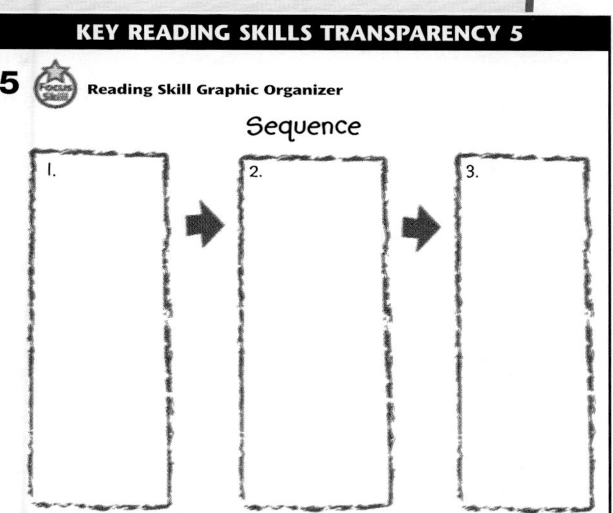

Life Skills

Life Skills are health-enhancing behaviors that can help students reduce risks to their health and safety.

Six Life Skills are reinforced throughout *Harcourt Health and Fitness*. The skill emphasized in this chapter is Make Responsible Decision.

POSTER 8
MAKE RESPONSIBLE DECISIONS

Building Good Character

Character education is an important aspect of health education. When children behave in ways that show good character, they promote the health and safety of themselves and others.

Six character traits are reinforced throughout *Harcourt Health and Fitness*. The trait emphasized in this chapter is Citizenship.

POSTER 2 CITIZENSHIP

Citizenship
Character
The boys are showing good citizenship by following school rules.
DO
Take pride in your school, community, state, and country.
Obey laws and rules and respect authority.
Be a good neighbor.
Help keep your school and neighborhood safe and clean.
Cooperate with others.
Protect the environment.
DON'T
Don't break rules and laws.
Don't waste natural resources.
Don't damage public property or the property of others.
Don't litter. Don't hurt the environment in other ways.
How have YOU shown good CITIZENSHIP today?

Resources

Coordinated School Health Program

Health Education
Health Services
Physical Education
Nutrition Services
Parent/ Community Involvement
Healthy School Environment
Counseling, Psychological, & Social Services
Health Promotion for Staff
CSHP

A Coordinated School Health Program endeavors to improve children's health and therefore their capacity to learn through the support of families, schools, and communities working together. The following information is provided to help classroom teachers be more aware of these resources.

The National Center for Chronic Disease and Health Promotion, part of the **CDC**, funds the Coordinated School Health Program. Visit its website for information about the eight components that make up this program.
www.cdc.gov/nccdphp/dash/

Each year, more than 200,000 children are injured on America's playgrounds. To address the concern for playground safety, the CDC and the **University of Northern Iowa** established the National Program for Playground Safety.
www.uni.edu/playground/

The best thing anyone can do to stay safe in and around the water is to learn to swim. The **American Red Cross** identifies specialized water activities and outlines ways to stay safe while enjoying those activities.
www.redcross.org/

The American Academy of Pediatric Dentistry (**AAPD**) recommends that dentists play an active role in encouraging the use of protective equipment for both organized and informal sporting activities.
www.aapd.org/

Other resources that support a Coordinated School Health Program:
- School-Home Connection
- Daily Physical Activity
- Daily Fitness Tips
- Activities: Home & Community
- Health Background: Webliography
- *Be Active! Resources for Physical Education*

Media Resources

Books for Students

Mattern, Joanne. ***Safety at Home.*** ABDO Publishing, 1999. Looks at potential dangers in the home and discusses ways to stay safe. **EASY**

Children's Hospital at Yale–New Haven. ***Now I Know Better: Kids Tell Kids About Safety***. Millbrook Press, 1996. Children describe emergencies; includes advice from emergency room doctors. **AVERAGE**

Gutman, Bill. ***Hazards at Home***. Twenty-First Century Books, 1996. Tells about potential dangers in the home and how to prevent accidents. **ADVANCED**

Books for Teachers and Families

Handal, Kathleen, MD. ***The American Red Cross First Aid and Safety Handbook.*** Little, Brown 1992. A guide to first aid based on materials used by the Red Cross.

National Safety Council. ***First Aid and CPR.*** Jones & Bartlett Publishers, 2000. Outlines the steps to victim resuscitation; diagrams included.

Free and Inexpensive Materials

Underwriter's Laboratories
Ask for a free copy of UL's room-by-room home safety tip guide.

Character Education
Has on-line teaching guides on topics such as conflicts and bullying.

Consumer Product Safety Commission
Request CPSC #383 checklist to correct situations that may lead to poisonings.

Federal Citizen Information Center
Ask for CPSC #627J checklist to ensure a safe home playground.

U.S. Fire Administration
Has free books, videotapes, and kits on fire prevention on their Kids Page.

To access free and inexpensive resources on the Web, visit
www.harcourtschool.com/health/free

Videos

First Aid for Students: Water Safety and Resuscitation. Sheridan House, 1994.

Home Alone: You're in Charge. Sunburst Communications, 1993.

Water Safety for Kids. Swim Safe Fundamentals, 1994.

These resources have been selected to meet a variety of individual needs. Please review all materials and websites prior to sharing them with students to ensure the content is appropriate for your class. Note that information, while correct at time of publication, is subject to change.

Visit **The Learning Site** for related links, activities, resources, and the health **Webliography.**

www.harcourtschool.com/health

Meeting Individual Needs

Below-Level

Have students focus on text structure. Before they read a section, have them preview it by looking at the headings, the pictures, and the questions at the end. Have students predict what the section will be about and write one question they want to answer from the reading.

Activities

- Make a List, p. 118
- Create a Display, p. 124

On-Level

Using prior knowledge can help students set a purpose for reading. Have them think about what they already know about the selection. Write their comments on a chart, and discuss areas where more information is needed. Ask students what they would like to learn more about.

Activities

- Make a Diagram, p. 118
- Make a Poster, p. 124

Challenge

Have students use the Internet or library resources to explore the history of a health-related subject. Have them make a time line on paper strips of facts or events related to the topic. They should write the related facts or events at appropriate points on the time line.

Activities

- Make a Public Announcement, p. 118
- Write a Song, p. 124

ESL/ELL

Language Workshop

Oral language can be developed through rhythmic activities. Have students repeat words and phrases rhythmically. Chants help students remember phrases and practice language skills. Have students slap knees or clap hands while saying words related to the chapter.

Activities

- Comprehensible Input, p. 122
- Background and Experience, p. 128

Curriculum Integration

Use these topics to integrate health into your daily planning.

Physical Education

- Daily Fitness Tip, pp. 116, 122, 128
- Daily Physical Activity, p. 115
- Beachball Rally, p. 129

Math

- The Necessity of Water, p. 120

Art

- Disaster Warning Posters, p. 119
- Safety Tags, p. 123

Social Studies

- Disasters in Your Area, p. 119

CHAPTER 5

Pages 114–133

CHAPTER SUMMARY

In this chapter, students

- learn how to respond to emergencies and to develop a family emergency plan.
- practice safety measures to prevent injuries at home, and in and near water.

Life Skills

Students *make decisions* about following family rules and staying safe.

Building Good Character

Students demonstrate good *citizenship* by obeying authorities in an emergency.

Literature Springboard

Use the poem "I Need My Knees, But No More Please" to spark interest in the chapter topic. See the Read-Aloud Anthology on page RA-6 of this *Teacher Edition*.

Prereading Strategies

SCAN THE CHAPTER Have students preview the chapter content by scanning the titles, headings, pictures, tables, and graphs. Ask volunteers to predict what they will learn. Use their predictions to determine their prior knowledge.

PREVIEW VOCABULARY Have students look up unfamiliar words in the Glossary.

Words I Know	Words I've Seen or Heard	New Words

Reading Skill

SEQUENCE To introduce or review this skill, have students use the Reading in Health Handbook, pp. 38–39. Teaching strategies and additional activities are also provided.

Students will have opportunities to practice and apply this skill throughout this chapter.

- Focus Skill Reading Mini-Lesson, p. 116
- Reading comprehension questions identified with the 
- *Activity Book* p. 23 (shown on page 120)
- Lesson Summary and Review, pp. 120, 125, 130
- Chapter Review and Test Preparation, pp. 132–133

Reading Skill

SEQUENCE To sequence is to place in order the events that take place. It is also the order of the steps for doing a task. Use the Reading in Health Handbook on pages 338–339 and this graphic organizer to help you read the health facts in this chapter.

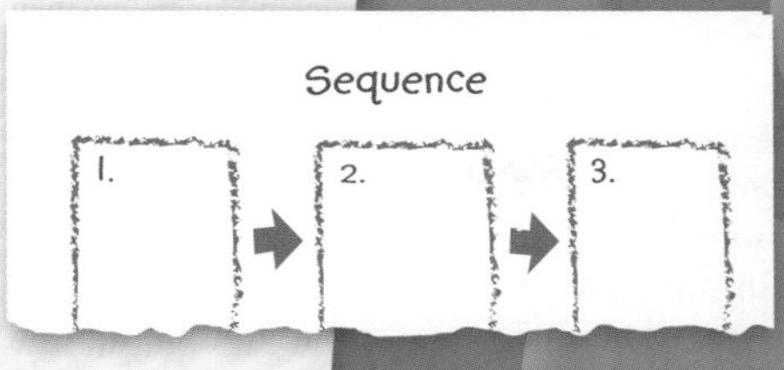

Health Graph

INTERPRET DATA Every year, hundreds of thousands of children go to emergency rooms for treatment of injuries. Of the causes shown in the graph, which results in the greatest number of injuries? How many more injuries are there from falls than from burns? From falls than from poisonings?

Unintentional Injuries
Children 5–14

Number of Injuries per Year: 0, 200,000, 400,000, 600,000, 800,000, 1,000,000, 1,200,000, 1,400,000
Cause of Injury: Falls, Burns, Poisonings

Daily Physical Activity

Enjoy being active. Keep your activities safe.

Be Active!
Use the selection Track 5, **Flexercise**, to practice safe warm-ups and exercises.

School-Home Connection

Distribute copies of the School-Home Connection (in English or Spanish). Have students take the page home to share with their families as you begin this chapter.

Follow Up Have volunteers share the results of their activities.

Supports the Coordinated School Health Program

TEACHING RESOURCES P. 31

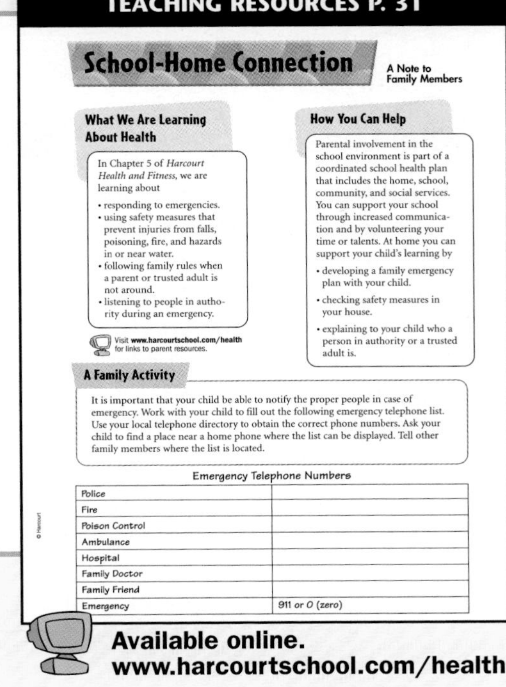

School-Home Connection

A Note to Family Members

What We Are Learning About Health

In Chapter 5 of *Harcourt Health and Fitness*, we are learning about

- responding to emergencies.
- using safety measures that prevent injuries from falls, poisoning, fire, and hazards in or near water.
- following family rules when a parent or trusted adult is not around.
- listening to people in authority during an emergency.

Visit **www.harcourtschool.com/health** for links to parent resources.

How You Can Help

Parental involvement in the school environment is part of a coordinated school health plan that includes the home, school, community, and social services. You can support your school through increased communication and by volunteering your time or talents. At home you can support your child's learning by

- developing a family emergency plan with your child.
- checking safety measures in your house.
- explaining to your child who a person in authority or a trusted adult is.

A Family Activity

It is important that your child be able to notify the proper people in case of emergency. Work with your child to fill out the following emergency telephone list. Use your local telephone directory to obtain the correct phone numbers. Ask your child to find a place near a home phone where the list can be displayed. Tell other family members where the list is located.

Emergency Telephone Numbers

Police	
Fire	
Poison Control	
Ambulance	
Hospital	
Family Doctor	
Family Friend	
Emergency	911 or 0 (zero)

© Harcourt

Available online.
www.harcourtschool.com/health

INTRODUCE THE CHAPTER

Health Graph

Interpret Data

Ask volunteers to explain what information the graph is presenting. **Which of the causes shown in the graph results in the greatest number of injuries?** falls

How many times more injuries are there from falls than from burns? roughly 25 (24.5) times

How many times more injuries are there from falls than from poisoning? 68

Daily Physical Activity

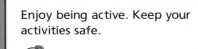

Use *Be Active! Music for Daily Physical Activity* with the Instant Activity Cards to provide students with movement activities that can be done in limited space. Options for using these components are provided beginning on page TR2 in this *Teacher Edition*.

Chapter Project

Be Safe, Not Sorry (*Assessment Guide* p. 58)

ASSESS PRIOR KNOWLEDGE Use students' initial ideas for the project as a baseline assessment of their understanding of chapter concepts. Have students complete the project as they work through the chapter.

PERFORMANCE ASSESSMENT The project can be used for performance assessment. Use the Project Evaluation Sheet, *Assessment Guide* p. 66.

LESSON 1

Pages 116–120

Objectives

- ► Recognize an emergency and know how to respond.
- ► Explain how to develop a family emergency plan.

When Minutes Count . . .

Assign the Quick Study, Lesson 1, Activity Book pp. 21–22 (shown on p. 117).

Program Resources

- ► Activity Book pp. 21–22, 23
- ► Transparencies 5, 25

Vocabulary

emergency p. 116,

family emergency plan p. 118

Daily Fitness Tip

Tell students that part of planning for emergencies is to practice and maintain the family emergency plan. Family members should review the plan every six months, conduct regular fire evacuations, replace stored water and food every six months, make sure fire extinguishers are charged, test smoke detectors monthly, and change smoke detector batteries at least once a year.

1. MOTIVATE

Ask students to brainstorm what comes to mind when they hear the word *emergency*. List their responses on the board. Then ask them to name actions that people should take in an emergency. List these also, and leave the lists on the board for students to refer to while studying this lesson.

LESSON 1 Responding to Emergencies

Lesson Focus
You can prepare for some emergencies or disasters. In an emergency, you can take steps to get help.

Why Learn This?
You can use what you learn to help yourself and others stay safe during a disaster.

Vocabulary
emergency
family emergency plan

Make an Emergency Phone Call

You see a house on fire in your neighborhood. This is an emergency. An **emergency** (ee•MER•juhn•see) is a situation in which help is needed right away. Other examples of emergencies are severe burns, severe bleeding, stopped breathing or stopped heartbeat, poisoning, drowning, and broken bones.

In an emergency, you must act quickly. The first thing to do is to tell an adult. If an adult isn't around, you must call for help.

For Emergencies

- Write down your name, your home address, your parents' or guardians' names, and their phone numbers at work.
- Post this list by a telephone in your home.

116

Reading Skill

Mini-Lesson

SEQUENCE Remind students that a sequence shows the order in which things occur. Have them practice this skill by responding to the Focus Skill question on page 117. Have students draw and complete the graphic organizer as you model it on the transparency.

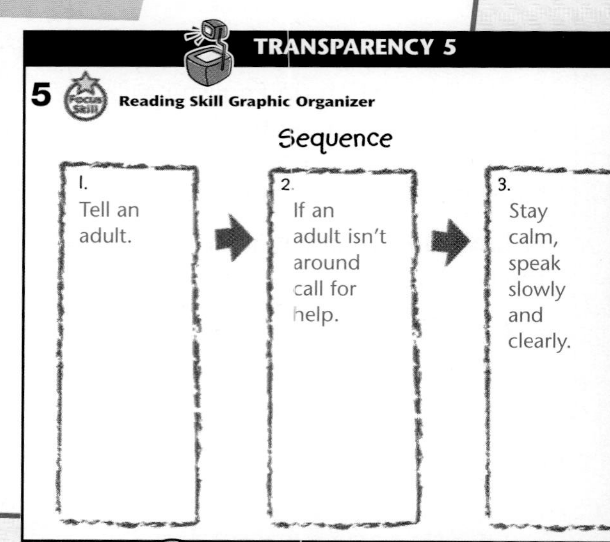

TRANSPARENCY 5
5 Reading Skill Graphic Organizer
Sequence
1. Tell an adult.
2. If an adult isn't around call for help.
3. Stay calm, speak slowly and clearly.

Interactive Transparencies available on CD-ROM.

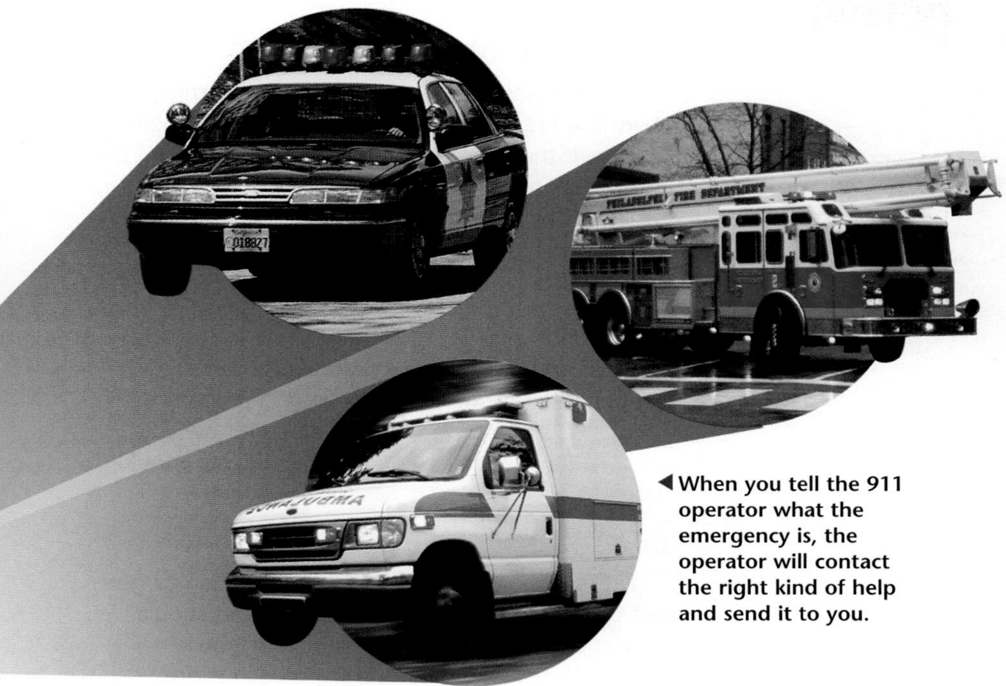

When you tell the 911 operator what the emergency is, the operator will contact the right kind of help and send it to you.

Communication skills are very important when you talk with a 911 operator. Remember to do the following:

- Stay calm.
- Speak slowly and clearly.
- Tell the 911 operator your name, the problem, the phone number you are calling from, and the address.
- Answer the operator's questions as completely as possible. If you are at home, you can read your *For Emergencies* list by your phone.
- Stay on the phone until the operator tells you to hang up.

SEQUENCE What is the first thing you should do in an emergency?
Tell an adult, if possible.

ACTIVITY

Life Skills

Communicate

Rena decides to practice giving information to an emergency operator. She knows that she needs to speak clearly. What else does Rena need to do? Use the steps for Communicating About a Health Need on pages 46–47.

QUICK STUDY, ACTIVITY BOOK PP. 21–22

CHAPTER 5 Name ______ Quick Study

Safe at Home

Directions
- Use lesson vocabulary in the Word Bank to complete each **Summary**.
- Read the section directions to complete each **Lesson Details**.

Word Bank
emergency hazard lifeguard family emergency plan

Lesson 1 pp. 116–120

Summary If an emergency happens, tell an adult or call 911. Deciding on escape routes from your home should be part of your family emergency plan.

Lesson Details The parts of a family emergency plan are listed in the left column. The reason each part is important is listed in the right column. Draw a line to match each part with the reason it is important.

Know your family contact	to know how to prepare for disasters.
Know what could happen	so family members will know everyone is safe.
Learn how to turn off utilities	to let someone in another city know you are safe.
Decide on escape routes	to get out of your home quickly.
Choose two meeting places	to prevent danger from water, gas, and electricity.

Lesson 2 pp. 122–125

Summary A slippery floor is an example of a hazard that can lead to a fall.

Lesson Details Hazardous Hilda does not know her safety rules. Listed below are five unsafe actions. Help Hilda keep herself and others safe. Write the safety rule for each behavior. The first one is done for you.

1. Hilda wants to stick a fork in the toaster to get out a piece of stuck bread.
   Don't stick metal objects into electrical appliances.
2. Hilda has a cough, so she reaches for the cough syrup.
   Never take medicine unless a parent or another trusted adult gives it to you.
3. Hilda leaves her backpack in the doorway.
   Be aware of what's going on around you.

© Harcourt

Name ______ Quick Study (continued)

4. With bare hands, Hilda reaches for a hot cup in the microwave.
   Use mitts to remove hot food or liquid from the microwave.
5. Hilda decides to spray a big bug with insect spray when her parents aren't around.
   Do not use insect sprays, cleaning products, or other household products without an adult's help.

Lesson 3 pp. 128–130

Summary At a swimming pool, the lifeguard has the authority to tell people to follow the rules.

Lesson Details Use pp. 128–130 to complete the graphic organizer.

Main Idea: Practicing water safety can help prevent injury.

Details:
1. Obey the lifeguard.
2. Don't jump into the pool backward.
3. Dive only into water 9 feet deep or more.
4. Don't dive from the side of a pool.
5. Wear a life jacket when you are on a boat.

© Harcourt

Available online.
www.harcourtschool.com/health

2. TEACH

Interpret Visuals—Tables

Review the steps for responding in an emergency on page 116. Give students lined index cards, and have them write their name, home address, home phone number, and parents' or guardians' names and phone numbers if they work outside the home. On the board, write a model card using your name. Tell students to fill in as much as they can and then take the cards home to have a family member help complete them. Students should post the card by a telephone in their home.

Critical Thinking Why is it important to act quickly and stay calm in an emergency? Possible answers: Getting help as soon as possible may help save a person's life; if you get excited, you may not speak clearly or may forget what to say; you will help the injured person stay calm, too.

Discuss

Discuss situations in which a person should call 911. Tell students that they should never call 911 unless it is an emergency because they can tie up the system for true emergencies and prevent people from getting needed help. However, they should always call 911 if they are in doubt about whether something is an emergency and no adult is present.

What are some situations that are not emergencies? Possible answers: finding out the starting time of an event; getting directions to a location; reporting a lost pet

Activity

Communicate Have students use the information in the box on page 116, in the main text on this page, and in the steps on pages 46–47 to write what Rena needs to do.

TEACH *continued*

Content-Area Reading Support

Using Titles and Headings Direct attention to the headings on these pages. Point out that the first heading, which identifies the overall topic, is in larger type than the other headings, which identify subtopics. Explain that type size and color are clues to the topic and organization of information in a passage. **How do the green subheads relate to the main head on the page?** They tell the main steps in making an emergency plan.

Discuss

Have a volunteer read aloud the first paragraph on this page.
What disasters could happen in the home or community? Possible responses: fire, electrical storm that knocks out the power, flood, tornado, earthquake, hurricane, blizzard, extremely hot weather
Students on occasion may find themselves at home alone. Explain that there are also safety guidelines that they and their parents can follow during these times. Tell students to go to page 356 of the Health and Safety Handbook for tips and safeguards for when they are home alone. Have students also explain how to develop a home-safety plan, such as for fire safety.

Quick Activity

It may be helpful for students to draw their entire home so that they can mark how to get out of the home through the door of their bedroom. They can use different-colored markers to show each escape route. Both routes should end at the meeting place outside.

When Minutes Count . . .

Transparency 25: Emergency Escape Plan can be used to present material in this lesson.
Interactive Transparencies available on CD-ROM.

Personal Health Plan

Real-Life Situation
Suppose you were writing down your family emergency plan.
Real-Life Plan
Write a list of people you could contact. Talk with your family about which person should be the family contact.

Make an Emergency Plan

An emergency can happen without warning. If there is a fire, you might need to leave your home quickly. If there is a storm, your electricity might be out for a long time. You can prepare for such situations by making a **family emergency plan**, a list of steps your family will take to stay safe during an emergency.

Know What Could Happen

Find out what kinds of natural disasters can happen where you live. Learn how to prepare for them and what to do if they happen. Know your community's warning signals and what you should do when they are given.

Decide on Escape Routes

If there is a fire in your home, you need to get out quickly. Your family emergency plan should have a drawing of each room in your house. Include two ways to escape from each room.

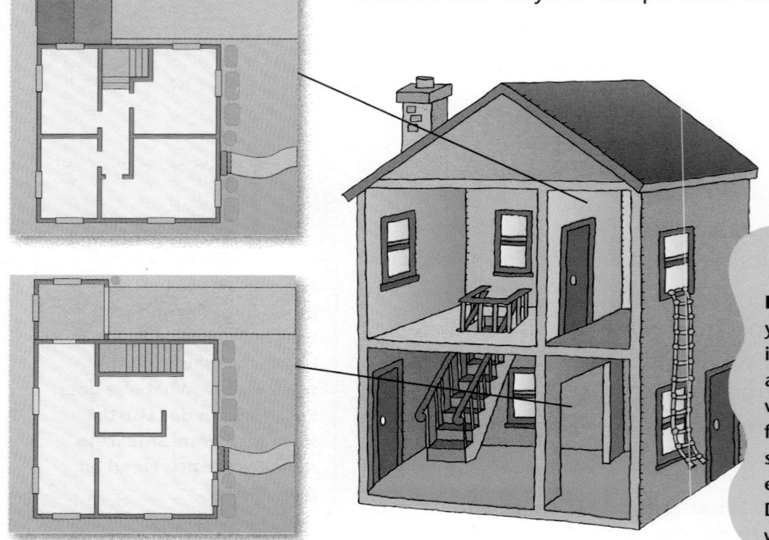

Quick Activity

Plan an Escape Sketch your bedroom, including the windows and doors. Write two ways you could escape from the room, and show these escape exits on your sketch. Decide whether you would need a ladder.

118

Meeting Individual Needs
Leveled Activities

BELOW-LEVEL Make a List Have students find the emergency numbers for the fire department, police department, poison control center, and ambulance service for their city or town. Have them copy these numbers onto a list.

ON-LEVEL Make a Diagram Ask students to make a diagram showing the different parts of a family emergency plan. Have them fill in as much information as possible, including a sketch of their entire home, and then take the diagram home to a parent or guardian for help in completing it.

CHALLENGE Make a Public Service Announcement Encourage students to write and present a public service announcement about the importance of making a family emergency plan and the steps involved.

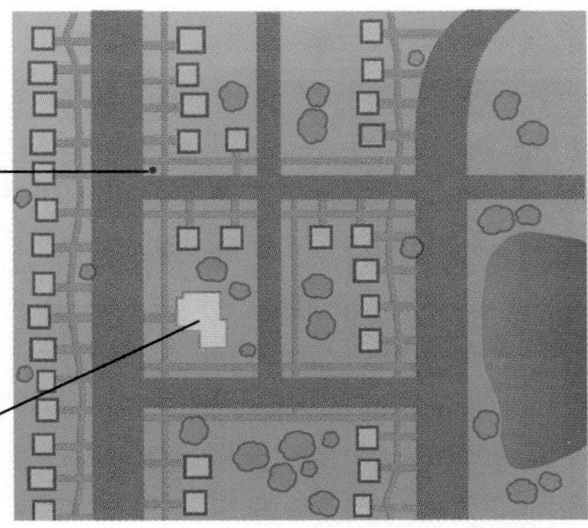

Know Your Family Contact

For a family contact, choose someone who lives in another city. Write down the person's name, address, and phone number. If a disaster happens and you become separated from your family, you should call this person to let him or her know where you are. If you are with your family, call to say the family is OK.

Learn How to Turn Off Utilities

Water, gas, and electricity are utilities. These may be damaged in an emergency and become dangerous. Ask a parent or another adult to show you how to shut them off.

Choose Two Meeting Places.

All members of your family should meet in the same place. One place should be near your home. Another place should be away from your neighborhood in case you can't return home.

MAIN IDEA AND DETAILS What is a family emergency plan? What are five things the plan should include?

It is a list of steps your family will take to stay safe during an emergency; know what could happen, decide on escape routes from your home, know your family contact, learn how to turn off utilities, and choose two meeting places.

119

Discuss

Ask students to identify the importance of taking personal responsibility for developing and maintaining a personal health plan for personal safety. Have them discuss possible meeting places outside their homes and away from their neighborhoods. If the emergency is sudden, such as a fire, meeting at a light pole or a large tree might be appropriate. A place away from your neighborhood might be a friend's or relative's house or a local storm shelter.

Critical Thinking Why is it important to have a place to meet during an emergency? It's important so that the family knows who is safe and who to look for. If someone does not appear at the meeting place, he or she may be trapped inside a house during a fire or may be in danger during another type of disaster, such as a weather emergency. Use this opportunity to ask students to explain how to develop a home emergency response plan, such as for fire safety.

Personal Health Plan

Plans should include:

- Names of several relatives or friends who live in another city or state
- A time that you will talk to your family about which person should be the family contact

This feature is designed to provide students with an opportunity to reflect on health decisions they are making in their personal lives. The Personal Health Plan should not be used to evaluate or assess students, nor should the results be shared among students.

Art

Disaster Warning Posters
Have students make posters giving disaster warning and preparedness information. They should create three-column tables on their posters, listing possible disasters for their area in the first column. In the other two columns, they should list warning signals that can be given for particular events and the various ways that people can prepare for such events.

Social Studies

Disasters in Your Area Divide the class into five groups, and assign each group one disaster or emergency that may occur in your area. For example, your area may experience floods, hurricanes, tornadoes, electrical storms, and heat waves. Have students use information they have accessed on disasters in their area to prepare a skit in which each student shows one action to stay safe.

3. WRAP UP

Lesson 1 Summary and Review

1. emergency; adult; 911; family emergency plan; utilities
2. any five items listed on this page
3. One way out may not be safe. You may have to go out a window because a door is blocked by fire.
4. Answers may include:

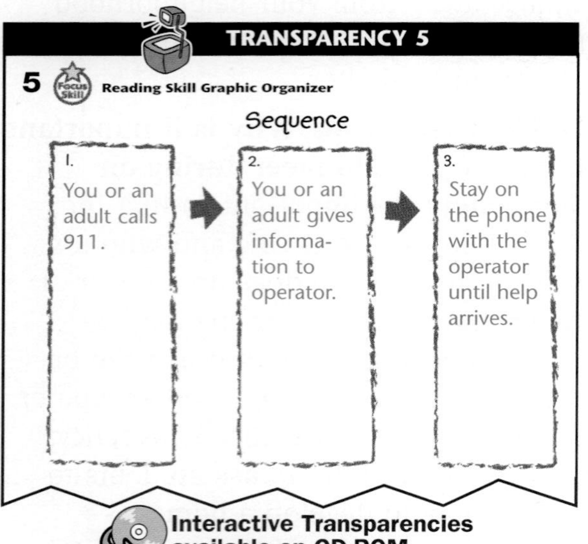

TRANSPARENCY 5
5 Reading Skill Graphic Organizer
Sequence
1. You or an adult calls 911.
2. You or an adult gives information to operator.
3. Stay on the phone with the operator until help arrives.
Interactive Transparencies available on CD-ROM.

5. Paragraphs should indicate that being prepared for emergencies can help prevent injury, help keep existing injuries from becoming worse, and help keep people safe if services are interrupted.

For **writing models** with examples, see *Teaching Resources* pp. 47–61. Rubrics are also provided.

When Minutes Count . . .

Quick Study Students can use *Activity Book* pages 21–22 (shown on p. 117) as they complete each lesson in this chapter.

Myth and Fact

Myth: Items in an emergency supply kit stay good forever. They don't need to be replaced unless you use them.

Fact: Medicine, batteries, water, and food do not stay good over a long time. Check expiration dates, and throw out items that have expired. Replace food and water every six months.

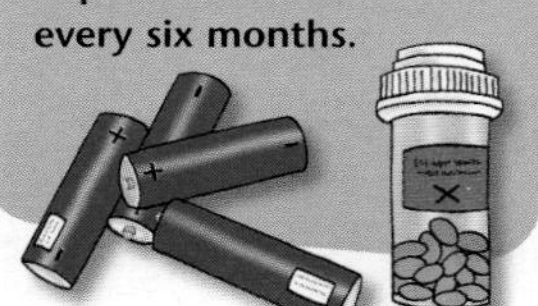

Make an Emergency Supply Kit

If an emergency happens, your family might be without electricity or running water. Plan for emergencies by keeping an emergency supply kit. Always keep it in the same place. Include the following supplies in your kit:

- canned fruits, vegetables, meats, and soups, plus a manual can opener
- plastic cups, plates, and eating utensils
- bottled water
- flashlight, battery-operated radio, and batteries
- clothes, shoes, and bedding
- first-aid kit and medicines

DRAW CONCLUSIONS Why is it important to have a family emergency supply kit?
because the family may be without electricity and running water during a disaster

Lesson 1 Summary and Review

1. **Summarize with Vocabulary**
   Use vocabulary and other terms from this lesson to complete the statements.
   An _____ is a situation in which help is needed right away. If someone is hurt, tell an _____ or call the number _____. Your family can follow a _____ in an emergency to help stay safe. Gas, water, and electricity are examples of _____.
2. Name five items that belong in an emergency supply kit.
3. **Critical Thinking** Why do you need to know two ways to escape from each room if a fire happens in your home?
4. **SEQUENCE** Draw and complete this graphic organizer to show what happens from the time you see an emergency until help arrives.

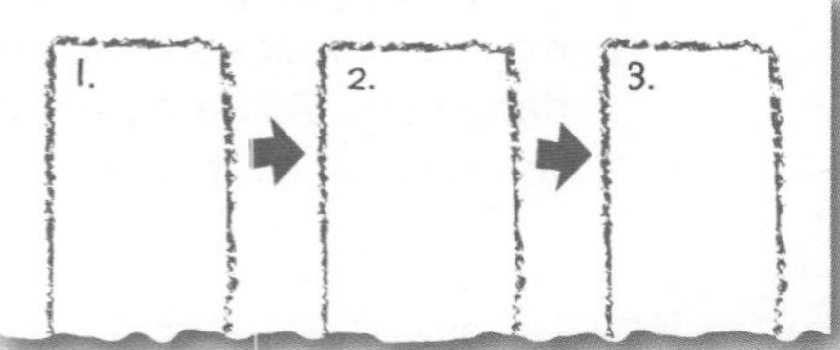

5. **Write to Express—Idea**

   Write a paragraph to tell why being prepared for an emergency is important. Include examples from this lesson or from what you already know.

120

Math

The Necessity of Water
Explain that the average person needs two quarts of water daily just for drinking. The person may also need an additional two quarts for sanitary purposes. Ask students to calculate how much stored water their family would need for drinking and for sanitation for three days during a disaster.

ACTIVITY BOOK P. 23

Name ____________

Focus Skill Reading Skill

Sequence

How Accidents Happen

Have you ever lined up dominoes and then touched one and watched all of them fall? What happens if you remove one domino from the line or move it so that the domino before it cannot touch it? All the other dominoes that follow will remain standing.

In the same way, many injuries occur because of an order, or sequence, of events. One event leads to another event. Here is a sequence.

1. the situation: the first thing that leads to the accident
2. the risky habit: a habit that is unsafe
3. the risky act: a behavior that is unsafe
4. the accident: the result of the risky act
5. the injury: the result of the accident

The following sentences that describe an accident are not in the correct order. Copy the graphic organizer below, and use it to put the events in the correct sequence. Then write one way each of the first three events could be changed to prevent the injury.

Ben leaves the floor wet. Ben's sister breaks her wrist when she falls. Ben lets his dog in from the rain, and the dog drips water on the floor. Ben's sister slips and falls on the wet floor. Ben doesn't notice the water on the floor, because he often doesn't notice unsafe conditions.

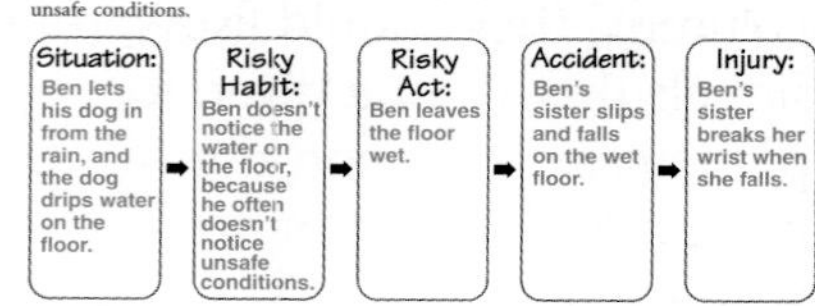

Situation:	Risky Habit:	Risky Act:	Accident:	Injury:
Ben lets his dog in from the rain, and the dog drips water on the floor.	Ben doesn't notice the water on the floor, because he often doesn't notice unsafe conditions.	Ben leaves the floor wet.	Ben's sister slips and falls on the wet floor.	Ben's sister breaks her wrist when she falls.

© Harcourt

Situation: Ben can dry off the dog when it enters the house.

Risky Habit: Ben can pay more attention to unsafe conditions.

Risky Act: Ben can mop up the water.

Available online.
www.harcourtschool.com/health

Citizenship

Building Good Character

Respecting Authority

In an emergency, an adult who has authority decides what to do. An adult in charge, such as a police officer or firefighter, may wear a uniform. But he or she also can be your parent, a teacher, or another adult. Being a good citizen means that you respect people who have authority. You cooperate and do what they say, to protect yourself and others from harm. Here are ways you can show respect for authority during an emergency drill or a real emergency:

- **Follow the instructions given by the adult in charge.**
- **Listen carefully. Don't interrupt when the person is talking. Ask questions if you don't understand what to do.**
- **Do what you are asked to do. Don't talk back to the person in authority.**
- **Don't fool around or make jokes. An emergency or even a drill is a serious situation.**
- **Help others obey authority. Don't ask them to break rules or laws.**

Activity

In small groups, think of an emergency situation. It might be a tornado, a loss of electric power for several days, or an injury to a person. Write a skit that shows how people should respect authority in that situation. Choose one member to act the role of the person in authority. Perform your skit for the class.

121

Building Good Character

Caring
Citizenship
Fairness
Respect
Responsibility
Trustworthiness

Objective

► Describe ways to demonstrate good citizenship during an emergency or a practice drill.

Program Resource

► Poster 2

BEFORE READING

Provide various emergency scenarios, and ask students to brainstorm people who might be in charge. Examples include a *parent* immediately after a fire breaks out at home, a *lifeguard* as a storm approaches a beach, and the *principal* when a tornado warning is sounded at school.

DISCUSS

Using the example of a fire drill at school, have students tell how they can follow each guideline in the passage to show respect for authority and be good citizens.

ACTIVITY

Advise students to use information in this chapter to prepare their skits. Have them illustrate each point in the passage. Stop at some point during each group's presentation to ask the class to discuss what might happen if the students were not showing respect for authority.

Using the Poster

Activity Discuss the information presented in the poster. Then have students use the ideas from their skits to add ways to show respect for authority. You may wish to have students make their own posters showing this information.

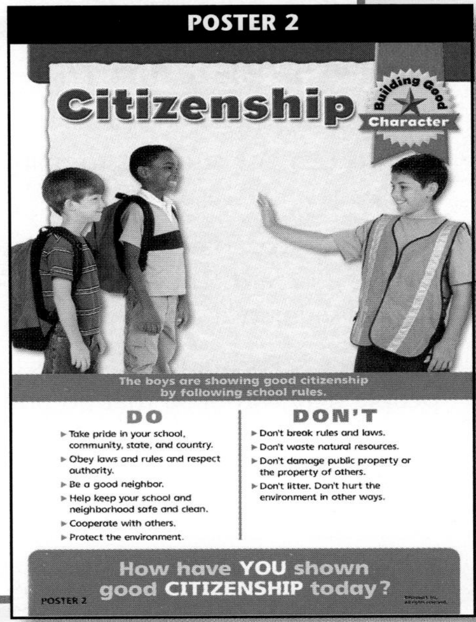

POSTER 2
Citizenship
Building Good Character
The boys are showing good citizenship by following school rules.
DO
► Take pride in your school, community, state, and country.
► Obey laws and rules and respect authority.
► Be a good neighbor.
► Help keep your school and neighborhood safe and clean.
► Cooperate with others.
► Protect the environment.
DON'T
► Don't break rules and laws.
► Don't waste natural resources.
► Don't damage public property or the property of others.
► Don't litter. Don't hurt the environment in other ways.
How have YOU shown good CITIZENSHIP today?
POSTER 2

LESSON 2
Pages 122–125

Objectives
- ► Identify strategies for preventing injuries in the home.
- ► Develop a fire safety plan.

When Minutes Count . . .
Assign the Quick Study, Lesson 2, Activity Book pp. 21–22 (shown on p. 117).

Program Resources
- ► Activity Book pp. 21–22
- ► Transparency 5

Vocabulary
hazard p. 122

Daily Fitness Tip
Caution students that they should never have lit candles in their bedrooms. Almost half of home candle fires start in a bedroom. Candle fires kill more people than fires from most other causes except smoking and children playing with fire.

For more information about safety rules and exercise, see *Be Active! Resources for Physical Education,* p. 177.

1. MOTIVATE
Optional Activity Materials ladder, chair or stool, heavy books, mobile

Have a ladder handy, but don't draw students' attention to it. Tell students you need to attach a mobile to the ceiling. While they watch, place an overturned trash can on the seat of the chair, and then place some heavy books on top of that.

Am I practicing safety measures if I get up on this chair? no

What could I do to reach the ceiling safely? use the ladder

At home, what is a safe way to reach for items high on a shelf or in a cupboard? use a sturdy stepladder, or ask an adult to help

LESSON 2 Staying Safe at Home

Lesson Focus
You can practice safety and watch out for hazards at home.

Why Learn This?
What you learn can help protect you and others from harm at home.

Vocabulary
hazard

Health & Technology

Preventing Kitchen Fires
Most food fires occur when food or oil overheats on the stove. The Consumer Product Safety Commission is developing technology that turns off burners when they get too hot, and fire extinguishers that put out cooking fires.

Prevent Injuries in the Home
You might be surprised to learn that many injuries are caused by accidents in the home. Using injury prevention can help. *Injury prevention* (IN•juh•ree prih•VEN•shuhn) means "keeping injuries from happening."

One way to prevent injuries is to practice *safety measures*, actions you take to stay safe. One safety measure is to get rid of or be careful around hazards. A **hazard** (HAZ•erd) is an object or condition that makes a situation unsafe. For example, electricity can be a hazard when it's not used properly.

122

ESL/ELL Support
COMPREHENSIBLE INPUT Help students understand the meaning of *hazard.*

Beginning Ask students to point to the hazards in the pictures on these two pages.

Intermediate Have students describe in their own words situations that involve a hazard. They should tell exactly what the hazard is and how it can cause injury.

Advanced Encourage students to write a story about a hazard and how people deal with it so that no one is injured.

Falls are the most common cause of home injuries. People fall in bathtubs, out of windows, and on stairs. Floors can be dangerous when they are wet or slippery.

Fires also cause many injuries in the home. Here are tips to prevent injuries from fire:

- Get permission before using an electrical or cooking appliance. Make sure you know how to use it.
- Know where fire extinguishers are.
- Make sure there are smoke detectors on every level of the house and in sleeping areas.

DRAW CONCLUSIONS What can you do to prevent injuries?
Practice safety measures.

Major Causes of Home Fires

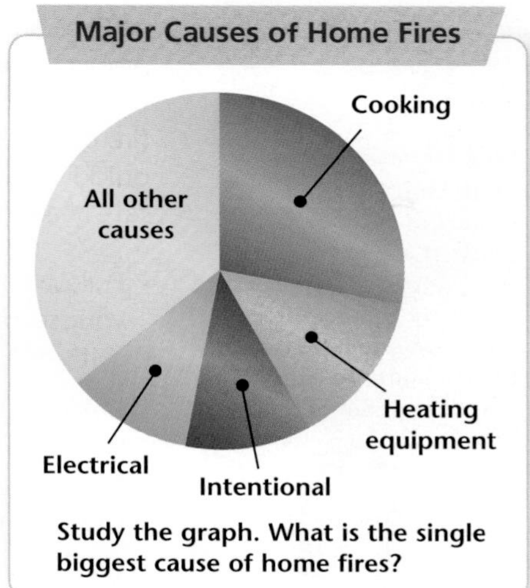

Study the graph. What is the single biggest cause of home fires?

Quick Activity

Look for Hazards Look at the picture on these two pages. What safety hazards can you find? Make a list of safety rules you might use at home to prevent injury from some of these hazards.

2. TEACH

Interpret Visuals—Graphs

Tell students that a circle graph tells the percentages of different parts of a whole. Help students estimate the single biggest cause of home fires. cooking

Quick Activity

Explain that while the single biggest cause of home fires is cooking, smoking causes the greatest number of fire-related deaths. Have students work in pairs to identify the safety hazards shown on these two pages and write how they would correct the hazards. Discuss their findings as a class.
Hazards may include overloading electric outlets, using electric appliances near water, leaving unused appliances plugged in, cooking food unattended, no hot mitts for handling hot food or liquid, metal objects in electrical appliances, objects on stairway, piles of paper, unattended candle burning, puddles of water on floor.

Discuss

Tell students that fires that start at night are especially dangerous.

Critical Thinking Why do you think this is true? Because people are asleep, the fire may go unnoticed for a long time.

Problem Solving How can the risk of injury from fires that start at night be reduced? by having working smoke detectors in sleeping areas

Teacher Tip

Checklist for Smoke Detectors Provide calendars, rulers, and $8^1/2$ in. x 11 in. sheets of poster board. Assist students in developing a schedule for testing the smoke detectors in their homes once a month and for changing the batteries twice a year (such as when changing to daylight savings time in April and back to standard time in October). Have them first draw their designs on a regular sheet of paper.

Art

Safety Tags Have students study samples of safety tags that are often attached to the cords of small appliances. Have them discuss how the manufacturers use symbols and words to convey the message on the tags. Then have students design safety tags for items that normally don't have them.

TEACH *continued*

Interpret Visuals—Pictures

Review the Stop, Drop, and Roll movements shown here. Emphasize that this lifesaving technique works when performed correctly. Ask volunteers to demonstrate these movements on a gymnastics mat. Be sure that they stop immediately, drop to the floor quickly, and cover their face as they roll back and forth.

Critical Thinking **Why is running when your clothes are on fire the worst thing you can do?** It fans the flames.

Content-Area Reading Support

Using Reference Words Direct attention to the last sentence in the first paragraph. Explain that the phrase *doing so* refers to an idea stated earlier in the paragraph. Have a volunteer identify the idea. the actions in the previous three sentences Point out to students that when they come across phrases such as *doing so*, they should be certain they understand the idea to which the phrase refers before moving on.

Health Background

Carbon Monoxide Carbon monoxide is an odorless, colorless gas that can cause illness and death. It can build up in enclosed spaces from fumes produced by stoves, heating systems, fireplaces, and motor vehicle exhaust. More than 500 Americans die from carbon monoxide poisoning each year. Carbon monoxide detectors should be installed in bedrooms and in every level of the home.

Source: *Centers for Disease Control and Prevention website*

Myth and Fact

Myth: You have several minutes to get out of a house if a fire starts.

Fact: A fire can double in size every minute. After a fire starts, you have two to three minutes to either put it out or get out of the house.

Stay Safe in a Fire

Fires are a major cause of injuries, loss of life, and property loss. Your family needs a plan to escape from your home in the event of a fire. Have a family fire drill every six months. Practice getting out quickly. Doing so can mean the difference between safety and danger. Here's what to do in a fire:

- Follow your escape route. If it's blocked, use your second route. Test any door you come to. If it's hot, leave it shut. Find a different way out.
- Crawl low, under the smoke. Hold a wet cloth over your nose and mouth.
- Meet outside at your family meeting place. DO NOT go back inside your house.
- Use a neighbor's phone to call 911.

DRAW CONCLUSIONS Why is it important for your family to have a fire drill every six months?
Possible answer: Everyone will know how to get out of the house quickly without thinking about it.

▲ **If your clothing catches on fire, STOP. Running fans the flames. Shout for help, but don't run.**

◀ **DROP to the floor or ground. Cover your face.**

▼ **ROLL back and forth slowly to put out the flames.**

124

Meeting Individual Needs
Leveled Activities

BELOW-LEVEL **Create a Display** Have students look through discarded magazines to find pictures of household products that are poisonous. They can mount the pictures on construction paper, add a title, and display them at school.

ON-LEVEL **Make a Poster** Encourage students to make posters listing safety rules for younger children to follow to prevent poisonings. The posters can be displayed at school and then taken home to be shared with younger siblings.

CHALLENGE **Write a Song** Suggest that students set to music the safety rules for what to do if a fire happens, using the tune of a popular song. They can perform the song at a school assembly meeting. Make sure they include *Stop, Drop, and Roll.*

Prevent Poisoning

Poisons are substances that cause harm when they enter the body. A poison can also be deadly. Poisons can be swallowed or breathed in, or they can get into your body through the skin. Cleaning products that are usually safe when used properly can be poisonous. Medicines taken improperly can be poisonous. Some plants are also poisonous if they are eaten. For these reasons, extra care should be taken to prevent injury. Follow these safety guidelines to prevent poisoning:

- Never take medicine unless a parent or another trusted adult says it's safe.
- Use arts and crafts supplies that are labeled *nontoxic*, meaning "not poisonous."
- Do not use insect sprays, bleach, paints, or other household products without an adult.

MAIN IDEA AND DETAILS What is the main idea of this section?
See list of safety guidelines on this page.

ACTIVITY

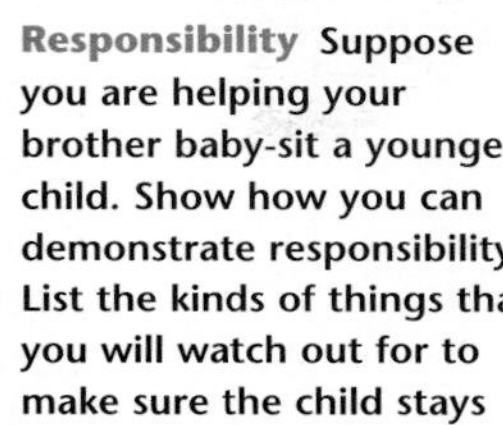

Building Good Character

Responsibility Suppose you are helping your brother baby-sit a younger child. Show how you can demonstrate responsibility. List the kinds of things that you will watch out for to make sure the child stays away from any poisonous products.

Lesson 2 Summary and Review

1. **Summarize with Vocabulary**
   Use vocabulary and other terms from this lesson to complete the statements.
   Being careful around a _____ is an example of a safety measure. When you keep injuries from happening, you are practicing _____. _____ are the most common cause of injuries in the home. Substances that cause harm when they enter the body are called _____.
2. **Critical Thinking** Why should your home have a fire extinguisher in the kitchen?
3. What are ways to prevent falls?
4. **SEQUENCE** Draw and complete this graphic organizer to show the steps you should take if a fire breaks out in your home.

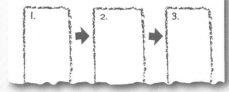

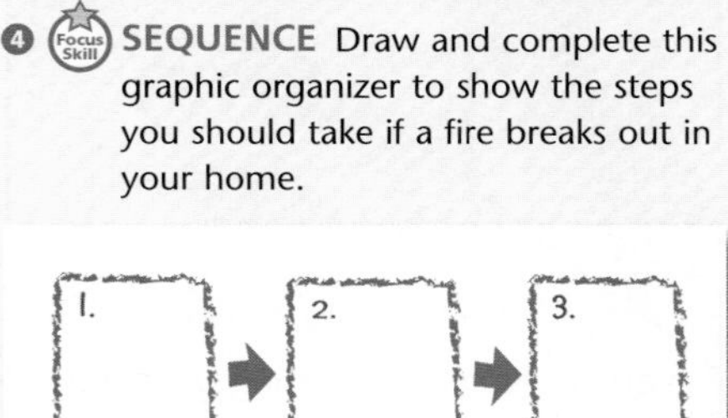

5. **Write to Inform—How-To**
   Write a list of safety rules to prevent poisonings. Post the rules in your home.

125

Activity

Responsibility Students should provide specific actions they would take, for example, always accompanying a child who can walk to make sure he or she does not taste or swallow any potential poison.

3. WRAP UP

Lesson 2 Summary and Review

1. hazard; injury prevention; falls; poisons
2. The biggest cause of fires in the home is cooking.
3. Possible answers: Use a handrail when going up and down stairs, don't pile papers and magazines on the floor, and be careful when walking on slippery or wet surfaces.
4. Answers may include:

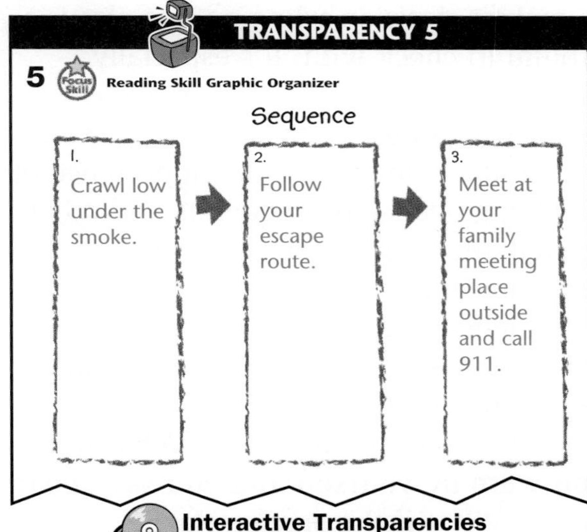

TRANSPARENCY 5
5 Reading Skill Graphic Organizer
Sequence
1. Crawl low under the smoke.
2. Follow your escape route.
3. Meet at your family meeting place outside and call 911.
Interactive Transparencies available on CD-ROM.

5. Paragraphs should include safety guidelines on this page.

For **writing models** with examples, see *Teaching Resources* pp. 47–61. Rubrics are also provided.

Teacher Tip

Fire Safety at School This lesson presents an excellent opportunity to review the fire escape route from your classroom. Show the map, and practice the route with your students. Consider demonstrating how to operate a fire extinguisher or having a school safety officer (if available) or community firefighter demonstrate. Stress that at school or at home, a person should always call 911 or the fire department BEFORE attempting to put out a fire.

When Minutes Count . . .

Quick Study Students can use *Activity Book* pages 21–22 (shown on p. 117) as they complete each lesson in this chapter.

Life Skills

Communicate
Make Responsible Decisions
Manage Stress
Refuse
Resolve Conflicts
Set Goals

Objectives

- Identify the steps for decision making.
- Use the decision-making steps to stay safe.

Program Resources

- Activity Book p. 24
- Poster 8

1. MOTIVATE

Tell students that sometimes it's difficult to make a decision when no one else is around to check with. It's especially scary when the decision you make is about your safety or the safety of others. Ask students to explain the importance of seeking guidance from parents and other trusted adults in making healthy decisions and solving problems. Explain to students that they are getting older and may need to know how to respond in certain situations to stay safe. Pose several "What if?" questions: **What if you were by yourself and you saw a car crash? What if the smoke alarm sounded? What if your friend fell off a bike and was hurt?**

2. TEACH

Direct students' attention to the pictures of Ken talking on the phone. Ask a student volunteer to read the lead-in paragraph.

Step 1

What are Ken's choices? He could go swimming without permission, tell Eddie they shouldn't swim without an adult present, or plan to go swimming when it's okay with their parents.

Make Responsible Decisions

About Staying Safe

Sometimes you are home alone and you need to make a decision. You can use the steps for **Making Responsible Decisions** to help you make healthful decisions about staying safe.

Ken's mother is next door when Ken's new friend, Eddie, calls. Eddie asks Ken to come to his house to swim. Eddie's parents aren't at home either. What should Ken do?

1 Find out about the choices you could make.

Ken could go swimming without asking his mother's permission, or he could tell Eddie they shouldn't swim without an adult present. They could also plan to go swimming at Eddie's when it's OK with their parents.

2 Eliminate choices that are against your family rules.

Ken knows that swimming without adult supervision is against his family's rules. It is also dangerous. He eliminates that choice.

126

Teacher Tip

Safety Log Have students log for a week the actions they take to make their homes safer. Advise them to use the information in this chapter to look for hazards.

Day of the Week ____________

My Action ________________

A Safe Result ______________

Be sensitive to the rules of families. Don't require students to share their log entries.

ACTIVITY BOOK P. 24

Name ______________________

Problem Solving

Life Skill

Make Responsible Decisions

Steps for Making Responsible Decisions

1. Find out about the choices you could make.
2. Eliminate choices that are against your family rules.
3. Ask yourself: What is the possible result of each choice? Does the choice show good character?
4. Make what seems to be the best choice.

Use the steps to help these students make responsible decisions.

A. Zalika has friends over for a slumber party. Some of the girls want to place lighted candles around Zalika's bedroom. This is against Zalika's family rules. Zalika's parents are already asleep. "Your parents won't know," says one of the girls.

- Explain what would be the most responsible decision for Zalika to make.

Possible answer: Zalika should eliminate the choice of lighting the candles because it is against the family rules. It does not matter whether her parents are asleep. Zalika can show she is trustworthy by following the rules. She should tell her friends that not lighting candles is a family rule and that this rule helps prevent fires.

B. Nardo and Soo are swimming at the community pool. It is against pool rules to jump into the pool backward. Nardo tries to talk Soo into diving in backward when the lifeguard isn't looking. "Come on," Nardo says. "Are you chicken?"

- What decision should Soo make to show responsibility and good character?

Possible answer: The best choice for Soo is to refuse to act in an unsafe way. Jumping into the pool backward could injure him or someone else. Soo would show good character by obeying pool rules, even when the lifeguard is not looking.

© Harcourt

Available online.
www.harcourtschool.com/health

3 **Ask yourself: What is the possible result of each choice? Does the choice show good character?**

If Ken goes swimming without first asking permission, his parents will be upset. If he talks to his parents, he and Eddie may be able to plan for a day that both his and Eddie's parents say is OK.

4 **Make what seems to be the best choice.**

Ken decides to talk to his parents. He'll plan a day when both he and Eddie can have permission to go swimming and there will be supervision. Eddie thinks that's a good idea.

Problem Solving

Nora is playing at Carmen's house. Carmen wants to use her older sister's electric hair-curling iron. Nora asks, "Do you have permission to use it?" Carmen says, "No, but I've watched my sister. I think I can do it." Use the steps for **Making Responsible Decisions** to help Nora. Come up with a response that Nora can give to Carmen that will demonstrate responsible decision making and also show Carmen how to respect her sister's belongings.

Using the Poster

Activity Ask a volunteer to describe what is being shown in the poster. Have students work in groups to use the pictures to compose a skit showing how to use the steps to make responsible decisions.

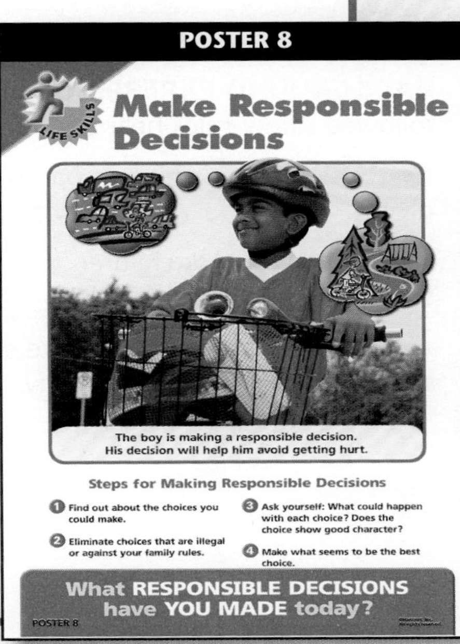
POSTER 8
LIFE SKILLS
Make Responsible Decisions
The boy is making a responsible decision. His decision will help him avoid getting hurt.
Steps for Making Responsible Decisions
1 Find out about the choices you could make.
2 Eliminate choices that are illegal or against your family rules.
3 Ask yourself: What could happen with each choice? Does the choice show good character?
4 Make what seems to be the best choice.
What RESPONSIBLE DECISIONS have YOU MADE today?
POSTER 8

Step 2

Why is it important for Ken to eliminate the choice that is against family rules? If he goes against family rules, he does not show respect for his parents. He does not show responsible behavior because he might get hurt if he goes swimming without an adult present.

Building Good Character

Tell students that being trustworthy means keeping your promises and being honest. Your family can count on you to follow family rules. You are reliable and can be trusted to do the right thing.

Step 3

Explain how each choice does or does not show good character. The first choice does not show good character; Ken is not being trustworthy if he disobeys family rules. The second choice shows that he is trustworthy and responsible because he follows family rules and practices safe behavior.

Step 4

What does Ken decide is his best choice? to go swimming at Eddie's house another time when he and Eddie have permission and supervision

Critical Thinking What happens as a result of Ken's choice? Possible answers: He shows his family he is trustworthy; he and Eddie stay safe.

3. WRAP UP

Problem Solving

Answers should reflect the steps for Making Responsible Decisions. Nora should not use the curling iron. She would show she is trustworthy by not disobeying Carmen's family rules. She would show she is responsible by following safety rules.

LESSON 3

Pages 128–130

Objectives

- ► Identify safety rules for swimming, diving, and boating.
- ► Describe how to respond to a water emergency.

When Minutes Count . . .

Assign the Quick Study, Lesson 3, Activity Book pp. 21–22 (shown on p. 117).

Program Resources

- ► Activity Book pp. 21–22, 25
- ► Transparency 5

Vocabulary

lifeguard p. 128

Daily Fitness Tip

Advise students to be aware of their swimming weaknesses and abilities. If they do not swim well or are uncomfortable in the water, they should wear a life jacket. Caution children not to use air-filled swimming aids (such as water wings) in place of life jackets. They give a false sense of security and can increase the risk of drowning.

1. MOTIVATE

Optional Activity Materials sand, shallow dish or pan of water, craft sticks, 2 in. x 3 in. self-stick notes, plastic cloth

Spread the sand around the container of water. Tell students that this represents a beach setting. The water can represent a swimming pool, ocean, or lake. Have students work in pairs to think of a safety rule for swimming, diving, or boating and write it on the self-stick note. Have students attach their rules to craft sticks and place each in the sand around the water. Alternatively, draw a beach setting on the board, and have students post the notes on the board.

LESSON 3 Staying Safe near Water

Lesson Focus
When you practice safety habits while swimming and boating, you help prevent injuries and death by drowning.

Why Learn This?
What you learn can help keep you and others safe around water.

Vocabulary
lifeguard

Stay Safe While Swimming

There's nothing like having fun in a swimming pool, a lake, or the ocean. However, people can be injured in or around water. Practicing water safety can help prevent injury. When you are at a swimming pool, follow these safety rules:

- Obey the **lifeguard**, a person who has special training to keep people safe in and around water.
- Don't run or push near the pool. Wet decks are slippery and hard.
- Don't bob underwater at the edge of the pool. Someone might come in on top of you.
- Don't jump in the pool backward.

If someone in the water needs help, yell for help. Find an adult. Do NOT get into the water. If the person is close enough, REACH—hold something long and strong out to the person. Hold on to something secure, such as a dock pole or a tree branch. ▶

If the person is too far away for you to reach, attach a rope to something that floats. Attach the other end to something secure. THROW the object to the person. ▶

ESL/ELL Support

BACKGROUND EXPERIENCE Invite children to discuss times they have followed safety rules near and in water.

Beginning Have children pantomime safety rules when swimming and diving.

Intermediate Ask children to draw and label pictures showing them swimming and diving safely.

Advanced Have children write a list of safety rules telling what a person should do and not do, and why.

Diving can result in serious injuries. Follow these safety rules when diving into water:

- Dive only in water 9 feet deep or more.
- Never dive into an above-ground pool.
- Dive only from the end of the diving board.
- Don't dive from the side of a pool.

SEQUENCE What is the first thing you should do if you see storm clouds or hear thunder while swimming? Get out of the water immediately.

Personal Health Plan

Real-Life Situation
Suppose you are planning to go to a public swimming pool.
Real-Life Plan
List three behaviors that you can practice to help you and others stay safe while swimming.

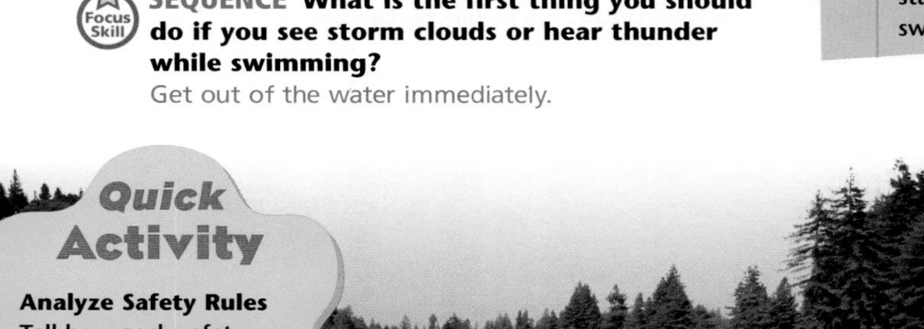

Quick Activity

Analyze Safety Rules Tell how each safety rule helps keep you and others safe around water. Draw a poster to illustrate each rule.

Rules for Water Safety

- Learn to swim.
- Wear sunscreen.
- Obey all signs.
- Be aware of weather and water conditions. Get out of the water immediately if you see storm clouds or hear thunder.
- Swim only when and where an adult is present.

129

2. TEACH

Interpret Visuals—Diagrams

Have a volunteer read the text for the Reach and Throw pictures and then describe the techniques being used.

Problem Solving What might you use to reach toward the person? Possible answers: a sturdy branch, the pole end of a pool skimmer, an oar

Critical Thinking Why should you hold on to something secure as you reach? so you don't fall into the water or get pulled in by the person

Quick Activity

Divide the class into groups and assign each group specific rules. Display the posters in a common area in the school.

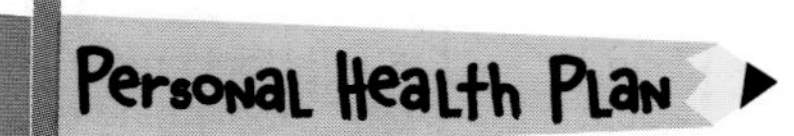

Personal Health Plan

Plans should include:

- three safety rules from these two pages.
- ways to practice the rules.

Health Background

Pool and Spa Hazard Since 1980 there have been more than 54 cases of children between ages 2 and 16 becoming trapped by their hair, arms, or legs in the drains of swimming pools or spas, resulting in injury or death. Long hair should be pinned up or kept away from suction drains. Missing or damaged drain covers should be reported and repaired.

Source: *Consumer Product Safety Council*

For more background, visit the **Webliography** in Teacher Resources at **www.harcourtschool.com/health**
Keyword injury prevention

Teacher Tip

Drowning Prevention Invite the physical education teacher to demonstrate the technique for drowning prevention if a person cannot get to solid land. Show pictures of the technique beforehand. Ask volunteers to describe and demonstrate the technique after the physical education teacher has modeled it.

Physical Education

Beachball Relay Write the rules in this lesson on separate pieces of paper, and attach removable tape to each. Divide the class into two teams. Give teams time to study the rules. Then tell students to close their books. Throw a beach ball to one team member, who says a rule and posts it on the board. Alternate play between the teams until all rules have been stated or one team cannot think of a rule.

3. WRAP UP

Lesson 3 Summary and Review

1. thunder; lifeguard; dive; life jacket
2. Possible answers: A person who runs around the pool could fall and get injured; a person who jumps in the pool backward could hit the side of the pool or jump on top of someone else; a person who dives in shallow water could hit the bottom and seriously injure his or her head or neck.
3. any of the safety rules listed on page 130
4. Answers may include:

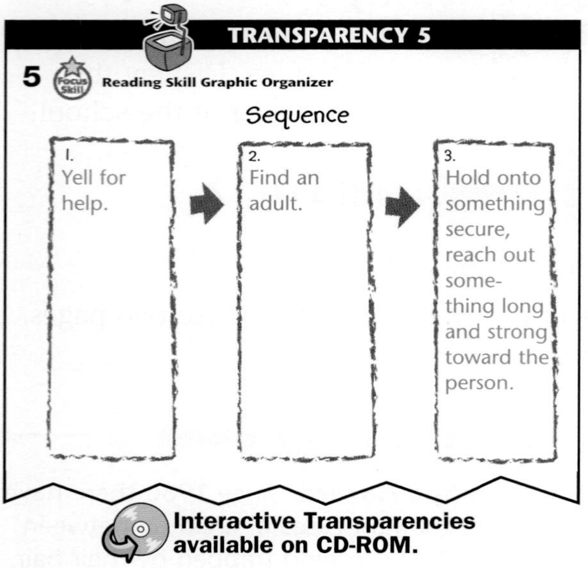

TRANSPARENCY 5
5
Reading Skill Graphic Organizer
Sequence
1. Yell for help.
2. Find an adult.
3. Hold onto something secure, reach out some-thing long and strong toward the person.

Interactive Transparencies available on CD-ROM.

5. Stories should include several safety rules presented in this lesson.

For **writing models** with examples, see *Teaching Resources* pp. 47–61. Rubrics are also provided.

When Minutes Count . . .

Quick Study Students can use *Activity Book* pages 21–22 (shown on p. 117) as they complete each lesson in this chapter.

Did You Know?

Many boating deaths of children could be prevented if children wore life jackets. A federal law requires any child under thirteen years old to wear a Coast Guard-approved life jacket when on a boat, unless the child is in an enclosed cabin.

Be Safe While Boating

More than 70 million people enjoy boating each year. Follow these safety rules while boating:

- Wear a life jacket. It will keep you afloat if you fall in the water.
- Don't make sudden movements or stand up. If you fall in the water, hold on to the boat.
- Make sure someone on shore knows where you are and when you plan to return.

CAUSE AND EFFECT What is an effect of wearing a life jacket on a boat?
staying safe if you fall in the water; the life jacket will keep you afloat.

◀ Never go out in a boat by yourself.

Lesson 3 Summary and Review

❶ **Summarize with Vocabulary**
Use vocabulary and other terms from this lesson to complete the statements.

Get out of the water if you hear _____. A person trained to help you be safe in or around water is a _____. You should _____ only in water 9 feet deep or more. Wear a _____ to keep you afloat.

❷ **Critical Thinking** What are three things that can happen if swimming-pool safety rules aren't followed?

❸ What are three tips for boating safety?

❹ **SEQUENCE** Draw and complete this graphic organizer to show what to do if someone in the water needs help and is close to you.

❺ **Write to Entertain—Short Story**
Write a story about a boy who goes swimming but doesn't know the safety rules. Have his friends tell him the rules so that no one gets hurt.

ACTIVITY BOOK P. 25

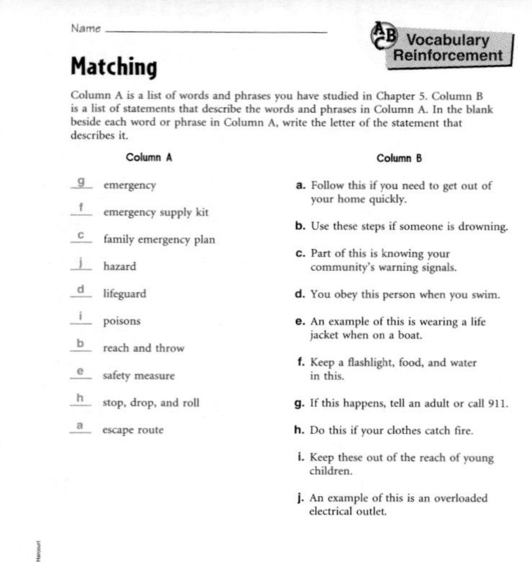

Name ________________

Vocabulary Reinforcement

Matching

Column A is a list of words and phrases you have studied in Chapter 5. Column B is a list of statements that describe the words and phrases in Column A. In the blank beside each word or phrase in Column A, write the letter of the statement that describes it.

Column A	Column B
g emergency	a. Follow this if you need to get out of your home quickly.
f emergency supply kit	b. Use these steps if someone is drowning.
c family emergency plan	c. Part of this is knowing your community's warning signals.
j hazard	d. You obey this person when you swim.
d lifeguard	e. An example of this is wearing a life jacket when on a boat.
i poisons	f. Keep a flashlight, food, and water in this.
b reach and throw	g. If this happens, tell an adult or call 911.
e safety measure	h. Do this if your clothes catch fire.
h stop, drop, and roll	i. Keep these out of the reach of young children.
a escape route	j. An example of this is an overloaded electrical outlet.

Available online.
www.harcourtschool.com/health

ACTIVITIES

Math

Calculate the Number of Fires Fire departments in the United States respond to one home fire about every hour. About how many fires is that in one day?

Science

Out of the Pool Predict the swimming conditions for your area or for another region of the country. Use weather forecasts in sources provided by your teacher to predict if the weather conditions will be safe for swimming. Use the same sources to check your predictions for a week.

Technology Project

Many electrical outlets have a device called a GFCI (ground-fault circuit-interrupter), which helps prevent shocks. Use the Internet to research how a GFCI works. Identify some types of appliances that have built-in shock protectors. Then use a computer to make a slide show to inform others about these devices.

For more activities, visit The Learning Site. www.harcourtschool.com/health

Home & Community

Practice Fire Drills Organize a family fire drill, using your family emergency plan. Each person should start in a different room and use one of the room's escape exits. The whole family should meet at the chosen location outdoors. Then discuss the drill, and decide how the family might improve its plan.

Career Link

The Coast Guard The Coast Guard is one of the armed forces in the United States. One of its goals is to enforce safety rules for people who boat for fun. Suppose you are a Coast Guard officer. Some people tell you that they don't understand why it's important to wear a life jacket if they know how to swim. What will you tell them?

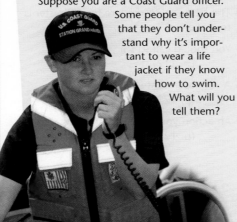

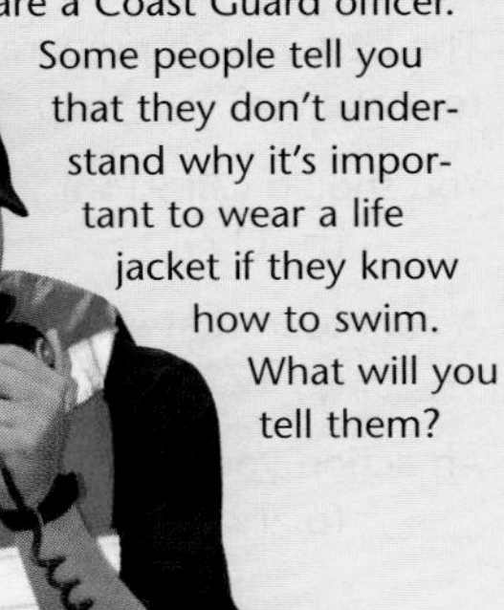

Career Link

The Coast Guard Students should recognize that wearing a life jacket may save a person's life if he or she falls out of a boat. The person could hit his or her head and become unconscious and start sinking. If the boat is damaged and the person is in the water for a long time, he or she might get tired and not be able to swim.

You may wish to have interested students find out what other duties the Coast Guard performs. For example, it provides homeland security in our nation's harbors and ports and along our coastlines. Since September 11, 2001, the Coast Guard has increased security measures.

For more information on health careers, visit the **Webliography** in Teacher Resources at **www.harcourtschool.com/health**
Keyword health careers

Activities

Math

According to the Centers for Disease Control, fire departments responded to 396,500 home fires in the United States in a recent year. Students can work out an approximate answer as follows: 60 seconds/minute x 60 minutes/hour x 24 hours/day x 365 days/year = 31,536,000 seconds. 31,536,000/80 = 394,200

Science

Provide daily newspapers or printouts from weather sites on the Internet. Students should recognize that swimming is not safe whenever thunderstorms are predicted. Optional: Many newspapers feature a UV (ultraviolet) index. Limiting outdoor activities, including swimming, during particular hours when the UV index is high is advised.

Home & Community

Remind students that the plan should show at least two ways to escape from every room. Suggest that an adult time the drill and that family members conduct several drills the first time they practice their escape drill. The family can make a goal of reducing the time to get out of the home.

Supports the Coordinated School Health Program

Technology Project

Students can use PowerPoint™ or other presentation software they have at home or at school. Ask the school library media specialist to assist students in developing their presentations. If computer access or presentation software is not available, students can illustrate their presentations by using art materials.

Chapter Review and Test Preparation

Pages 132–133

Reading Skill 5 pts. each

1. Stop, Drop, and Roll
2. Stay calm, call an adult, or call 911

Use Vocabulary 5 pts. each

3. Injury prevention
4. family emergency plan
5. emergency
6. hazard
7. safety measure

Check Understanding 5 pts. each

8. C, Tell an adult.
9. H, boy pushing boy
10. B, knowing the phone number of the nearest fire department
11. J, smoke detector
12. D, can opener
13. J, stop, drop, roll
14. C, what the problem is
15. G, Don't run or push near the pool.

Think Critically 5 pts. each

16. A young child might drink the paint thinner, thinking it is juice.
17. You might fall out of the boat, or be injured and not be able to swim.

Chapter Review and Test Preparation

Reading Skill

SEQUENCE

Copy this graphic organizer, and then use it to answer questions 1 and 2.

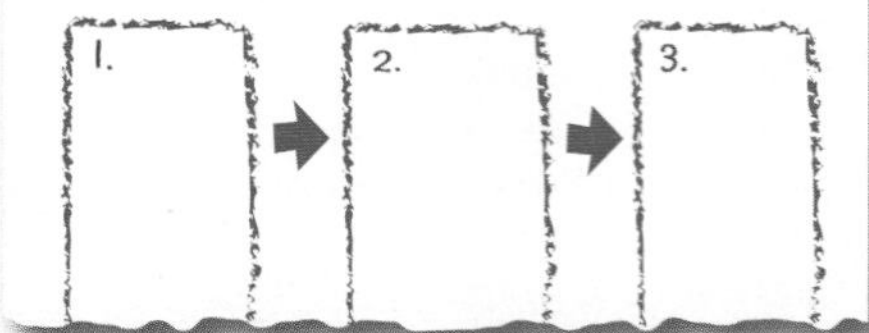

1 What steps should you take if your clothes catch fire?

2 What should you do in an emergency?

Use Vocabulary

Fill in the blanks with the correct terms to complete the sentences.

3 _____ means "keeping injuries from happening." (p. 122)

4 The best way to prepare for a disaster is to make a(n) _____. (p. 118)

5 You should call 911 if you see a(n) _____. (p. 117)

6 A condition that is NOT safe is a(n) _____. (p. 122)

7 An action you take to stay safe is a(n) _____. (p. 122)

Check Understanding

Choose the letter of the correct answer.

8 What is the first thing you should try to do in an emergency? (p. 116)

A Write down your phone number.
B Speak slowly and clearly.
C Tell an adult.
D Call the nearest hospital.

9 Which of the following can be a hazard when you are swimming? (p. 128)

F

H

G

J

10 Which of the following is **NOT** an important part of a family emergency plan? (pp. 118–119)

A having two ways to escape from each room
B knowing the phone number of the nearest fire department
C having two meeting places outside
D knowing your family contact

11 A _____ can alert you if a fire breaks out. (p. 123)

F 911 operator
G hazard
H fire extinguisher
J smoke detector

132

Formal Assessment

ASSESSMENT GUIDE P. 31

5 Name ______________ **Chapter Test**

Safe at Home

Write the letter of the best answer on the line at the left.

C 1. A(n) _____ is a situation in which help is needed right away.
A response B hazard C emergency D appliance

G 2. The first thing to do in an emergency is to _____.
F communicate G tell an adult H leave the area J go for help

C 3. You should learn your community's _____.
A disaster B first aid C warning signals D emergency

J 4. A family emergency plan should have two _____ routes from each room.
F emergency G disaster H warning J escape

A 5. You should know how to turn off _____ such as water and gas.
A utilities B contacts C escapes D radios

J 6. A(n) _____ is a an unsafe condition.
F response G emergency H warning J hazard

A 7. _____ are substances that cause harm when they enter the body.
A Poisons B Hazards C Injuries D Utilities

G 8. A _____ has special training to keep people safe around water.
F firefighter G lifeguard H police officer J surfer

C 9. The label *nontoxic* means the product is _____.
A not flammable B not sinkable C not poisonous D not electrical

H 10. If your clothes catch on fire, do **NOT** _____.
F yell G move H run J crawl

© Harcourt

ASSESSMENT GUIDE P. 32

Name ______________

Match each phrase in Column A with the phrase in Column B that completes a true statement.

	Column A		Column B
d	11. When you call 911,	a	have a fire drill every six months.
e	12. You can prepare for emergencies	b	should have two ways to escape from each room.
c	13. When you are on a boat,	c	always wear a life jacket.
b	14. A family escape route	d	be sure to speak slowly and clearly.
a	15. A family should	e	by having a family emergency plan.

Write *T* or *F* to show whether the sentence is true or false.

T 16. If a door is hot during a fire, you should keep it closed.

F 17. If there is a fire in your home, the first thing you should do is call 911.

F 18. One smoke detector can protect an entire house.

F 19. If you are swimming as a thunderstorm approaches, the safest place is in the water.

T 20. A family should replace the food, water, and batteries in an emergency supply kit every six months.

© Harcourt

12 Becca is planning foods to put in her emergency supply kit. Tell what's missing under "Supplies." (p. 120)

Emergency Supply Kit

Food	Supplies for Food
canned tuna, peanut butter, crackers	plates, forks and spoons, cups

A salt
B jelly
C napkins
D can opener

13 If your clothing catches on fire, which of the following should you do? (pp. 124–125)

F shout, drop, roll
G run, shout, roll
H jump, drop, roll
J stop, drop, roll

14 What does a 911 operator need to know if you call about an emergency? (p. 117)

A that you are worried
B the name of your school
C what the problem is
D the location of your emergency supply kit

15 Which of the following rules can help keep you safe while swimming? (p. 128)

F Jump in the pool backward.
G Don't run or push near the pool.
H At the edge of the pool, bob underwater.
J If a storm is coming, stay in the water until you see lightning.

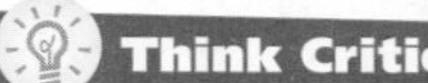

Think Critically

16 Your older brother is using paint thinner. He pours what is left over into an empty juice bottle. Why is this action unsafe?

17 When you're in a boat, why is it important to wear a life jacket even if you know how to swim?

Apply Skills

18 **BUILDING GOOD CHARACTER**
Citizenship You see someone throwing rocks at bottles floating in the swimming area of the lake where you swim. Later you see a boy and a girl getting ready to go for a swim there. What can you do to be a good citizen and to show caring for others?

19 **LIFE SKILLS**
Make Decisions Your sister comes home from school and rushes upstairs. She drops her backpack on the stairs. When you mention it, she says, "I'll pick it up later." Use the steps for Making Responsible Decisions to explain to her how her behavior can harm your family or keep it safe.

Write About Health

20 **Write to Inform—Explanation** Write about a time when you or someone you know had an accident. Explain how the accident could have been prevented. Describe what you can do in the future to prevent that type of accident.

133

Apply Skills 5 pts. each

18. Students should recognize that the activity witnessed is creating a possible swimming safety hazard. Students should arrive at the decision to tell the lifeguard, if there is one present, that there is possible danger. If a lifeguard is not present, the individuals themselves should be warned of the possible danger.

19. Answers will vary. Students should show that they used each step of the decision-making process.

Write About Health 5 pts.

20. Students should demonstrate that they understand that most accidents can be prevented.

Performance Assessment

Use the Chapter Project and the rubric provided on the Project Evaluation Sheet. See *Assessment Guide* pp. 18, 58, 66.

Portfolio Assessment

Have students select their best work from the following suggestions:

- Leveled Activities, p. 118
- Quick Activity, p. 123
- Write to Inform, p. 120
- Activities, p. 131

See *Assessment Guide* pp. 12–16.

ASSESSMENT GUIDE P. 33

Name ______________

Complete the chart below by filling in the appropriate spaces.

21. Family Emergency Plan	22. Emergency Supply Kit
• Know what could happen. • Plan escape routes. • Choose a family contact. • Know what could happen. • Turn off utilities. • Choose two meeting places.	• canned food and a manual can opener • plastic cups, plates, forks, and spoons • bottled water • flashlight, battery-operated radio, and batteries • first-aid kit and medicines

Explain why the following actions are bad ideas. Tell what kind of hazard each is. Possible answers are given.

23. Sally has four prescription pills left in a large bottle. She decides to save space and put the pills in a smaller bottle.

Putting the pills in a different bottle is a poison hazard. Sally may not remember what the pills are, what they are for, or how often to take them. Also, they may look like another medicine, and another family member may take them by mistake and get sick.

24. Before his soccer game, Tom heats a can of soup on the stove. While the soup is heating, to save time, he decides to take a shower.

Putting something on the stove to cook and then leaving the room is a fire hazard. Tom might take so long in the shower that the soup boils away and the pan starts a fire.

25. Lila gets out of the house safely and checks in with her family during a small kitchen fire. It looks as if the fire is out, so she goes back into the house to look for Buzzard, the cat.

Lila cannot be sure the fire is completely out. It could start up again. If it did, no one would think to look for her because she already checked in.

© Harcourt

CHAPTER 6

Safe Away From Home

Lesson	Pacing	Objectives	Reading Skills
Introduce the Chapter pp. 134–135		• Preview chapter concepts.	**Draw Conclusions** pp. 135, 332–333
1 Staying Safe Outdoors pp. 136–140	1 class period	• Identify strategies for avoiding injuries when camping and hiking, and during cold and hot weather. • Describe appropriate responses during weather emergencies.	**Draw Conclusions** pp. 137, 140 • Compare and Contrast, p. 138 • Cause and Effect, p. 139 • Sequence, p. 140
Building Good Character p. 141		• Describe ways to show responsibility during outdoor activities by being a positive role model.	
2 Staying Safe on the Road pp. 142–145	1 class period	• Identify personal behaviors to prevent injuries when skating, skateboarding, biking, and riding in a motor vehicle. • Discuss the use of safety gear and equipment to avoid injuries when traveling.	**Draw Conclusions** pp. 142, 143, 145 • Summarize, p. 145
Life Skills p. 146–147	1 class period	• Identify steps for resolving conflicts. • Apply conflict-resolution skills to handle conflicts with friends.	
3 Staying Safe in a Conflict pp. 148–152	3 class periods	• Identify strategies for avoiding deliberate injuries. • Develop and use skills to avoid, resolve, and cope with conflicts.	**Draw Conclusions** pp. 148, 152 • Compare and Contrast, p. 149 • Main Idea and Details, p. 151 • Summarize, p. 152
Activities p. 153		• Extend chapter concepts.	
Chapter Review pp. 154–155	1 class period	• Assess chapter objectives.	

Vocabulary	Program Resources
	Music CD Teaching Resources, p. 33
flood lightning hurricane tornado	Transparency 2 Activity Book, pp. 26–28
	Poster 5
air bag	Transparency 2 Activity Book, pp. 26–27
	Activity Book, p. 29 Poster 11
bully gang weapon	Transparency 2 Activity Book, pp. 26–27, 30
	The Learning Site www.harcourtschool.com
	Assessment Guide, pp. 34–36

Interactive Transparencies available on CD-ROM.

Reading Skill

These reading skills are reinforced throughout this chapter and one skill is emphasized as the Focus Skill.

- **Draw Conclusions**
- Compare and Contrast
- Identify Cause and Effect
- Identify Main Idea and Details
- Sequence
- Summarize

KEY READING SKILLS TRANSPARENCY 2

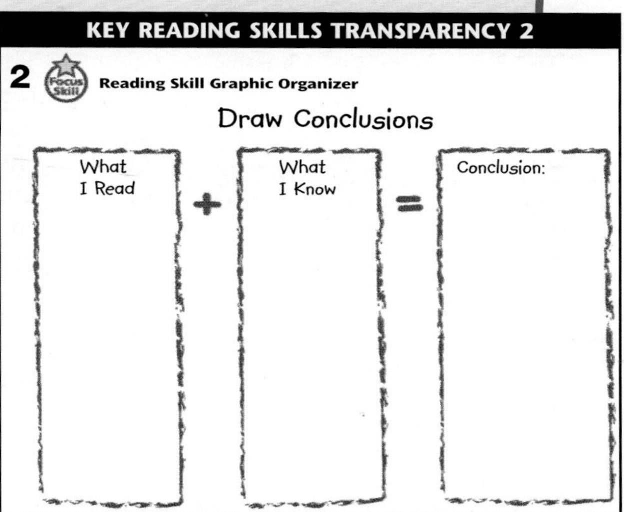

Life Skills

Life Skills are health-enhancing behaviors that can help students reduce risks to their health and safety.

Six Life Skills are reinforced throughout *Harcourt Health and Fitness*. The skill emphasized in this chapter is Resolve Conflicts.

POSTER 11 RESOLVE CONFLICTS

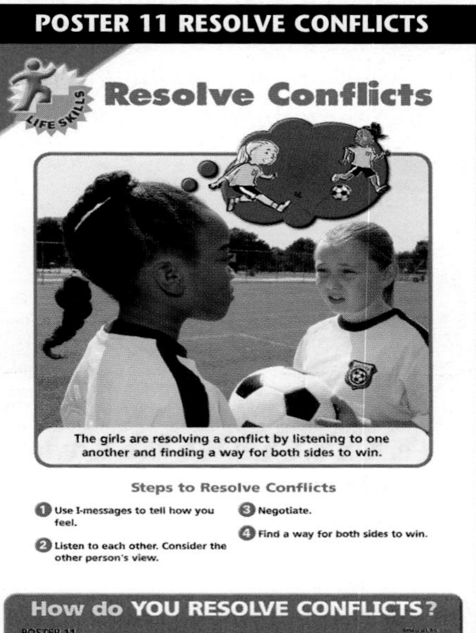

Resolve Conflicts
The girls are resolving a conflict by listening to one another and finding a way for both sides to win.
Steps to Resolve Conflicts
1 Use I-messages to tell how you feel.
2 Listen to each other. Consider the other person's view.
3 Negotiate.
4 Find a way for both sides to win.
How do YOU RESOLVE CONFLICTS?

Building Good Character
Express feelings, needs, and wants in appropriate ways.

Character education is an important aspect of health education. When children behave in ways that show good character, they promote the health and safety of themselves and others.

Six character traits are reinforced throughout *Harcourt Health and Fitness*. The trait emphasized in this chapter is Responsibility.

POSTER 5 RESPONSIBILITY

Keep yourself safe.
Keep trying. Do your best.

Set goals and work toward them.

Don't do things that are unsafe or that destroy property.

Don't deny or make excuses for your mistakes.
Don't leave your work for others to do.
Don't lose or misuse your belongings.

Resources

Coordinated School Health Program

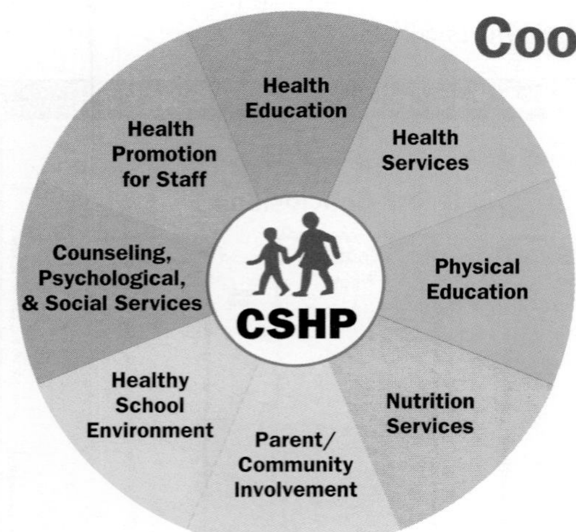

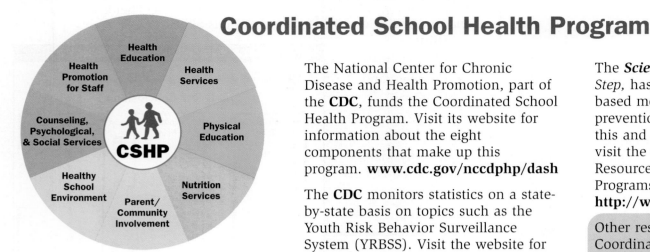

A Coordinated School Health Program endeavors to improve children's health and therefore their capacity to learn through the support of families, schools, and communities working together. The following information is provided to help classroom teachers be more aware of these resources.

The National Center for Chronic Disease and Health Promotion, part of the **CDC**, funds the Coordinated School Health Program. Visit its website for information about the eight components that make up this program. **www.cdc.gov/nccdphp/dash**

The **CDC** monitors statistics on a state-by-state basis on topics such as the Youth Risk Behavior Surveillance System (YRBSS). Visit the website for more information. **www.cdc.gov/nccdphp/dash/state_info/**

The **National Institute of Mental Health** works to assist children and adolescents who have been victims of or witnesses to violent and/or catastrophic events. **www.nimh.nih.gov/outline/traumatic.cfm**

The ***Science-Based Program***, *Second Step,* has been identified as a research-based model program for the prevention of violence in schools. For this and other exemplary programs, visit the California Healthy Kids Resource Center: Research-Validated Programs. **http://www.californiahealthykids.org**

Other resources that support a Coordinated School Health Program:
- School-Home Connection
- Daily Physical Activity
- Daily Fitness Tips
- Activities: Home & Community
- Health Background: Webliography
- *Be Active! Resources for Physical Education*

Media Resources

Books for Students

Loy, Jessica. ***Follow the Trail: A Young Person's Guide to the Great Outdoors.*** Henry Holt and Company, 2003. A beginner's safety guide to camping and hiking. **EASY**

Polland, Barbara Kay. ***We Can Work It Out: Conflict Resolution for Children.*** Tricycle Press, 2000. Explains various ways for children to resolve conflicts. **AVERAGE**

Schulson, Rachel Ellenberg. ***Guns: What You Should Know.*** Albert Whitman and Company, 1999. Warns of the danger of guns. **ADVANCED**

Books for Teachers and Families

Manoff, David H., and Stephen N. Vogel. ***Mosby's Outdoor Emergency Medical Guide.*** Mosby Year Book, 1996. Offers help to the untrained person.

Schmidt, Teresa M. ***Daniel the Dinosaur Learns to Stand Tall Against Bullies.*** Johnson Institute, 1996. Explains aggressive behavior.

Free and Inexpensive Materials

Elkind + Sweet/Live Wire Media
Request a free preview of their video "Prevent Violence with Groark."

Bureau of Alcohol, Tobacco, and Firearms
Gang Resistance Education and Training (GREAT) program provides classroom instruction on preventing youth violence.

U.S. Fire Administration
Has free books, videotapes, and kits on fire prevention on their Kids Page.

National Highway Traffic Safety Administration
Ask for safety items from their catalog.

To access free and inexpensive resources on the Web, visit **www.harcourtschool.com/health/free**

Videos

Bicycle Safety Camp: A Kid's Guide to Bike Safety. Capstone Entertainment, 1996

Guns and Violence in Schools. Educational Video Network, 1999.

First Aid and CPR. Educational Video Network, 2002.

These resources have been selected to meet a variety of individual needs. Please review all materials and websites prior to sharing them with students to ensure the content is appropriate for your class. Note that information, while correct at time of publication, is subject to change.

Visit **The Learning Site** for related links, activities, resources, and the health **Webliography.**

www.harcourtschool.com/health

Meeting Individual Needs

Below-Level

Ask students to tell where they find answers to questions. If the answer is in the text, they write *Here* on a self-stick note and attach it to the page. If the answer is on more than one page, they write *Think and Search* on that note. They write *On My Own* if they have to answer it themselves.

Activities

- Make a Checklist, p. 138
- Make a Mural, p. 150

On-Level

Using graphic aids can help students understand information given in text. Tell students that maps, graphs, diagrams, time lines, and pictures help convey the meaning of text. Have them look for graphic aids and tell what information is given and how it is helpful.

Activities

- Identify Plant and Animal Hazards, p. 138
- Perform a Skit, p. 150

Challenge

Have students write idiomatic expressions related to health topics. Idioms might include being *green with envy, feeling blue, having a bone to pick,* or being *chilled to the bone.* Have students illustrate both the figurative and literal meanings.

Activities

- Read a Book, p. 138
- Debate, p. 150

ESL/ELL

Learning Log

Students can use a Learning Log to record new information gained from text. Have students write a newspaper article about a topic related to the chapter content. Encourage students to include information in their articles that answers the questions *who, what, when, where,* and *why*.

Activities

- Comprehensible Input, p. 139
- Background and Experience, p. 142

Curriculum Integration

Use these topics to integrate health into your daily planning.

Integrated Language Arts/Reading Skills

- Role-Play, p. 144
- Practicing "I" Messages, p. 151

Physical Education

- Daily Fitness Tip, pp. 136, 142, 148
- Daily Physical Activity, p. 135
- Identifying Bike Trails, p. 143

Science

- Reading a Windchill Table, p. 140
- Inventions That Save Lives, p. 145

Art

- Peaceful Solutions Comic Strip, p. 149

CHAPTER 6

Pages 134–155

CHAPTER SUMMARY

In this chapter, students

- identify safety measures to prevent injuries outdoors, in motor vehicles, and in weather emergencies.
- examine ways to resolve conflicts and avoid violence.

Life Skills

Students *resolve conflicts* between friends.

Building Good Character

Students show *responsibility* by being positive role models.

Consumer Health

Students *make buying decisions* about helmets and *analyze media messages* about conflicts.

Literature Springboard

Use the article "Defusing Difficult Situations" to spark interest in the chapter topic. See the Read-Aloud Anthology on page RA-7 of this *Teacher Edition*.

Prereading Strategies

SCAN THE CHAPTER Have students preview the chapter content by scanning the titles, headings, pictures, graphs and tables. Ask volunteers to predict what they will learn. Use their predictions to determine their prior knowledge.

PREVIEW VOCABULARY Have students preview the chapter vocabulary and sort the words into two lists—familiar words and unfamiliar words. Have students look up unfamiliar words in the Glossary.

Words I Know	Words I've Seen or Heard	New Words

Reading Skill

DRAW CONCLUSIONS To introduce or review this skill, have students use the Reading in Health Handbook, pp. 332–333. Teaching strategies and additional activities are also provided.

Students will have opportunities to practice and apply this skill throughout this chapter.

- Focus Skill Reading Mini-Lesson, p. 136
- Reading comprehension questions identified with the 
- *Activity Book* p. 28 (shown on p. 140)
- Lesson Summary and Review, pp. 140, 145, 152
- Chapter Review and Test Preparation, pp. 154–155

Reading Skill

DRAW CONCLUSIONS Sometimes when you read a lesson, not all of the information is provided. You have to use information from the passage plus what you already know to draw a conclusion. Use the Reading in Health Handbook on pages 332–333 and this graphic organizer to help you.

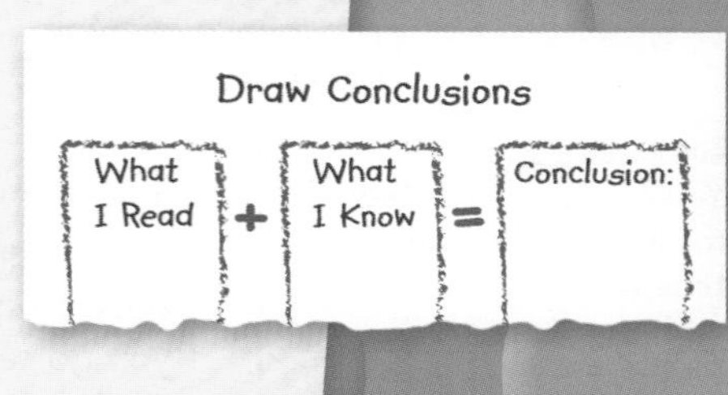

Health Graph

INTERPRET DATA Thunderstorms are the most frequent type of dangerous storm in the United States. The danger comes from lightning.

1. How many more thunderstorms does Florida have than Texas? Than Indiana? Than California?
2. Why is a person at higher risk of getting struck by lightning in Florida than in the other states shown?

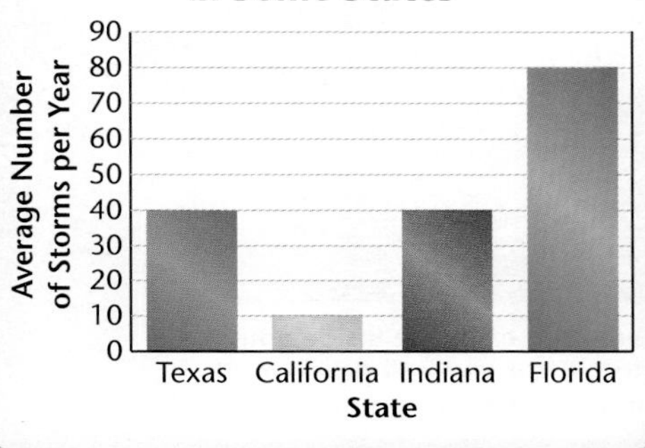

Daily Physical Activity

You can be active and safe outdoors. Help your body stay healthy.

Be Active!
Use the selection Track 6, **Muscle Mambo**, to move your heart and other muscles toward good health.

135

INTRODUCE THE CHAPTER

Health Graph

Interpret Data

Ask a volunteer to explain what the graph shows.

How many times more thunderstorms does Florida have than Texas? two times **than Indiana?** two times **than California?** eight times

Why is a person at higher risk of getting struck by lightning in Florida than in any other state? because Florida has the greatest number of thunderstorms and thunderstorms bring lightning

Which states have the same number of thunderstorms every year? Texas and Indiana

Daily Physical Activity

Use *Be Active! Music for Daily Physical Activity* with the Instant Activity Cards to provide students with movement activities that can be done in limited space. Options for using these components are provided beginning on page TR2 in this *Teacher Edition.*

Chapter Project

Dos and Don'ts *(Assessment Guide* p. 58*)*

ASSESS PRIOR KNOWLEDGE Use students' initial ideas for the project as a baseline assessment of their understanding of chapter concepts. Have students complete the project as they work through the chapter.

PERFORMANCE ASSESSMENT The project can be used for performance assessment. Use the Project Evaluation Sheet (rubric), *Assessment Guide* p. 67.

School-Home Connection

Distribute copies of the School-Home Connection (in English or Spanish). Have students take the page home to share with their families as you begin this chapter.

Follow Up Have volunteers share the results of their activities.

Supports the Coordinated School Health Program

TEACHING RESOURCES P. 33

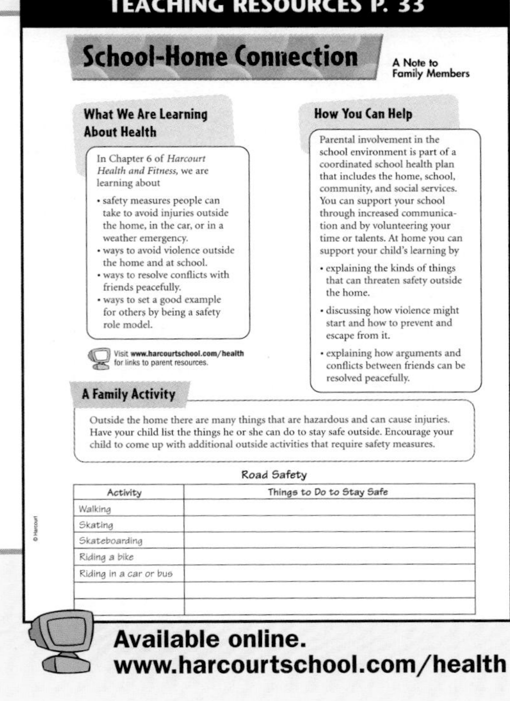

School-Home Connection

A Note to Family Members

What We Are Learning About Health

In Chapter 6 of *Harcourt Health and Fitness,* we are learning about

- safety measures people can take to avoid injuries outside the home, in the car, or in a weather emergency.
- ways to avoid violence outside the home and at school.
- ways to resolve conflicts with friends peacefully.
- ways to set a good example for others by being a safety role model.

Visit **www.harcourtschool.com/health** for links to parent resources.

How You Can Help

Parental involvement in the school environment is part of a coordinated school health plan that includes the home, school, community, and social services. You can support your school through increased communication and by volunteering your time or talents. At home you can support your child's learning by

- explaining the kinds of things that can threaten safety outside the home.
- discussing how violence might start and how to prevent and escape from it.
- explaining how arguments and conflicts between friends can be resolved peacefully.

A Family Activity

Outside the home there are many things that are hazardous and can cause injuries. Have your child list the things he or she can do to stay safe outside. Encourage your child to come up with additional outside activities that require safety measures.

Road Safety

Activity	Things to Do to Stay Safe
Walking	
Skating	
Skateboarding	
Riding a bike	
Riding in a car or bus	

© Harcourt

Available online.
www.harcourtschool.com/health

LESSON 1
Pages 136–140

Objectives
- ► Identify strategies for avoiding injuries when camping and hiking, and during cold and hot weather.
- ► Describe appropriate responses during weather emergencies.

When Minutes Count . . .
Assign the Quick Study, Lesson 1, Activity Book pp. 26–27 (shown on p. 137).

Program Resources
- ► Activity Book pp. 26–28
- ► Transparency 2

Vocabulary
flood p. 139, **lightning** p. 139, **hurricane** p. 139, **tornado** p. 139

Daily Fitness Tip
Children perspire less than adults and reach a higher core body temperature before they begin to sweat. Remind students to drink more fluids in warm and hot weather, regardless of their activity levels. They should not wait until they're thirsty to drink. They should avoid liquids that contain caffeine or large amounts of sugar; these cause a person to lose more body fluids.

1. MOTIVATE

Optional Activity Materials
sunscreen and insect repellent

Ask students to name some activities they enjoy while camping or hiking and some safety measures they practice while doing them. Display the materials and ask the following questions.

How does sunscreen protect your health? It reduces damage to the skin from the sun.

Why is it important to guard against insect bites? Bites and stings from insects such as ticks and mosquitoes can cause diseases.

LESSON 1

Staying Safe Outdoors

Lesson Focus
You can practice safety measures while spending time outdoors.

Why Learn This?
You can protect yourself and others from injuries when you are outdoors.

Vocabulary
flood
lightning
hurricane
tornado

Camping and Hiking

Spending time outdoors can be fun, but you need to stay safe. The last thing you want when you go camping or hiking is to become injured or ill. The pictures on these two pages give some tips for staying safe while camping. Here are other tips to follow when you are outdoors:

- Wear sunscreen, even on cold or cloudy days.
- Don't go hiking by yourself. If you get lost, stay where you are. Wear a whistle and use it.
- Take along a first-aid kit.

Don't wear loose, flowing clothing that can easily catch fire.
Make sure an adult is present when a campfire is burning.
Quick Activity
Identify Precautions
What safety precautions can you identify in this picture?
Keep a bucket of water nearby to put out your campfire.
Build the campfire inside a fire ring. Clear away all dead wood and leaves from the ring.

136

Reading Skill

Mini-Lesson

DRAW CONCLUSIONS
Remind students that when they read, they often use what they already know to draw conclusions. Have them practice this skill by responding to the Focus Skill question on page 137. Have students draw and complete the graphic organizer as you model it on the transparency.

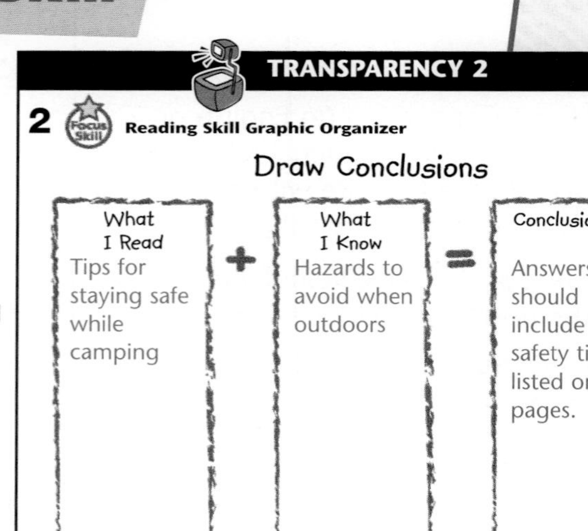

Interactive Transparencies available on CD-ROM.

Make sure the tent is secure and waterproof.
Use a cooler with ice or ice packs to store foods that can spoil.
Look for dangers on the ground, such as broken glass, thorns, or fallen branches.
Do not go near wild animals.

▲ poison ivy

▲ poison oak

▲ poison sumac

Most wild animals are usually afraid of people. But if you get too close, a wild animal may bite you. Going near a young animal can also be dangerous. The mother might be nearby and could attack you to protect her young.

Ticks and insects, such as mosquitoes, can carry germs that cause diseases. Use a repellent and keep your skin covered. Wear long pants and shirts with long sleeves. If you get a tick on you, ask an adult to remove it. Watch for stinging insects.

Some people react to posion ivy, posion oak, or posion sumac. These plants can cause skin redness, itching, and a rash. Avoid touching any plant with leaves in groups of three. If you do touch one of these plants, wash your skin with plenty of soap and water.

DRAW CONCLUSIONS How can you stay safe when camping?
Answers should include the safety tips listed on these pages.

Information Alert!

West Nile Virus West Nile virus is spread by mosquitoes. It first appeared in the U.S. in 1999, reaching Texas in 2002. Find out the number of cases in your state.

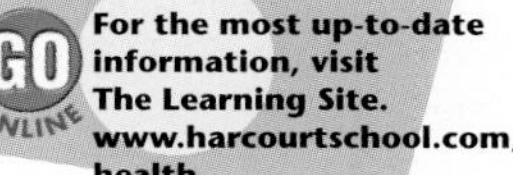

For the most up-to-date information, visit The Learning Site. www.harcourtschool.com/health

137

QUICK STUDY, ACTIVITY BOOK PP. 26–27

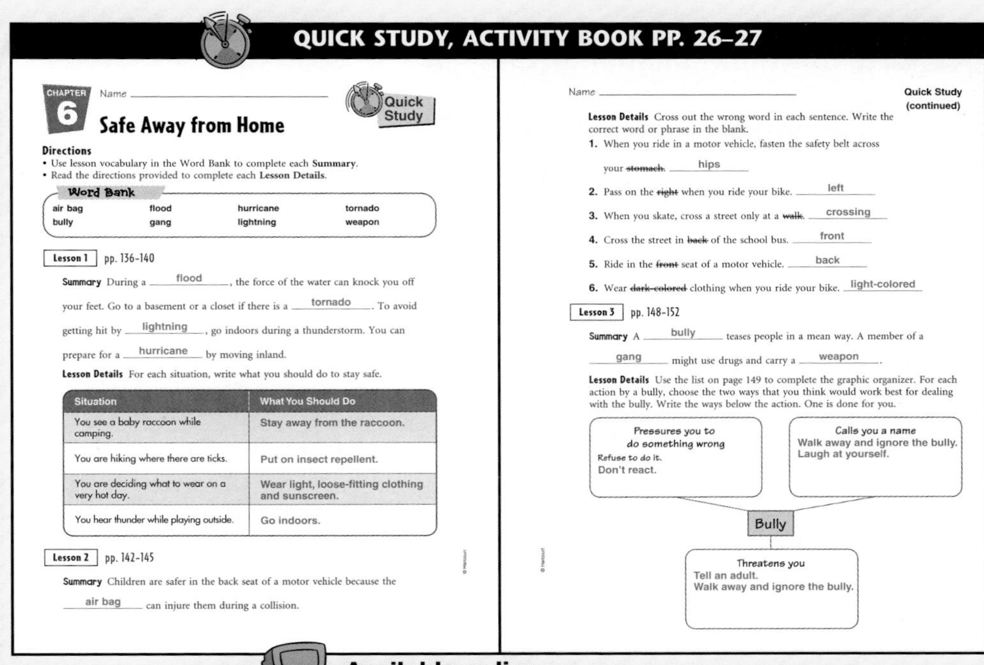

CHAPTER 6 Name ______

Safe Away from Home

Quick Study

Directions
- Use lesson vocabulary in the Word Bank to complete each **Summary**.
- Read the directions provided to complete each **Lesson Details**.

Word Bank

air bag	flood	hurricane	tornado
bully	gang	lightning	weapon

Lesson 1 pp. 136-140

Summary During a __flood__, the force of the water can knock you off your feet. Go to a basement or a closet if there is a __tornado__. To avoid getting hit by __lightning__, go indoors during a thunderstorm. You can prepare for a __hurricane__ by moving inland.

Lesson Details For each situation, write what you should do to stay safe.

Situation	What You Should Do
You see a baby raccoon while camping.	Stay away from the raccoon.
You are hiking where there are ticks.	Put on insect repellent.
You are deciding what to wear on a very hot day.	Wear light, loose-fitting clothing and sunscreen.
You hear thunder while playing outside.	Go indoors.

Lesson 2 pp. 142-145

Summary Children are safer in the back seat of a motor vehicle because the __air bag__ can injure them during a collision.

Name ______ Quick Study (continued)

Lesson Details Cross out the wrong word in each sentence. Write the correct word or phrase in the blank.

1. When you ride in a motor vehicle, fasten the safety belt across your ~~stomach.~~ __hips__
2. Pass on the ~~right~~ when you ride your bike. __left__
3. When you skate, cross a street only at a ~~walk~~. __crossing__
4. Cross the street in ~~back~~ of the school bus. __front__
5. Ride in the ~~front~~ seat of a motor vehicle. __back__
6. Wear ~~dark-colored~~ clothing when you ride your bike. __light-colored__

Lesson 3 pp. 148-152

Summary A __bully__ teases people in a mean way. A member of a __gang__ might use drugs and carry a __weapon__.

Lesson Details Use the list on page 149 to complete the graphic organizer. For each action by a bully, choose the two ways that you think would work best for dealing with the bully. Write the ways below the action. One is done for you.

Bully

Pressures you to do something wrong
Refuse to do it.
Don't react.

Calls you a name
Walk away and ignore the bully.
Laugh at yourself.

Threatens you
Tell an adult.
Walk away and ignore the bully.

© Harcourt

Available online.
www.harcourtschool.com/health

2. TEACH

Quick Activity

As students do the Quick Activity, list on the board the safety precautions they identify. Then have students explain how each of these precautions helps to keep a person safe.

Content-Area Reading Support

Using Paragraph Structure Have students read the text and explain how each paragraph relates to the lesson title. Each paragraph deals with different aspects of safety precautions for activity outdoors. Point out that each paragraph introduces a new aspect of various things to consider. Urge students to pay particular attention to the first sentence of a paragraph because it may state the topic or main idea of the paragraph. Comment that paragraphs in textbooks are often organized this way.

Discuss

Problem Solving How else can you stay safe on a camping trip? Possible answers: Listen to the weather report before leaving; don't touch hot pots without a potholder; don't wander away from the campsite alone or without permission.

Critical Thinking Why is it important to keep all food, even food that won't spoil, in tightly sealed containers? The smell of food can attract wild animals.

Critical Thinking Explain the importance of washing if you should come in contact with plants like poison ivy, oak, or sumac. Some people have allergic reactions from contact with plants like these. Point out that oils from these plants can be spread by contact. That's why you need to wash thoroughly whatever part of you touches, even clothing, such a plant. For more details about first aid for skin rashes and insect bites see page 347 or *Teaching Resources* page 103.

TEACH *continued*

Discuss

Problem Solving What are some other ways to stay warm and dry to avoid injury in cold weather? Stay indoors; if you get wet, change into dry clothes quickly; wear ski masks and scarves for added warmth and protection from cold and wind.

Draw Conclusions

Why is it important to drink plenty of fluids when the weather is hot? You lose body fluids through sweating and need to replace those fluids.

Critical Thinking What does it mean if you start to shiver? You're getting cold.

What should you do if you continue to shiver? Guide students to recognize that they need to go indoors to warm up. Sunglasses are also important in winter. Snow can reflect sunlight causing glare.

Health Background

Hypothermia A condition in which the core body temperature drops below 95°. It's usually caused by extended exposure to cold temperatures without adequate protective clothing or while wearing wet clothing. People suffering from hypothermia often experience confusion, lack of coordination, and slurred speech. This serious condition requires immediate first aid and medical assistance.

Hyperthermia A general term referring to heat-related illnesses. Heatstroke, one of the most common forms of hyperthermia, is especially dangerous. The body temperature rises above 104°. Signs of heatstroke include dry, flushed skin; rapid pulse; confusion; and lack of sweating. Heatstroke should be treated by experienced medical personnel as quickly as possible.

Source: *National Institutes of Health*

For more background, visit the **Webliography** in Teacher Resources at **www.harcourtschool.com/health** **Keyword** first aid

Head coverings or earmuffs protect your ears from frostbite.

Your head and neck lose heat more quickly than other parts of your body.

Wearing several layers of clothing helps keep in your body heat.

An outer waterproof layer keeps moisture away from your body. The middle layer lets air pass through and pulls wetness away from your body. The lining helps hold in heat.

Mittens allow your fingers to warm each other.

Waterproof shoes or boots keep your feet dry.

Tips for Winter Safety

- ☐ Never skate, sled, or ski alone or after dark.
- ☐ Wear brightly colored clothing.
- ☐ Stay out of the paths of others.
- ☐ Don't sled or ski in areas that have trees, fences, rocks, poles, traffic, or roads.
- ☐ Avoid skiing or sledding on icy, steep, or bumpy hills.

Hot and Cold Weather

Summer can be a great time to have fun. But be careful of the heat. If you get too hot, you can become faint or dizzy or feel sick to your stomach. In very hot weather, wear light, loose-fitting clothing. Rest often in the shade. Drink plenty of water. Be sure to wear sunscreen to protect your skin.

You can have fun in cold weather too, but your body can lose a lot of heat. It may not be able to keep itself warm. Getting too cold can be dangerous. Dress in layers to keep warm. Very cold weather can damage your skin. Be sure to stay covered up. You should wear sunscreen.

COMPARE AND CONTRAST **How are safety rules for hot and cold weather alike and different?** Alike: You should wear sunscreen in both types of weather. Different: In hot weather, wear light, loose clothing. In cold weather, wear layers of clothing.

138

Meeting Individual Needs
Leveled Activities

BELOW-LEVEL **Make a Checklist** Have pairs of students make a checklist of safety precautions to take when participating in various outdoor activities.

ON-LEVEL **Identify Plant and Animal Hazards** Have students find out what types of plant and animal hazards, such as poison ivy, ticks, or bears, are common in your area. Have students report their findings to the class.

CHALLENGE **Read a Book** Work with the media specialist to help students choose a story or book about a child who has an outdoor adventure and was not prepared or did not follow safety rules. Have students write a one-page alternative storyline with the character following safety rules they have learned.

Weather Emergencies

Storms are dangerous because high winds, lightning, and floods can occur. A **flood** is an overflow of water onto normally dry land. Floods can sweep away people and property.

CAUSE AND EFFECT Tell what can happen as a result of storms.
High winds, lightning, and floods can occur.

Thunderstorms can bring strong winds, heavy rain, lightning, and flash floods. **Lightning** is a large release of electricity. It can injure or kill people, cause fires, and damage property.

A **hurricane** is a storm that forms over an ocean and covers a large area. It brings strong winds, heavy rain, and floods.

A **tornado** is an extremely strong windstorm. Its winds spin in a funnel-shaped cloud. Tornadoes can flatten houses and other buildings and lift cars and trucks.

139

ESL/ELL Support

COMPREHENSIBLE INPUT Help students practice what to do in various weather emergencies.

Beginning Give students index cards on which you have drawn a weather emergency. Have students choose a card and act out what to do in the emergency.

Intermediate Assign a type of weather emergency to each pair of students. Have the pair write two sentences telling what to do in the emergency.

Advanced Ask students to design a pamphlet telling people what to do in various weather emergencies.

Discuss

Tell students that an average thunderstorm lasts about 30 minutes and affects an area about 15 miles in diameter. In an average year, 16 million thunderstorms occur worldwide. Some thunderstorms produce heavy rains, flash floods, strong winds, hail, or tornadoes. All thunderstorms produce lightning.

Problem Solving How can you find out if a storm is headed your way? listen to a radio or watch TV

Critical Thinking Why is it important to have a battery-operated radio on hand? in case the power goes out during a storm

Interpret Visuals—Pictures

Direct students' attention to the photographs of the tornado, lightning, and hurricane. Ask a volunteer to describe similarities and differences.

Suppose you were outdoors and you heard thunder in the distance. What should you do and why? Get indoors as quickly as possible to avoid danger from lightning that comes with thunderstorms. Stay indoors until the storm passes. Students can look ahead to page 140 to check their responses.

Where do hurricanes form? over an ocean

Critical Thinking Which parts of the country are likely to be affected by hurricanes and why? areas along the coasts, because hurricanes form over oceans

Critical Thinking Why would a person be safer from a tornado below ground than at ground level? Possible answer: Tornadoes cause damage as they touch the ground.

3. WRAP UP

Lesson 1 Summary and Review

1. Lightning, tornado, hurricane, floods
2. Students should cite safety rules from pages 136–137, such as keep a bucket of water nearby, have adult supervision, and build the fire in a fire ring.
3. Leave the porcupine alone because it's a wild animal and may bite; its mother might be nearby and the mother might attack using its quills.
4. Possible answers:

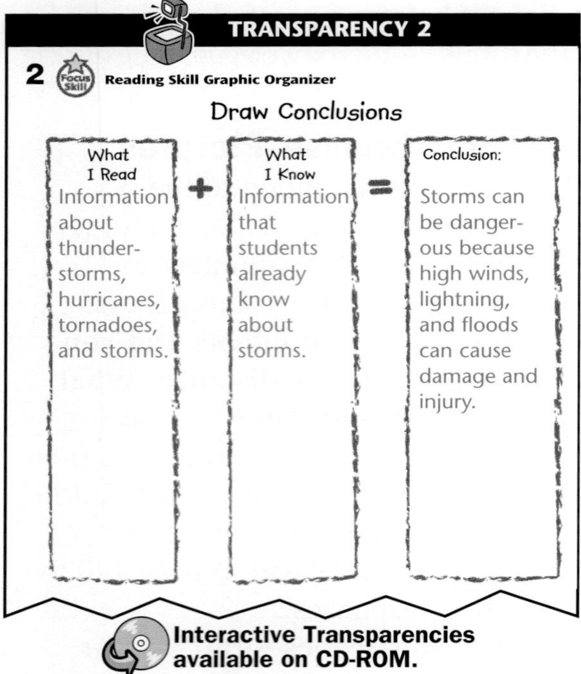
TRANSPARENCY 2

2 Reading Skill Graphic Organizer

Draw Conclusions

What I Read	+	What I Know	=	Conclusion:
Information about thunderstorms, hurricanes, tornadoes, and storms.		Information that students already know about storms.		Storms can be dangerous because high winds, lightning, and floods can cause damage and injury.

Interactive Transparencies available on CD-ROM.

5. Answers should include safety rules on how to stay warm in cold weather.

For **writing models** with examples, see *Teaching Resources* pp. 47–61. Rubrics are also provided.

When Minutes Count . . .

Quick Study Students can use *Activity Book* pages 26–27 (shown on p. 137) as they complete each lesson in this chapter.

Did You Know?
Lightning strikes Earth about one hundred times each second. A lightning bolt can have a temperature of more than 60,000 degrees Fahrenheit. That's hotter than the surface of the sun!

Safety in Bad Weather

The best way to stay safe in bad weather is to be prepared. If bad weather occurs, follow your family emergency plan. Listen to TV and radio reports.

SEQUENCE **What can you do before a thunderstorm to help keep safe?**

Quickly get inside a building or motor vehicle.

What to Do in Bad Weather

Type of Weather	What You Should Do
Blizzard	Dress in layers of wool or silk to keep in body heat. If you are in a car, do not leave it.
Hurricane	Bring toys and bicycles indoors. Move inland away from the coast, if you are told to do so.
Thunderstorm	Quickly get inside a building or motor vehicle. If you are outdoors, crouch down. Don't lie flat.
Tornado	Stay away from windows. Go to a basement, a closet, or a bathroom without windows.

Lesson 1 Summary and Review

1. **Summarize with Vocabulary**
   Use vocabulary from this lesson to complete the statements.
   _____ from a thunderstorm can cause fires. A storm called a _____ can pick up a truck. A _____ forms over an ocean. It can bring a _____, which can sweep away people and property.
2. How can you prevent a campfire from getting out of control?
3. **Critical Thinking** While hiking, your friend sees a baby porcupine and wants to get closer. What would you tell her?
4. **DRAW CONCLUSIONS** Draw and complete this graphic organizer to show why some storms are dangerous.

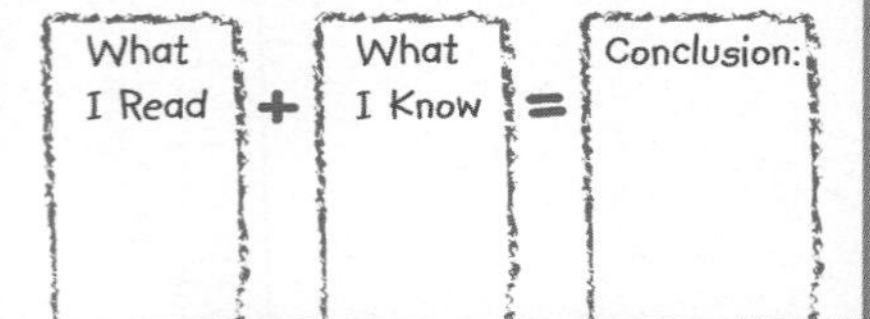
What I Read
What I Know
Conclusion:

5. **Writing to Inform—How-To** 
   Suppose your family is going on vacation in a very cold climate. Write about what you and your family can do to stay safe when you are outdoors on your vacation.

140

ACTIVITY BOOK P. 28

Name ______________

Reading Skill

Draw Conclusions

Safety Online

Suppose you receive an e-mail from someone you don't know. The person says she is 10 years old and wants to be your pen pal. Can you believe what this person is telling you? You can't see or hear the person. What people tell you online may or may not be true.

Some adults who are looking for children to harm use the computer to contact children. They may write nice messages and offer gifts to gain your trust. Then they might send pictures that make you uncomfortable. They may ask to meet you in person.

Follow safety rules when you use the computer. Visit only websites that your parents say are OK. If a person you don't know writes to you, tell your parents. They can tell you if it's safe to write back. Tell your parents if anyone sends you a mean message or one that makes you feel uncomfortable. Never give your last name, address, or phone number on any website (even on those you are allowed to visit) unless your parents have approved.

Which of the following conclusions can you draw from this passage? Write the conclusion in the circle of the graphic organizer. Then write three details.

A. All strangers who write to you online tell lies about themselves.
B. You can stay safe online by following safety rules.
C. It is OK to write back to a stranger who sends you a nice message online.

Possible answers:

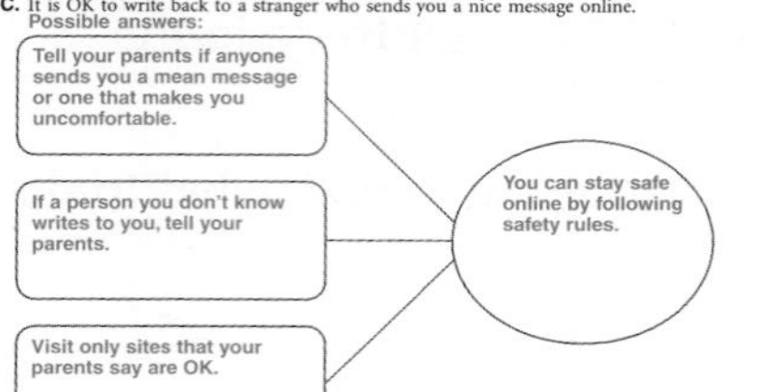
Tell your parents if anyone sends you a mean message or one that makes you uncomfortable.
If a person you don't know writes to you, tell your parents.
Visit only sites that your parents say are OK.
You can stay safe online by following safety rules.

Available online.
www.harcourtschool.com/health

Science

Reading a Windchill Table
Use print or online sources to copy or print out a windchill table from the National Weather Service. Explain to students that wind can carry heat away from the body. High winds increase the likelihood of hypothermia or frostbite (freezing of body tissue). Distribute several copies of the table, and help students interpret how to read it. Discuss how windchill affects what people wear and how long they can stay outside.

Responsibility

Building Good Character

Being a Positive Role Model

Positive role models set good examples for others. They behave in responsible ways that keep themselves and others safe. Below are tips on how you can be a positive role model, especially during outdoor activities. Notice that the first letters of the tips combine to spell **MODEL.**

- **Mind laws, rules, and people in authority.** If the lifeguard tells you to leave the pool, do it. Others will follow your example because they know you are responsible.
- **Observe unsafe situations and take action.** While on a picnic, you notice lightning in the distance. Tell your family so that all of you can pack up and leave the area.
- **Decide to resist pressure to take wrong actions.** A friend wants you to sneak out of your campsite with him while others are sleeping. Be a positive role model by refusing to go.
- **Examine your behavior to see how it helps or harms others.** When you skate, make sure you do not get in the way of others.
- **Look out for the safety of others.** On a hike, you discover a friend has forgotten her sunscreen. You share yours.

Activity

By sharing ideas, your class can learn ways to be positive role models. For one school week, choose one tip to follow each day, and write down what you did. At the end of the week, share your descriptions with your class.

141

Building Good Character

Caring
Citizenship
Fairness
Respect
Responsibility
Trustworthiness

Objective

► Describe ways to show responsibility during outdoor activities by being a positive role model.

Program Resource

► Poster 5

BEFORE READING

Ask students to describe a person who is a positive role model. Point out that everyone can be a positive role model by behaving responsibly. Have volunteers give examples of responsible behaviors that they practice or have observed that encourage people to behave responsibly.

DISCUSS

As you read aloud each tip, ask students to tell why each behavior shows that the person is responsible. Guide students to recognize how each behavior helps prevent injury. Solicit additional examples of behaviors for each tip, and write these on the board.

ACTIVITY

Suggest that each student work with a classmate all week to describe ways in which a tip was followed. Students can discuss their ideas and help each other recognize situations in which they are acting as positive role models. Students also can ask their parents for help. Student descriptions can serve as a springboard for classroom discussions.

Using the Poster

Activity After students discuss the poster, have them choose their favorite example of being a positive role model from the descriptions they generated. Partners can work together to create a poster and display it in a school location related to the topic. For example, a poster about obeying the coach could be displayed in the gymnasium. Display posters in a hallway outside the classroom.

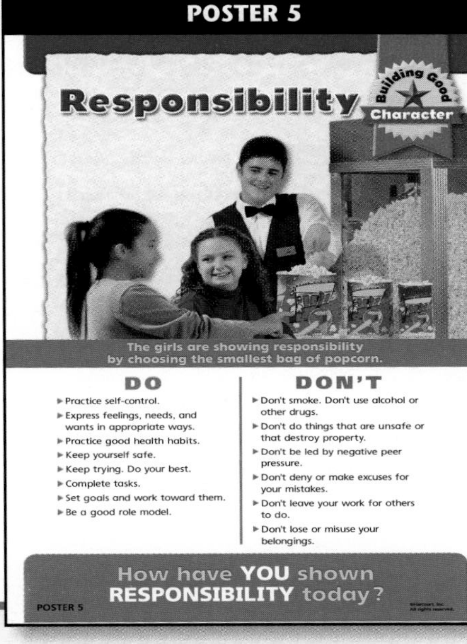
POSTER 5
Responsibility
Building Good Character
The girls are showing responsibility by choosing the smallest bag of popcorn.
DO
► Practice self-control.
► Express feelings, needs, and wants in appropriate ways.
► Practice good health habits.
► Keep yourself safe.
► Keep trying. Do your best.
► Complete tasks.
► Set goals and work toward them.
► Be a good role model.
DON'T
► Don't smoke. Don't use alcohol or other drugs.
► Don't do things that are unsafe or that destroy property.
► Don't be led by negative peer pressure.
► Don't deny or make excuses for your mistakes.
► Don't leave your work for others to do.
► Don't lose or misuse your belongings.
How have YOU shown RESPONSIBILITY today?
POSTER 5

LESSON 2
Pages 142–145

Objectives
► Identify personal behaviors to prevent injuries when skating, skateboarding, biking, and riding in a motor vehicle.
► Discuss the use of safety gear and equipment to reduce injuries when traveling.

When Minutes Count . . .
Assign the Quick Study, Lesson 2, Activity Book pp. 26–27 (shown on p. 137).

Program Resources
► Activity Book pp. 26–27
► Transparency 2

Vocabulary
air bag p. 144

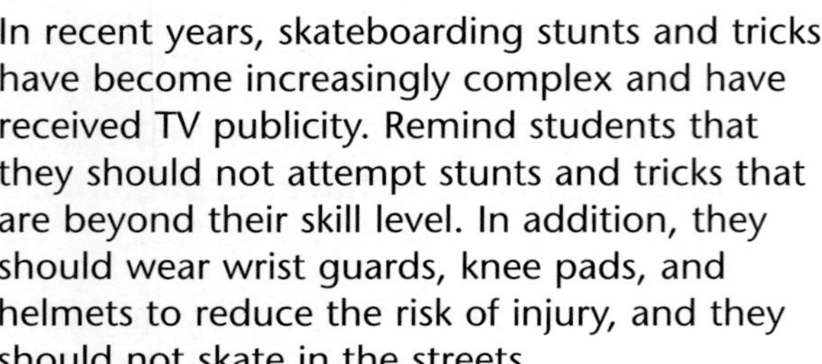

In recent years, skateboarding stunts and tricks have become increasingly complex and have received TV publicity. Remind students that they should not attempt stunts and tricks that are beyond their skill level. In addition, they should wear wrist guards, knee pads, and helmets to reduce the risk of injury, and they should not skate in the streets.

For more about skating and skateboarding safety, see *Be Active! Resources for Physical Education* p. 187.

1. MOTIVATE

Ask students to imagine that they are planning a bike ride.

What will you wear? Possible answer: helmet, light- or bright-colored clothing

What equipment on your bike do you need to check before you start? Possible answer: Check that there is the correct amount of air in the tires, that the brakes work, and that the bike has reflectors.

Ask students to identify the importance of taking personal responsibility for maintaining a personal health plan for personal safety.

LESSON 2 Staying Safe on the Road

Lesson Focus
Proper safety equipment and safety rules can keep you safe when you travel.

Why Learn This?
You will know how to stay safe when you bike, skate, skateboard, or ride in a motor vehicle.

Vocabulary
air bag

Biking

I am easier to see.

Riding your bike is a great way to travel. Following these safety rules can reduce your risk when you ride:

- Ride in a street, road, or bike path. Don't ride alone.
- Ride in a straight line near the right-hand side of the road. Pass on the left.
- Follow traffic signs and safety laws.
- Use the proper hand signals for stops and turns.
- Slow down around people on foot.
- Watch out for doors opening from parked cars.
- Don't ride at night.

CAUSE AND EFFECT **What is an effect of wearing bright or light-colored clothing when biking?**

Make sure you wear a helmet. In many places, it's the law.
Wear bright or light-colored clothing. Make yourself easy to see.
Use a basket, not a backpack.
Sound a horn or bell to help others hear you coming.
Wear closed-toe shoes to avoid foot injuries. Do not wear loose clothing that may catch in the chain or wheels.

ESL/ELL Support

BACKGROUND AND EXPERIENCE Invite children to discuss the safety rules they follow when riding on a bike or in a motor vehicle.

Beginning Point to the pictures of safety gear shown with the children riding the bike and in the car. Ask students to name each piece of equipment.

Intermediate Have students describe the safety gear that should be worn when biking and riding in a car, and how each piece helps reduce the risk of injury. Students can look at the pictures in the text if needed.

Advanced Encourage students to make up catchy slogans for bumper stickers to encourage people to wear the proper equipment when riding on a bike or in a car.

Skating and Skateboarding

Skating and skateboarding can be fun. They give you a chance to play with your friends. The exercise can help you stay healthy and fit. However, your experience is fun only if you don't get hurt. To stay safe, wear the proper safety gear. Also stay safe by following these rules:

- Skate on the sidewalk or paths for skating—not in the street. Watch out for rocks, bumps, and holes.
- If you lose your balance, crouch down so that you won't have far to fall. Relax and try to roll.

Focus Skill **DRAW CONCLUSIONS Why is it important to follow safety rules when you skate?**

It is important to follow safety rules to keep from getting hurt.

Quick Activity

Identify Safety Gear Identify the safety gear this person is wearing. How does it keep a skater safe?

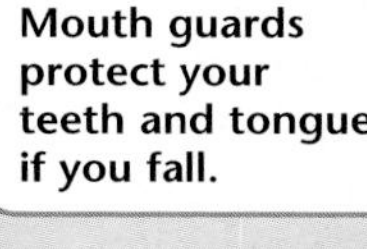

Mouth guards protect your teeth and tongue if you fall.

A helmet will protect your head in case there is a collision or fall.

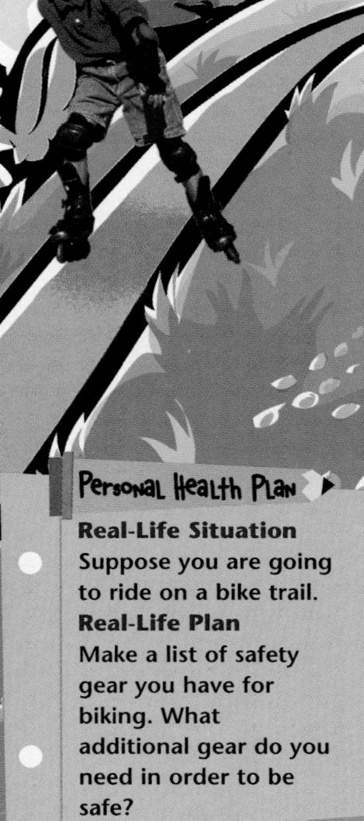

Wrist guards help prevent bones in your arms and wrists from breaking if you fall.

Knee and elbow pads protect you from bruises and broken bones.

Closed, nonslip shoes keep you from slipping.

Personal Health Plan

Real-Life Situation
Suppose you are going to ride on a bike trail.

Real-Life Plan
Make a list of safety gear you have for biking. What additional gear do you need in order to be safe?

143

Physical Education

Identifying Bike Trails
Improving access is key to helping people get plenty of physical activity. Students may not be aware of locations where they and their families can ride bikes safely. Research (or assign students to do this) designated bike trails in your town or county. Bring in a map, and help students locate the bike trails. Suggest that they try the bike trails with their families. Review with the students safety rules for biking.

Teacher Tip

Evaluating Helmet Features
Bring several helmets to class, and point out the features students should look for, including proper fit (helmet should fit low, just above the eyebrows), a hard shell, a crushable liner, a layer of padding, a strong strap and buckle, and a label or tag that says *ANSI, Snell, CPSC,* or *ASTM* (organizations that set safety standards). Allow students to examine the helmets.

2. TEACH

Personal Health Plan

Plans should include:
- Wear a helmet.
- Have a horn or bell.
- Use a basket or backpack.
- Wear bright or light-colored clothing. that isn't loose.
- Wear closed-toed shoes.

For more bike safety information, see pages 352–353 of the Health and Safety Handbook.

Interpret Visuals—Pictures

Ask volunteers to read the captions on both of these pages. As a class, discuss the safety tips shown. Guide students to understand how each tip helps reduce the risk of injury. Solicit additional safety tips, such as yelling "Passing on your left!" before passing pedestrians. Remind students that walking people have the right of way. Caution students that wrist guards should not be worn when riding a scooter because they can make steering difficult.

Content-Area Reading Support

Using Text Format Direct attention to the lists of safety rules on every page in this lesson. Point out that the colon is used to draw attention to what follows it, in this case a list of rules. Explain that the rules could have been written one after another as part of the paragraph. However, listing them on separate lines gives them greater importance and makes each rule easier to read.

Discuss

Critical Thinking Why wouldn't you want to wear headphones while skating? They keep you from hearing important sounds like cars or other moving vehicles that you need to avoid.

Quick Activity

Students' responses should include helmet, knee and elbow pads, wrist guards, and mouth guard.

TEACH *continued*

Interpret Visuals—Pictures

Call attention to the picture of the children in the car. Ask how the children are practicing safety. Have students read the list of passenger safety rules, and discuss the importance of each.

Discuss

Problem Solving What would you say to someone who put his or her arm out the window of a moving car? Use a reason in your answer. Possible answer: Tell the person to bring his or her arm back in the car because something could strike and injure it, or the arm could get caught on something outside the window.

Critical Thinking Why is riding in the back of an open pickup truck dangerous? Passengers can't be buckled in; in an accident they can be thrown out of the truck or crushed.

Interpret Visuals—Graphs

Tell students that a circle graph tells the percentages of different parts of a whole. Help students estimate the answers by dividing the graph into eighths, with each eighth representing 12.5 percent of the circle. More are using safety belts; more than half.

Health Background

Safety Belts Save Lives Safety-belt use continues an upward trend since national surveys began in 1994. In June 2002, safety-belt use in the United States was 75 percent. A 2 percent increase in belt use translates into an additional 6 million users. The NHTSA estimates that safety belts saved 147,246 lives in the period 1975–2001. This excludes children under the age of nine, who should be in child safety seats.

Source: *National Highway Traffic Safety Administration*

For more background, visit the **Webliography** in Teacher Resources at **www.harcourtschool.com/health**
Keyword injury prevention

Health & Technology

Safer Air Bags The National Highway Traffic Safety Administration (NHTSA) is responsible for standards for air bag safety. It is looking at changes in technology to make air bags safer. One idea is to have the air bag system sense the weight of the passenger. The air bag would inflate with less force for a light passenger than for a heavier one. Another idea is to let the driver turn off the air bag system for the passenger seat.

Riding in a Motor Vehicle

Safety belts can save lives. You should always wear one when you ride in a motor vehicle. Know how to wear a safety belt correctly.

- Fasten the lap belt snugly across your hips, not across your stomach.
- Use a booster seat if you are less than 4 feet 9 inches tall and weigh less than 80 pounds. The lap belt should not cross your face or neck.
- Don't share your safety belt with anyone else.
- Don't distract the driver. Always speak softly to other passengers.
- Don't play with the windows or seats.
- Don't play with sharp objects or drink from a bottle, can, or cup while the vehicle is moving.

An **air bag** is a device in a motor vehicle that inflates, or blows up like a balloon, during a crash. Air bags protect people in the front seats but not people in the back seats. Air bags inflate quickly, and the force can injure a child in the front seat. For this reason, you should always ride in the back seat.

144

Language Arts

Role-Play Set up four chairs, two in a row side-by-side, to simulate the seats of a car. Have groups of students act out getting in the car at home, traveling to the store, and then returning home. In each group, one or two students can act as parents and the remaining students can be children of various ages.

Teacher Tip

School-Bus Safety Discuss with students the reasons for safety rules on and around a school bus. Arrange several desks together to resemble seats on a bus. Then have students role-play waiting for a bus, getting on the bus, and riding on the bus. Encourage students to be role models when riding the bus.

Follow these safety rules for riding a bus:

- Stand at least 6 feet away from the curb while you are waiting to get on.
- Cross the street at least 10 feet in front of the bus.
- Make sure the driver sees you. Never walk behind the bus.
- Use the handrails to avoid falls.
- Stay seated at all times.
- Keep your head and arms inside the bus.
- Don't distract the bus driver.

SUMMARIZE Explain how to correctly wear a safety belt.

Follow the steps listed on page 144.

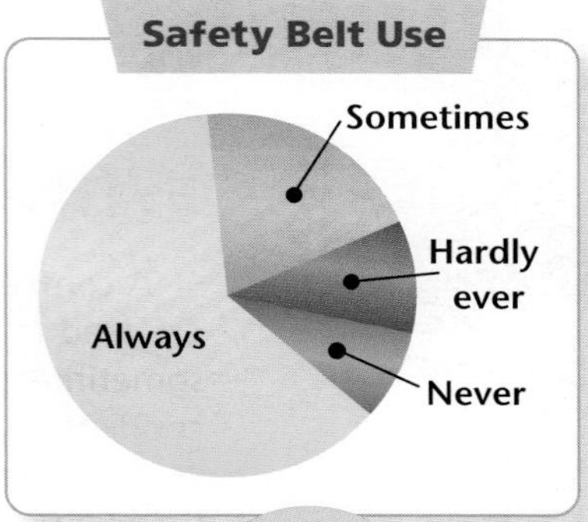

Quick Activity

Interpret Graphs
How does the amount of people who always use safety belts compare to the amount who never use them?

Lesson 2 Summary and Review

1. **Summarize with Vocabulary**
   Use vocabulary and other terms from this lesson to complete the statements.
   When you skate or bike, wear a _____ to protect your head from injury. Don't bike at _____. Always wear your _____ when you ride in a car. Ride in the back seat to avoid injury from an _____ if it inflates. Use the _____ on the bus to avoid falls.
2. What should you do if you start to fall when you are skating or skateboarding?
3. **Critical Thinking** List the safety gear to wear when biking. Which is the most important?
4. **DRAW CONCLUSIONS** Draw and complete this graphic organizer to show details about following safety rules on a bus.

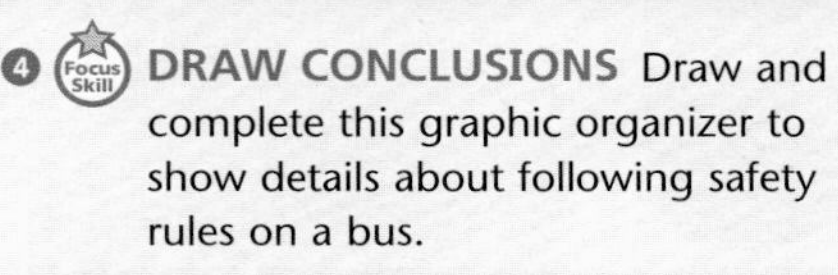

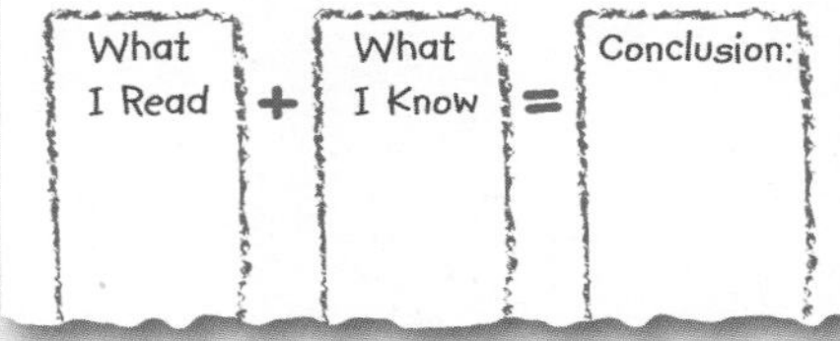

5. **Write to Inform—Explanation**
   Write a paragraph telling why everyone should wear safety belts.

Science

Inventions That Save Lives
Have students investigate inventions that have helped make automobiles safer for drivers and passengers. Students may wish to make a time line or other graphic to show the sequence of the development of automobile safety features. Make sure students understand that safety equipment is effective only when people use it correctly. Ask students to write a brief paragraph on the importance of healthful behaviors when riding in a motor vehicle.

Quick Activity

More than three times as many people wear safety belts than those who don't. Those who sometimes do is more than double the number of those who never do.

3. WRAP UP

Lesson 2 Summary and Review

1. helmet, night, safety belt, air bag, handrails
2. Crouch down, relax, and try to roll.
3. helmet, bright- or light-colored clothing, closed-toe shoes, clothing that will not catch in the chain or wheels; the helmet because it protects your brain and your head.
4. Possible conclusion statement:

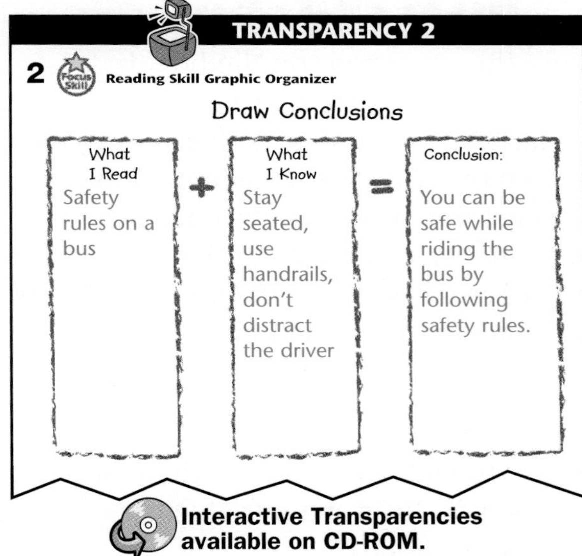

TRANSPARENCY 2
2
Reading Skill Graphic Organizer
Draw Conclusions
What I Read
Safety rules on a bus
+
What I Know
Stay seated, use handrails, don't distract the driver
=
Conclusion:
You can be safe while riding the bus by following safety rules.
Interactive Transparencies available on CD-ROM.

5. Paragraphs should include that wearing a safety belt is the most important safety rule when riding in a motor vehicle.

For **writing models** with examples, see *Teaching Resources* pp. 47–61. Rubrics are also provided.

When Minutes Count . . .

Quick Study Students can use *Activity Book* pages 26–27 (shown on p. 137) as they complete each lesson in this chapter.

Life Skills

Communicate
Make Responsible Decisions
Manage Stress
Refuse
Resolve Conflicts
Set Goals

Objectives

- ► Identify steps for resolving conflicts.
- ► Apply conflict-resolution skills to handle conflicts with friends.

Program Resources

- ► Activity Book p. 29
- ► Poster 11

1. MOTIVATE

Write this statement on the board: *Friends can disagree and still remain friends.* Ask students whether they agree or disagree with this statement. Make a class list of reasons supporting each position. Have students discuss times they have disagreed with friends and how they handled the situations.

2. TEACH

Direct students' attention to the first photograph. Read the introductory paragraphs aloud.

Step 1

What is the difference between an "I" message and a "you" message? Lead students to recognize that an "I" message tells how the speaker feels. A "you" message puts blame on the other person.

Critical Thinking **Suppose Tamara says, "I get upset when you don't play fair!" Is this an effective "I" message?** Lead students to recognize that it is not effective because it is accusing the other person rather than focusing on an observable behavior.

Resolve Conflicts

With Friends

A conflict is a disagreement. Sometimes conflicts can lead to unsafe situations. Even friends disagree sometimes. It's important to resolve, or work out, conflicts if you want to remain friends and stay safe. You can use the steps to **Resolve Conflicts** to help you work out conflicts without fighting or getting angry.

Tamara doesn't think April is playing fair because she doesn't pass the ball. April thinks Tamara hogs the ball. How can Tamara and April resolve this conflict peacefully?

1 Use "I" messages to tell how you feel.

Tamara tells April, "I get upset when the ball is not passed to me."

2 Listen to the other person. Consider that person's point of view.

April says she's angry with Tamara for not sharing the ball so other players can have chances to make goals.

Teacher Tip

Practicing Listening Skills Ask students to generate a list of effective listening skills as you write them on the board. Examples include *Make eye contact, Focus on what the speaker is saying instead of what you will say next, Don't interrupt,* and *Don't fold your arms.* Call on individual students to demonstrate each skill as you say a few words to that student.

ACTIVITY BOOK P. 29

Name ____________________

Problem Solving

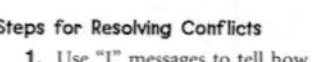

Life Skill

Resolve Conflicts

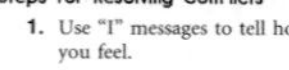

Steps for Resolving Conflicts

1. Use "I" messages to tell how you feel.
2. Listen to the other person. Consider the other person's point of view.
3. Negotiate.
4. Compromise on a solution.

Tell how these students could resolve their conflicts.

A. Jamila and Carlita are working together on a social studies project. Jamila wants to do a skit for their presentation. Carlita wants to make a diorama. The girls start to argue.

- Explain how Jamila and Carlita can come up with a solution that is agreeable to both of them.

Possible answers: discuss which type of presentation would show the information best; agree to do one activity on this project and the other activity on another project. Students may also suggest that the girls ask their teacher to help them resolve their conflict.

B. Austin goes to Nathan's house after school. They are deciding what to do. Nathan wants to play a board game. Austin wants to play basketball. Austin says angrily, "You never want to do what I want!" He looks as if he wants to fight.

- How is Austin not following the steps for resolving conflicts? What can Nathan say to prevent the boys from fighting?

Possible answer: Austin is not using "I" messages. Nathan can use an "I" message such as "I don't want to fight. Let's settle this another way." Possible compromises are to draw straws or flip a coin to decide what to play and to play one game first and the other later or another day.

© Harcourt

Available online.
www.harcourtschool.com/health

3 Negotiate.

April says maybe they should play on different teams. Tamara says they could try to pass the ball more.

4 Compromise on a solution.

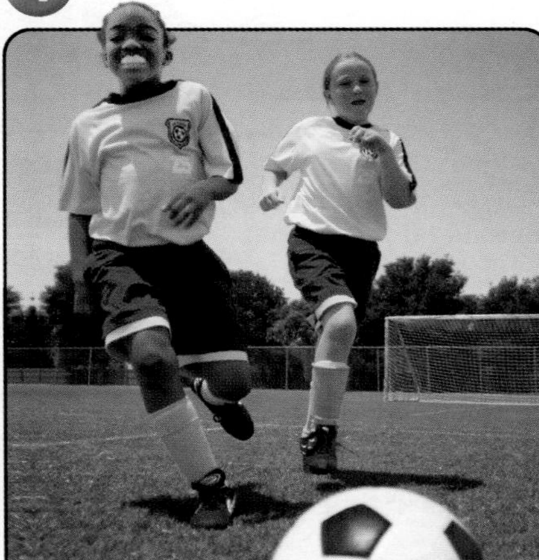

Tamara and April agree that they can each give up the ball more often. Players in scoring positions will have chances to make goals, and the team will do better.

Problem Solving

Victor and his brother Jerome are at the playground. Jerome is crawling on top of the horizontal ladder. He knows this is unsafe. Victor tries to persuade Jerome to stop. Jerome tells Victor to mind his own business. There are other children under the ladder. How can Victor and Jerome use the steps to **Resolve Conflicts** to resolve their conflict? Explain how their solution can also demonstrate responsibility for the safety of the other children playing there.

147

Step 2
What do Tamara and April learn when they listen to each other? They learn how the other one feels.

Step 3
How do the girls negotiate? They each suggest different things to try.

Step 4
How do the girls compromise on a solution? They agree that the best solution is to pass the ball more so all players have a chance to score.

Critical Thinking Why is this a good solution? Possible answers: They can stay on the same team. They won't hurt each other. They will have more fun playing.

Building Good Character

Point out that when people resolve conflicts peacefully, they are being fair to one another. When people are fair, they do not judge other people's behavior. They give other people time to talk. They listen to them. They make a sincere effort to settle their disagreement and do not insist on getting their way all the time.

3. WRAP UP

Problem Solving

Answers should reflect the steps to Resolve Conflicts. Victor can explain that the rule about not crawling on top of the ladder is to keep people safe. He can suggest an alternative activity for Jerome that is safe and fun. Victor also can ask his parents or other adults he knows at the playground for help.

Using the Poster

Activity Organize students in groups of four or five. Give each group an index card on which you have written a scenario in which two friends disagree. Direct students to refer to the poster to help them apply the steps to resolve the conflict in their situation. Encourage students to role-play their scenario and solution for the class.

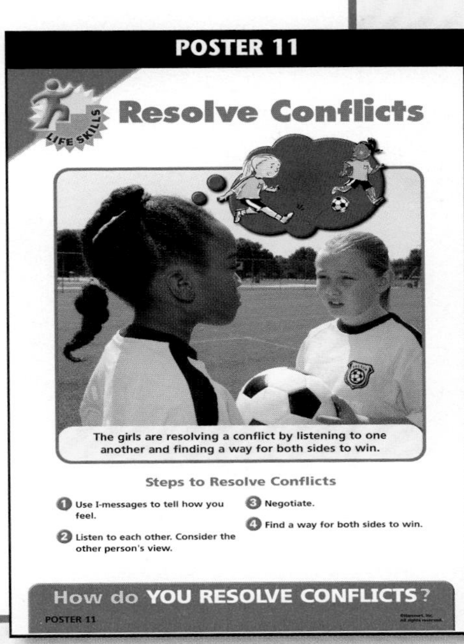

POSTER 11
Resolve Conflicts
LIFE SKILLS
The girls are resolving a conflict by listening to one another and finding a way for both sides to win.
Steps to Resolve Conflicts
1 Use I-messages to tell how you feel.
2 Listen to each other. Consider the other person's view.
3 Negotiate.
4 Find a way for both sides to win.
How do YOU RESOLVE CONFLICTS?
POSTER 11

LESSON 3
Pages 148–152

Objectives
- Identify strategies for avoiding deliberate injuries.
- Develop and use skills to avoid, resolve, and cope with conflicts.

When Minutes Count . . .
Assign the Quick Study, Lesson 3, Activity Book pp. 26–27 (shown on p. 137).

Program Resources
- Activity Book pp. 26–27, 30
- Transparency 2

Vocabulary
bully p. 149, **gang** p. 150, **weapon** p. 151

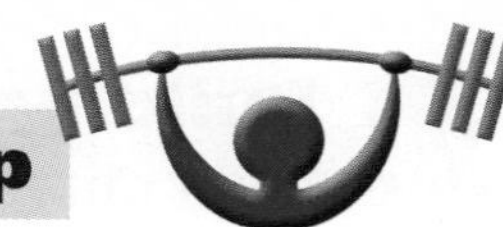

Daily Fitness Tip
Humor can defuse a tense situation and check a bully's attack. Encourage students to enlist the aid of teachers and parents to devise and practice appropriate humorous comebacks to typical bully tactics. Caution students not to try humor if a bully threatens physical harm, but instead to get away quickly.

For more guidelines on resolving conflicts during physical activities, see *Be Active! Resources for Physical Education* p. 209.

1. MOTIVATE
Share the following poem with students:

If I fight	*If I fight*
I might	*I might*
Get a cut or	*Lose control*
Break a bone	*Lose a friend*
Someone else's	*Lose my life.*
Or my own.	*The fight will end.*

What kinds of things can happen when people fight? Possible answers: people suffer cuts and broken bones; friendships end; people can get killed.

LESSON 3 Staying Safe in a Conflict

Lesson Focus
You can resolve conflicts without fighting. You can learn skills to avoid getting hurt as a result of violence.

Why Learn This?
When you practice these skills, you reduce your risk of injury.

Vocabulary
bully
gang
weapon

Resolving Conflict
Conflict among people is normal. There are ways to resolve conflicts without fighting. Here are some suggestions:

- Stay calm. Keep your voice even and quiet.
- Speak respectfully. Do not call the other person names. Say "Please," "Thank you," and "I'm sorry."
- Agree that there is a problem. Listen to the other side. Try to see things the way others see them.
- Identify choices to end the conflict. Each person should compromise, or give a little.
- Leave if another person threatens you.

Focus Skill **DRAW CONCLUSIONS** **Why is it important to resolve conflicts peacefully?**

If the conflict isn't resolved peacefully, a fight might break out and someone might get hurt.

Quick Activity
Resolving a Problem Look at the picture. Write how you would go about resolving the conflict these students are having.

Teacher Tip
Bully-Proof Your School Most students are neither bullies nor victims, but they can band together to support victims of bullying or report it when they see it happen. Encourage students to create a class organization against bullying. Solicit ideas for how such an organization would work. Help students suggest ways to get students in other classes involved.

▲ A bully may tease others in a mean way, call them names, shove them, or trip them.

Dealing with Bullies

Your friends tease you in a friendly way. Someone else starts teasing you in a mean way. This bully continues to pick on you. A **bully** is a person who hurts or frightens others. Bullies usually try to bother people who are different or alone. Being picked on by a bully is no fun. Here are some ways to help keep a bully from hurting or frightening you:

- Don't react or say anything. Keep your cool.
- Don't push, kick, or hit the bully.
- Laugh at yourself. Bullies often leave people alone who don't get angry.
- Refuse if a bully pressures you to do something.
- Walk away and ignore the bully.
- Get help from an adult if a bully threatens you or keeps bothering you.

COMPARE AND CONTRAST What is the difference between teasing from a friend and teasing from a bully? Teasing from a friend is friendly; teasing from a bully is mean and can be hurtful.

ACTIVITY

Life Skills

Refuse Tyler tells Takai to steal a calculator from someone's backpack. He says Takai is "chicken" if he doesn't do it. How can Takai use refusal skills in this situation?

149

Teacher Tip

Bullies Some students may be uncomfortable with some of the content in this lesson because they have been victims of bullies, have bullied others, or have family members who have experienced such problems. Respect the feelings of these students, and keep class participation in any discussion of bullying or other forms of violence voluntary.

Art

Peaceful Solutions Comic Strip After students study the information on page 148, work with them to generate a list of situations that could lead to disagreements among children their age. Have partners select one of the situations and discuss ways that an argument could be resolved without a fight. Students can illustrate the situation and resolution in a large comic strip that can be posted in a hallway or the cafeteria.

2. TEACH

Quick Activity

Have students make a list of possible solutions. As students role-play, remind them to use the suggestions for resolving conflicts. Ask volunteers to present their solutions to the class.

Activity

Refuse Ask a volunteer to review refusal skills. Suggest students read pages 198–199 for more information on refusal skills. Encourage students to describe how they could be applied to this situation. Lead students to recognize that it takes courage to stand up for one's values.

Interpret Visuals—Pictures

Ask volunteers to describe what is happening in the picture on page 148 and what they think might have led to the disagreement. Have a student read the suggestions for resolving conflicts without fighting. Then ask students to discuss how the children in the picture can resolve their conflict by using one or more of these methods.

Discuss

Discuss other forms that bullying can take, such as phone calls, dirty tricks, threatening notes, or taking others' possessions. Ask students to explain the importance of seeking guidance from trusted adults in solving problems.

Critical Thinking Which tips for dealing with a bully have you tried? Why do you think these work? Answers will vary. Ask students to share other strategies that have worked.

TEACH *continued*

Content-Area Reading Support

Using Paragraph Structure Direct attention to the following sentence in the first paragraph: *If a conflict does get out of control, it may lead to physical force, or violence.* Point out that *if* is a signal word indicating an event or condition that could happen. The words after the comma show a possible consequence or a suggested course of action related to the *if* words. Ask students to find the other three *if* sentences in this paragraph and to analyze the relationship of the *if* words to the words after the comma.

Discuss

Ask students to identify strategies for avoiding deliberate injuries such as gang violence and accidents at school and home. Also ask them to identify negative characteristics of social groups such as gangs. Tell students that people sometimes start a conflict because they are angry and the anger gets out of control. Anger is a normal emotion, but a person should deal with anger without getting violent.

Problem Solving What are other signs that a person is angry? Possible answers: shouting, calling a person names, getting up close in a person's face

Critical Thinking What are acceptable ways to express your anger? Possible answers: Tell the person that you are angry without losing your temper or fighting; write in a journal; talk to a friend or parents. Make sure students recognize the importance of talking about their feelings so that their parents can help them deal with their anger.

Consumer Activity

Students' paragraphs should conclude that the media are promoting the idea that fighting is a reasonable way to resolve a conflict. Media could demonstrate conflict resolution strategies. Students should state specific strategies.

Avoid fights by following these guidelines.

Fights

- Walk away if you see a fight.
- Avoid fighting. Instead, talk things out.
- Keep it light. No problem is worth fighting about.
- Get away if a person tries to harm you.

Consumer Activity

Analyze Media Messages Many TV shows, video games, and movies show people fighting to resolve conflicts. Write a paragraph explaining a better, more positive message about resolving conflicts.

Avoiding Violence

Most conflicts don't end in a fight. If a conflict does get out of control, it may lead to physical force, or *violence*. The use of physical force can result in harm to someone. If you are trying to resolve a conflict, carefully observe the other person. Watch for signs that the person is becoming angry or may become violent. Some signs are a clenched fist or jaw, a red face, and a shaking body. If you see any of these signs, back off. If you are near a fight, don't try to stop it. You might get injured. Get away. Find an adult to help.

Another way to avoid violence is to stay away from gangs. A **gang** is a group of people who often use violence. They often commit crimes, use drugs, and carry weapons.

150

Meeting Individual Needs
Leveled Activities

BELOW-LEVEL Make a Mural Have students divide mural paper into four equal sections, one for each action that may be taken to avoid a fight. Form four groups and have each group illustrate one section of the mural.

ON-LEVEL Perform a Skit Have pairs or groups of students brainstorm a situation involving a conflict that they might experience. Then have them write and perform a skit in which the conflict is resolved.

CHALLENGE Debate Have teams of students debate whether violence should be shown on television and in movies.

Gangs

- Avoid being alone.
- Stay away from gang members.
- Stay away from places where gang members hang out.
- Tell an adult if someone asks you to join a gang.

Weapons

- Never touch a gun, even if you think it is a toy.
- Stay away from people who carry weapons.
- Tell an adult if you see a person with a weapon.

A **weapon** is an object that is used to injure or threaten someone. A weapon can be a gun, a knife, or even a baseball bat. Police officers carry weapons as part of their job. Some adults keep weapons in their homes for protection against attackers. Others use weapons for hunting and for target shooting.

Weapons also may be used by terrorists. *Terrorism* is the use of violence to promote a cause. You don't always know where or when a terrorist attack might occur. However, you'll be safer if you stay calm. Do as your family, your teacher, or another person in charge tells you.

MAIN IDEA AND DETAILS **What's the most important action you can take to avoid violence? Name several ways to do this.**
Follow the suggested safety steps listed on these pages.

ACTIVITY

Building Good Character

Citizenship Schools do not allow weapons. Good citizens obey rules and laws. Suppose you know that a classmate has brought a knife to school in his or her backpack. What should you do?

Activity

Citizenship Lead students to recognize that it is not "tattling" to tell a teacher about the knife or some other weapon. Someone could be seriously injured. Students also should not touch the knife. Good citizens obey rules and laws to protect and respect each other.

Discuss

Draw Conclusions Why is it important to tell your parents if someone asks you to join a gang or threatens you? Possible answers: Parents can talk to the parents of the gang members if they are students, or they can contact the authorities. Parents also can help find other ways for you to be safe, such as making sure you do not go places where gang members are present.

Health Background

Making Schools Safe Effective prevention, intervention, and crisis response strategies operate best in schools that focus on academic achievement and maintain high standards. Children are taught that they are responsible for their actions, and all children are valued and respected. The school demonstrates a climate of caring and a sense of community. Students can safely report potential school violence without fear of reprisals.

Source: *A Guide to Safe Schools, U.S. Department of Education*

GO ONLINE For more background, visit the **Webliography** in Teacher Resources at **www.harcourtschool.com/health** **Keyword** violence prevention

Teacher Tip

Talking About Terrorism With reports of terrorism and security alerts continually appearing in news reports, students may understandably feel anxious. If students voice concerns about attacks in the United States, be honest and tell them there are no guarantees that it won't happen again. Reassure them that our government takes steps to prevent further terrorist attacks. These precautions may actually make people safer than they were in the past.

Language Arts

Practicing "I" Messages Model "I" messages and appropriate body language when resolving a conflict (eye contact, arms down, speaking calmly). Give students scenarios (for example, someone bumped you in the hallway), and have them work in groups to make a dialogue with the person with whom they are angry. Encourage them to practice these communication skills.

3. WRAP UP

Lesson 3 Summary and Review

1. bully, weapon, gang, violence
2. Try not to react; don't try pushing, kicking, or hitting the bully; try not to get mad, laugh at yourself; refuse to be pressured; walk away if you can and get the help of an adult.
3. Never touch a gun, even if you think it is a toy; stay away from people who carry weapons; tell an adult if you see a person with a weapon.
4. Possible answers:

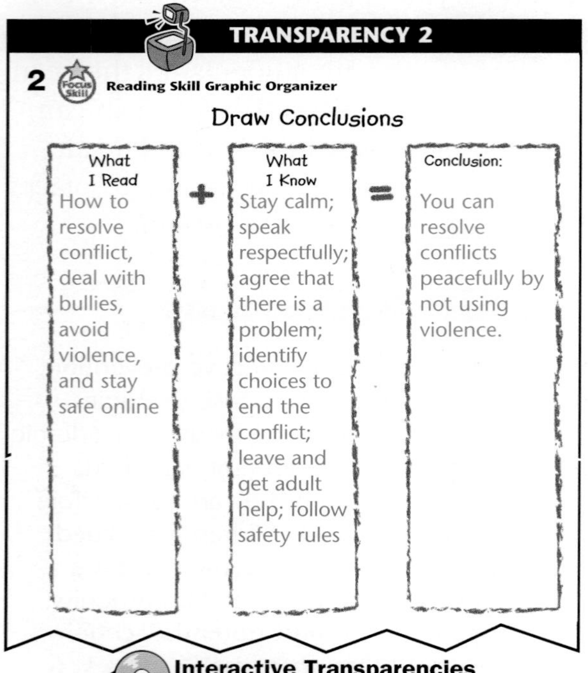
TRANSPARENCY 2

2 Reading Skill Graphic Organizer

Draw Conclusions

What I Read	+	What I Know	=	Conclusion:
How to resolve conflict, deal with bullies, avoid violence, and stay safe online	+	Stay calm; speak respectfully; agree that there is a problem; identify choices to end the conflict; leave and get adult help; follow safety rules	=	You can resolve conflicts peacefully by not using violence.

Interactive Transparencies available on CD-ROM.

5. Paragraphs should include points such as avoid being alone, stay away from gang members, stay away from places where gang members hang out; tell an adult if someone asks you to join a gang.

For **writing models** with examples, see *Teaching Resources* pp. 47–61. Rubrics are also provided.

When Minutes Count . . .

Quick Study Students can use *Activity Book* pages 26–27 (shown on p. 137) as they complete each lesson in this chapter.

Staying Safe Online

You can use the Internet for many things. It can be helpful for schoolwork. You may be allowed to play games on it. You can use it to stay in touch with friends. The Internet is like a city you can visit without leaving your home. Just as in a real city, there are places you don't want to visit. There are also people you don't want to meet. To stay safe online, you should follow some safety rules.

SUMMARIZE List rules for being safe online. See the bulleted list.

STAYING SAFE ONLINE

- Follow family rules for going online.
- Don't give out personal information, such as your name, address, school, telephone number, or picture.
- Tell your parents or guardian if you come across information or get a message that makes you uncomfortable.
- Never agree to meet in person someone you've only met online.

Lesson 3 Summary and Review

1 Summarize with Vocabulary

Use vocabulary and other terms from this lesson to complete the statements.

A person who trips someone on purpose is a _____. A gun is one type of _____. Members of a _____ may hurt people and commit crimes. The use of physical force to harm someone is _____.

2 Critical Thinking Suppose you ignore or try to avoid a bully, but he or she keeps bothering you. What can you do?

3 What are ways to stay safe from weapons?

4 DRAW CONCLUSIONS Draw and complete the graphic organizer to show how to resolve conflicts.

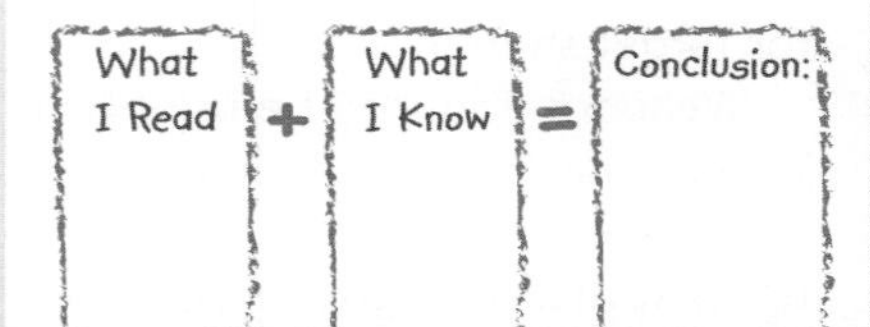

5 Write to Inform—How-To 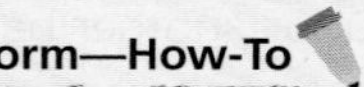

Write a paragraph that tells students in your school how to avoid gangs.

ACTIVITY BOOK P. 30

Name ________

Vocabulary Reinforcement

Complete the Puzzle

Use the clues to complete the puzzle.

Across

4. a powerful windstorm
5. a storm that forms over an ocean and covers a large area
7. a person who hurts or frightens others
8. a group of people who often use violence

Down

1. an object that is used to injure or threaten someone
2. an overflow of water onto normally dry land
3. a large release of electricity
6.–7. a safety item that inflates in a motor vehicle during a collision

Available online. www.harcourtschool.com/health

ACTIVITIES

Language Arts

Weapon Safety Poster
With a small group, write tips on weapon safety. Draw pictures to go with your tips. Display your posters in hallways or on bulletin boards where other students can see them.

Physical Education

Teamwork Games
Make up some games that are good for relieving stress brought about by conflict situations. Ask the physical education teacher to suggest types of activities that are physically active. In your games, include activities that require teamwork.

Technology Project

Weather radios broadcast information from the National Weather Service 24 hours a day. Announcers alert people about dangerous weather so they can be prepared. With a partner, find out what a thunderstorm watch and warning are. Then create your own broadcast telling listeners about an approaching storm. Provide safety guidelines. "Broadcast" your message to your class.

For more activities, visit The Learning Site. www.harcourtschool.com/health

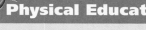

Home & Community

Promote Safety Belt Use
Make posters urging people to wear safety belts. With permission, hang the posters in stores and meeting places in your community.

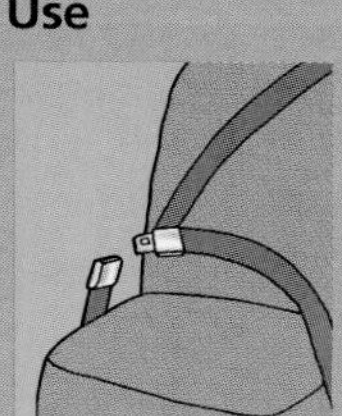

Career Link

FEMA Worker
FEMA is the short name for the Federal Emergency Management Agency. FEMA workers help people before and after weather emergencies or other disasters. Suppose you are a FEMA worker. How would you help people get ready for a hurricane?

153

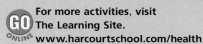

Career Link

FEMA Worker FEMA workers have many different roles. They teach people how to prepare for a disaster and how to make their homes as safe as possible. FEMA workers help repair homes and work with city officials to fix public buildings that have been damaged. FEMA also trains firefighters and emergency workers.

Students may want to access print or online references to find out how people can make their homes safe when a hurricane is predicted. Students also may want to find out the qualifications for becoming a FEMA worker.

For more information on health careers, visit the **Webliography** in Teacher Resources at **www.harcourtschool.com/health**
Keyword health careers

Activities

Language Arts

Remind students that their posters should promote safety, not violence. Encourage students to work as partners or in small groups to share ideas. Circulate frequently to make sure the illustrations and messages are appropriate.

Physical Education

Tell students that physical activity helps people cope with stress. In addition to playing the games, demonstrate stretching and deep-breathing exercises or ask the physical education teacher to do this.

Home & Community

Provide references for students to access information about your state's laws on safety-belt use. Help students to interpret this information and use it in their posters. Send a letter home with students asking parents to help place the posters in places that their family frequents, such as the public library or places where the parents are employed.

Supports the Coordinated School Health Program

Technology Project

A "watch" is a weather alert that lets people know that severe weather, such as a thunderstorm or a tornado, may occur. A "warning" means that severe weather has been spotted in a particular area. Provide modeling for how to word a weather broadcast by bringing in a weather radio and allowing students to hear a broadcast of current weather conditions in your area. If you have a TV in your room, have students view a local or national channel giving weather reports. To help make this activity as authentic as possible, provide props, such as a microphone, and encourage students to refer to local towns and landmarks in their presentations.

Chapter Review and Test Preparation

Pages 154–155

Reading Skill 5 pts. each

1. [What I read] information from pages 150–151; [What I know] information will vary based on student experience; [Conclusion] You could get hurt.
2. [What I read] information from pages 136–137; [What I know] information will vary based on student experience; [Conclusion] to prevent fires from spreading out of control

Use Vocabulary 5 pts. each

3. A, air bag
4. F, tornado
5. B, bully
6. D, lightning
7. E, terrorism
8. C, flood
9. G, weapon

Check Understanding 5 pts. each

10. B, Walk away and ignore the bully.
11. H, helmet
12. D, tell an adult if asked to join a gang
13. G, hurricane
14. D, Tell an adult.
15. G, sitting on plants with three leaves

Think Critically 5 pts. each

16. Do not respond to the person and tell my parents or guardian immediately.
17. sunscreen

Chapter Review and Test Preparation

Reading Skill

DRAW CONCLUSIONS

Draw and then use this graphic organizer to answer questions 1 and 2.

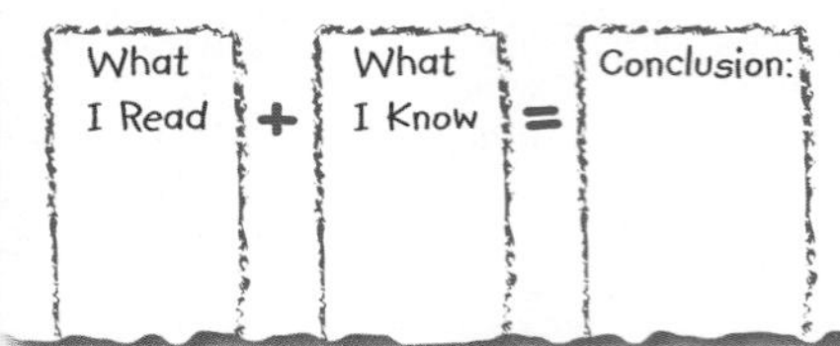

1 Why might it be a good idea to walk away if you suspect someone is a gang member?

2 What is the purpose of a fire ring, and why do you suppose it works to prevent fires from spreading?

Use Vocabulary

Match each term in Column B with its meaning in Column A.

Column A	Column B
3 It inflates during a car crash	**A** air bag
4 Funnel-shaped cloud	**B** bully
5 One who hurts others	**C** flood
6 Large release of electricity	**D** lightning
7 Violence to promote a cause	**E** terrorism
8 Overflow of water	**F** tornado
9 Object used to injure someone	**G** weapon

Check Understanding

Choose the letter of the correct answer.

10 Suppose a bully trips you in the hallway. What should you do? (p. 149)

A Yell at the bully.
B Walk away and ignore the bully.
C Trip the bully.
D Laugh at the bully.

11 Which piece of safety gear should you wear when you skate, skateboard, and bike? (pp. 142–143)

F

H

G

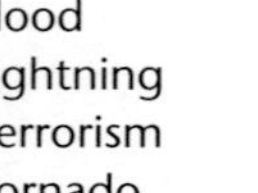

J

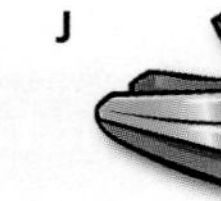

154

Formal Assessment

ASSESSMENT GUIDE P. 34

6 Name ______ Chapter Test

Safe Away from Home

Match each term below to a sentence. Write the letter of the correct term on the line to the left of the sentence.

a lightning **b** bully **c** terrorism **d** flood **e** air bag **f** precaution **g** gangs **h** hurricane **i** weapon **j** tornado

g 1. Groups of people that often use violence to get their way
b 2. A person who hurts or frightens others
d 3 An overflow of water onto normally dry land, able to sweep away people and property
i 4. An object that can be used to hurt or threaten someone
c 5. The use of violence to promote a cause
a 6. A large release of electricity that can injure or kill people and cause fires
f 7. Care taken before a dangerous situation occurs
h 8. A storm that forms over an ocean and has strong winds and heavy rain
e 9. A device, found in a motor vehicle, that blows up like a balloon during a collision
j 10. A storm in which winds spin in a funnel shape and can flatten buildings

© Harcourt

ASSESSMENT GUIDE P. 35

Name ______

Write *T* or *F* to show whether the sentence is true or false.

F 11. If you get lost while hiking, you should try to find your way back.
F 12. The air is so cold in winter that the sun's rays cannot burn your skin.
T 13. Wrist guards and kneepads are pieces of the safety gear for skateboarding.
F 14. If you are outside during a thunderstorm, the safest thing to do is to lie flat.
F 15. The safest place for children riding in a car is in the front seat.

Write the letter of the best answer on the line at the left.

D 16. If you are caught in a thunderstorm, it is best to move ______.
A under a tree or tent
B to a swimming pool
C down to lie flat on the ground
D inside a building or automobile

H 17. During cold weather, your ______ lose heat more quickly than other parts of your body.
F toes and feet **H** head and neck
G fingers and hands **J** fingers and toes

A 18. One important piece of safety gear for biking is ______.
A a helmet **C** a backpack
B an air bag **D** loose clothing

J 19. The safest place for an infant in a car is ______.
F in its mother's lap **H** lying on the back seat
G in a child safety seat in front **J** in a child safety seat in back

B 20. A useful way to deal with bullies or a gang is to ______.
A talk back **C** join forces
B walk away **D** fight back

© Harcourt

12 You can stay safe from gangs if you _____. (p. 150)
A keep silent if asked to join a gang
B go places by yourself
C hang out where they hang out
D tell an adult if asked to join a gang

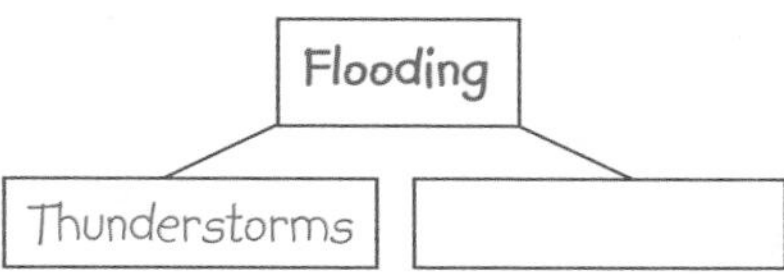

13 Which is another cause of flooding? (p. 139)
F lightning
H tornado
G hurricane
J blizzard

14 If you find a gun, what should you do? (p. 151)
A Keep it a secret.
B Show it to your friends.
C Look at it closely to see if it is a toy.
D Tell an adult.

15 You are camping and notice people doing the following. Which is unsafe? (p. 137)
F applying bug repellent
G sitting on plants with three leaves
H putting out the campfire
J watching some squirrels from several feet away

Think Critically

16 You are online when a person you do not know e-mails you. He says he has a really cool video game you can play if you meet him after school. What should you do?

17 What should you always wear outdoors in any kind of temperature and for any activity?

Apply Skills

18 **BUILDING GOOD CHARACTER**
Responsibility You have just learned to skateboard. Your friends are more skilled than you. They are pushing you to go faster and do tricks you are not ready for. What do you say to your friends? Apply what you know about being responsible to keep yourself and others safe.

19 **LIFE SKILLS**
Resolve Conflicts You are trying to resolve a conflict with a classmate. Suddenly his face turns red, he clenches his fist, and he begins yelling. Use what you know about resolving conflicts to tell what you should do next.

Write About Health

20 **Write to Inform—Description** Write a paragraph explaining what can happen if a person gets overheated in hot weather. Describe safety rules that can help for hot weather.

155

ASSESSMENT GUIDE P. 36

Name __________

Possible answers are given.

21. Name one useful way to deal with bullies and gangs, as well as with weapons. Explain why it is useful.
You can deal with bullies, weapons, and gangs by walking away from them. This is useful because it lessens the chance that you will become injured.

22. Name one piece of safety gear that is useful for biking, skateboarding, and riding a scooter. Explain why it is useful.
A helmet is the most useful piece of safety gear for these three activities. A helmet will protect a rider's face, head, and brain from serious injury during a fall.

23. Name one safety rule that is useful for biking, skateboarding, and sledding, as well as skiing. Explain why it is useful.
Do not go biking, skateboarding, sledding, or skiing after dark. It is difficult for others to see you, and that may cause an accident. Also, if you become lost, it will be more difficult for others to find you in the dark.

24. What can you do to help yourself stay safe in all kinds of bad weather? Explain why it is useful.
You can be prepared by knowing what to do when bad weather happens. Families can follow the family emergency plan. They can listen to radio reports and follow any safety instructions local authorities issue.

25. Name one safety rule useful for riding on a bus as well as in a car.
Do not distract the driver. Both the bus driver and the car driver must be able to keep their attention on driving. Distracting the driver puts everyone in the bus or car at risk for injury.

© Harcourt

Apply Skills 5 pts. each

18. Answers will vary but should include that being responsible means a person acts in ways that keep self and others safe.

19. Get away from the person because he may become violent.

Write About Health 5 pts.

20. Answers will vary but should mention that a person can become dizzy, faint, or nauseated. Guidelines should include wearing light, loose-fitting clothing; resting often in the shade; drinking plenty of water; and wearing sunscreen.

Performance Assessment

Use the Chapter Project and the rubric provided on the Project Evaluation Sheet. See *Assessment Guide* pp. 18, 58, 67.

Portfolio Assessment

Have students select their best work from the following suggestions:

- Leveled Activities, p. 138
- Quick Activity, p. 143
- Write to Inform, p. 145
- Activities, p. 153

See *Assessment Guide* pp. 12–16.

CHAPTER 7

Guarding Against Disease

Lesson	Pacing	Objectives	Reading Skills
Introduce the Chapter pp. 156–157		• Preview chapter concepts.	**Compare and Contrast** pp. 157, 330–331
1 **Why People Become Ill** pp. 158–160	1 class period	• Understand what disease is, and how it affects the body. • Distinguish between communicable and noncommunicable diseases.	**Compare and Contrast** pp. 159, 160
Building Good Character p. 161		• Learn to be more caring by identifying ways to help those who are ill.	
2 **Communicable Diseases** pp. 162–165	1 class period	• Understand that diseases are caused by pathogens. • Distinguish among viruses, bacteria, and fungi as different types of pathogens. • Identify ways that pathogens can be spread.	**Compare and Contrast** p. 165 • Cause and Effect, p. 163 • Main Idea and Details, p. 165
3 **Fighting Communicable Diseases** pp. 166–171	3 class periods	• Describe the immune system's function as a defense against pathogens. • Identify ways of helping the body defend itself against disease.	**Compare and Contrast** p. 171 • Draw Conclusions, pp. 167, 171 • Sequence, p. 168 • Summarize, p. 169
Life Skills pp. 172–173	1 class period	• Learn to identify situations that are stressful. • Use the steps to manage stress to help lead a more healthful life.	
4 **Noncommunicable Diseases** pp. 174–179	3 class periods	• Identify noncommunicable diseases and their symptoms. • Understand how noncommunicable diseases can be managed.	**Compare and Contrast** p. 179 • Draw Conclusions, pp. 174, 178 • Main Idea and Details, pp. 175, 176 • Summarize, p. 177 • Cause and Effect, p. 179
5 **Live a Healthful Lifestyle** pp. 180–182	1 class period	• Identify healthful lifestyle choices that help prevent illness. • Understand how resistance, managing stress, and abstinence from tobacco help prevent disease.	**Compare and Contrast** p. 182 • Draw Conclusions, p. 181 • Cause and Effect, p. 182
Activities p. 183		• Extend chapter concepts.	
Chapter Review pp. 184–185	1 class period	• Assess chapter objectives.	

Vocabulary	Program Resources
	Music CD Teaching Resources, p. 31
disease communicable disease noncommunicable disease	Transparency 1 Activity Book, pp. 31–33
	Poster 1
pathogen virus bacteria fungi infection	Transparency 1 Activity Book, pp. 31–32
immune system antibodies immunity vaccine	Transparency 1 Activity Book, pp. 31–32
	Activity Book, p. 34 Poster 9
cancer allergy asthma diabetes arthritis	Transparency 1 Activity Book, pp. 31–32
resistance abstinence	Transparency 1 Activity Book, pp. 31–32, 35
	The Learning Site www.harcourtschool.com
	Assessment Guide, pp. 37–39

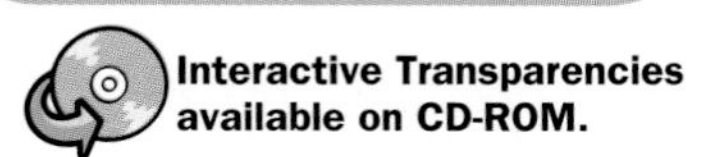

Reading Skill

These reading skills are reinforced throughout this chapter and one skill is emphasized as the Focus Skill.

- **Compare and Contrast**
- Draw Conclusions
- Identify Cause and Effect
- Identify Main Idea and Details
- Sequence
- Summarize

KEY READING SKILLS TRANSPARENCY 1

1  **Reading Skill Graphic Organizer**

Compare and Contrast

Topic: Communicable and Noncommunicable Diseases

Alike	Different

POSTER 9 MANAGE STRESS

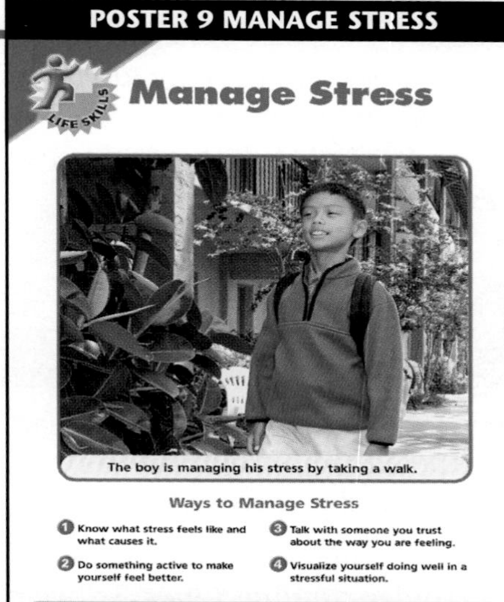

Manage Stress
The boy is managing his stress by taking a walk.
Ways to Manage Stress
1 Know what stress feels like and what causes it.
2 Do something active to make yourself feel better.
3 Talk with someone you trust about the way you are feeling.
4 Visualize yourself doing well in a stressful situation.
How have YOU MANAGED STRESS today?

Life Skills

Life Skills are health-enhancing behaviors that can help students reduce risks to their health and safety.

Six Life Skills are reinforced throughout *Harcourt Health and Fitness*. The skill emphasized in this chapter is Manage Stress.

Building Good Character

Character education is an important aspect of health education. When children behave in ways that show good character, they promote the health and safety of themselves and others.

Six character traits are reinforced throughout *Harcourt Health and Fitness*. The trait emphasized in this chapter is Caring.

POSTER 4 CARING

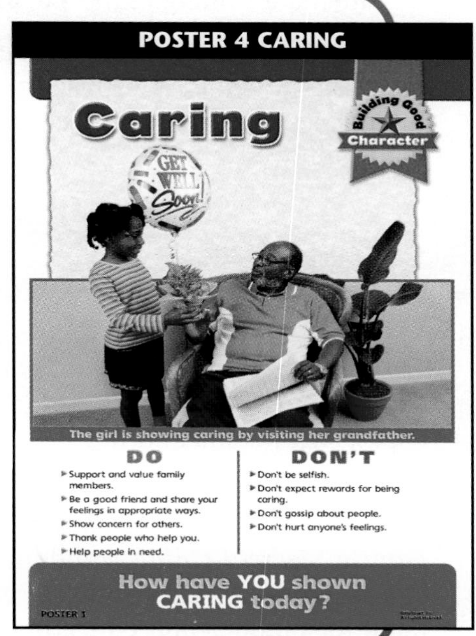

Caring
Building Good Character
The girl is showing caring by visiting her grandfather.
DO
Support and value family members.
Be a good friend and share your feelings in appropriate ways.
Show concern for others.
Thank people who help you.
Help people in need.
DON'T
Don't be selfish.
Don't expect rewards for being caring.
Don't gossip about people.
Don't hurt anyone's feelings.
How have YOU shown CARING today?

Resources

Coordinated School Health Program

Health Education
Health Services
Physical Education
Nutrition Services
Parent/ Community Involvement
Healthy School Environment
Counseling, Psychological, & Social Services
Health Promotion for Staff
CSHP

A Coordinated School Health Program endeavors to improve children's health and therefore their capacity to learn through the support of families, schools, and communities working together. The following information is provided to help classroom teachers be more aware of these resources.

Children, including babies, can have high blood pressure. The **American Heart Association** recommends that all children have yearly blood pressure check. *The AHA Kids Cookbook* contains recipes for dishes that are low in fat and cholesterol. **www.americanheart.org/**

BAM! (Body and Mind) from the **CDC** contains various health topics for kids. *Disease Detectives* provides students with information about germs and preventing disease. **www.bam.gov/**

Myths and facts about influenza and the common cold are explained by the American Lung Association (**ALA**) along with guidelines for the prevention and treatment of these common illnesses. **www.lungusa.org/**

The Comprehensive Health Education Foundation (**C.H.E.F.®**) and the National Middle School Association (**NMSA**) work to improve the health of young adolescents by supporting the Coordinated School Health Programs addressing HIV/AIDS prevention and other health issues. **www.chef.org/age/school.php**

Other resources that support a Coordinated School Health Program:

- School-Home Connection
- Daily Physical Activity
- Daily Fitness Tips
- Activities: Home & Community
- Health Background: Webliography
- *Be Active! Resources for Physical Education*

Media Resources

Books for Students

Vander Hook, Sue. ***Diabetes.*** Smart Apple Media, 2001. An in-depth look at this disease. EASY

Landau, Elaine. ***Allergies (Understanding Illness).*** Twenty-First Century Books, 1995. Explains the symptoms, diagnoses, and treatments for allergies. AVERAGE

Benziger, John. ***The Corpuscles Meet the Virus Invaders.*** Corpuscles Intergalactica, 1990. Fun facts about the immune system. ADVANCED

Books for Teachers and Families

Brody, Jane E. ***Jane Brody's Cold and Flu Fighter.*** W. W. Norton, 1995. Offers advice on preventing and coping with colds and flu.

Clayman, Charles B., MD, Ed. ***The American Medical Association Family Medical Guide.*** Random House, 1994. An excellent reference book for families and educators.

Free and Inexpensive Materials

Federal Citizen Information Center
Ask for #507K, *Got a Sick Kid?,* which explains how to give right medication in the right dosage.

The American Heart Association
Receive up to five free copies of *What Every Teacher Should Know,* #65-3535

The American Lung Association
Subscribe to free e-mail newsletter on topics such as *Asthma Buster Alerts.*

Johnson & Johnson Companies
Has a wall calendar with tips and advice for managing diabetes.

American Institute for Cancer Research
Ask for *Simple Steps to Prevent Cancer,* which suggests changes to diet and lifestyle.

To access free and inexpensive resources on the Web, visit **www.harcourtschool.com/health/free**

Videos

Vitamins and Your Health. Educational Video Network, 1997.

Medicine (Tell Me Why: Volume 15). Penguin Productions, 1987.

All About Health and Hygiene. Schlessinger Media, 2001.

These resources have been selected to meet a variety of individual needs. Please review all materials and websites prior to sharing them with students to ensure the content is appropriate for your class. Note that information, while correct at time of publication, is subject to change.

Visit **The Learning Site** for related links, activities, resources, and the health **Webliography.**

www.harcourtschool.com/health

Meeting Individual Needs

Below-Level

Before reading a section of the text, ask students to think about how the topic relates to them personally. Have students write their responses in their health journals and include what they hope to learn about the topic. Remind students that their journals are private.

Activities

- First Line of Defense Collage, p. 166
- Flash Cards, p. 174
- What Is...?, p. 178
- Healthful Lifestyles Posters, p. 180

On-Level

Students can increase their understanding by asking questions during reading. Point out the questions at the end of each section. Explain that good readers ask themselves *who*, *what*, *when*, *where*, or *why* questions as they read. Have students pause during reading to ask questions.

Activities

- Name That Defense, p. 166
- Making a Table, p. 174
- Anatomy Chart, p. 178
- Healthful Choices Skit, p. 180

Challenge

To help students acquire problem-solving skills, have them identify a problem relating to the topic of this chapter. Have students use construction paper, craft sticks, glue, and scissors to make puppets. Then have them act out the problem and possible solutions.

Activities

- A Day in the Life, p. 166
- Current Research, p. 174
- Noncommunicable Disease Report, p. 178
- Take a Survey, p. 180

ESL/ELL

Learning Log

Students can use a Learning Log to help them summarize a section using five key points. After reading a section aloud, ask students to tell five things they learned. On the board, write the five most important facts in clear, simple language. Have students copy them into their Learning Logs.

Activities

- Background and Experience, p. 162
- Comprehensible Input, pp. 171, 176

Curriculum Integration

Use these topics to integrate health into your daily planning.

Integrated Language Arts/Reading Skills

- Short Stories, p. 181

Math

- Multiplying Bacteria, p. 169

Music

- Immunization Song, p. 170

Science

- Germ Theory, p. 163
- Beaver Fever, p. 165
- Food-Allergic Reaction, p. 177

Physical Education

- Daily Fitness Tip, pp. 158, 162, 166, 174, 180
- Daily Physical Activity, p. 157

Art

- Health Brochures, p. 179

Social Studies

- Uncommon Diseases in the U.S., p. 163
- Smallpox, p. 167

CHAPTER 7

Pages 156–185

CHAPTER SUMMARY

In this chapter, students

- ► learn about communicable and noncommunicable diseases.
- ► identify ways to prevent disease.
- ► understand why a healthful diet plays an important part in preventing disease.

Life Skills

Students learn how to *manage stress* at a doctor's office.

Building Good Character

Students show that they are *caring* by learning how to help others.

Consumer Health

Students *analyze* advertisements and media messages.

Literature Springboard

Use the excerpt from *No Measles, No Mumps for Me to* spark interest in the chapter topic. See the Read-Aloud Anthology on page RA-8 of this *Teacher Edition.*

Prereading Strategies

SCAN THE CHAPTER Have students preview the chapter content by scanning the titles, headings, pictures, tables, and graphs. Assess prior knowledge by asking volunteers to speculate on what they will learn.

PREVIEW VOCABULARY As students scan the chapter, have them write down unfamiliar words that they find. Have students look up unfamiliar words in the Glossary.

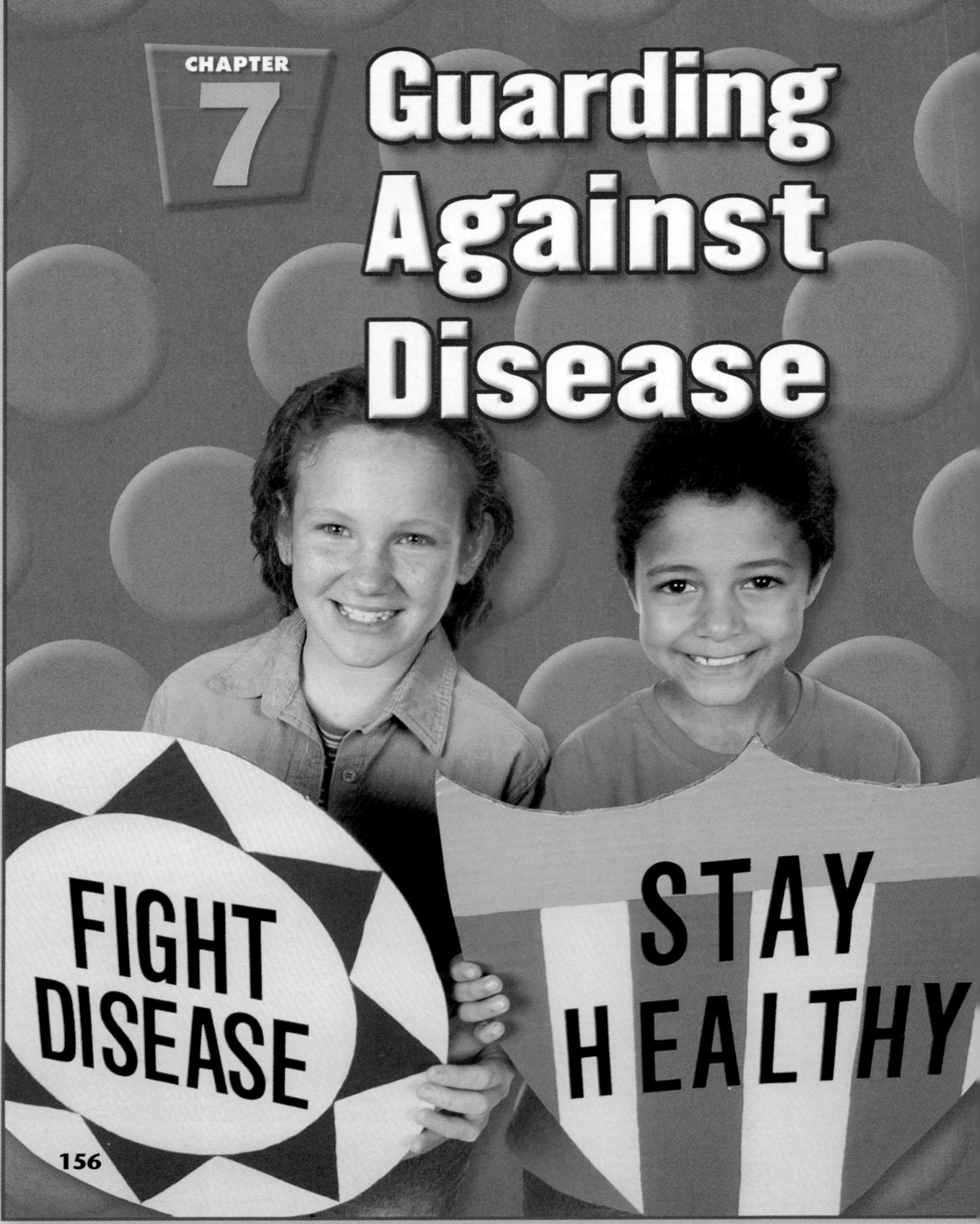

Reading Skill

COMPARE AND CONTRAST To introduce or review this skill, have students use the Reading in Health Handbook, pp. 330–331. Teaching strategies and additional activities are also provided.

Students will have opportunities to practice and apply this skill throughout this chapter.

- Focus Skill Reading Mini-Lesson, p. 158
- Reading comprehension questions identified with the 
- *Activity Book* p. 33 (shown on p. 160)
- Lesson Summary and Review, pp. 160, 165, 171, 179, 182
- Chapter Review and Test Preparation, pp. 184–185

Reading Skill

COMPARE AND CONTRAST When you compare, you tell how two or more things are alike. When you contrast, you tell how they are different. Use the Reading in Health Handbook on pages 330–331 and this graphic organizer to help you read the health facts in this chapter.

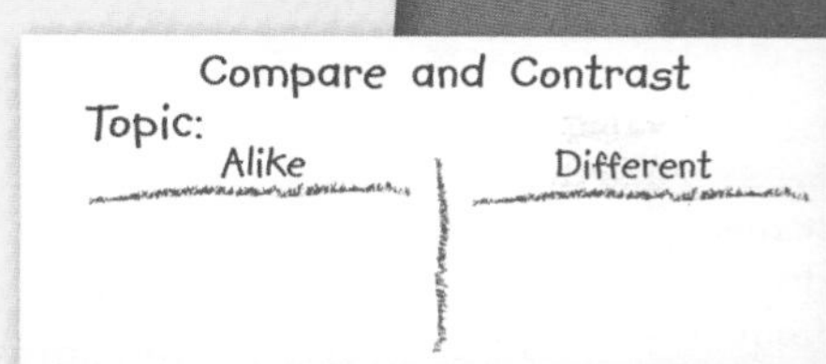

Health Graph

INTERPRET DATA Public health in the United States improved greatly in the twentieth century. Cleaner water for personal use was one main reason for this. Another reason was the development of vaccines (vak•SEENZ). Describe how the number of whooping cough (pertussis) cases changed from the 1940s to the 1970s.

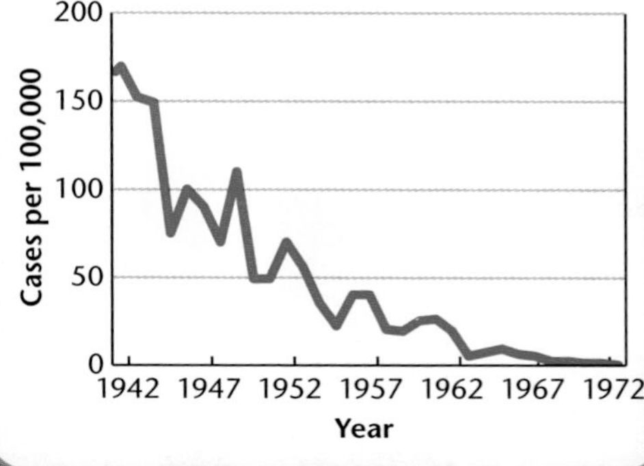

Daily Physical Activity

Protect yourself and others from disease. Stay fit and healthy.

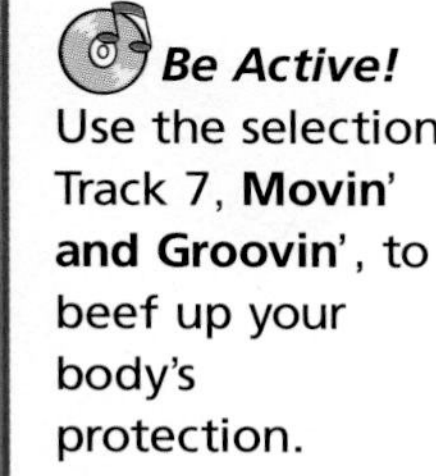

Be Active! Use the selection Track 7, **Movin' and Groovin'**, to beef up your body's protection.

INTRODUCE THE CHAPTER

Health Graph

Interpret Data

Ask for volunteers to explain what information the graph is presenting.

Describe how the number of whooping cough (pertussis) cases changed from the 1940s to the 1970s. According to the graph, the number of cases declined gradually.

What is the general trend in the number of cases of whooping cough? Did the number of cases go up, go down, stay the same, or vary during the 1940s through the 1970s? Cases of whooping cough rose and fell over the years until the disease died out about 1980; between the 1940s and the 1970s cases rose dramatically and then decreased, with occasional surges.

Daily Physical Activity

Use *Be Active! Music for Daily Physical Activity* with the Instant Activity Cards to provide students with movement activities that can be done in limited space. Options for using these components are provided beginning on page TR2 in this *Teacher Edition.*

Chapter Project

Battling Dangerous Pathogens (*Assessment Guide* p. 59)

ASSESS PRIOR KNOWLEDGE Use students' initial ideas for the project as a baseline assessment of their understanding of chapter concepts. Have students complete the project as they work through the chapter.

PERFORMANCE ASSESSMENT The project can be used for performance assessment. Use the Project Evaluation Sheet (rubric), *Assessment Guide* p. 68.

School-Home Connection

Distribute copies of the School-Home Connection (in English or Spanish). Have students take the page home to share with their families as you begin this chapter.

Follow Up Have volunteers share the results of their activities.

Supports the Coordinated School Health Program

TEACHING RESOURCES P. 35

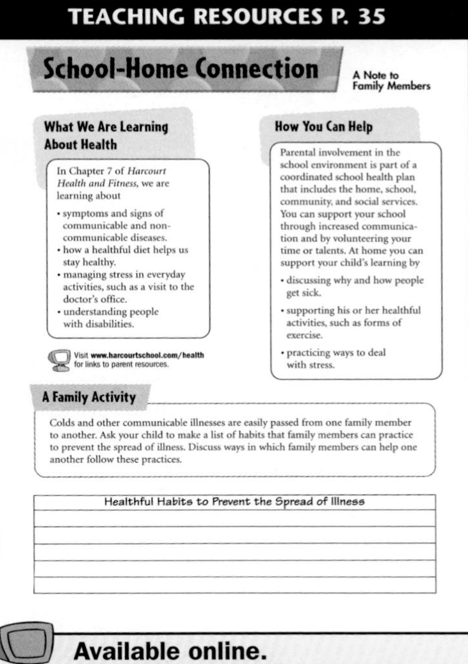

School-Home Connection A Note to Family Members

What We Are Learning About Health

In Chapter 7 of *Harcourt Health and Fitness*, we are learning about

- symptoms and signs of communicable and noncommunicable diseases.
- how a healthful diet helps us stay healthy.
- managing stress in everyday activities, such as a visit to the doctor's office.
- understanding people with disabilities.

Visit www.harcourtschool.com/health for links to parent resources.

How You Can Help

Parental involvement in the school environment is part of a coordinated school health plan that includes the home, school, community, and social services. You can support your school through increased communication and by volunteering your time or talents. At home you can support your child's learning by

- discussing why and how people get sick.
- supporting his or her healthful activities, such as forms of exercise.
- practicing ways to deal with stress.

A Family Activity

Colds and other communicable illnesses are easily passed from one family member to another. Ask your child to make a list of habits that family members can practice to prevent the spread of illness. Discuss ways in which family members can help one another follow these practices.

Healthful Habits to Prevent the Spread of Illness

Available online.
www.harcourtschool.com/health

LESSON 1
Pages 158–160

Objectives

- ► Understand what disease is, and how it affects the body.
- ► Distinguish between communicable and noncommunicable diseases.

When Minutes Count . . .
Assign the Quick Study, Lesson 1, Activity Book pp. 31–32 (shown on p. 159).

Program Resources

- ► Activity Book pp. 31–33
- ► Transparency 1

Vocabulary

disease p. 158,
communicable disease p. 158,
noncommunicable disease p. 159

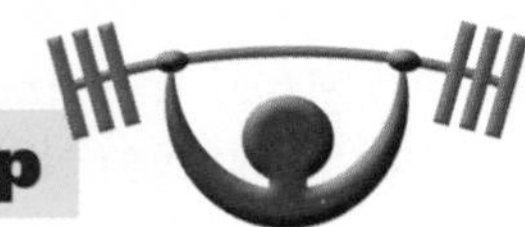

Daily Fitness Tip

Becoming ill is never fun. It's important to do what we can to keep our bodies as healthy as possible. Staying healthy requires day-to-day effort and includes eating a healthful diet and getting regular exercise. Remind students that staying healthy helps the brain work better, too!

1. MOTIVATE

Have students stand up and jump in place for fifteen seconds. When they are done and sitting again, ask them how the jumping made them feel. (CAUTION: Determine any physical limitations of students before having them participate in this activity.)

How would being ill change the way you were able to jump? Students might respond that they would tire more easily or lose their breath. Some might say they would not be able to jump for fifteen seconds if they were very ill.

Why People Become Ill

Lesson Focus
People get ill with diseases that can spread from person to person and diseases that cannot spread from person to person.

Why Learn This?
You can use what you learn to help prevent disease and to help other people who are ill.

Vocabulary
disease
communicable disease
noncommunicable disease

Everybody Gets Ill

Jeff felt sick, so he told his mother. His mother felt Jeff's head, and it felt warm. Together, they went to see the doctor.

Like Jeff, everyone gets ill from disease sometimes. A **disease** (dih•ZEEZ) is a condition that damages or weakens part of the body. When you have a disease, your body doesn't work as it should.

Jeff had the flu, a communicable disease. A **communicable** (kuh•MYOO•nih•kuh•buhl) **disease** is an illness that can spread from person to person. Someone in Jeff's class had the flu. The flu spread to Jeff. Then Jeff spread the flu to his mother. Colds, flu, pinkeye, and strep throat are also communicable diseases.

158

Mini-Lesson

COMPARE AND CONTRAST
Remind students that when they compare, they tell how things are alike. When they contrast, they tell how they are different. Have them practice this skill by answering the Focus Skill question on page 159. Have students draw and complete the graphic organizer you model it on the transparency.

TRANSPARENCY 1

1 Reading Skill Graphic Organizer

Compare and Contrast

Topic: Communicable and Noncommunicable Diseases

Alike	Different
Both are forms of illness.	Communicable diseases can be passed from person to person. Noncommunicable diseases cannot be passed from person to person.

Interactive Transparencies available on CD-ROM.

An illness that does not spread from one person to another is a **noncommunicable** (nahn•kuh•MYOO•nih•kuh•buhl) **disease**. *Asthma*, *allergies*, and *cancer* are types of noncommunicable diseases. So are heart disease and diabetes.

Noncommunicable diseases have many causes. Some, such as diabetes, are more common in some families than in others. Things that pollute air and water can cause other diseases, including cancer. Sometimes unhealthful habits, such as eating a lot of high-fat foods, can cause noncommunicable diseases. Also, people who use tobacco have a much greater chance than nonsmokers of getting cancer and heart disease.

COMPARE AND CONTRAST How are communicable and noncommunicable diseases alike and different?

Alike: Both are forms of illness. Different: Communicable diseases can be passed from person to person; noncommunicable diseases cannot.

Information Alert!

Influenza, or flu, is a major cause of illness. Each year in the United States, flu causes about 36,000 deaths and sends 114,000 people to the hospital. Find out how you can help protect yourself against flu.

GO ONLINE **For the most up-to-date information, visit The Learning Site. www.harcourtschool.com/health**

Trace the spread of flu from Jeff to his mother. How do you think the disease was spread? What do you think Jeff's mother could have done to avoid catching flu?▶

159

2. TEACH

Interpret Visuals—Pictures

Direct students' attention to the pictures on both pages. Point out how unaware we are when disease-causing organisms, such as those that cause flu, enter or exit our body. Discuss the questions asked about the picture. Emphasize the importance of healthful habits to help prevent the spread of disease.

Content-Area Reading Support

Using Respellings Direct attention to the phonetic respelling: kuh • MYOO • nih • kuh • buhl. Explain that respellings show how words are pronounced. Point out that the dots in the respelling divide the word into syllables and that capital letters indicate the stressed, or accented, syllable.

Discuss

Critical Thinking What kinds of foods can help cause noncommunicable diseases? Refer students to Chapter 3, pages 61 and 66–69 for examples. Ask students to make a list of high-fat foods that should be avoided.

Health Background

Poliomyelitis One of the worst disease epidemics was the spread of poliomyelitis, better known as polio, in the United States between 1942 and 1953. Other severe epidemics occurred in Europe and Asia. The disease is caused by the polio virus, which is thought to enter the body through the mouth. Once it is in the nervous system, the virus produces symptoms ranging from headache and fever to paralysis of voluntary muscles. International efforts to eliminate polio were established by the World Health Assembly and named STOP (Stop Transmission of Polio). The goal of STOP is to eliminate polio worldwide.

Source: *Britannica.com, Encarta Plus, Center for Disease Control and Preventions websites*

For more background, visit the **Webliography** in Teacher Resources at **www.harcourtschool.com/health**
Keyword diseases

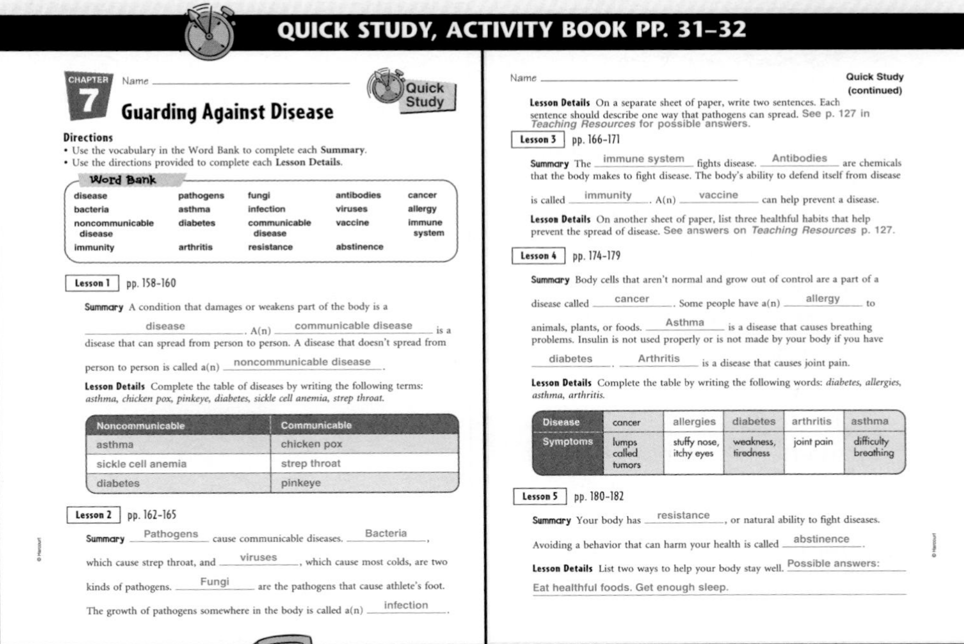

QUICK STUDY, ACTIVITY BOOK PP. 31–32

CHAPTER 7 Name ______

Guarding Against Disease

Quick Study

Directions
- Use the vocabulary in the Word Bank to complete each **Summary**.
- Use the directions provided to complete each **Lesson Details**.

Word Bank

disease	pathogens	fungi	antibodies	cancer
bacteria	asthma	infection	viruses	allergy
noncommunicable disease	diabetes	communicable disease	vaccine	immune system
immunity	arthritis	resistance	abstinence	

Lesson 1 pp. 158-160

Summary A condition that damages or weakens part of the body is a disease. A(n) communicable disease is a disease that can spread from person to person. A disease that doesn't spread from person to person is called a(n) noncommunicable disease.

Lesson Details Complete the table of diseases by writing the following terms: *asthma, chicken pox, pinkeye, diabetes, sickle cell anemia, strep throat.*

Noncommunicable	Communicable
asthma	chicken pox
sickle cell anemia	strep throat
diabetes	pinkeye

Lesson 2 pp. 162-165

Summary Pathogens cause communicable diseases. Bacteria, which cause strep throat, and viruses, which cause most colds, are two kinds of pathogens. Fungi are the pathogens that cause athlete's foot. The growth of pathogens somewhere in the body is called a(n) infection.

© Harcourt

Name ______ **Quick Study (continued)**

Lesson Details On a separate sheet of paper, write two sentences. Each sentence should describe one way that pathogens can spread. See p. 127 in *Teaching Resources* for possible answers.

Lesson 3 pp. 166-171

Summary The immune system fights disease. Antibodies are chemicals that the body makes to fight disease. The body's ability to defend itself from disease is called immunity. A(n) vaccine can help prevent a disease.

Lesson Details On another sheet of paper, list three healthful habits that help prevent the spread of disease. See answers on *Teaching Resources* p. 127.

Lesson 4 pp. 174-179

Summary Body cells that aren't normal and grow out of control are a part of a disease called cancer. Some people have a(n) allergy to animals, plants, or foods. Asthma is a disease that causes breathing problems. Insulin is not used properly or is not made by your body if you have diabetes. Arthritis is a disease that causes joint pain.

Lesson Details Complete the table by writing the following words: *diabetes, allergies, asthma, arthritis.*

Disease	cancer	allergies	diabetes	arthritis	asthma
Symptoms	lumps called tumors	stuffy nose, itchy eyes	weakness, tiredness	joint pain	difficulty breathing

Lesson 5 pp. 180-182

Summary Your body has resistance, or natural ability to fight diseases. Avoiding a behavior that can harm your health is called abstinence.

Lesson Details List two ways to help your body stay well. Possible answers: Eat healthful foods. Get enough sleep.

© Harcourt

Available online. www.harcourtschool.com/health

Personal Health Plan

Plans should include get plenty of rest, drink lots of fluids, wash hands regularly, stay away from people who have colds.

3. WRAP UP

Lesson 1 Summary and Review

1. disease, Communicable diseases, noncommunicable diseases, chronic diseases, acute diseases
2. Possible answers: colds and flu. Other communicable diseases include strep throat, pinkeye, and ear infections
3. Avoiding contact with others, reduces the chances of passing the disease to others.
4. Responses may include:

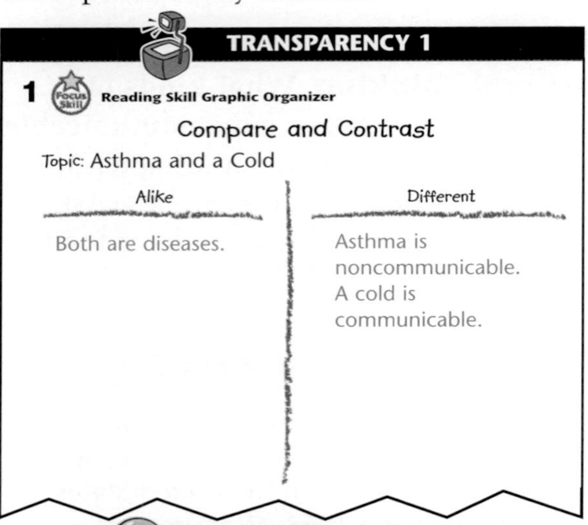

TRANSPARENCY 1

1 Reading Skill Graphic Organizer

Compare and Contrast

Topic: Asthma and a Cold

Alike	Different
Both are diseases.	Asthma is noncommunicable. A cold is communicable.

Interactive Transparencies available on CD-ROM.

5. Possible answer: Amos might say that he feels warm, his throat feels scratchy and dry, and he is tired. Amos has an acute communicable disease.

For **writing models** with examples, see *Teaching Resources* pp. 47–61. Rubrics are also provided.

When Minutes Count . . .

Quick Study Students can use *Activity Book* pages 31–32 (shown on p. 159) as they complete each lesson in this chapter.

Personal Health Plan

Real-Life Situation
Suppose that you have a cold and need to take care of yourself.

Real-Life Plan
Write a paragraph describing some things you would do to take care of yourself. Also include some healthful behaviors that you should practice all the time.

When Getting Well Takes Time

Most communicable diseases are acute diseases. An *acute* (uh•KYOOT) disease lasts only a short time. Colds and flu are examples of acute diseases.

Chronic (KRAH•nik) diseases last a long time, sometimes months or even years. An allergy is an example of a chronic disease.

COMPARE AND CONTRAST
How are acute and chronic illnesses alike and different?

Alike: Both are forms of illness. Different: An acute disease lasts only a short time, whereas a chronic disease lasts for a long time.

Mr. Kelly gets oxygen from a portable tank to help him breathe. He has a chronic lung disease called emphysema.

Lesson 1 Summary and Review

1. **Summarize with Vocabulary**
   Use vocabulary and other terms from this lesson to complete the statements.
   _____ is another name for *illness*. _____ can be passed from person to person but _____ ones cannot. Diseases that last a long time are called _____. Other diseases, called _____, last only a short time.
2. Give two examples of acute diseases.
3. **Critical Thinking** Why is it best for you to stay home from school when you have a communicable disease?
4. **COMPARE AND CONTRAST** Draw and complete this graphic organizer to show how asthma and a cold are alike and different.

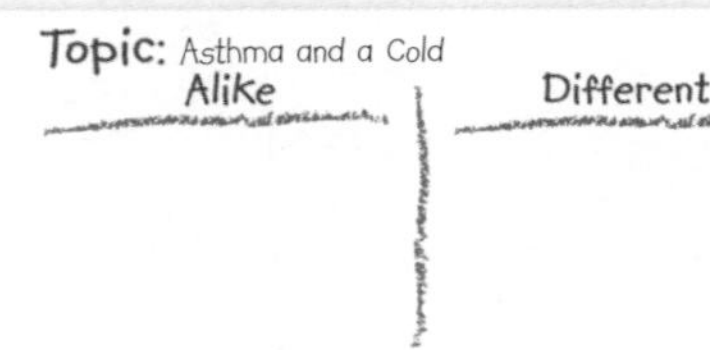

5. **Write to Inform—Description**
   Amos has a fever, a sore throat, and a cough. How can Amos explain how he feels? In your answer, include whether his disease is communicable or noncommunicable and whether it is chronic or acute.

160

Teacher Tip

Acute Illness Make sure students understand that most (although not all) communicable diseases are acute. This means that they come on suddenly and last for a short time. A person can get over the disease and no longer be infected or contagious to other people. This is true even if the disease has long-term effects. There are many survivors of polio, for example, who have been disabled by the disease for life. However, they're no longer infected with the virus and aren't contagious.

ACTIVITY BOOK P. 33

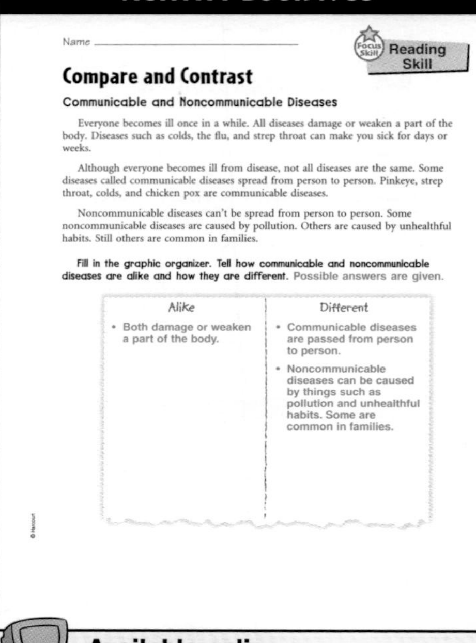

Name ______________________

Reading Skill

Compare and Contrast

Communicable and Noncommunicable Diseases

Everyone becomes ill once in a while. All diseases damage or weaken a part of the body. Diseases such as colds, the flu, and strep throat can make you sick for days or weeks.

Although everyone becomes ill from disease, not all diseases are the same. Some diseases called communicable diseases spread from person to person. Pinkeye, strep throat, colds, and chicken pox are communicable diseases.

Noncommunicable diseases can't be spread from person to person. Some noncommunicable diseases are caused by pollution. Others are caused by unhealthful habits. Still others are common in families.

Fill in the graphic organizer. Tell how communicable and noncommunicable diseases are alike and how they are different. Possible answers are given.

Alike	Different
• Both damage or weaken a part of the body.	• Communicable diseases are passed from person to person. • Noncommunicable diseases can be caused by things such as pollution and unhealthful habits. Some are common in families.

© Harcourt

Available online.
www.harcourtschool.com/health

Caring

Building Good Character

Help People Who Are Ill

Another type of health condition is a disability—a mental or physical problem that keeps the body from working as it should. People who have illnesses or disabilities want to be treated with care and understanding. Here are some tips to help you to be more caring:

- **Visit. People with some chronic noncommunicable illnesses may miss a lot of school. They might like to have you visit them at home.**
- **Get to know someone with a disability. Think about how an illness or disability would affect you and how you would want to be treated.**
- **Never tease. If you hear or see schoolmates making fun of a person with an illness or disability, ask them to stop, or tell an adult. Pages 268–276 can help you be a good role model.**
- **Help a person with a physical disability if you can. Be aware of the person's feelings. Like everyone else, people with disabilities like to do as much as they can on their own.**

Activity

Suppose a classmate uses a wheelchair. Brainstorm how you could adapt group activities to include this student. List ideas for involving a variety of individuals with differences in your activities.

161

Building Good Character

Caring
Citizenship
Fairness
Respect
Responsibility
Trustworthiness

Objective

► Learn to be more caring by identifying ways to help those who are ill.

Program Resources

► Poster 1

BEFORE READING

Ask students to identify similarities in which healthy environments can be promoted in schools and communities. Brainstorm with students some ways to show care and understanding. After discussing how to be caring and understanding in general, lead a discussion about ways to demonstrate care and understanding to those who are ill or disabled.

DISCUSS

After students have read the page, ask if they can add any suggestions to the list. Write these suggestions on the board.

ACTIVITY

Help students get started with the activity by thinking of one or two suggestions as a class. Remind students that the purpose of the activity is not to win the game but to think of ways to be more caring to people who are disabled.

Using the Poster

Activity Have students design posters about ways to care for others.

Display Students' posters can be displayed in a location that is visible to all students, such as the school cafeteria, school entrance, auditorium, or another common area.

POSTER 1
Caring
Building Good Character
Get Well Soon!
The girl is showing caring by visiting her grandfather.
DO
► Support and value family members.
► Be a good friend and share your feelings in appropriate ways.
► Show concern for others.
► Thank people who help you.
► Help people in need.
DON'T
► Don't be selfish.
► Don't expect rewards for being caring.
► Don't gossip about people.
► Don't hurt anyone's feelings.
How have YOU shown CARING today?
POSTER 1

LESSON 2
Pages 162–165

Objectives
- ► Understand that diseases are caused by pathogens.
- ► Distinguish among viruses, bacteria, and fungi as different types of pathogens.
- ► Identify ways that pathogens can be spread.

When Minutes Count . . .
Assign the Quick Study, Lesson 2, Activity Book pp. 31–32 (shown on p. 159).

Program Resources
- ► Activity Book pp. 31–32
- ► Transparency 1
- ► Growth, Development, and Reproduction pp. 58–65

Vocabulary
pathogen p. 162, **virus** p. 162, **bacteria** p. 162, **fungi** p. 163, **infection** p. 163

Daily Fitness Tip
The body's immune system fights infection by destroying pathogens when they enter the body. A strong immune system is an important part of staying healthy. Regular exercise and a healthful diet help the immune system function properly and efficiently.

1. MOTIVATE
Write the term *germ theory* on the board.

What do you think the term *germ theory* means? Accept all reasonable answers. Responses will probably reflect what students think of when they hear or read the word *germ*. Explain that *germ* is another word for *pathogen*. Tell students that in the late 1800s, Robert Koch, along with two other scientists, Louis Pasteur and Joseph Lister, developed the germ theory. This theory states that "a specific disease is caused by a specific type of microorganism [germ]."

LESSON 2

Communicable Diseases

Lesson Focus
Communicable diseases are caused by pathogens.

Why Learn This?
By knowing how pathogens are spread, you can promote health at home and at school.

Vocabulary
pathogens
virus
bacteria
fungi
infection

Causes of Disease
Pathogens (PATH•uh•juhnz) are organisms or viruses that cause communicable diseases. There are several kinds of pathogens. A **virus** (VY•ruhs) is the smallest kind. Viruses multiply inside the cells of living things. Viruses cause colds, flu, chicken pox, and many other diseases.

Bacteria (bak•TIR•ee•uh) are one-celled living things that also can cause disease. Most bacteria are harmless. In fact, your body needs many kinds of bacteria. But a few kinds of bacteria cause diseases, including pinkeye, ear infections, and strep throat.

◄ German scientist Robert Koch (1843–1910) proved that certain kinds of bacteria cause certain diseases. Before his work, people thought that "bad air" caused most diseases.

ESL/ELL Support
BACKGROUND AND EXPERIENCE Invite students to discuss times when they or someone they know has been sick with flu or cold. Help students understand how infection by a virus affects how people feel and act.

Beginning Ask students to draw a picture of someone who is healthy and active, and a picture of someone who is ill or not feeling well.

Intermediate Ask students to write a simple sentence that describes how they feel when they are sick.

Advanced Ask students to write a list of adjectives that describe how they feel when they are sick, such as *tired, sleepy,* or *feverish.*

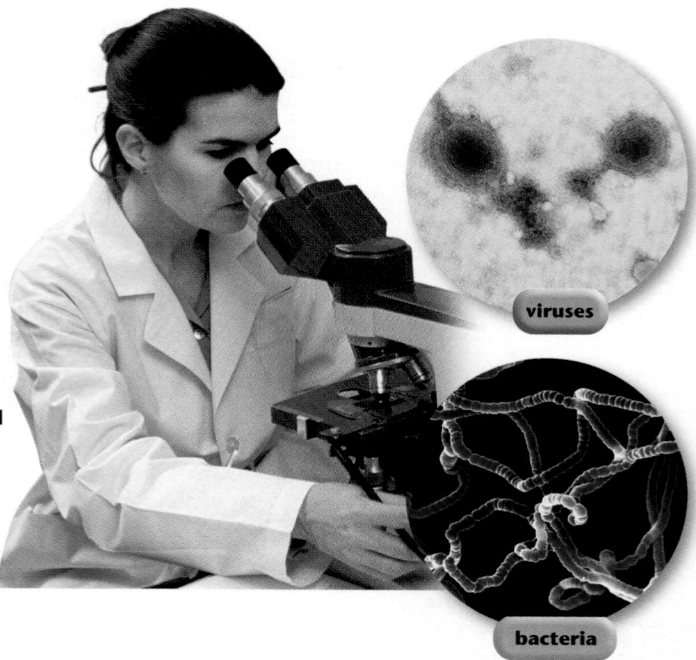

This lab technician is observing some pathogens through a microscope. Bacteria and many fungi are so small that this is the only way to see them. Viruses are even smaller. They can be seen only by using a very powerful electron microscope.▶

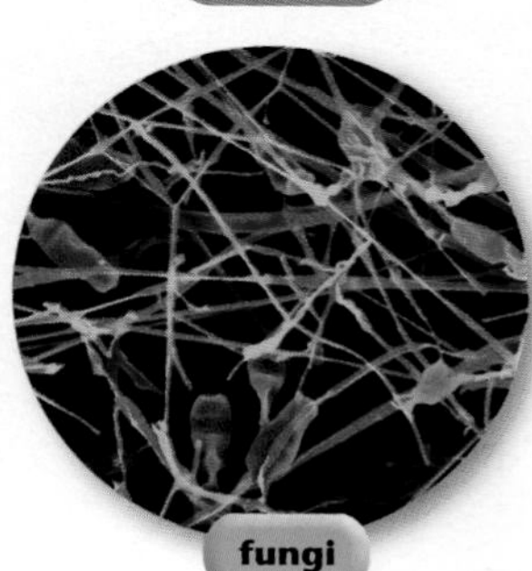

fungi

Fungi (FUN•jy) are another kind of pathogen. Fungi are small, simple living things such as yeasts and molds. As with bacteria, not all fungi cause disease. The fungi that do cause disease often affect the skin. Two examples are athlete's foot and ringworm. Athlete's foot is a fungus infection of the skin between the toes. Ringworm is actually not a worm, but a fungus that causes itchy, red skin.

All pathogens multiply, or grow in large numbers. An **infection** (in•FEK•shuhn) is the growth of pathogens somewhere in the body. If your body gets an infection, you may become ill.

CAUSE AND EFFECT **What can happen when pathogens enter a person's body?**
The person can get an infection and become ill.

163

2. TEACH

Interpret Visuals—Pictures

Ask students to identify different pathogens, such as viruses, bacteria, and fungi. Have students study the pictures of pathogens on this page. Discuss the similarities and differences between them. Point out the size difference between viruses and bacteria. Many bacteria are hundreds or thousands of times larger than most viruses.

Content-Area Reading Support

Using Signal Words Direct attention to the first sentence in the first paragraph. Point out that the phrase *another kind of pathogen* signals that other kinds of pathogens have been mentioned. Ask students to recall what those pathogens are.

Discuss

Critical Thinking Where can pathogens infect and multiply in the body? Possible answers: on the skin, in the throat or nose, in the stomach. Remind students that pathogens can multiply anywhere in or on the body.

Health Background

Ringworm In the 1800s, ringworm was commonly spread by contact with barbers, schoolchildren, and theater seats. This well-known skin infection is not caused by a worm at all, but by one of various kinds of fungi. The disease is easily identified by the rapidly growing circular patches of rough, reddened skin that heals from the center outward. Hence the name ringworm. Today, ringworm can be transmitted by infected people, pets, towels, hairbrushes, or other contaminated objects. Some infections disappear with no treatment at all. In other cases, a topical antifungal medication is applied to the infected area, or other ringworm medication is taken by mouth.

Source: *National Institutes of Health*

Social Studies

Uncommon Diseases in the U.S. Have students research an infectious disease that is not common in the United States today, but is common in other countries or was common in the past. Examples include bubonic plague, malaria, African sleeping sickness (trypanosomiasis), and cholera. Ask students to find out what the symptoms of the disease are, how it spreads, what kind of pathogen causes it, and how it has affected life in the areas where it is, or was, common.

Teacher Tip

Through the Microscope
Illustrate the difference between light and electron microscopes by showing pictures of both. Light microscopes use light waves to create a magnified image, while electron microscopes use electrons. A light microscope can magnify about 2,000 times. Electron microscopes can magnify almost 1,000,000 times. Because viruses are so small, they can be viewed only by using an electron microscope.

TEACH *continued*

Interpret Visuals—Pictures

Direct attention to the pictures on this page showing how pathogens can be spread. Using the pictures as a model, ask students for examples of things people can do to prevent the spread of infection to others. Possible answers: Cover your mouth or nose when sneezing or coughing; always wash your hands after petting or handling an animal; avoid people who are ill.

Content-Area Reading Support

Using Typographic Clues Direct attention to the word in italics in the second paragraph—*contaminated*. Point out that using italics emphasizes a word's importance. Add that the word's definition is often included in the same paragraph.

Discuss

Explain that fungi, bacteria, and viruses are three kinds of organisms that cause disease. Parasites are another. Parasites range from tiny one-celled protozoa such as *giardia* to invertebrates such as tape worms and lice.

Critical Thinking With all these pathogens out there, why aren't we sick all the time? Our bodies have many natural ways of combating disease. Pathogens aren't really everywhere; they need special conditions to live, grow, and multiply.

Growth, Development, and Reproduction An optical lesson about sexually transmitted diseases is provided in this supplement on pp. 58–65. Use this component in compliance with state and local guidelines.

How Pathogens Spread

Pathogens can spread in many different ways. For example, you use a pencil that someone who is ill has used. Pathogens from the pencil can get onto your hands. If you don't wash your hands, you could pass the pathogen to your mouth or eyes. You could also pass the pathogen to someone else.

Something that contains pathogens is *contaminated* (kuhn•TAM•uh•nayt•id). Water, air, and food can spread pathogens. If you drink contaminated water, for example, you will probably get sick.

▼ When someone coughs or sneezes, droplets with pathogens can be sprayed into the air. If you are nearby, you may breathe in those pathogens.

164

Science

Germ Theory The work of many scientists contributed to the development of the germ theory. Assign pairs of students to research scientists Joseph Lister, Dimitri Iwanowski, Pierre Bretonneau, Anton van Leeuwenhoek, Louis Pasteur, and Robert Koch and develop short presentations to give the rest of the class about their individual contributions to the development of the germ theory.

Pathogens multiply in food that is spoiled or is not properly prepared. When you eat spoiled or contaminated food, you may get food poisoning. Some forms of food poisoning can make you very ill or even kill you.

Some pathogens can spread from one food to another. Some are spread when people who handle foods don't wash their hands. Others multiply whenever food is left out of the refrigerator. See pages 126–128 for a reminder of ways that you can avoid food poisoning and food contamination.

▲ Stream water often looks clean, but it might not be safe to drink. Take drinking water with you when you go hiking.

▲ Animals such as insects and birds sometimes spread pathogens to people.

MAIN IDEA AND DETAILS **Name four ways that pathogens can be spread. Give an example for each.**

Answers should include the methods outlined on pages 164–165.

Lesson 2 Summary and Review

1. **Summarize with Vocabulary**
   Use vocabulary from this lesson to complete the statements.
   There are several types of _____ that cause disease. They include _____, _____, and _____. If any of them multiply in your body, you can get a(n) _____.
2. Name three illnesses caused by viruses and three caused by bacteria.
3. **Critical Thinking** If your best friend has a cold, what are two ways that the pathogens in your friend's body could be spread to you?
4. **COMPARE AND CONTRAST** Draw and complete this graphic organizer to show how bacteria and viruses are alike and different.

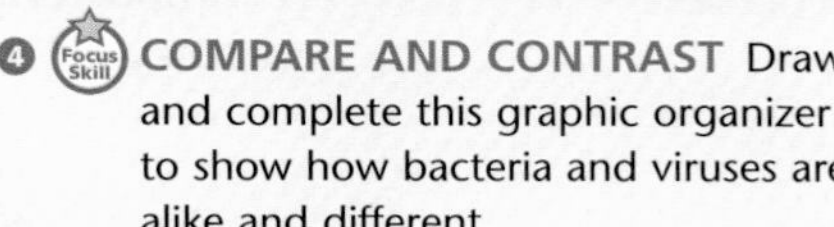

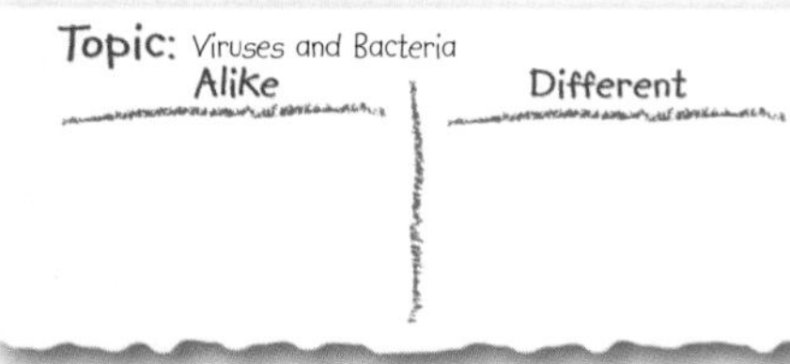

5. **Write to Inform—How-To**
   Jamie wants to help his father prepare breakfast. Make a list of things Jamie can do to make sure he doesn't spread pathogens as he helps prepare breakfast.

Science

Beaver Fever One of the most highly contagious protozoan pathogens is *Giardia lamblia*. The cysts of *Giardia* are found in contaminated water and, when taken in orally, infect the small intestine. An outbreak in Canada's Banff National Park a few years ago was thought to have been caused by beavers infected with the human strain of *Giardia*; hence the nickname "beaver fever." The protozoan is named after nineteenth-century French biologist Alfred M. Giard.

3. WRAP UP

Lesson 2 Summary and Review

1. pathogens, viruses, bacteria, fungi, infection
2. Colds, flu, and chicken pox are caused by viruses. Pinkeye, ear infections, and strep throat are almost always caused by bacteria.
3. Breathing in droplets from the air when your friend sneezes or coughs, and touching objects used by the ill friend are two ways the cold virus can spread.
4. Responses may include:

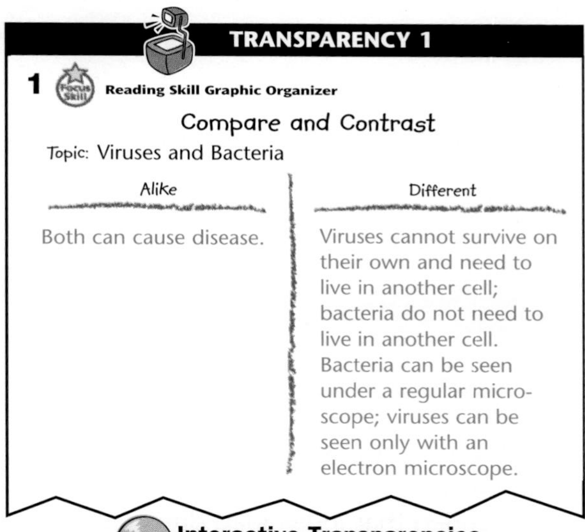

TRANSPARENCY 1
1 Reading Skill Graphic Organizer
Compare and Contrast
Topic: Viruses and Bacteria
Alike
Different
Both can cause disease.
Viruses cannot survive on their own and need to live in another cell; bacteria do not need to live in another cell. Bacteria can be seen under a regular microscope; viruses can be seen only with an electron microscope.

Interactive Transparencies available on CD-ROM.

5. Sample response: Jamie doesn't use spoiled or contaminated food. He doesn't use food that was supposed to be in the refrigerator but sat out instead. He washes his hands before he handles the food. Also refer to tips on pages 85–86.

For **writing models** with examples, see *Teaching Resources* pp. 47–61. Rubrics are also provided.

When Minutes Count . . .

Quick Study Students can use *Activity Book* pages 31–32 (shown on p. 159) as they complete each lesson in this chapter.

LESSON 3
Pages 166–171

Objectives
- ► Describe the immune system's function as a defense against pathogens.
- ► Identify ways of helping the body defend itself against disease.

When Minutes Count . . .
Assign the Quick Study, Lesson 3, Activity Book pp. 31–32 (shown on p. 159).

Program Resources
- ► Activity Book pp. 31–32
- ► Transparency 1, 20
- ► Growth, Development, and Reproduction pp. 66–72

Vocabulary
immune system p. 166,
antibodies p. 167, **immunity** p. 167,
vaccine p. 170

Daily Fitness Tip

Water makes up about 60 percent of the human body by weight. It's important to drink water throughout the day to replace that lost through various bodily functions. It's recommended that individuals drink eight 8-ounce glasses of water each day.

1. MOTIVATE

To introduce the idea that the skin is the body's first line of defense against pathogens, ask students to describe what a scab is. Most students will say that it is a crusty patch of dried blood and pus that forms on the skin after a scrape or injury.

What would happen if a scab didn't form after the skin had been cut or scraped? The injury would continue to bleed, and germs would have a way of entering the bloodstream.

What can you do to help a cut or scrape heal? Possible answers: don't pick at a scab, cover with a bandage, keep it clean

LESSON 3

Fighting Communicable Diseases

Lesson Focus
You can help your body fight disease.

Why Learn This?
You can use what you learn about preventing disease to promote health at home and at school.

Vocabulary
immune system
antibodies
immunity
vaccine

Your Body Fights Disease

You are ill. Your throat hurts. You're coughing, you have a fever, and your body aches. You have symptoms of flu. *Symptoms* (SIMP•tuhmz) are signs or physical feelings of a disease.

You don't get ill every day. You are usually healthy because your body defends itself against pathogens. Your body's defenses are described on the next page. If pathogens get past your first defenses, your immune system goes to work. The **immune** (ih•MYOON) **system** is the body system that fights disease. White blood cells are an important part of the immune system because they kill pathogens.

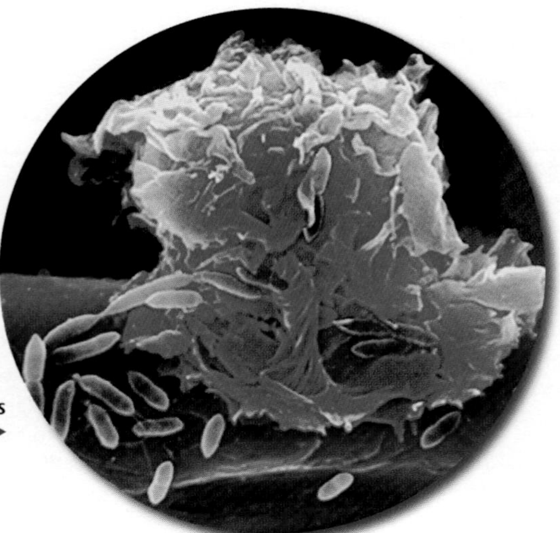

You have several kinds of white blood cells. Some surround pathogens and destroy them. ►

Meeting Individual Needs
Leveled Activities

BELOW-LEVEL **First Line of Defense Collage** Have students collect pictures and photographs from magazines and newspapers that represent the different parts of the body that act as a first line of defense against pathogens, for example, ears, eyes, nose, and skin. Students can arrange their pictures on a sheet of construction paper to make a collage.

ON-LEVEL **Name That Defense** Show students pictures of different parts of the body that act as the body's first line of defense against pathogens (nose, ears, mouth, stomach, eyes, throat, skin). Have students explain how each body part protects against invading pathogens.

CHALLENGE **A Day in the Life** Ask students to write a short story about a day in the life of an antibody that fights invading pathogens. Encourage students to be as creative as possible with their stories and to add illustrations.

Some white blood cells fight pathogens by making antibodies. **Antibodies** (AN•tih•bahd•eez) are chemicals that the body makes to fight disease.

An antibody attaches itself to a pathogen and tries to destroy it. If the pathogen is not destroyed, white blood cells then attack and destroy it.

Once your body has made antibodies for a pathogen, the antibodies stay in the body. Some stay for several months. Some stay your whole life. If that pathogen ever attacks again, your body usually has enough antibodies to keep you from getting ill. The body's ability to defend itself against certain kinds of pathogens is called **immunity** (ih•MYOON•uh•tee).

Did You Know?

A fever, or above-normal body temperature, is a symptom of many diseases. A fever shows that your body is fighting an infection. It is a normal response of the body to foreign invaders such as bacteria and viruses.

DRAW CONCLUSIONS **If you have had a certain viral disease, can you get that disease again? Explain.** No. Your body recognizes the pathogen and makes antibodies to destroy it before it can multiply and cause the disease.

The Body's Defenses

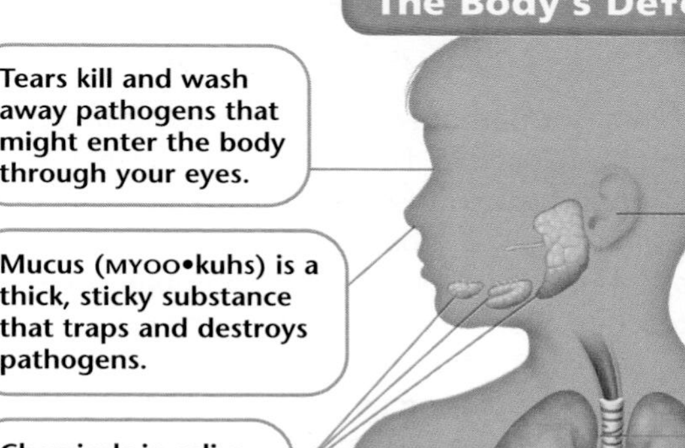

Tears kill and wash away pathogens that might enter the body through your eyes.
Mucus (MYOO•kuhs) is a thick, sticky substance that traps and destroys pathogens.
Chemicals in saliva, the liquid in your mouth, kill many pathogens.
The skin's tough outer layers block many pathogens from entering your body. Sweat on skin may destroy some pathogens, too.
Earwax traps pathogens that might enter through your ears.
Cilia (SIL•ee•uh) are small hairs that line the body's air passages. Cilia help move pathogens out of the body.
Chemicals in the digestive juices in your stomach kill many pathogens.

Social Studies

Smallpox It is thought that smallpox originated more than 3,000 years ago in India or Egypt. An intensive global campaign of vaccination has eliminated this disease from the world population. Since the population might once again be exposed to this disease, vaccinations for smallpox have been reintroduced. Help students research areas of the world that were affected by smallpox. Use a world map to point out where these countries are located.

2. TEACH

When Minutes Count . . .

Transparency 20: Body Defenses can be used to present material in this lesson. *Interactive Transparencies available on CD-ROM.*

Interpret Visuals—Pictures

After students have studied the diagram on this page, ask them to close their books. Point to each body part and ask for volunteers to explain how that body part helps defend against pathogens.

Content-Area Reading Support

Using Typographic Clues Direct attention to the words that are highlighted. Point out that, in each case, a definition either follows or precedes the highlighted word. Advise students to pay special attention to sentences that contain highlighted words because they usually give the meaning of the word.

Discuss

Ask students to recall when they have had a fever. **What does it feel like to have a fever?** Make a list of words that students use to describe how they feel. Remind students that this is the body's normal response to invading pathogens.

Health Background

Vaccines Active or passive immunity against a specific pathogen can be produced by the administration of a vaccine. A vaccine is a suspension of weakened or killed microorganisms, toxins, or antibodies. The first vaccine was developed by Edward Jenner in 1796. Jenner had observed that milkmaids who had been infected with cowpox were resistant to smallpox. He therefore used the cowpox virus to create vaccines that protected people against smallpox. Jenner's discovery helped eliminate smallpox as a worldwide disease.

Source: *Centers for Disease Control and Prevention website*

For more background, visit the **Webliography** in Teacher Resources at **www.harcourtschool.com/health** **Keyword** diseases

TEACH *continued*

Quick Activity

Students will probably list sneezing and touching another person as ways that pathogens are spread. Ways to avoid the spread of pathogens would be to cover the mouth and nose when sneezing, and to wash hands frequently.

Discuss

Critical Thinking How does keeping hands clean help prevent infection? Keeping hands clean helps wash off bacteria and other pathogens that get on the hands when touching objects and people.

Why is it especially important for students to stay home when they are ill? Infection can spread quickly from student to student, and even to teachers.

Problem Solving What should you do if you are at school and feel ill? You should ask your teacher for permission to see the school nurse. You should also avoid touching other students.

Growth, Development, and Reproduction An optical lesson about HIV/AIDS is provided in this supplement on pp. 66–72. Use this component in compliance with state and local guidelines.

Quick Activity

Avoiding Disease Look at this picture. With a partner, come up with a list of two or three ways you see pathogens being spread. For each example you list, write ways to avoid or kill the pathogens. Present your work in a table.

▲ Why is this student's friend avoiding contact?

Myth and Fact

Myth: Soap is what kills bacteria when you wash your hands.

Fact: Rubbing your hands together loosens dead skin cells. Soap makes the pathogens on those cells stay suspended (floating) in the warm water, so that you can rinse them off your hands.

Help Your Body Avoid Disease

You can avoid pathogens by not touching things someone ill has touched. For example, pinkeye is a bacterial eye infection. If someone with pinkeye rubs his or her eyes, the bacteria get on the person's hands. The bacteria can get on objects he or she touches, too. If you touch the same objects and then touch your eyes, you could get pinkeye. Pathogens can also be spread through coughing and sneezing. Stay away from people who have a communicable disease, such as flu or a cold.

Hospitals and medical offices have rules to follow to avoid the spread of disease. Your school might ask you to stay home if you are ill. Following rules can help you avoid disease.

SEQUENCE **You have flu. Your mother takes your temperature. Then she has something to eat without washing her hands. What might happen next?**

Accept either of the following: The flu virus enters your mother's body; your mother gets flu.

168

Teacher Tip

Washing Your Hands To help limit the spread of disease in your classroom, always have a supply of soap. Limit your use of antibacterial soap. Overuse of these soaps can cause bacteria to become resistant. Washing properly with adequate soap and water gets rid of most bacteria. Have students routinely wash their hands before and after recess, snack time, and lunch. Students should also wash their hands after any science, or art activities.

Practice Healthful Habits

One of the best ways to avoid disease is to keep your hands clean. Wash your hands often. Always wash before eating, after using the bathroom, and after playing with pets. Use soap and warm water. Rub your hands together for at least 15 seconds. You should also avoid touching your eyes, nose, and mouth.

Remember, bacteria can enter your body if you cut your skin. Wash cuts with clean water. Follow the tips on pages 350–351. Another way to avoid disease is by obeying school rules that say not to share combs, drinks, or foods. Practicing healthful habits can help avoid the spread of disease.

SUMMARIZE How can you keep pathogens from spreading?

Personal Health Plan

Real-Life Situation
Pathogens can spread from objects and surfaces that people touch every day.
Real-Life Plan
Make a list of three surfaces or objects in your classroom. Next to your list write down what you can do to protect yourself from the spread of pathogens. Refer to the additional information about hand washing on page 34.

▼ How are these students helping keep pathogens from spreading?

through keeping clean, following rules that help avoid the spread of disease, and supporting efforts that promote health.

Personal Health Plan

Student lists should include:

- pencils and pens. (Use only your own pencil or pens.)
- table, desk, and countertops. (Keep all surfaces clean.)
- doorknobs. (Wash all doorknobs daily; wash hands regularly)

Content-Area Reading Support

Using Title and Headings Direct attention to the heading on this page. Point out that this heading identifies the overall topic, is in larger type, and is in a different color from the rest of the information on the page. Explain that type size and color are clues to the topic and organization of information in a text passage.

Discuss

How can not sharing combs or brushes help prevent the spread of disease?
Pathogens can live on hair and can spread when combs and brushes are shared.

Ask students to identify specific school rules that could help prevent the spread of disease.

Math

Multiplying Bacteria Some bacteria multiply very quickly. *E. coli* bacteria reproduce every 20 minutes under ideal conditions. In the right conditions, one *E. coli* bacterium can multiply to more than a million bacteria in less than four hours. Have students compute how long it would take one *E. coli* bacterium to grow to a colony of 16 bacteria. 80 minutes

Life Skills

Pages 172–173

Communicate
Make Responsible Decisions
Manage Stress
Refuse
Resolve Conflicts
Set Goals

Objectives

- Learn to identify situations that are stressful.
- Use the steps to manage stress to help lead a more healthful life.

Program Resources

- Activity Book p. 34
- Poster 9

1. MOTIVATE

Optional Activity Materials pictures or photographs of people doing positive things in stressful situations (performers, athletes, businesspeople, law enforcement officers, and so on)

Display the images. Allow students time to study them. Ask students to identify what is stressful about each situation shown in the pictures. Then ask students to describe how the people might turn their stress into something positive.

2. TEACH

Direct students' attention to the photographs of Jason thinking about getting a shot.

Step 1

How does Jason know he's feeling stress? He's feeling nervous and he has a stomachache.

Step 2

What's causing Jason to feel nervous? He must go to a doctor's office for a shot.

Manage Stress

at the Doctor's Office

Everybody feels stress sometimes. Stress is mental or emotional strain. Learning to manage stress is an important part of staying healthy. The steps to **Manage Stress** can help you.

Jason needs a tetanus shot, so he must go to the doctor's office. Just thinking about the shot gives Jason a stomachache. How can he deal with the stress?

1 Know what stress feels like and what causes it.

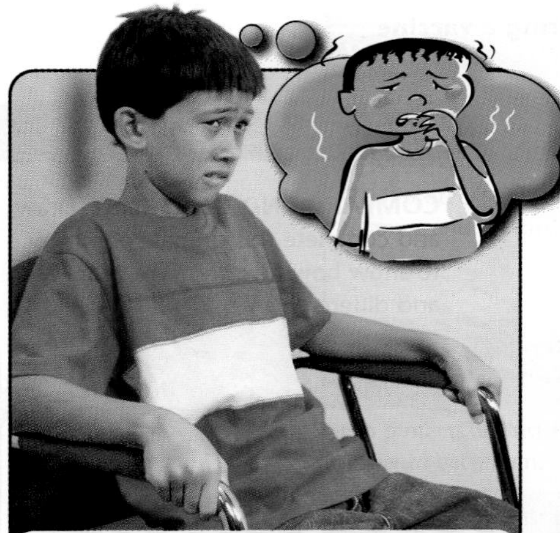

Jason is feeling nervous. He gets stressed when he visits the doctor's office.

2 Try to determine the cause of the stress.

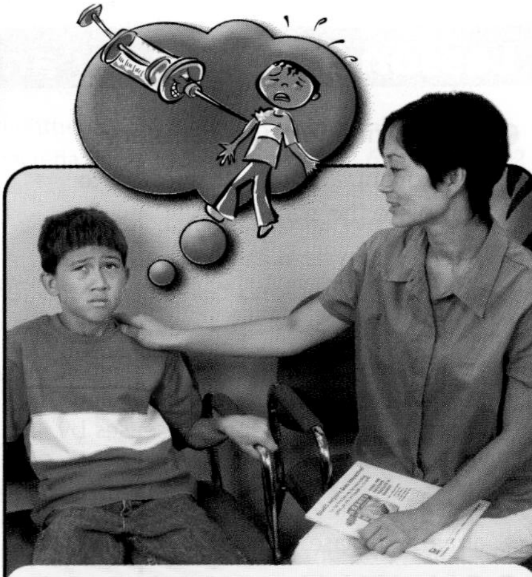

Jason doesn't like getting shots. He knows they hurt. He also knows thinking about getting a shot gives him stress.

172

Teacher Tip

Role-Play Ask students to make a list of three or four positive things they can think of the next time they visit a doctor's office or clinic. Then try this role-playing activity. Have students work in pairs with one acting as the receptionist who greets patients. Have the other student be a patient arriving for an appointment. Students acting as patients are to think of one of the positive things from their list. Some students may want to think out loud. Remind pairs to switch roles.

ACTIVITY BOOK P. 34

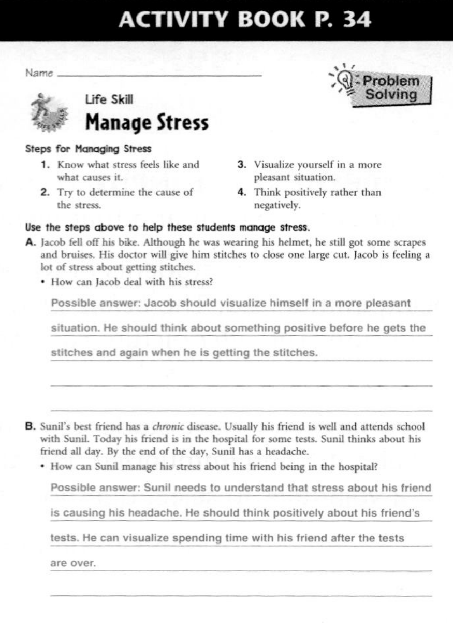

Name ______________

Problem Solving

Life Skill

Manage Stress

Steps for Managing Stress

1. Know what stress feels like and what causes it.
2. Try to determine the cause of the stress.
3. Visualize yourself in a more pleasant situation.
4. Think positively rather than negatively.

Use the steps above to help these students manage stress.

A. Jacob fell off his bike. Although he was wearing his helmet, he still got some scrapes and bruises. His doctor will give him stitches to close one large cut. Jacob is feeling a lot of stress about getting stitches.

- How can Jacob deal with his stress?

Possible answer: Jacob should visualize himself in a more pleasant situation. He should think about something positive before he gets the stitches and again when he is getting the stitches.

B. Sunil's best friend has a *chronic* disease. Usually his friend is well and attends school with Sunil. Today his friend is in the hospital for some tests. Sunil thinks about his friend all day. By the end of the day, Sunil has a headache.

- How can Sunil manage his stress about his friend being in the hospital?

Possible answer: Sunil needs to understand that stress about his friend is causing his headache. He should think positively about his friend's tests. He can visualize spending time with his friend after the tests are over.

© Harcourt

Available online.
www.harcourtschool.com/health

3 Visualize yourself in a more pleasant situation.

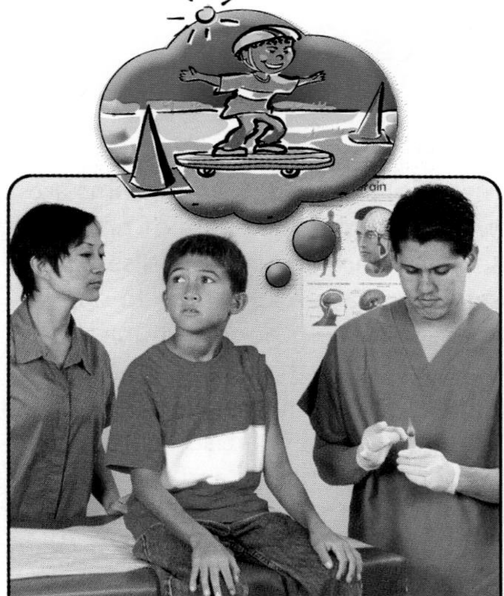

Jason decides to look away and to think of something that he enjoys. He imagines himself on his skateboard with his friend.

4 Think positively rather than negatively.

Jason finds that thinking about something pleasant helps relieve his stress. He hardly feels the shot.

Problem Solving

Natalie's grandmother has a chronic illness. Natalie is so upset and worried that she can't sleep. She knows that this much stress can harm her own health, but she does not know what to do about it. Use the steps to **Manage Stress** to help Natalie. Suggest ways that she can demonstrate caring to her grandmother, which will help her handle the stress that she feels herself.

Using the Poster

Activity Have students work in pairs to create posters about managing stress.

Display Students' posters can be displayed in a location such as the cafeteria or entrance to the school to remind all students of ways to manage stress.

POSTER 9
Manage Stress
The boy is managing his stress by taking a walk.
Ways to Manage Stress
1 Know what stress feels like and what causes it.
2 Do something active to make yourself feel better.
3 Talk with someone you trust about the way you are feeling.
4 Visualize yourself doing well in a stressful situation.
How have YOU MANAGED STRESS today?

Step 3

What does Jason decide to think about instead of thinking about the shot? He imagines he is on his skateboard with his friend.

Building Good Character

Remind students that when they practice the steps to manage stress they are practicing responsibility. They are identifying their feelings and learning how to turn a stressful situation into a positive one. Remind students to practice being responsible by asking the following questions when they feel stressed: Why am I feeling stressed? Have I felt this way before? How can I turn my stressful thoughts into positive ones?

Critical Thinking When would be the best time for Jason to start practicing the steps for managing stress? Jason should practice the steps for managing stress as soon as he knows that he is feeling nervous.

Step 4

How did thinking of something positive help relieve Jason's stress? It helped Jason focus on something positive instead of on the shot.

3. WRAP UP

Problem Solving

Natalie can show that she cares about her grandmother's feelings by visiting her, spending time talking with, reading to, or having a meal with her. By helping her grandmother feel better, Natalie will relieve her own stress about her grandmother's illness.

LESSON 4
Pages 174–179

Objectives
- ► Identify noncommunicable diseases and their symptoms.
- ► Understand how noncommunicable diseases can be managed.

When Minutes Count . . .
Assign the Quick Study, Lesson 4, Activity Book pp. 31–32 (shown on p. 159).

Program Resources
- ► Activity Book pp. 31–32
- ► Transparency 1

Vocabulary
cancer p. 175, **allergy** p. 176, **asthma** p. 177, **diabetes** p. 178, **arthritis** p. 179

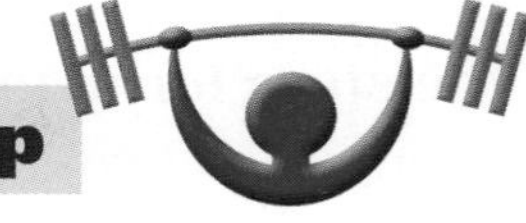

Daily Fitness Tip
Staying flexible helps keep joints healthy. Along with regular exercise, it is important to stretch the muscles on a regular basis. This acts to increase circulation in and around the joints and helps prevent arthritis.

For more information about exercise, see *Be Alert! Resources for Physical Education* p. 163.

1. MOTIVATE
Help students understand the meaning of the word *noncommunicable.* **What does communicate mean?** Students might say that *communicate* means "to tell something." Emphasize that when somebody communicates, he or she is sharing words and ideas.

What would it mean to "noncommunicate" with somebody? Students might respond that noncommunicating would mean *not* sharing words or ideas with somebody.

Discuss the idea that, just as *noncommunication* means "not to share ideas and words," a noncommunicable disease is a disease that cannot be shared.

LESSON 4

Noncommunicable Diseases

Lesson Focus
Some diseases cannot be spread from person to person.

Why Learn This?
You can make choices that lower your risk of disease.

Vocabulary
cancer
allergy
asthma
diabetes
arthritis

Heart Disease
Ms. Cole has heart disease. Its symptoms are chest pain, weakness, and shortness of breath. Heart diseases are noncommunicable diseases. These diseases often take a long time to appear. Some people are born with noncommunicable diseases, while others get them over time.

Ms. Cole's heart disease may have been caused by her not getting enough exercise or from not eating right. Poor health habits and smoking can increase a person's risk for getting heart disease. Heart disease is the leading cause of death among adults in the United States.

DRAW CONCLUSIONS **Did Ms. Cole catch heart disease? Explain.**
No. Heart disease is a noncommunicable disease.

Health & Technology
It's Electric Doctors can do a test called an electrocardiogram, or EKG, to find out if the heart is working properly. An EKG can show doctors that a patient has heart disease before the disease gets bad.

◄ Ms. Cole is having a stress test. While she exercises on the treadmill, her heartbeat rate and blood pressure are being checked.

174

Meeting Individual Needs
Leveled Activities

BELOW-LEVEL Flash Cards Have students work together in pairs to learn the noncommunicable diseases discussed in this lesson. Ask each pair to create a flash card for each disease. Each card should have the name of the disease on one side and the symptoms of the disease on the other side.

ON-LEVEL Making a Table Have students make a table to organize the information in this lesson. The table should have three columns. The names of the noncommunicable diseases can be listed in the first column, the symptoms of each disease in the second column, and the treatment for each disease in the third column.

CHALLENGE Current Research Ask students to research the kinds of treatment that are currently available for one of the noncommunicable diseases discussed in this lesson. Students can prepare short reports and present their findings to the class.

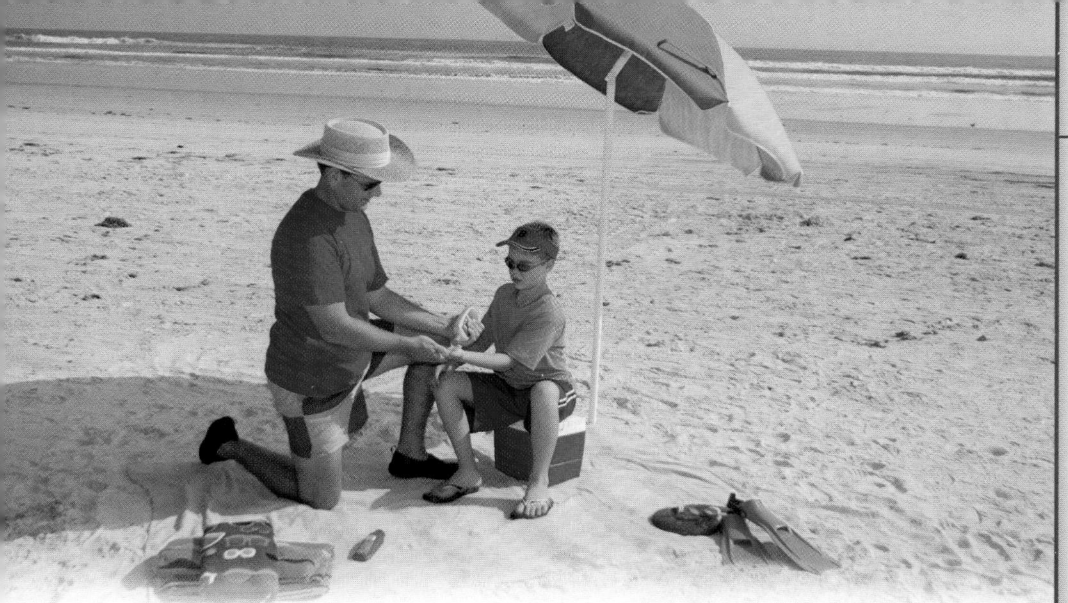

▲ You can get skin cancer if your skin is exposed to too much sunlight. Using sunscreen helps prevent this form of the disease. What other protection is the boy using?

Cancer

Some people get cancer. **Cancer** occurs when body cells that are not normal grow out of control. Cancer cells often form lumps called tumors. Cancer can occur in nearly every part of the body, including the bones and blood. Cancer can also spread from one part of the body to another. Cancer is the second-leading cause of death in the United States.

Scientists know what causes some forms of cancer. Tobacco, for example, is one cause. There are many other kinds of cancers for which scientists still do not know the cause. The sooner a cancer in the body is found, the more likely it can be treated successfully.

MAIN IDEA AND DETAILS **What is cancer, and in what parts of the body can it occur?**

Cancer occurs when cells that aren't normal grow out of control. It can occur in almost any part of the body.

Did You Know?

Skin cancer is the most common type of cancer in humans. More than 1 million cases are found each year. People who have light skin, get sunburned easily, and have a family history of skin cancer have greater chances of getting this disease than other people.

175

Teacher Tip

Healthy Heart Diet Rules

1. Total fat intake in one day should be less than 30 percent of the total calories.
2. Saturated fat intake in one day should be less than 10 percent of the total calories.
3. Cholesterol intake for one day should be no more than 300 milligrams.
4. Sodium intake for one day should be no more than 2,400 milligrams or one teaspoon.

2. TEACH

Interpret Visuals—Pictures

Have students look at the woman on the treadmill. Ask students why they think this test is called a stress test. Students will probably respond that the test measures how much the heart is *stressed* by the exercise on the treadmill.

Content-Area Reading Support

Using Paragraph Structure Direct attention to the last paragraph on the page. Point out that the first sentence states the topic of the paragraph, *causes some forms of cancer*. The other sentences give examples of known causes of some forms of cancer.

Health Background

Congenital Heart Defects The term *congenital heart defects* refer to a variety of malformations or defects of the heart or its major vessels that are present at birth. Although they are rare, congenital heart defects occur in approximately 8 out of every 1,000 children. The result of most congenital heart defects is an obstruction of blood flow in the heart or its vessels. About half of the babies who are born with congenital heart defects require medical or surgical treatment. In many cases, the cause of congenital heart defects is unknown. The factors that have been identified are genetic or chromosomal abnormalities, certain medications or alcohol or drug abuse during pregnancy, and maternal viral infection in the first part of pregnancy.

Source: *Yale University School of Medicine Heart Book*

TEACH *continued*

Interpret Visuals—Graphs

According to the graph, the most common allergy is hay fever. **What are the least common allergies shown on the graph?** seafood and peanuts

Discuss

Critical Thinking **Suppose you are allergic to bee stings and are planning a week's vacation. What precautions could you take in planning your stay?** Possible answers: Stay away from bees or places where bees might be; take medications along, and don't forget them when you go for a walk; remind your family and friends about your allergy, and explain what they should do if you get stung; find out where the nearest doctor, clinic, or emergency room is as soon as you arrive.

How can you be a caring friend of someone who has allergies to certain things? You can be aware of the things that your friend is allergic to; you can remind your friend to take his or her allergy medication.

Some Common Allergies	
Substance	**Symptoms**
Pollen from grasses, trees, or weeds	stuffy, runny nose; sneezing; itchy eyes; red eyes; puffy eyes
Foods such as eggs, nuts, milk products, soy, fish, wheat, peas, or shellfish	itchy mouth and throat; diarrhea; vomiting; hives; difficulty breathing
Plants such as poison ivy or poison oak	red, itchy patches on the skin; sometimes blisters
Furry animals such as dogs, cats, or rabbits	itchy eyes; runny nose; rash; difficulty breathing

Which substances are likely to cause rashes on the skin? plants, furry animals **Which can cause difficulty breathing?** foods, furry animals

◀ This cat's scratching could make someone's eyes water and cause sneezing.

◀ Allergies can cause asthma attacks. A person who is allergic to grass should stay away from mowing. The exhaust from the mower could also cause an attack.

Numbers of People with Common Allergies in the United States

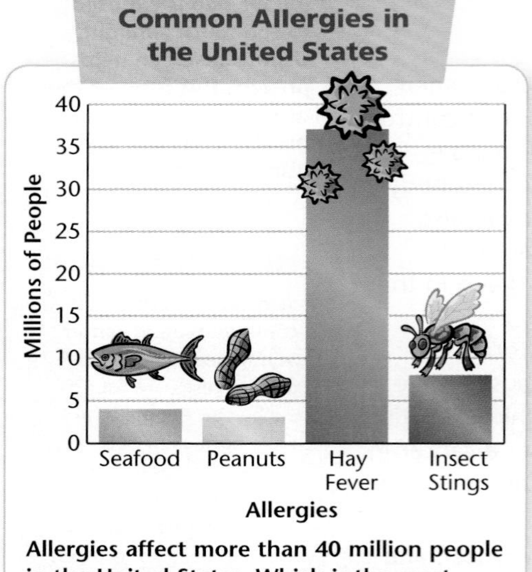

Allergies affect more than 40 million people in the United States. Which is the most common allergy shown on the graph?

Allergies

An **allergy** (AL•er•jee) is a noncommunicable disease in which a person's body reacts badly to a certain thing. People can be allergic to animals, plants, medicines, and even foods. Some allergic reactions are so severe that they can cause death.

If you have allergies, you should avoid the things you are allergic to. Medicines can help make the symptoms go away and can even save your life if you have a severe reaction. Some people can get shots for their allergies. Over time, they no longer have allergic reactions.

MAIN IDEA AND DETAILS **What symptoms might suggest that you have an allergy to cats?** Possible answer: Your eyes water and you sneeze each time you get near a cat.

ESL/ELL Support

COMPREHENSIBLE INPUT Help students understand what allergies are and how they can be treated.

Beginning Ask students to act out how a person with an allergy to cats might react if a cat jumps into his or her lap. Other examples might involve somebody who is allergic to a certain flower and is presented with a bouquet of those flowers.

Intermediate Have students draw pictures of people experiencing an allergic reaction to something.

Advanced Ask students to write a paragraph that includes the following information: the definition of the word *allergy*, one example of an allergy, and possible treatments.

Asthma

Keiko has asthma. **Asthma** (AZ•muh) is a noncommunicable disease of the respiratory system. Her asthma attacks can be scary. Her chest feels tight. She has trouble breathing, and she coughs or wheezes.

These attacks are caused by allergies, cigarette smoke, and dust. Cold weather and exercise can also cause them. Keiko has more attacks than usual if she has a cold or other disease that affects the lungs.

Asthma cannot be cured, but some children outgrow the disease. A doctor can find out what things cause the attacks and tell ways to avoid them. Doctors can also give medicines to help people manage the disease.

SUMMARIZE What is asthma, and how can you get help for it?
Students should use the information above.

Myth and Fact

Myth: People with asthma should never exercise.
Fact: Exercise is important for good health. People with asthma usually can avoid attacks when they exercise by not exercising too long. They can also take medicine before exercising.

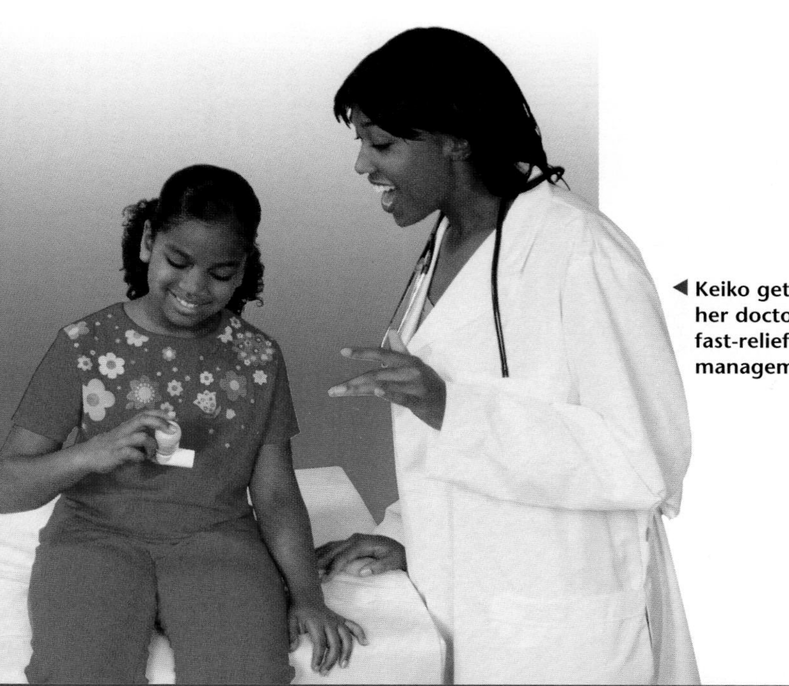

◀ Keiko gets directions from her doctor on the use of a fast-relief inhaler for proper management of her asthma.

Science

Food-Allergic Reaction When a particular food is eaten and an allergic reaction occurs, many things happen in the body. First, the immune system reacts to the food item as if it were a harmful substance. Trying to protect the body, the immune system produces large amounts of histamines and chemicals that affect the respiratory, digestive, and cardiovascular systems. Using this information, have students make a flowchart representing what happens during a food-allergic reaction.

Discuss

Help students understand the difference between allergies and asthma.

Compare and Contrast

How are asthma and allergies alike? How are they different? Both are noncommunicable diseases. Asthma, which affects the respiratory system, can be caused by allergies. Allergies happen when a person's body reacts badly to a certain thing (allergen).

Many allergies are outgrown as bodies mature. Babies are sometimes allergic to certain foods but, as they grow older, the allergy disappears. Ask volunteers to talk about any allergies they may have had when they were babies.

Problem Solving You have invited a friend over for dinner. During dinner, your pet cat comes into the room and lies down under the dinner table. During dinner your friend complains of an upset stomach and irritated mouth. What might you conclude from your friend's symptoms? It is likely that your friend probably had an allergic reaction to a food item that was served for dinner rather than an allergy to the cat. The latter usually affects the respiratory system (nose and lungs).

TEACH *continued*

Consumer Activity

Reliable sources of information can be found on the Internet at government or educational sites.

Content-Area Reading Support

Using Respellings Direct attention to the phonetic respelling DY · UH · BEET · EEZ. Explain that respellings show how words are pronounced. Point out that the dots in the respelling divide the word into syllables and that capital letters indicate the stressed, or accented, syllable.

Interpret Visuals—Pictures

Ask students to describe what Nancy is doing in the photograph. Nancy has type 1 diabetes, a condition where the body doesn't make insulin. If the body doesn't use insulin properly, another condition, type 2 diabetes, occurs. Point out to students that many diabetics must give themselves injections of insulin every day in order to keep their blood sugar level normal.

Discuss

Critical Thinking How could you explain diabetes in the simplest possible way? Students might respond that diabetes is a condition in which the body is unable to maintain a normal blood sugar level.

Health Background

Obesity and Type 2 Diabetes Over the past ten years the percentage of Type 2 diabetes among children has increased by twenty percent. Out of those diagnosed, eighty-five percent were considered obese. Most children are diagnosed with Type 2 diabetes during the years of middle to late puberty. However, with the increase of overweight and less active children, doctors are predicting that even younger children will be diagnosed with this disease.

Source: *American Academy of Pediatrics website*

For more background, visit the **Webliography** in Teacher Resources at **www.harcourtschool.com/health** **Keyword** diseases

Consumer Activity

Analyze Advertisements and Media Messages Many medicines and supplies are sold for diabetes and arthritis. Look for ads in magazines and other resources to learn more about each. Use the tips for getting reliable health information on pages 49–50 and pages 53–54.

Diabetes

Nancy has **diabetes** (dy•uh•BEET•eez), a disease that occurs if the body stops making insulin or stops using it properly. Insulin (IN•suh•lin) is a substance that helps body cells take up sugar from the blood. People who have diabetes feel weak and tired.

When sugar cannot enter body cells, it builds up in the blood. High blood sugar causes many health problems. If diabetes is not treated, blood vessels as well as the heart, kidneys, and eyes can be damaged.

Diabetes cannot be cured, but it can be treated. People with diabetes must follow a balanced diet, get regular exercise, and measure their blood sugar levels. Some take insulin or other medication.

DRAW CONCLUSIONS Why do people with diabetes feel weak and tired?

Since their bodies have trouble taking up sugar from the blood, their cells are not getting the energy they need.

Nancy is learning how to measure her blood sugar level. If it is too high, she will get a shot of insulin. Nancy has to take insulin every day to control her blood sugar level. ▶

178

Meeting Individual Needs
Leveled Activities

BELOW-LEVEL What Is...? On large index cards, have students write out simple questions like *What is diabetes? What is asthma? What is heart disease?* Then have them write answers to the questions on the back of each card. Students can quiz each other, using the cards.

ON-LEVEL Anatomy Chart Display a simple chart of the human body and ask students to label the parts of the body that are affected by asthma, arthritis, heart disease, allergies, and diabetes.

CHALLENGE Noncommunicable Disease Report Have students choose one of the diseases discussed in this lesson and write an in-depth report on it. Encourage students to include information about current research, treatments, and, if applicable, cures.

Arthritis

Will's grandmother has **arthritis** (ar•THRYT•is), a noncommunicable disease in which one or more of the body's joints become swollen and painful. Joints are places, such as wrists and knees, where your body bends. These joints can be red, swollen, stiff, and painful. Some mornings Will's grandmother is so stiff that it is hard for her to get out of bed.

There is no cure for arthritis, but doctors can give medicines to help the pain and swelling. A physical therapist taught Will's grandmother daily stretches that help keep full motion in her joints. She also takes walks and swims often.

CAUSE AND EFFECT **Will's grandmother rotates her wrists in an exercise. How does this help her arthritis?**
It can help her wrists stay flexible.

▲ **Walking helps Will's grandmother stay limber and also helps her manage stress by taking her mind off her disease.**

Lesson 4 Summary and Review

1. **Summarize with Vocabary** — **Summarize with Vocabulary**
   Use vocabulary and other terms from this lesson to complete the statements.
   _____ diseases are not caused by pathogens. These diseases include _____, which affects the joints, and _____, which affects the level of sugar in the blood. _____ develops when cells that are not normal grow out of control.
2. Name some things that can cause an allergic reaction.
3. **Critical Thinking** If you were planning a snack for yourself and a friend who has diabetes, what foods would you select?
4. COMPARE AND CONTRAST Draw and complete this graphic organizer. Use the term on this list that tells best how cancer and heart diseases are alike: *noncommunicable, serious, deadly.*

5. **Write to Inform—Description**
   Suppose that one of your friends has just found out that he or she has cancer. Describe one or two ways you could show your friend that you care.

179

3. WRAP UP

Lesson 4 Summary and Review

1. Noncommunicable, arthritis, diabetes, Cancer
2. Animals, plants, medications, and certain foods can cause allergic reactions.
3. Raw vegetables, a little cheese and crackers, unpeeled fruits, some milk, or nuts might be good snack choices for a diabetic.
4. Responses may include:

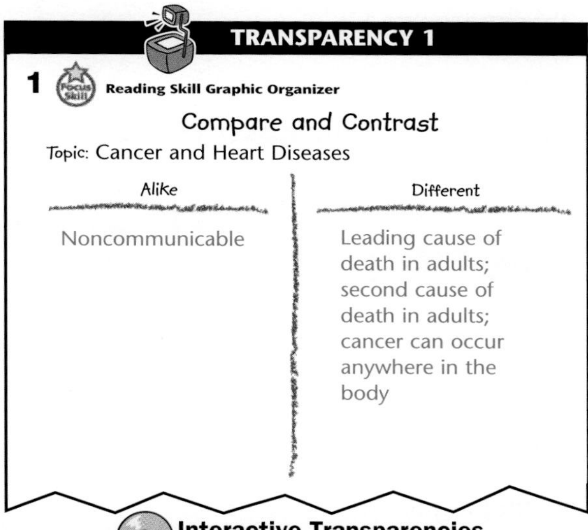

TRANSPARENCY 1
1 Reading Skill Graphic Organizer
Compare and Contrast
Topic: Cancer and Heart Diseases
Alike
Different
Noncommunicable
Leading cause of death in adults; second cause of death in adults; cancer can occur anywhere in the body

Interactive Transparencies available on CD-ROM.

5. Answers will vary, but students may mention including the friend in activities whenever possible, offering help if the friend needs it, and taking books and assignments to the friend when he or she has to miss school.

For **writing models** with examples, see *Teaching Resources* pp. 47–61. Rubrics are also provided.

When Minutes Count . . .

Quick Study Students can use *Activity Book* pages 31–32 (shown on p. 159) as they complete each lesson in this chapter.

Teacher Tip

Food Allergies Many students have allergies to common foods such as peanut butter, cow's milk, wheat, and berries. Students with specific food allergies might eat foods that are slightly different from those many other children eat (for example, cashew butter, soy milk, goat's milk, rice flour, or sunflower butter). Help prevent students with food allergies from feeling unusual or deprived because they are unable to eat certain foods.

Art

Health Brochures Have students create informational brochures about either heart disease, diabetes, or arthritis. Tell students to include a description of the disease and how it affects the body, precautions people who have the disease must take, and ways the disease can be treated or managed.

LESSON 5

Pages 180–182

Objectives

- Identify healthful lifestyle choices that help prevent illness.
- Understand how resistance, managing stress, and abstinence from tobacco help prevent disease.

When Minutes Count . . .

Assign the Quick Study, Lesson 5, Activity Book pp. 31–32 (shown on p. 159).

Program Resources

- Activity Book pp. 31–32, 35
- Transparency 1

Vocabulary

resistance p. 180, **abstinence** p. 182

Daily Fitness Tip

Mental fitness is as important as physical fitness in preventing illness and living a healthful lifestyle. Keep your attitude positive and healthful by getting plenty of sleep at night, eating regular balanced meals, and exercising regularly.

1. MOTIVATE

Help students create a healthful lifestyle checklist. Give each student an index card, and have him or her write *My Healthful Lifestyle Checklist* at the top of the card. Then have students use their answers to the following questions to complete their checklist.

What choices have you made so far today that will help you have a healthful lifestyle? Some students may respond that they had a healthful breakfast, got plenty of sleep, took a shower or bath, brushed their teeth, or exercised.

What things could you do to improve your healthful lifestyle? Some students may respond that they could make better food choices, go to bed earlier, or get more exercise.

Live a Healthful Lifestyle

Lesson Focus
A healthful lifestyle lowers your chances of getting ill.

Why Learn This?
Setting and meeting personal health goals and managing stress can help you feel good and stay well.

Vocabulary
resistance
abstinence

Ways to Stay Well

The choices you make about such things as what to eat and what activities to take part in all affect your health. A healthful lifestyle can help you stay well.

Eating healthful foods gives your body the energy that it needs to be active, fight diseases, and repair itself. Exercise helps prevent heart disease and some types of diabetes. It also helps your body fight off pathogens. Getting enough sleep helps your body grow and repair itself.

By making healthful lifestyle choices, you protect your body's resistance. **Resistance** (rih•ZIS•tuhnts) is your body's natural ability to fight off diseases on its own. The higher your resistance, the less often you will become ill, and the sooner you will get well when you do.

▲ What are these children doing to stay healthy and keep up their resistance?

180

Meeting Individual Needs
Leveled Activities

BELOW-LEVEL Healthful Lifestyle Posters Have students create posters that feature healthful lifestyle choices. Posters should be colorful and eye-catching. Suggest to students that they show at least three different choices that contribute to a healthful lifestyle.

ON-LEVEL Healthful Choices Skit Have students work in small groups to write and perform a skit that compares the results of a healthful lifestyle choice and a nonhealthful lifestyle choice. Students can perform their skits for their own class as well as for others.

CHALLENGE Take a Survey Have students survey at least 25 persons to see how they answer the following question: *What are the three most important ways to live a healthful lifestyle?* Students can compile the results of the survey and present their findings to the rest of the class.

▲ When Bobbie is feeling a lot of stress, she relaxes with a good book.

Quick Activity

Setting Goals Use the information in this lesson to help you set three personal-health goals for preventing illness. Write your goals on a poster, and post it in a place where you will see the goals every day.

Managing stress is another important part of a healthful lifestyle. Everybody has stress from time to time. Sometimes stress comes from outside, for example, from school. Other times stress comes from you. Perhaps you tell yourself that you're not smart enough. Stress you put on yourself can be the hardest of all.

It's important to know the difference between normal stress and unhealthful stress. Feeling a little nervous before a big game might help you play better. But feeling stressed all the time is the kind of stress you need to get rid of. Too much stress can reduce your body's resistance to disease and can make you ill.

DRAW CONCLUSIONS **Why might a person who has problems at home get colds more often than one who doesn't?**

Someone who is stressed might have lower resistance to disease than someone who is not stressed.

Consumer Activity

Accessing Valid Health Information A number of TV and magazine ads say that taking large amounts of vitamins will strengthen your resistance. Don't believe all the ads that you see. Talk with a parent or guardian or doctor before adding vitamins or minerals to your diet.

Language Arts

Short Stories Have students write a short story that describes how the main character turns unhealthful stress into positive stress. Encourage students to pick a source of stress that is familiar to them. Suggest that they illustrate their stories as well. Finished stories can be read aloud or displayed for other students to read.

2. TEACH

Interpret Visuals—Pictures

After students look at the picture on this page, have them discuss why reading is an activity that helps some people relax. **What are some other ways to relax?** Students might respond that walking the dog, listening to music, drawing, or chatting with friends helps them relax.

Quick Activity

Encourage students to choose goals that are realistic and obtainable. Remind them that they may want to revise or change their goals from time to time.

Consumer Activity

Remind students that media advertising may not be entirely truthful. Many claims about products in TV and magazine ads are not 100 percent accurate. Point out that before acting on any claim, you should investigate further. Check a valid health information source or talk to someone you can trust.

Health Background

Stress When a person is under stress, a number of physiological changes occur. Hormones such as adrenaline and cortisol are released. The heart beats faster and blood pressure increases. Blood moves quickly to the brain and muscles in order to help the person think and act quickly. This can be useful in the short term but dangerous in the long term. When a person is under prolonged stress, the brain and the rest of the body don't have time to recover. The stress can affect the heart, blood vessels, immune system, and digestive system. Long-term stress can cause heart disease, memory impairment, depression, and increased susceptibility to other diseases. There is also a lot of evidence that severe stress (such as that experienced during violent events like combat and abuse) can cause brain damage, resulting in conditions such as post-traumatic stress disorder, anxiety, depression, and dissociative disorders.

Source: *Emory University*

3. WRAP UP

Lesson 5 Summary and Review

1. resistance, healthful, exercise, Abstinence (or Abstaining)
2. Accept any answers that reflect healthful lifestyle choices.
3. Tobacco smoke causes some kinds of cancers and heart diseases. Smoke can also cause asthma attacks. Cigarette smoke can weaken the body's immune system.
4. Responses may include:

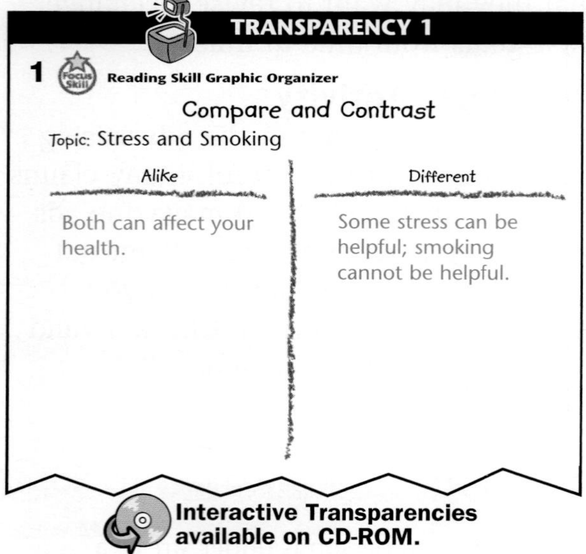

TRANSPARENCY 1

1 Reading Skill Graphic Organizer

Compare and Contrast

Topic: Stress and Smoking

Alike	Different
Both can affect your health.	Some stress can be helpful; smoking cannot be helpful.

Interactive Transparencies available on CD-ROM.

5. Responses will vary but should include information from this and previous lessons about healthful and unhealthful foods and the effects on health (including resistance to heart disease) of a high- or low-fat diet.

For **writing models** with examples, see *Teaching Resources* pp. 47–61. Rubrics are also provided.

When Minutes Count . . .

Quick Study Students can use *Activity Book* pages 31–32 (shown on p. 159) as they complete each lesson in this chapter.

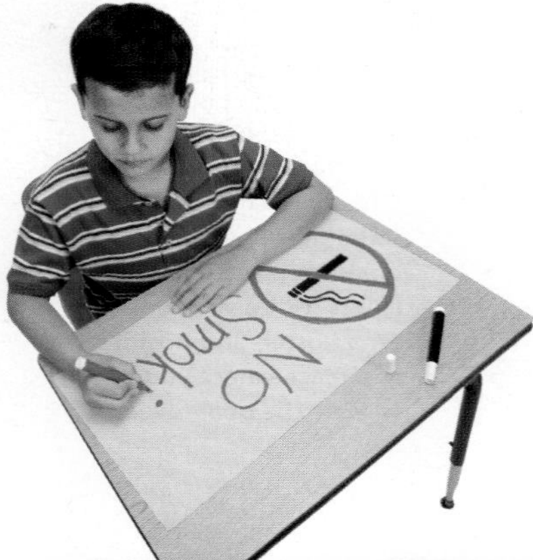

▼ Even if you don't smoke, avoiding tobacco smoke can be difficult. Jamal is making a poster to remind people that smoking is unhealthful for everyone.

Avoiding Tobacco

One of the most important things you can do to protect your health is to avoid tobacco. Smoking can cause many diseases, including cancer, heart disease, and asthma. It also weakens your resistance to disease.

People who choose not to use tobacco are practicing abstinence. **Abstinence** (AB•stuh•nuhnts) is avoiding a behavior that can harm the health. One reason it is important to abstain from tobacco is that it is addictive, or hard to give up. Practicing abstinence is a healthful lifestyle choice.

CAUSE AND EFFECT How does using tobacco affect a person's health?

Lesson 5 Summary and Review

1. **Summarize with Vocabulary**
   Use vocabulary and other terms from this lesson to complete the statements.
   You can increase your _____ to disease by making wise lifestyle choices. Choosing _____ foods and getting enough _____ are very important. Practicing _____ from tobacco is also important.
2. What things could you do to improve your body's resistance?
3. **Critical Thinking** If you know someone your age who smokes, what can you say to persuade and help that person to quit?
4. **COMPARE AND CONTRAST** Draw and complete this graphic organizer to show how the effects of stress and smoking are alike and different.

Topic: Stress and Smoking

Alike	Different

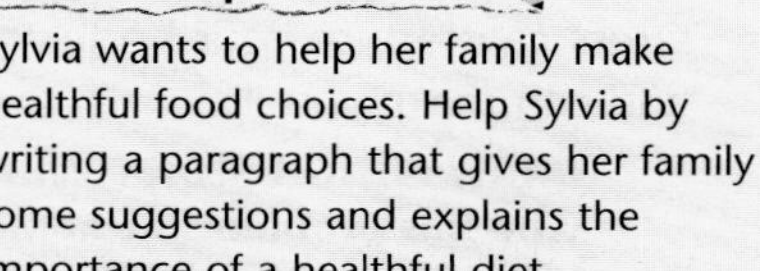

5. **Write to Express—Idea**
   Sylvia wants to help her family make healthful food choices. Help Sylvia by writing a paragraph that gives her family some suggestions and explains the importance of a healthful diet.

182 Smoking weakens resistance to disease. It can cause asthma, heart disease, and several forms of cancer.

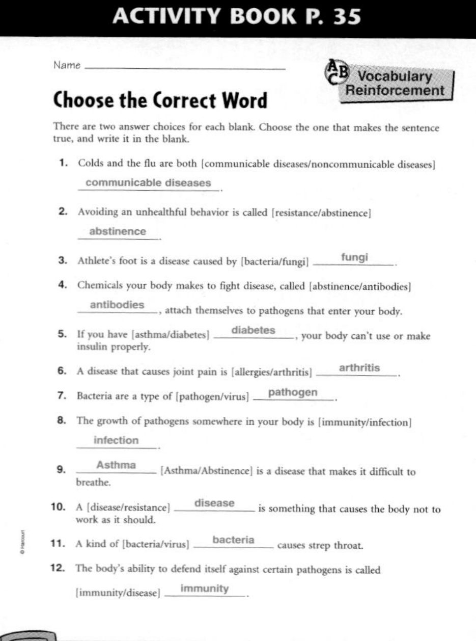

ACTIVITY BOOK P. 35

Name ____________

Vocabulary Reinforcement

Choose the Correct Word

There are two answer choices for each blank. Choose the one that makes the sentence true, and write it in the blank.

1. Colds and the flu are both [communicable diseases/noncommunicable diseases] communicable diseases.
2. Avoiding an unhealthful behavior is called [resistance/abstinence] abstinence.
3. Athlete's foot is a disease caused by [bacteria/fungi] fungi.
4. Chemicals your body makes to fight disease, called [abstinence/antibodies] antibodies, attach themselves to pathogens that enter your body.
5. If you have [asthma/diabetes] diabetes, your body can't use or make insulin properly.
6. A disease that causes joint pain is [allergies/arthritis] arthritis.
7. Bacteria are a type of [pathogen/virus] pathogen.
8. The growth of pathogens somewhere in your body is [immunity/infection] infection.
9. Asthma [Asthma/Abstinence] is a disease that makes it difficult to breathe.
10. A [disease/resistance] disease is something that causes the body not to work as it should.
11. A kind of [bacteria/virus] bacteria causes strep throat.
12. The body's ability to defend itself against certain pathogens is called [immunity/disease] immunity.

© Harcourt

Available online. www.harcourtschool.com/health

ACTIVITIES

Science

Research Bacteria Most bacteria are not pathogens. In fact, many bacteria in our bodies actually protect us from diseases. Research good bacteria. Find out how some of these bacteria help us. Use an encyclopedia or other library resource in your research. Present your findings in an oral report.

Home & Community

Communicating Talk with your family about what you've learned about good health habits and how they can keep pathogens from spreading. Write on note cards two or three of the health habits that you discuss. Post the note cards on the refrigerator or another place where family members will see them and be reminded to act healthfully.

Math

Calculate the Cost If one pack of cigarettes costs $4.00, how much would it cost to smoke one pack of cigarettes every day for one year? For two years? How much would it cost to smoke two packs of cigarettes every day for one year? For two years?

Career Link

Licensed Practical Nurse (LPN)
Under the guidance of physicians or registered nurses, licensed practical nurses care for sick or injured people. Many LPNs work in nursing homes. Suppose that you are an LPN working in a nursing home. You provide care for a woman who has arthritis. The woman feels sad because she misses living in her own home. Write some tips to help your patient manage her disease and handle her stress.

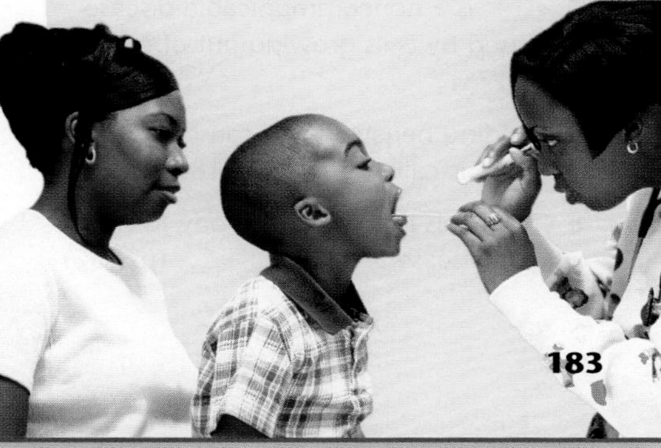

Technology Project

Use a computer to make a slide presentation of about seven tips for creating a healthful lifestyle. Present your slide show to your classmates and family.

For more activities, visit The Learning Site. www.harcourtschool.com/health

183

Activities

Science

One example of a helpful bacterium is lactobacillus, which helps the digestive system process dairy products. Encourage students to include images of the bacteria they chose for their reports.

Math

Research the current price of a pack of cigarettes to be sure students are using an accurate price. Emphasize to students what the financial impact of a habit such as smoking can be. Help students think of other, more beneficial items for which the money spent on cigarettes could be used.

Home & Community

Suggest to students that they invite other family members to suggest their own healthful habits to include on the note cards.

Supports the Coordinated School Health Program

Technology Project

Have students present their slide shows to the rest of the class. Afterward, guide students in a class discussion about healthful lifestyle tips. Other grades might also benefit.

Career Link

Licensed Practical Nurse (LPN) Students might say that they would find out what the patient misses most about her home. Perhaps similar items could be brought to her nursing-home room. It might also help to know what kind of music, books, or activities the patient enjoys. By including these things in the patient's environment, she may not feel as lonely. Having the patient engage in light movement or exercise would help manage her illness.

GO ONLINE For more information on health careers, visit the **Webliography** in Teacher Resources at **www.harcourtschool.com/health**
Keyword health careers

Chapter Review and Test Preparation

Pages 184–185

Reading Skill 5 pts. each

1. Both are diseases.
2. Communicable diseases can be spread from person to person; noncommunicable diseases cannot be spread from person to person.

Use Vocabulary 5 pts. each

3. pathogens
4. immune
5. symptoms
6. Cancer
7. abstinence
8. antibodies
9. disease
10. vaccines
11. Arthritis

Check Understanding 5 pts. each

12. C, cilia
13. G, resistance
14. A, fungi
15. F, [fruits/vegetables]

Think Critically 5 pts. each

16. Ted will not get allergies from Marianne because allergies are noncommunicable diseases. Allergies are not caused by pathogens, so Marianne's allergies cannot be spread when she sneezes.
17. Because heart disease runs in Matt's family, he has a greater chance of getting it than people in families where heart disease is rare. Matt can lower his risk by making healthful lifestyle choices; for example, by eating a diet that is low in fat and abstaining from the use of tobacco.

Chapter Review and Test Preparation

Reading Skill

COMPARE AND CONTRAST

Draw and then use this graphic organizer to answer questions 1 and 2.

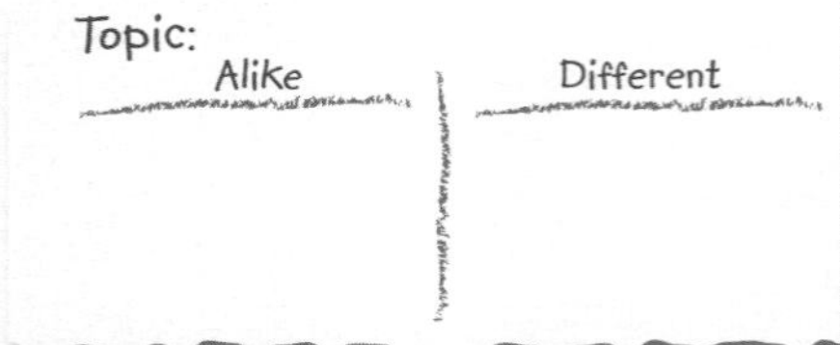

1 Write how communicable and noncommunicable diseases are alike.

2 Write how communicable and noncommunicable diseases are different.

Use Vocabulary

Use a term from this chapter to complete each sentence.

3 Communicable diseases are caused by _____. (p. 162)

4 The body system that fights disease is the _____ system. (p. 166)

5 Signs or physical feelings of disease are _____. (p. 166)

6 _____ is a noncommunicable disease caused by cells growing out of control. (p. 175)

7 Avoiding behavior that can harm your health is called _____. (p. 182)

8 Chemicals made by the body to help fight disease are called _____. (p. 167)

9 An illness is a(n) _____. (p. 158)

10 Substances made to prevent certain diseases are called _____. (p. 170)

11 _____ is a noncommunicable disease in which one or more of the body's joints become swollen and painful. (p. 179)

Check Understanding

Choose the letter of the correct answer.

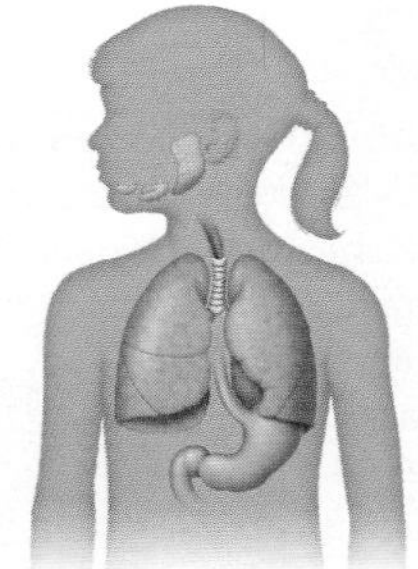

12 Small hairs that line the body's air passages are called _____. (p. 167)

A saliva **C** cilia
B mucus **D** fur

13 Your body's natural ability to fight off diseases on its own is called _____. (p. 180)

F antibody **H** defense
G resistance **J** immunity

184

Formal Assessment

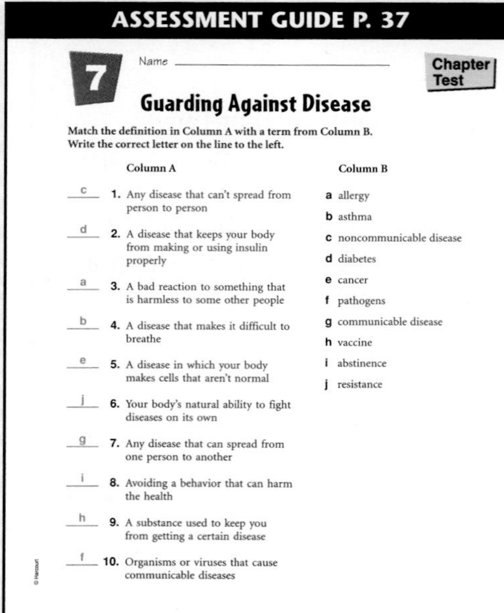

ASSESSMENT GUIDE P. 37

7 Name ____________ Chapter Test

Guarding Against Disease

Match the definition in Column A with a term from Column B. Write the correct letter on the line to the left.

	Column A	Column B
c	1. Any disease that can't spread from person to person	a allergy
d	2. A disease that keeps your body from making or using insulin properly	b asthma
a	3. A bad reaction to something that is harmless to some other people	c noncommunicable disease
b	4. A disease that makes it difficult to breathe	d diabetes
e	5. A disease in which your body makes cells that aren't normal	e cancer
j	6. Your body's natural ability to fight diseases on its own	f pathogens
g	7. Any disease that can spread from one person to another	g communicable disease
i	8. Avoiding a behavior that can harm the health	h vaccine
h	9. A substance used to keep you from getting a certain disease	i abstinence
f	10. Organisms or viruses that cause communicable diseases	j resistance

© Harcourt

ASSESSMENT GUIDE P. 38

Name ____________

Write the letter of the correct answer on the line at the left.

C 11. The body system that fights disease is the _____.
A pathogen C immune system
B infection D vaccine

J 12. _____ is a noncommunicable disease that causes joint pain.
F Asthma H Antibodies
G Allergies J Arthritis

A 13. Which of these can be used to prevent a certain disease?
A vaccine C infection
B diabetes D pathogens

G 14. The growth of pathogens in your body causes _____.
F allergy H asthma
G infection J cancer

A 15. Pinkeye, ear infections, and strep throat are caused by _____.
A bacteria C vaccines
B viruses D fungi

Write *T* or *F* to tell if the statements are true or false.

F 16. Asthma is a communicable disease.

T 17. White blood cells are a part of the immune system.

T 18. Abstinence from tobacco is a healthful decision.

T 19. Some kinds of fungi are pathogens.

T 20. Too much stress can reduce your body's resistance to disease.

© Harcourt

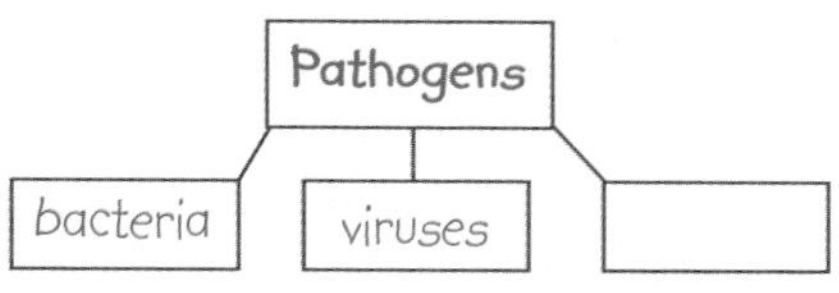

14 What pathogens are missing from the graphic organizer? (p. 163)
A fungi
B vaccine
C insulin
D mucus

15 If you are trying to prevent the spread of pathogens, which of these should you do? (p. 169)

F 

H 

G 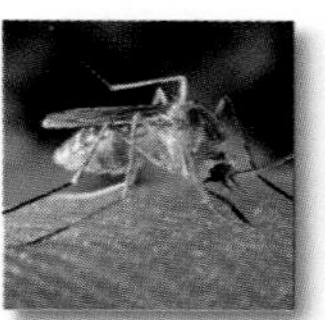

J 

Think Critically

16 Marianne has allergies. If Marianne sneezes on Ted, will he get allergies too? Explain your answer.

17 Several people in Matt's family have heart disease. Describe Matt's chances of getting heart disease. Tell how Matt can lower his chances.

Apply Skills

18  **LIFE SKILLS**
Manage Stress Suppose you are nervous about going onstage in your first play. Explain what you could do to feel more relaxed.

19 **BUILDING GOOD CHARACTER**
Caring After studying this chapter, you decide to help your friends and family take better care of their health. What are some ways that you can set a good example?

Write About Health

20 **Write to Inform—Explanation** Amy needs a booster shot, but she is scared. She has complained so much that her mom is about to give in and let Amy put off the booster. Write a note explaining why Amy needs to get her booster on time.

185

ASSESSMENT GUIDE P. 39

Name ____________

21. Describe one thing every person can do to help prevent skin cancer.
Possible answer: Using sunscreen can help reduce the chance of getting skin cancer.

Draw two pictures, each showing something you can do to increase your body's resistance to disease. Under each picture, write a sentence describing what you have drawn.

22. Possible answer: Eat a healthful diet.

23. Possible answer: Get plenty of exercise.

Pathogens can easily spread from person to person in the classroom. Strep throat, pinkeye, flu, and colds are all commonly spread from person to person in schools.

24. Write a paragraph that describes ways that pathogens spread from person to person in a classroom.
Possible answer: Pathogens spread from person to person in several ways. For example, if I use someone's pencil, and that person is ill, the pathogens can get onto my hands. Coughing and sneezing can also spread pathogens from person to person.

25. Describe one way to reduce the number of pathogens passed from person to person in the classroom.
Possible answers: regular hand washing; staying home when sick; not sharing hats, drinking glasses, and so on

Apply Skills 5 pts. each

18. Answers will vary but should refer to the stress-managing steps. Possible answer: You could recognize that you are feeling stress, perhaps because many people will be watching; pretend that you are performing at home, and tell yourself that you are going to give your best performance ever.

19. Answers will vary but may include choosing healthful foods, getting regular exercise, and managing stress by thinking positively.

Write About Health 5 pts.

20. Students should point out that getting a booster on time is important for Amy to keep her own immunity and to protect others from the disease. Some students may mention the importance of cooperating with parents and health-care providers to stay well.

Performance Assessment

Use the Chapter Project and the rubric provided on the Project Evaluation Sheet. See *Assessment Guide* pp. 18, 59, 68.

Portfolio Assessment

Have students select their best work from the following suggestions:

- Leveled Activities, p. 166
- Quick Activity, p. 168
- Write to Inform, p. 171
- Activities, p. 183
- See *Assessment Guide* pp. 12–16.

CHAPTER 8

Medicines, Drugs, and Your Health

Lesson	Pacing	Objectives	Reading Skills
Introduce the Chapter pp. 186–187		• Preview chapter concepts.	**Summarize** pp. 187, 340–341
1 **Medicines Affect the Body** pp. 188–193	3 class periods	• Recognize that medicines are drugs that help the body. • Distinguish between prescription and over-the-counter medicines.	**Summarize** pp. 189, 192, 193 • Sequence, p. 190 • Cause and Effect, p. 191
2 **Substances That Can Be Harmful** pp. 194–197	1 class period	• Recognize that some common substances, such as caffeine and OTC medicines, can be addictive. • Describe the harmful effects of caffeine and inhalants.	**Summarize** pp. 195, 197 • Draw Conclusions, p. 196 • Cause and Effect, p. 197
Life Skills pp. 198–199	1 class period	• Identify skills needed to refuse OTC medicines. • Use refusal skills to say *no* to over-the-counter medicines.	
3 **Marijuana and Cocaine** pp. 200–204	3 class periods	• Recognize the dangerous effects of marijuana and cocaine. • Recognize that cocaine use can lead to immediate addiction.	**Summarize** pp. 201, 204 • Draw Conclusions, pp. 202, 204 • Compare and Contrast, p. 203
Building Good Character p. 205		• Demonstrate responsibility by recognizing the importance of practicing self-control.	
4 **Refusing Drugs** pp. 206–209	1 class period	• Explain why saying *no* to drugs is a healthful decision. • Demonstrate how to say *no* to illegal drugs.	**Summarize** pp. 207, 209
5 **How Drug Abusers Can Get Help** pp. 210–212	1 class period	• Recognize the warning signs of drug use. • Identify people and organizations that can help with drug recovery.	**Summarize** pp. 210, 212 • Draw Conclusions, p. 212
Activities p. 213		• Extend chapter concepts.	
Chapter Review pp. 214–215	1 class period	• Assess chapter objectives.	

Vocabulary	Program Resources
	Music CD Teaching Resources, p. 37
medicine drug side effects prescription prescription medicines over-the-counter medicines dose expiration date	Transparency 6 Activity Book, pp. 36–38
addiction caffeine inhalants	Transparency 6 Activity Book, pp. 36–37
	Activity Book, p. 39 Poster 10
illegal drug marijuana drug dependence cocaine	Transparency 6 Activity Book, pp. 36–37
	Poster 5
self-respect peer pressure	Transparency 6 Activity Book, pp. 36–37
	Transparency 6 Activity Book, pp. 36–37, 40
	The Learning Site www.harcourtschool.com
	Assessment Guide, pp. 40–42

Interactive Transparencies available on CD-ROM.

Reading Skill

These reading skills are reinforced throughout this chapter and one skill is emphasized as the Focus Skill.

Summarize

- Draw Conclusions
- Identify Cause and Effect
- Identify Main Idea and Details
- Sequence
- Summarize

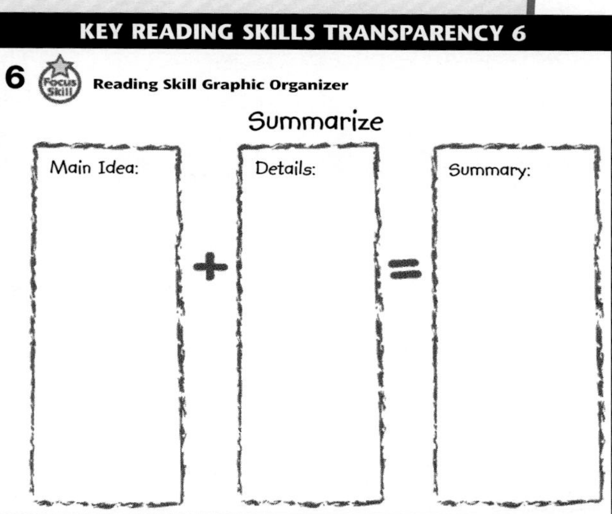

Life Skills

Life Skills are health-enhancing behaviors that can help students reduce risks to their health and safety.

Six Life Skills are reinforced throughout *Harcourt Health and Fitness*. The skill emphasized in this chapter is Refuse.

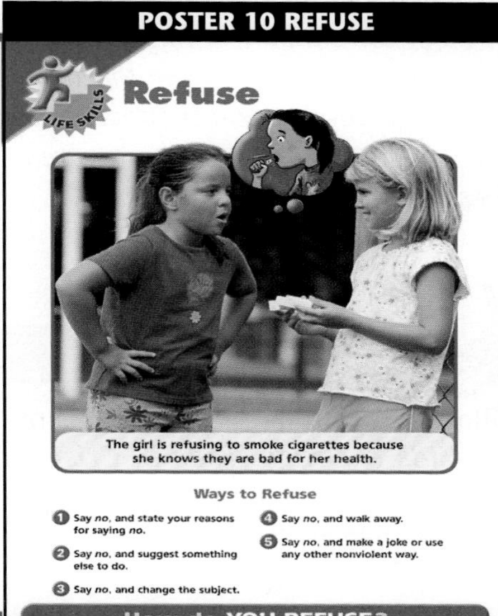

POSTER 10 REFUSE
Refuse
The girl is refusing to smoke cigarettes because she knows they are bad for her health.
Ways to Refuse
1 Say no, and state your reasons for saying no.
2 Say no, and suggest something else to do.
3 Say no, and change the subject.
4 Say no, and walk away.
5 Say no, and make a joke or use any other nonviolent way.
How do YOU REFUSE?

Building Good Character
The girls are showing responsibility by choosing the smallest bag of popcorn.
Express feelings, needs, and wants in appropriate ways.

Character education is an important aspect of health education. When children behave in ways that show good character, they promote the health and safety of themselves and others.

Six character traits are reinforced throughout *Harcourt Health and Fitness*. The trait emphasized in this chapter is Responsiblity.

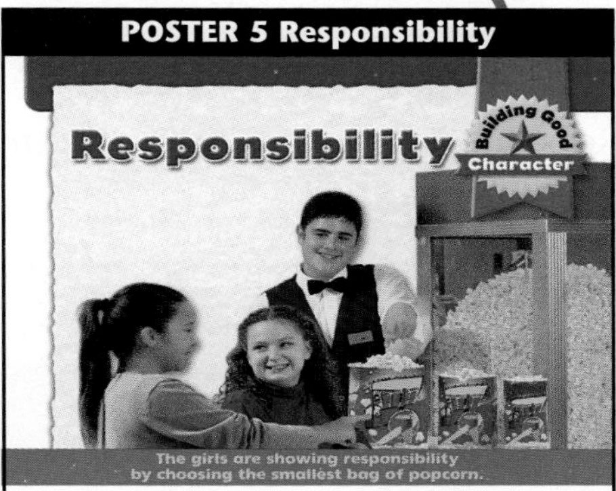

Keep yourself safe.
Keep trying. Do your best.
Complete tasks.
Set goals and work toward them.

Don't do things that are unsafe or that destroy property.

Don't deny or make excuses for your mistakes.
Don't leave your work for others to do.
Don't lose or misuse your belongings.

Resources

Coordinated School Health Program

Health Education
Health Services
Physical Education
Nutrition Services
Parent/ Community Involvement
Healthy School Environment
Counseling, Psychological, & Social Services
Health Promotion for Staff
CSHP

A Coordinated School Health Program endeavors to improve children's health and therefore their capacity to learn through the support of families, schools, and communities working together. The following information is provided to help classroom teachers be more aware of these resources.

The National Institute of Drug Abuse (**NIDA**), an arm of the National Institutes of Health (NIH) offers the guide *Preventing Drug Use Among Children and Adolescents.* This guide provides important research-based concepts and information to develop and carry out effective drug abuse prevention programs.
www.health.nih.gov/

The **American Junior Red Cross** invites students to participate in Youth Volunteer programs, including Community Services. They can serve as mentors to peers or younger children on substance abuse prevention and other major youth issues.
www.redcross.org/services/youth/

The ***Science-Based Program****, Too Good for Drugs,* has been identified as a research-based model program for the prevention of alcohol and tobacco use. For this and other exemplary programs, visit the Center for Substance Abuse Prevention: Model Programs.
http://modelprograms.samhsa.gov/

Other resources that support a Coordinated School Health Program:
- School-Home Connection
- Daily Physical Activity
- Daily Fitness Tips
- Activities: Home & Community
- Health Background: Webliography
- *Be Active! Resources for Physical Education*

Media Resources

Books for Students

Dilaura, Cynthia, and M. D. Devore. ***Kids & Drugs (Kids in Crisis).*** Abdo Publishing, 1994. Description of drugs with a narrative illustration. **EASY**

Sanders, Pete, and Steve Myers. ***What Do You Know About Drugs?*** Gloucester Press, 2000. Uses color photos and cartoons to address the issue of drug abuse. **AVERAGE**

Royston, Angela. ***Inhalants (Learn to Say No!).*** Heinemann Library, 2000. Discusses inhaling substances and the risks involved. **ADVANCED**

Books for Teachers and Families

Kuhn, Cynthia; Scott Swartzwelder, Ph.D.; Wilkie Wilson, Ph.D. ***Just Say Know: Talking with Kids About Drugs and Alcohol.*** W. W. Norton, 2002. Enforces reasons for staying healthy and making the right decisions.

Thomas, Peggy. ***Medicines from Nature.*** Twenty-First Century Books, 1997. A fascinating text on new and more effective medications.

Free and Inexpensive Materials

National Clearinghouse for Alcohol and Drug Information
Ask for free copies of the research-based guide, *Preventing Drug Use Among Children and Adolescents.*

Social Studies School Service
Ask for its Health Education catalog containing topics such as drug prevention activities.

Central Intelligence Agency
Has a Homepage for Kids on topics such as heroin and CIA drug-related publications such as *From Flowers to Heroin.*

To access free and inexpensive resources on the Web, visit
www.harcourtschool.com/health/free

Videos

You Can Refuse. Comprehensive Health Education, 1991.

Inhalants. United Learning, 1998.

The Boy Who Was Swallowed by the Drug Monster. STARS, 1994.

These resources have been selected to meet a variety of individual needs. Please review all materials and websites prior to sharing them with students to ensure the content is appropriate for your class. Note that information, while correct at time of publication, is subject to change.

Visit **The Learning Site** for related links, activities, resources, and the health **Webliography.**

www.harcourtschool.com/health

Meeting Individual Needs

Below-Level

Study strategies help students retain what they've read. Make cards showing the letters **K**, **W**, and **L** to stand for *What I **K**now*, *What I **W**ant to Know*, and *What I **L**earned*. Hold up a card at the proper time during a lesson as students write their responses.

Activities

- Perform a Skit, p. 190
- Write Acrostics, p. 194
- Write Poems, p. 202
- Make a Picture Album, p. 208

On-Level

When students adjust their reading rate, they can often comprehend more facts and details in a nonfiction passage. Explain that a selection that includes a lot of facts and details should be read more slowly than a passage that is intended for entertainment.

Activities

- Make Labels, p. 190
- Research Substance Abuse, p. 194
- Evaluate Gateway Drugs, p. 202
- Make Flash Cards, p. 208

Challenge

Challenge students to locate information in text quickly. Give students a list of vocabulary terms and provide self-stick notes. Have students race a partner to skim the selection for the terms, placing a note on each word after locating it.

Activities

- Identify Reliable Sources, p. 190
- Make a Graphic Organizer, p. 194
- Drugs and Creativity, p. 202
- Write Ads, p. 208

ESL/ELL

Reading Workshop

Challenge students to locate information in text quickly. Give students a list of vocabulary terms and provide self-stick notes. Have students race a partner to skim the selection for the terms, placing a note on each word after locating it.

Activities

- Language and Vocabulary, p. 196
- Comprehensible Input, pp. 201, 207
- Background and Experience, p. 210

Curriculum Integration

Use these topics to integrate health into your daily planning.

Integrated Language Arts/Reading Skills

- Exploring Personal Benefits, p. 203
- Make a Semantic Map, p. 203
- Conduct an Interview, p. 204
- Say *No* with Humor, p. 209

Math

- Cost Per Dose, p. 191
- Costs of Illegal Drug Use, p. 204

Physical Education

- Daily Fitness Tip, pp. 188, 194, 200, 206, 210
- Daily Physical Activity, p. 187

Drama

- Act Out a Skit, p. 198
- Now Hear This, p. 211

Social Studies

- Food and Drug Administration, p. 195
- Laws and Drug Use, p. 200
- Media Messages, p. 206

CHAPTER

Pages 186–215

CHAPTER SUMMARY

In this chapter, students

- ► learn the rules for safe over-the-counter medicine and prescription medicine use.
- ► learn how medicines, caffeine, and inhalants affect the body in harmful ways.
- ► learn about the harmful effects of illegal drugs, including marijuana and cocaine, and how to say *no* to anyone who offers these drugs.

Life Skills
Students practice *refusing* to use over-the-counter medicines.

Building Good Character
Students show *responsibility* by practicing self-control.

Consumer Health
Students *make a buying decision* after comparing the costs of OTC medicines.

Literature Springboard

Use the selection "How Medicine Came" from *The Circle of Thanks: Native American Poems and Songs of Thanksgiving* to spark interest in the chapter topic. See the Read-Aloud Anthology on page RA-9 of this *Teacher Edition.*

Prereading Strategies

SCAN THE CHAPTER Have students preview the chapter content by scanning the titles, headings, pictures, and graphs. Ask them to predict what they will learn. Use their predictions to determine their prior knowledge.

PREVIEW VOCABULARY Have students look up unfamiliar words in the Glossary.

CHAPTER 8

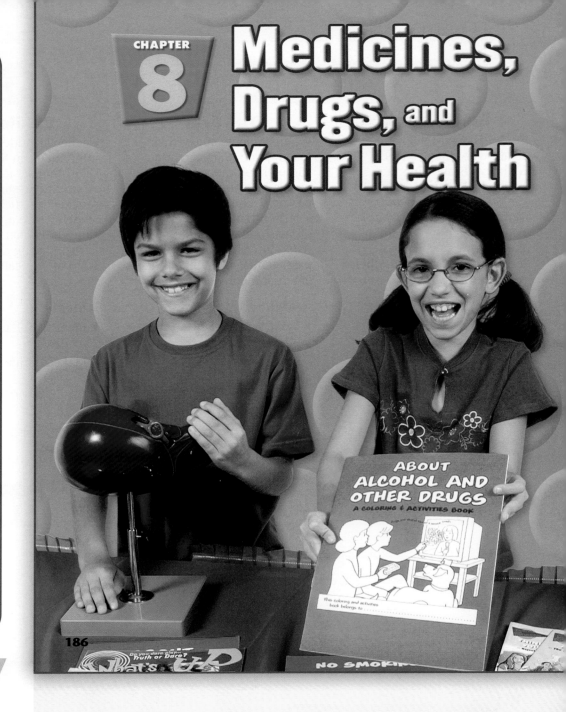

Medicines, Drugs, and Your Health

186

Reading Skill

SUMMARIZE To introduce or review this skill, have students use the Reading in Health Handbook, pp. 340–341. Teaching strategies and additional activities are also provided.

Students will have opportunities to practice and apply this skill throughout this chapter.

- Focus Skill Reading Mini-Lesson, p. 188
- Reading comprehension questions identified with the 
- *Activity Book* p. 38 (shown on p. 193)
- Lesson Summary and Review, pp. 193, 197, 204, 209, 212
- Chapter Review and Test Preparation, pp. 214–215

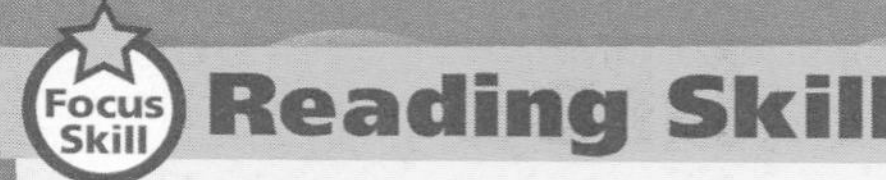

Reading Skill

SUMMARIZE A summary is a short statement that includes the main ideas and most important details in a passage. Use the Reading in Health Handbook on pages 340–341 and this graphic organizer to help you read the health facts in this chapter.

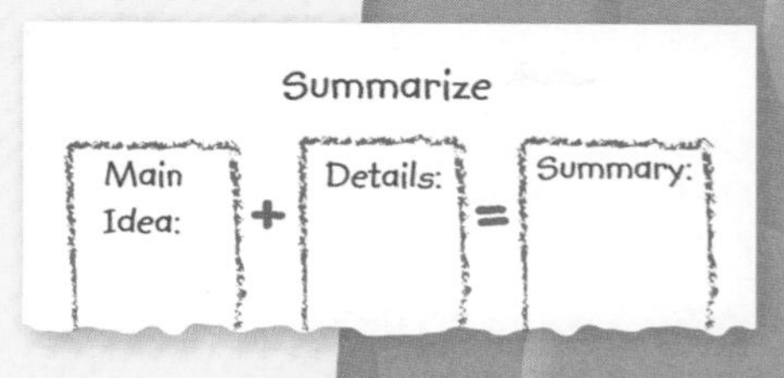

Health Graph

INTERPRET DATA Did you ever hear "Everyone is doing it"? Information about marijuana use among students ages 12 to 17 tells a different story. Do most teenagers use marijuana? What does this graph tell you?

Marijuana Use Among Students
Ages 12–17

	Number of Marijuana Users per 100 Students
Ever	about 28
Past year	about 21
Past 30 days	about 11

Daily Physical Activity

Keep your body healthy. Stay active and drug free.

Be Active! Use the selection Track 8, **Jumping and Pumping**, make your body feel better.

INTRODUCE THE CHAPTER

Health Graph

Interpret Data

Ask volunteers to describe the information presented in the graph.

Do most teenagers use marijuana? Less than one-third of the students have ever tried marijuana. So, most teenagers in this age group do NOT use marijuana.

Draw students' attention to the Focus Reading Skill. Ask a volunteer to read aloud the description of a summary.

Critical Thinking Summarize what the graph tells about marijuana use among 12–17-year-olds. Less than one-third of them have ever tried marijuana, even fewer have tried it in the last year, and only 11 percent have used it in the last month. From this information, you can summarize that most young people have not, and do not, use marijuana.

Daily Physical Activity

Use *Be Active! Music for Daily Physical Activity* with the Instant Activity Cards to provide students with movement activities that can be done in limited space. Options for using these components are provided beginning on page TR2 in this *Teacher Edition.*

School-Home Connection

Distribute copies of the School-Home Connection (in English or Spanish). Have students take the page home to share with their families as you begin this chapter.

Follow Up Have volunteers share the results of their activities.

Supports the Coordinated School Health Program

TEACHING RESOURCES P. 37

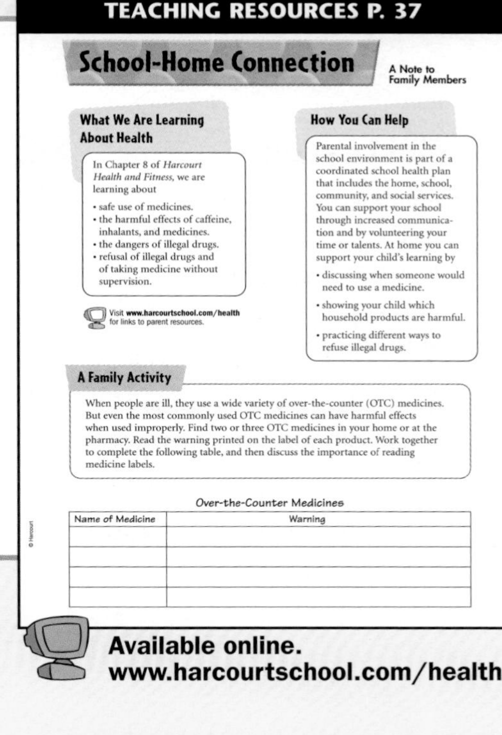

School-Home Connection — A Note to Family Members

What We Are Learning About Health

In Chapter 8 of *Harcourt Health and Fitness*, we are learning about
- safe use of medicines.
- the harmful effects of caffeine, inhalants, and medicines.
- the dangers of illegal drugs.
- refusal of illegal drugs and of taking medicine without supervision.

Visit www.harcourtschool.com/health for links to parent resources.

How You Can Help

Parental involvement in the school environment is part of a coordinated school health plan that includes the home, school, community, and social services. You can support your school through increased communication and by volunteering your time or talents. At home you can support your child's learning by
- discussing when someone would need to use a medicine.
- showing your child which household products are harmful.
- practicing different ways to refuse illegal drugs.

A Family Activity

When people are ill, they use a wide variety of over-the-counter (OTC) medicines. But even the most commonly used OTC medicines can have harmful effects when used improperly. Find two or three OTC medicines in your home or at the pharmacy. Read the warning printed on the label of each product. Work together to complete the following table, and then discuss the importance of reading medicine labels.

Over-the-Counter Medicines

Name of Medicine	Warning

Available online.
www.harcourtschool.com/health

Chapter Project

Drug Alert (*Assessment Guide* p. 59)

ASSESS PRIOR KNOWLEDGE Use students' initial ideas for the project as a baseline assessment of their understanding of chapter concepts. Have students complete the project as they work through the chapter.

PERFORMANCE ASSESSMENT The project can be used for performance assessment. Use the Project Evaluation Sheet (rubric), *Assessment Guide* p. 69.

LESSON 1

Pages 188–193

Objectives

- ► Recognize that medicines are drugs that help the body.
- ► Distinguish between prescription and over-the-counter medicines.

When Minutes Count . . .

Assign the Quick Study, Lesson 1, Activity Book pp. 36–37 (shown on p. 189).

Program Resources

- ► Activity Book pp. 36–38
- ► Transparency 6

Vocabulary

medicine p. 188, **drug** p. 188, **side effects** p. 189, **prescription** p. 190, **prescription medicines** p. 190, **over-the-counter medicines** p. 191, **dose** p. 191, **expiration date** p. 192

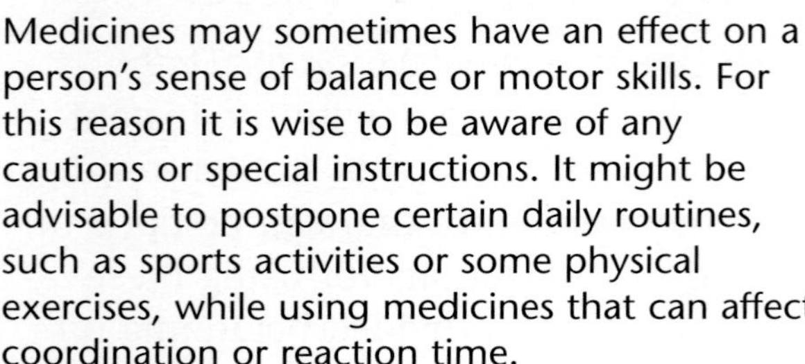

Daily Fitness Tip

Medicines may sometimes have an effect on a person's sense of balance or motor skills. For this reason it is wise to be aware of any cautions or special instructions. It might be advisable to postpone certain daily routines, such as sports activities or some physical exercises, while using medicines that can affect coordination or reaction time.

1. MOTIVATE

Think of a time when you didn't feel well. What did you do to feel better? Possible answers: went to bed, rested, and took medicine

When your parent or guardian gives you a medicine, what might you want to know about it? Possible answer: what the medicine will taste like

Tell students that in this lesson they will learn answers to questions they may have about medicines.

LESSON 1 Medicines Affect the Body

Lesson Focus
Medicines can be helpful if they are used properly.

Why Learn This?
Learning how to use medicines safely can help you stay healthy.

Vocabulary
medicine
drug
side effects
prescription
prescription medicine
over-the-counter medicines
dose
expiration date

Medicines Are Drugs

Has a parent or guardian ever given you a pill for a cold or put antibiotic cream on a cut? Then you have some idea of what a medicine is.

A **medicine** (MED•uh•suhn) is a drug used to prevent, treat, or cure a health problem. A **drug** is a substance other than food that changes the way the body works. All medicines are drugs, but not all drugs are medicines. Pain relievers and antibiotic creams are medicines. Drugs that are not medicines do not prevent, treat, or cure health problems. Instead, they can cause health problems and if misused can hurt you.

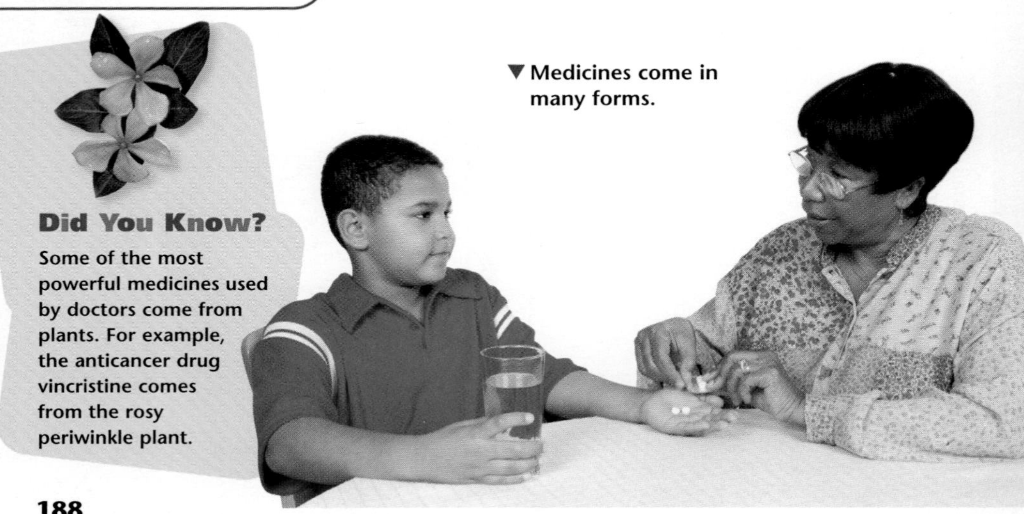

▼ Medicines come in many forms.

Did You Know?
Some of the most powerful medicines used by doctors come from plants. For example, the anticancer drug vincristine comes from the rosy periwinkle plant.

188

Reading Skill

Mini-Lesson

SUMMARIZE Remind students that a summary is a short statement that includes the main idea and most important details in a passage. Have them practice this skill by answering the Focus Skill question on page 189. Have students draw and complete the graphic organizer as you model it on the transparency.

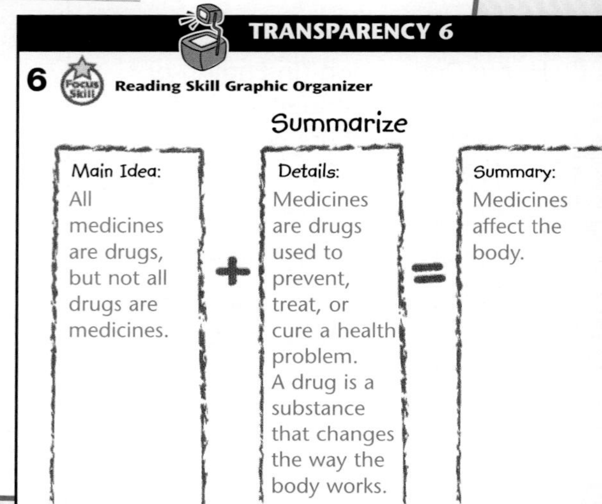

TRANSPARENCY 6
6 Reading Skill Graphic Organizer
Summarize
Main Idea:
All medicines are drugs, but not all drugs are medicines.
+
Details:
Medicines are drugs used to prevent, treat, or cure a health problem.
A drug is a substance that changes the way the body works.
=
Summary:
Medicines affect the body.

Interactive Transparencies available on CD-ROM.

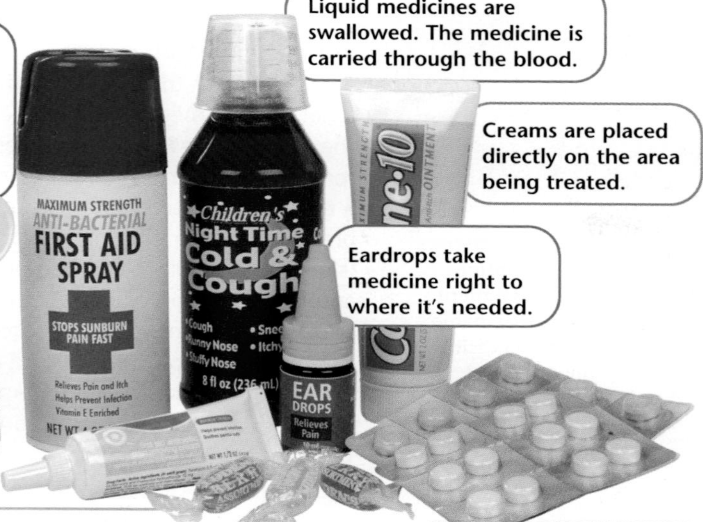

The medicine in some sprays is breathed in. An inhaler is used to take the medicine into the lungs.
Liquid medicines are swallowed. The medicine is carried through the blood.
Creams are placed directly on the area being treated.
Eardrops take medicine right to where it's needed.
Sucking on these cough drops releases medicine right where it's needed, to help you feel better.
Some pills are chewed, then swallowed. The medicine dissolves in the stomach and is carried through the blood.
MAXIMUM STRENGTH
ANTI-BACTERIAL
FIRST AID
SPRAY
STOPS SUNBURN PAIN FAST
Children's
Night Time
Cold &
Cough
EAR
DROPS
Relieves
Pain

▲ Medicines come in many forms. The way a medicine is used depends on its purpose.

When you are hurt or ill, your parents or other trusted adults decide if you need medicine. They decide how much and what kind of medicine to give you. They teach you to use medicines properly so that when you are old enough to take them yourself, they do not harm you.

Even when used properly, medicines may have side effects. **Side effects** are unwanted changes in the body caused by a medicine. Doctors and pharmacists can tell you about a medicine's side effects. Most are not harmful. If you feel worse after taking a medicine, always tell a trusted adult.

Myth and Fact

Myth: Medicines are different from drugs.

Fact: The word *drug* can refer to medicines—helpful drugs that cure or treat illness. Other times, the word *drug* refers to substances that do not help or prevent illness, but can harm the user.

Focus Skill **SUMMARIZE Explain the similarities and the differences between medicines and drugs.**

Medicines are drugs used to prevent, treat, or cure a health problem. Drugs are substances other than food that change the way the body works, and do not prevent, treat, or cure health problems, but cause them.

2. TEACH

Discuss

Draw students' attention to the pictures and captions of the various forms of medicines. **How do liquid medicines and pills work differently from eardrops and cough drops?** Liquid medicines and pills carry medicine through the body, while eardrops and cough drops release medicine right where it is needed.

Critical Thinking Why might you have side effects from a medicine, and what should you do if you notice any? Sometimes a medicine will cause an unwanted change in the body. If you notice any side effects from a medicine, you should tell a trusted adult.

Health Background

Medicines That Cause Problems The Food and Drug Administration (FDA) often issues an alert about any problems caused by a particular medicine. It sometimes recommends that the medicine be removed from the market. The news media usually alert the public when this happens, and alerts are posted on the FDA website as well. People taking a medicine for which an alert has been issued should consult their doctors to find out how a medicine change will affect their treatment.

Source: *United States Food and Drug Administration website*

For more background, visit the **Webliography** in Teacher Resources at **www.harcourtschool.com/health**
Keyword medicines

QUICK STUDY, ACTIVITY BOOK PP. 36–37

CHAPTER 8 Name ____________ Quick Study

Medicines, Drugs, and Your Health

Directions
- Use lesson vocabulary in the Word Bank to complete each **Summary**.
- Read the directions provided to complete each **Lesson Details**.

Word Bank

addiction	dose	expiration date	marijuana	prescription
caffeine	drug	illegal drug	peer pressure	recovery
cocaine	drug dependence	inhalants	over-the-counter medicines	self-respect

Lesson 1 pp. 188–193

Summary A ___drug___ changes the way the body works. ___Over-the-counter medicines___, which you can buy at the store, and ___prescription___ medicines, which a doctor orders, should be taken with care. Make sure you take the right amount, or ___dose___, and that the ___expiration date___ has not passed.

Lesson Details How are drugs and medicines alike? How are they different?
Possible answer: Both change the way the body works. Medicines treat health problems; illegal drugs cause health problems.

Lesson 2 pp. 194–197

Summary A repeated strong desire for a drug is a sign of ___addiction___. ___Caffeine___ is a drug found in coffee. Fumes from household products used as drugs are ___inhalants___.

Name ____________ Quick Study (continued)

Lesson Details Write how each of the following drugs affects the body.
Inhalants: Possible answers: damage the brain and other organs; cause clumsiness, headaches, nausea, confusion, memory loss, and death
Caffeine: Possible answers: makes the heart beat too fast, makes you nervous, and keeps you from sleeping

Lesson 3 pp. 200–204

Summary One drug that is against the law is ___marijuana___, which comes from the hemp plant. Another ___illegal drug___ is ___cocaine___, which comes from the coca plant. People who need drugs to feel normal have ___drug dependence___.

Lesson Details Below are some effects of drugs. Write *C* if the effect is from cocaine, *M* if from marijuana, and *M* and *C* if from both drugs.

1. ___M___ affects learning and memory
2. ___C___ can cause heart attacks
3. ___C, M___ causes confusion
4. ___M___ can cause cancer

Lesson 4 pp. 206–209

Summary People who like themselves have ___self-respect___. They do not give in to ___peer pressure___, or do things because their friends want them to.

Lesson Details Write three ways to say *no* to drugs.
I can say, "No, I don't want to hurt my body." "No, I don't want to get into trouble." "No, it's against the law."

Lesson 5 pp. 210–212

Summary People who take drugs can get help. There are many organizations that can help with ___recovery___, or stopping drug use.

Lesson Details Imagine that you have a friend who is using drugs. What should you do? On another sheet of paper, write at least two ways you could help.
See p. 128 in *Teaching Resources* for answers.

© Harcourt

Available online.
www.harcourtschool.com/health

TEACH *continued*

Content-Area Reading Support

Using Typographic Clues Draw students' attention to the vocabulary terms that are highlighted in color. Point out that a definition follows most highlighted terms. Encourage students to pay special attention to sentences that contain highlighted vocabulary terms because they usually give the meaning of the term.

Discuss

Sometimes people don't get over an illness because they don't take medicines properly, either because they don't follow directions or they believe that taking more or less of a medicine will be better for them. Ask students for examples that describe the proper use of prescription medications. Have them identify the use of prescription medication.

Critical Thinking Before writing you a prescription, why does a doctor ask your parents if you're taking any other medicines? Doctors want to make sure that the medicine they prescribe won't have a harmful reaction with medicines you're already taking. They also want to make sure that you don't take too much of one kind of medicine. They need to know whether to tell you to stop taking the medicines you're already taking.

Interpret Visuals—Pictures

What information does the pharmacist put on a prescription medicine label? He or she includes the name, address, and phone number of the pharmacy, the doctor's name, the name and strength of the medicine, and instructions telling how much of the medicine to take and how often.

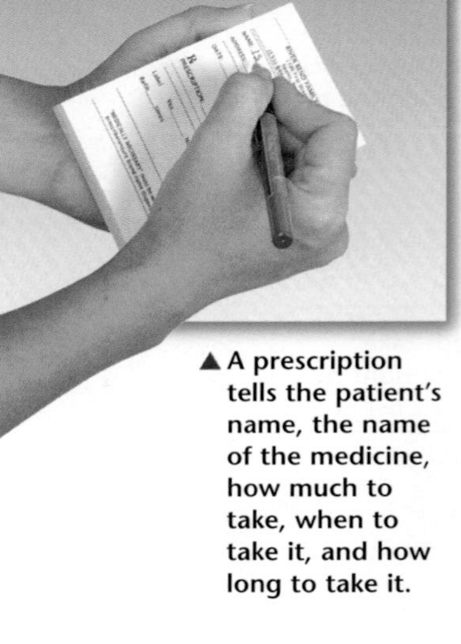

▲ A prescription tells the patient's name, the name of the medicine, how much to take, when to take it, and how long to take it.

Prescription Medicines

For some health problems, you need to see a doctor. After the doctor carefully decides what kind of medicine you need, he or she writes a prescription. A **prescription** (prih•SKRIP•shuhn) is a doctor's order for a medicine. When an adult takes the prescription to a pharmacy, a pharmacist (FAR•muh•sist) fills the order for the medicine and labels the container. Medicine that an adult can buy only with a doctor's order is called a **prescription medicine**. A prescription medicine is meant for just one person. Never take another person's prescription medicine. This can be dangerous to your health.

SEQUENCE What are the steps for getting a prescription medicine?

Go to a doctor, get a prescription, go to a pharmacy, and have the pharmacist fill the order.

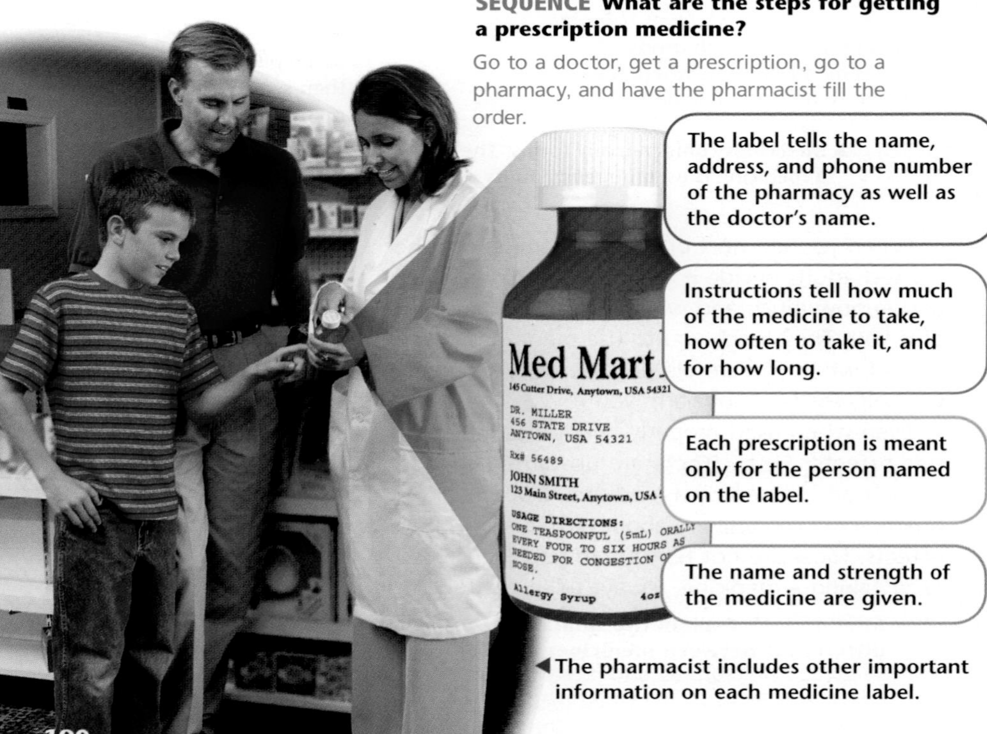

Med Mart
145 Cutter Drive, Anytown, USA 54321
DR. MILLER
456 STATE DRIVE
ANYTOWN, USA 54321
Rx# 56489
JOHN SMITH
123 Main Street, Anytown, USA
USAGE DIRECTIONS:
ONE TEASPOONFUL (5mL) ORALLY
EVERY FOUR TO SIX HOURS AS
NEEDED FOR CONGESTION
Allergy Syrup
The label tells the name, address, and phone number of the pharmacy as well as the doctor's name.
Instructions tell how much of the medicine to take, how often to take it, and for how long.
Each prescription is meant only for the person named on the label.
The name and strength of the medicine are given.

◀ The pharmacist includes other important information on each medicine label.

190

Meeting Individual Needs
Leveled Activities

BELOW-LEVEL Perform a Skit Have students write and perform a skit that reflects the steps a person must go through in order to obtain a prescription medicine.

ON-LEVEL Make Labels Have students make a label for an imaginary prescription medicine. They should make up the information needed for the label, including the dosage and frequency for someone their age or weight, along with other required information.

CHALLENGE Identify Reliable Sources Remind students of the importance of identifying reliable sources of personal health information. This lesson identifies doctors and pharmacists. Challenge students to identify other reliable sources of health information. (Answers might include the school nurse, library references, websites affiliated with reputable health agencies, and so on.)

◀ Labels on OTC medicines tell people what they can be properly used for. What are the uses for this medicine?

Over-the-Counter Medicines

For some health problems, you don't need to see a doctor. Your parents or guardians may give you a medicine from a drugstore or a grocery store. Medicines that can be bought without a prescription are called **over-the-counter medicines**, or OTC medicines. Many pain relievers, antibiotic creams, and cough medicines are OTC medicines.

The label on an OTC medicine tells what health problem the medicine treats and the dose. The **dose** is the amount of the medicine that you should take every time you use it.

OTC medicines can be harmful if taken incorrectly. Never take an OTC medicine on your own. Tell a parent or another trusted adult if you do not feel well.

CAUSE AND EFFECT **When can OTC medicines be harmful?**

OTC medicines can be harmful if taken incorrectly.

Quick Activity

Read and Compare Look at the prescription medicine label on page 190 and the OTC medicine label above. How are they alike and different?

Consumer Activity

Make a Buying Decision At a drugstore or a grocery store, find three OTC cough medicines with the same active ingredients. Compare the costs of the medicines. Which is the best value?

191

Discuss

Ask students to identify examples of the use of non-prescription medication, such as over-the-counter medicines. Have them describe labels found on OTC medicines.

How do labels help people use OTC medicines safely? They have warnings that indicate who should avoid taking the medicines.

What should you do if you don't feel well and think you need an OTC medicine? Tell a parent or another trusted adult.

Consumer Activity

In general, students are likely to find that for medicines with the same ingredients, store-brand or generic OTC medicines are the best value.

Quick Activity

Both labels list the name of the medicine, expiration date, and dose. They both also say how often the medicine should be taken. The OTC label describes the medicine's uses, but this information isn't found on a prescription label. A prescription label lists the name, address, and phone number of the pharmacy as well as the doctor's name. This information isn't found on an OTC label.

Math

Cost Per Dose Extend the Consumer Activity by challenging students to calculate the cost *per dose* of each of three OTC medicines containing the same active ingredient. Have students find out if the medicine formerly determined to be the best value is still the best value when evaluated on a per-dose (rather than per-ounce or per-milliliter) basis.

Teacher Tip

Medicine Abuse When used as directed, OTC and prescription medicines are usually safe. However, some medicines, despite their legitimate uses, produce mood-altering effects that make them prone to abuse. Intense marketing and commercialism have resulted in commonly abused prescription medicines, including narcotic pain relievers, sedatives, and over-the-counter medicines. Remind students that medicines should be taken only when absolutely necessary.

Health Background

Aspirin Tell students that people under 20 should never use any form of aspirin. This common OTC fever-reducer and pain-reliever, found in many OTC preparations, can trigger a life-threatening condition called Reye's syndrome.

Source: *National Reye's Syndrome Foundation website*

For more background, visit the **Webliography** in Teacher Resources at **www.harcourtschool.com/health**
Keyword medicines

TEACH *continued*

Activity

Caring Chad should tell a responsible adult, such as a parent, teacher, family doctor, or school guidance counselor.

Discuss

Ask students to identify examples of the use of prescription medication. Invite volunteers to read each of the safety rules shown on these pages.

Critical Thinking Why must parents and other adults who care for you learn the safe use of medicines? so that medicines are used correctly and do not harm you

Problem Solving What are some important things parents should check for before buying an OTC medicine? expiration date and unbroken safety seal

Critical Thinking Why is it dangerous to buy medicines with a broken or missing safety seal? Possible answer: Someone may have put something harmful into the container.

Critical Thinking Why is it important to keep medicine in the package it comes in? The original package has important information about the medicine, such as its proper use, dose and frequency, and expiration date.

Critical Thinking You've learned many things about medicine safety. Why do you think that it's important for you to know these things, even though you can take medicine only from a parent or another trusted adult? One day you will be responsible for your own medical care.

Interpret Visuals—Graphs

What information does the graph provide about the effectiveness of safety caps on medicines? Possible answer: The use of safety caps on medicines has prevented some poisoning among children.

ACTIVITY

Building Good Character

Caring Chad is worried about his older sister. She is always taking medicine, even though she's not sick. Chad wants to talk with someone about his sister, but he is worried that she will get into trouble. What actions would best show that Chad cares about his sister?

Safe Use of Medicines

Everyone must learn the safe use of medicines. For example, medicines should not be used if the expiration date has passed. The **expiration date** (eks•puh•RAY•shuhn) tells you the last date it is safe to take the medicine. Always check a medicine's expiration date. The safety seal should also be checked. Medicine should not be bought if the seal is broken. Whenever you take medicine, follow the rules on the Medicine Safety Checklist.

▼ Always have a parent or another trusted adult give you medicine. Never take *any* medicine on your own.

Medicine Safety Checklist

- Take medicines only from a parent or another trusted adult—never on your own.
- Follow directions on the medicine label.
- Do NOT use a medicine after its expiration date.
- Do NOT take another person's medicine.
- Do NOT buy an OTC medicine with a broken or missing safety seal.
- Do NOT crush or break capsules or pills without a doctor's permission.
- Store medicines in a locked cabinet, out of the reach of small children.
- If a medicine makes you ill or has side effects, tell an adult.

Teacher Tip

Vitamin Safety Because vitamins are both available over the counter and used to promote good health, many people believe that they are safer than other OTC medicines. In fact, vitamins can be toxic when taken in amounts that exceed the United States Recommended Daily Allowances (USRDA). Remind students that they should use the same safety rules for vitamins as they use for other medicines.

Teacher Tip

More Medicine Safety Tips Students may share these safety tips with their families.

- Look at the package carefully before taking any medicine. If it looks suspicious in any way, don't take it.
- Examine the shape and size of the pills or capsules. If a pill or capsule is different from the others, don't take the medicine.
- Take medicine with water, not juice or milk, unless otherwise directed by a physician.

Throw away medicine that is too old to use. Age can make medicines change. They might not work or might cause harmful effects.

Child-resistant safety caps are used on many medicines. ▶

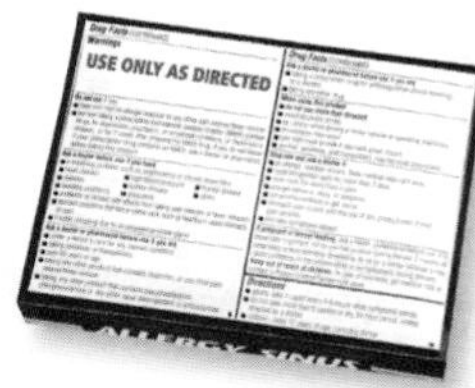

◀ Always follow the directions on the label. This includes taking the right dose at the right time.

Children Under 5 Poisoned by Medicines

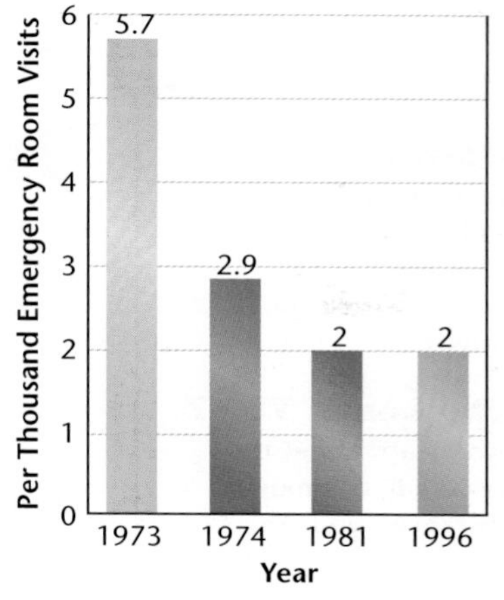

In 1972 a law about the use of safety caps on medicines was passed. How has this helped keep small children safe and healthy?

SUMMARIZE How can you use medicines safely?

Lesson 1 Summary and Review

❶ **Summarize with Vocabulary**

Use vocabulary from this lesson to complete the statements.

_____ change the way the body works. Those used to treat or cure illnesses are called _____. _____ can be bought without a doctor's order, but _____ can not.

❷ **Critical Thinking** Distinguish between helpful and harmful medicines and drugs.

❸ OTC medicine labels describe the health problem the medicine treats. Prescription medicine labels do not. Why not?

❹ **SUMMARIZE** Draw and complete this graphic organizer to describe the information found on a prescription medicine label.

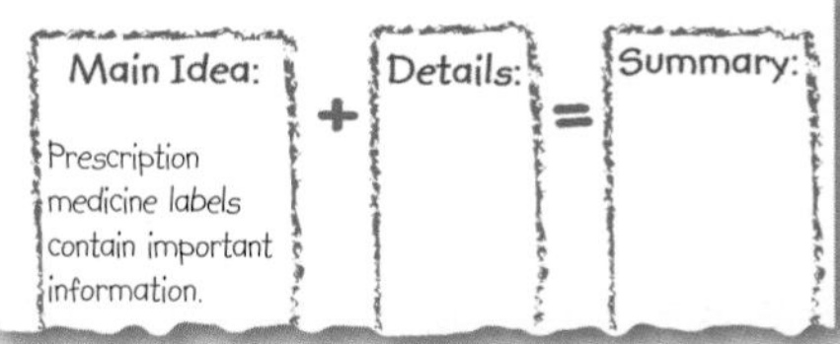

❺ **Write to Inform—How-To**

Write a pamphlet designed to teach your family how to use medicines safely.

Answers should reflect an understanding of the rules on page 192, as well as those in the Medicine Safety Checklist.

193

ACTIVITY BOOK P. 38

Name ________________

Reading Skill

Summarize

Medicines

When you get sick, one of the ways you can get better is by taking medicine. There are two main kinds of medicines. The first is the kind your parent or other adult family member might buy for you, called over-the-counter (OTC) medicine. The other is the kind your doctor writes an order for, called prescription medicine.

Over-the-counter medicines are drugs such as pain relievers and cough medicines. If you have a cut, an adult might put OTC antibiotic cream on your cut to keep it from getting infected. You can buy OTC medicines in places like drugstores and grocery stores.

If you have visited the doctor with a health problem, he or she may have prescribed a medicine for you. That means that the doctor wrote an order for a medicine that would help you feel better. Your parent or another adult probably took the prescription to a pharmacy. The pharmacist got the medicine ready.

No matter what kind of medicine you use, you need to be careful with it. Medicine can only help make you better if you take it the way the doctor ordered or the way the label on the OTC medicine tells you to take it. If you take the medicine incorrectly, you might get sick or not get well. For medicine to do its work, the people taking medicine have to do theirs, too.

Add the details and summary to the graphic organizer.

Main Idea: Medicines can help make you well. + Details: Over-the-counter medicines include pain relievers and cough medicines. They can be bought in drug stores and grocery stores. Prescription medicines are ordered by a doctor. You can get them in a pharmacy. It is important to follow the directions on the label. = Summary: When taken properly, medicines help a person who is ill get well.

© Harcourt

Available online.
www.harcourtschool.com/health

3. WRAP UP

Lesson 1 Summary and Review

1. Drugs; medicines; Over-the-counter (OTC); prescription
2. Drugs that are swallowed go to all parts of the body through the blood. Medicines put on the skin affect just the skin and have fewer side effects.
3. You go to a doctor for a particular problem, and the doctor writes the prescription for your particular problem only. But when you buy an OTC medicine, you haven't talked to a doctor about your problem, so the OTC label needs to provide information about the health problem it will treat.
4. Possible answers:

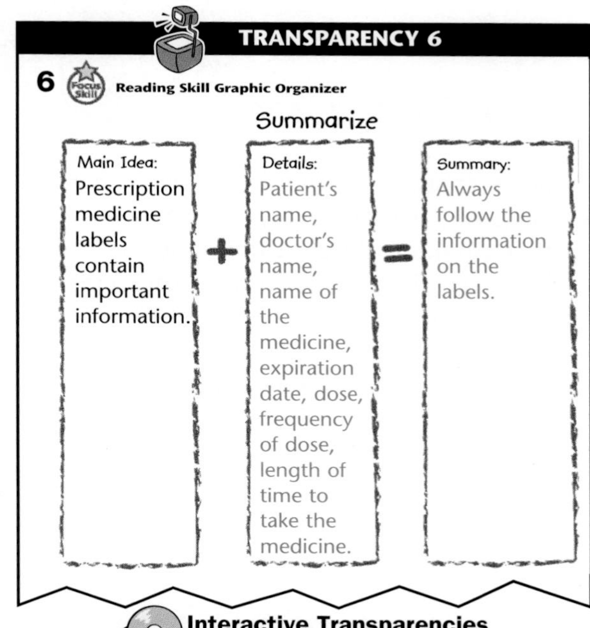

TRANSPARENCY 6
6
Reading Skill Graphic Organizer
Summarize
Main Idea:
Prescription medicine labels contain important information.
+
Details:
Patient's name, doctor's name, name of the medicine, expiration date, dose, frequency of dose, length of time to take the medicine.
=
Summary:
Always follow the information on the labels.

Interactive Transparencies available on CD-ROM.

5. Students' pamphlets should show an understanding of the medicine safety rules presented on pages 192–193.

For **writing models** with examples, see *Teaching Resources* pp. 47–61. Rubrics are also provided.

When Minutes Count . . .

Quick Study Students can use *Activity Book* pages 36–37 (shown on p. 189) as they complete each lesson in this chapter.

LESSON 2
Pages 194–197

Objectives
- ► Recognize that some common substances, such as caffeine and OTC medicines, can be addictive.
- ► Describe the harmful effects of caffeine and inhalants.

When Minutes Count . . .
Assign the Quick Study, Lesson 2, Activity Book pp. 36–37 (shown on p. 189).

Program Resources
- ► Activity Book pp. 36–37
- ► Transparency 6

Vocabulary
addiction p. 195, **caffeine** p. 196, **inhalants** p. 197

Daily Fitness Tip
Medicine cabinets should be cleaned out on a regular basis, perhaps every six or twelve months. An adult should throw out any medicine past its expiration date; medicines that have changed color, have a residue at the bottom, or have an "off" odor; creams or ointments that have changed color or separated; the remains of eyedrops, which are susceptible to fungus; and any leftover prescription medicines.

1. MOTIVATE
Ask students to recall how their body felt when they were very frightened. **How did your body feel?** Answers will vary, but are likely to include that their hearts beat fast and they felt nervous.

Tell students that in this lesson, they will learn about a drug called caffeine that can make the heart beat very fast and make the user feel nervous. Point out that OTC medicines and household products are usually safe when used as intended but can be harmful when misused.

LESSON 2

Substances That Can Be Harmful

Lesson Focus
Common household products and OTC medicines can be harmful if they are misused.

Why Learn This?
If you learn about the dangers of common substances, you are less likely to be harmed by them.

Vocabulary
addiction
caffeine
inhalants

Harmful Effects and Misuse
You probably have heard about the dangers of drugs. Did you know that common substances around your home can also be dangerous?

OTC medicines can clear your stuffy nose. They can take away pain, soothe a sore throat, or stop an itch. But OTC medicines can harm you if you misuse them.

Some people misuse medicines. In most cases they simply don't read the labels or follow the directions. Medicines can be harmful to your body if you take more than the right dose. They can be harmful if you take them more often than you should or for the wrong reasons.

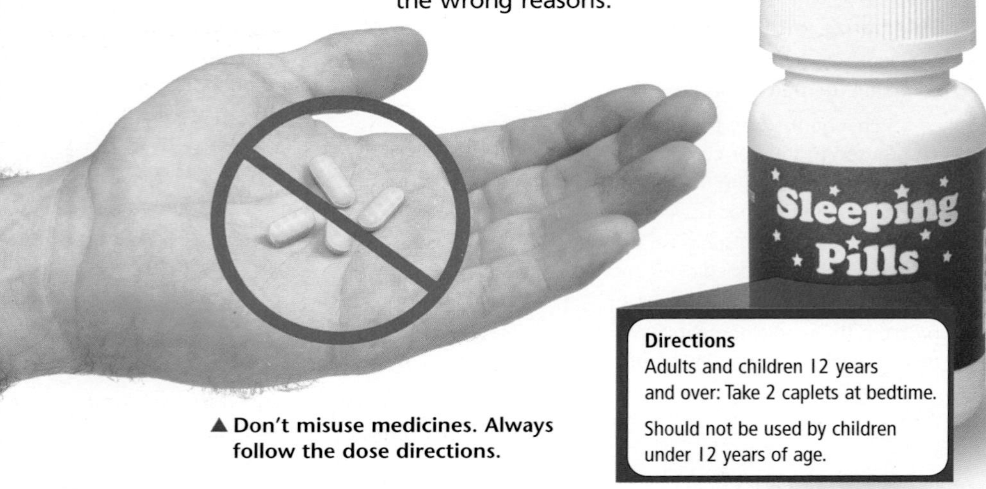

Sleeping Pills
Directions
Adults and children 12 years and over: Take 2 caplets at bedtime.
Should not be used by children under 12 years of age.

▲ Don't misuse medicines. Always follow the dose directions.

194

Meeting Individual Needs
Leveled Activities

BELOW-LEVEL **Write Acrostics** Have students demonstrate their understanding of addiction by writing acrostic puzzles that use the word *addiction.*

ON-LEVEL **Research Substance Abuse** Have students use library and Internet resources to investigate some OTC drugs that people abuse. Have them make posters to illustrate their findings.

CHALLENGE **Make a Graphic Organizer** Have students research different OTC cough and cold medicines, including antihistamines, decongestants, antitussives, and expectorants. Have them find out what each treats, its ingredients, how it works, and side effects that may result if the medicine is misused. Encourage students to organize their findings in a chart that can be displayed in the classroom.

▼ OTC medicines can impair a user's driving ability and may cause car crashes.

Misuse of some medicines can cause car crashes. For example, some medicines make people feel sleepy. This affects the way they drive.

The misuse of medicines and drugs can lead to addiction. An **addiction** (uh•DIK•shuhn) is a craving that makes a person use a drug even when he or she knows it is harmful. People who are addicted to a drug feel sick if they don't use it. It's very hard for them to stop using the drug. No one can predict who is likely to develop an addiction.

Information Alert!

The Food and Drug Administration (FDA) Some OTC diet aids contain dangerous drugs. Diet aids are not considered medicines. Congress is trying to change laws so that the FDA can remove unsafe diet aids from stores.

For the most up-to-date information, visit The Learning Site. www.harcourtschool.com/health

Focus Skill **SUMMARIZE Describe when medicines can be harmful.**

They can be harmful if people take too much of them, take them too often, or take them for the wrong reason. They are also harmful when they lead to addiction.

2. TEACH

Interpret Visuals—Pictures

Draw students' attention to the picture of the car crash.

Critical Thinking How can OTC medicines cause car crashes? They can make people sleepy and affect their ability to drive.

Problem Solving How can adults be responsible and stay safe when they need to take medicine? They can read the label to make sure that the medicine doesn't cause drowsiness. If the medicine might make them sleepy, they should avoid driving.

Discuss

What is addiction? It's a craving that makes a person use a drug even when he or she knows it's harmful.

Critical Thinking Think about the abuse of medicines and the use of illegal drugs. In what ways is the use of each of them alike? Both involve using substances in a way that's harmful to the body, and both can cause addiction.

Problem Solving What's the best way to avoid addiction to OTC medicines? Use OTC medicines correctly. **What's the best way to avoid addiction to other kinds of drugs?** Don't take them.

Social Studies

Food and Drug Administration This federal agency was established in 1906 in response to complaints about untested chemical additives in food. Encourage students to find out more about the Food and Drug Administration and its responsibilities by visiting its website.

Teacher Tip

Emergency Protocol Discuss with students what they should do if someone they are with overdoses or has an adverse reaction to a drug. Reinforce the concept that they and most other people don't possess the ability to judge the severity of a medical situation, and cannot handle such emergencies on their own. They should *always* notify a responsible adult immediately and call 911 for medical assistance.

TEACH *continued*

Content-Area Reading Support

Using Typographic Clues Remind students that by reading the sentences that precede, include, and follow highlighted vocabulary terms, they can find clues to the terms' meanings. Encourage students to pay special attention to the sentence that contains the term because it usually defines the term.

Where is the term *caffeine* defined? in the first sentence

Why is it important to also pay attention to the sentences that follow the definition? They give more information about the term *caffeine*.

Discuss

What are caffeine's effects? It speeds up the heart and makes most people feel more awake.

Critical Thinking How does the amount of caffeine change the way caffeine affects the body? In small amounts, caffeine isn't harmful to most people. But too much caffeine can make the heart work too hard, make the user nervous, and keep the user from sleeping.

Problem Solving How can you avoid becoming addicted to caffeine? by choosing water, juice, milk, or other caffeine-free drinks

Plans might include

- avoiding sodas, chocolate drinks, and other beverages in the machine that you know have caffeine.
- selecting a beverage from the machine that you know doesn't have caffeine, such as milk or water.

Personal Health Plan

Real-Life Situation
Suppose you are about to choose a drink from a soda machine. You know that drinks with little or no caffeine are more healthful than ones with a lot of caffeine.

Real-Life Plan
Write how you might avoid choosing a drink with caffeine.

Caffeine

Caffeine (ka•FEEN) is a drug found in coffee, tea, chocolate, and some soft drinks. Like all drugs, caffeine changes the way you feel, think, and act. It speeds up the heart and makes most people feel more awake.

Small amounts of caffeine will not harm most people. However, too much caffeine can be harmful. Caffeine can make your heart beat too fast. It can make you nervous and keep you from sleeping. People can become addicted to caffeine. To avoid these effects, choose water, milk, or other caffeine-free drinks.

DRAW CONCLUSIONS How can reading a beverage label help you make a healthful drink decision? You can read to see if the drink has caffeine and, if so, how much.

Compare these drinks. Which has the most caffeine? The least? ▼

Some kinds of water contain vitamins, caffeine, and even sugar.
This sports drink has more than 50 mg of caffeine.
Iced tea has about 30 mg of caffeine per cup.
A cup of coffee has about 75 mg of caffeine.
Colas aren't the only soft drinks with caffeine. Other soft drinks with caffeine are root beer and some brands of orange soda.
SPORT DRINK
WATER + PLUS
ORANGE SODA

ESL/ELL Support

LANGUAGE AND VOCABULARY Words with unusual spellings may confuse students. Help them analyze the spelling and pronunciation of the word *caffeine*.

Beginning Help students understand that the word *caffeine* has an unusual spelling, in which the *i* following the *e* isn't pronounced. Have them repeat the word after you use it in a sentence. (Actually, one *f*, the *i*, and the final *e* are silent.)

Intermediate Have students write simple sentences using the word *caffeine*. Remind them that the term's spelling is unusual and includes letters that aren't pronounced.

Advanced Challenge students to list other words—in English or in their first languages—that contain letters that aren't pronounced.

Inhalants

Some chemicals when mixed can produce harmful fumes. Many household products give off dangerous fumes. When these fumes are used as a drug, they are called **inhalants** (in•HAY•luhnts). The fumes from these products are poisonous and should not be breathed.

Inhalants can cause clumsiness, headache, nausea, confusion, and memory loss. They can damage the brain and other organs. They can even cause death. Some people die the very first time they breathe the poisons. Others become addicted to inhalants.

CAUSE AND EFFECT What should you do if you have to use a product that gives off fumes?
If the products you use give off fumes, you need to make sure that the room where you are has enough fresh air.

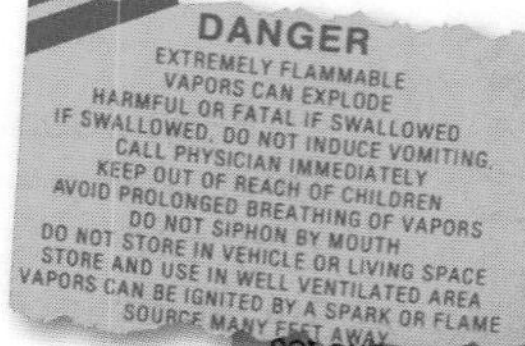

EXTREMELY FLAMMABLE
VAPORS CAN EXPLODE
HARMFUL OR FATAL IF SWALLOWED
IF SWALLOWED, DO NOT INDUCE VOMITING.
CALL PHYSICIAN IMMEDIATELY
KEEP OUT OF REACH OF CHILDREN
AVOID PROLONGED BREATHING OF VAPORS
DO NOT SIPHON BY MOUTH
DO NOT STORE IN VEHICLE OR LIVING SPACE
STORE AND USE IN WELL VENTILATED AREA
VAPORS CAN BE IGNITED BY A SPARK OR FLAME

▼ **When used where there is plenty of fresh air, these products are safe. When inhaled directly, the fumes are poisonous.**

Lesson 2 Summary and Review

❶ **Summarize with Vocabulary**
Use the vocabulary from this lesson to complete the statements.

An _____ is a craving a person has to use a drug. The drug _____ is found in coffee, tea, and some soft drinks. Common household products that give off fumes can also cause addiction if they are used as drugs called _____.

❷ How can reading the label before using a household product protect you from harm?

❸ **Critical Thinking** Why is it important to know how caffeine affects your body?

❹ **SUMMARIZE** Draw and complete this graphic organizer to describe how common substances can be harmful.

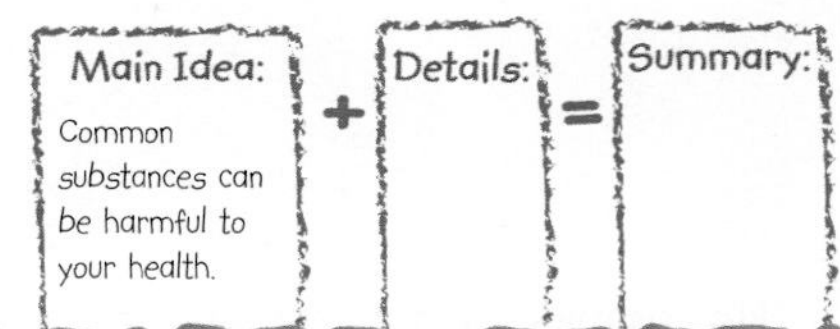

❺ **Write to Express—Business Letter**
Draft a letter asking the maker of your favorite soft drink how much caffeine the product has.

Cultural Connection

Caffeine Culture Caffeine has played a social role in many cultures throughout human history. One such example is afternoon tea in England. Have students investigate the role of caffeine in various cultures and write a report to share with the rest of the class.

3. WRAP UP

Lesson 2 Summary and Review

1. addiction; caffeine; inhalants
2. The label tells how to use the product safely.
3. If you know the effects of the drug, you'll know why it's important to limit it.
4. Possible answers:

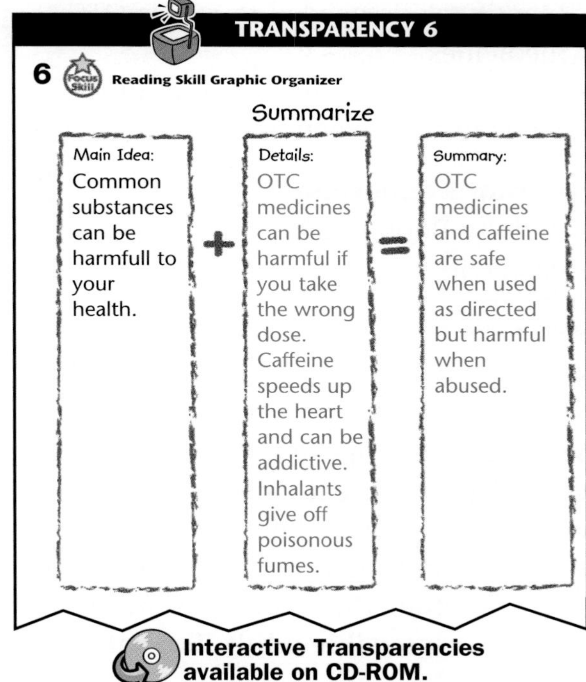

TRANSPARENCY 6
6 Reading Skill Graphic Organizer
Summarize
Main Idea: Common substances can be harmfull to your health.
+
Details: OTC medicines can be harmful if you take the wrong dose. Caffeine speeds up the heart and can be addictive. Inhalants give off poisonous fumes.
=
Summary: OTC medicines and caffeine are safe when used as directed but harmful when abused.
Interactive Transparencies available on CD-ROM.

5. Check students' letters.

For **writing models** with examples, see *Teaching Resources* pp. 47–61. Rubrics are also provided.

When Minutes Count . . .

Quick Study Students can use *Activity Book* pages 36–37 (shown on p. 189) as they complete each lesson in this chapter.

Life Skills

Communicate
Make Responsible Decisions
Manage Stress
Refuse
Resolve Conflicts
Set Goals

Objectives

- ► Identify skills needed to refuse OTC medicines.
- ► Use refusal skills to say *no* to over-the-counter medicines.

Program Resources

- ► Activity Book p. 39
- ► Poster 10

1. MOTIVATE

Why do you suppose that you're warned never to eat candy that isn't wrapped? You don't know if it's safe. **How is accepting a medicine from someone other than your parent or another responsible adult like eating unwrapped candy?** You don't know if the medicine is safe for you to take.

Critical Thinking Why do you need a parent or another trusted adult to give you medicine? Parents and other trusted adults know the rules of medicine safety.

2. TEACH

Direct students' attention to the photographs and steps on this page.

Step 1

What reason does Sofia give Lucy for saying *no*? She isn't allowed to take any medicine unless her parents give it to her.

Critical Thinking Why do parents have rules about taking medicine? to keep their children safe

Refuse

OTC Medicines

People sometimes think OTC medicines are safer than prescription medicines. That's why they might try OTC medicines they don't need. Using the steps for **Refusing** can help you refuse medicines you don't need.

Lucy and Sofia are studying together. Lucy says her brother gave her some caffeine pills. He said they would help her stay awake. She offers one to Sofia.

1 Say *no* firmly, and state your reasons for saying so.

"No, thanks," Sofia says. "I'm not allowed to take medicine unless my parents give it to me."

2 Remember a consequence, and keep saying *no*.

"Try one. It helps me stay awake so I can study," Lucy says. Sofia says, "But it might make you sick."

Drama

Act Out a Skit Have students present Sofia and Lucy's interaction as a skit. Encourage students to work in pairs to act out the scenario presented on this page as well as other ways for refusing OTC medicines, such as situations involving caffeine drinks versus water or dealing with a headache using an OTC or prescribed medicine. Then allow students to perform their skits for the rest of the class.

ACTIVITY BOOK P. 39

Name ____________________

Problem Solving

Life Skill
Refuse

Steps for Refusing OTC Medicines

1. Say *no* firmly, and state your reasons for saying *no*.
2. Remember a consequence, and keep saying *no*.
3. Suggest something else to do.
4. Repeat *no* and walk away.

Tell how these students can use the steps for refusing OTC medicines.

A. Jason tells Ben he has something to show him. He shows Ben some medicine in a bottle. "I got it from Seth," Jason says. "He says it's for coughs but it makes you feel really good."

- What should Ben tell Jason? Write how Ben could use the steps above to help him refuse the medicine.

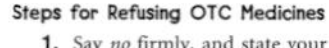

Possible answer: Ben could say that he won't take someone else's medicine because it could make him sick. Ben could ask Jason to go for ice cream with him instead. If Jason still insists that they try the medicine, Ben can refuse again and walk away.

B. Jennifer is with Marcy when Marcy opens her purse and pulls out a package of pills. "I saw these at home. The package says they give you energy. I really need some energy. Do you want one, too?"

- How could Jennifer say *no*? Write how she could use the steps above to refuse the pills.

Possible answer: Jennifer could tell Marcy that she won't take the pills because she knows she shouldn't take medicine that she doesn't need. If Marcy insists, Jennifer could tell her that she already has plenty of energy and doesn't want to get into trouble. She could suggest that a snack might give Marcy energy. If Marcy still wants them to take the pills, Jennifer can tell her that she will see her later and can leave.

© Harcourt

Available online.
www.harcourtschool.com/health

3 **Suggest something else to do.**

"Besides, you don't need pills to stay awake," Sofia says. "Why don't you just go to bed earlier?"

4 **Repeat *no* and walk away.**

"Just one won't hurt," Lucy offers. "No. I don't need pills to stay awake. I'll see you later," Sofia says as she walks away.

Problem Solving

Richard finds a package of OTC pills on his big brother's desk. When his friend Cory comes over, Richard shows the pills to him. He suggests that they each take a pill and see what happens.

Explain the importance of refusal skills. How can Cory use the steps for **Refusing** to refuse the pill? Explain how his decision can demonstrate caring for his health.

Using the Poster

Activity Have students write and perform skits showing situations in which young people refuse to use drugs.

Display Poster 10 to remind students of the steps for making responsible decisions.

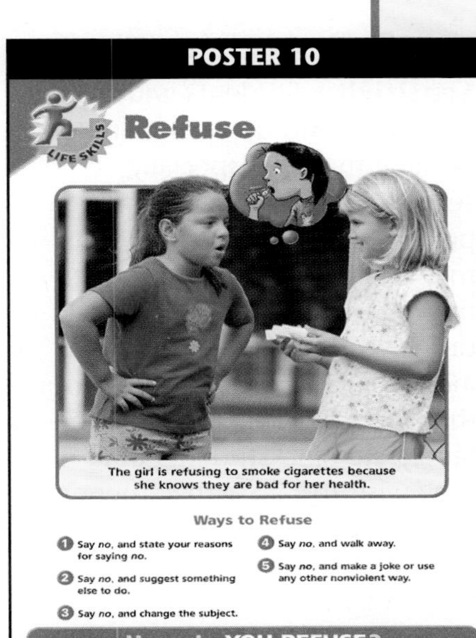

POSTER 10
LIFE SKILLS
Refuse
The girl is refusing to smoke cigarettes because she knows they are bad for her health.
Ways to Refuse
1 Say no, and state your reasons for saying no.
2 Say no, and suggest something else to do.
3 Say no, and change the subject.
4 Say no, and walk away.
5 Say no, and make a joke or use any other nonviolent way.
How do YOU REFUSE?
POSTER 10

Step 2

What consequence does Sofia remember? that she could get sick

Problem Solving What other consequences might Sofia think of? Possible answers: She'll get in trouble if she breaks the rules about taking medicine; caffeine can be harmful to you.

Step 3

What alternative does Sofia suggest? going to bed earlier

Critical Thinking Why does Sofia make this suggestion? If Lucy gets enough sleep, she won't need pills to stay awake.

Building Good Character

Remind students that when making any decision, they should consider how the decision shows good character. Here are questions they can ask themselves: Am I being trustworthy and responsible? Am I following my family's rules?

Step 4

How does Sofia respond when Lucy pressures her to take "just one" pill? She says *no* again and walks away.

Critical Thinking Why does Sofia tell Lucy, "I'll see you later"? She wants Lucy to know that she still wants to be her friend, but not if she takes the pill.

3. WRAP UP

Problem Solving

Answers will vary. Students might suggest that Cory can tell Richard *no*, because it's unsafe to take OTC medicines that you don't need. He might tell Richard that the pills could have side effects. Cory might suggest that they shoot baskets instead. And finally, he can walk away from Richard. If Cory does these things, he shows that he cares about what happens to himself—that he has self-respect.

LESSON 3
Pages 200–204

Objectives
- Recognize the dangerous effects of marijuana and cocaine.
- Recognize that cocaine use can lead to immediate addiction.

When Minutes Count . . .
Assign the Quick Study, Lesson 3, Activity Book pp. 36–37 (shown on p. 189).

Program Resources
- Activity Book pp. 36–37
- Transparency 6

Vocabulary
illegal drug p. 200, **marijuana** p. 200, **drug dependence** p. 201, **cocaine** p. 202

Daily Fitness Tip
The hours when students are most likely to experiment with drugs are after school before parents come home or during summer vacations, when they have a lot of time to "hang out." Have students brainstorm safe activities that can fill these hours.

1. MOTIVATE
Ask students what their goals are or what plans they have for their lives. Explain to them that reaching a goal takes discipline and work. Remind students that illegal drug use can ruin their plans and keep them from achieving their goals. Lives can also be ruined because of illegal drug use. People are often hurt and die.
What does this tell you about the effects that drugs can have on you?
Drugs change the way you feel and think. They put you in danger and can ruin your life.

LESSON 3

Marijuana and Cocaine

Lesson Focus
Marijuana and cocaine are illegal drugs that can harm the body and lead to addiction.

Why Learn This?
Learning the dangers of using marijuana and cocaine will make it easier for you to refuse to use them.

Vocabulary
illegal drug
marijuana
drug dependence
cocaine

Marijuana
Some drugs are so harmful that they are illegal (ih•LEE•guhl). An **illegal drug** is a drug that is not a medicine and that is against the law to sell, buy, have, or use. A drug abuser is someone who uses illegal drugs. Drug abusers harm their health and break the law. They often spend time in jail.

Marijuana (mair•uh•WAHN•uh) is an illegal drug made from the hemp plant. It is sometimes called grass or pot. Marijuana users usually smoke it.

▼ It is illegal to grow marijuana in the United States. Illegally grown marijuana is destroyed, and the people who grow it are arrested.

Teacher Tip
Sensitivity Students with family members who use marijuana or cocaine may be especially sensitive to the concepts presented in this lesson. Some may become defensive or deny the potential dangers of these drugs. Without singling out individual students, acknowledge that drug use affects everyone in a family. Remind students that, if they wish to talk with someone about a family drug problem, they should seek the counsel of a trusted adult.

Social Studies
Laws and Drug Use Many states have different penalties regarding the possession and use of illegal drugs. Have students research the penalties in your state for buying, selling, or possessing marijuana. Have students report their findings in a graphic organizer.

▲ It is illegal to buy, sell, or use marijuana.

Most states give drug users a fine and jail time for buying, selling, or using marijuana. ▶

Marijuana harms users' health. It has more than 400 substances in it. Marijuana use can lead to dependence on the drug. **Drug dependence** is the need to take a drug just to feel normal.

Smoking marijuana causes breathing and heart problems and makes it hard for the body to fight infections. It can also cause cancer.

SUMMARIZE How does marijuana use affect the body?

It causes breathing and heart problems, makes it hard for the body to fight infections, and can cause cancer.

Did You Know?

At one time, drug experts did not think that marijuana use was dangerous. The latest evidence shows that marijuana *is* harmful.

2. TEACH

Interpret Visuals—Pictures

Draw students' attention to the series of pictures on these pages.

Where does marijuana come from? It comes from the hemp plant. **What happens when it's found growing?** It's destroyed. **What happens to the people who grow marijuana?** They're arrested.

Discuss

Remind students that the consequences of using marijuana aren't just legal problems.

What are some of the physical effects of marijuana use? breathing and heart problems, problems fighting infections, and cancer

Problem Solving What's the best way to avoid the negative effects of marijuana use? Avoid marijuana and people who buy, sell, or use it.

ESL/ELL Support

COMPREHENSIBLE INPUT The term *illegal* does not represent a concrete object. Clarify with students the consequences of engaging in illegal activities.

Beginning Role-play with students a situation in which illegal drug use results in being arrested, handcuffed, and taken away in a police car.

Intermediate Have students describe situations in which activities would be illegal.

Advanced Encourage students to write stories about the consequences faced by someone who has used illegal drugs.

TEACH *continued*

Discuss

Critical Thinking What should you do if you find a packet of cocaine or a vial of crack? Guide students to respond that they shouldn't touch it and should tell a trusted adult about it immediately. Remind students that illegal drug use has consequences not only for the individual, but also for the user's family and for the community.

In families, parents sometimes discover their child has a serious cocaine (or other drug) problem when they find money, jewelry, or other valuables missing from their home. Often, their first reaction is to deny there is a problem, rather than confront the drug abuser.

Critical Thinking Why is it dangerous to deny a drug problem within a family? Possible answers: The user doesn't get help; the family suffers; the drug problem gets worse.

Activity

Manage Stress Students might make the following suggestions for managing stress without using drugs: listen to music; talk to a friend or parent about how you are feeling; try a hobby; be physically active in some way; get exercise.

ACTIVITY

Life Skills

Manage Stress

Some drug users say they use drugs to relieve stress. However, there are safe, healthful ways to manage stress. Name some things you can do to manage stress and stay drug-free.

Cocaine

Cocaine (koh•KAYN) is a powerful drug made from the leaves of the coca plant. Cocaine affects the way a user feels. But the feelings last for only a short time.

Crack is a solid form of cocaine. It causes the same effects as cocaine, only faster. Crack is probably one of the most addictive illegal drugs.

Dependence on cocaine can happen after using the drug just once. The drug abuser often needs more and more of the drug to get the same effect. This can lead to serious illness or death.

Cocaine and crack are illegal drugs. Some cocaine and crack users commit crimes to get money to buy drugs. People who sell or use cocaine often get arrested and spend time in jail.

DRAW CONCLUSIONS **Why might users of crack and cocaine lose friends and family?** Using cocaine is both unhealthful and illegal. Users often spend time in jail. These things destroy healthful relationships with friends and family members.

▼ Cocaine is responsible for almost a third of all drug-related emergency room visits.

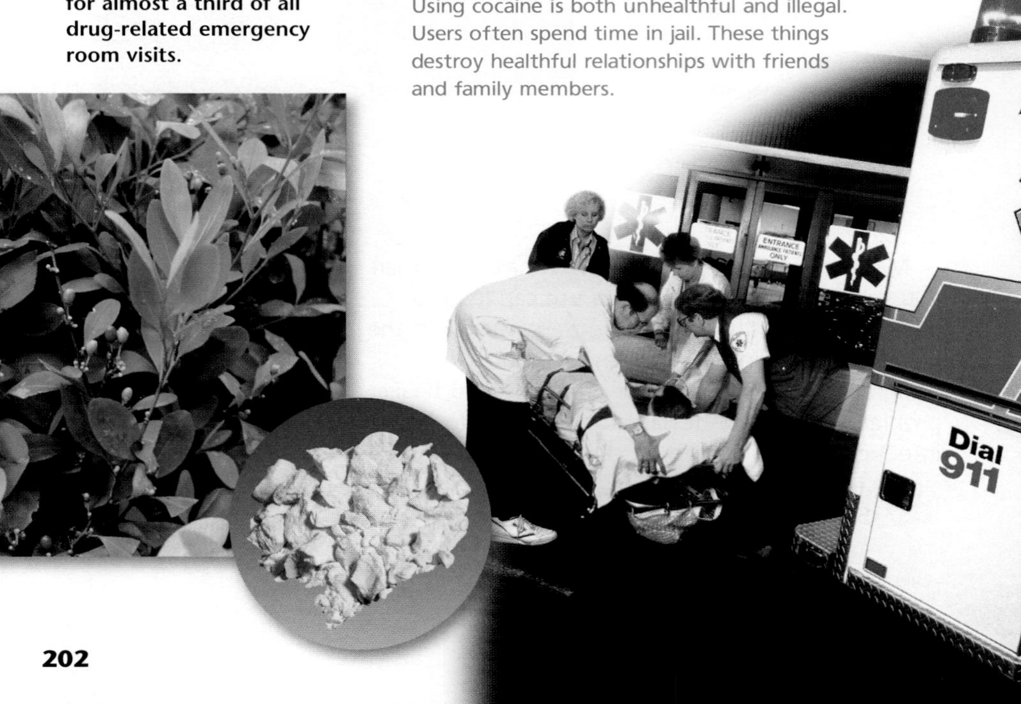

202

Meeting Individual Needs
Leveled Activities

BELOW-LEVEL **Write Poems** Encourage students to write poems warning peers not to use drugs. Invite students to share their poems with the rest of the class.

ON-LEVEL **Evaluate Gateway Drugs** Have students define the term *gateway drug*. In particular, challenge them to discuss how using marijuana, tobacco, and inhalants can "open the gate" for more serious drug problems.

CHALLENGE **Drugs and Creativity** To illustrate the fallacy that drugs enhance creativity, challenge students to compile a list of famous musicians, artists, and actors whose lives ended due to the use of illegal drugs. Emphasize the devastation that use of illegal drugs causes individuals.

Effects of Marijuana and Cocaine

Marijuana

- trouble learning
- trouble remembering
- confusion
- nervousness
- trouble judging time and distance
- heart works harder
- lung damage
- cancer

Cocaine

- confusion and anger
- nervousness, sadness, and sleeplessness
- seizures
- heart works harder
- chest pain
- higher blood pressure
- heart failure
- heart attack
- trouble breathing
- lung damage
- cancer

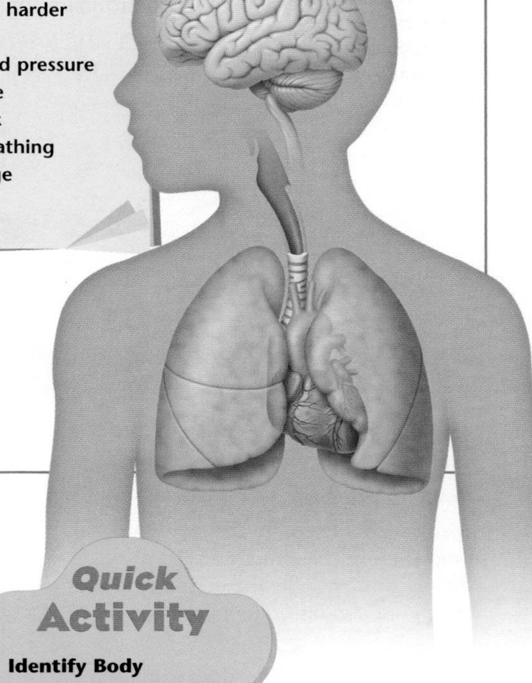

COMPARE AND CONTRAST
What effects are the same for marijuana use and cocaine use? What effects are different?

Responses should reflect a comparison of the common and different effects listed above.

Quick Activity

Identify Body Systems Make a table showing which body system these drugs affect and each organ affected. You can refer to pages 12–14 and 20–23 if you need help.

Language Arts

Exploring Personal Beliefs
Encourage students to write in journals their feelings about drug use. Reassure them that their privacy will not be violated, so they should feel free to express their feelings. If students wish to discuss their feelings, remind them that they can always confide in a trusted adult, such as a parent, doctor, nurse, or school counselor.

Content-Area Reading Support

Using Text Format Draw attention to the format of the text below the heading on this page—bulleted lists inside text boxes. Explain that a change in format, such as the way text is arranged on this page, often signals a change in the kind of information conveyed.

How is this information different from the information on page 202? The text on page 202 presents ideas in paragraph form. The boxed text on this page presents two lists of factual information about effects of drugs on parts of the body.

Urge students to pay attention to a change in the format of text on a page and to be ready for a change in the type of information it presents.

Discuss

Point out that even small doses of cocaine can cause seizures or death—there is no way to predict who will suffer the worst side effects. One use can be fatal.

What mental effects do marijuana and cocaine have in common? Which mental effects are different? Both can cause confusion and nervousness. Cocaine can also cause anger, sleeplessness, sadness, and seizures, while marijuana causes problems with memory, learning, and judging time and distance.

Quick Activity

Students should identify the brain: nervous system; heart: circulatory system; lungs: respiratory system.

Quick Activity

Possible answers: $200 a month; $300 in six weeks; $2,600 a year at $50 a week.

3. WRAP UP

Lesson 3 Summary and Review

1. illegal drugs; drug user; community
2. You can't learn and remember things well when you use marijuana.
3. Cocaine is an illegal drug made from the leaves of the coca plant. Its effects are described on pages 202–203.
4. Possible answers:

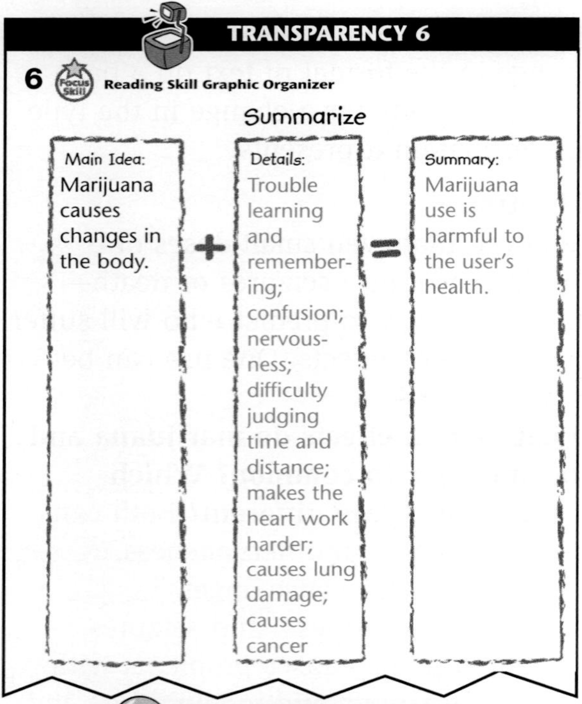

TRANSPARENCY 6
6 Reading Skill Graphic Organizer
Summarize
Main Idea:
Marijuana causes changes in the body.
Details:
Trouble learning and remembering; confusion; nervousness; difficulty judging time and distance; makes the heart work harder; causes lung damage; causes cancer
Summary:
Marijuana use is harmful to the user's health.

Interactive Transparencies available on CD-ROM.

5. Students' pamphlets should reflect an understanding of the effects of the drugs, as shown on page 203.

For **writing models** with examples, see *Teaching Resources* pp. 47–61. Rubrics are also provided.

When Minutes Count . . .

Quick Study Students can use *Activity Book* pages 36–37 (shown on p. 189) as they complete each lesson in this chapter.

Quick Activity

Calculate the Cost of Drug Abuse Drugs harm drug abusers, families, and their community. If a drug abuser is spending $50 a week on drugs, how much is he or she spending in a month? six weeks? one year?

Effects of Drug Use on Others

You know that drug use is harmful to the drug user. Did you know that it also hurts others? Family members suffer when they live with the effects of drug use. Even the community is affected. Drug users often end up in car crashes that injure others.

Law enforcement and drug treatment cost a great deal of money. There are many hospital, legal, and jail expenses due to drug abuse. Because tax dollars help pay for these expenses, everyone is hurt by drug use.

DRAW CONCLUSIONS
How does drug abuse affect people who do not use drugs?

Lesson 3 Summary and Review

1. **Summarize with Vocabulary**
Use vocabulary and other terms from this lesson to complete the statements.
Marijuana and cocaine are _____. A person who abuses these drugs is called a _____. Drugs harm not only the person who uses them, but also his or her family and the _____.
2. **Critical Thinking** Why does marijuana use make it hard to do well in school?
3. What is cocaine, and what are some of its effects on the body?
4. **SUMMARIZE** Draw and complete this graphic organizer to show how marijuana use affects the body.

5. **Write to Inform—How-To**
Imagine that you want to teach a younger child how to say *no* to marijuana and cocaine use. Write a how-to pamphlet that describes the effects of the drugs and teaches refusal skills.

Families who live with a drug user suffer from the effects of drug use. People pay the high costs of drug use through tax dollars that could be spent on other things.

Math

Costs of Illegal Drug Use The use of illegal drugs costs the American people billions of dollars each year. Encourage students to use library or Internet resources to find out about such costs (tax dollars for law enforcement, jail expenses, expenses to businesses for employees who lose time from work, hospital and drug treatment costs, etc.). Have the class display these costs in a chart and estimate the total. (Recent estimates are about $110 billion annually.)

Language Arts

Conduct an Interview
Challenge students to interview a school resource officer. Have them schedule a time for an interview and prepare questions in advance. For example, they might ask the officer for information and suggestions on how they as students can help prevent the use of illegal drugs at their school and in their community. Have students write summaries of their findings and present them to the rest of the class.

Responsibility

Building Good Character

Practicing Self-Control

Responsible people know that their actions affect others. They use self-control. They choose actions that will not harm others or themselves. Here are some ways to practice self-control.

- **Use good judgment in what you do. Make good decisions.**
- **Do NOT choose actions that harm yourself or others.**
- **Do NOT do anything that is against your family's rules or against the law.**
- **Remember that your actions have short-term and long-term effects.**
- **Think of your long-term goals. Do NOT do things that will harm your future.**
- **Be responsible for your own actions. Do NOT give in to peer pressure. See page 207 for more about peer pressure.**

Activity

Take turns practicing self-control with a friend. Suppose that you have been offered drugs. How would you use self-control to say *no*? What questions would you ask yourself before deciding what to do? What things would you think about before saying *no*?

205

Building Good Character

Caring
Citizenship
Fairness
Respect
Responsibility
Trustworthiness

Objective

► Demonstrate responsibility by recognizing the importance of practicing self-control.

Program Resource

► Poster 5

BEFORE READING

Ask students to revisit the Medicine Safety Checklist on page 193. Point out to students that when practicing self-control to follow these rules, people show responsibility and help keep themselves and others safe.

DISCUSS

After students read the page, ask them to describe strategies for self-control. Write their responses on the board. Then ask students to explain how the actions of individuals impact others. When an individual uses self-control and follows rules and laws, he or she makes the community safer for everyone.

ACTIVITY

To demonstrate responsibility through self-control, students might ask themselves the following questions before making a decision about the drug offer:

- Will my decision hurt me?
- Will it harm others?
- Does my decision follow the law?
- Will my decision have long-term effects that will harm my future?

Using the Poster

Activity Ask students to think of other ideas to add to the poster.

Display Poster 5 to remind students of ways to show respect for authority and the law. The poster can be displayed in the classroom, school cafeteria, or another common area.

POSTER 5

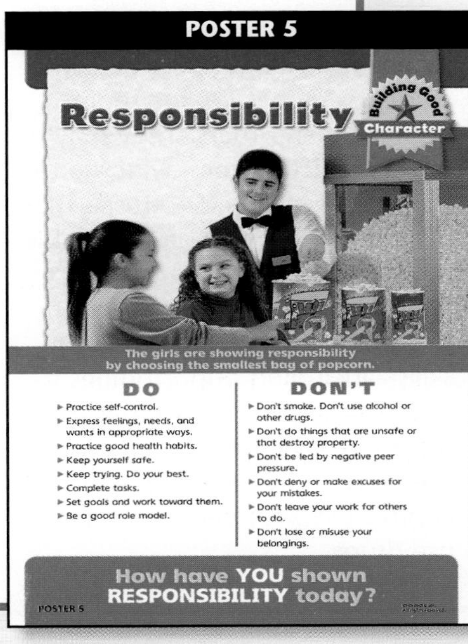
Responsibility
Building Good Character
The girls are showing responsibility by choosing the smallest bag of popcorn.
DO
► Practice self-control.
► Express feelings, needs, and wants in appropriate ways.
► Practice good health habits.
► Keep yourself safe.
► Keep trying. Do your best.
► Complete tasks.
► Set goals and work toward them.
► Be a good role model.
DON'T
► Don't smoke. Don't use alcohol or other drugs.
► Don't do things that are unsafe or that destroy property.
► Don't be led by negative peer pressure.
► Don't deny or make excuses for your mistakes.
► Don't leave your work for others to do.
► Don't lose or misuse your belongings.
How have YOU shown RESPONSIBILITY today?
POSTER 5

LESSON 4
Pages 206–209

Objectives

- Explain why saying *no* to drugs is a healthful decision.
- Demonstrate how to say *no* to illegal drugs.

When Minutes Count . . .
Assign the Quick Study, Lesson 4, Activity Book pp. 36–37 (shown on p. 189).

Program Resources

- Activity Book pp. 36–37
- Transparency 6

Vocabulary

self-respect p. 206,

peer pressure p. 207

Daily Fitness Tip

Teens are more susceptible to peer pressure than are young children. Therefore, the more practice students have saying *no* to drugs now, the easier it will be for them to actually say *no* when they are teens. Provide students with lots of practice throughout the year saying *no* to drugs and to negative peer pressure that could lead them to harm.

For more guidelines about illegal drugs and your physical fitness, see *Be Active! Resources for Physical Education* p. 171.

1. MOTIVATE

Tape a large sheet of butcher paper to the board. Ask students: **How many different ways can you think of to say *no*?** Possible answers: "Forget it!" "I'm not interested." "No, thanks!" "No way!" Ask a volunteer to list the responses on the butcher paper. Tell students that the paper will remain displayed in the classroom for this lesson and for Lesson 5. Invite students to add to the list as they learn or think of new ways to say *no*.

Refusing Drugs

Lesson Focus
Knowing the facts about drugs makes it easier to say *no* to them.

Why Learn This?
When you refuse drugs, you have a better chance to stay healthy.

Vocabulary
self-respect
peer pressure

Refusing Is a Healthful Decision

Refusing drugs is one of the most healthful decisions you can make. It helps you build **self-respect**, the feeling you have about yourself when you like yourself and are proud of what you do. Saying *no* to drugs helps you keep your body safe from harm and keep your mind clear. It means you obey the law and want to stay out of trouble. It allows you to do the things that are important to you and to go after your goals.

Quick Activity

Demonstrate Ways to Refuse Drugs Use the reasons shown here to help you and a partner role-play refusing drugs. Take turns offering one another drugs and saying *no*. List your reasons for saying *no*.

▼ **Respect Yourself:** "I don't need drugs to feel good about myself."

▲ **Feel Healthy:** "I don't want to hurt my body."

206

Teacher Tip

Practice Makes Perfect Some students, by nature, are more hesitant than others. They may have a difficult time saying *no* to their peers, and their refusals may be weak. They may be vulnerable to manipulation by persistent peers. Offer these students extra support to demonstrate refusal skills—including opportunities to role-play saying *no*—so that they feel more comfortable, and are therefore more assertive, when confronted with peer pressure to use drugs.

Social Studies

Media Messages Television strongly influences perceptions of and behavior related to drug use. Encourage students to note situations involving peer pressure and drug use as they watch TV with their families. Challenge them to role-play positive outcomes of refusal in the same situations. For example, if a teen in a television show accepts a cigarette or beer, have students role-play ways in which the character could have said *no*.

There are many reasons to refuse drugs. Remember what you learned about drugs. When you know the risks of using drugs, saying *no* to drugs is easy.

Only you can decide what is right for you. When you make a decision to refuse drugs, stick to it. Do not give in to peer pressure. **Peer pressure** is the strong influence people your own age can have on you. It can create a desire to follow the crowd and do what others are doing. Others may tell you that using drugs is cool. Is putting your health at risk a cool thing to do? Peer pressure is *negative* if someone wants you to do something you know is wrong. Most people do not use drugs. Ask yourself: Do you want to harm your body?

SUMMARIZE Explain why you should resist peer pressure to use drugs.

Using drugs is unhealthful, is against the law, destroys relationships with friends and family, is not respectful to yourself, and keeps you from doing well in school and achieving your goals.

Personal Health Plan

Real-Life Situation
Saying *no* to drugs helps you stay healthy. It shows that you respect yourself and others. Saying *no* lets you pay attention to the important things in your life.
Real-Life Plan
Write how you might say *no* to drugs. How does saying *no* help you stay healthy?

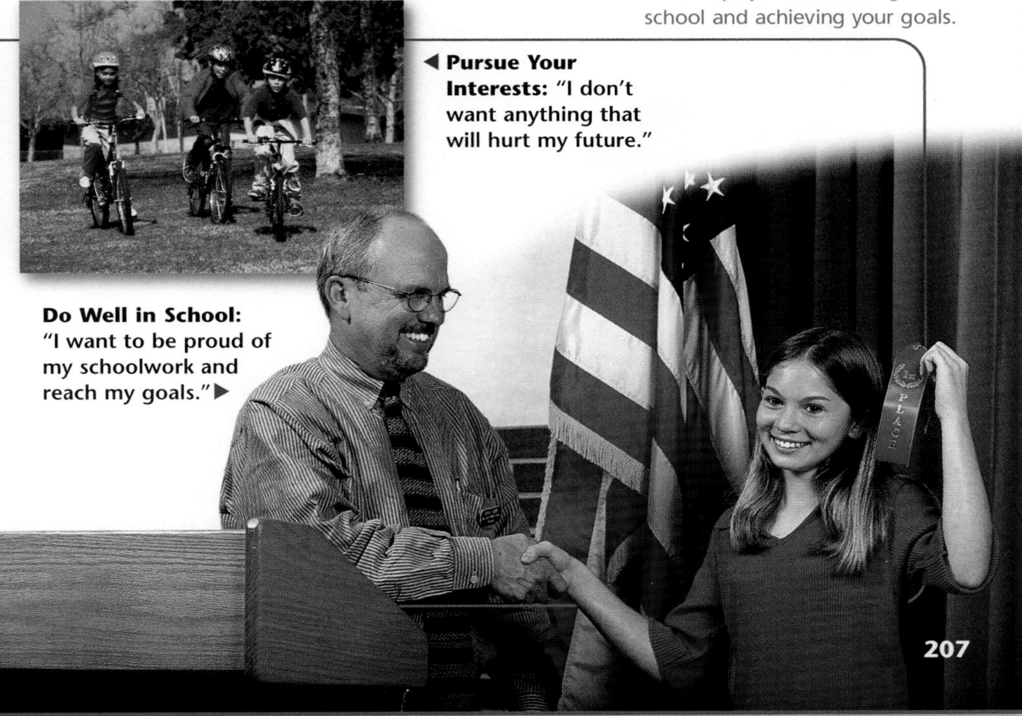

◀ **Pursue Your Interests:** **"I don't want anything that will hurt my future."**

Do Well in School: **"I want to be proud of my schoolwork and reach my goals."** ▶

207

ESL/ELL Support

COMPREHENSIBLE INPUT The term *peer pressure* is a noun, but it doesn't represent a concrete object. Help students understand the concept of peer pressure.

Beginning Role-play with students several situations in which peer pressure is applied. With simple language, model saying *no*.

Intermediate Have students describe situations in which they've experienced peer pressure and how they said *no*.

Advanced Have students write a script for a skit in which the protagonist is confronted with—and resists—peer pressure.

2. TEACH

Personal Health Plan

Plans might include:

- Saying *no* and stating your reasons for not using drugs.
- Remembering a consequence of drug use and keep saying *no*.
- Suggesting something else to do.
- Ignoring the person.
- Reversing the peer pressure.
- Using humor.
- Changing the subject.
- Staying with people who refuse to use drugs.
- Walking away.

Saying *no* helps you stay healthy because you are more able to avoid health problems connected with drug addiction, such as being ill a lot, being unable to fight infections, and not eating well.

Content-Area Reading Support

Using Text Format Direct attention to the caption for each of the photographs on these pages. Have students explain in their own words the relationship between the photographs, the captions, and the lesson. The captions and photographs describe and illustrate how refusing to use drugs is a healthful decision—the topic of the lesson.
Encourage students to take time to study the photographs and captions, as they contain important information not included in the regular text passages.

Quick Activity

Ask students to explain the dangers of yielding to peer pressure by assessing risks and consequences. Reasons for saying *no* to drugs should include the consequences of using drugs—illness, social and legal problems—and the understanding of how much drugs can damage your life. This can give students the motivation to say *no* to drugs when being influenced by peer pressure.

TEACH *continued*

Discuss

Write the following reasons for drug use on the board:

- to feel grown-up
- curiosity
- to feel that you belong
- to feel good
- to rebel against family rules
- to take risks

Ask students to add other reasons young people might use drugs. Encourage students to analyze the listed reasons for drug use. Ask them to list alternatives for the use of other substances.

Critical Thinking What would you tell someone who used these excuses for drug use? Possible answers: Using drugs is not a mature thing to do—most adults don't use any drugs at all. Taking drugs doesn't feel good, especially after you've become addicted to them. There are more healthful ways to fit in, such as joining activities and organizations. You can express yourself in other ways that won't harm your health, such as in the clothes you wear or the way you style your hair. The consequences aren't worth the risks.

Consumer Activity

Students might say that most adults shown on TV shows and commercials are young, glamorous, and shapely. This is not a normal view of most people, since normally people are different sizes, weights, and body shapes. If all people tried to look like people on TV, a lot of people could harm themselves trying or end up being unhealthful. People are naturally different.

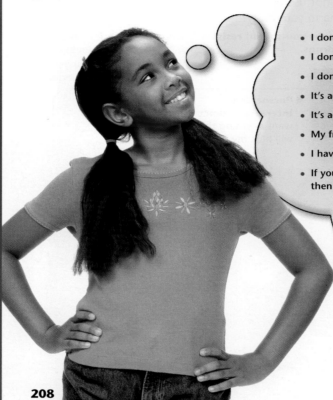

Consumer Activity

Analyze Media Messages TV shows can give a false idea of what is normal. Look at adults on some TV shows and commercials. How do they compare with the real adults you know? Explain why the influence of the media should be resisted.

Ways to Say *No* to Drugs

If you are ever tempted to try drugs, think about what might happen. If you use drugs, you will have to deal with the harm they do to your body. You will have to deal with the problems you could cause your family and your friends. If you are caught, you will also have to deal with the law.

It is *your* responsibility to keep yourself healthy and safe. Other people can give you reasons to avoid drugs, but you are the only one who can decide to say *no* to drugs. You are the only one who can stick to that decision.

Ways to say *No*:

- I don't want to hurt my body.
- I don't want to get into trouble.
- I don't want to disappoint my family.
- It's against the law.
- It's against my family rules.
- My friends don't use drugs.
- I have better things to do.
- If you are trying to get me to use drugs, then you are not my friend.

◀ This girl has thought about how she will say *no* to drugs. How will you say *no*? It helps to have a plan. Then you can say *no* with confidence.

208

Meeting Individual Needs
Leveled Activities

BELOW-LEVEL Make a Picture Album On lined index cards, have students draw "photos" of themselves resisting peer pressure to use drugs. Students should caption their "photos" and display them in an album.

ON-LEVEL Make Flash Cards Have each student make five flash cards, each of which states a way to refuse drugs. Then divide the class into small groups. Have the groups use the flash cards to role-play responses to situations in which they are offered drugs.

CHALLENGE Write Ads Have each student write and illustrate an ad warning against drug use. Tell students to use factual information about drug use to help students say *no*. Display the ads on the bulletin board.

What will you say if someone tries to get you to use drugs? Having a plan can help you say *no* with confidence. One way to avoid being tempted is to have friends who don't abuse drugs. Another way is to go to places where drugs are not used. Getting involved with activities you enjoy will help you find friends who don't use drugs.

Organizations in your community may offer activities for people your age. Check out a community center, your school, or a religious center for fun things to do. You might join a sports team, a club, or a musical group.

If you have a problem, don't turn to drugs. Instead, talk with a parent or another trusted adult about your problem.

▼ **If you have a problem, talk with your parents or other trusted adults.**

Focus Skill **SUMMARIZE Identify ways to cope with or seek assistance when confronted with situations involving drugs.**

Lesson 4 Summary and Review

1. **Summarize with Vocabulary**
   Use vocabulary and other terms from this lesson to complete the statements.
   If you know the ways that drugs can harm you, it is easier to resist _____. Planning ways to say *no* can make it easier to _____. Refusing drugs will help you like yourself and feel proud of your actions and will help build _____.
2. **Critical Thinking** Why is it important to talk to a trusted adult to get help with your problems?
3. What are three healthful alternatives to drug use?
4. Focus Skill **SUMMARIZE** Draw and complete this graphic organizer to show ways to refuse drugs.

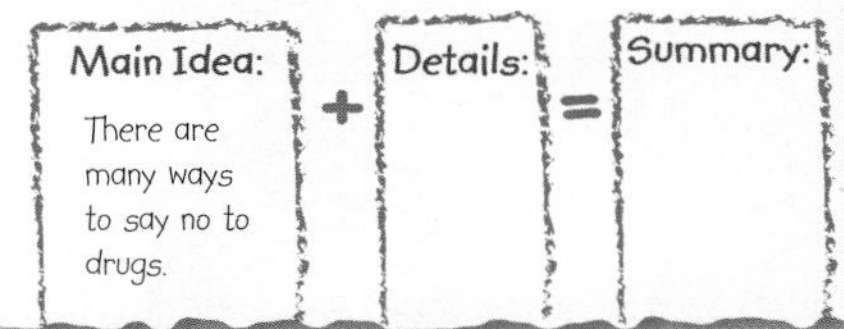

5. **Write to Express— Solution to a Problem**

   Write about how you would respond if you are ever offered drugs.

Have a plan, remember reasons for saying *no*, choose friends who are drug-free, become involved in activities, and talk about problems with a trusted adult instead of turning to drugs. 209

3. WRAP UP

Lesson 4 Summary and Review

1. peer pressure; refuse (say *no*); self-respect
2. Adults can offer support and encouragement in finding ways to refuse drugs. If you have a problem, they can help you find a solution because they have more experience and may have faced the problem themselves when they were your age.
3. Possible answers: joining a sports team or club; becoming involved in school activities; doing art projects; helping others
4. Possible responses:

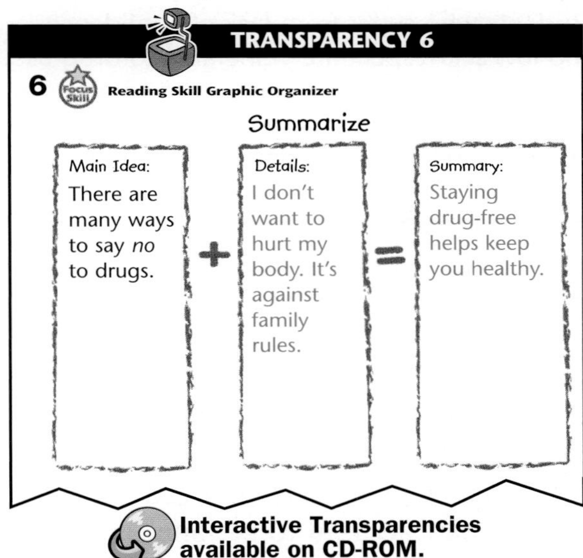

TRANSPARENCY 6
6 Reading Skill Graphic Organizer
Summarize
Main Idea:
There are many ways to say no to drugs.
Details:
I don't want to hurt my body. It's against family rules.
Summary:
Staying drug-free helps keep you healthy.
Interactive Transparencies available on CD-ROM.

5. Answers will vary but should reflect an understanding of the physical, social, and legal consequences of drug abuse, as contrasted with the positive outcomes of refusing drugs.

For **writing models** with examples, see *Teaching Resources* pp. 47–61. Rubrics are also provided.

Teacher Tip

Family Matters Healthy families provide the tools necessary for building self-respect. Unfortunately, not all parents are able to provide their children with unconditional love and the sense that they are lovable, capable people. This is especially true in homes where drug use is a problem. If you know students who are confronted with drug use at home, gently guide them to meet with counselors or become involved in activities and organizations that promote a sense of self-worth.

Language Arts

Say *No* with Humor Some students might find that using humor makes it easier and more comfortable to say *no* to drugs. Have students work in small groups to develop a list of humorous or clever drug refusals. Then invite them to role-play to demonstrate refusal skills to drugs. The humorous ways may be added to the list begun at the beginning of this lesson.

When Minutes Count . . .

Quick Study Students can use *Activity Book* pages 36–37 as they complete each lesson in this chapter.

LESSON 5
Pages 210–212

Objectives

- ► Recognize the warning signs of drug abuse.
- ► Identify people and organizations that can help with drug recovery.

When Minutes Count . . .
Assign the Quick Study, Lesson 5, Activity Book pp. 36–37 (shown on p. 189).

Program Resources

- ► Activity Book pp. 36–37, 40
- ► Transparency 6

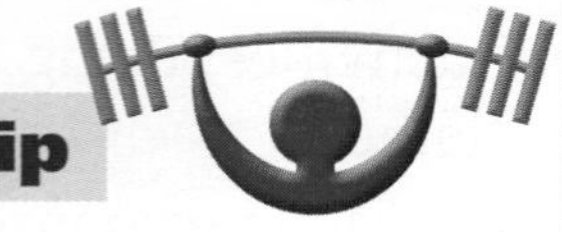

Daily Fitness Tip

Students who suffer from lack of confidence and low self-respect are vulnerable to drug use. If you suspect a student has turned to drugs or may soon turn to drugs to cope with personal problems, refer the student to the school guidance counselor.

1. MOTIVATE

Share the following scenario with students:
Matt is worried about his fifteen-year-old cousin, Tim. They used to be very close, but Tim's behavior has changed. He is quieter than he used to be, and he stays away from home a lot. When he does go home, he avoids his family. He often says he is not hungry and does not eat with his family. He stays in his room with the door closed most of the time. His family is worried.

His grades in school are dropping because he often skips school. He no longer plays the sports he used to enjoy. And he doesn't seem to care about how he looks. He doesn't bathe, change clothes, or comb his hair.

What do you think may have caused Tim's change in behavior? drug use

Problem Solving What would you do if you were Matt? Talk to my parents or to Tim's parents.

LESSON 5 How Drug Abusers Can Get Help

Lesson Focus
It's important to know the warning signs of a drug problem and where to go for help.

Why Learn This?
You can use what you learn to get help for yourself, family members, or friends who might need it.

Know the Warning Signs

People who abuse drugs need help. If you know the warning signs of drug abuse, you may be able to get help for someone you know who might be using drugs. Once a person admits that he or she has a drug problem, that person can get help.

Changes in mood and behavior are clues that a person might be using drugs. Drug abusers might be nervous or tired. They might get angry easily. Some users may avoid friends and stop doing things they used to enjoy. Others might not seem to care about how they look. Or their grades may drop, and they may not do well in other activities.

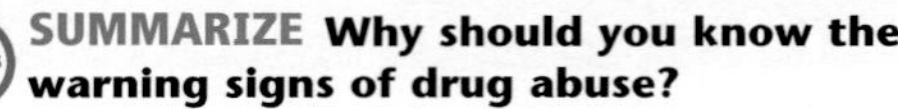

SUMMARIZE Why should you know the warning signs of drug abuse?
If you know the signs of drug use, you may be able to get help for the user.

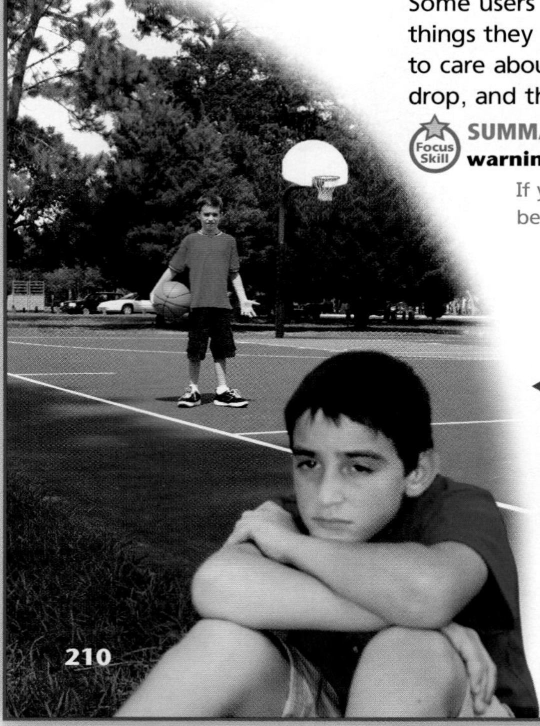

◄ Does a friend suddenly seem moody or sad? Has he or she stopped doing things with you? Your friend might have a drug problem and need help.

ESL/ELL Support

BACKGROUND AND EXPERIENCE Tailor the lesson to the needs of students by ascertaining what they already know about the warning signs of drug abuse.

Beginning Ask students to act out what they already know about the warning signs of drug abuse. Role-play for them the warning signs they are not yet familiar with.

Intermediate Have students write a list of the warning signs of drug abuse.

Advanced Have students use the text to create a graphic organizer summarizing the warning signs of drug abuse.

Tell a trusted adult. ▶

When Does Someone Need Help?

Yes answers to one or more of these questions might mean you need to find help for yourself or someone else.

- Do you have friends who use drugs?
- Have your friends tried to get you to use drugs?
- Have you ever used drugs just for fun?
- Have you ever taken OTC medicines just to improve your mood?
- Do you have friends who sell drugs?

Take Action

You might think that someone else's drug problem is not your business. You might think that you will hurt the user if you tell others about the problem. But taking illegal drugs is harmful. Trying to help the user is the caring thing to do.

If you, a friend, or a family member needs help, talk with your parents or other trusted adults. They will know how to get help. If a parent or guardian needs help, speak to another adult you trust.

There are organizations that can help with recovery, the process a user goes through to stop taking drugs. You can find the names of these organizations in a school or community library.

2. TEACH

Interpret Visuals—Pictures

Draw students' attention to the picture on page 210. Use this as an opportunity to ask students to give examples of ways to identify the abuse of prescription medicines and over-the-counter medicines.

What signs of harmful drug use might this person be showing? The person has removed himself from his friends. He is not playing with them, and he looks sad.

Critical Thinking **Is everyone who shows the behaviors mentioned on page 210 abusing drugs? Explain.** Students will likely recognize that the behaviors could be due to problems other than drug abuse, such as depression or disappointment.

Problem Solving **What would be the best thing for you to do if you knew someone who showed the warning signs of harmful drug use but you didn't know if drugs were a problem?** Students should recognize that people showing these kinds of behaviors need help no matter what is causing the behavior. Students should state that it is important to tell a trusted adult.

For more help on what to do when others use drugs and information on having a drug-free school, refer students to the Health and Safety Handbook pp. 354–355.

Drama

Now Hear This! Encourage students to write and record a series of public service announcements geared to helping their peers identify the signs of drug use. If possible, allow students to broadcast their announcements over the school's public address system.

Teacher Tip

Treatment Information

National Clearinghouse for Alcohol and Drug Information, P.O. Box 2345, Rockville, MD 20847, (800) 729-6686

National Council on Alcoholism and Drug Dependence, Public Information Office, 20 Exchange Place, Suite 2902, New York, NY 10005, (800) 622-2255

National Drug and Alcohol Treatment Referral Hotline, (800) 662-4357, directs people to counselors and resources.

3. WRAP UP

Lesson 5 Summary and Review

1. warning signs; recovery
2. tell a responsible adult
3. Possible answers: mood changes; sadness; tiredness; anger; avoiding friends and family; avoiding usual activities and interests
4. Possible responses:

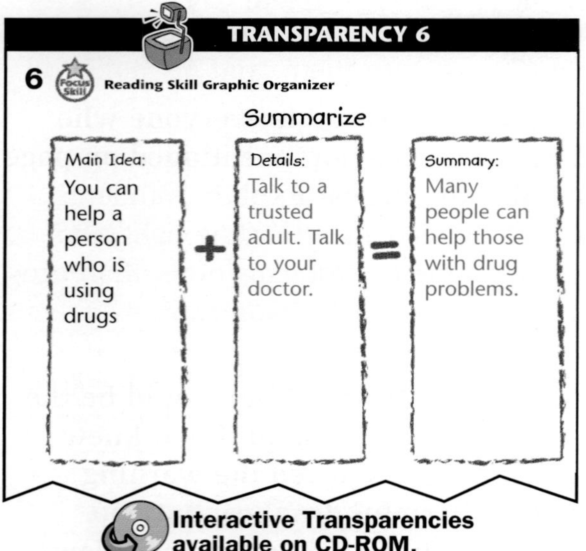

Interactive Transparencies available on CD-ROM.

5. Answers might include any changes in appearance, behavior, or mood, such as those mentioned on page 210.

For **writing models** with examples, see *Teaching Resources* pp. 47–61. Rubrics are also provided.

When Minutes Count . . .

Quick Study Students can use *Activity Book* pages 36–37 as they complete each lesson in this chapter.

▼There are people in your family, school, and community to talk with about drug problems.

▲Your parents

▲Your doctor

▲Your teacher, school nurse, or counselor

▲Another trusted adult

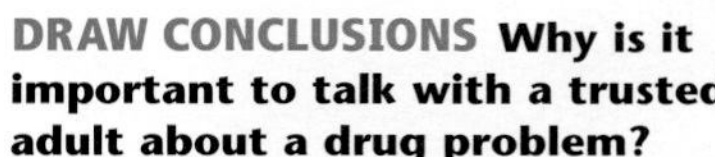

DRAW CONCLUSIONS Why is it important to talk with a trusted adult about a drug problem?

A trusted adult can find the best way to get help for a person with a drug problem.

Lesson 5 Summary and Review

1. **Summarize with Vocabulary**
   Use terms from this lesson to complete the statements.
   Mood swings and poor grades may be _____ of drug use. Many organizations can help drug users with _____, the process of stopping drug use.
2. **Critical Thinking** What should you do if you think a friend has a drug problem?
3. List three warning signs of drug use.
4. **SUMMARIZE** Draw and complete this graphic organizer to show how you can take action to help someone who wants to stop using drugs.

Main Idea: You can help a person who is using drugs.
Summary: Many people can help those with drug problems.
+
Details:
=
Summary:

5. **Write to Inform—How-To**
   Write how to tell if someone you know has a possible drug problem.

ACTIVITY BOOK P. 40

Name ______________

Vocabulary Reinforcement

Use Word Meanings

Underline the term that makes the sentence correct.

1. (Recovery Self-respect) is the process of stopping drug use.
2. If you have an (addiction, illegal drug,) you have a craving that makes you use a drug.
3. The drug (cocaine marijuana) is from the hemp plant.
4. A (recovery drug) is a substance that changes the way your body works.
5. Fumes from household products that are used as drugs are (prescription drugs. inhalants.)
6. Two examples of (drug dependence illegal drugs) are cocaine and marijuana.
7. (Over-the-counter medicines Prescription medicines) are drugs you can buy without a doctor's order.
8. When your friends try to get you to do something, that is called (self-respect. peer pressure.)
9. You have (self-respect drug dependence) when you need to take a drug to feel normal.
10. (Caffeine Marijuana) is a drug found in coffee.

© Harcourt

Available online. www.harcourtschool.com/health

Teacher Tip

Speaking from Experience
Invite a substance abuse counselor to speak to students about his or her personal experiences. To locate a volunteer, contact drug treatment facilities in your area. Encourage students to prepare questions in advance, focusing on how substance abuse affects individuals, their families and friends, and the community. Also encourage students to explore the ongoing nature of the recovery process.

ACTIVITIES

Science

Caffeine-Containing Plants Do some research on plants that contain caffeine, such as coffee beans, tea leaves, and cola nuts. Find out how these plants are used in food and beverage products and where they come from.

Physical Education

Find Your Heart Rate Find your heart rate by holding your first two fingers at the base of your jaw line or at the inside of your wrist. Then count heartbeats for fifteen seconds, and multiply that number by four to find the heart rate. Report on how using large amounts of caffeine might affect a person's heart rate.

Technology Project

Think of the ways drug use affects each member of a family. Use a computer to make a slide presentation showing the effects of one person's drug use on each family member. Present your slide show to your family or classmates. If a computer is not available, you can draw a flowchart on paper or make overhead transparencies.

For more activities, visit The Learning Site. www.harcourtschool.com/health

Home & Community

Communicating Discuss with family members the information and safety rules you have learned about taking medicines. Make a medicine safety checklist like the one shown on page 192 to post near places where medicines are stored.

Career Link

Drug Rehabilitation Counselor Drug rehabilitation counselors help people who have problems with drug addictions. They help users identify the behaviors and problems that cause their addictions. They have counseling sessions for individual users, their families, or groups. The counselors work closely with doctors to help an addict overcome his or her addiction. Describe how you might try to help someone if you were a drug rehabilitation counselor.

213

Career Link

Drug Rehabilitation Counselor Have students make a list of suggestions a drug rehabilitation counselor might talk to a person about. Encourage students to use their lists to role-play a situation between a drug counselor and someone who asks for help.

For more information on health careers, visit the **Webliography** in Teacher Resources at **www.harcourtschool.com/health**
Keyword health careers

Activities

Science

Students might be further challenged to find out how caffeine is taken out of coffee and tea to make decaf beverages.

Physical Education

Students may want to try doing some physical activity and then retaking their pulse rates to see what effect activities have on heart rate. Make sure students don't have any health conditions before having them attempt this activity. Discuss reasons why athletes might avoid caffeine and alcohol.

Home & Community

Discuss various places where medicines might be stored in a home (medicine cabinet or another cabinet, refrigerator, and so on). Students could post a medicine safety checklist at each of these locations throughout the home.

CSHP **Supports the Coordinated School Health Program**

Technology Project

Have students present their slide shows or flow charts to their classmates or family. Encourage them to discuss ways in which drug use affects each member of a family.

Chapter Review and Test Preparation

Pages 214–215

Reading Skill 5 pts. each

1. Possible answers: Have a parent or another trusted adult give medicine; keep medicines in the packages they come in; throw away old medicines; follow the label's instructions; never take someone else's medicine; never crush pills without a doctor's permission; store medicines out of the reach of small children and in a locked cabinet.
2. Possible answers: makes it hard to learn and remember things; causes confusion and nervousness; makes it hard to judge time and distance; makes the heart work harder; damages the lungs; causes cancer

Use Vocabulary 5 pts. each

3. C, peer pressure
4. A, side effects
5. D, medicine
6. E, dose
7. F, recovery
8. B, drug abuser

Check Understanding 5 pts. each

9. C, self-respect
10. J, work toward your goals
11. A, It caused the number to drop.
12. J, all of the above
13. B, over-the-counter medicines
14. G, go to a doctor, get a prescription, go to a pharmacy
15. C, It causes lung cancer.

Think Critically 5 pts. each

16. It should not be given to a child under twelve years of age, unless directed by a doctor.
17. If you know the warning signs of drug use, you can get help for friends or family members who might need it.

Chapter Review and Test Preparation

Reading Skill

SUMMARIZE

Copy this graphic organizer, and then use it to answer questions 1 and 2.

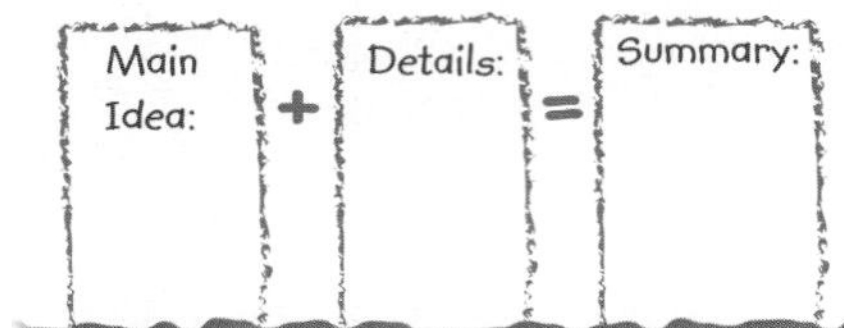

1 How can medicines be used safely?

2 How does marijuana affect the body?

Use Vocabulary

Match each term in Column B with its meaning in Column A.

Column A	Column B
3 Influence from others	**A** side effects
4 Changes caused by a medicine	**B** drug abuser
5 Drug used to prevent or treat a health problem	**C** peer pressure
6 Amount of medicine taken	**D** medicine
7 Stopping the use of drugs	**E** dose
8 Someone who uses illegal drugs	**F** recovery

Check Understanding

9 The feeling you have about yourself when you like yourself is called _____. (p. 206)

A addiction **C** self-respect
B peer pressure **D** dependence

10 Refusing drugs allows you to _____. (pp. 206–207)

F do poorly in school
G hurt your family relationships
H lose self-respect
J work toward your goals

11 How did the use of safety caps affect the number of children poisoned by medicines? (p. 193)

A It caused the number to drop.
B It did not change the number.
C It caused more children to be hurt.
D None of these.

12 Using marijuana can cause _____. (pp. 200–201, 203, 204)

F health problems **H** legal problems
G family problems **J** all of the above

13 Medicines that can be bought without a doctor's order are called _____. (p. 191)

A cough medicines
B over-the-counter medicines
C prescription medicines
D antibiotics

214

Formal Assessment

ASSESSMENT GUIDE P. 40

8 Name ______ Chapter Test

Medicines, Drugs, and Your Health

Read about each feeling or action. Then match each term below to one of the descriptions. Write the correct letter on the line to the left of the description.

a peer pressure **b** refuses **c** responsibility **d** self-respect

b 1. What Billy does when he is asked to try illegal drugs
a 2. What Billy feels when his friends push him to use drugs
d 3. What Billy feels when he says, "No, I have better things to do."
c 4. What Billy shows if he tells a trusted adult about a friend who uses drugs

Write *T* or *F* to show whether each statement is true or false.

F 5. If you take the correct dose of medicine, you will never get side effects.
T 6. An illegal drug is a drug that is not a medicine and is against the law to sell, buy, have, or use.
F 7. Drug users are not breaking the law. They are just trying new experiences.
T 8. Marijuana is an illegal drug made from the hemp plant.
F 9. Heavy marijuana use never leads to drug dependence.
F 10. Cocaine is another name for marijuana.

© Harcourt

ASSESSMENT GUIDE P. 41

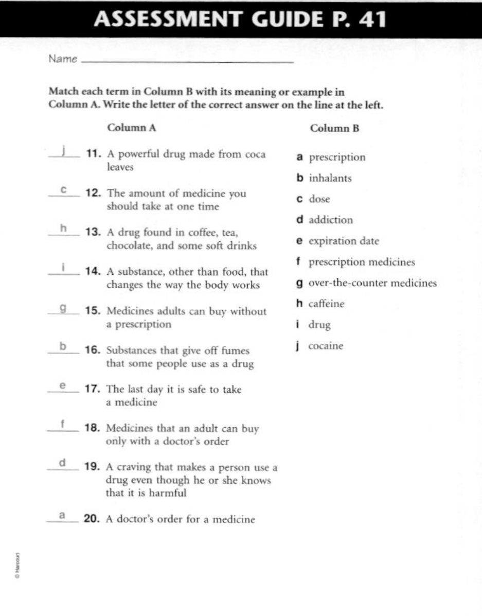

Name ______

Match each term in Column B with its meaning or example in Column A. Write the letter of the correct answer on the line at the left.

Column A	Column B
j 11. A powerful drug made from coca leaves	**a** prescription
c 12. The amount of medicine you should take at one time	**b** inhalants
h 13. A drug found in coffee, tea, chocolate, and some soft drinks	**c** dose
i 14. A substance, other than food, that changes the way the body works	**d** addiction
g 15. Medicines adults can buy without a prescription	**e** expiration date
b 16. Substances that give off fumes that some people use as a drug	**f** prescription medicines
e 17. The last day it is safe to take a medicine	**g** over-the-counter medicines
f 18. Medicines that an adult can buy only with a doctor's order	**h** caffeine
d 19. A craving that makes a person use a drug even though he or she knows that it is harmful	**i** drug
a 20. A doctor's order for a medicine	**j** cocaine

© Harcourt

14 Which of the following belongs in the blank? (p. 190)

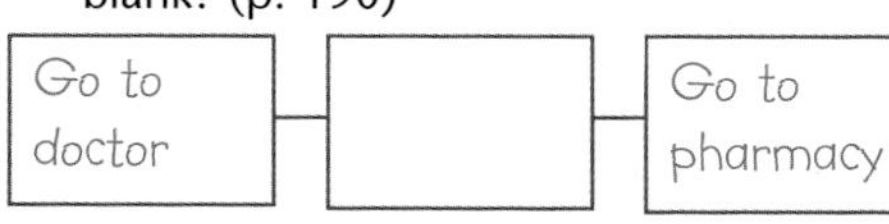

- **F** try OTC medicine, get prescription, go to pharmacy
- **G** go to doctor, get prescription, go to pharmacy
- **H** go to pharmacy, get prescription, go to doctor
- **J** go to doctor, go to pharmacy, get prescription

15 Which does **NOT** describe an effect of cocaine on the body? (p. 203)

- **A** It makes it hard to learn.
- **B** It makes the heart work harder than it should.
- **C** It causes lung cancer.
- **D** It makes it hard to breathe.

Think Critically

16 Study the OTC medicine label shown. What does it tell you about the safety of this medicine for someone your age?

> **Directions**
> Adults and children 12 years and over: Take 2 caplets at bedtime.
>
> Should not be used by children under 12 years of age.

17 Why is it important to know the warning signs of drug abuse?

Apply Skills

18 **BUILDING GOOD CHARACTER**
Responsibility One of your friends has started hanging around with people who use drugs. He has stopped doing activities he used to enjoy. His clothes look messy, too. You think he might be using drugs, but you don't want to get him into trouble. What is the best way to show responsibility in what you know about your friend's situation?

19 **LIFE SKILLS**
Refuse Suppose you have just returned from a long hike. Your legs are tired, and your feet hurt. Your friend offers you some medicine to make you feel better. What do you do? Explain how you will respond to your friend.

Write About Health

20 **Write to Inform—Description** Imagine that you are participating in a school health fair. Create a pamphlet that describes how medicines can be harmful as well as helpful.

Apply Skills 5 pts. each

18. Tell a trusted adult about your concerns so that your friend can get help.

19. You should never take a medicine unless a parent or another trusted adult gives it to you. Instead, you could try alternatives such as taking a hot bath, rubbing your feet, or putting your feet up. Students should include the decision-making process in their answers.

Write About Health 5 pts.

20. Pamphlets should include the harmful effects of inhaling fumes from common household products.

Performance Assessment

Use the Chapter Project and the rubric provided on the Project Evaluation Sheet. See *Assessment Guide* pp. 18, 59, 69.

Portfolio Assessment

Have students select their best work from the following suggestions:

- Leveled Activities, p. 190
- Quick Activity, p. 203
- Write to Inform, p. 193
- Activities, p. 213

See *Assessment Guide* pp. 12–16.

ASSESSMENT GUIDE P. 42

21. Underline the behaviors that might be warning signs of someone taking drugs.

- sudden bursts of anger
- friendliness
- changes in mood
- poor health habits
- poor schoolwork
- excellent schoolwork
- a lot of fighting
- great sense of humor

22. Suppose your best friend has a problem with inhalants. Suggest someone your friend might talk to about this problem.

Accept the name of any trusted adult in the student's family, school, or wider community, e.g., doctor, parents, teacher, religious leader.

Suppose that you were going to teach the class about drugs. Choose one of the drugs from the list. Write two ways this drug can affect people's bodies or minds.

inhalants marijuana cocaine caffeine

Accept any of the following answers:

23. INHALANTS: clumsiness, headache, nausea, confusion, memory loss, brain damage, death; MARIJUANA: lung damage including cancer, makes heart work harder, brain changes including difficulty learning, remembering, and judging time or distance, confusion, nervousness;

24. COCAINE: mood changes, makes heart work harder, seizures, heart failure and heart attack, difficulty breathing, lung damage, cancer; CAFFEINE: speeds up the heart, trouble sleeping, nervousness

25. Your little sister can't read. Draw a picture to show her a rule for the safe use of medicines.

Drawings should reflect rules such as the following: never take medicine on your own, don't take someone else's medicine, take medicine only from a trusted adult, tell an adult if a medicine makes you feel ill. Accept any reasonable interpretation of the rules listed on pages 192–193.

© Harcourt

CHAPTER 9 Harmful Effects of Alcohol and Tobacco

Lesson	Pacing	Objectives	Reading Skills
Introduce the Chapter pp. 216–217		• Preview chapter concepts.	**Cause and Effect** pp. 217, 330–331
1 **How Tobacco Harms Body Systems** pp. 218–223	2 class periods	• Describe tobacco products and the harm they cause to the body. • Explain why some young people begin smoking and why stopping is difficult.	**Cause and Effect** pp. 219, 223 • Sequence, p. 221 • Draw Conclusions, p. 223
2 **How Alcohol Harms Body Systems** pp. 224–229	3 class periods	• Describe alcohol and the harm it causes to body systems and behavior. • Identify some effects of problem drinking.	**Cause and Effect** pp. 227, 229 • Draw Conclusions, p. 225
3 **Saying *No* to Alcohol and Tobacco** pp. 230–233	1 class period	• Demonstrate strategies for refusing the use of alcohol and tobacco. • Discuss ways to resist peer pressure to use alcohol and tobacco.	**Cause and Effect** pp. 231, 233 • Main Idea and Details, p. 233
Life Skills pp. 234–235	1 class period	• Identify ways to say *no*. • Practice ways to refuse alcohol and tobacco.	
4 **Tobacco and Alcohol Users Can Get Help** pp. 236–238	1 class period	• List warning signs of alcohol and tobacco use. • Name sources of help for alcohol or tobacco users.	**Cause and Effect** p. 238 • Summarize, p. 237 • Draw Conclusions, p. 238
Building Good Character p. 239		• Identify ways to show trustworthiness by reporting dangerous situations.	
5 **Tobacco, Alcohol, and the Media** pp. 240–242	1 class period	• Understand the purpose of tobacco and alcohol advertisements. • Identify how truthful or misleading an advertisement is.	**Cause and Effect** p. 242 • Compare and Contrast, p. 241 • Draw Conclusions, p. 242
Activities p. 243		• Extend chapter concepts.	
Chapter Review pp. 244–245	1 class period	• Assess chapter objectives.	

Vocabulary	Program Resources
	Music CD Teaching Resources, p. 39
nicotine tar	Transparency 3 Activity Book, pp. 41–43
alcohol intoxicated alcoholism	Transparency 3 Activity Book, pp. 41–42
	Transparency 3 Activity Book, pp. 41–42
	Activity Book, p. 44 Poster 10
	Transparency 3 Activity Book, pp. 41–42
	Poster 6
	Transparency 3 Activity Book, pp. 41–42, 45
	The Learning Site www.harcourtschool.com
	Assessment Guide, pp. 43–45

Interactive Transparencies available on CD-ROM.

Reading Skill

These reading skills are reinforced throughout this chapter and one skill is emphasized as the Focus Skill.

Identify Cause and Effect

- Draw Conclusions
- Compare and Contrast
- Identify Main Idea and Details
- Sequence
- Summarize

KEY READING SKILLS TRANSPARENCY 3

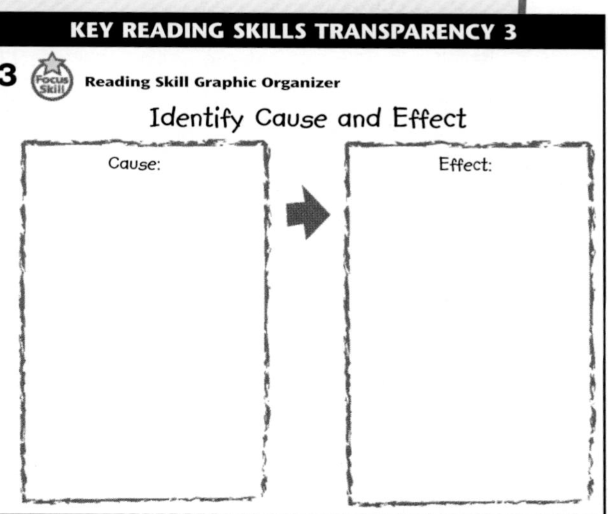
3 Reading Skill Graphic Organizer

Identify Cause and Effect

Cause:

Effect:

Life Skills

Life Skills are health-enhancing behaviors that can help students reduce risks to their health and safety.

Six Life Skills are reinforced throughout *Harcourt Health and Fitness*. The skill emphasized in this chapter is Refuse.

POSTER 10 REFUSE

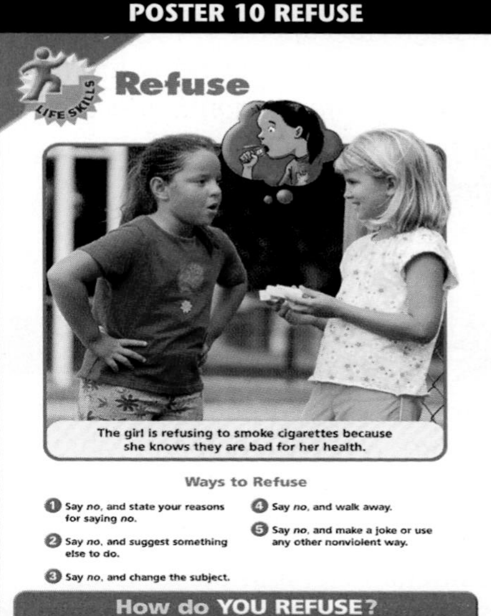

Refuse
The girl is refusing to smoke cigarettes because she knows they are bad for her health.
Ways to Refuse
1 Say no, and state your reasons for saying no.
2 Say no, and suggest something else to do.
3 Say no, and change the subject.
4 Say no, and walk away.
5 Say no, and make a joke or use any other nonviolent way.
How do YOU REFUSE?

Building Good Character

Character education is an important aspect of health education. When children behave in ways that show good character, they promote the health and safety of themselves and others.

Six character traits are reinforced throughout *Harcourt Health and Fitness*. The trait emphasized in this chapter is Trustworthiness.

POSTER 6 TRUSTWORTHINESS

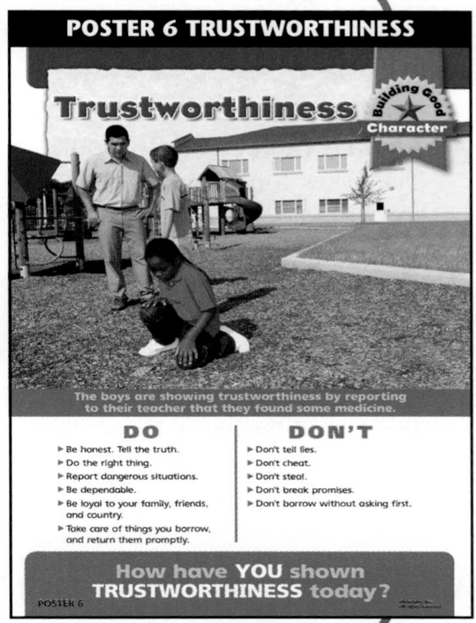

Resources

Coordinated School Health Program

Health Education
Health Services
Physical Education
Nutrition Services
Parent/ Community Involvement
Healthy School Environment
Counseling, Psychological, & Social Services
Health Promotion for Staff
CSHP

A Coordinated School Health Program endeavors to improve children's health and therefore their capacity to learn through the support of families, schools, and communities working together. The following information is provided to help classroom teachers be more aware of these resources.

Books for Students

Royston, Angela. ***Tobacco (Learn to Say No!)***. Heinemann Library, 2000. Discusses tobacco's damaging effects on the body. **EASY**

Sanders, Pete, and Steve Myers. ***Drinking Alcohol (What Do You Know About)***. Copper Beech Books, 1997. Explains why people drink and where to go to get help. **AVERAGE**

Sanders, Pete, and Steve Myers. ***Smoking (What Do You Know About)***. Copper Beech Books, 1996. Discusses the harmful effects of smoking. **ADVANCED**

Books for Teachers and Families

Lang, Susan S., and Beth H. Marks. ***Teens & Tobacco: A Fatal Attraction***. Twenty-First Century Books, 1996. Written for teens but helpful for adults who work with youth.

Wilmes, David J. ***Alcohol Is a Drug Too:***

The National Center for Chronic Disease and Health Promotion, part of the **CDC**, funds the Coordinated School Health Program. Visit its website for information about the eight components that make up this program.
www.cdc.gov/nccdphp/dash/

Statistics indicate that people make decisions about smoking very early in life, usually at about the age of 16. About 80 percent of all adults who smoke began before the age of 18. Visit the **American Heart Association** for Tobacco-Free Background Information.
www.americanheart.org/

Kids who drink are more likely to be victims of violent crime, to be involved in alcohol-related traffic crashes, and to have serious school-related problems.

Media Resources

What Happens to Kids When We're Afraid to Say No. Johnson Institute, 1993. Challenges adults who are charged with modeling for youth.

Free and Inexpensive Materials

National Clearinghouse for Alcohol and Drug Information
Ask for free copies of their research-based guide, *Preventing Drug Use Among Children and Adolescents*; also has topics such as "A Lesson Learned About Alcohol from Harry Potter and the Sorceror's Stone."

Social Studies School Service
Request a copy of its Health Education catalog containing sample lessons from activity books and a poster on dangers of smoking.

The American Lung Association
Request the free e-mail newsletter on topics such as the Tobacco Control Tribune.

To access free and inexpensive resources on the Web, visit
www.harcourtschool.com/health/free

The **National Institute on Alcohol Abuse and Alcoholism**, an arm of the National Institutes of Health, publishes *Make a Difference: Talk to Your Kids About Alcohol.* **www.health.nih.gov/**

The **CDC** advises that tobacco-related oral lesions are common in children who use smokeless tobacco. The lesions occur in 35 percent of snuff users and 20 percent of chewing tobacco users.
www.cdc.gov/OralHealth/

Other resources that support a Coordinated School Health Program:

- School-Home Connection
- Daily Physical Activity
- Daily Fitness Tips
- Activities: Home & Community
- Health Background: Webliography
- *Be Active! Resources for Physical Education*

Videos

Breath of Life: Our Respiratory System. Rainbow Educational Media, 1992.

"The Talk": Tobacco, Alcohol, and Other Drugs. Boo Boo Productions, 1999.

The Trouble with Tobacco. Rainbow Educational Media, 1996.

These resources have been selected to meet a variety of individual needs. Please review all materials and websites prior to sharing them with students to ensure the content is appropriate for your class. Note that information, while correct at time of publication, is subject to change.

Visit **The Learning Site** for related links, activities, resources, and the health **Webliography.**

www.harcourtschool.com/health

Meeting Individual Needs

Below-Level

To help students recognize letter patterns in words, have them go through the chapter on a "word hunt." For example, tell them that you are looking for any word that contains *er* as in *emergency*. Write the words on the board, and circle the *er* in each one.

Activities

- Make Truthful Ads, p. 220
- Conduct an Interview, p. 226
- Make Collages, p. 232
- Write Ads, p. 238

On-Level

Encourage students to jot down key words or concepts that are unclear. If something does not make sense, remind students that they may have missed an important point. Tell them to reread the passage, focusing on the context of the key words.

Activities

- Make Charts, p. 220
- Make a Display, p. 226
- Write Stories, p. 232
- Make Lists, p. 238

Challenge

Have students use a minimum number of vocabulary words to make up brief stories or dialogues. Students can write their stories or dialogues on paper and then record them. Have other students listen for the words in context and tell the meanings.

Activities

- Conduct Interviews, p. 220
- Estimate BAL by Body Weight, p. 226
- Perform a Puppet Show, p. 232
- Make a Database, p. 238

ESL/ELL

Reading Workshop

After reading a section of the text, have students think of two questions to ask a volunteer seated in the "answer chair." Students take turns asking the questions. When the student in the "answer chair" has answered two questions correctly, another student can take a turn.

Activities

- Comprehensible Input, pp. 228, 231, 236

Curriculum Integration

Use these topics to integrate health into your daily planning.

Integrated Language Arts/Reading Skills

- Write a Script, p. 222
- Warning Labels, p. 225
- Feelings About Drinking and Driving, p. 229
- Newspaper Editorial, p. 233
- Have a Debate, p. 240
- Advertising Messages, p. 241

Math

- Smoking Costs, p. 234

Physical Education

- Daily Fitness Tip, pp. 218, 224, 230, 236, 240
- Daily Physical Activity, p. 217

Science

- Investigate Nicotine, p. 221
- Alcohol Breakdown, p. 224
- Reaction Time, p. 227

Social Studies

- Alcohol Laws, p. 225
- No More Liquor Ads, p. 230
- Cigarette Ads, p. 241

Art

- Pamphlets, p. 229

CHAPTER
9
Pages 216–245

CHAPTER SUMMARY

In this chapter, students

- learn the harmful effects of alcohol and tobacco and why people use them.
- learn to recognize the warning signs of a person's needing help for a tobacco or alcohol problem and where to get it.

Life Skills
Students practice ways to *refuse* tobacco and alcohol and to overcome negative peer pressure.

Building Good Character
Students practice *trustworthiness* about reporting dangerous situations.

Consumer Health
Students *analyze* advertising and media messages.

Literature Springboard

Use the excerpt from "Where There's SMOKE" to spark interest in the chapter topic. See the Read-Aloud Anthology on page RA-10 of this *Teacher Edition.*

Prereading Strategies

SCAN THE CHAPTER Have students preview the chapter content by scanning the titles, headings, pictures, and graphs. Ask volunteers to speculate on what new information they will learn. Use their predictions to determine their prior knowledge.

PREVIEW VOCABULARY As students scan the chapter, point out the vocabulary words listed at the beginning of each lesson. Pronounce each word, and have students repeat the word. Invite volunteers to offer the meanings of any words they recognize. Ask students to look up each word in the Glossary.

CHAPTER 9

Harmful Effects of Tobacco and Alcohol

216

Reading Skill

IDENTIFY CAUSE AND EFFECT To introduce or review this skill, have students use the Reading in Health Handbook, pp. 334–335. Teaching strategies and additional activities are also provided.

Students will have opportunities to practice and apply this skill throughout this chapter.

- Focus Skill Reading Mini-Lesson, p. 218
- Reading Skill questions identified with the 
- *Activity Book* p. 43 (shown on p. 223)
- Lesson Summary and Review, pp. 223, 229, 233, 238, 242
- Chapter Review and Test Preparation, pp. 244–245

Reading Skill

IDENTIFY CAUSE AND EFFECT
Effect is what happens. Cause is the reason, or why, it happens. Use the Reading in Health Handbook on pages 334–335 and this graphic organizer to help you read the health facts in this chapter.

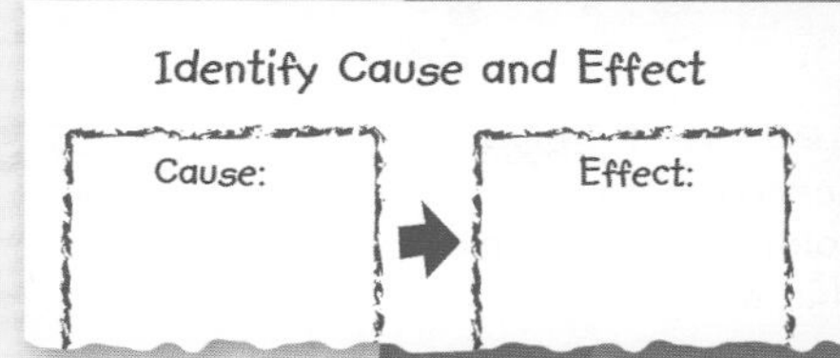

Health Graph

INTERPRET DATA In the 1920s, it was against the law to drink alcohol in the United States. At that time, Americans drank less alcohol than at any other time in history. How did the amount of alcohol drunk by American adults change from 1934 to 1980?

Yearly Amount of Alcohol Drunk by American Adults

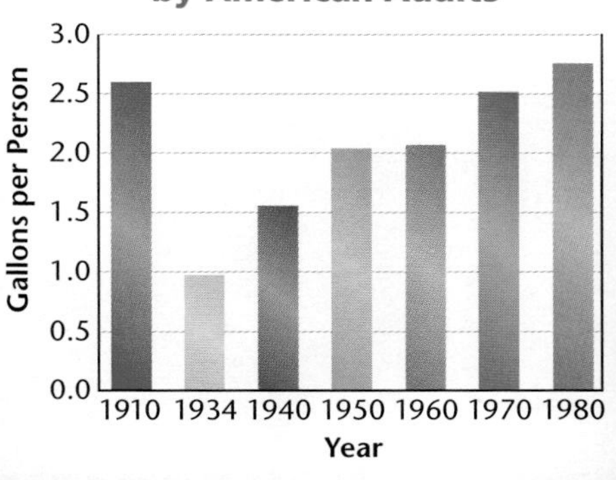

Daily Physical Activity

You can stay healthy and free from effects of tobacco and alcohol. Be physically active.

Be Active!
Use the selection Track 9, **Hop To It**, to practice some healthful activity choices.

INTRODUCE THE CHAPTER

Health Graph

Interpret Data

Ask for volunteers to explain what information the graph is presenting.

How has the amount of alcohol used by American adults changed from 1934 to 1980? It decreased after 1934 and increased after 1940.

How many gallons of alcohol did the average adult drink in 1980? 2.76 gallons

What year did the average adult drink the least amount of alcohol? 1934

Daily Physical Activity

Use *Be Active! Music for Daily Physical Activity* with the Instant Activity Cards to provide students with movement activities that can be done in limited space. Options for using these components are provided beginning on page TR2 in this *Teacher Edition.*

Chapter Project

Don't Let the Ads Fool You! (*Assessment Guide* p. 60)

ASSESS PRIOR KNOWLEDGE Use students' initial ideas for the project as a baseline assessment of their understanding of chapter concepts. Have students complete the project as they work through the chapter.

PERFORMANCE ASSESSMENT The project can be used for performance assessment. Use the Project Evaluation Sheet (rubric), *Assessment Guide* p. 70.

School-Home Connection

Distribute copies of the School-Home Connection (in English or Spanish). Have students take the page home to share with their families as you begin this chapter.

Follow Up Have volunteers share their list of smoking cessation programs.

Supports the Coordinated School Health Program

TEACHING RESOURCES P. 39

School-Home Connection A Note to Family Members

What We Are Learning About Health

In Chapter 9 of *Harcourt Health and Fitness*, we are learning about
- the reasons people use tobacco and alcohol and the harmful effects these drugs have on the body.
- signs that someone has a problem with alcohol or tobacco.
- ways to say *no* to alcohol and tobacco and to deal with peer pressure.

Visit www.harcourtschool.com/health for links to parent resources.

How You Can Help

Parental involvement in the school environment is part of a coordinated school health plan that includes the home, school, community, and social services. You can support your school through increased communication and by volunteering your time or talents. At home you can support your child's learning by
- discussing the use of tobacco and alcohol in your community.
- explaining why a person might need help to stop using alcohol or tobacco.
- role-playing ways your child can refuse tobacco and alcohol.

A Family Activity

With your child, research local programs that are available to help people stop using tobacco. Look in a local telephone directory, read ads in local newspapers, or call a local hospital to find out about resources for those who want to stop using tobacco. Help your child enter your findings in the table below.

Local Stop-Smoking Programs

Name of Program	Where It Meets	When It Meets	Phone Number

Available online.
www.harcourtschool.com/health

LESSON 1
Pages 218–223

Objectives
- ► Describe tobacco products and the harm they cause the body.
- ► Explain why some young people begin smoking and why stopping is difficult.

When Minutes Count . . .
Assign the Quick Study, Lesson 1, Activity Book pp. 41–42 (shown on p. 219).

Program Resources
- ► Activity Book pp. 41–43
- ► Transparency 3

Vocabulary
nicotine p. 219, **tar** p. 219

Daily Fitness Tip
Nonsmokers who are exposed to environmental tobacco smoke (ETS) absorb nicotine and other compounds just as smokers do. The greater the exposure to ETS, the greater the levels of harmful compounds in the body. Remind students to avoid ETS by politely asking those who are smoking to move away from them or to designated smoking areas during recreational events.

For more guidelines about tobacco and your physical fitness, see *Be Active! Resources for Physical Education* p. 169.

1. MOTIVATE
Optional Activity Materials 6-inch square of cloth, petroleum jelly, paper-towel tube

Hold a piece of cloth around the end of a paper-towel tube while you blow into the open end of the tube. Allow students to place their hands so they can feel the breath as it passes through the cloth. Explain that the cloth represents the tiny air sacs inside the lungs that allow oxygen to pass through when we breathe. Then coat the cloth with petroleum jelly and again blow through the tube. Explain that this coating represents the tar that smoke leaves inside the lungs.

LESSON 1

How Tobacco Harms Body Systems

Lesson Focus
Tobacco products contain many chemicals that harm the body.

Why Learn This?
Understanding that tobacco is a harmful drug can help you refuse to use it.

Vocabulary
nicotine
tar

Tobacco
The brown material inside a cigarette is called tobacco. It comes from dried leaves of the tobacco plant. When people smoke cigarettes, they breathe tobacco smoke into their lungs. It can harm the lungs and other parts of the body.

Another kind of tobacco—chewing tobacco—comes in small bags. People who use chewing tobacco put small wads of it into their mouths. Snuff is another tobacco product. People suck on pinches of it that they put in their mouths.

▼ The use of tobacco products is dangerous. In many places, it is against the law for people under 18 years old to use tobacco products.

218

Reading Skill

Mini-Lesson
IDENTIFY CAUSE AND EFFECT Remind students that effect is what happens. Cause is the reason, or why, it happens. Have them practice this skill by responding to the Focus Skill question on p. 219. Have students draw and complete the graphic organizer as you model it on the transparency.

TRANSPARENCY 3

3 Reading Skill Graphic Organizer

Identify Cause and Effect

Cause:	Effect:
Smoking tobacco	Tobacco smoke contains harmful chemicals that can hurt the lungs and other parts of the body.

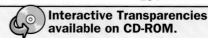

Interactive Transparencies available on CD-ROM.

Harmful Chemicals in Cigarette Smoke

Other

Nicotine

Carbon Monoxide

Tar

▲ Most chemicals in cigarette smoke are harmful. Just a little nicotine can kill a person.

Quick Activity

Interpret Graphs Look at the circle graph on this page. What chemical is found the most in cigarette smoke? How do the other chemicals compare to this chemical?

All forms of tobacco contain nicotine. **Nicotine** is a very addictive chemical that speeds up the nervous system. People addicted to nicotine have a constant need, or craving, for this chemical. They find it hard to stop using nicotine.

Another dangerous chemical in tobacco smoke is tar. **Tar** is a dark, sticky material that coats the lungs and air passages of smokers. Tar buildup makes it hard for a smoker to breathe.

Tobacco smoke also contains many other harmful chemicals. In fact, tobacco smoke contains more than 4,000 chemicals. About 50 of those chemicals are known to cause cancer.

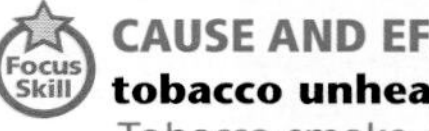

CAUSE AND EFFECT Why is smoking tobacco unhealthful? Tobacco smoke contains harmful chemicals that can hurt the lungs and other parts of the body.

▲ Diseased lung tissue

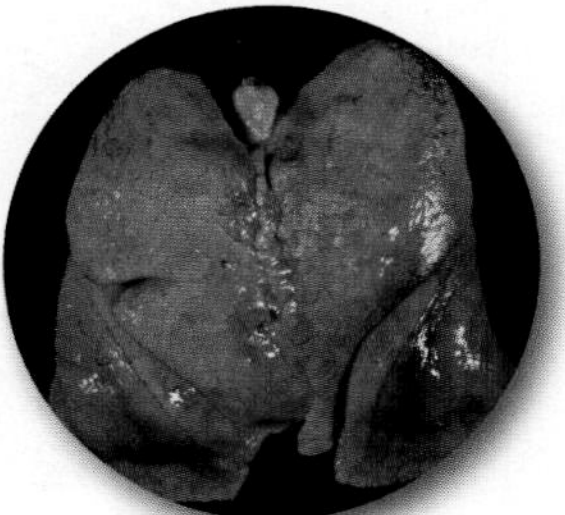

▲ Healthy lung tissue

219

QUICK STUDY, ACTIVITY BOOK PP. 41–42

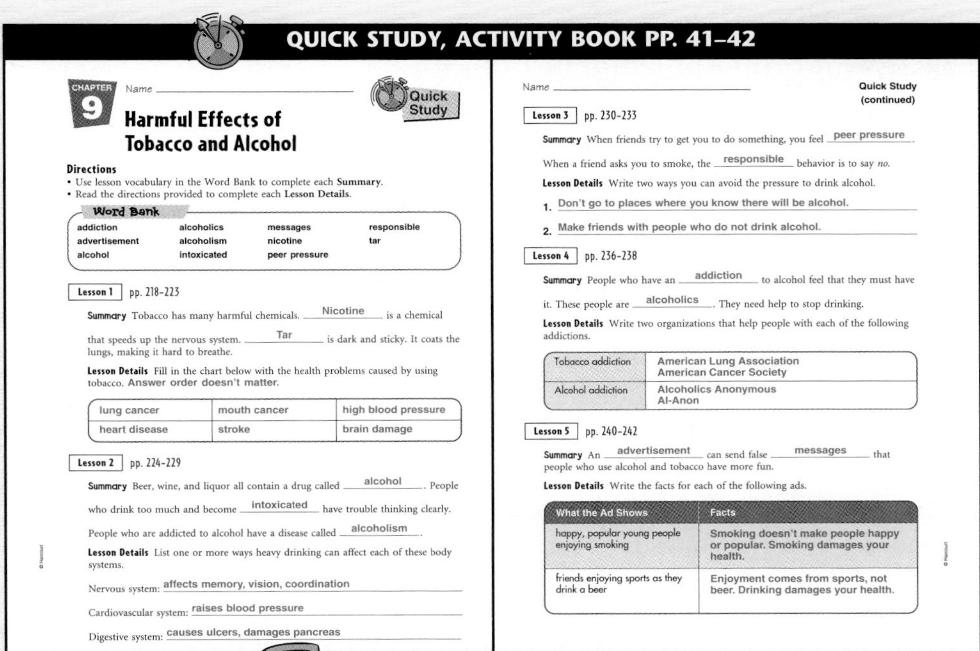

CHAPTER 9 Name ____________ Quick Study

Harmful Effects of Tobacco and Alcohol

Directions
- Use lesson vocabulary in the Word Bank to complete each **Summary**.
- Read the directions provided to complete each **Lesson Details**.

Word Bank

addiction	alcoholics	messages	responsible
advertisement	alcoholism	nicotine	tar
alcohol	intoxicated	peer pressure	

Lesson 1 pp. 218–223

Summary Tobacco has many harmful chemicals. Nicotine is a chemical that speeds up the nervous system. Tar is dark and sticky. It coats the lungs, making it hard to breathe.

Lesson Details Fill in the chart below with the health problems caused by using tobacco. Answer order doesn't matter.

lung cancer	mouth cancer	high blood pressure
heart disease	stroke	brain damage

Lesson 2 pp. 224–229

Summary Beer, wine, and liquor all contain a drug called alcohol. People who drink too much and become intoxicated have trouble thinking clearly. People who are addicted to alcohol have a disease called alcoholism.

Lesson Details List one or more ways heavy drinking can affect each of these body systems.

Nervous system: affects memory, vision, coordination

Cardiovascular system: raises blood pressure

Digestive system: causes ulcers, damages pancreas

Name ____________ Quick Study (continued)

Lesson 3 pp. 230–233

Summary When friends try to get you to do something, you feel peer pressure. When a friend asks you to smoke, the responsible behavior is to say *no.*

Lesson Details Write two ways you can avoid the pressure to drink alcohol.

1. Don't go to places where you know there will be alcohol.
2. Make friends with people who do not drink alcohol.

Lesson 4 pp. 236–238

Summary People who have an addiction to alcohol feel that they must have it. These people are alcoholics. They need help to stop drinking.

Lesson Details Write two organizations that help people with each of the following addictions.

Tobacco addiction	American Lung Association American Cancer Society
Alcohol addiction	Alcoholics Anonymous Al-Anon

Lesson 5 pp. 240–242

Summary An advertisement can send false messages that people who use alcohol and tobacco have more fun.

Lesson Details Write the facts for each of the following ads.

What the Ad Shows	Facts
happy, popular young people enjoying smoking	Smoking doesn't make people happy or popular. Smoking damages your health.
friends enjoying sports as they drink a beer	Enjoyment comes from sports, not beer. Drinking damages your health.

© Harcourt

Available online.
www.harcourtschool.com/health

2. TEACH

Quick Activity

Carbon monoxide is found in most cigarette smoke. Smoke also contains about half as much nicotine and almost the same amount of tar.

Interpret Visuals—Graphs

Have students examine the graph showing the components of cigarette smoke. Remind students that when a cigarette is smoked, these substances are released into the air. Ask students to describe ways in which smoking pollutes. Write their examples on the board.

Discuss

How does tar affect people's ability to breathe? Tar builds up in the lungs and air passages and makes it harder to breathe.

Critical Thinking Why is it dangerous for someone who is pregnant to smoke? Poisons affect the baby along with the mother.

Health Background

Bidi Cigarettes A new health threat to children is bidis (also beedies and beadies). These small cigarettes resemble marijuana joints. Bidis come in flavors such as vanilla, strawberry, and mango. Bidi use concerns health officials because a bidi is more dangerous than a regular cigarette. Bidi smoke contains about five times the tar and at least three times the nicotine and carbon monoxide of regular cigarette smoke. Children appear to choose bidis because they are wrongly perceived to be less dangerous than regular cigarettes, are trendy, and are less expensive than many other forms of tobacco.

Source: *Campaign for Tobacco-Free Kids, National Conference of State Legislators, Senator Dick Durbin website*

For more background, visit the **Webliography** in Teacher Resources at **www.harcourtschool.com/health**
Keyword tobacco

TEACH *continued*

Content-Area Reading Support

Using Graphics Direct students' attention to the illustrations on this page. Point out that each illustration or photograph has a caption next to it. Ask a volunteer to read each caption aloud. Point out that the caption helps explain the message of an illustration or photograph. Encourage students to take time to study the captions in their textbooks, since they contain important information not included in the regular passages of text.

Discuss

One of the main ways children learn is by copying adults they admire, such as teachers and famous people.

Critical Thinking **Why is it important for teachers and famous people, such as TV and sports stars, to act wisely and safely around others?** Some people, especially children, may copy their behaviors.

Health Background

Health Statistics More than 400,000 Americans die each year from smoking-related diseases. That is one in five of all deaths, more than from cocaine, heroin, alcohol abuse, auto wrecks, homicides, and suicides combined. Tobacco use is considered to be the largest preventable cause of premature death and disability in the United States.

Source: *Centers for Disease Control and Prevention, University Health Center websites*

For more background, visit the **Webliography** in Teacher Resources at **www.harcourtschool.com/health**
Keyword tobacco

The Trap of Tobacco

Most adults who use tobacco started when they were young. They may have tried tobacco because they were curious. Or they may have started smoking because friends asked them to try it. Others may have tried chewing tobacco because they saw famous baseball players using it.

Many young people see adults using tobacco. They see people using it on television or in movies. Some young people think that using tobacco is a way to act grown-up. What they don't know is that most adult users of tobacco wish they had never started using it! They want to quit, but they have a hard time doing so.

▲ Tobacco use may seem like fun, but it causes more problems than it's worth! Smoking can make you lose your friends and your health.

Meeting Individual Needs
Leveled Activities

BELOW-LEVEL **Make Truthful Ads** Discuss with students the harmful effects of tobacco and the fact that advertising makes smoking look inviting. Students should design advertisements that truthfully depict the harmful effects of tobacco. Encourage them to write catchy slogans that warn others about the hazards of smoking.

ON-LEVEL **Make Charts** Pairs of students can make charts that show the dangers of tobacco products to smokers, nonsmokers who are exposed to ETS, and users of smokeless tobacco products. Have students share their charts with the rest of the class.

CHALLENGE **Conduct Interviews** Ask students to interview former smokers by asking questions such as *When and why did you first begin to smoke? What effects did smoking have on your health? Why did you decide to stop? Did you get any special help in breaking your habit?* Have students share brief summaries of their interview with the rest of the class.

▲ Smoking is not cool. It makes your breath and clothes smell bad and your teeth turn yellow.

Many people cough the first time they smoke. They might get dizzy or have an upset stomach. These are warning signs that cigarette smoke is harmful. People's bodies are telling them not to smoke.

Some first-time users will stop smoking, but many will smoke again and again. Soon, the body gets used to the smoke. In a short time, quitting becomes hard for the smoker. The person begins to crave the nicotine in cigarettes. The smoker may get nervous or depressed when he or she doesn't smoke. He or she has become addicted to nicotine.

SEQUENCE **Explain how the social aspects of smoking can lead to an addiction to tobacco.** You see others smoking. It looks inviting. You try a cigarette, and then again. Soon you crave a cigarette. If you don't smoke, you get nervous and depressed. You become addicted.

221

Interpret Visuals—Pictures

Direct students' attention to the picture, and have volunteers describe what is happening.

Critical Thinking **Does smoking make this woman attractive?** Accept all reasonable answers, such as No, it makes her smell bad.

Content-Area Reading Support

Using Reference Words Direct attention to the following sentence: *These are warning signs that cigarette smoke is harmful.* Point out that the word *these* represents an entire idea. Call on a volunteer to explain what *these* represents. (coughing, getting dizzy, having an upset stomach)

Suggest that as students read, they pay attention to words such as *this, that, these,* and *those,* pausing if necessary to be sure they understand the ideas the words refer to.

Science

Investigate Nicotine In addition to being a dangerous drug in tobacco, nicotine is a poison used by gardeners as a pesticide. Invite students to talk to a gardener or botanist who uses nicotine to protect plants from pests. Students should find out what precautions the gardener takes to protect himself or herself from the nicotine.

Teacher Tip

Smokeless Tobacco Snuff (or dip) and chewing tobacco are more addictive than cigarettes because each pinch contains as much nicotine as two cigarettes. Also, saliva pulls more of the nicotine out of the tobacco than smoking does. The withdrawal symptoms of people quitting smokeless tobacco have been rated by users as more severe than those of alcohol withdrawal.

TEACH *continued*

Interpret Visuals—Pictures

Have students describe what the picture on this page illustrates. Then invite volunteers to read the callout boxes aloud. If students have difficulty recognizing some of the organs discussed in the callout boxes, refer them to the drawings of the human body systems on pages 12–13, 21, and 22. Emphasize that tobacco affects many parts of the body, not just the lungs.

Discuss

In January 1993 the Environmental Protection Agency officially declared ETS a known human carcinogen, classifying it as an environmental hazard equivalent to asbestos and other hazardous substances. The report stated that ETS is a serious health risk for nonsmokers, particularly children.

Problem Solving Suppose you want to avoid breathing environmental tobacco smoke, but someone lights up a cigarette near you. How can you politely ask the person not to smoke near you? Possible answer: "Would you please smoke outside?"

Health Background

Environmental Tobacco Smoke ETS is a mixture of sidestream smoke (emitted from burning tobacco products between puffs) and mainstream smoke (exhaled by the smoker). Sidestream smoke contains higher concentrations of toxic and cancer-causing chemicals than directly inhaled smoke. Each year, nearly 3,000 deaths are attributed to ETS. ETS is also responsible for increased lower-respiratory-tract infections and other respiratory problems in children.

Source: *National Cancer Institute, Environmental Health Center, American Lung Association websites*

For more background, visit the **Webliography** in Teacher Resources at **www.harcourtschool.com/health**
Keyword tobacco

Information Alert!

Effects of Tobacco
Many effects of tobacco are well known, but scientists are still discovering others.

For the most up-to-date information, visit The Learning Site. www.harcourtschool.com/health

Harmful Effects of Tobacco

Smoking can change a person's health. Over time, a smoker is much more likely than a nonsmoker to develop cancer and other diseases.

Cancers caused by tobacco use are lung cancer and mouth cancer. Lung cancer grows in a smoker's lungs. It blocks the lungs' air passages and can cause death. Mouth cancer happens most often in people who use chewing tobacco and snuff. To treat it, doctors often must cut away part of the face, lips, or tongue to remove the cancer. Some cancers can't be treated and can lead to death.

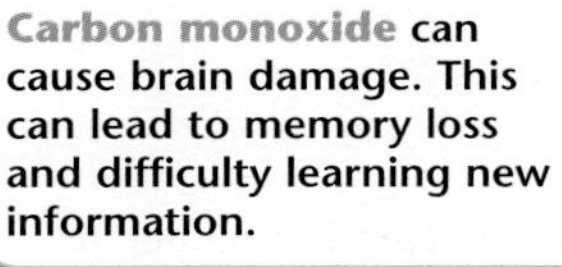

Carbon monoxide can cause brain damage. This can lead to memory loss and difficulty learning new information.

Nicotine shrinks blood vessels. This makes the heart work harder. This condition can lead to high blood pressure, heart disease, and stroke.

Tar coats the lungs and air passages. This leads to coughs and diseases of the lungs and air passages.

◀ Your health and fitness can be ruined if you use tobacco or alcohol products.

Teacher Tip

Children of Smokers Some of your students may have family members who use tobacco. These students may experience confused feelings as they become aware of the dangers of ETS. Help students understand that they may not be able to influence a family member's choice to smoke. However, they can resolve to be smoke-free adults. Emphasize the medical and social facts regarding the hazardous effects of tobacco use without conveying judgment on smokers.

Language Arts

Write a Script Divide the class into groups of four. Explain that each group is to write a script for a talk show about the dangers of smoking. Encourage students to choose one member to be the host and to have the other three students in the group adopt opposing views about tobacco use. Suggest that students consult a variety of sources for information.

Tobacco users are more likely to develop heart disease and high blood pressure than nonsmokers. That's because the gases in cigarette smoke take the place of oxygen in the blood. The heart has to work much more to get the oxygen the body needs.

Environmental tobacco smoke (ETS) is smoke in the air. It can cause the same diseases in nonsmokers as in smokers. ETS comes from burning cigarettes, pipes, or cigars and from smoke that is breathed out by smokers.

Children who live with smokers are likely to get infections and develop asthma more often than children who live in smoke-free homes.

DRAW CONCLUSIONS Describe the short-term and long-term effects of tobacco use.

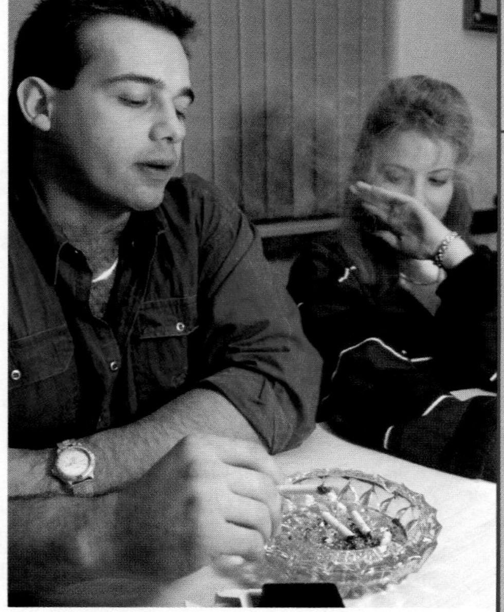

▲ ETS is not only a bother—it can also make you ill.

Lesson 1 Summary and Review

1 Summarize with Vocabulary

Use vocabulary and other terms from this lesson to complete the statements.

When somebody smokes _____, he or she breathes in dangerous chemicals such as the sticky, black substance called _____. Also, smokers become addicted to _____. These chemicals are released into the air as _____.

2 Critical Thinking What are two short-term and two long-term social effects of tobacco use?

3 List three harmful chemicals in tobacco.

4 CAUSE AND EFFECT Draw and complete this graphic organizer to show how choosing to use tobacco products affects the body.

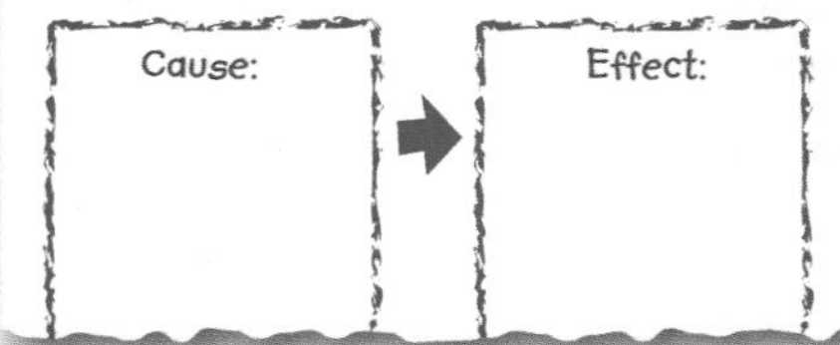

5 Write to Inform—Explanation

Interview an adult who started smoking cigarettes as a child. Ask if he or she regrets the decision now.

The heart has to beat faster and breathing may become harder as the body tries to get the oxygen it needs. The body becomes addicted to tobacco. Continued smoking then effects physical, mental, social, and legal aspects of your life.

ACTIVITY BOOK P. 43

Name ____________

Focus Skill **Reading Skill**

Identify Cause and Effect

Long-Term Use of Tobacco

Whenever tobacco is used, the poison nicotine enters the blood. This drug is addictive—it makes a person crave more nicotine. Nicotine raises the blood pressure, which can lead to heart disease. Tobacco smoke also contains other poisons, such as carbon monoxide, a deadly gas. Carbon monoxide keeps oxygen from reaching the blood. People smoke tobacco in cigarettes, cigars, and pipes.

When a person smokes or breathes other people's smoke, his or her lungs become coated with tar. Over time, the tar can build up enough to block the flow of air to the lungs. This can lead to many lung diseases, such as lung cancer. It can cause the airways in the lungs to become permanently blocked.

Smokeless tobacco is chewing tobacco or snuff. With this form of tobacco, nicotine enters the bloodstream through the blood vessels in the mouth. It can cause sores to form inside the mouth. Over time, these sores can become cancer of the lips, tongue, cheeks, or throat. Smokeless tobacco is even more addictive than smoking tobacco because more nicotine enters the body with each use.

Fill in the graphic organizer with the effects of long-term use of smoking tobacco and smokeless tobacco.

Cause: long-term use of smoking tobacco ➡ Effects: raises the blood pressure; leads to heart disease; causes lung diseases such as cancer; causes airways in the lungs to become blocked

Cause: long-term use of smokeless tobacco ➡ Effects: raises the blood pressure; causes sores in the mouth that can become cancer of the lips, tongue, cheeks, or throat

Available online.
www.harcourtschool.com/health

3. WRAP UP

Lesson 1 Summary and Review

1. tobacco, tar, nicotine, environmental tobacco smoke
2. Possible short-term effects: bad breath, clothes that smell bad; possible long-term effects: nervous or depressed, may lose friends
3. carbon monoxide, nicotine, tar
4. Possible answers include:

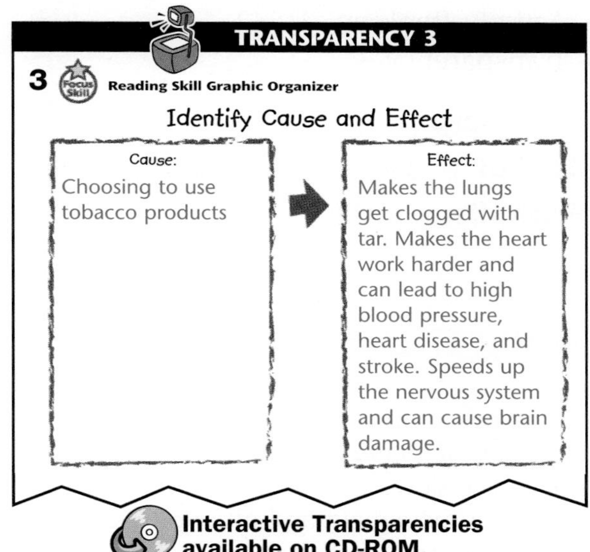
TRANSPARENCY 3

3 Focus Skill Reading Skill Graphic Organizer

Identify Cause and Effect

Cause: Choosing to use tobacco products ➡ Effect: Makes the lungs get clogged with tar. Makes the heart work harder and can lead to high blood pressure, heart disease, and stroke. Speeds up the nervous system and can cause brain damage.

Interactive Transparencies available on CD-ROM.

5. The paragraph should explain why the person first started to smoke (for example, peer pressure). Then the paragraph should relate reasons the adult regrets his or her decision to smoke.

For **writing models** with examples, see *Teaching Resources* pp. 47–61. Rubrics are also provided.

When Minutes Count . . .

Quick Study Students can use *Activity Book* pages 41–42 (shown on p. 219) as they complete each lesson in this chapter.

LESSON 2
Pages 224–229

Objectives
- Describe alcohol and the harm it causes body systems and behavior.
- Identify some effects of problem drinking.

When Minutes Count . . .
Assign the Quick Study, Lesson 2, Activity Book pp. 41–42 (shown on p. 219).

Program Resources
- Activity Book pp. 41–42
- Transparency 3

Vocabulary
alcohol p. 224, **intoxicated** p. 228, **alcoholism** p. 229

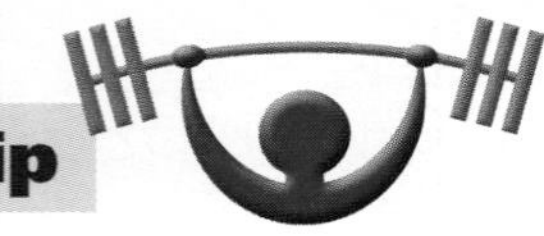

Daily Fitness Tip

Alcohol consumption can affect the body. The activity of the nervous system can become impaired or slowed. Reflexes and motor skills needed for movement and other physical activity may not function properly, leaving an individual vulnerable to physical injury and harm. Remind students that drinking alcohol is dangerous.

For more guidelines about alcohol and your physical fitness, see *Be Active! Resources for Physical Education* p. 171.

1. MOTIVATE

Bring to class various containers labeled in fluid ounces, such as a 12-oz beverage can, a 5.5-oz juice can, and a 1-oz vanilla extract bottle, to help students compare the usual serving sizes of beer, wine, and liquor.

Critical Thinking Which beverage—beer, wine, or liquor—contains the least alcohol in one sip? beer (2 to 6 percent alcohol)

Which beverage contains the most alcohol in one sip? liquor (40 to 57 percent alcohol)

LESSON 2

How Alcohol Harms Body Systems

Lesson Focus
Alcohol is an addictive drug that can harm the body and affect behavior.

Why Learn This?
Knowing the dangers of alcohol can help you refuse to use it.

Vocabulary
alcohol
intoxicated
alcoholism

Alcohol

Alcohol is a drug found in beer, wine, and liquor. The use of alcohol is legal only for adults 21 years of age and older. When a person drinks alcohol, it enters the blood. The amount of alcohol in a person's blood is called the *blood alcohol level (BAL)*. The more a person drinks, the higher his or her BAL will become.

Alcohol changes the way people feel, act, and think. It also changes the way the body works. After drinking alcohol, a person may find it is hard to walk or to speak clearly. The size and age of a person affect the way his or her body reacts to alcohol. A small person will have a higher BAL than someone larger who drinks the same amount.

These effects are based on a 150-pound adult. People who weigh less may have these effects with fewer drinks.▶

How Alcohol Affects the Body

Number of Beers	BAL	Effect on a Person's Body
1 beer	0.015	reduced concentration, reflexes slowed
2 beers	0.04	short-term memory loss
4 beers	0.1	seven times more likely to have a car crash if driving
12 beers	0.3	vomiting/unconsciousness

224

Cultural Connection

Religious, Cultural, or Family Traditions You may wish to invite volunteers to share personal knowledge of family, cultural, or religious practices and attitudes regarding alcohol. Students will represent a range of backgrounds, as some religions use wine in a ritual manner and others completely prohibit its use by members. Likewise, some family customs may involve alcohol at major celebrations only, at dinner, or not at all.

Science

Alcohol Breakdown The breakdown of alcohol into carbon dioxide, water, and energy by enzymes in the liver takes place at the rate of $^{1}/_{3}$ ounce per hour. Have students research to find out more about the chemical reactions that occur with alcohol, such as the flammability of its vapors and effects on living things. Students can pair up and report to the rest of the class the results of their research.

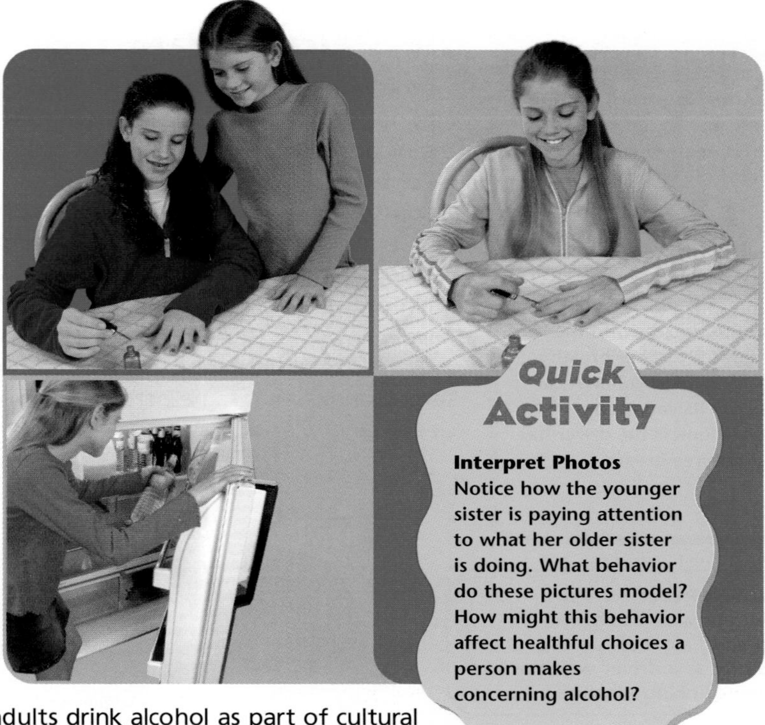

Quick Activity

Interpret Photos
Notice how the younger sister is paying attention to what her older sister is doing. What behavior do these pictures model? How might this behavior affect healthful choices a person makes concerning alcohol?

Some adults drink alcohol as part of cultural events, or celebrations. For example, some people drink champagne at weddings. Others drink a small amount of wine as part of religious ceremonies.

Some adults drink to relax or because they feel lonely, nervous, or depressed. These people may become addicted and need alcohol more often.

Some young people see adults or their peers using alcohol, so they want to try it. They are curious about its effects. They think drinking alcohol will make them seem grown-up. Many young people think that drinking alcohol is a fun activity. Others may try alcohol because their friends pressure them to try it. They want to feel like they are part of a group.

DRAW CONCLUSIONS List three reasons a young person may want to try alcohol.

Possible answers: peer pressure, seeing adults use it, curiosity about it, belief that alcohol will help the user have more fun, wanting to seem grown-up

225

2. TEACH

Interpret Visuals—Tables

Have students point to each heading in the table on page 224 as you explain the contents of each column. Make sure students understand each effect described in the table. Also, help them understand that 0.015 BAL means a person has between 1 percent and 2 percent (1.5 percent) alcohol level in the blood. At the very least, help them understand that 0.3 BAL is much more than 0.015 BAL.

Critical Thinking Is it safe to drink one beer and drive a car? no, because one beer could slow the reflexes and reduce concentration of some people

Why is it dangerous for young people to drink alcohol? They have smaller bodies, so even one drink could give them a high BAL. Also, young people are likely to feel the effects of alcohol more strongly than adults.

Quick Activity

Have volunteers describe what is taking place in the series of photographs on this page. Students should relate that the younger girl copies her older sister because she admires her and is influenced by her. The younger girl may also copy unhealthful behaviors of her older sister. In doing so, the younger girl may copy behaviors that are injurious, such as drinking alcohol.

Social Studies

Alcohol Laws Have students contact your state's alcoholic beverage control agency to learn about the alcohol laws in your state. Ask students to prepare a report or poster summarizing their findings. Ask them to find out the legal drinking age and BALs in your state as well as the penalties for driving while intoxicated.

Language Arts

Warning Labels Tell students to imagine that the government has decided to include a warning label on all alcoholic beverage containers and it is the students' responsibility to write the label. The label should include only factual information that will inform drinkers of the dangers of drinking alcohol.

TEACH *continued*

Discuss

Suggest that students review the nervous, digestive, and circulatory systems in Chapter 1, on pages 12–14, 16–19, and 20–23. As students read the next few pages, have them note the various body systems that are affected by alcohol use.

Interpret Visuals—Pictures

Ask students to describe what they think is taking place in the picture. Then have volunteers read the caption and the boxes aloud. Make sure students understand each of the effects of alcohol and how these can affect the skills a person needs to drive safely.

Critical Thinking Why is it important to see clearly and to think and act quickly when driving? Possible answers: Something could be in the road ahead; other cars can appear suddenly; it is important to see road signs and lane markings.

Problem Solving Suppose the person in the picture has been drinking and is getting ready to drive. What would you say and do if you were the person in the passenger seat? Possible answer: I would tell the person that it is unsafe to drink and drive; take away the car keys.

Content-Area Reading Support

Using Text Format Draw students' attention to the Effects of Alcohol. Point out that bulleted lists and texts often carry important information.

Have a volunteer read the Effects of Alcohol aloud. Ask students if they know of other effects of alcohol use. Remind students that alcohol is a drug and thus may affect each individual differently.

Health & Technology

Ignition Interlock System
Every year in the United States, more than 16,000 people die in alcohol-related car crashes. A new technology, called an ignition interlock system (IIS), may help lower this number. A driver would have to breathe into the IIS to have his or her breath analyzed for alcohol. A car with an IIS cannot be started unless the driver has alcohol-free breath.

Ways Alcohol Harms the Body

You've learned that food is slowly digested into nutrients that are small enough to enter the bloodstream. Alcohol does not need to be digested. Instead, it goes directly into the bloodstream from the stomach and small intestines. Blood quickly carries alcohol to the brain.

Alcohol slows down the brain. Because the brain controls the body's functions, alcohol can have many effects. After just one drink, an average-size adult might feel relaxed. After several drinks, that same person might feel ill, sleepy, angry, or depressed.

Effects of Alcohol

- difficulty walking
- memory loss
- blurred vision
- slurred speech
- decreased ability to think clearly
- dizziness

Slowed Reaction Time
A driver who has been drinking alcohol can't react as quickly as a driver who has not been drinking alcohol.

Lack of Coordination
Steering, braking, and speeding up all depend on coordinating different muscles. Alcohol makes it hard to control muscles.

Dizziness
Alcohol can make a person feel dizzy. This can affect vision, which is important to driving.

Difficulty Thinking
Alcohol makes it hard for a person to think clearly. A driver who has been drinking alcohol is not able to make clear, quick decisions about traffic and road conditions.

226

Meeting Individual Needs
Leveled Activities

BELOW-LEVEL Conduct an Interview Have students ask an adult who does not drink alcohol why he or she chooses not to drink. Have them share their findings with the rest of the class.

ON-LEVEL Make a Display Ask students to clip newspaper articles about alcohol-related car crashes. Have students mount the articles on construction paper and write several sentences summarizing each article. Display the articles in the classroom.

CHALLENGE Estimate BAL by Body Weight Help students understand the increased effects of alcohol in people who weigh less than 150 pounds. Students can estimate their size compared with a 150-pound adult by dividing their estimated body weight into 150. Then help them multiply this figure times the BAL levels shown in the table on page 224.

Long-term use of alcohol can damage the brain. Drinking too much alcohol can cause heart disease. Heavy drinking can damage other organs too, especially the liver. The liver cleans the blood of poisons. Alcohol affects the liver's ability to work. That may lead to cirrhosis. Cirrhosis is a liver disease that results from drinking too much alcohol. Cirrhosis can cause death.

Many people who drink do not eat well. Alcohol makes it hard for the body to absorb nutrients from food. The health of someone who drinks a lot may suffer because the body doesn't get all the nutrients it needs.

Personal Health Plan ▶

Real-Life Situation
Suppose a friend invites you to a party where you know alcohol will be served.

Real-Life Plan
Make your own plans. Invite your friend to come to your activity instead. Write down some suggestions for some fun things that you could do.

CAUSE AND EFFECT List two short-term and two long-term effects of alcohol use.

Possible short-term effects: dizziness, memory loss; possible long-term effects: brain damage, malnutrition, heart disease, cirrhosis

Health behaviors affect body systems. For example, choosing to drink alcohol can harm your nervous, cardiovascular, and digestive systems. ▶

Nervous System
Heavy drinking damages parts of the brain linked with memory, vision, and coordination.

Cardiovascular System
Alcohol makes the heart beat faster and raises blood pressure. Heavy drinking can permanently raise blood pressure.

Digestive System
Heavy drinking can lead to sores in the stomach, called ulcers. Alcohol can also damage the pancreas, causing severe pain and vomiting.

Personal Health Plan ▶

Suggestions of fun things to do could include going to a movie, having a sleepover, going to a sports event, playing a game, or watching a movie at home.

Interpret Visuals—Pictures

Have students point to each body part as volunteers read the boxed text describing the effects of alcohol on those organs and systems. Repeat, rephrase, or demonstrate the descriptions as necessary to help students understand each effect. Then ask students to list the body systems and organs shown in the picture that are affected by drinking alcohol. (Digestive System: stomach, pancreas; Cardiovascular System: heart; Nervous System: brain)

Health Background

Further Effects of Alcohol Additional effects of alcohol on the body not shown on this page include cancer of the mouth, throat, and digestive system; destruction of enzymes in the digestive system; and hypertension (sustained high blood pressure) if a person drinks more than three drinks a day. It takes weeks for blood pressure to return to normal after drinking stops.

Source: *Bowles Center for Alcohol Studies, University of Georgia*

For more background, visit the **Webliography** in Teacher Resources at **www.harcourtschool.com/health**
Keyword alcohol

Science

Reaction Time Invite students to work in pairs to study reaction time. One student should suspend a ruler vertically above the hand of the other. The thumb and index finger of that person should surround the 0 mark on the ruler but not touch it. As the first student drops the ruler, the second should catch it. The number on the ruler at which he or she catches it gives a relative indication of reaction time. Students can make several trials, comparing their reaction times.

Drama

Skit Organize the class into groups, and have each group write a short skit about possible things that could happen to a group of students who get together to drink. Once the skits have been written, have the students discuss what the skits had in common. For example, all the skits ended with people hurt, ill, or in trouble with parents or the law.

TEACH *continued*

Discuss

The word *intoxicate* comes from the Latin *intoxicare*, which means "to poison."

Critical Thinking How is alcohol like a poison? Possible answer: It has harmful effects on the body, just as a poison does.

Critical Thinking Name three activities you do well now that you probably could not do well if you were intoxicated. Accept all reasonable answers, such as complete schoolwork and puzzles and participate in games, sports, and hobbies.

What changes would drinking alcohol cause that would prevent you from doing well in these activities? Possible answers: slowed thinking, inability to concentrate, poor decision making, loss of memory

What are some of the effects of problem drinking on the ability to work? Possible answers: The drinker may miss work or do a poor job. The drinker may lose his or her job.

What are some effects of problem drinking on schoolwork? The drinker may not be able to concentrate and may lose interest in school or get low grades.

Critical Thinking How is alcoholism like falling dominoes? With alcoholism, one problem causes another, just as one falling domino causes others to fall.

Did You Know?

Car crashes are the leading cause of death for Americans who are 20 or younger. A large number of these crashes are due to alcohol use.

Alcohol Can Affect Behavior

A problem drinker is often drunk, or intoxicated (in•TAHK•suh•kay•tuhd). Being **intoxicated** means being strongly affected by too much alcohol. Problem drinkers don't behave as they would if they were not drinking. They have trouble thinking clearly and making good decisions. They may get into serious situations that hurt themselves and others.

Problem drinkers often miss work. They do poorly when they are at work. They may have trouble keeping a job. Young drinkers can't concentrate well and often miss school. As they lose interest in their classes, their grades fall.

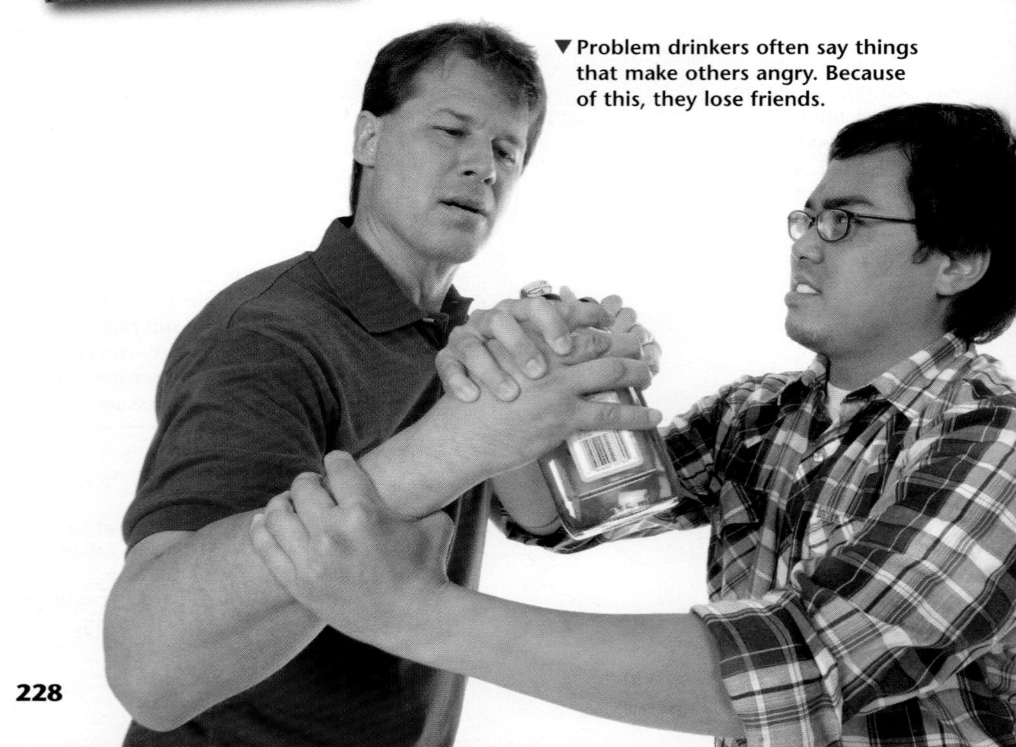

▼ Problem drinkers often say things that make others angry. Because of this, they lose friends.

ESL/ELL Support

COMPREHENSIBLE INPUT Students may have difficulty understanding the effects of alcohol. Propose that the graphic organizer for Identify Cause and Effect (pages 334–335) be used to clarify effects.

Beginning Have each student write one effect of alcohol use on an index card. Put the cards in a "hat." Have a volunteer pull a card and act out the effect. Other students should guess the effect.

Intermediate Have students draw on index cards cartoon figures that illustrate short-term and long-term effects of alcohol. Tell students to label the drawings.

Advanced Have students write stories in which someone suffers the effects of drinking alcohol. Students should describe the consequences of alcohol's adverse effects.

Problem drinkers are often addicted to alcohol. They cannot stop drinking without help. They have a disease called **alcoholism**. A person who has this disease is called an alcoholic.

The families of alcoholics often suffer. Family members feel pain and frustration at not being able to live without worry. A family member who is an alcoholic cannot be depended upon to help in everyday chores or responsibilities. Alcoholics can't think about the needs of others—not even family members. Alcohol makes some people say hurtful things and become violent. They may hurt others or be arrested by the police. Their behavior can change from day to day.

CAUSE AND EFFECT What are some social and legal consequences of alcoholism?

legal effect: getting arrested for drunk driving or for being violent; social effect: losing friends or hurting family members

Myth and Fact

Myth: Alcohol is safer than illegal drugs.

Fact: Alcohol can be just as addictive and damaging to your health as other drugs.

▲ Alcoholism affects every part of an alcoholic's life.

Lesson 2 Summary and Review

1 Summarize with Vocabulary

Use vocabulary and other terms from this lesson to complete the statements.

When people drink too much _____, they become drunk, or _____. Long-term use of alcohol can lead to _____. Many _____ develop the liver disease _____.

2 List three mental effects of drinking alcohol.

3 Critical Thinking How is the blood alcohol level related to body weight?

4  **CAUSE AND EFFECT** Draw and complete this graphic organizer to show how choosing to drink alcohol affects body systems.

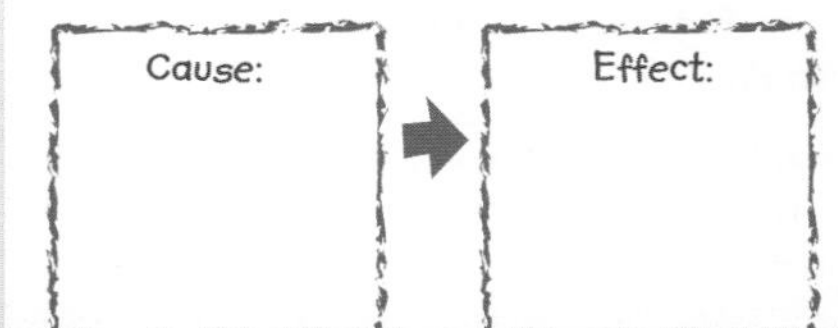

5 Write to Inform—Explanation

Write a paragraph explaining why NOT drinking alcohol is a responsible behavior. Explain how this choice can affect one's health.

Language Arts

Feelings About Drinking and Driving Have students assess their feelings about drinking alcohol. Then have them summarize orally their feelings about drinking and driving.

Art

Pamphlets Organize the class into groups. Each group should have at least one writer, one editor, and one artist. Have the groups create pamphlets that emphasize the short-term effects of alcohol. You may wish to arrange for the pamphlets to be displayed in your school's library.

3. WRAP UP

Lesson 2 Summary and Review

1. alcohol, intoxicated, alcoholism, alcoholics, cirrhosis
2. Possible answer: memory loss, decreased ability to think clearly, brain damage
3. After drinking the same amount of alcohol, a person who is small will have a higher BAL than will someone who is large.
4. Possible effects include:

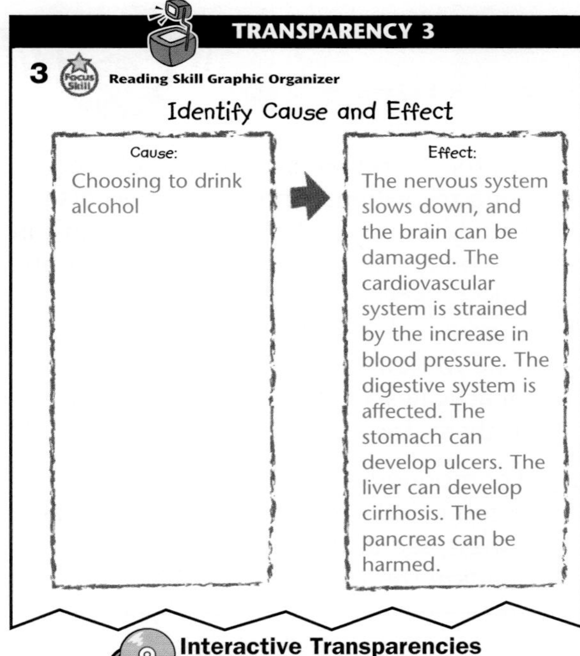
TRANSPARENCY 3

3 Reading Skill Graphic Organizer

Identify Cause and Effect

Cause:	Effect:
Choosing to drink alcohol	The nervous system slows down, and the brain can be damaged. The cardiovascular system is strained by the increase in blood pressure. The digestive system is affected. The stomach can develop ulcers. The liver can develop cirrhosis. The pancreas can be harmed.

Interactive Transparencies available on CD-ROM.

5. The student should write that not abusing alcohol is key to a healthy body and mind and is the responsible choice because it does not break family rules and laws.

For **writing models** with examples, see *Teaching Resources* pp. 47–61. Rubrics are also provided.

When Minutes Count . . .

Quick Study Students can use *Activity Book* pages 41–42 (shown on p. 219) as they complete each lesson in this chapter.

LESSON 3
Pages 230–233

Objectives
- Demonstrate strategies for refusing alcohol and tobacco.
- Discuss ways to resist peer pressure to use alcohol and tobacco.

When Minutes Count . . .
Assign the Quick Study, Lesson 3, Activity Book pp. 41–42 (shown on p. 219).

Program Resources
- Activity Book pp. 41–42
- Transparency 3

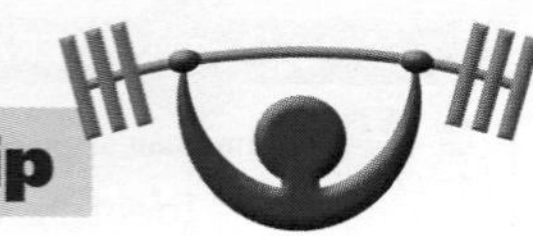

Daily Fitness Tip

Students may find that alcohol and tobacco use during recreational and sporting events is widespread. However, alcohol and tobacco can harm the body and should not be thought of as harmless. Peers who try to encourage use of these products should be resisted. The body works fine without alcohol and tobacco, and physical activities are much more healthful without them, too.

For more guidelines about refusing alcohol and tobacco and your physical fitness, see *Be Active! Resources for Physical Education* pp. 169–171.

1. MOTIVATE

Invite two volunteers to the front of the class. Explain that one has the role of persuading the other to smoke a cigarette. The other has the role of refusing. Allow students to play out their roles. Invite class members to suggest reasons a person might give to back up his or her decision to say *no*. List the suggestions on the board as they are given.

LESSON 3

Saying *No* to Alcohol and Tobacco

Lesson Focus
Knowing the facts about alcohol and tobacco use can help prepare you to refuse them.

Why Learn This?
Saying *no* to alcohol and tobacco can help you be safe and healthy.

Be Prepared to Say *No*

Many adults choose not to use tobacco or alcohol. You, too, have a choice. Someday, someone may offer you alcohol or tobacco. What will you say?

Earlier in this chapter, you learned about the harmful effects of these products. For many people, knowing about the harmful effects of alcohol and tobacco is enough for them to choose to say *no*. But there are other important reasons for saying *no*.

Ways to Say *No*
- Politely say *no* and walk away.
- Say that you have something else to do.
- Explain that you won't use these products because of their health risks.
- Explain that it is against the law for young people to use these products.
- Change the subject.

◀ Practice different ways to say *no* so that you will know what to do if someone offers you alcohol or tobacco.

Social Studies

No More Liquor Ads Point out to students that while beer and wine are commonly featured in TV commercials, liquor is not. Tell them that this was not always the case. Students should find out when and why such liquor ads were eliminated.

Teacher Tip

Positive Peer Pressure Tell students that peer pressure can be negative, involving situations that are harmful, dangerous, or illegal. It can also be positive—for example, one student might encourage another to study for a test, learn a new sport, or refuse harmful substances. Have students brainstorm ways they could influence their peers in positive ways. Then have them role-play situations in which they use those skills.

It is against the law for young people to use alcohol and tobacco. If you are caught using these products, you could be fined or arrested. Your family will be upset. If you break the rules of your family and use these products, you may lose your family's trust.

Some people refuse to use alcohol and tobacco because tobacco makes them feel ill and alcohol makes them feel nervous, sad, or out of control. Others refuse to let alcohol and tobacco rule their lives. People who want to live a healthful lifestyle know that alcohol and tobacco use should be avoided. They have more fun and feel better without using these drugs.

CAUSE AND EFFECT Explain why it is responsible behavior for you to say *no* if someone offers you alcohol or tobacco.

Saying *no* to alcohol and tobacco is a responsible behavior because of their harmful effects on the body; using them is against the law for young people; they can cause family problems; using alcohol and tobacco can make the user ill, nervous, sad, or out of control; people feel better without using them.

Did You Know?

A pack of cigarettes costs about $3.85. If an 18-year-old person smokes a pack of cigarettes a day until the age of 75 and the cost never even changes, he or she will spend more than $80,000 on cigarettes! Imagine what you could buy with that much money!

▼ Knowing why other people don't use alcohol and tobacco can help you prepare to say *no*.

Alcohol and Tobacco Use
If You Say *Yes*—
You may develop lung, heart, or liver disease. Your breath, clothing, and hair will smell. You are more likely to be in a car crash or a fire. You may have problems at home or at school. You may become depressed or angry. You may be arrested.
If You Say *No*—
Your organs are more likely to be healthy. You are more likely to be alert and in control. Your body is more likely to be healthy, and you will have more energy. You will have a better chance to do your best.

ESL/ELL Support

COMPREHENSIBLE INPUT Help students identify reasons to refuse alcohol and tobacco.

Beginning Have students draw pictures of what could happen to them if they use alcohol or tobacco.

Intermediate Have students go over the text on this page and make a list of all the reasons given for avoiding alcohol and tobacco.

Advanced Have students make a table that classifies the reasons listed on this page for avoiding alcohol and tobacco as *social, physical,* or *legal*.

2. TEACH

Content-Area Reading Support

Using Charts and Graphs Direct students to the Ways to Say *No* list on page 230, and ask volunteers to read the suggestions. Then invite them to rephrase each suggestion as if they were actually saying *no* to someone, such as, "No, thanks; I have something else to do."

Since saying *no* is such an important skill to learn, encourage students to use the Ways to Say *No* in a different way. Split the class into five groups—one for each bulleted point in the list. Have each group develop a scene around the method of saying *no*. Have each group perform the scene in front of the rest of the class.

Direct students to the Alcohol and Tobacco Use box on this page. Point out that this box shows two choices and the effects of each choice. Have students identify the two choices and read the effects. Ask students what else they might add to the chart.

Discuss

Point out to students that the legal age for buying alcohol and tobacco products ranges from 18 to 21, depending on the state where you live.

Critical Thinking Why is it illegal for young people to buy alcohol and tobacco products? Possible answers: Alcohol and tobacco products can seriously harm a young person's health. Young people feel the effects of alcohol more than adults. If you start good habits when you are young, you may not use these products as an adult.

TEACH *continued*

Personal Health Plan

Accept all reasonable answers. Plans may include the following:

- Go to parents for help.
- Talk to a school counselor or teacher.
- Stay friends with other students who do not use alcohol or tobacco.

Discuss

After students read the information about peer pressure, ask the following:

What do you think the expression *being pressured* or *feeling pressured* means? Possible answer: Someone is trying to persuade you to do something, and you don't want to do it.

What are some fun, safe things you could do instead of drinking alcohol or smoking? Accept reasonable responses.

Critical Thinking Why is it important to speak up and say how you feel when you don't want to use tobacco or alcohol? Possible answers: Others may think you want to go along with their ideas if you remain silent; they may mistake silence for agreement.

Activity

Responsibility Possible answer: If Lorna smokes, she may have problems breathing when she plays basketball. She may get lung cancer or other lung diseases. The responsible choice would be to choose not to smoke and to end friendships with those asking her to smoke. If Lorna does these two things, she will be healthier and have better friends.

Personal Health Plan

Real-Life Situation
Your brother's friends are in the park, smoking cigarettes. They ask you to try smoking.

Real-Life Plan
Write a plan to say *no.* As part of your plan, make a list of ways that you can get help saying *no* to tobacco use.

Dealing with Peer Pressure

In Chapter 8 you learned that peer pressure can sometimes affect you. Sometimes friends get you to do healthful things, such as playing sports or studying. Sometimes friends may try to get you to use alcohol and tobacco. The best way to say *no* to alcohol and tobacco is to avoid peer pressure to use them.

No | **Yes**

There are plenty of activities you can do to have fun without using alcohol or tobacco. ▶

232

Meeting Individual Needs
Leveled Activities

BELOW-LEVEL Make Collages Ask students to write at the top of a sheet of poster board one of the steps for refusing tobacco or alcohol. Students should then cut out and mount on the poster board magazine pictures that show young people in group situations. Encourage students to look for pictures of healthy young people.

ON-LEVEL Write Stories Invite students to write short stories about how a person their age refuses alcohol or tobacco and, as a result, increases his or her self-respect. Encourage volunteers to place their stories in a classroom reading center.

CHALLENGE Perform a Puppet Show Suggest that students write a script for a puppet show explaining how to say *no* to an offer of tobacco or alcohol. They can practice their puppet show for classmates and then perform it for younger students at the school.

Young people often find it hard not to give in to peer pressure. You can avoid peer pressure by staying away from people who use alcohol and tobacco. Don't go to places where alcohol is being served to young people. Make friends with people who share your decision not to use these drugs. Finally, if the pressure becomes too much, always seek help from a parent or another trusted adult, such as a teacher, who will help you resist this kind of peer pressure.

MAIN IDEA AND DETAILS List other things you can do instead of using alcohol or tobacco.

Possible answers: paint, play a musical instrument, play a sport, read, go out with friends to a movie

Make friends with other alcohol-free and tobacco-free students! ▼

ACTIVITY

Building Good Character

Responsibility **Lorna loves to play basketball. Lately, her friends have been asking her to smoke cigarettes. What could happen to Lorna if she chooses to smoke? What responsible choice could Lorna make? What might result from that choice?**

Lesson 3 Summary and Review

1. **Summarize with Vocabulary**
   Use terms from this lesson to complete the statements.
   Some people choose to use tobacco or alcohol because of _____, which can be resisted by learning how to say _____ to these drugs.
2. **Critical Thinking** What are some of the reasons people choose to use alcohol or tobacco?
3. Identify ways to cope with or seek assistance when confronted with situations involving alcohol and tobacco.
4. **CAUSE AND EFFECT** Draw and complete this graphic organizer to show how knowing how to refuse alcohol and tobacco can affect a person's mental and physical health.

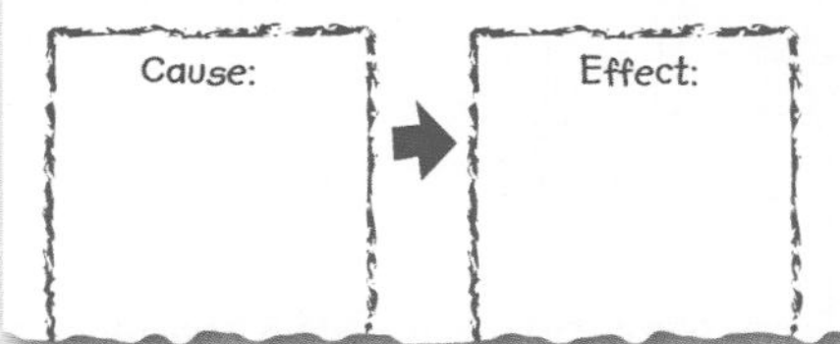

5. **Write to Inform—Description**
   Write a paragraph describing how adult family members and school staff can be role models for healthy behaviors such as not using tobacco and alcohol.

Language Arts

Newspaper Editorial Have students write an editorial for a local newspaper about the effects of drunk driving on your community and what students think can be done about it.

Teacher Tip

Social Standards Teaching students to say *no* to alcohol is complicated by our culture's double standards for drinking. Adults advocate sobriety, yet the media sometimes present drinking as highly desirable or comical. Thus, teaching students to say *no* to alcohol requires the support of parents and the community.

3. WRAP UP

Lesson 3 Summary and Review

1. peer pressure, *no*
2. Possible answers: to feel grown-up, because of peer pressure, out of curiosity, because they think it's cool
3. Possible answers: Say *no* and walk away; say that you have something else to do; explain that you won't use them because of their health risks; seek help from a parent or another trusted adult.
4. Possible answers:

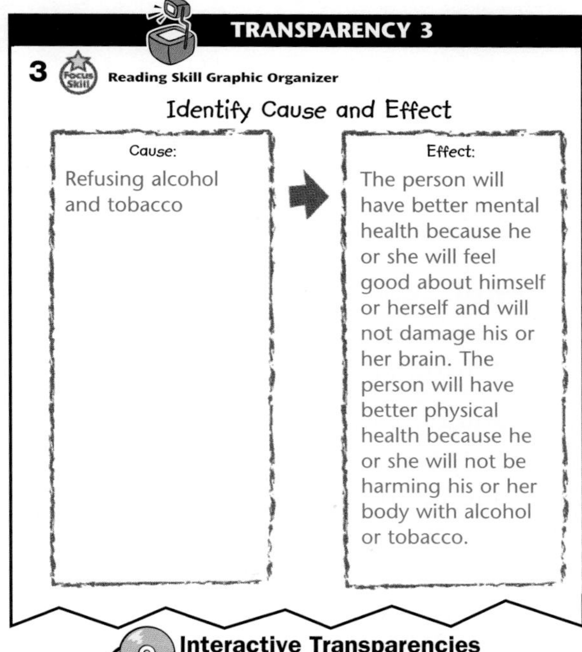

TRANSPARENCY 3

3 Reading Skill Graphic Organizer

Identify Cause and Effect

Cause:	Effect:
Refusing alcohol and tobacco	The person will have better mental health because he or she will feel good about himself or herself and will not damage his or her brain. The person will have better physical health because he or she will not be harming his or her body with alcohol or tobacco.

Interactive Transparencies available on CD-ROM.

5. Students' paragraphs should discuss how young people often look up to adults for ways to behave. If young people are with adults who don't use tobacco and use alcohol responsibly, young people are likely to follow their example.

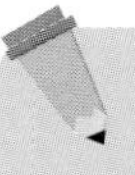

For **writing models** with examples, see *Teaching Resources* pp. 47–61. Rubrics are also provided.

When Minutes Count . . .

Quick Study Students can use *Activity Book* pages 41–42 (shown on p. 219) as they complete each lesson in this chapter.

Life Skills

Communicate
Make Responsible Decisions
Manage Stress
Refuse
Resolve Conflicts
Set Goals

Objectives

- ► Identify ways to say *no*.
- ► Practice ways to refuse alcohol and tobacco.

Program Resources

- ► Activity Book p. 44
- ► Poster 10

1. MOTIVATE

Optional Activity Materials: various magazines such as *Time, Newsweek, Sports Illustrated*

Invite students to look through the magazines for cigarette ads to analyze. Ask students to look at what the people in the ads are doing. Are they smoking? Many ads feature people who aren't smoking engaged in active sports.

2. TEACH

Direct students' attention to the pictures of Rodney and Kevin in the first panel.

Step 1

Critical Thinking How do you think Kevin's parents would feel if they knew Kevin wanted to try a cigarette? Possible answers: shocked, angry, embarrassed, sad

Step 2

What does Rodney suggest they do instead of smoking cigarettes? play soccer

REFUSE

To Use Alcohol and Tobacco

Someone may someday offer you alcohol or tobacco. Using the steps to **Refuse to Use Alcohol and Tobacco** can help you say *no* and can help you make a healthful choice.

Rodney's friend Kevin is thinking about trying to smoke tobacco. Some students have asked Kevin to join them while they smoke some cigarettes. Kevin wants Rodney to come with him. How can Rodney refuse?

1 Say *no* and tell why not.

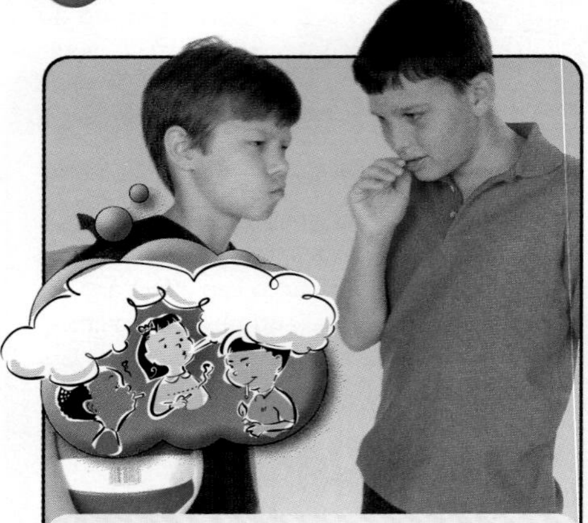

"Some of the guys are going to try some cigarettes after school. Want to come?" asks Kevin. "*No*. Smoking is against the law, and it's bad for you," Rodney says.

2 Suggest something else to do.

"Come on. Everybody does it. It's the cool thing to do," Kevin says. "Not me. Let's go play some soccer instead," says Rodney.

234

Math

Smoking Costs To reinforce ways to refuse tobacco, have students use a calculator to find out how much money a person who smokes one pack a day would save (daily, weekly, monthly, yearly) by stopping smoking completely. Check the price of cigarettes in your area so that students can complete the calculations.

ACTIVITY BOOK P. 44

Name ____________

Problem Solving

Life Skill
Refuse

Steps for Refusing to Use Alcohol and Tobacco

1. Say *no* and tell why not.
2. Suggest something else to do.
3. Reverse the peer pressure.
4. Repeat *no* and walk away. Leave the door open for the other person to join you.

Use the steps to tell how these students could say *no*.

A. Keisha's friend Leilani has a friend named Mel who smokes. One day Keisha and Leilani stop to talk to Mel. Mel pulls out a cigarette and asks Keisha if she wants to try it.

- How could Keisha say *no*? Write the steps that could help her.

Possible answers: Keisha could tell Mel *no*. She could say she doesn't want to get hooked and her parents don't want her to use tobacco. Then she could suggest that she and Leilani walk home and watch TV. She could say, "I hate the smell of cigarette smoke." Keisha could invite Mel to come and watch TV, too.

B. Jake is at a school party in a park. A friend, Moe, has brought a bottle of beer to the party. He tells Jake to meet him in a hidden corner of the park to have a sip.

- How could Jake refuse? Write how he could use the steps above to help him say *no*.

Possible answers: Jake could tell Moe *no* and say that drinking at a school party can get them into trouble because it's against school rules. Then he could say, "Let's go play ball." Jake could also say, "I don't want to drink beer and upset my parents." He could say that he doesn't want to have beer breath. Then he could walk away, asking again if Moe wants to play ball.

© Harcourt

Available online. www.harcourtschool.com/health

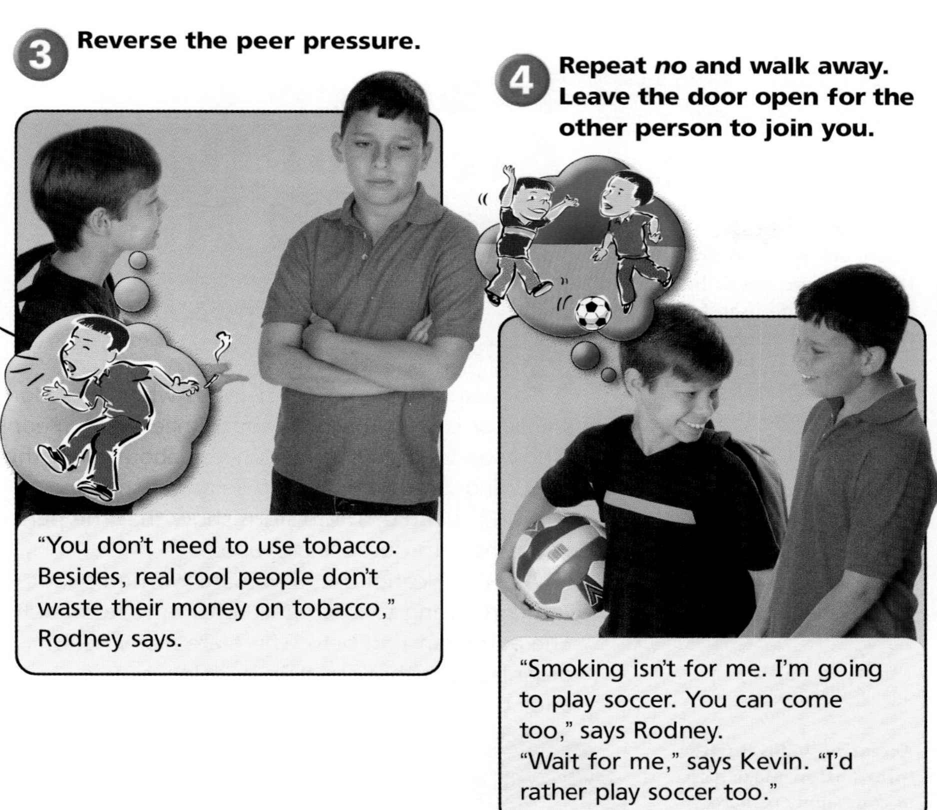

3 Reverse the peer pressure.
"You don't need to use tobacco. Besides, real cool people don't waste their money on tobacco," Rodney says.
4 Repeat *no* and walk away. Leave the door open for the other person to join you.
"Smoking isn't for me. I'm going to play soccer. You can come too," says Rodney.
"Wait for me," says Kevin. "I'd rather play soccer too."

Problem Solving

Celia and Mattie walk home together after school every day. One day, they see a friend from class with some older students. Their friend calls them over, saying, "Celia, Mattie, do you want to try a cigarette?" Use the steps to **Refuse to Use Alcohol and Tobacco** to describe how Celia and Mattie might respond and reverse the peer pressure. Explain how Celia and Mattie's behavior might demonstrate caring for their friend's health.

Using the Poster

Activity Have students write and perform skits that show different ways to refuse alcohol and tobacco.

Display Poster 10 to remind students of the different ways of refusing.

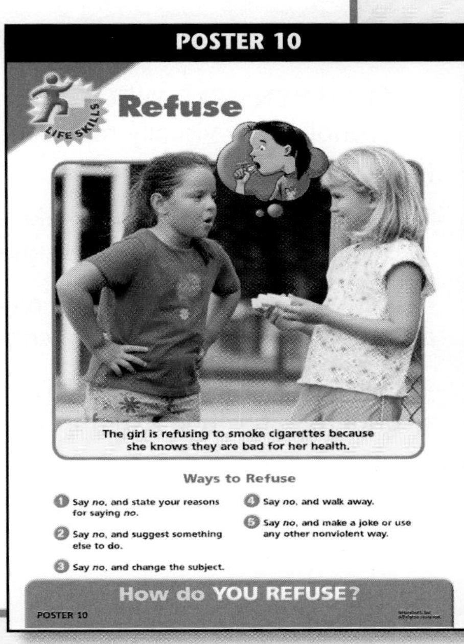

Critical Thinking **What else could Rodney suggest to help Kevin get his mind off smoking?** Possible answers: suggest they do an activity he knows Kevin enjoys; let Kevin know he still would like to spend time with him but not if Kevin smokes cigarettes

Step 3

Problem Solving **What is another way Rodney could have reversed the peer pressure?** Possible answer: Tell Kevin that smoking is a stupid thing to do.

Building Good Character

Remind students that when making any decision, they should consider how the decision shows trustworthiness. Have them discuss how refusing to smoke shows that Rodney is trustworthy.

Step 4

How do you know that Rodney's offer to have Kevin join him worked? Kevin says, "Wait for me. I'd rather play soccer too."

3. WRAP UP

Problem Solving

Students may suggest a variety of ways that Mattie and Celia can refuse to smoke by reversing the peer pressure. Students should also mention that some sort of positive peer pressure would show that they care about their friend's health.

LESSON 4
Pages 236–238

Objectives
- List warning signs of alcohol and tobacco use.
- Name sources of help for alcohol or tobacco users.

When Minutes Count . . .
Assign the Quick Study, Lesson 4, Activity Book pp. 41–42 (shown on p. 219).

Program Resources
- Activity Book pp. 41–42
- Transparency 3

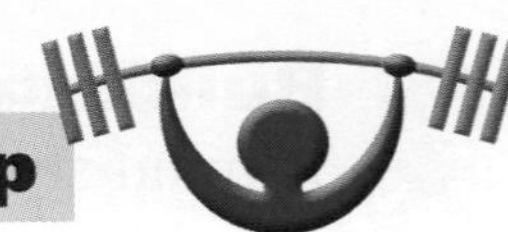

Daily Fitness Tip

Alcoholism can have a definite effect on physical fitness. Remind students that anyone with a problem related to alcohol is welcome in Al-Anon, an organization for family members of alcoholics. Al-Anon's support can help with recovery and a return to a more healthful lifestyle.

For more guidelines about alcohol and tobacco use and your physical fitness, see *Be Active! Resources for Physical Education* pp. 169–171.

1. MOTIVATE

Read the following proverbs from Benjamin Franklin's *Poor Richard's Almanac.* Explain that a proverb is a wise saying.

Drink does not drown care,
But waters it, and makes it grow faster.

He that spills the rum loses that only;
He that drinks it often loses both that and himself.

Drunkenness, that worst of Evils,
Makes some men Fools, some Beasts, some Devils.

When the Wine enters, out goes the Truth.

Check students understanding of what each proverb means. Make sure students understand that *care* means "worries." Describe what it means to "lose . . . himself."

Tobacco and Alcohol Users Can Get Help

Lesson Focus
There are warning signs that a person needs help in quitting the use of tobacco and alcohol.

Why Learn This?
Knowing about the sources of help for users of tobacco and alcohol may allow you to help yourself and others.

Help for Users of Tobacco or Alcohol

Tobacco users who get nervous when they don't smoke or chew tobacco probably need help. People who hide tobacco use feel uneasy about what they are doing. So do those who lie about smoking or chewing tobacco. These signs show that the person needs help to quit using tobacco.

As with alcohol use, if you are worried about someone using tobacco, talk with a trusted adult. The adult can find help. There are many health organizations that can help people who are addicted to tobacco.

Consumer Activity

Accessing Valid Health Information Make a list of community resources for people who are addicted to tobacco. Who do you think are the best people to ask about products that help tobacco users overcome their addiction?

▼ Talk to your parents if you're worried about someone's tobacco or alcohol use.

Joanie sees her sister smoking with friends. She thinks her sister might have a problem. ▶

236

ESL/ELL Support

COMPREHENSIBLE INPUT Help students understand the warning signs of alcoholism by visually representing each sign through either pictures or pantomiming.

Beginning Have students make a picture chart showing signs of alcoholism. Each of the listed signs should be represented by a drawing.

Intermediate Have students read the list of warning signs of alcoholism and then talk about why an alcoholic might exhibit the listed signs.

Advanced Have students review the short-term and long-term effects of alcohol use and then extend the list of warning signs of alcoholism.

Some organizations are the American Lung Association and the American Cancer Society. There are some products that can help tobacco users overcome their addiction. Nicotine gums and patches can help people reduce their need for nicotine. The best prevention is to never start using tobacco.

Have you ever been afraid to ask someone for help? Alcoholics need help. It's hard for them to stop drinking. They may be afraid to ask for help.

If you are worried about someone who uses alcohol, there are warning signs of alcoholism that you should know. The signs, listed here, can help you decide if an alcohol user needs help. You may also notice that the user has trouble doing things most people do normally. For example, young users may not do schoolwork or home chores. Adult users may forget to pay their bills. All alcoholics need help.

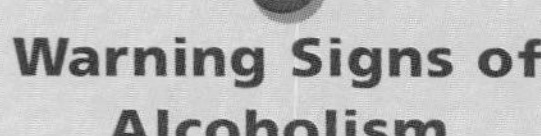

Warning Signs of Alcoholism

1. Often seems tired
2. Has an unhealthful diet
3. Often misses school or work
4. Has trouble controlling moods
5. Gets angry when he or she drinks
6. May not wash hair or clothing
7. Smells like alcohol

SUMMARIZE List three people you can turn to if you know someone with a tobacco problem.

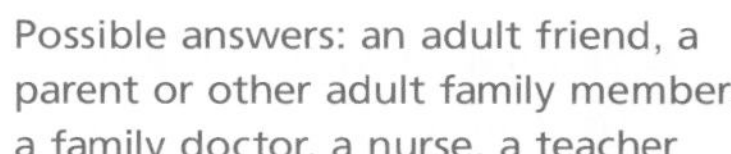

Possible answers: an adult friend, a parent or other adult family member, a family doctor, a nurse, a teacher

237

2. TEACH

Consumer Activity

The American Lung Association and the American Cancer Society are health organizations that provide community resources for tobacco addicts. Health professionals such as doctors or nurses are the best people to ask about products that help tobacco users overcome their addiction to tobacco.

Interpret Visuals—Pictures

Help students recognize that the pictures on these pages tell a story. Before students read the lesson, ask volunteers to tell what is happening in each picture. Then have them read the captions to verify their ideas.

Critical Thinking What are some difficulties for family members when someone in the family has a problem with tobacco or alcohol? Students' answers may include information from the text, as well as prior or personal knowledge, or inferences, such as the fact that a person with an alcohol or tobacco problem might lie about, deny, or cover up the problem.

Content-Area Reading Support

Using Text Format Direct students' attention to the list of Warning Signs of Alcoholism. Have students read it and point out how it connects to the lesson. Both the lesson and the list discuss how to recognize an alcoholic. Point out that textbooks often use boxes in the side column to highlight or summarize information.

Teacher Tip

Recovery Programs Programs such as Alcoholics Anonymous, Nicotine Anonymous, Al-Anon, and Alateen are based on peer support and honest and confidential sharing of personal experiences. Most twelve-step programs rely on a spiritual, nondenominational focus of belief in and reliance on a higher power. Other programs, such as Rational Recovery, use a format that avoids spirituality as a necessary component.

Teacher Tip

Children Exposed to Alcohol or Tobacco Abuse Some of your students may have experienced the destructive consequences of a family member who has an alcohol or a tobacco problem. Broaching these subjects may bring up confused emotions in these students. Protect students from feeling singled out regarding this subject, and be prepared to provide compassionate support if a student confides in you.

Activity

Communicate Remind students about trusted adults.

3. WRAP UP

Lesson 4 Summary and Review

1. Alcoholics, Alcoholics Anonymous, Al-Anon, the American Lung Association, the American Cancer Society
2. Possible answer: The person seems tired, often misses school or work, and doesn't have a healthful diet.
3. Drinking and smoking harm both the user and the user's family.
4. Possible answers:

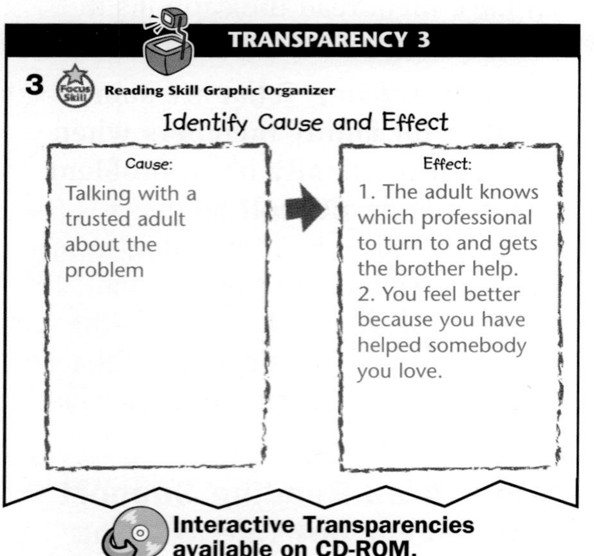

TRANSPARENCY 3
3 Reading Skill Graphic Organizer
Identify Cause and Effect
Cause:
Talking with a trusted adult about the problem
Effect:
1. The adult knows which professional to turn to and gets the brother help.
2. You feel better because you have helped somebody you love.

Interactive Transparencies available on CD-ROM.

5. Students should write that it is difficult to quit using alcohol or tobacco, as both are addictive drugs. They should mention the support groups and organizations named in this lesson and concerned friends and relatives as places and people who can help.

For **writing models** with examples, see *Teaching Resources* pp. 47–61. Rubrics are also provided.

When Minutes Count . . .

Quick Study Students can use *Activity Book* pages 41–42 (shown on p. 219) as they complete each lesson in this chapter.

ACTIVITY

Life Skills

Communicate

Curt's mother is an alcoholic. Sometimes when his mother is drinking, she yells at Curt and he feels hurt. Name some trusted adults Curt could talk to. What could Curt say to these adults? Use the steps for Communicating shown on pages 46–47.

More Help for Alcohol Users

Where can you go for help if you're worried about someone's alcohol use? Talk to an adult you trust, such as a parent, another relative, or a family friend. You could also talk to a teacher, counselor, school nurse, family doctor, or religious leader. Telling someone else about the problem might help you feel better.

Don't worry that telling someone will hurt the person with the alcohol problem. The adult you talk to may be able to find help for the alcoholic. There are many programs to help alcoholics and their families. Alcoholics Anonymous (AA) and Al-Anon are just two.

DRAW CONCLUSIONS Why is it important for an alcoholic to get help?
An alcoholic's drinking affects not only him or her, but also the family. He or she may need support to get help.

Lesson 4 Summary and Review

1. **Summarize with Vocabulary**
   Use terms from this lesson to complete the statements.
   Tobacco users can get support from organizations such as _____ and _____. _____ and their family members can go to organizations such as _____ or _____ for help with their alcohol problems.
2. What are three signs that a person is an alcoholic?
3. **Critical Thinking** Why should alcoholics and tobacco users try to stop their addictions?
4. **CAUSE AND EFFECT** Draw and complete this graphic organizer to show two possible effects of talking with a trusted adult about a brother's alcohol problem.

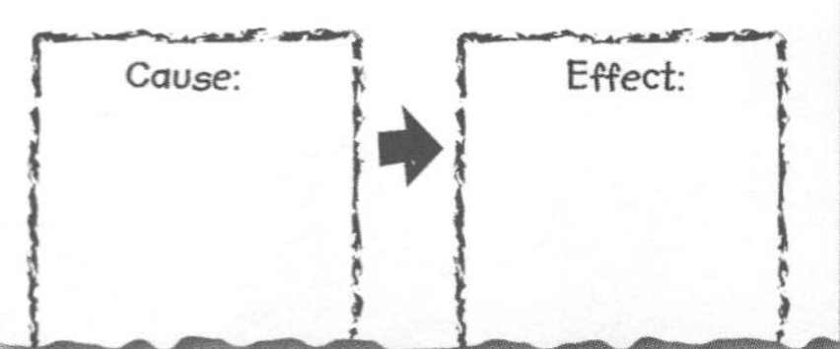

5. **Write to Inform—Explanation**
   Write about why it may be difficult for a user of tobacco or alcohol to quit. Write how a user can find help to recover from his or her addiction.

Meeting Individual Needs
Leveled Activities

BELOW-LEVEL Write Ads Invite students to write want ads for an alcohol treatment counselor. In the ads, students should mention any special qualities applicants for this job should have.

ON-LEVEL Make Lists Ask students to make three lists explaining why it might be hard to ask for help with an alcohol or tobacco problem. The first list should be from the point of view of a person who has the problem, the second list from the point of view of a family member, and the third list from the point of view of a friend of the family.

CHALLENGE Make a Database Suggest that students use the media center to find out about agencies that offer assistance to those who have a drinking problem or to those with family members who have a drinking problem. Help students construct a database of local addresses and phone numbers other students could access when using the media center.

Trustworthiness

Building Good Character

Report Dangerous Events

Trustworthiness involves being honest, telling the truth, and keeping promises so that people know they can count on you. You are trustworthy when you report dangerous events. Reporting dangerous events makes your home, community, and school safer. You should report dangerous events, such as when you

- **see young people drinking alcohol**
- **see young people using tobacco**
- **see people fighting**
- **smell smoke or gas**
- **see somebody who is hurt or unconscious**
- **see a stranger around your home or on school grounds**

You can report these events to

- **a parent**
- **another adult relative**
- **a teacher**
- **your school counselor**
- **your school principal**
- **a police officer**
- **another trusted adult**

Activity

With a friend, role-play how to report a dangerous event. Be sure to tell the person playing the trusted adult what you saw, where it was, and how long ago you saw it.

239

Building Good Character

Caring
Citizenship
Fairness
Respect
Responsibility
Trustworthiness

Objective

► Identify ways to show trustworthiness by reporting dangerous situations.

Program Resource

► Poster 6

BEFORE READING

Have students discuss why it is important to report a dangerous situation. Lead students to realize that they should not handle a dangerous situation alone, and that it should be reported so that a responsible adult can help deal with the situation.

DISCUSS

After students have read the page, have them close their books and restate situations that should be reported to a trusted adult. Have students think of other situations that should also be reported.

ACTIVITY

Be sure that students understand the instructions for the activity. Explain to students that they should remember to tell the trusted adult important details. They should tell the adult *what* has happened, *who* it happened to and who was there, *where* it happened, and *when* it happened.

Using the Poster

Activity Suggest that students design and display posters about trustworthiness and reporting dangerous situations.

Display Poster 6 to remind students of ways to be trustworthy. Students' posters can be displayed in the classroom, school cafeteria, or other common areas.

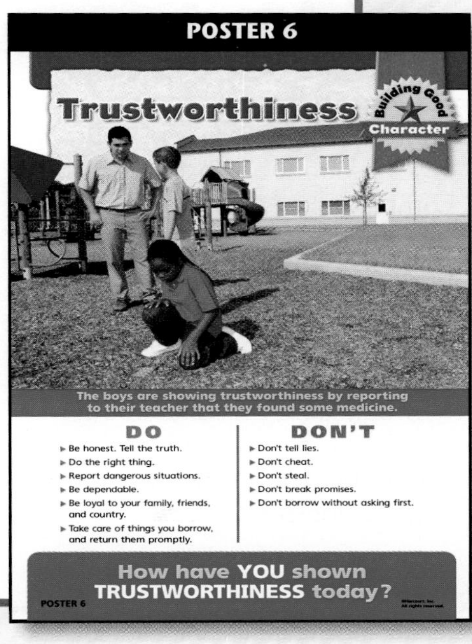

POSTER 6
Trustworthiness
Building Good Character
The boys are showing trustworthiness by reporting to their teacher that they found some medicine.
DO
Be honest. Tell the truth.
Do the right thing.
Report dangerous situations.
Be dependable.
Be loyal to your family, friends, and country.
Take care of things you borrow, and return them promptly.
DON'T
Don't tell lies.
Don't cheat.
Don't steal.
Don't break promises.
Don't borrow without asking first.
How have YOU shown TRUSTWORTHINESS today?
POSTER 6

LESSON 5
Pages 240–242

Objectives
- Understand the purpose of tobacco and alcohol advertisements.
- Identify how truthful or misleading an advertisement is.

When Minutes Count . . .
Assign the Quick Study, Lesson 5, Activity Book pp. 41–42 (shown on p. 219).

Program Resources
- Activity Book pp. 41–42, 45
- Transparency 3

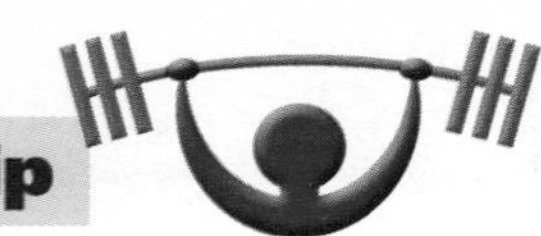

Daily Fitness Tip

Most tobacco and alcohol advertisers do not portray their products in ways that clearly indicate the harmful effects that they can have on physical health. Remind students that all these products can do them physical harm and do not have a part in any kind of physical fitness activities or fitness plan.

For more guidelines about alcohol and tobacco use and your physical fitness, see *Be Active! Resources for Physical Education* p. 169.

1. MOTIVATE

Tell students that an American Lung Association study determined that more than 80 percent of the top box office movies featured some form of tobacco use. When you consider that less than 25 percent of American adults smoke, this use of tobacco in movies seems extremely exaggerated.

Critical Thinking Why do you think tobacco use is shown so frequently in movies? Students may suggest that movie directors think smoking makes actors look hip, sophisticated, and so forth. Explain to students that tobacco companies pay stars to smoke in movies as an advertisement for their products.

LESSON 5

Tobacco, Alcohol, and the Media

Lesson Focus
Advertisers and the media do not always present alcohol and tobacco in a truthful manner.

Why Learn This?
Understanding the purpose of ads can help you make good decisions about not using tobacco and alcohol.

The Job of Advertising

Companies that make tobacco and alcohol products use advertisements, or ads, to send messages. They want you to think that people who use their products have lots of fun. The people in the ads are young and attractive. They wear stylish clothes and drive high-priced cars. Advertisers want young people to think that using alcohol and tobacco is exciting, fun, and healthful.

Cigarette companies are not allowed to advertise on television. But you still might see the names of their products in other places—in magazines or displayed at sporting and cultural events.

▼ The job of advertising is to sell products, not to show the truth.

BEACH BEER
For a fun time on the beach!
BEER

Language Arts

Have a Debate In recent years, an increasing number of court cases brought against tobacco companies by former smokers or their family members have relied on the idea that tobacco companies used false advertising to entice people to smoke and did not tell people that smoking was harmful. Hold a debate about whether tobacco companies should be held liable for smoking-related illnesses.

Teacher Tip

Alcohol Advertisements
According to the Federal Trade Commission, beer and wine companies spend about $600 million a year on television ads and $90 million on print ads. These figures do not include the advertisement expenditures of liquor companies. Both television and print ads are placed in youth-oriented magazines and programs. Ask students to discuss why they think this is so.

Beer makers use TV commercials to advertise their products during sporting events and other popular programs. They hope you will think that drinking beer is fun and exciting.

Alcohol products are sometimes advertised on billboards, in magazines, and on the radio. It's important to know that what is shown in tobacco and alcohol ads is not true. Alcohol and tobacco can't make you happy, popular, or successful. The truth is, alcohol and tobacco use may ruin your health, cause you to lose friends, and keep you from doing well at school or work.

COMPARE AND CONTRAST How do alcohol and tobacco ads compare with the facts about these drugs?
Alcohol and tobacco ads tell you that using these drugs will make you have fun. But these drugs make you smell, may make you lose friends, and are not healthful for you.

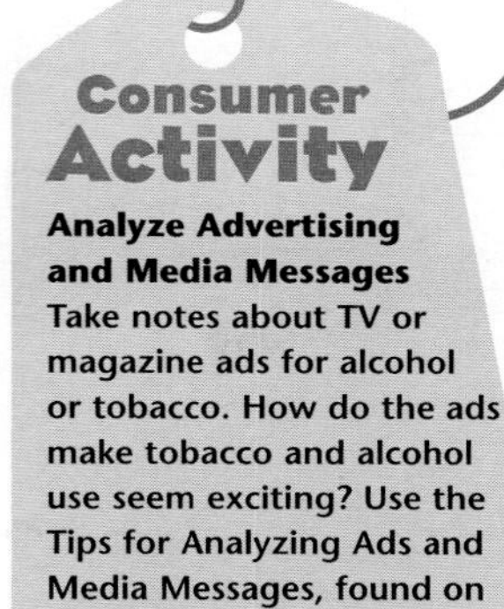

Consumer Activity

Analyze Advertising and Media Messages
Take notes about TV or magazine ads for alcohol or tobacco. How do the ads make tobacco and alcohol use seem exciting? Use the Tips for Analyzing Ads and Media Messages, found on pages 49–50, to help.

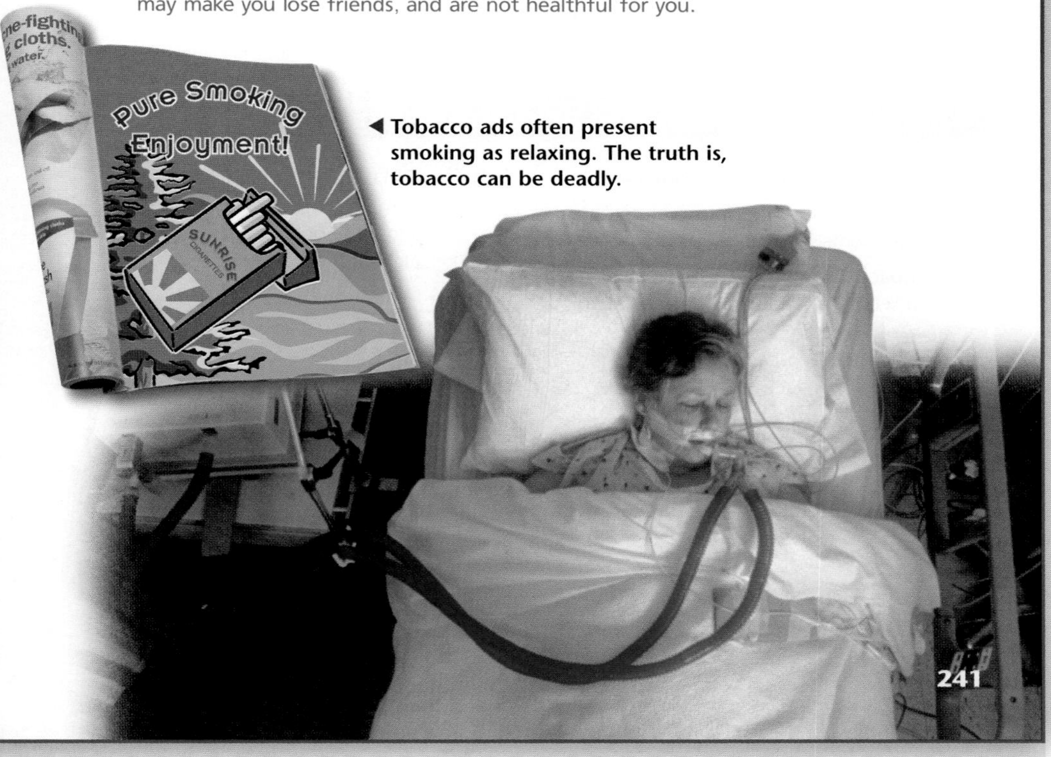

◀ Tobacco ads often present smoking as relaxing. The truth is, tobacco can be deadly.

241

2. TEACH

Consumer Activity

You may wish to collect or record tobacco or alcohol ads to discuss in class. Such ads often show sports events or include people who appear to be attractive and physically fit. Help students contrast the physical abilities needed for sports with the negative effects of tobacco and alcohol use.

Critical Thinking Tobacco and alcohol advertisers show tobacco and alcohol as exciting and fun. Is this true? Why or why not? Possible answer: It's not true because tobacco and alcohol are drugs that can cause addiction, illness, and death.

Interpret Visuals—Pictures

Direct students' attention to the illustration of a cigarette ad on page 240. Ask volunteers to read the caption. Encourage them to tell how the picture beside the ad tells the real truth about tobacco.

Critical Thinking Explain which of the two images is more truthful. The image of the sick person is more truthful because it shows what smoking can do to a person. The ad shows somebody practicing a sport—something that is actually difficult for a smoker to do.

Social Studies

Cigarette Ads Cigarette companies were the largest advertisers on TV and radio until Congress banned their ads. However, cigarette makers counter the ban by financing sports and other events on TV. Tobacco companies also get their products in movies by paying stars to use their brands. Cigarette manufacturers are now leaders in magazine and newspaper ads. Ask students to gather tobacco ads from newspapers and magazines.

Language Arts

Advertising Messages Have students make a bulletin board about messages from ads. Label the top half *What Advertisers Want You to Think.* Label the bottom half *What You Know Is True.* Have students put drawings or magazine clippings on the top portion to illustrate the messages that alcohol and tobacco companies give to the public. On the bottom half, have students place similar items to express the truth about alcohol and tobacco.

Quick Activity

Students' posters should have an anti-smoking or anti-drinking message.

3. WRAP UP

Lesson 5 Summary and Review

1. ads, buy or use, truth
2. The media portray use of alcohol and tobacco as being cool, fun, exciting, or healthful.
3. Possible answer: These messages do not tell the truth about alcohol and tobacco. They are only trying to sell you something.
4. Possible answers include:

TRANSPARENCY 3

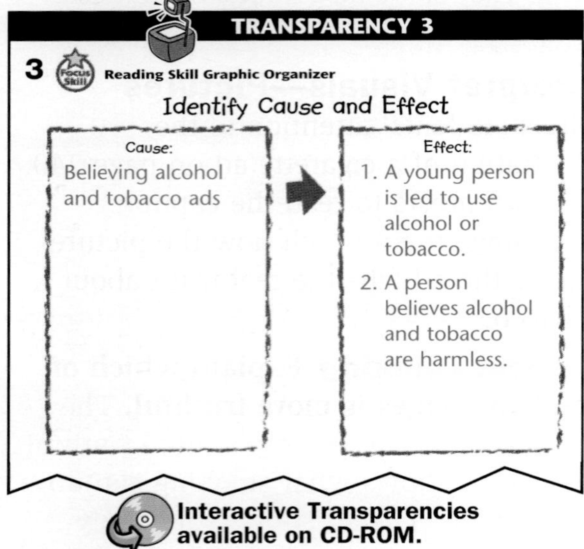

3 Reading Skill Graphic Organizer
Identify Cause and Effect
Cause:
Believing alcohol and tobacco ads
Effect:
1. A young person is led to use alcohol or tobacco.
2. A person believes alcohol and tobacco are harmless.

Interactive Transparencies available on CD-ROM.

5. Students' paragraphs should tell how media messages could make alcohol and tobacco seem cool or exciting. This belief could persuade a person to buy and use these products. If a person uses these products often, his or her health could be harmed.

For **writing models** with examples, see *Teaching Resources* pp. 47–61. Rubrics are also provided.

When Minutes Count . . .

Quick Study Students can use *Activity Book* pages 41–42 (shown on p. 219) as they complete each lesson in this chapter.

Quick Activity

Make a Poster Many organizations publish ads or brochures that tell the truth about alcohol and tobacco. Make an anti-alcohol or anti-tobacco poster that one of these organizations could use.

▲ **Information is available that tells the truth about alcohol and tobacco use.**

Resist False Media Messages

Look at ads for alcohol or tobacco on billboards, in magazines, or on television. Think about what really happens to people who use alcohol or tobacco. People who use these drugs have a greater risk for disease and injury. They really don't have much fun either. Knowing these facts can help you resist the false messages in ads about alcohol and tobacco.

DRAW CONCLUSIONS Why is it important that you know the facts about alcohol and tobacco when you see ads? Knowing the facts about these d will help you know that advertise are trying to get you to buy the product, not tell you the truth.

Lesson 5 Summary and Review

1. **Summarize with Vocabulary**
   Use terms from this lesson to complete the statements.
   Tobacco and alcohol companies use _____ to sell their products. These companies want you to _____ their products. You need to know the _____ about alcohol and tobacco product ads.
2. How do ads show alcohol and tobacco?
3. **Critical Thinking** Why should you resist false media messages about the use of alcohol and tobacco?
4. **CAUSE AND EFFECT** Draw and complete this graphic organizer to show the possible effects of believing alcohol and tobacco ads.

5. **Write to Inform—Description** 
   Write a paragraph describing how media messages can influence a person's health-related buying choices.

242

ACTIVITY BOOK P. 45

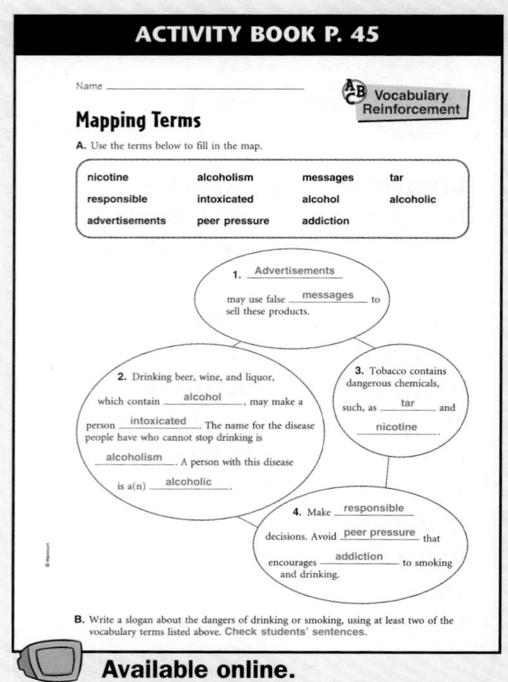

Name ______

Vocabulary Reinforcement

Mapping Terms

A. Use the terms below to fill in the map.

nicotine	alcoholism	messages	tar
responsible	intoxicated	alcohol	alcoholic
advertisements	peer pressure	addiction	

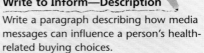

1. Advertisements may use false messages to sell these products.

2. Drinking beer, wine, and liquor, which contain alcohol, may make a person intoxicated. The name for the disease people have who cannot stop drinking is alcoholism. A person with this disease is a(n) alcoholic.

3. Tobacco contains dangerous chemicals, such as tar and nicotine.

4. Make responsible decisions. Avoid peer pressure that encourages addiction to smoking and drinking.

B. Write a slogan about the dangers of drinking or smoking, using at least two of the vocabulary terms listed above. Check students' sentences.

Available online. www.harcourtschool.com/health

ACTIVITIES

Science

Make a Body Atlas Decorate a bulletin board with a full-size picture of the human body, showing organs that are affected by alcohol and tobacco. Color the organs that are affected by tobacco one color. Use another color to show the organs affected by alcohol.

Social Studies

Historic Beverages When settlers first came to North America, people drank beverages other than water. Find out what they drank. Did any of these beverages have alcohol in them? How were they made? Write a magazine article that reports your findings.

Technology Project

Use the Internet to research an organization such as Mothers Against Drunk Driving (MADD), SADD, AA, Al-Anon, or Alateen. Write a report about the resources the organization has to help someone overcome an alcohol problem. If you do not have access to a computer, find a book about one of these organizations.

For more activities, visit The Learning Site. www.harcourtschool.com/health

Home & Community

Promote Health Talk to your classmates about ways to say *no* to tobacco and alcohol use. Make posters that show your ideas. Hang the posters in your school library, where other students can see them. Then take your poster home and share what you have learned with your family.

Career Link

Social Worker Social workers help people with many kinds of problems. Imagine that you are a social worker. An alcoholic father and his family have come to you for help. Write a list of things that you think the family should do to overcome their problems. Be sure to include in your list some organizations that help alcoholics and their families.

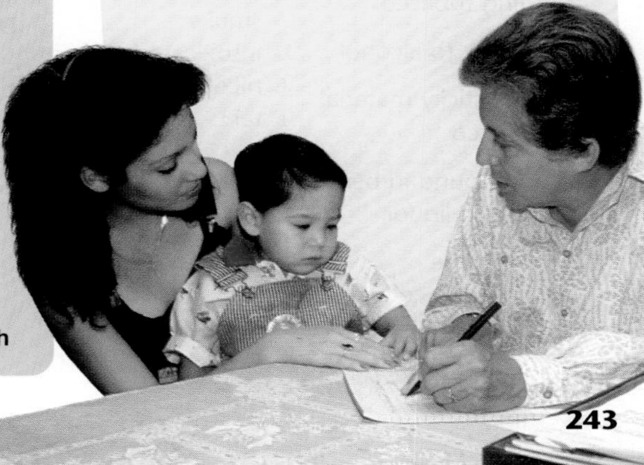

243

Career Link

Social Worker Some students may not know that the educational background needed for being a social worker can vary. For those interested in doing a broad spectrum of work in this field, there are educational degree programs that specialize and offer master's degrees. Remind students that they can find the names of programs for alcoholics and their families in Lesson 4 of this chapter.

For more information on health careers, visit the **Webliography** in Teacher Resources page at **www.harcourtschool.com/health**
Keyword health careers

Activities

Science

If a full-size picture of the human body is not available, students may use butcher paper to outline one human body and draw in several of the major organs of the body. They may use Chapter 1 of the textbook as a reference.

Social Studies

Have students work with a partner to conduct research. After students write their magazine articles, encourage them to read the articles to the rest of the class.

Home & Community

Tell students that many posters have catchy phrases that help people remember their messages. You may want to find some anti-tobacco and anti-alcohol posters to show students as examples.

Supports the Coordinated School Health Program

Technology Project

You may want to help students with their Internet search. Encourage each student to research a different organization. Allow students to read their reports to the rest of the class.

Chapter Review and Test Preparation

Pages 244–245

Reading Skill 5 pts. each

1. Possible answers: Smoking cigarettes can make the user feel nervous. Alcohol slows down nerve messages. Heavy drinking damages the brain.
2. Possible answers: Nicotine in tobacco shrinks blood vessels, making the heart work harder to pump blood. This condition can lead to high blood pressure, heart disease, and stroke. Alcohol makes the heart beat faster, raising blood pressure. Heavy drinking can permanently raise blood pressure.

Use Vocabulary 5 pts. each

3. D, intoxicated
4. C, environmental tobacco smoke
5. B, alcoholism
6. F, tar
7. A, alcohol
8. E, nicotine

Check Understanding 5 pts. each

9. D
10. F, Make friends who don't do drugs.
11. B, American Lung Association
12. H, mouth cancer
13. D, oxygen
14. H, has more energy
15. A, to improve health

Think Critically 5 pts. each

16. Most adult smokers are addicted.
17. Sample answer: If people know that tobacco and alcohol use harms their health, they might think twice about using these products.

Chapter Review and Test Preparation

Reading Skill

CAUSE AND EFFECT

Draw and then use this graphic organizer to answer questions 1 and 2.

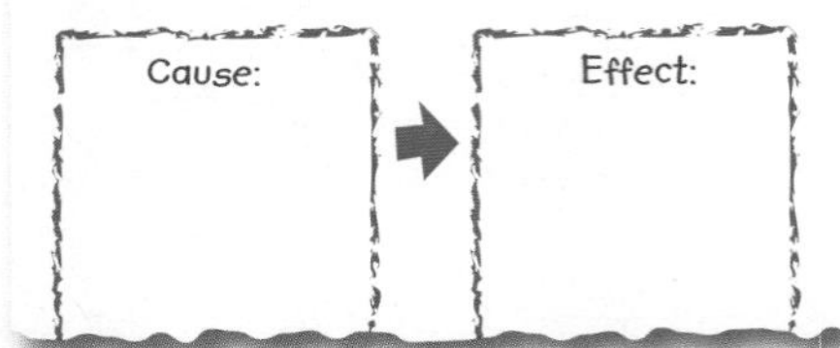

1 Write two effects that alcohol and tobacco have on the nervous system.

2 Write two effects that alcohol and tobacco have on the cardiovascular system.

Use Vocabulary

Match each term in Column B with its meaning in Column A.

Column A	Column B
3 Strongly affected by alcohol	**A** alcohol
4 Smoke in the air from burning tobacco	**B** alcoholism
5 Addiction to alcohol	**C** environmental tobacco smoke
6 A dark, sticky material in tobacco	**D** intoxicated
7 A drug found in beer, wine, and liquor	**E** nicotine
8 An addictive substance in tobacco	**F** tar

Check Understanding

9 Which of the following has about 50 cancer-causing chemicals? (p. 219)

A

C

B

D

10 Which is one way to avoid harmful peer pressure? (pp. 232–233)
F Make friends who don't do drugs.
G Go to parties where alcohol is available.
H Don't practice refusal skills.
J Choose friends who use tobacco.

11 Which group could help somebody quit smoking? (p. 237)
A Alcoholics Anonymous
B American Lung Association
C Al-Anon
D none of these

244

Formal Assessment

ASSESSMENT GUIDE P. 43

9

Name ______

Chapter Test

Harmful Effects of Tobacco and Alcohol

Write *T* or *F* to show if the statements are true or false.

T 1. Cigarette tobacco is made from the dried leaves of the tobacco plant.
T 2. If you see a friend using tobacco, you should tell a trusted adult.
F 3. Only cigarettes contain nicotine.
F 4. An intoxicated person usually does well at his or her job.
T 5. Environmental tobacco smoke is dangerous to others.
F 6. Alcohol is a drug found in cigarettes.
T 7. Some people start smoking when they are young because they see famous people smoking.
F 8. Tobacco is a powerful drug that is used to kill insects on crops.
T 9. Tobacco causes both lung cancer and mouth cancer.
T 10. Tar is a dangerous substance found in tobacco smoke.

© Harcourt

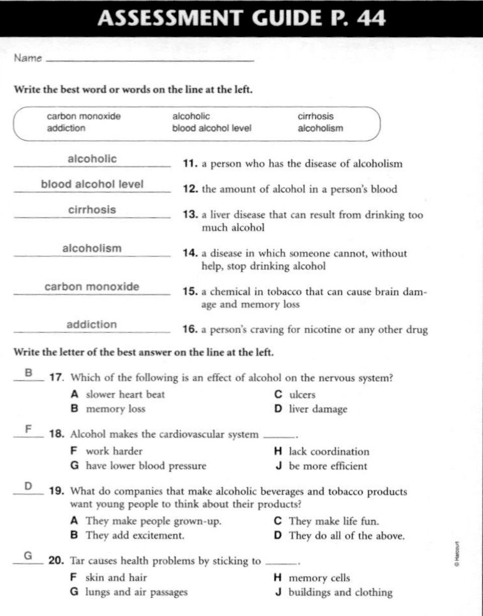

ASSESSMENT GUIDE P. 44

Name ______

Write the best word or words on the line at the left.

carbon monoxide	alcoholic	cirrhosis
addiction	blood alcohol level	alcoholism

alcoholic 11. a person who has the disease of alcoholism
blood alcohol level 12. the amount of alcohol in a person's blood
cirrhosis 13. a liver disease that can result from drinking too much alcohol
alcoholism 14. a disease in which someone cannot, without help, stop drinking alcohol
carbon monoxide 15. a chemical in tobacco that can cause brain damage and memory loss
addiction 16. a person's craving for nicotine or any other drug

Write the letter of the best answer on the line at the left.

B 17. Which of the following is an effect of alcohol on the nervous system?
A slower heart beat **C** ulcers
B memory loss **D** liver damage

F 18. Alcohol makes the cardiovascular system ______.
F work harder **H** lack coordination
G have lower blood pressure **J** be more efficient

D 19. What do companies that make alcoholic beverages and tobacco products want young people to think about their products?
A They make people grown-up. **C** They make life fun.
B They add excitement. **D** They do all of the above.

G 20. Tar causes health problems by sticking to ______.
F skin and hair **H** memory cells
G lungs and air passages **J** buildings and clothing

© Harcourt

Smoking cigarettes	—	Lung cancer
Chewing tobacco	—	

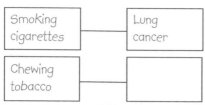

12 Which disease would best complete this graphic organizer? (p. 222)

F cirrhosis **H** mouth cancer
G heart disease **J** alcoholism

13 Gases in cigarette smoke take the place of _____ in the blood. (p. 223)
A nicotine **C** nitrogen
B carbon monoxide **D** oxygen

14 Which of the following is **NOT** a sign of alcoholism? (p. 237)
F clothes not clean
G seems tired
H has more energy
J often gets angry

15 People start using tobacco or alcohol for all of the following reasons **EXCEPT**_____. (pp. 220, 225)
A to improve health
B peer pressure
C to feel grown-up
D curiosity

Think Critically

16 Since smoking is dangerous, why do so many adults continue to do it?

SURGEON GENERAL'S WARNING: Smoking Causes Lung Cancer, Heart Disease, Emphysema, And May Complicate Pregnancy

17 Study the warning label shown above. Similar warnings appear on alcohol bottles and cans. How would this warning help people refuse to use the product?

Apply Skills

18 **BUILDING GOOD CHARACTER**
Trustworthiness You are walking to class one day when you see some students sharing a beer outside the school. What should you do?

19 **LIFE SKILLS**
Refuse Some older students start talking to you after school one day. You're really excited to have their attention. Then one of them offers you a cigarette. What should you do?

Write About Health

20 **Write to Inform—Description**
Describe how using alcohol or tobacco makes life less fun.

ASSESSMENT GUIDE P. 45

Name ____________

Alcohol affects many parts of the body. Tell how each part of the body labeled in the diagram might be affected by alcohol.

Liver
Stomach

21. liver cirrhosis; difficulty in cleaning blood of poisons

22. digestive system stomach ulcers; pancreatic damage, more difficulty in absorbing nutrients from food

23. Cheryl's sister Arlene is in high school. Cheryl sees that Arlene is acting strangely. Look at the list Cheryl made about Arlene's behavior.

- She often skips school.
- She is failing some classes.
- She doesn't bathe often.
- She gets very angry for no reason.

What might be Arlene's problem?
alcohol abuse

24. Cheryl wants to help her sister. Write Cheryl a note with an idea of where to go for help for Arlene.
Possible answer: Dear Cheryl, You could get help from a trusted adult, such as a parent, another family member, or a close family friend. A teacher, counselor, school nurse, or family doctor could also help you and Arlene. Your friend, [student's name]

25. Arlene and her friends also smoke cigarettes. They've all decided to try to stop smoking and drinking. Write the name of a program that can help with a drinking problem. Write the name of a program that can help people stop smoking.
Alcohol problem: Alcoholics Anonymous; Al-Anon
Tobacco problem: American Lung Association; American Cancer Society

Apply Skills 5 pts. each

18. Answers will vary but should include reporting the situation to a trusted adult.

19. Answers will vary but should include some way to refuse, such as refuse to accept (say *no*) the offer of the cigarette.

Write About Health 5 pts.

20. Using tobacco and alcohol makes playing sports harder, can make the user feel tired or sick, and could cause you to lose friends.

Performance Assessment

Use the Chapter Project and the rubric provided on the Project Evaluation Sheet. See *Assessment Guide* pp. 18, 60, 70.

Portfolio Assessment

Have students select their best work from the following suggestions:
- Leveled Activities, p. 220
- Quick Activity, p. 242
- Write to Inform, p. 229
- Activities, p. 243

See *Assessment Guide* pp. 12–16.

CHAPTER

10 Your Needs and Feelings

Lesson	Pacing	Objectives	Reading Skills
Introduce the Chapter pp. 246–247		• Preview chapter concepts.	**Main Idea and Details** pp. 247, 336–337
1 Learning About Yourself pp. 248–251	1 class period	• Identify personality traits. • Describe how a good attitude and a positive self-concept contribute to self-confidence and high self-esteem.	**Main Idea and Details** pp. 249, 251 • Draw Conclusions, p. 250 • Compare and Contrast, p. 251
2 We All Have Needs pp. 252–255	1 class period	• Identify the four basic physical needs. • Identify examples of basic emotional, mental, and social needs. • Recognize how setting goals helps people meet their needs.	**Main Idea and Details** p. 255 • Summarize, p. 253 • Sequence, p. 255
3 We All Have Feelings pp. 256–259	1 class period	• Identify feeling and recognize safe ways to express them. • Describe self-control strategies and steps for anger management.	**Main Idea and Details** p. 259 • Compare and Contrast, p. 257 • Sequence, p. 259
4 The Challenge of Friendship pp. 260–265	3 class periods	• Recognize shared interests, goals, and values as factors in friendship. • Identify and practice effective strategies for resolving conflicts by using negotiation and compromise. • Describe characteristics needed to be a responsible friend and family member.	**Main Idea and Details** p. 265 • Cause and Effect, p. 261 • Draw Conclusions, p. 263
Life Skills pp. 266–267	1 class period	• Identify skills to resolve conflicts. • Explain and apply conflict resolution skills.	
5 Working with Others pp. 268–272	3 class periods	• Explain the importance of respecting differences in people. • Describe how people can work together to help others. • Learn ways to make a difference as a role model.	**Main Idea and Details** pp. 271, 272 • Draw Conclusions, p. 268 • Cause and Effect, p. 269 • Summarize, p. 272
Building Good Character p. 273		• Recognize the importance of caring by being a good friend. • Describe the qualities of a good friend.	
6 Dealing with Peer Pressure pp. 274–276	1 class period	• Describe how peer pressure works and how you can respond to it effectively. • Explain how a strong self-concept can help you avoid the influences of negative peer pressure. • Demonstrate refusal and negotiation skills to enhance health.	**Main Idea and Details** p. 276 • Compare and Contrast, p. 275 • Sequence, p. 276
Activities p. 277		• Extend chapter concepts.	
Chapter Review pp. 278–279	1 class period	• Assess chapter objectives.	

Vocabulary	Program Resources
	Music CD Teaching Resources, p. 41
self-concept **self-confidence**	Transparency 4 Activity Book, pp. 46–48
basic needs **privacy** **goal**	Transparency 4 Activity Book, pp. 46–47
self-control	Transparency 4 Activity Book, pp. 46–47
conflict **conflict resolution** **negotiate** **compromise**	Transparency 4 Activity Book, pp. 46–47
	Activity Book, p. 49 Poster 11
compassion **role model**	Transparency 4 Activity Book, pp. 46–47
	Poster 1
	Transparency 4 Activity Book, pp. 46–47, 50
	The Learning Site www.harcourtschool.com
	Assessment Guide, pp. 46–48

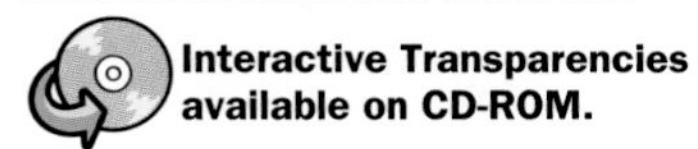
Interactive Transparencies available on CD-ROM.

Reading Skill

These reading skills are reinforced throughout this chapter and one skill is emphasized as the Focus Skill.

- **Identify Main Idea and Details**
- Draw Conclusions
- Identify Cause and Effect
- Compare and Contrast
- Sequence
- Summarize

KEY READING SKILLS TRANSPARENCY 4

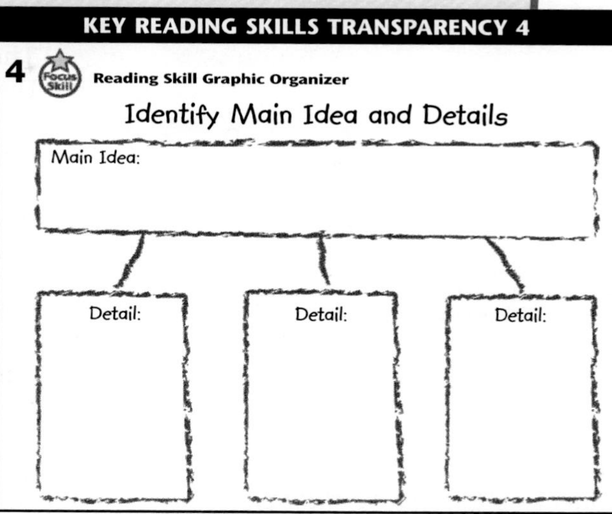
4 Reading Skill Graphic Organizer

Identify Main Idea and Details

Main Idea:

Detail: | Detail: | Detail:

Life Skills

Life Skills are health-enhancing behaviors that can help students reduce risks to their health and safety.

Six Life Skills are reinforced throughout *Harcourt Health and Fitness*. The skill emphasized in this chapter is Resolve Conflicts.

POSTER 11 RESOLVE CONFLICTS

Resolve Conflicts
LIFE SKILLS
The girls are resolving a conflict by listening to one another and finding a way for both sides to win.
Steps to Resolve Conflicts
1 Use I-messages to tell how you feel.
2 Listen to each other. Consider the other person's view.
3 Negotiate.
4 Find a way for both sides to win.
How do YOU RESOLVE CONFLICTS?
POSTER 11

Building Good Character

Character education is an important aspect of health education. When children behave in ways that show good character, they promote the health and safety of themselves and others.

Six character traits are reinforced throughout *Harcourt Health and Fitness*. The trait emphasized in this chapter is Caring.

POSTER 1 CARING

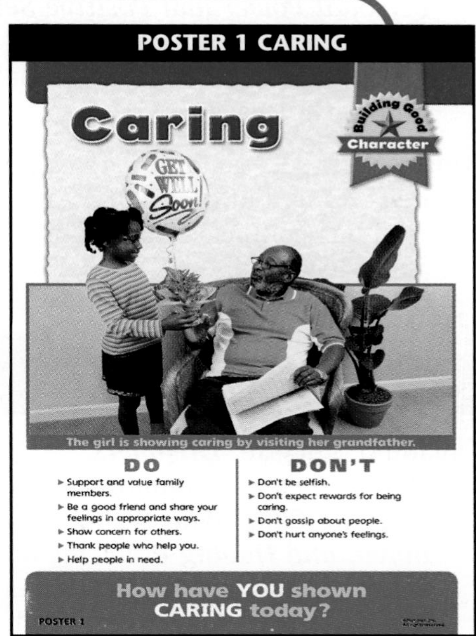

Caring
Building Good Character
GET WELL Soon!
The girl is showing caring by visiting her grandfather.
DO
Support and value family members.
Be a good friend and share your feelings in appropriate ways.
Show concern for others.
Thank people who help you.
Help people in need.
DON'T
Don't be selfish.
Don't expect rewards for being caring.
Don't gossip about people.
Don't hurt anyone's feelings.
How have YOU shown CARING today?
POSTER 1

Resources

Coordinated School Health Program

Health Education
Health Services
Physical Education
Nutrition Services
Parent/ Community Involvement
Healthy School Environment
Counseling, Psychological, & Social Services
Health Promotion for Staff
CSHP

A Coordinated School Health Program endeavors to improve children's health and therefore their capacity to learn through the support of families, schools, and communities working together. The following information is provided to help classroom teachers be more aware of these resources.

The National Center for Chronic Disease and Health Promotion, part of the **CDC**, funds the Coordinated School Health Program. Visit its website for information about the eight components that make up this program. **www.cdc.gov/nccdphp/dash/**

Post-traumatic stress disorder (PTSD) is an anxiety disorder that can develop after exposure to a terrifying event in which grave physical harm occurred or was threatened. The **National Institute of Mental Health** works to assist children who have been victims of or witnesses to these events. **www.nimh.nih.gov/outline/traumatic.cfm**

The **CDC** monitors statistics on a state-by-state basis on topics such as the Youth Risk Behavior Surveillance System (YRBSS). **www.cdc.gov/nccdphp/dash/state_info**

The National Association of State Boards of Education **(NASBE)** explains ways that schools can help children prevent skin cancer, the most common form of cancer in the United States, in the publication *Fit, Healthy, and Ready to Learn! A School Health Policy Guide.* **www.nasbe.org/**

Other resources that support a Coordinated School Health Program:

- School-Home Connection
- Daily Physical Activity
- Daily Fitness Tips
- Activities: Home & Community
- Health Background: Webliography
- *Be Active! Resources for Physical Education*

Media Resources

Books for Students

Smith, David J. ***If the World Were a Village: A Book About the World's People.*** Kids Can Press, 2002. Helps children appreciate the diversity among the world's people. **EASY**

Kaufman, Gershen. ***Stick Up for Yourself! Every Kid's Guide to Personal Power and Positive Self-Esteem.*** Free Spirit Publishing, 1999. Challenges children to make proper choices. **AVERAGE**

Kinsey-Warnock, Natalie. ***The Night the Bells Rang.*** Puffin, 2000. A farm boy who has conflicts with his brother and a local bully. **ADVANCED**

Books for Teachers and Families

Palladino, Lucy Jo. ***Dreamers, Discoverers, & Dynamos: How to Help the Child Who Is Bright, Bored, and Having Problems in School.*** Ballantine Books, 1999. Examines the "Edison-trait" and creative children who have trouble in school.

Kaufman, Gershen. ***A Teacher's Guide to Stick Up for Yourself: A 10-Part Course in Self-Esteem and Assertiveness for Kids.*** Free Spirit Publishing, 2000. Explores the problems children face such as learning and liking oneself.

Free and Inexpensive Materials

Federal Citizen Information Center
Receive free express e-mail on the FirstGov for Kids site. This informative government site has a wide range of topics on its KidsHealth page that deals with topics such as feelings and related emotional and social issues. Also has information about social groups such as the National 4-H Web page.

To access free and inexpensive resources on the Web, visit **www.harcourtschool.com/health/free**

Videos

Peer Pressure. United Learning, 1998.

Looking from the Inside/Out. AIT Productions, 1996.

Dilemma: He's Different. Educational Video Network, 1994.

These resources have been selected to meet a variety of individual needs. Please review all materials and websites prior to sharing them with students to ensure the content is appropriate for your class. Note that information, while correct at time of publication, is subject to change.

Visit **The Learning Site** for related links, activities, resources, and the health **Webliography.**

www.harcourtschool.com/health

Meeting Individual Needs

Below-Level

To practice study strategies, students can fold a paper to form two columns. In the left column, they write questions they may have before or while they read. In the right column, they write the page number where they found the answer.

Activities
- Describe Traits, p. 250
- Make Calm-Down Posters, p. 258
- Make a Friendship Web, p. 260
- Make a Map, p. 268
- Say *No*, p. 274

On-Level

If students are having difficulty explaining what a paragraph was about, work with a small group to discuss how summarizing helps with comprehension. Have them tell or list the main points of the section. This will help them understand and remember what they read.

Activities
- Analyze Traits, p. 250
- Write Poems, p. 258
- Read a Story, p. 260
- Investigate Braille, p. 268
- Use Positive Peer Pressure, p. 274

Challenge

Have students write a cinquain poem from the text. Have students follow this pattern in their poems: Line 1: a one-word title; Line 2: two adjectives describing the title; Line 3: three action verbs; Line 4: four words expressing feelings; Line 5: a one-word synonym for the title.

Activities
- Think Positively, p. 250
- Learn About Facial Expressions, p. 258
- Perform a Skit, p. 260
- Sign Language, p. 268
- Make a Scene, p. 274

ESL/ELL

Vocabulary Workshop

Before reading, write each new vocabulary term on the board, pronounce it, and have students repeat it. Give the meanings and cite examples. Then whisper each term to a different volunteer. The volunteers act out their terms or draw pictures about them for others to guess.

Activities
- Language and Vocabulary, p. 254
- Comprehensible Input, p. 264
- Background and Experience, p. 270

Curriculum Integration

Use these topics to integrate health into your daily planning.

Integrated Language Arts/Reading Skills
- No Islands, p. 252
- Resolving a Conflict, p. 262
- Friendship Bulletin Board, p. 265
- Identifying Role Models, p. 272

Math
- Making Graphs, p. 261

Music
- Feelings, p. 256

Science
- Conflicts Between Humans and Animals, p. 263
- Saving Energy, p. 271

Physical Education
- Daily Fitness Tip, pp. 248, 252, 256, 260, 268, 274
- Daily Physical Activity, p. 247
- Reducing Stress, p. 259
- Working Together, p. 271

Art
- Wants and Needs, p. 253
- Masks, p. 257

Social Studies
- Meeting Basic Needs, p. 255
- Conflicts Between and Within Nations, p. 262

CHAPTER
10
Pages 246–279

CHAPTER SUMMARY

In this chapter, students

- ► examine specific ways in which each person is unique and special.
- ► learn effective strategies for managing feelings and friendship.
- ► recognize the importance of working and treating each other with respect and compassion.

Life Skills
Students practice *resolving conflicts* at school.

Building Good Character
Students learn that being *caring* is a way to be a good friend.

Consumer Health
Students *analyze* advertisements and media messages.

Literature Springboard

Use the poem "My Puppy" to spark interest in the chapter topic. See the Read-Aloud Anthology on page RA-11 of this *Teacher Edition*.

Prereading Strategies

SCAN THE CHAPTER Have students preview the chapter content by scanning the titles, headings, pictures, tables, and graphs. Ask volunteers to predict what they'll learn. Use their responses to determine their prior knowledge.

PREVIEW VOCABULARY As students scan the chapter, invite them to sort vocabulary into familiar and unfamiliar words. Have students look up unfamiliar words in the Glossary.

Words I Know	Words I've Seen or Heard	New Words

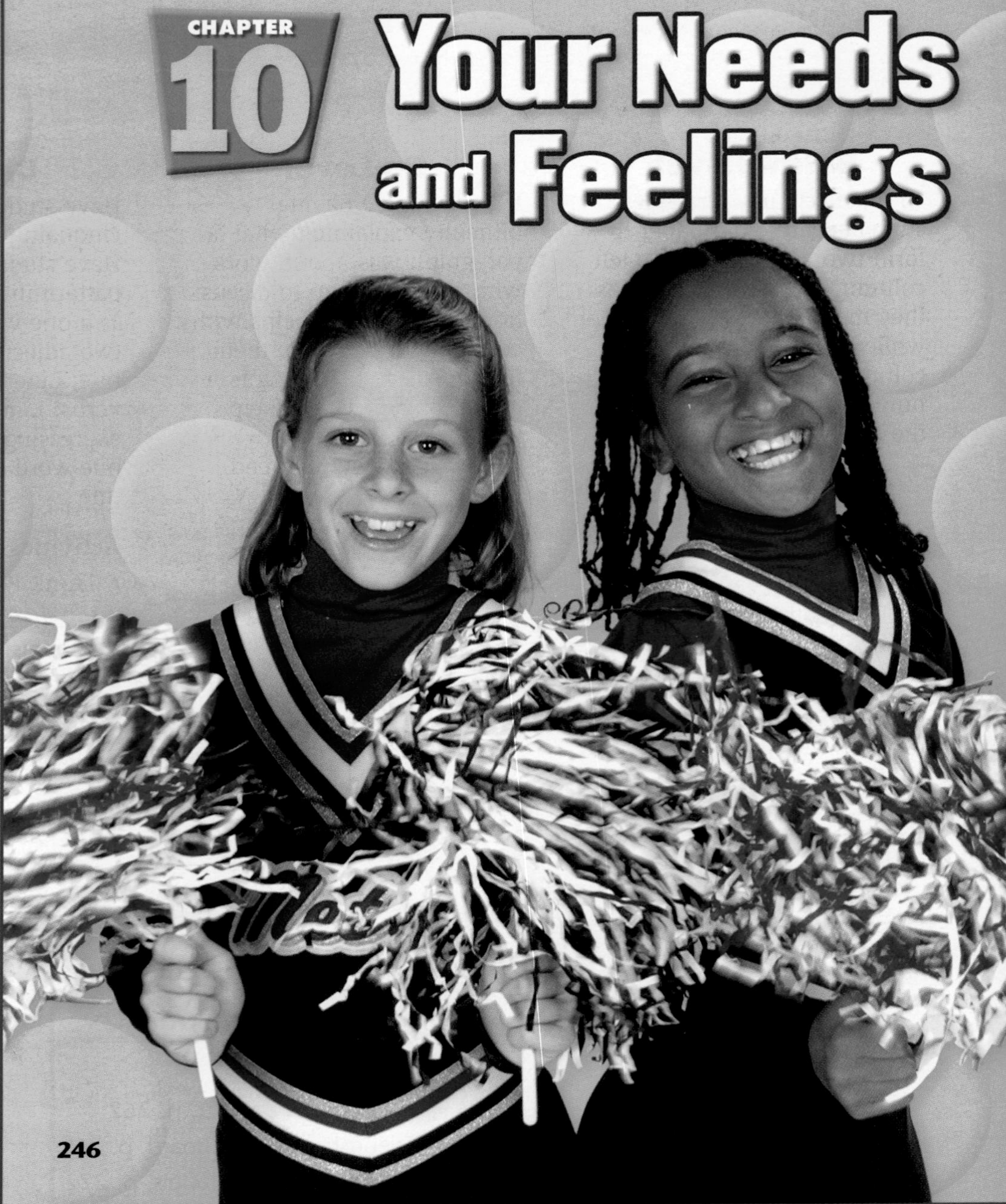

Reading Skill

IDENTIFY MAIN IDEA AND DETAILS To introduce or review this skill, have students use the Reading in Health Handbook, pp. 336–337. Teaching strategies and additional activities are also provided.

Students will have opportunities to practice and apply this skill throughout this chapter.

- Focus Skill Reading Mini-Lesson, p. 248
- Reading comprehension questions identified with the 
- *Activity Book* p. 48 (shown on page 251)
- Lesson Summary and Review, pp. 251, 255, 259, 265, 272, 276
- Chapter Review and Test Preparation, pp. 278–279

Reading Skill

IDENTIFY MAIN IDEA AND DETAILS The main idea is the most important thought in a passage. Details tell about the main idea and help you understand it. Use the Reading in Health Handbook on pages 336–337 and this graphic organizer to help you read and understand the information in this chapter.

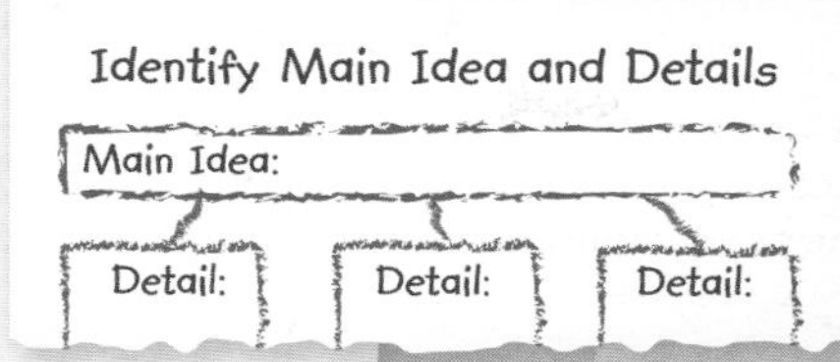

Health Graph

INTERPRET DATA A magazine for young people asked readers what bothered them the most. This graph shows how they replied. What bothered these young people even more than a test?

What Bothers You?

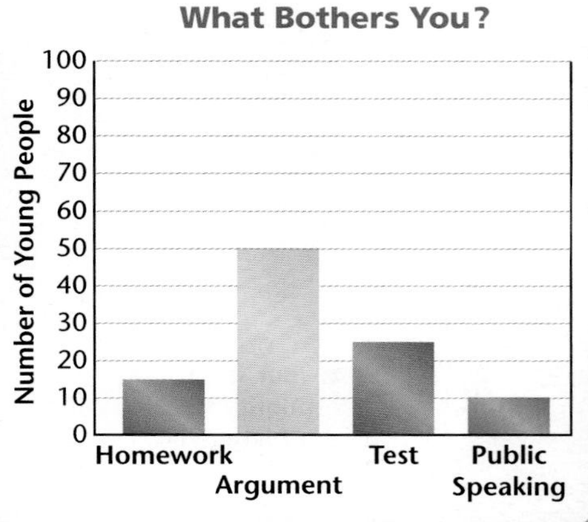

Daily Physical Activity

You can feel better about yourself. Be physically active, and exercise.

Be Active!
Use the selection Track 10, **Super Stress Buster**, to relax you and give your mood a boost.

INTRODUCE THE CHAPTER

Health Graph

Interpret Data

Invite volunteers to explain what the graph shows.

What bothered these young people even more than a test? having an argument

Do you think that's also true of the students in your class? Students may agree or disagree. If they disagree, ask what they think bothers their class most.

What bothered the students in this survey the least? public speaking

Do you think that's also true of your class? Students may agree or disagree.

Daily Physical Activity

Use *Be Active! Music for Daily Physical Activity* with the Instant Activity Cards to provide students with movement activities that can be done in limited space. Options for using these components are provided beginning on page TR2 in this *Teacher Edition*.

Chapter Project

Conflict Resolution (*Assessment Guide* p. 60)

ASSESS PRIOR KNOWLEDGE Use students' initial ideas for the project as a baseline assessment of their understanding of chapter concepts. Have students complete the project as they work through the chapter.

PERFORMANCE ASSESSMENT The project can be used for performance assessment. Use the Project Evaluation Sheet (rubric), *Assessment Guide* p. 71.

School-Home Connection

Distribute copies of the School-Home Connection (in English or Spanish). Have students take the page home to share with their families as you begin this chapter.

Follow Up Have volunteers share the results of their activities.

Supports the Coordinated School Health Program

TEACHING RESOURCES P. 41

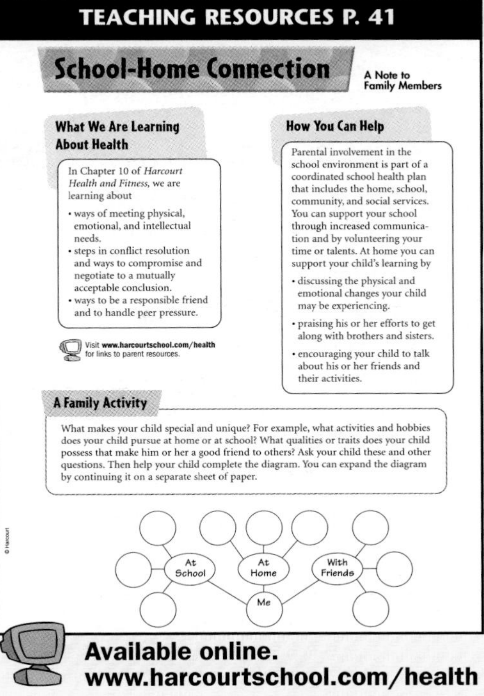

School-Home Connection

A Note to Family Members

What We Are Learning About Health

In Chapter 10 of *Harcourt Health and Fitness,* we are learning about

- ways of meeting physical, emotional, and intellectual needs.
- steps in conflict resolution and ways to compromise and negotiate to a mutually acceptable conclusion.
- ways to be a responsible friend and to handle peer pressure.

Visit **www.harcourtschool.com/health** for links to parent resources.

How You Can Help

Parental involvement in the school environment is part of a coordinated school health plan that includes the home, school, community, and social services. You can support your school through increased communication and by volunteering your time or talents. At home you can support your child's learning by

- discussing the physical and emotional changes your child may be experiencing.
- praising his or her efforts to get along with brothers and sisters.
- encouraging your child to talk about his or her friends and their activities.

A Family Activity

What makes your child special and unique? For example, what activities and hobbies does your child pursue at home or at school? What qualities or traits does your child possess that make him or her a good friend to others? Ask your child these and other questions. Then help your child complete the diagram. You can expand the diagram by continuing it on a separate sheet of paper.

At School
At Home
With Friends
Me

© Harcourt

Available online.
www.harcourtschool.com/health

LESSON 1
Pages 248–251

Objectives
► Identify personality traits.
► Describe how a good attitude and a positive self-concept contribute to self-confidence and high self-esteem.

When Minutes Count . . .
Assign the Quick Study, Lesson 1, Activity Book pp. 46–47 (shown on p. 249).

Program Resources
► Activity Book pp. 46–48
► Transparency 4
► Growth, Development, and Reproduction pp. 12–25

Vocabulary
self-concept p. 248,
self-confidence p. 248

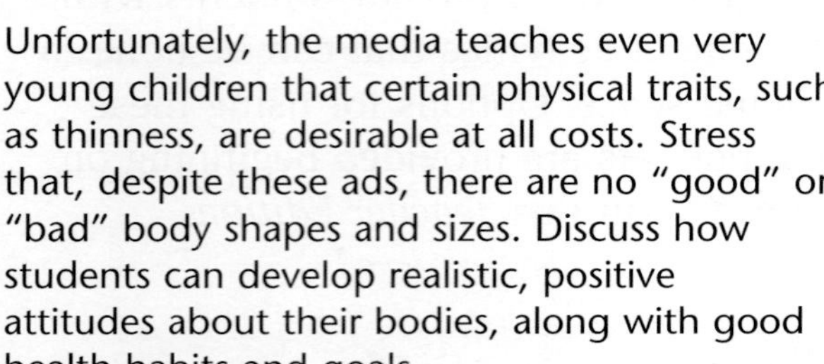
Daily Fitness Tip
Unfortunately, the media teaches even very young children that certain physical traits, such as thinness, are desirable at all costs. Stress that, despite these ads, there are no "good" or "bad" body shapes and sizes. Discuss how students can develop realistic, positive attitudes about their bodies, along with good health habits and goals.

1. MOTIVATE
Ask students to think of someone they know and one term that tells something about how this person looks. Possible responses: tall, brown eyes, red hair, boy Ask volunteers to share the terms they chose, but not the names of the people. Have students think of a word or phrase that tells something about this person, such as an interest or skill. Possible responses: likes to swim, plays the guitar, is good at math, tells funny jokes Don't require students to share their words or phrases. Caution those who do to be sensitive to the feelings of others.

LESSON 1 Learning About Yourself

Lesson Focus
Learning about yourself helps you appreciate who you are.

Why Learn This?
Knowing who you are helps you make healthful decisions and get along well with others.

Vocabulary
self-concept
self-confidence

Getting to Know You
In Chapter 1, you learned *traits* are the physical characteristics or other qualities that make you special. People are also described by their traits. For example, one person might be friendly. Someone else might be shy.

Knowing your traits gives you a picture of yourself. The picture you have of yourself most of the time is your **self-concept**. If your self-concept is positive, you have self-respect. *Self-respect* means that you value yourself and your ideas.

A positive self-concept leads to *self-confidence* and *self-esteem*. **Self-confidence** means that you are sure of yourself. You can handle most problems. When you have self-esteem, you respect yourself and are happy with yourself.

▲ Your family helps you have respect for yourself and your abilities.

When you have self-respect, you always try your best.▼

▲ Your self-concept might include having athletic skills.

248

Reading Skill

Mini-Lesson
MAIN IDEA AND DETAILS
The main idea is the most important thought in a passage. Details tell about the main idea. Have students practice this skill by answering the Focus Skill question on page 249. Have them draw and complete the graphic organizer as you model it on the transparency.

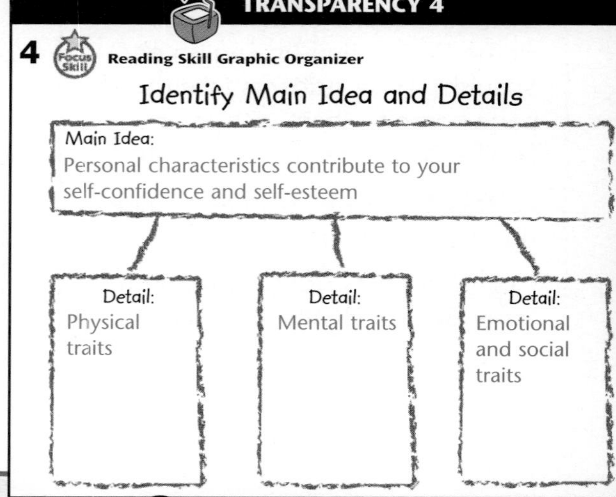

Interactive Transparencies available on CD-ROM.

▲ Self-confidence gives you the courage to challenge yourself.

In addition to physical traits, you also have mental, emotional, and social traits.

Your mental and emotional traits affect the way you think, learn, and act. These traits might include a good memory or a sense of humor. One of your traits might be a *talent*, or natural ability. You may play the violin or draw well.

Your social traits affect the way you act with others. Maybe you are a leader. Maybe you prefer to work on your own. You might be a good listener. Perhaps friends turn to you for help.

Your many traits make you who you are. Knowing your traits helps you learn about yourself.

MAIN IDEA AND DETAILS Explain how personal characteristics contribute to your self-confidence and self-esteem.
Physical, mental, emotional, and social traits help shape your self-concept and your feelings of self-confidence and self-esteem.

Did You Know?

Every year, about one million people from 150 countries compete in the Special Olympics. The athletes all take this oath: "Let me win. But if I cannot win, let me be brave in the attempt."

249

2. TEACH

Discuss

Explain that *mental traits* determine how you learn. For example, some people learn better by watching a demonstration, while others learn better by listening to an explanation. Some are quick learners, and others take more time. Mental traits can also include musical or artistic abilities.

Emotional traits determine how you handle feelings. Do you share them with others or keep them to yourself? Do people describe you as serious or humorous at times? Are you patient or impatient?

Interpret Visuals—Pictures

Have students look at the pictures on page 248. Ask them to describe this boy's physical traits. Then have them guess the boy's mental, emotional, and social traits, based on clues in the pictures.

Do people sometimes share the same traits? Yes; people can share traits but not always in exactly the same way.

Critical Thinking Do you think two people can have exactly the same traits? This is not likely, as even identical twins can have different ways of learning. Plus, one might be a leader and the other a team member.

Point out that we can describe people by what we can see and by what we can't see. This lesson will help students think about all the ways that each person is different and special.

Growth, Development, and Reproduction

An optional lesson about adolescence and emotional changes is provided in this supplement on pp. 12–25. Use this component in compliance with state and legal guidelines.

QUICK STUDY, ACTIVITY BOOK PP. 46–47

CHAPTER 10 Name ________ Quick Study

Your Needs and Feelings

Directions
- Use the vocabulary in the Word Bank to complete each **Summary**.
- Use the section directions to complete each **Lesson Details**.

Word Bank

basic needs	conflict	negotiate	role model	self-control
compassion	conflict resolution	peer pressure	self-concept	
compromise	goal	privacy	self-confidence	

Lesson 1 pp. 248–251

Summary The way you picture yourself is your self-concept. When you are sure of yourself, you have self-confidence.

Lesson Details Fill in the ending of each sentence.

A social trait I have is Possible answer: being a leader.

A mental or emotional trait I have is Possible answer: a good sense of humor.

A physical trait I have is Possible answer: brown hair.

Lesson 2 pp. 252–255

Summary The needs that all people have are basic needs. A social need you might have is time by yourself, or privacy. A goal is something you are willing to work for.

Lesson Details There are four basic needs. Fill in the diagram with these needs, and give an example of each. Possible examples are given.

basic needs: physical: food; social: time alone; mental: knowing math; emotional: love

© Harcourt

Name ________ Quick Study (continued)

Lesson 3 pp. 256–259

Summary People who express their feelings calmly have self-control.

Lesson Details Write the steps to help manage anger.

1. Stop what you are doing.
2. Cool down by counting to ten.
3. Think about what's going on.
4. Take action by walking away.

Lesson 4 pp. 260–265

Summary When friends disagree, they have a conflict. They can solve their disagreement through conflict resolution. They can work together, or negotiate, to find a compromise.

Lesson Details How can you find a friend? Write a sentence that tells how.

Possible answer: I could join a sports team or join a club.

Lesson 5 pp. 268–272

Summary When you understand the feelings of others, you have compassion. A role model is someone who sets a good example.

Lesson Details Write a sentence telling how you can make a difference in your community or your school. Possible answer: I can try to help new people feel welcome, and I can help with the food drive in town.

Lesson 6 pp. 274–276

Summary Positive peer pressure from your friends can help you choose activities that help yourself and the community.

Lesson Details Write an example of one positive and one negative influence you could have on a friend. Possible examples are given.

Positive: working on a food drive Negative: cheating on a test

© Harcourt

Available online.
www.harcourtschool.com/health

TEACH *continued*

Discuss

Write these two headings on the board: *Can Change* and *Cannot Change.* Invite students to suggest traits to list under each heading.

Critical Thinking Why is it important to understand which traits we can change and which we can't change? We must learn to accept some things as they are. When we can accept ourselves, we are better able to accept others.

How could making a positive change affect your self-confidence? You'll feel better about yourself and more in control of your life.

Problem Solving A friend is always late. She says, "That's just the way I am. I can't change." What could you say to her? Possible answer: While we can't change our height or color, we can change much of our behavior, especially when it's rude to others.

Activity

Respect Benjamin can plan his time so he can do his best on the report. Doing his best will show that he respects himself and his skills and abilities.

ACTIVITY

Building Good Character

Respect You have a science report due this Friday and you want to get a good grade. List things you can do to reach this goal. How will your work show you respect yourself?

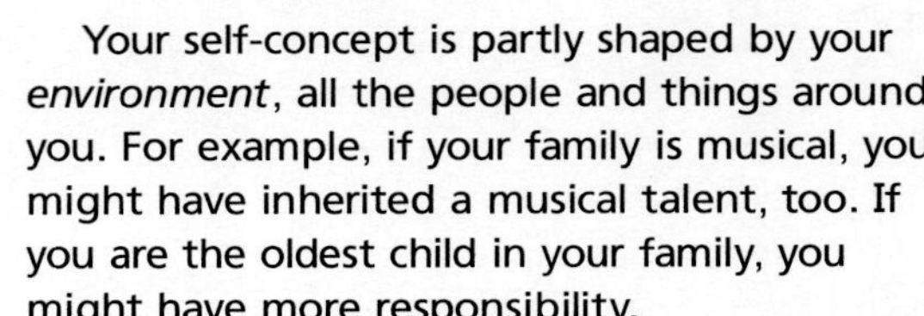

What Makes You Special

Your self-concept is partly shaped by your *environment*, all the people and things around you. For example, if your family is musical, you might have inherited a musical talent, too. If you are the oldest child in your family, you might have more responsibility.

You cannot change most of your physical traits. You can, however, change some of your other traits. If your family is not musical, you can still learn to play an instrument. Maybe you have a temper. You can find ways to control that behavior. If speaking to a group makes you nervous, you can change that, too. If you change your traits and behaviors, you can change your self-concept.

DRAW CONCLUSIONS Think of a trait someone might want to change. How could changing that trait change his or her self-concept?

Possible answer: If you become more comfortable speaking in front of a group, you may begin to see yourself as a good public speaker.

You have talents and skills you can develop.▼

250

Health Background

Heredity Explain that genes determine inherited traits. At conception, each child receives genes from both parents. These genes carry the instructions for what the child will look like, such as hair and skin color and height. Because of these genes, we often resemble our parents. Some genes pass on musical or artistic talents. Some people also inherit genes that give them dimples or allow them to roll their tongues.

Source: *The Nemours Foundation website*

For more background, visit the **Webliography** in Teacher Resources at **www.harcourtschool.com/health**
Keyword growth and development

Meeting Individual Needs Leveled Activities

BELOW-LEVEL Describe Traits Have students write these headings: *physical, mental, emotional,* and *social.* Ask them to list at least one trait for themselves under each heading.

ON-LEVEL Analyze Traits Have students list two traits for themselves in each of the four categories. Then have them identify which of those traits they could change and which they couldn't change.

CHALLENGE Think Positively Have small groups think of positive and negative ways to describe the same trait, such as *slim* and *skinny*. Discuss the advantages of describing your traits in positive ways.

Valuing Yourself

Your self-concept is also shaped by your attitude. *Attitude* is how you look at things. You respect yourself and your skills if you have a positive attitude. If you have a negative attitude, you expect to do poorly.

If you expect to do poorly, you probably will. If you expect to do well, you probably will. The more successes you have, the more confidence you gain. Your attitude then becomes more positive.

Learn more about yourself. What is your self-concept? What are your abilities? After you know yourself, you can decide which traits to value and which ones to change.

COMPARE AND CONTRAST How are *self-concept* and *self-respect* different?
Self-concept is the picture you have of yourself. *Self-respect* means valuing yourself and your ideas.

Tips for Building Self-Confidence

- Focus on the things you do well.
- Look at problems as learning experiences.
- Believe in yourself and your ability to make wise decisions.
- Be realistic about your abilities.

Lesson 1 Summary and Review

1. **Summarize with Vocabulary** Use vocabulary and other terms from this lesson to complete the statements.
Your _____ is how you picture yourself. When you value your own ideas, you show _____. When you are sure of yourself, you have _____. Everyone has qualities, or _____, that make them special. Your self-concept is shaped by your _____.
2. What traits do most family members share?
3. **Critical Thinking** How can you demonstrate personal characteristics that contribute to self-confidence and self-esteem.
4. **MAIN IDEA AND DETAILS** Draw and complete this graphic organizer to show two more things that are part of self-concept.

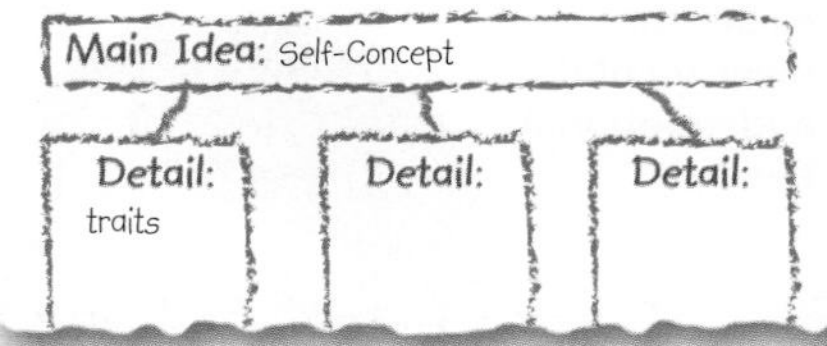

5. **Write to Inform—Description** Choose a character in a story you have read. Describe some physical, mental, emotional, and social traits of this character.

Discuss

Hold up a glass half filled with water. **Is this glass half empty or half full?** Discuss which response shows a positive attitude. Invite students to describe other events in a positive and a negative way.

3. WRAP UP

Lesson 1 Summary and Review

1. self-concept; self-respect; self-confidence; traits; attitude
2. physical traits, such as skin/hair/eye color; mental traits, such as artistic ability; emotional traits, such as a sense of humor; social traits, such as friendliness
3. Every person has a different combination of traits.
4. Possible answers:

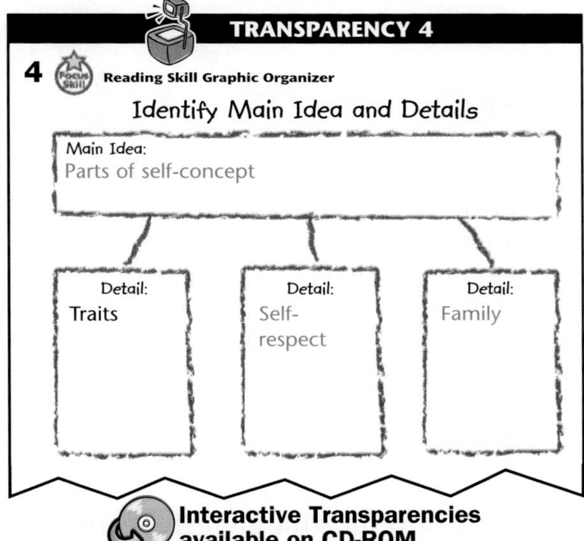

TRANSPARENCY 4
4 Reading Skill Graphic Organizer
Identify Main Idea and Details
Main Idea: Parts of self-concept
Detail: Traits
Detail: Self-respect
Detail: Family

Interactive Transparencies available on CD-ROM.

5. Students' descriptions should list the physical, mental, emotional, and social traits of their chosen character.

For **writing models** with examples, see *Teaching Resources* pp. 47–61. Rubrics are also provided.

Quick Study Students can use *Activity Book* pages 46–47 (shown on p. 249) as they complete each lesson in this chapter.

Cultural Connection

Graph an Inherited Trait Have students find out how many classmates can roll their tongue at the sides. Then help them make a circle or bar graph that shows how many students can and can't roll their tongues. Remind students that this is an inherited physical trait.

ACTIVITY BOOK P. 48

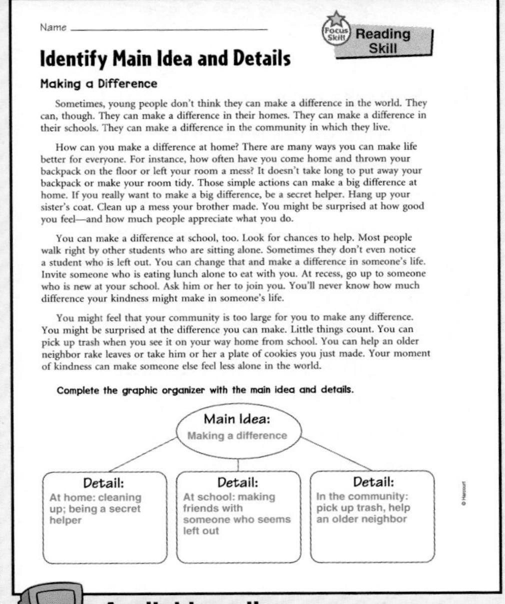

Name ______

Reading Skill

Identify Main Idea and Details

Making a Difference

Sometimes, young people don't think they can make a difference in the world. They can, though. They can make a difference in their homes. They can make a difference in their schools. They can make a difference in the community in which they live.

How can you make a difference at home? There are many ways you can make life better for everyone. For instance, how often have you come home and thrown your backpack on the floor or left your room a mess? It doesn't take long to put away your backpack or make your room tidy. Those simple actions can make a big difference at home. If you really want to make a big difference, be a secret helper. Hang up your sister's coat. Clean up a mess your brother made. You might be surprised at how good you feel—and how much people appreciate what you do.

You can make a difference at school, too. Look for chances to help. Most people walk right by other students who are sitting alone. Sometimes they don't even notice a student who is left out. You can change that and make a difference in someone's life. Invite someone who is eating lunch alone to eat with you. At recess, go up to someone who is new at your school. Ask him or her to join you. You'll never know how much difference your kindness might make in someone's life.

You might feel that your community is too large for you to make any difference. You might be surprised at the difference you can make. Little things count. You can pick up trash when you see it on your way home from school. You can help an older neighbor rake leaves or take him or her a plate of cookies you just made. Your moment of kindness can make someone else feel less alone in the world.

Complete the graphic organizer with the main idea and details.

Main Idea: Making a difference
Detail: At home: cleaning up; being a secret helper
Detail: At school: making friends with someone who seems left out
Detail: In the community: pick up trash, help an older neighbor

© Harcourt

Available online. www.harcourtschool.com/health

LESSON 2

Pages 252–255

Objectives

- Identify the four basic physical needs.
- Identify examples of basic emotional, mental, and social needs.
- Recognize how setting goals helps people meet their needs.

When Minutes Count . . .

Assign the Quick Study, Lesson 2, Activity Book pp. 46–47 (shown on p. 249).

Program Resources

- Activity Book pp. 46–47
- Transparency 4
- Growth, Development, and Reproduction pp. 26–33

Vocabulary

basic needs p. 252, **privacy** p. 254, **goal** p. 254

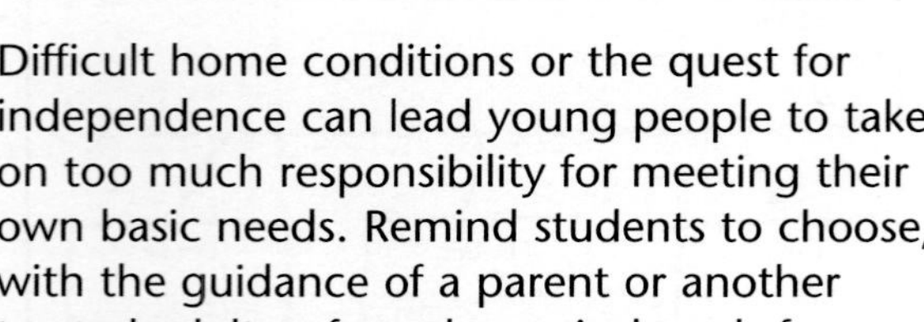

Daily Fitness Tip

Difficult home conditions or the quest for independence can lead young people to take on too much responsibility for meeting their own basic needs. Remind students to choose, with the guidance of a parent or another trusted adult, safe and practical goals for themselves.

1. MOTIVATE

Tell students to imagine that they are going to live on Mars. What would they need to survive? a shelter from heat and cold, air, food, water Point out that all of us have the same basic needs. Adults help young children meet these needs. Being a responsible adult means meeting your own basic needs and possibly the needs of others.

Explain that this lesson will help students learn more about their needs and wants—and how to meet them.

LESSON 2 We All Have Needs

Lesson Focus
All people have physical, mental, emotional, and social needs.

Why Learn This?
As you get older, you will be responsible for meeting your own needs through the choices you make and the goals you set.

Vocabulary
basic needs
privacy
goal

Your Basic Needs

People all have physical, mental, emotional, and social needs. These are called **basic needs**.

To stay healthy, you need food, water, clean air, and a place to live. These are your physical needs. When you were a baby, your family met all of your physical needs. Now that you are older, you can meet some of these needs. For example, you get your own snacks or drinks. When you are grown-up, you will meet all of your physical needs.

You also have wants. *Wants* are things you would like to have. You *need* to eat food, but you may *want* to eat a hamburger. You may not need a hamburger. You just want one!

Everyone has physical needs. People can help each other meet mental and emotional needs. ▶

252

Teacher Tip

Be Sensitive Be careful not to imply that all families meet their children's physical or emotional needs. Children who live in dysfunctional homes may feel even more isolated if they believe that everyone else enjoys a supportive and loving family life. If you become concerned about specific students, follow your school district's guidelines for handling the situation.

Language Arts

No Islands Explain that about 400 years ago, a writer named John Donne wrote, "No man is an island, entire of itself." Explain that Donne meant everyone is connected and people depend on other people. Ask students if they think this belief still applies today. Challenge them to write their own statements that express the same idea.

Mental needs include thinking, learning, and using your mind. For example, you need to know math so you can count, use money, and measure. You learned to read so you can read words and enjoy a story. To use your mind, you might read new books or learn how to play a new game.

Emotional needs include love, security, and a feeling of belonging. Everyone needs to feel accepted. You need to be able to talk with others about your feelings and personal thoughts. You need to trust others and feel that they trust you.

Your family probably meets most of your emotional needs. Friends and other people also help meet your emotional needs.

SUMMARIZE What is a physical need? It is something you need to stay healthy, including food, water, clean air, and a place to live.

Quick Activity

Interpret an Illustration List the physical needs this picture shows being met. Then write a paragraph describing any emotional and mental needs that the picture shows are being met.

253

2. TEACH

Content-Area Reading Support

Using Signal Words Direct students' attention to the first paragraph on this page. Point out that the first sentence states the main idea: *Mental needs include thinking, learning, and using your mind.* Have a volunteer read the second sentence. *For example, you need to know math . . .*

Explain that *for example* signals that the detail sentences in the paragraph contain examples of the main idea. Urge students to pay attention to signal words and phrases so they can better understand how ideas are connected.

Discuss

Ask students to identify positive characteristics of social groups.

Problem Solving Rudy says, "But, Mom, I need that brand of jeans!" What is the problem here? Rudy doesn't *need* a certain brand of jeans; he just wants it.

Critical Thinking Why do some people confuse their needs with their wants? Possible answer: They don't know the difference.

How can you meet your mental needs? Possible answers: by reading, learning new things like problem-solving skills

How can you meet your emotional needs? Possible answers: by spending time with family; by making friends and being a friend; by being trustworthy and finding others to trust

Quick Activity

Physical needs being met: food, water, clean air, a place to live. Possible emotional needs being met: love, security, feeling of belonging, acceptance. Possible mental needs being met: reading to learn new ideas, possibly doing math homework, exchanging ideas

Art

Wants and Needs Have students use available art media, such as clay, charcoal, watercolors, collage, photographs, or other forms, to express the difference between wants and needs. Encourage students to think of ways to show that needs are necessary for survival, while wants are personal preferences.

Teacher Tip

Wants Are OK Stress that it's not wrong to want something. We all want things, including many things we don't need. Still, students must realize that they can meet their basic needs in many ways. They need clothes to shelter them from the weather, but they don't need a certain brand of clothes. They need to drink water, but it doesn't have to be an expensive brand name.

TEACH *continued*

Interpret Visuals—Pictures

Have students study the family members shown on this page. Discuss how their social needs might change from time to time. **When might parents want some time alone?** Possible answers: after they've had a very busy day, when they need to make an important decision **When might young people want to be with friends or family members?** Possible answers: when they're happy, sad, working on a project, and so on **When might young people want to be alone?** Possible answers: when they need to make a decision, when they're tired, when they want to read, after they've been with people all day

Guide students to recognize that most people enjoy having some time alone. Then ask students to name some activities they might do when they are alone. Answers may include reading, playing video games, riding a bike, thinking, planning, or day-dreaming. **What are some goals that fourth graders might have?** Possible answers: getting a project or chore done, raising a grade, learning a new skill, earning money to buy something special **How can setting goals help you meet your needs?** Setting goals helps you focus on what you need or want and plan a way to get it.

Consumer Activity

Help students recognize that the media sets standards for social relationships that are often unrealistic and tend to encourage people to go to great lengths—and great expense—to fit in with their friends. The media often suggests that being part of a group is the measure of success and the only route to happiness. Point out that many people are content being alone, despite the images in ads, commercials, and many television shows. Ask students for examples that demonstrate healthy ways of gaining attention.

Consumer Activity

Analyze Ads and Media Messages If you watch television this week, pay attention to any messages about social needs. Do people seem to always be with other people? Is anyone ever happy alone? What influence do you think these shows or ads have on your social needs?

Social Needs and Setting Goals

Social needs include getting attention. They also include being part of a group. They can also include time to be alone.

Almost everyone likes to get attention. You also appreciate being able to express yourself. When you were a baby, you got attention mostly by crying. Now you can talk to people and express your needs. You can raise your hand in school if you have a question. Politely asking for someone's attention is another healthy way of getting attention.

People have different social needs. For example, you might need **privacy** (PRY•vuh•see), or time by yourself. You might be the only one in your family who wants a quiet place to read.

People might have different social needs at different times.▼

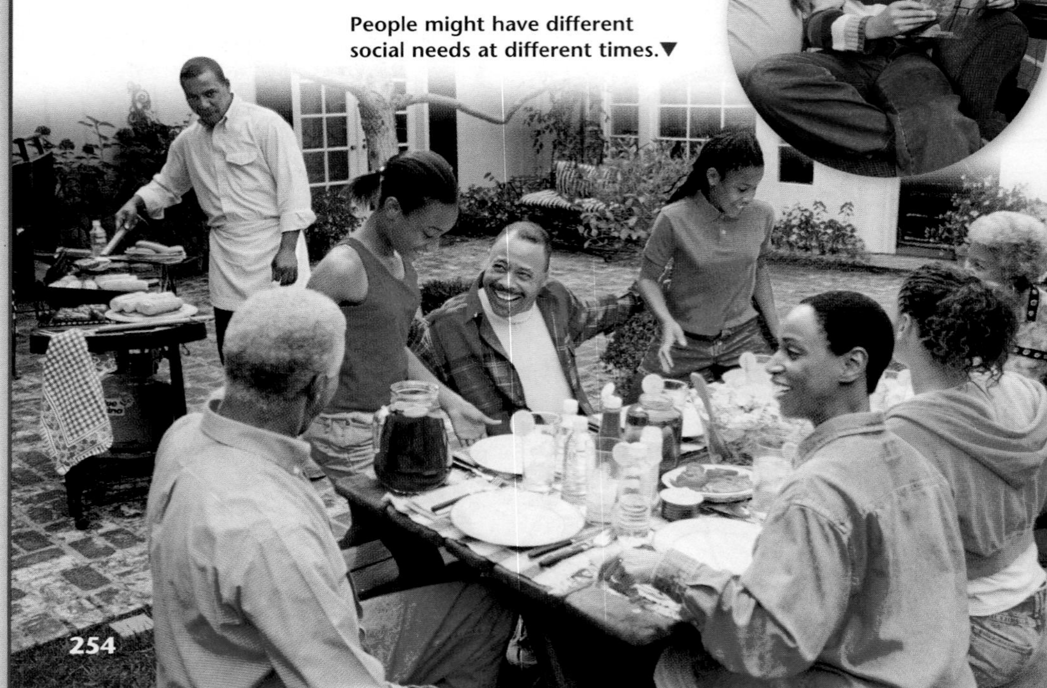

254

ESL/ELL Support

LANGUAGE AND VOCABULARY The words *need* and *want*, used as nouns, are abstract and may confuse students. Students may also be confused by the general category of food and specific kinds of food.

Beginning Have students gather together pictures of kinds of food, drinks, and homes. Put the pictures of food in one group, the drinks in another, and the homes in a third group. Hold up several pictures from one group and say, for example, "We eat food. Food is a need. These are all food." Ask students to repeat your sentences.

Intermediate Show students the pictures of food. Say, "We need food, but we want tacos (hold up picture), or we want a peanut butter sandwich (hold up picture)." Ask students to help complete each sentence.

Advanced Have students look at the pictures and write their own sentences about needs and wants.

As you get older, you will be responsible for meeting more of your own needs and wants. Learning to set goals will help with this. A **goal** is something you are willing to work for. The tips here show how to set and meet a goal.

Be clear about your goals. For example, if your goal is to get to school on time every day, work on things to help you reach the goal. What takes up your time each morning? Look at ways to save time. As you work toward your goal, check your progress. Are you getting closer to meeting your goal? Do you need to do something different?

Meeting your needs will be up to you someday. If you know how to set and meet goals, you'll be ready!

How to Set and Meet Goals

- Set a goal.
- Plan the steps to meet your goal. Will you need help? How long will it take?
- Work toward your goal.
- Evaluate your progress, and make any necessary changes.

SEQUENCE What should you do after you set a goal? Plan the steps you will take to meet your goal.

Lesson 2 Summary and Review

1. **Summarize with Vocabulary** Use vocabulary and other terms from this lesson to complete the statements.
   To stay healthy, you must meet your _____. Things you would like to have are called _____. Having someone to trust is an _____ need. Many people like to have time alone, so they need _____. To meet a need or a want, you can set a _____.
2. Name a mental need. How do people meet this need?
3. **Critical Thinking** Describe three healthy ways that you can get attention.
4. **MAIN IDEA AND DETAILS** Draw and complete this graphic organizer to show three important details about a goal.

5. **Write to Inform—Narration** Tell about a goal you worked to meet. For example, your goal might have been to get on a team, make a new friend, earn money, or learn a new skill.

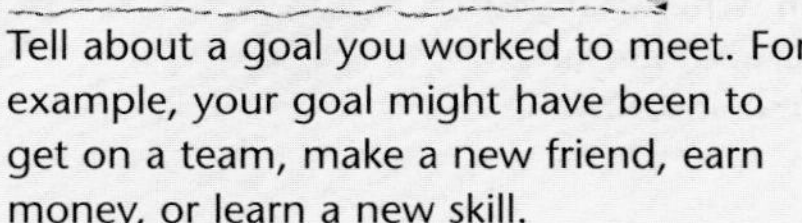

Interpret Visuals—List

Ask students if they can think of steps that could be added to the list. Possible addition: Celebrate reaching your goal.

3. WRAP UP

Lesson 2 Summary and Review

1. physical needs; wants; emotional; privacy; goal
2. Thinking, learning, and using the mind are mental needs. They may be met by reading, studying, and learning.
3. Possible answers: They share their feelings with family and friends who love and accept them.
4. Possible answers:

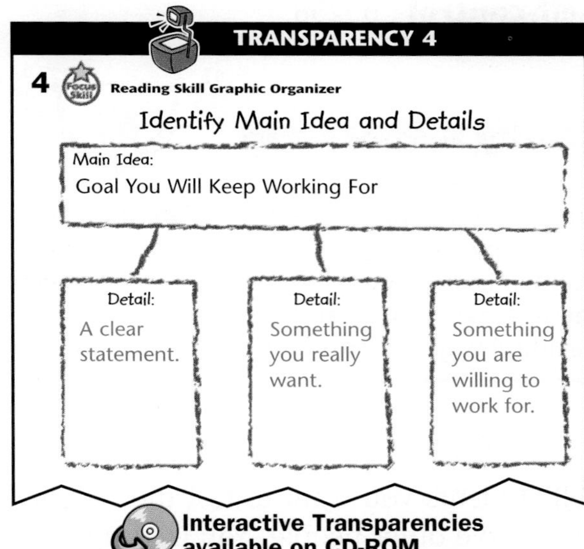

TRANSPARENCY 4
4 Reading Skill Graphic Organizer
Identify Main Idea and Details
Main Idea:
Goal You Will Keep Working For
Detail:
A clear statement.
Detail:
Something you really want.
Detail:
Something you are willing to work for.

Interactive Transparencies available on CD-ROM.

5. Students' responses should explain the goal they set and the steps they took to meet their goal.

For **writing models** with examples, see *Teaching Resources* pp. 47–61. Rubrics are also provided.

Teacher Tip

Coping with Disaster Students may be particularly vulnerable after a disaster, such as a hurricane, flood, plane crash, fire, or terrorist attack. Some may worry about their safety, while others may think the disaster is their fault in some way. Encourage, but don't push, them to talk about their feelings. Be a good listener when they are ready to talk. They might also express their feelings through art, music, or play. Help students realize that grieving can take time.

Social Studies

Meeting Basic Needs Help students identify regions in the world where people have trouble meeting their basic needs, even for clean water. The United Nations Children's Fund (UNICEF) is a good place to start. Of course, there may be places close to—or in—your own community where people struggle to meet their needs. Students might consider ways they could help.

When Minutes Count . . .

Quick Study Students can use *Activity Book* pages 46–47 (shown on p. 249) as they complete each lesson in this chapter.

LESSON 3
Pages 256–259

Objectives
- ► Identify feelings and recognize safe ways to express them.
- ► Describe self-control strategies and steps for anger management.

When Minutes Count . . .
Assign the Quick Study, Lesson 3, Activity Book pp. 46–47 (shown on p. 249).

Program Resources
- ► Activity Book pp. 46–47
- ► Transparency 4
- ► Growth, Development, and Reproduction pp. 26–28, 32–33

Vocabulary
self-control p. 258

Daily Fitness Tip

Stress that people of all ages sometimes feel sad, angry, and frightened. These feelings are normal. Learning how to recognize them, keep them under control, and express them in healthful ways is important to growing up.

1. MOTIVATE

Tell students you want to test their ability to observe other people. You'll turn your back. When you turn around, they're to explain how you feel.

Carry out this exercise several times, using facial expressions and other body language to show that you are tired, angry, worried, and so on. Don't say anything.

I didn't tell you how I was feeling. How did you know? by the way you stood or sat, by the look on your face, by your gestures

Explain that this lesson will help students learn more about their feelings and ways to manage them.

LESSON 3

We All Have Feelings

Lesson Focus
You can learn to express your feelings in ways that help you feel in control.

Why Learn This?
Part of growing up is learning to express your feelings in ways that help you feel confident and help you get along with others.

Vocabulary
self-control

Your Feelings

You have the same feelings as everyone else, but you may not share the same feelings at the same time. For example, you might feel happy about a school field trip, but a friend might be anxious about it. Understanding what you feel and why you feel it is an important part of growing up. Learning about feelings can help you get along with others.

Feelings are not good or bad, but feelings that are uncomfortable can be a warning signal. When you feel angry or afraid, something is not always right. If you feel that you are being abused, or bothered physically, emotionally, or in a way that violates your privacy, talk to a parent or trusted adult.

Quick Activity

Interpret Photographs Study these pictures. Then write what you think each person is feeling and why.

256

Music

Feelings Invite students to bring in a recording or the lyrics to their favorite song about feelings. Remind students that only appropriate songs and lyrics can be shared. They might even make up their own song about feelings. The song might be sad or funny. Provide time for students to share their songs by singing them or playing a recording. Discuss the diversity of feelings and ways to express them.

Teacher Tip

Bulletin Board Have students cut out magazine photographs illustrating different feelings to add to the bulletin board. If there is time, have students talk about some of the photographs. What feeling is being expressed in the photo? For example, how can you tell a person is angry, scared, excited, or stressed? Remind students to write their names on the backs of all items they add to the bulletin board.

You might try to hide uncomfortable feelings, but your body often gives you away. *Body language* is movements, such as frowning or slouching, that can express your real feelings.

One uncomfortable feeling is *stress*. You can feel stress when you have too much to do. Stress can show in tense shoulders. Your face can look pained from a headache or a stomachache.

Grief is another uncomfortable feeling. Grief is a great sadness. For example, you might feel grief after the loss of a pet or of a family member.

If you feel grief, tell someone. Helping others is another way to deal with grief. Exercise and writing are also good ways to cope with grief.

COMPARE AND CONTRAST Which do you think tells more about someone's feelings—words or body language? Why? Accept reasonable responses. Possible answer: Body language. People might say they feel okay, but their body language shows how they really feel.

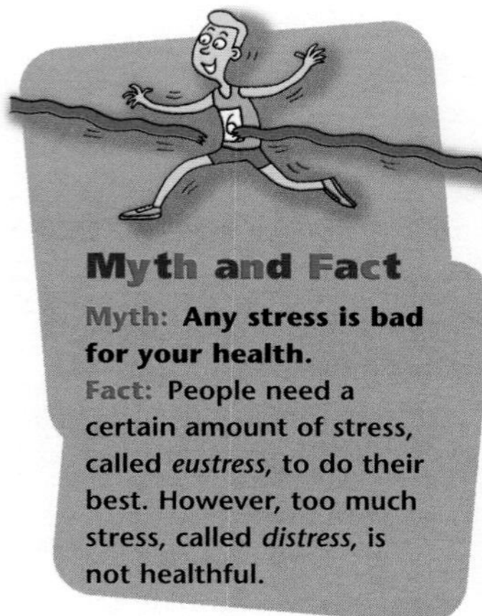

Myth and Fact

Myth: Any stress is bad for your health.

Fact: People need a certain amount of stress, called *eustress*, to do their best. However, too much stress, called *distress*, is not healthful.

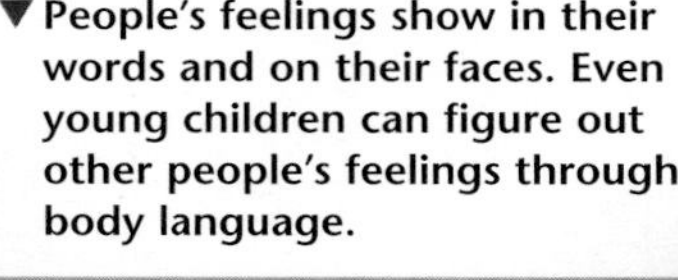

▼ **People's feelings show in their words and on their faces. Even young children can figure out other people's feelings through body language.**

257

Teacher Tip

Good Stress, Bad Stress Tell students that a little stress is good for them. When they feel a little nervous before giving a presentation or playing in an important game, this eustress, or "good" stress, helps their body work at its peak so they do their best. However, if they are constantly worried about getting things done or meeting others' expectations, stress turns into distress. Distress, or "bad" stress, is hard on their body.

Art

Masks Have students make papier-mâché or paper-plate masks that show different feelings. Then have them find or write stories that involve feelings and, if they can, wear their masks as they read or tell the stories to the class or a small group. A group might work together to make several masks for a story that involves several feelings.

2. TEACH

Quick Activity

Accept reasonable interpretations of the photographs. Caution students not to jump to conclusions based on a person's facial expression. People may look angry when they're actually confused, or worried when they're sad. Students need to consider all they know about the situation, in addition to the person's facial expression.

Discuss

Discuss the term "trusted adult" with students. Explain that sometimes their parents or guardians may not be nearby when they need help. Students should be encouraged to identify other adults whom they can trust in the absence of their parents or legal guardians. Such "trusted adults" should be individuals well known to the child and MAY include grandparents, teachers, counselors, nurses, doctors, fire fighters, police officers, and neighbors.

Describe the importance of dealing with emotions appropriately and how they affect thoughts and behaviors. Possible answers: Your feelings warn you when things are not right in your life. They tell you when something is wrong or unsafe for you. You need to be aware of your feelings so you can control them and express them in healthful ways.

Lessons that provide strategies for teaching about child abuse, including sexual exploitation, are provided on pages TR30–TR33. Lessons are also provided in the optional component *Growth, Development, and Reproduction*, pp. 26–33. Use these lessons and components in compliance with state and local guidelines.

TEACH *continued*

Interpret Visuals—Pictures

Ask students what made the older child in the picture angry. **How is she calming down? What are some other good ways to calm down?** Possible answers: She is asking for an explanation; take deep breaths, write in a journal, get some exercise, listen to soothing music, talk to a friend or trusted adult.

Critical Thinking Why does it help to know several ways to calm down? Possible answers: Sometimes you don't have time to exercise or listen to music; knowing several ways to calm down means you can choose the one that best fits the situation.

Discuss

Critical Thinking Do we all get angry about the same things? Why or why not? Guide students to recognize that certain things, such as name-calling, anger most people. However, other things anger some people and not others. For example, some people get angry when someone is late, yet others may not.

Health Background

Anger and Your Body When we're stressed or angry, our bodies react with a "fight or flight" response. To prepare for battle or flight, our bodies release adrenaline and other hormones into our bloodstream. The adrenaline gives us more energy—and sometimes causes our body or hands to shake. Our heart rate increases, and blood rushes to our large muscles and away from our digestive system. This sometimes causes "butterflies" in our stomach. We breathe faster to get more oxygen to our muscles. Our muscles tighten and get ready for action. Our pupils dilate, and our sight sharpens. We are ready for the enemy! Often, however, the only enemy is our perception of danger.

Source: *Mind/Body Education Center website*

For more background, visit the **Webliography** in Teacher Resources at **www.harcourtschool.com/health**
Keyword human body

Did You Know?
Self-control can also mean you choose what actions you will take in situations. Self-control involves making choices about what you will do or will not do. You do not have self-control if you let your friends make decisions for you.

Controlling Your Feelings

Part of growing up is learning how to express your feelings responsibly. When you express feelings calmly, you have **self-control**. Like any skill, self-control takes practice.

For example, imagine that someone keeps teasing you at school. You begin to feel angry. Your face gets red, and your stomach hurts. Your hands curl into fists, and you feel like hitting. Finally you shout, "Stop that!" You might even call the teaser names.

You are out of control, and it's not a comfortable feeling. You can, however, learn how to manage your anger and stay in control. Then you can *choose* how to respond to your anger.

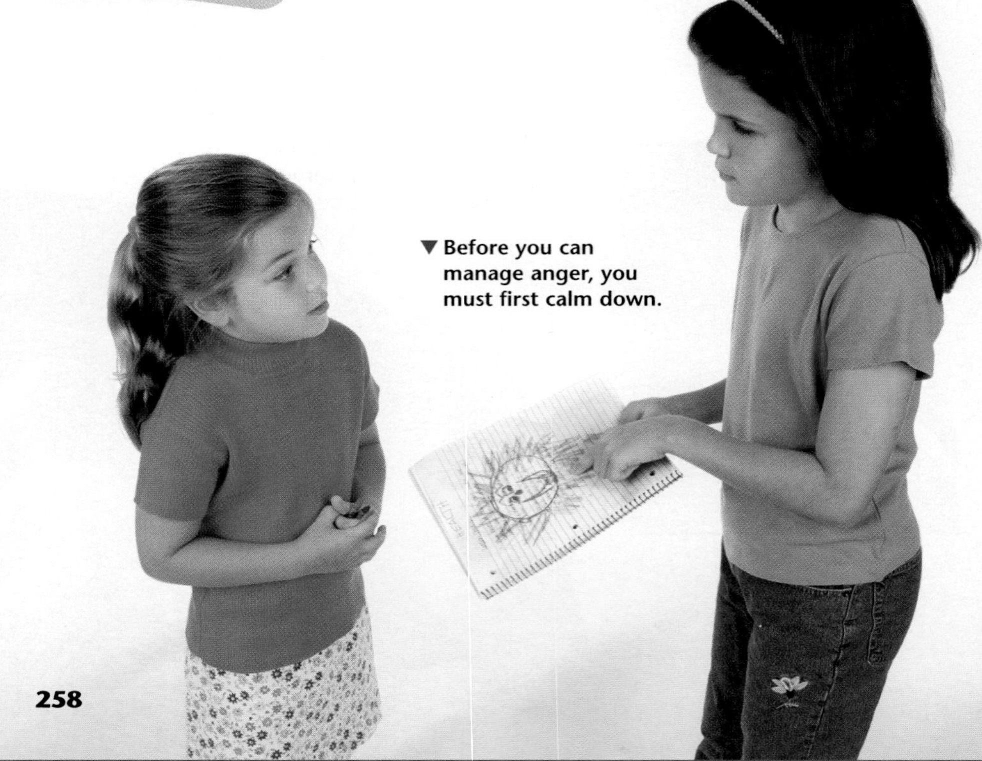

▼ Before you can manage anger, you must first calm down.

258

Meeting Individual Needs Leveled Activities

BELOW-LEVEL Make Calm-Down Posters Have students make posters showing ways to calm down when angry. Display the posters in the classroom or in hallways.

ON-LEVEL Write Poems Ask students to write poems or short stories about a time when a young person was angry but controlled his or her feelings. Stress that they don't have to write about themselves, but their poems or stories must be realistic.

CHALLENGE Learn About Facial Expressions Help students use the Internet and books to find examples of nonhuman facial and body expressions. Many animal expressions are similar to some human expressions, though they mean different things. Students can make a chart showing 5 or 6 different expressions and their meanings.

The steps shown can help you manage angry feelings and stay in control. You might use an "I" message to express your feelings. An "I" message tells someone how you feel without placing blame on him or her. You might say, "I feel very angry and I wish this would stop." You might also try acting as though the teasing doesn't bother you. Laughing or making light of it may cause the teaser to lose interest.

Another way to become responsible for yourself is to learn how to deal with uncomfortable feelings. When you are in control, you choose how you will express your feelings.

SEQUENCE What should you do before you express feelings of anger?
Stop what you are doing, calm down, and think about what is happening.

Steps for Anger Management

1. Stop what you are doing or saying.
2. Calm down by counting to ten or by taking long, slow breaths.
3. Think about what is happening.
4. Take action—either walk away or express your feelings calmly in "I" messages.

Lesson 3 Summary and Review

1. **Summarize with Vocabulary** Use the vocabulary and other terms from this lesson to complete the statements.
   People express their feelings with words and _____. Someone who has too much to do might feel _____. When a pet dies, you might feel _____. When you express feelings calmly, you have _____.
2. **Critical Thinking** Why is it important to know what you are feeling?
3. Identify types of physical or emotional abuse and ways that you could seek help from a parent or another trusted adult.
4.  **MAIN IDEA AND DETAILS** Draw and complete this graphic organizer by providing two more details to explain the main idea.

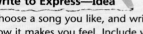

5. **Write to Express—Idea** Choose a song you like, and write about how it makes you feel. Include why you think the song makes you feel that way.

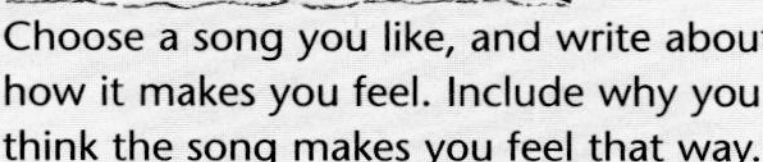

Physical Education

Reducing Stress The school's physical education teacher might help you identify simple stretching and deep-breathing exercises to teach the class as a way to relax and reduce stress. If you play music during this activity, avoid New Age or other types that might have religious connotations for some people. Instead, choose quiet and soothing music such as a Mozart violin concerto.

Teacher Tip

Self-Control Explain that controlling your feelings isn't the same as going along with others' unhealthful or unwise decisions. If students object to their friends' decisions, they need to say so. If friends are being disrespectful, they need to express their feelings about the situation calmly, using an "I" message. At the same time, they must control how they express their feelings and keep in mind that they might have misunderstood the situation.

Discuss

Describe the steps for anger management. **What kinds of things make you angry?** Invite volunteers to describe situations that make them angry (without naming others involved) and tell how they would use the steps to respond in a healthful way.

3. WRAP UP

Lesson 3 Summary and Review

1. body language; stress; grief; self-control
2. If you know how you feel, you can choose how to cope with that feeling; you have self-control.
3. You might do or say something you'll regret later.
4. Possible answers:

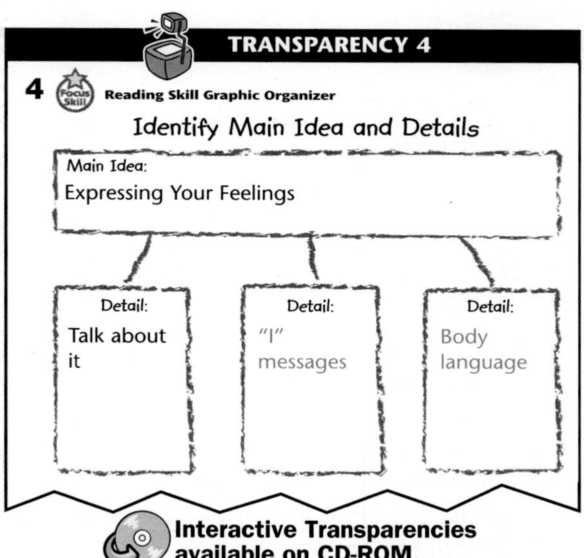

5. Students should write about the feelings they have and explain why they think they have those feelings.

For **writing models** with examples, see *Teaching Resources* pp. 47–61. Rubrics are also provided.

When Minutes Count ...

Quick Study Students can use *Activity Book* pages 46–47 (shown on p. 249) as they complete each lesson in this chapter.

LESSON 4
Pages 260–265

Objectives

- ► Recognize shared interests, goals, and values as factors in friendship.
- ► Identify and practice effective strategies for resolving conflicts by using negotiation and compromise.
- ► Describe characteristics needed to be a responsible friend and family member.

When Minutes Count . . .

Assign the Quick Study, Lesson 4, Activity Book pp. 46–47 (shown on p. 249).

Program Resources

- ► Activity Book pp. 46–47
- ► Transparency 4
- ► Growth, Development, and Reproduction pp. 29–31

Vocabulary

conflict p. 262, **conflict resolution** p. 262, **negotiate** p. 263, **compromise** p. 263

Daily Fitness Tip

Many fourth graders have already experienced negative peer pressure. Remind them that friends who urge them to do something that's wrong or unsafe aren't really friends. A real friend wouldn't ask them to do something that's dangerous or against their values or school or family rules.

For more guidelines on handling friendships, see *Be Active! Resources for Physical Education* p. 207.

1. MOTIVATE

Write these quotations on the board:
The only way to have a friend is to be a friend.—Ralph Waldo Emerson
Be slow in choosing a friend, slower in changing.—Benjamin Franklin
Have volunteers read the quotations aloud, and discuss whether students agree with one or both.

The Challenge of Friendship

Lesson Focus
Knowing how to solve conflicts and keep friends is a valuable skill.

Why Learn This?
The ideas in this lesson will help you be a true friend.

Vocabulary
conflict
conflict resolution
negotiate
compromise

The Value of Friends

Friends meet your social need to belong to a group. Friends, along with your family, encourage and support you.

You probably have several friends. Friendships often begin between people who share an interest or a goal. You might have friends in different places. For example, you might see some friends only at school. Others may be where you live.

You can express different parts of yourself through different friends. For example, your friends in art class may know you as a painter. Friends you skate with may know you as an athlete.

You and your friends may share the same feelings as well as the same goals and interests.

▼Friends can help you have self-respect.

Meeting Individual Needs
Leveled Activities

BELOW-LEVEL Make a Friendship Web On a large sheet of paper, have students draw a central circle and label it *Friends*. Have students think of qualities that make a good friend and add their ideas to make a web. Display the finished product in the classroom.

ON-LEVEL Read a Story Encourage students to share their favorite stories about friendship. If they don't have one, have them go to the media center to find a story they enjoy and would recommend to others.

CHALLENGE Perform a Skit Ask students to distinguish between disagreeing, arguing, and fighting. Have students perform skits showing how these three are alike and how they are different.

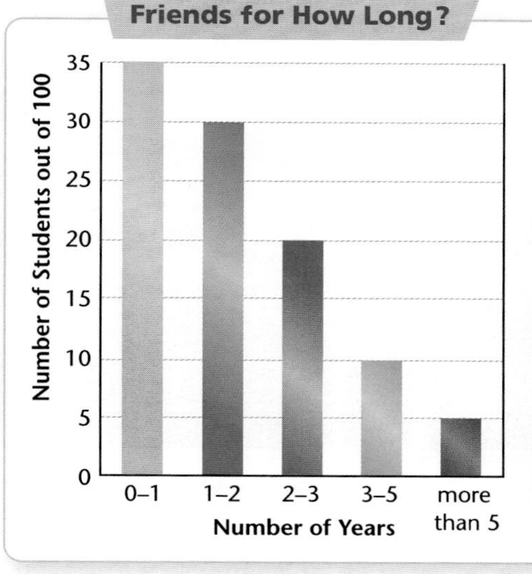

Quick Activity

Interpret a Graph How long had the largest group of students known their friends? What else can you tell about friendships by studying the bar graph?

Some friendships last a lifetime. Some last only a day or two. Young people often make new friends as their interests change.

If a friend starts spending time with someone else, don't be sad. This is normal. You will probably find a new friend soon, too.

To find a friend quickly, join a club or group. Then you may find a friend who likes the same things you do. Maybe your school has a club you would like to join. You could find a friend there who likes to do things you do. Or you could join a sports team.

Making and keeping friends takes practice. Still, having friends is worth the effort. Just remember that to have a friend, you must be a friend.

CAUSE AND EFFECT Describe some appropriate ways that you have used to make new friends.
responses may include shared interests and goals

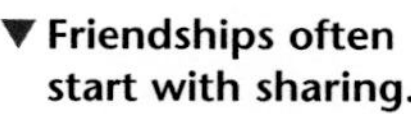

▼ Friendships often start with sharing.

261

2. TEACH

Content-Area Reading Support

Using Graphs Have students explain how the bar graph on this page relates to the lesson. It shows how long some young people have known their friends; making and keeping friends is the lesson topic. Discuss whether the information shown on the graph would be clearer if it were written in a paragraph. Probably not; graphs and charts show complex information in a form that can be easily understood.

Quick Activity

The largest group of students had known their friends for a year or less. One interpretation of the graph: many friendships among young people don't last long. Ask students to suggest some reasons for these short friendships. Possible answers: changing interests, moving away, changing schools

Discuss

Why should you be slow in choosing or changing friends? Possible answer: You need to choose carefully so you pick someone you can trust and who shares your values. Even good friends have disagreements at times. In most cases, this isn't a good reason to change friends.

Problem Solving What are some ways that students in our school can find new friends? Ask students to name specific clubs, groups, classes, or teams at your school that a student might join to find new friends.

Math

Making Graphs Have students conduct a survey like the one shown, of their own or another class. If they survey their own class, ask students to write on slips of paper how long they have known their best friend and turn in the papers anonymously. This will avoid embarrassing those who have no best friend or may have just broken up with a friend. Read the results and let students separate them into groups and make a bar graph. Compare your graph to the one shown.

Teacher Tip

Friendship Challenges This topic may be uncomfortable if students have trouble making friends, have recently broken up with a best friend, or are new to the school. Emphasize practical, positive ways to make and keep friends and to solve conflicts. Point out that people of all ages have friendship problems from time to time. Call only on volunteers during class discussions. Remind students that volunteering to help offers opportunities to meet people of all ages.

TEACH *continued*

Activity

Communicate Ask students to analyze strengths and weaknesses in personal skills. Students might suggest looking at ways to communicate better, such as writing notes or learning how to understand and use signing with the deaf friend. Efforts to improve the communication and understanding will show caring and consideration.

Interpret Visuals—List

Have students read Friendship Rules. **Which rule would be easiest to follow? Which would be hardest?** Accept reasonable answers, but ask students to explain their thinking.

What can happen if people start calling someone a bully, a sissy, or another name? Guide students to understand that labeling people is unfair. People who care about other people's feelings don't say such hurtful things.

What rule would you add to this list? Discuss whether each suggested rule would be valuable.

Discuss

Point out that some people argue as a way of getting attention. Have students think of more positive ways to get attention. List their ideas on the board. Possible answers: by helping others, by being brave or courageous, by learning a new skill

What are the benefits of resolving conflicts peacefully? Possible answers: maintains friendships, avoids hurt or angry feelings, avoids verbal or physical violence, keeps control of feelings

Friends have conflicts at times, but they usually can resolve them fairly and stay friends.▼

ACTIVITY

Life Skills

Communicate

You have difficulty communicating with a friend who is deaf. Analyze your strengths and weaknesses. Then explain how improving your communication skills can demonstrate consideration for your friend.

Solving Conflicts with Friends

Do you and any of your friends ever get angry at one another? It is normal for friends to have conflicts at times. You cannot avoid them. A **conflict** is a disagreement that happens when people have different needs or wishes. You can learn how to resolve conflicts and remain friends by using conflict resolution. **Conflict resolution** (rez•uh•LOO•shuhn) is the solving of problems you and your friends may have. Learning to resolve conflicts can also help you when you are an adult. Following rules like those below can also help.

- Don't talk behind each other's backs.
- Tell the truth.
- Avoid hurtful comments and put-downs.
- Solve disagreements peacefully.
- Set up a time to talk about problems.
- Listen to each other carefully.

262

Social Studies

Conflicts Between and Within Nations Choose a conflict or war, past or present, that students may be aware of. Ask them to define the conflict in terms of different needs or wants. Help the class apply the steps for conflict resolution, pages 266–267, to the conflict to show how it might have been (or might still be) resolved peacefully. Students interested in conflicts between nations might analyze one on their own and apply the conflict resolution process.

Language Arts

Resolving a Conflict Remind students that when friends are angry, it sometimes causes hurt feelings. Ask them to write a story about a time when a friend hurt their feelings. In the story, have them tell how they and the friend made up. Then have them write a new ending that could have happened if they had used better communication and conflict resolution skills.

When you and your friends have problems, you can **negotiate** (nih•GOH•shee•ayt). That is, you can work together to resolve the conflict. You might decide on a compromise (KAHM•pruh•myz). A **compromise** is a kind of solution in which each side gives up some of what it wants.

Suppose you want to sit in the cafeteria with a new student at school. Your best friend wants just the two of you to sit together, as usual. You and your friend could negotiate and find a compromise. You might sit with the new student one day and with your best friend the next day. Maybe your best friend will join you and the new student. Many conflicts have a workable solution.

Ways to Handle Disagreements

- Ignore small problems.
- Laugh at the problem together.
- Say you're sorry and forgive each other.
- If the problem is serious, you should both walk away. Maybe you can resolve the conflict later or ask an adult for help.

DRAW CONCLUSIONS How does finding a compromise help resolve conflicts?

It helps each person get part of what he or she wants.

Quick Activity

Interpret Photographs What do you think these two friends are arguing about? How might they resolve this conflict?

Quick Activity

Accept any reasonable opinions regarding the subject of this argument. As students brainstorm possible reasons, help them recognize that there are conflicts in all friendships. Conflicts are normal and are to be expected when two or more people work together. You might help students choose a realistic reason for the conflict shown and resolve it through role-play. Ask them to explain the steps in conflict resolution. They can apply the steps for conflict resolution, pages 266–267.

Interpret Visuals—List

Ask students to read and evaluate the tips on the list. **Which tip would work best? In what situations? Which tip might make things worse in a certain situation? Why?**

Teacher Tip

Disagree! Students must not negotiate or compromise when someone suggests an activity that they know is wrong, unsafe, or against school or family rules. Then they must protect their safety, follow their values, and stand up for their beliefs. If a friend suggests an unsafe activity once, they might help the friend see why it's unwise. If a friend often suggests unsafe activities, they shouldn't be concerned about maintaining the friendship. This person isn't a good friend.

TEACH *continued*

Interpret Visuals—Pictures

Draw students' attention to the picture on this page. Have them suggest possible conflicts that the boy might be discussing with his father. If you wish, ask pairs of volunteers to role-play the conversation. Each pair will choose a different conflict and role-play what the father might be telling the boy.

Discuss

Why are parents, teachers, coaches, school counselors, religious leaders, and other trusted adults good sources of advice if you're having a conflict with a friend? They've experienced conflicts with friends, family members, co-workers, and others. They've learned which behaviors make the conflict worse and which behaviors help solve it. They might also think of solutions that a younger person might not be aware of.

Critical Thinking **Describe healthy ways you can respond to disrespectful behavior.** Possible answers: control your feelings, not insult or attack the other person, listen respectfully to the other person's opinions, find a way to negotiate and compromise

Critical Thinking **What would a responsible person do during a conflict with family members?** Guide students to recognize that they should behave the same with family members as they would with friends—be respectful and control their feelings.

What is the biggest challenge of friendship? Possible answers: knowing if someone is really your friend; having a friend break up with you; finding new friends Ask students to suggest healthful ways to meet each challenge, using what they have learned from this lesson.

Growth, Development, and Reproduction An optional lesson about harassment is provided in this supplement on pp. 29–31. Use this component in compliance with state and local guidelines.

Did You Know?

Nearly 1,000 students took a friendship survey. About 730 of them were happy with their friendships, while 95 were not. Another 125 were not sure how they felt. How does that compare with how you and your friends feel?

Getting Help for Harassment

You and your friends can settle most of your conflicts. But at times when you both get angry it is good to seek the help of a parent or another trusted adult. Talking to an adult might help you think of a solution. Maybe an adult can help you both talk things out.

A situation that may require you to seek the help of a parent or trusted adult is harassment. *Harassment* is when someone teases or bothers you repeatedly in a hurtful way. An older person can offer help and suggestions on how to deal with harassment.

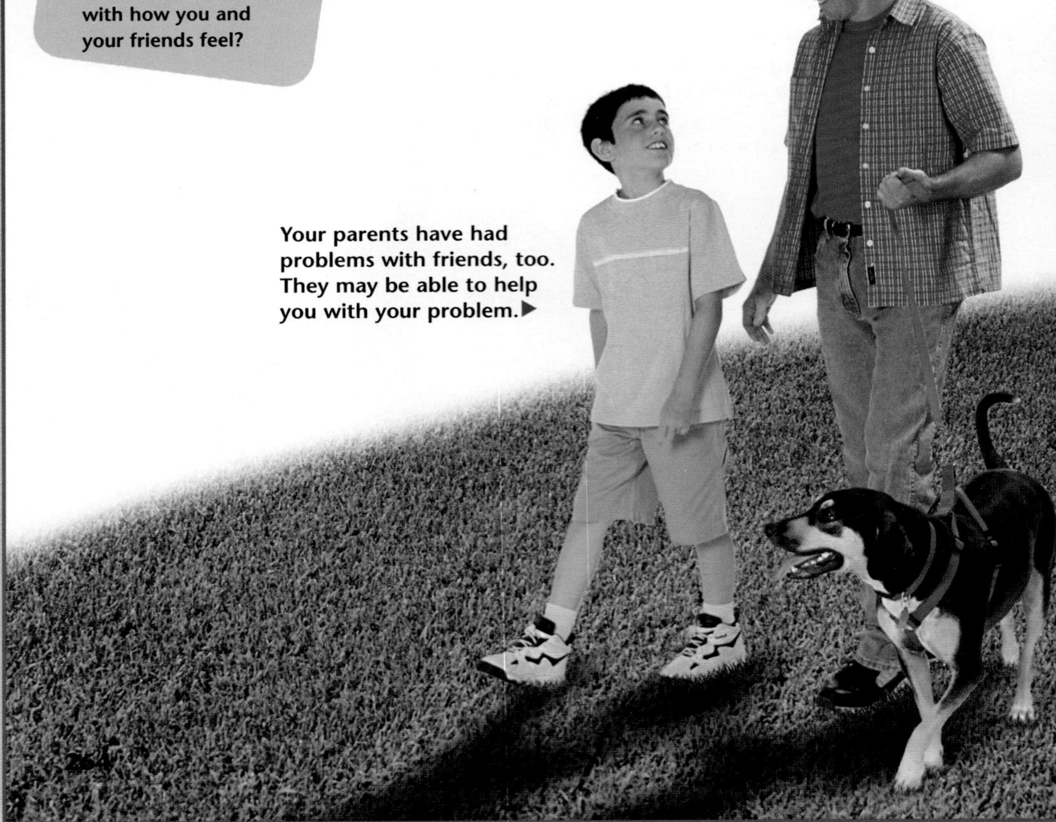

Your parents have had problems with friends, too. They may be able to help you with your problem. ▶

264

ESL/ELL Support

COMPREHENSIBLE INPUT The term *conflict* is an abstract noun. Clarify this concept with students.

Beginning Pantomime with a student a conflict over a book. You say, "I want to read it." The student says, "I want to read it, too." Then pantomime making the decision to take turns reading it or to read it together.

Intermediate Have students name typical conflicts at school. Then discuss several of them. What is the problem? How could it be solved?

Advanced Ask students to write a conversation in which two students resolve a conflict. Provide time for them to read their work aloud.

Someone who wants you to do things that make you uncomfortable is not a true friend. If he or she asks you to go against your values, talk with a parent or another trusted adult. It may be time to make new friends—friends who share your values.

There's nothing wrong with friends having different opinions. True friends respect each other. They can agree to disagree about things.

 **MAIN IDEA AND DETAILS What is harassment and how can you get help?**

Myth and Fact

Myth: You are responsible for what your friends do.

Fact: Each person is responsible for his or her own decisions. If your friend makes a poor decision, however, you should encourage him or her to make a better one.

A school counselor can help you sort out your feelings about a friendship.▶

Lesson 4 Summary and Review

1. **Summarize with Vocabulary**
   Use the vocabulary from this lesson to complete these statements.
   A _____ is a disagreement between people. People can try to resolve conflicts through _____. When you work together to solve a problem, you _____. Sometimes you reach a _____, in which each side gives up some of what it wants.
2. Why is it normal for friends to have conflicts?
3. **Critical Thinking** Why is it important to stand up for your values, even if you lose a friend?
4.  **MAIN IDEA AND DETAILS** Draw and complete this graphic organizer. In the boxes, name three places where you could find a friend.

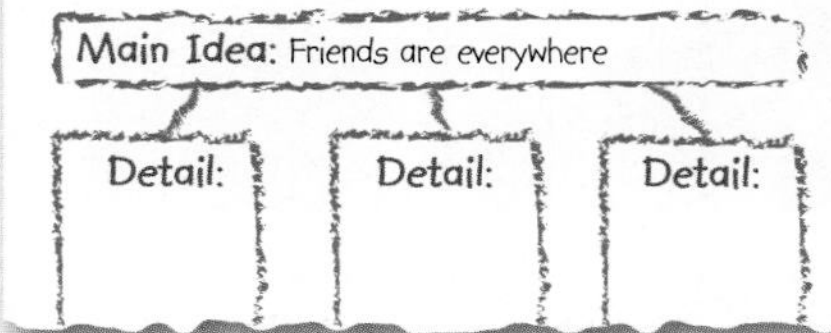

5. **Write to Inform—How-To**
   Describe the qualities of a good friend.

Possible answer: Harassment is when someone teases or bothers you in a hurtful way; talk to parents and other trusted adults if you are being harassed.

3. WRAP UP

Lesson 4 Summary and Review

1. conflict; conflict resolution; negotiate; compromise
2. Two people are very likely to have different opinions and ideas, which can lead to conflict.
3. Standing up for your values shows self-respect and self-confidence. True friends respect each other's rights to have different opinions. If you lose a friend because you stand up for your values, you haven't lost much.
4. Possible answers:

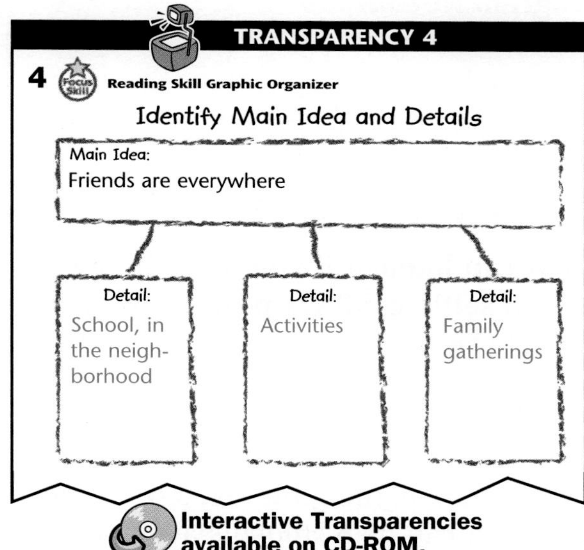

Interactive Transparencies available on CD-ROM.

5. Students' paragraphs should include ways to choose a friend, such as finding someone with similar interests and values. They should also explain how to make a friend, perhaps by doing an activity with the other person. In addition, students should describe the qualities of a true friend, such as trust and respect.

For **writing models** with examples, see *Teaching Resources* pp. 47–61. Rubrics are also provided.

Language Arts

Friendship Bulletin Board Encourage students to gather pictures of activities that friends can do together and display them as a collage on a classroom bulletin board. Students might include pictures of people being friends: helping each other, listening, and so on. They might also add lyrics from their favorite songs about friendship.

Teacher Tip

Classroom Visit Invite the school counselor to tell the class how he or she helps students resolve conflicts and, perhaps, find friends. Before the visit, let the counselor know what students have been learning about conflict resolution, negotiation, and compromise. Encourage students to ask questions. They might submit written questions to you. You can choose some to pass on to the counselor.

When Minutes Count . . .

Quick Study Students can use *Activity Book* pages 46–47 (shown on p. 249) as they complete each lesson in this chapter.

Life Skills

Communicate
Make Responsible Decisions
Manage Stress
Refuse
Resolve Conflicts
Set Goals

Objectives

- Identify skills needed to resolve conflicts.
- Explain and apply conflict resolution skills.

Program Resources

- Activity Book p. 49
- Poster 11

1. MOTIVATE

What can happen if you don't know how to settle conflicts peacefully?
Possible answers: you can lose friends, no one will want to work with you, you can get a reputation as a bully, people may be angry with you
Explain that learning the steps of conflict resolution can help students avoid all these problems.

2. TEACH

Direct students' attention to the photographs of Joe and Ashley.
What is the conflict in this situation?
Both students want to use the classroom computer at the same time.

Step 1
Critical Thinking How will using "I" messages help the students solve this problem? "I" messages allow both of them to explain their side of the problem without insulting or attacking the other person. Guide students to realize that some conflicts can be solved just by both sides understanding what the other person wants.

Resolve Conflicts
At School

Every day you face conflicts. It's easy to become angry, but you can use the steps for **Resolving Conflicts** to settle conflicts peacefully.

Joe wants to use the classroom computer, but Ashley is using it. They are both working on reports that must be finished in class before lunch.

1 Use "I" messages to tell how you feel.

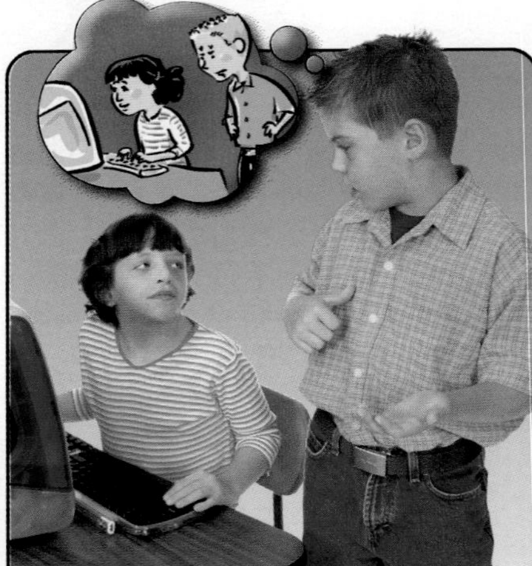

Joe says, "Ashley, I'm worried. I have to get my report done. I need to use the computer now."

2 Listen to each other. Consider the other person's point of view.

Ashley says, "I have to finish my report, too. I was here first. You can use the computer later."

Teacher Tip

Conflicts at Home Be sensitive to the fact that some students may not see conflicts resolved peacefully at home. You might also discuss the fact that the steps of conflict resolution are meant to be used in conflicts between young people. If students are having a conflict with their parents, they need to listen respectfully and do as the parent directs. Using an "I" message might be inappropriate in student/parent conflicts.

ACTIVITY BOOK P. 49

Name ____________

Life Skill
Resolve Conflicts

Steps for Resolving Conflicts at School

1. Use "I" messages to tell how you feel.
2. Listen to each other. Consider the other person's point of view.
3. Ask for a mediator.
4. Find a way for both sides to win.

Use the steps to help these students resolve their conflicts.

A. Both Ellen and Rosa want to share a locker with Lana. Each girl says that Lana agreed to share a locker with her. Ellen says, "Lana and I have been friends longer, so we should share a locker." Rosa says, "Lana and I have already talked about how we will decorate our locker."

- Think about how the friends could resolve their conflict. Write the steps that could help them.

Possible answer: They decide to ask their teacher to act as mediator. She suggests that Ellen and Rosa share a locker and that Lana and another friend have the locker next to Ellen and Rosa's. The friends decide they can accept that solution.

B. Carl and Neil are assigned to work together on a report. Carl wants to write a report about World War II. Neil wants to write a report about the space flights to the moon. Neither wants to write about the other person's topic.

- How can Carl and Neil work together? Write how they can use the steps to help them resolve their conflict.

Possible answer: The boys might ask a teacher to help them resolve the conflict. The teacher might suggest that they pick a topic they are both interested in.

© Harcourt

Available online.
www.harcourtschool.com/health

3 **Ask for a mediator. A mediator is someone who listens to both sides of a problem and helps find a fair solution.**

Joe says, "That won't help. Let's ask Ms. Williams what to do." Ashley agrees. They ask their teacher to act as mediator.

4 **Find a way for both sides to win.**

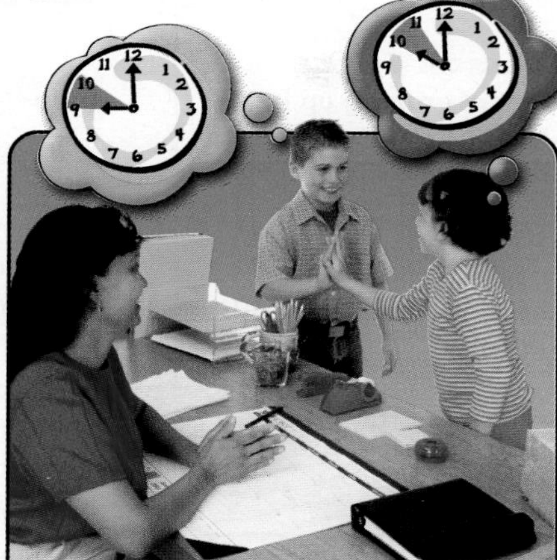

Ms. Williams suggests a schedule. Ashley will use the computer for an hour, and then Joe will use it. Both of them are happy with that.

Problem Solving

Joe and Ashley resolved their conflict even though Ashley is deaf. Ashley reads Joe's lips. Joe understands Ashley's signing.

Suppose you were working on a project with a student who is deaf. In what ways could you communicate with the student? Describe how this would demonstrate consideration for the student.

Using the Poster

Activity Suggest that students design and display posters about setting goals. Students' posters can be displayed in the classroom, school cafeteria, or other common areas.

Display Poster 11 to remind students of the steps used to set goals.

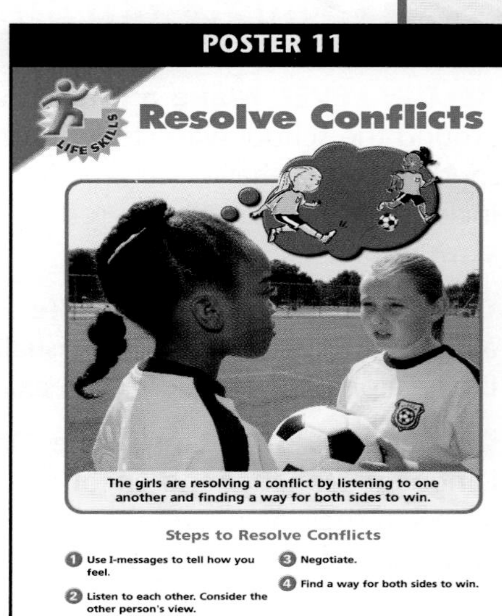

POSTER 11
LIFE SKILLS
Resolve Conflicts
The girls are resolving a conflict by listening to one another and finding a way for both sides to win.
Steps to Resolve Conflicts
1 Use I-messages to tell how you feel.
2 Listen to each other. Consider the other person's view.
3 Negotiate.
4 Find a way for both sides to win.
How do YOU RESOLVE CONFLICTS?
POSTER 11

Step 2

Why does it help to listen to the other person's point of view? Possible answer: You might not know what is actually bothering the other person; listening may help you find an easy resolution to the problem. You might learn something new.

Step 3

Who are some possible mediators at school? teachers, counselors, coaches, and peer mediators (students trained to help others resolve conflicts)

Building Good Character

Remind students that resolving conflicts peacefully is a way to show that they care about others' needs and feelings. When you care about someone, you're willing to negotiate and compromise so that conflicts are resolved fairly.

Step 4

What's another way to resolve this conflict that both Joe and Ashley could accept? Accept reasonable answers. Perhaps Joe or Ashley could use a computer in the library or another classroom.

What might have happened if Joe and Ashley had not resolved this conflict peacefully? Possible answer: They might have wasted time arguing, with neither one finishing his or her report.

3. WRAP UP

Problem Solving

Students might suggest writing notes, listening carefully to each other, speaking slowly, or using sign language as ways to communicate. The care and way that these are attempted would demonstrate their consideration.

LESSON 5

Pages 268–272

Objectives

- ► Explain the importance of respecting differences in people.
- ► Describe how people can work together to help others.
- ► Learn ways to make a difference as a role model.

When Minutes Count . . .
Assign the Quick Study, Lesson 5, Activity Book pp. 46–47 (shown on p. 249).

Program Resources

- ► Activity Book pp. 46–47
- ► Transparency 4

Vocabulary

compassion p. 268,
role model p. 272

Daily Fitness Tip

Make sure students understand that this lesson relates mostly to their relationships with people their own age. Unfortunately, students need to be somewhat wary about working with older children and adult strangers, some of whom might take advantage of a youngster's friendly attitude.

For more about working with others during physical activities, see *Be Active! Resources for Physical Fitness* p. 195.

1. MOTIVATE

Have you ever heard a person say, "Put yourself in my shoes"? What does this mean? Help students understand that when you "stand in someone else's shoes," you let yourself see things from that person's point of view.

What might you learn when you look at a problem from someone else's point of view? You gain some idea of how that person feels; you see how that person is affected by the problem.

Explain that in this lesson students will learn the skill of looking at problems and situations from other points of view.

Working with Others

Lesson Focus
Part of growing up is learning how to work respectfully with others.

Why Learn This?
Respecting differences helps you get along with others.

Vocabulary
compassion
role model

Understanding Others

Imagine going to a school where no one makes fun of you. No one teases you for getting glasses or a new haircut. New students are welcomed. Someone with a *disability* (dis•uh•BIL•uh•tee), a physical or mental impairment, is included in groups and activities.

How can you help make a school like that? You can help by keeping an open mind. You can show respect and compassion for others. When you have **compassion** (kuhm•PASH•uhn), you understand the needs and feelings of others. You help someone who is having a bad day because you know how that can feel.

DRAW CONCLUSIONS How can showing compassion help friends feel good about themselves? Compassion helps friends feel cared for and accepted.

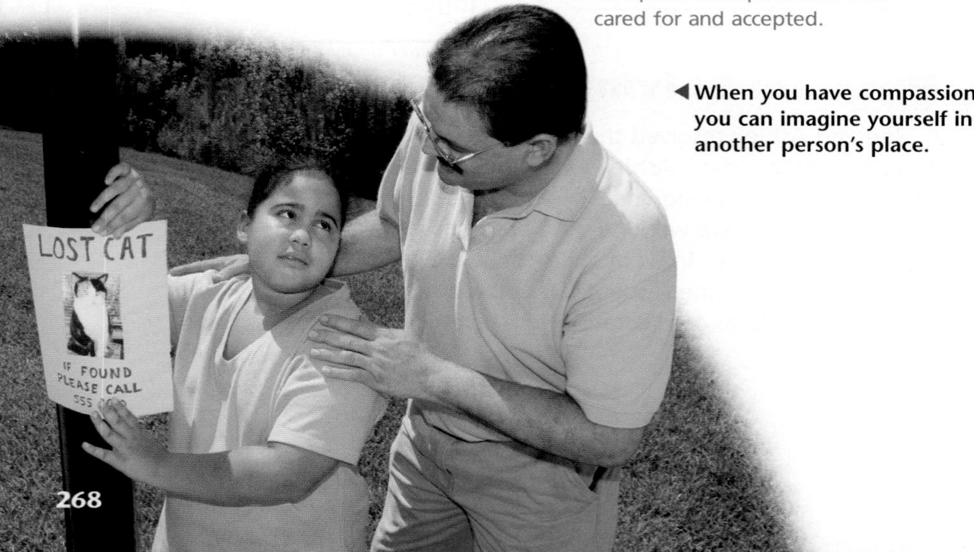
LOST CAT
IF FOUND
PLEASE CALL

◄ When you have compassion, you can imagine yourself in another person's place.

Meeting Individual Needs
Leveled Activities

BELOW-LEVEL Make a Map Give students a map of the school. Walk around the school with students and mark on the map all the accommodations that have been made for people with disabilities. These might include ramps, stalls in the rest rooms, TDD devices in the office, and signs in Braille.

ON-LEVEL Investigate Braille Have students find out how the alphabet for people who are visually impaired was developed. Provide a Braille alphabet for students to examine.

CHALLENGE Sign Language Obtain a copy of the American Sign Language alphabet and encourage students to learn how to sign the letters in their own name and the names of some classmates. They might also learn how to greet someone in sign language.

▲ We can see some of our differences. However, many differences do not show on the outside.

Dealing with Differences

You might feel nervous when you first meet someone who is different from you. Perhaps he or she is from another country or speaks with an accent. Maybe the person has a problem speaking or has trouble saying some words. If you listen closely, you may understand the words. You can ask questions to see if you understand. For example, you might ask, "Are you looking for the cafeteria?"

Besides these examples, people may be different in other ways. The more you get to know others, the more you will notice ways you are all the same.

You do not have to be friends with everyone. Still, you can get along with others and respect their right to be different from you.

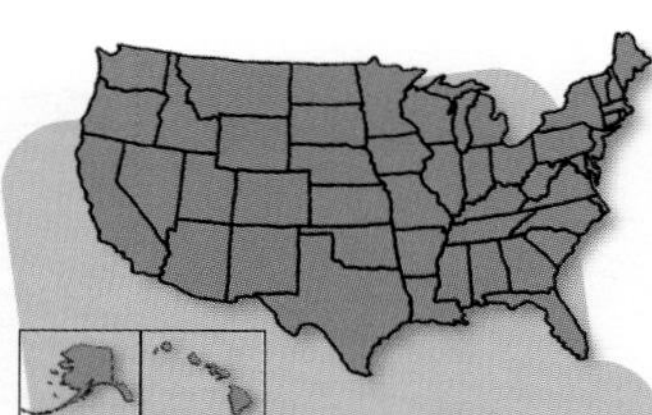

Did You Know?

By the year 2050, almost half the people living in the United States will be Hispanic, African American, Asian, or from the Pacific Islands.

CAUSE AND EFFECT **How might someone with a speech defect or someone who does not speak English feel if you took the time to speak with him or her?**
He or she would probably be pleased and feel accepted.

Cultural Connection

Greetings! Ask students who speak languages other than English to teach the class how to greet people in those languages. For example, they might teach the class how to say "Hello," "How are you?" "Please," "Thank you," and "Would you like to play/eat/walk with us?" Post the phrases on a bulletin board to help students remember them. Encourage students to greet each other in various languages whenever possible.

Teacher Tip

Listen! Throughout this lesson and the entire chapter, demonstrate and encourage active listening as a way to work effectively with others, build positive relationships, and show respect and caring. Remind students that they can show nonverbally that they're listening by looking at the speaker, leaning forward, and not interrupting. They can also show verbally that they're listening by making comments and asking questions to show their interest.

2. TEACH

Content-Area Reading Support

Using Respellings Point out the phonetic respellings of *disability* and *compassion* on page 268. Explain that respellings show how words are pronounced. The dots divide the word into syllables, and the capital letters show which syllable should be stressed, or accented. Have students identify the accented syllable in each word, and ask volunteers to pronounce the words. Point out that respellings can help students pronounce unfamiliar words and recognize words with unfamiliar spellings.

Discuss

Critical Thinking Have students read the last paragraph on this page.
Why is it important to know that you don't have to be friends with everyone?
Possible answers: Then you won't feel pressured to go along with an unsafe idea just to be someone's friend; you'll be free to choose friends who share your interests and values.

Health Background

Majority/Minority Census experts predict that by the year 2050 just a little over half of the residents of the United States (52.8 percent) will be non-Hispanic white people. The second largest group will be Hispanic people (24.3 percent), followed by African American people (13.2 percent), Asian and Pacific Islanders (8.9 percent), and Native Americans (0.8 percent). By the year 2070, non-Hispanic whites will be only 46.8 percent of the population.

Source: *United States Census Bureau website*

For more background, visit the **Webliography** in Teacher Resources at **www.harcourtschool.com/health**
Keyword family life

TEACH *continued*

Interpret Visuals—Pictures

Discuss each picture on these two pages with the class.

Who is helping in this picture? Who is being helped? Guide students to recognize all the ways that the helpers benefit from their own actions: they feel good about themselves and their abilities; they become a positive role model for others; they might make new friends; others will be more willing to help them when they need it.

Discuss

Critical Thinking **How old do you have to be to make a difference in someone else's life?** Help students realize that even a very young child can make a difference by showing caring and concern for others.

If we were to display pictures of people making a difference at our school, what might we show? Possible answers: students picking up trash inside and outside the school; students serving as tutors or helping younger children with other schoolwork and projects; students refusing to go along with an activity that's against school rules; students including others in their groups and activities

Quick Activity

Accept reasonable suggestions from students. Communities and situations may vary. Encourage students to discuss with their parents additional ways that they can help out in their home, school, or community.

Quick Activity

Interpret Photographs Look at these pictures of ways students make a difference. Then write three ways that you can make a difference in your community.

Making a Difference

You can make a difference in your home, at school, and in your community. You might not make the news. But you and the people you help will know what you do.

You can make a difference at home. If you have younger brothers or sisters, you know that they might cry or scream to demand things. You can teach them to get attention in other ways. You can practice listening and find ways to be helpful. When you respect your family's rules, you show that you are responsible and caring.

You can make a difference at school, too. You can show compassion and respect for other students and for teachers. Try seeing things from their points of view.

ESL/ELL Support

BACKGROUND AND EXPERIENCE Invite students to describe ways to show compassion, work with others, and make a difference.

Beginning Pantomime ways to show compassion and help others, such as picking up books after someone drops them. Invite students to pantomime other ways of helping others.

Intermediate Ask students to use simple sentences to describe effective ways to help others and work together.

Advanced Have students make a list of three or four guidelines that will help people work together. For example: Listen carefully to others' opinions.

At school, you can make sure that everyone is included in activities. You can welcome new students and discourage hurtful teasing. You can help keep the classrooms and other areas clean. By doing these things and encouraging others to do the same, you show respect for your school, the people in it, and yourself.

You can also make a difference in your community. Visit people in care centers, or volunteer to help in youth programs. You can make a difference all by yourself. You already have the skills you need!

Focus Skill **MAIN IDEA AND DETAILS** **Explain the three important points made on these two pages.**

By yourself, you can make a difference at home, at school, and in your community.

Personal Health Plan

Real-Life Situation
Suppose you want to be more of a help at home.

Real-Life Plan
Write a plan that you can follow to help you meet this goal.

271

Discuss

Problem Solving How can we encourage people to imitate behavior that is good? Possible answers: by encouraging good behavior; by not paying attention to behavior that is not good; by praising those who are good; by giving recognition to those who do good

Use the opportunity to ask students to identify negative characteristics of social groups, such as the cliques described on page 272.

Personal Health Plan

Student lists should include:

- talking with parents or family members
- ideas including common daily activities
- goals that are realistic

This feature is designed to provide students with an opportunity to reflect on health decisions they are making in their personal lives. The Personal Health Plan should not be used to evaluate or assess students, nor should the results be shared among students.

Science

Saving Energy Students might make a difference in their school or community by starting or helping with a recycling project. For example, they might set out containers and put up posters encouraging students and staff to recycle scrap paper or plastic products used in the cafeteria. Help students identify pick-up services or drop-off points for the recycled materials.

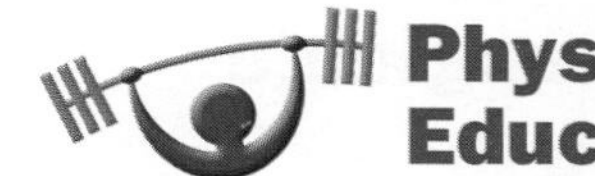

Physical Education

Working Together Ask the physical education teacher to lead or suggest cooperative games in which teams must work together in order to succeed. Afterward, ask students which behaviors helped their team succeed. What might they have done better?

Health Background

Statistics on Volunteerism A survey showed that 73 percent of America's young people believe they can make a difference in their communities. About 70 percent of people ages 15 to 21 have volunteered in their communities. Teenagers volunteer about 2.4 billion hours annually, which is worth $34.3 billion. Young people who volunteer only one hour a week are half as likely to smoke or use alcohol or other drugs. Students who volunteer are also more likely to succeed in school and three times more likely to continue to volunteer as adults. Teenagers are nearly four times more likely to volunteer if someone asks them to do it.

Sources: *Do Something: Young People's Involvement Survey*

For more background, visit the **Webliography** in Teacher Resources at **www.harcourtschool.com/health**
Keyword community/environmental health

Consumer Activity

Tell students first to make a list of the qualities found in a positive role model. Students can use their list to help decide if the character is a good role model.

3. WRAP UP

Lesson 5 Summary and Review

1. compassion; disability; role model
2. The more you learn about someone who is different from you, the more you can understand that person and find things in common with him or her.
3. Possible answer: Some young people think they must do big things to make a difference. But small things make a difference, too.
4. Possible answers:

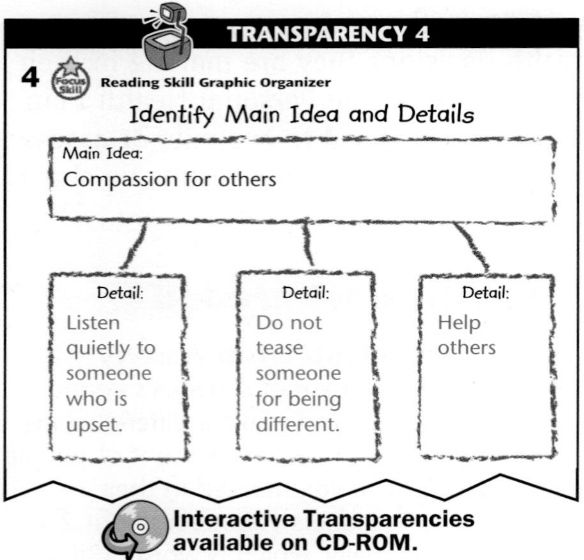

TRANSPARENCY 4

4 Reading Skill Graphic Organizer

Identify Main Idea and Details

Main Idea: Compassion for others

Detail: Listen quietly to someone who is upset.

Detail: Do not tease someone for being different.

Detail: Help others

Interactive Transparencies available on CD-ROM.

5. Students' letters might suggest ways that the community could provide activities for people in the community.

For **writing models** with examples, see *Teaching Resources* pp. 47–61. Rubrics are also provided.

When Minutes Count ...

Quick Study Students can use *Activity Book* pages 46–47 (shown on p. 249) as they complete each lesson in this chapter.

Consumer Activity

Analyze Ads and Media Messages Watch a television show that has a character in it who is about your age. Take notes about what he or she says and does. Is this character a good role model? Why or why not?

Setting good examples encourages others to make a difference, too.

Setting an Example

When you make a difference, you serve as a role model. A **role model** is someone who sets a good example. When you set a good example, you encourage others to do the same, and they can make a difference, too. Another way you can make a difference is by not being a member of a clique. A *clique* (KLEEK) is a group that excludes other people.

Some adults also serve as role models. By observing how they behave, you can learn to be honest, to follow rules and laws, and to respect others. Some adults are role models because they make healthful choices about food, exercise, and safety. You can encourage others by being a positive role model. How many people did you encourage today?

SUMMARIZE Why should young people set good examples?

Lesson 5 Summary and Review

1. **Summarize with Vocabulary** Use vocabulary and other terms from the lesson to complete these statements.

   When we try to understand others' needs and feelings, we show ____. Some students face challenges because they have a physical or mental ____. When we try to make a difference, we serve as a ____.

2. "The more you learn, the less you fear." How does this statement relate to respecting differences?
3. **Critical Thinking** Explain why you would not be a good role model if you were a member of a clique.
4. **MAIN IDEA AND DETAILS** Draw and complete this graphic organizer by adding three ways to show compassion.

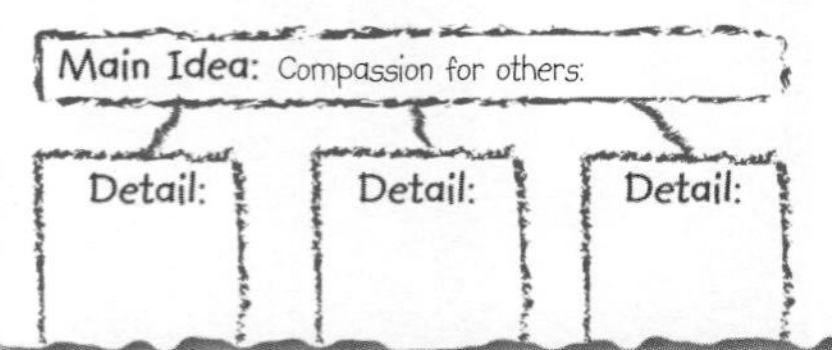

5. **Write to Express—Business Letter** How could your community be more compassionate to people, such as the elderly or the disabled? Explain your idea in a letter to the editor of your local newspaper.

272

Language Arts

Identifying Role Models Help students brainstorm positive role models. List them on the board. These people might be living or not, people in your community, or national heroes. They might be members of students' families or school staff. Then have students choose a role model and work with a partner, if you wish. Ask them to write a one-page report explaining why that person is someone to be admired.

Teacher Tip

Helping Out Ask students, school staff, and PTA/PTO leaders about community projects that could use your students as helpers. There might be something they could do in the classroom to help with a project in the community. Or students might read to younger children at your school or visit a nursing home or daycare center within walking distance, with parental and school permission, of course.

Caring

Building Good Character

Being a Good Friend

How can you be a good friend? The most important thing to remember is to treat others as you want them to treat you. Here are some things you can do.

- **Communicate clearly, share your feelings, and encourage your friend to share his or hers. This is important when you have a disagreement. Explain your point of view, and then listen to your friend's viewpoint.**
- **Show compassion, if your friend is having a bad day. Use your best listening skills. Sometimes you can show support just by being there.**
- **Show respect. Your friend has a right to disagree, just as you have a right to your own opinion.**
- **Take responsibility for your words and actions. If you have accidentally hurt your friend's feelings, apologize. Be ready to forgive if your friend has hurt you.**
- **Be open-minded. Are you passing up a really good friend because he or she is different from you in some way?**

Activity

Keep a friendship journal. Every night for two weeks, write down the ways you showed friendship that day. Did you invite a new student to eat with you at lunch? Did you find a way for a friend who has a disability to be a part of your basketball game? You can be caring at home, too. After two weeks, review your journal. Describe how your observations helped contribute to self-confidence and self-esteem.

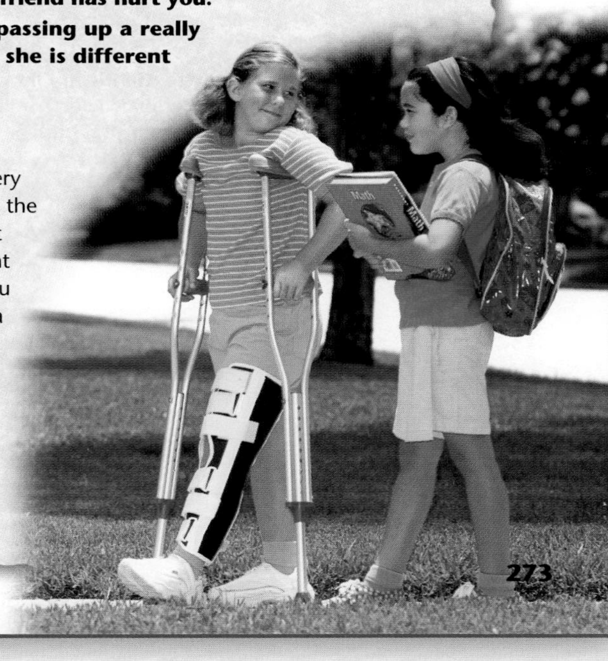

273

Building Good Character

Caring
Citizenship
Fairness
Respect
Responsibility
Trustworthiness

Objectives

- ► Recognize the importance of caring by being a good friend.
- ► Describe the qualities of a good friend.

Program Resource

- ► Poster 1

BEFORE READING

Brainstorm with students some ways to show caring at school and at home. Then ask why it's important to show caring to your friends. If you don't show your friends that you care, they may look for another friend who does.

DISCUSS

After students have read the page, ask **Which guideline listed here is the most difficult to carry out? Why? Which is the easiest? Which guideline is the most important? What other guidelines would you add to the list?** Responses will vary.

ACTIVITY

Don't ask students to share their journals with classmates. Explain that the journals provide a private place to record their progress in making new friends and in becoming a better friend. At the end of the two weeks, you might invite volunteers to explain how their journals helped them strengthen their friendship skills. You might also comment (without embarrassing anyone) on caring actions you have observed among students during the two weeks.

Using the Poster

Activity Suggest students design and display posters about being a good listener.

Display Poster 1 to remind students of ways to show fairness. Students' posters can be displayed in the classroom.

POSTER 1
Caring
Building Good Character
GET WELL Soon!
The girl is showing caring by visiting her grandfather.
DO
Support and value family members.
Be a good friend and share your feelings in appropriate ways.
Show concern for others.
Thank people who help you.
Help people in need.
DON'T
Don't be selfish.
Don't expect rewards for being caring.
Don't gossip about people.
Don't hurt anyone's feelings.
How have YOU shown CARING today?
POSTER 1

LESSON 6

Pages 274–276

Objectives

- Describe how peer pressure works and how you can respond to it effectively.
- Explain how a strong self-concept can help you avoid the influences of negative peer pressure.
- Demonstrate refusal and negotiation skills to enhance health.

When Minutes Count . . .
Assign the Quick Study, Lesson 6, Activity Book pp. 46–47 (shown on p. 249).

Program Resources

- Activity Book pp. 46–47, 50
- Transparency 4
- Growth, Development, and Reproduction pp. 44–46

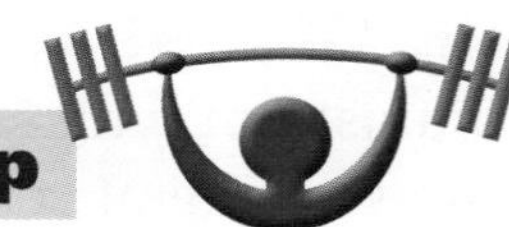

Daily Fitness Tip

Students can't avoid peer pressure, but their health and well-being depend on their ability to tell whether the pressure is negative or positive. Their well-being also depends on their willingness to resist peer pressure when it's negative. Stress that a confident person won't give in to negative peer pressure.

1. MOTIVATE

Let's say you want a friend to play [a game your students enjoy] with you, but the friend doesn't want to. How can you convince your friend to play the game? Possible answers: beg, argue, compromise with him or her

Are you using peer pressure? Why or why not? Guide students to realize that persuading someone your age to do something is using peer pressure.

Remind students that peer pressure isn't always bad. You can pressure your friends to do healthful, helpful, fun things, too. This lesson will help students tell negative peer pressure from positive peer pressure. Ask students to explain the influence of peer pressure on an individual's emotional health.

LESSON 6

Dealing with Peer Pressure

Lesson Focus
Knowing how to recognize the two kinds of peer pressure can help you know how to respond to peer pressure.

Why Learn This?
When you resist negative peer pressure, you help build a strong self-concept. You also encourage your friends to do the same.

Kinds of Peer Pressure

In Chapter 8, you learned that *peer pressure* is the strong influence someone your own age can have on you. Remember that peer pressure is *negative* if someone wants you to do something you know is wrong. For example, someone wants you to let him or her look at your paper during a test.

Peer pressure can be *positive*, too. For example, some friends may want you to help collect food for a food drive. Positive peer pressure doesn't ask you to do something wrong. It helps you build a strong self-concept. A strong self-concept can help you resist negative peer pressure.

▼ Did you ever invite friends to join you in a fun, healthful game or sport? If you did, you used positive peer pressure.

274

Meeting Individual Needs
Leveled Activities

BELOW-LEVEL **Say *No*** Have students role-play different ways to refuse negative peer pressure. You should be the one pressuring them, so that they don't practice a negative skill. Here are some ways to say *no*: give a reason or an excuse, suggest another activity, use humor, say *no* again, walk away.

ON-LEVEL **Use Positive Pressure** Ask each student to think of a way to apply positive peer pressure and try it. The next day, ask for feedback on what they did.

CHALLENGE **Make a Scene** Ask students, perhaps working with a partner, to think of a challenging situation involving negative peer pressure and write it like a scene from a play. Tell them to show how a character successfully resists the pressure.

How do you deal with peer pressure? First, determine if it is positive or negative pressure. You might ask yourself these questions:

- Does this activity go against my values?
- Would my parents approve?
- What might happen if I do this?
- How will I feel about myself afterward?
- Is this something I want to do?

After you answer these questions, you will know if you should say "Let's do it!" or "No way!"

COMPARE AND CONTRAST What is the difference between positive and negative peer pressure?

Positive peer pressure does not influence you to do something that you know is wrong. Negative peer pressure does.

Health & Technology

Pocket Keyboard Staying in touch with friends is getting easier. Soon you may be able to fold up a full-size keyboard for your cell phone and put it in your pocket. Wires can now be woven into cloth. The cloth can then be made into a keyboard.

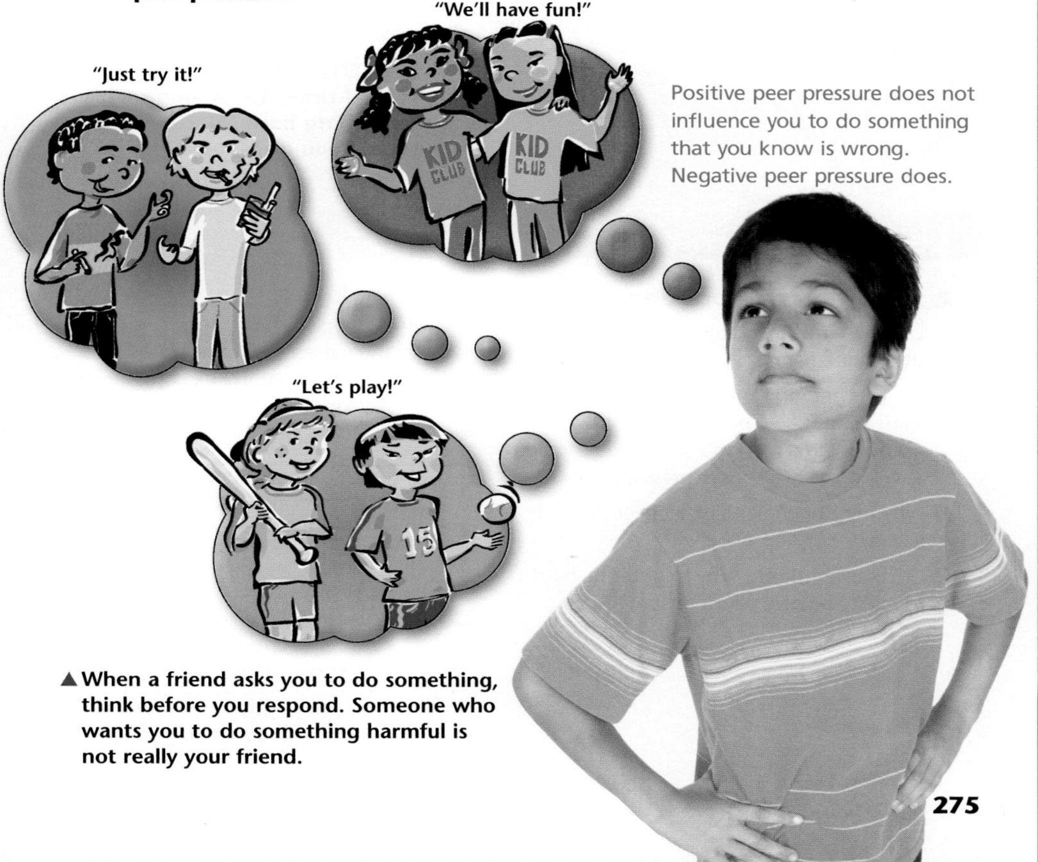

▲ **When a friend asks you to do something, think before you respond. Someone who wants you to do something harmful is not really your friend.**

275

Teacher Tip

Attitudes Help students distinguish between passive, assertive, and aggressive refusals. A passive refusal is uncertain and easily pushed aside. An assertive person stands up straight and shows confidence. An aggressive person stands too close and talks too loud. This over-response may encourage verbal or physical violence.

2. TEACH

Interpret Visuals—Pictures

Have students study each activity pictured on this page. **Which ones involve positive peer pressure?** playing ball, joining a club **Negative peer pressure?** trying cigarettes

What are other examples of positive peer pressure? Possible answers: urging someone not to smoke, to wear a safety helmet while skating or riding bikes, to study for a test, to include a new student in a game

Explain why the influences of negative peer pressure should be resisted. Possible answers: You might try illegal drugs, cheat, shoplift, lie, or break family rules.

Discuss

Problem Solving What can you do if a friend uses negative peer pressure? Guide students to recognize that everyone makes mistakes. Young people often don't think things through and may suggest something that sounds like fun without considering the consequences. Often, if someone points out the possible results, such as losing their parents' trust or getting into trouble, this friend will no longer want to do the activity. However, students may know someone who keeps suggesting harmful activities and won't take *no* for an answer. For their own health and well-being, they should avoid this person.

Critical Thinking Do adults have to deal with peer pressure, too? Why or why not? Help students realize that everyone is pressured to do things by peers, even parents and grandparents. We all have to think about the consequences so we know whether to participate or refuse to get involved.

Growth, Development, and Reproduction An optional lesson about maturity and reproduction is provided in this supplement on pp. 44–46. Use this component in compliance with state and local guidelines.

Discuss

How can peer pressure affect your physical and social health? Possible answers: It can affect what you eat, how much you exercise, and how much you sleep; It can help you choose or change friends; it can lead to fun or trouble.

3. WRAP UP

Lesson 6 Summary and Review

1. Peer pressure; Positive; *no*, negative
2. They assume that *pressure* can only be something that is negative.
3. Possible answers: You don't want to make your friends angry; you want to look cool and fit in with a group; you want people to like you.
4. Possible answers:

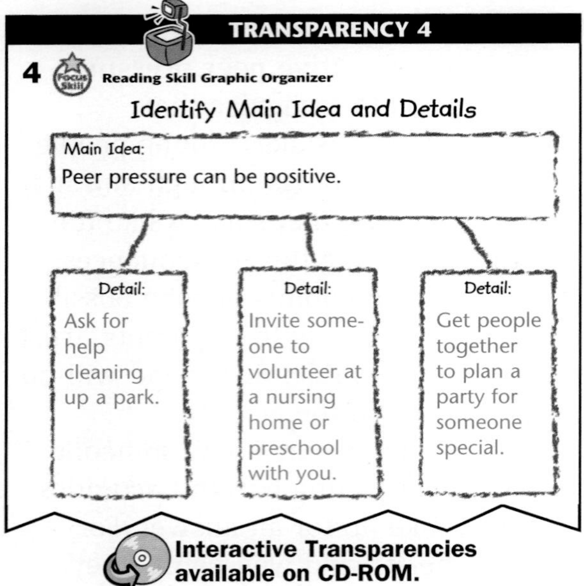
TRANSPARENCY 4

4 Reading Skill Graphic Organizer

Identify Main Idea and Details

Main Idea: Peer pressure can be positive.

Detail:	Detail:	Detail:
Ask for help cleaning up a park.	Invite someone to volunteer at a nursing home or preschool with you.	Get people together to plan a party for someone special.

Interactive Transparencies available on CD-ROM.

5. Possible uses of positive peer pressure: asking someone to study for a test, go to a ball game, try out for a team, the school band, or a play.

For **writing models** with examples, see *Teaching Resources* pp. 47–61. Rubrics are also provided.

When Minutes Count . . .

Quick Study Students can use *Activity Book* pages 46–47 (shown on p. 249) as they complete each lesson in this chapter.

▼ You can use peer pressure to encourage your friends to do their best.

Saying *No*

How can you say *no* to negative peer pressure? Sometimes friends just need you to set an example. Suggest a more healthful activity. They may go along with your idea.

You might tell why you won't do the harmful activity. For example, "It's not safe to swim without a lifeguard." You could make a joke. Say, "I can't believe you want to do that!" If they still want to do something harmful, walk away.

Do not give in to negative peer pressure. Your friends will admire your courage. Use positive peer pressure. True friends will respect you for it!

SEQUENCE You have refused several times to go along with something harmful. Now what should you do?
You should walk away.

Lesson 6 Summary and Review

1. **Summarize with Vocabulary** Use the terms from this lesson to complete these statements.
   _____ is getting someone your age to do something. _____ peer pressure is encouraging a friend to study. You should say _____ to _____ peer pressure.
2. Why might people think all peer pressure is bad?
3. **Critical Thinking** Why might it be hard to resist negative peer pressure?
4. **MAIN IDEA AND DETAILS** Draw and complete this graphic organizer to show examples of positive peer pressure. Do not use examples from the lesson.

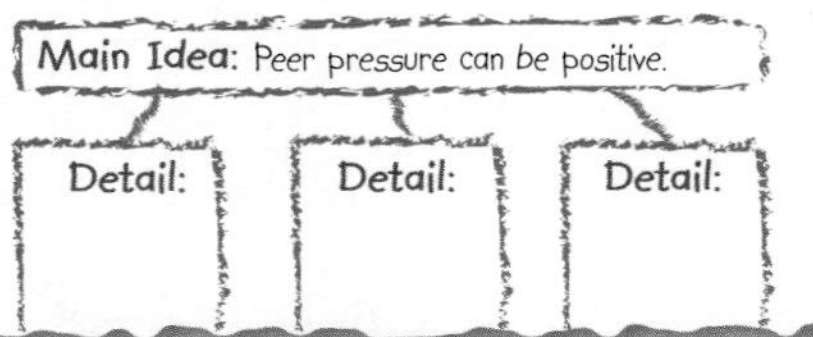

5. **Write to Inform—How-To** 
   Explain how you might use peer pressure to ask a friend to do something positive.

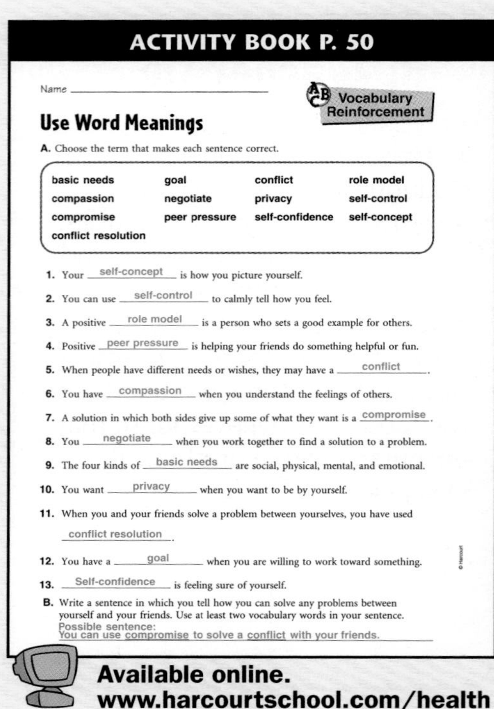
ACTIVITY BOOK P. 50

Name ______

Vocabulary Reinforcement

Use Word Meanings

A. Choose the term that makes each sentence correct.

basic needs	goal	conflict	role model
compassion	negotiate	privacy	self-control
compromise	peer pressure	self-confidence	self-concept
conflict resolution			

1. Your self-concept is how you picture yourself.
2. You can use self-control to calmly tell how you feel.
3. A positive role model is a person who sets a good example for others.
4. Positive peer pressure is helping your friends do something helpful or fun.
5. When people have different needs or wishes, they may have a conflict.
6. You have compassion when you understand the feelings of others.
7. A solution in which both sides give up some of what they want is a compromise.
8. You negotiate when you work together to find a solution to a problem.
9. The four kinds of basic needs are social, physical, mental, and emotional.
10. You want privacy when you want to be by yourself.
11. When you and your friends solve a problem between yourselves, you have used conflict resolution.
12. You have a goal when you are willing to work toward something.
13. Self-confidence is feeling sure of yourself.

B. Write a sentence in which you tell how you can solve any problems between yourself and your friends. Use at least two vocabulary words in your sentence.
Possible sentence:
You can use compromise to solve a conflict with your friends.

Available online.
www.harcourtschool.com/health

ACTIVITIES

Science

Plants Have Needs Like you, plants have needs. Do some research to find out about some of the needs of plants. Then do an experiment to see for yourself. Select three plants of the same type and size. Put each plant in a different environment in your home. Observe and compare their growth after a month.

Physical Education

Reducing Stress Pick a partner and find out about exercises that can help reduce stress. Consider talking to a physical education teacher for ideas. Then share what you have learned with the rest of the class. One partner could explain what the other is demonstrating. Then you could switch roles.

Technology Project

Make an outline of the main ideas and the important details of this chapter. Use a computer to make slides of the outline, if possible. Or make colorful posters of your outline.

For more activities, visit The Learning Site. www.harcourtschool.com/health

Home & Community

Communicating Share what you have learned about resolving conflicts. Make a poster to show at least four ways to resolve conflicts with friends. Display your poster in a hallway outside your classroom, in the media center, or at home for your family.

Career Link

School Counselor Suppose you are the counselor in your school. A teacher has sent Benjamin to you. Other students are upset because Benjamin keeps teasing them. Benjamin does not understand why the other students are making such a big deal out of it. Explain how you would help settle this conflict.

277

Career Link

School Counselor School counselors help students plan their careers, may offer guidance on adjustment or relationship problems, and help secure any needed academic or other assistance. They may also counsel parents. Many counselors supervise peer mediation programs.

Students may suggest that the counselor follow the steps in conflict resolution to help Jed and Benjamin better understand each other's point of view and find a way to get along together.

For more information on health careers, visit the **Webliography** in Teacher Resources at **www.harcourtschool.com/health**
Keyword health careers

Activities

Science

Students should begin with three nearly identical plants. To test the plants' need for light, they might put one in a dark closet, one in a dim corner, and one in a sunny window. To test plants' need for water, students might water one plant generously, one sparingly, and one not at all. Urge students to test for light *or* for water—so they know which one is affecting the plant's growth.

Physical Education

Allow time for partners to demonstrate their exercises for the class. If you have students with physical limitations, include some exercises that they can do, too.

Home & Community

Obtain necessary permission to display the posters in locations outside of your classroom. When the study of this topic is complete, have students take their posters home to use as a reference for resolving conflicts.

Supports the Coordinated School Health Program

Technology Project

Urge students to use the headings and subheadings in the lessons as they outline the main ideas and important details in this chapter. If they don't have access to a computer, they might make their slides with construction paper. Perhaps you can provide letter stencils to make the headings.

Chapter Review and Test Preparation

Pages 278–279

Reading Skill 5 pts. each

1. Possible answers: curly hair, brown eyes; good memory, good at math; impatient, giggly; shy, outgoing
2. Possible answers: curly hair, brown eyes (physical); good memory, good at math (mental); impatient, giggly (emotional); shy, outgoing (social)

Use Vocabulary 5 pts. each

3. D, self-confidence
4. B, self-control
5. F, privacy
6. C, role model
7. A, compromise
8. E, disability

Check Understanding 5 pts. each

9. B, basic needs
10. H, trait
11. D, compassion
12. F, peer pressure
13. B, Laugh at the other person.
14. H, conflict
15. A, negotiate

Think Critically 5 pts. each

16. Situations will vary. Possible ways to stay in control: find a way to cool off, express your feelings with an "I" message, listen to the other person's viewpoint, walk away.
17. Ask yourself questions such as these: Does this activity go against my values? Would my parents approve? What might happen if I do this? How will I feel about myself afterward? Is this something I want to do? The answers will tell you whether the pressure is positive and will have good consequences or negative and will lead to trouble.

Chapter Review and Test Preparation

Reading Skill

MAIN IDEA AND DETAILS

Draw and then use this graphic organizer to answer questions 1 and 2.

1 Write a different trait in each box.

2 Label each trait as *physical, mental, emotional,* or *social.*

Use Vocabulary

Match each term in Column B with its meaning in Column A.

Column A	Column B
3 Feeling sure of yourself	**A** compromise
4 Ability to express feelings calmly	**B** self-control
5 Time by yourself	**C** role model
6 Someone who sets a good example	**D** self-confidence
7 A solution in which each side gives up some of what it wants	**E** disability
8 A physical or mental impairment	**F** privacy

Check Understanding

Choose the letter of the correct answer.

9 What must you meet in order to stay healthy? (p. 252)
A goals
B basic needs
C wants
D role models

10 Being shy is a _____. (p. 248)
F need
G want
H trait
J goal

11 What is the older boy showing? (p. 268)
A self-confidence
B peer pressure
C conflict resolution
D compassion

278

Formal Assessment

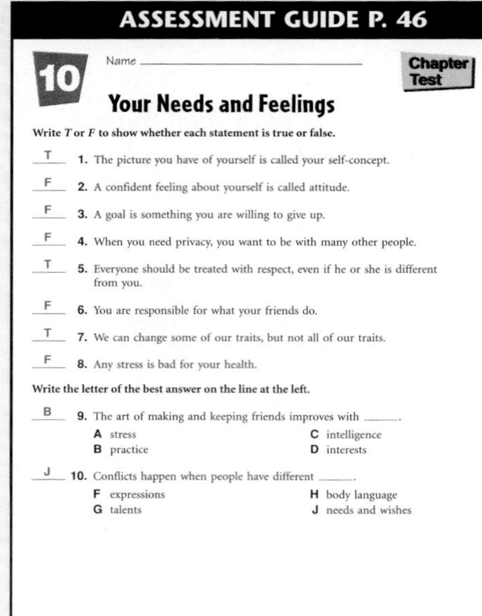

ASSESSMENT GUIDE P. 46

10 Name ______________ Chapter Test

Your Needs and Feelings

Write *T* or *F* to show whether each statement is true or false.

T 1. The picture you have of yourself is called your self-concept.
F 2. A confident feeling about yourself is called attitude.
F 3. A goal is something you are willing to give up.
F 4. When you need privacy, you want to be with many other people.
T 5. Everyone should be treated with respect, even if he or she is different from you.
F 6. You are responsible for what your friends do.
T 7. We can change some of our traits, but not all of our traits.
F 8. Any stress is bad for your health.

Write the letter of the best answer on the line at the left.

B 9. The art of making and keeping friends improves with _____.
A stress **B** practice **C** intelligence **D** interests

J 10. Conflicts happen when people have different _____.
F expressions **G** talents **H** body language **J** needs and wishes

© Harcourt

ASSESSMENT GUIDE P. 47

Name ______________

C 11. Conflict resolution can help you keep friends by _____.
A winning arguments **B** ignoring their ideas **C** solving problems **D** finding games

G 12. Which situation describes a compromise?
F We both go last. **G** We take turns going first. **H** We both get to go first. **J** You get to go first.

C 13. One way to negotiate is to _____.
A focus on small problems **B** choose a new friend **C** listen to each other's ideas **D** insist that you're right

F 14. To meet your goals, you must _____.
F plan the steps **G** exercise self-esteem **H** play on the steps **J** become a role model

C 15. Peer pressure is negative if it pushes you to _____.
A learn new skills **B** feel good about yourself **C** go against your values **D** build a strong self-concept

G 16. Which is an important friendship rule?
F Don't compromise. **G** Don't say mean things. **H** Use peer pressure. **J** Avoid conflicts.

Match each term below to a feeling or action described. Write the correct letter on the line to the left of the description.

a stress **b** self-control **c** compassion **d** grief

c 17. Liza sees her friend Dee looking sad. She knows that Dee's mom has been sick. Liza imagines how sad and scary that might be.
b 18. Sean feels like fighting because his friend lied to him. Instead Sean decides to talk with his friend when they both calm down.
d 19. Julia's favorite cat has been gone for two weeks. Julia doesn't think he'll be back. She feels very sad and just wants to cry.
a 20. Benjamin has an important math test tomorrow. He has studied for it, but he's not sure that he really understands the problems.

© Harcourt

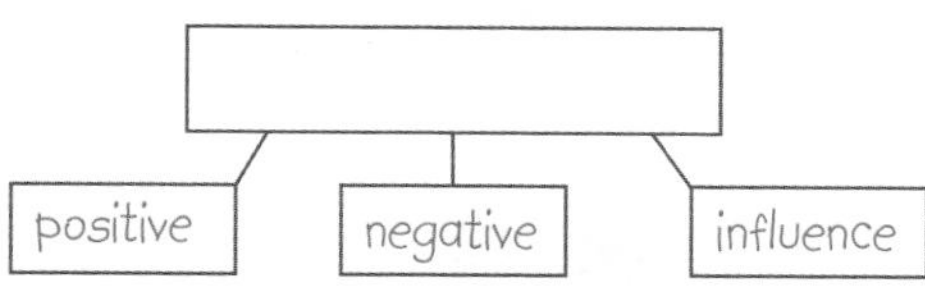

12 Which term goes in the top box? (p. 274)
F peer pressure
G conflict resolution
H basic needs
J compromise

13 Which of these is **NOT** a step in conflict resolution? (pp. 266–267)
A Explain how you feel.
B Laugh at the other person.
C Listen to the other person.
D Find a way for both sides to win.

14 Your brother has just grabbed the last cookie, and you tell him it was yours. You are having a _____. (p. 262)
F compromise
G compassion
H conflict
J conflict resolution

15 A classmate says that he will write the group's report if you present it to the class. He is trying to _____ with you. (p. 263)
A negotiate
B conflict
C respect
D joke

Think Critically

16 Describe a time when a person might lose self-control. How could that person stay in control?

17 Describe something a friend might encourage you to do. How can you decide if this peer pressure is positive or negative?

Apply Skills

18 **BUILDING GOOD CHARACTER**
Caring A classmate is teasing another student about his new shoes. How can you show this boy that you are a friend?

19 **LIFE SKILLS**
Resolve Conflicts Suppose that you and your friend want to play a sport together after school, but you each like a different sport. How could you resolve this conflict peacefully?

Write About Health

20 **Write to Inform—Explanation** Explain why young people need to learn how to use self-control when expressing their feelings.

279

ASSESSMENT GUIDE P. 48

Name ____________________

Everyone has basic physical, mental, emotional, and social needs. Complete the chart by listing two needs each person might have.

Person	Needs
21. a newborn baby	Possible answers: food, cuddling, love, safety, clean clothes and diapers, medical attention, being talked to
22. a fourth grader	Possible answers: food, shelter, clean clothes, friends, schooling, love, security, exercise, medical attention, privacy

Learning the steps for managing anger is an important part of growing up. List the two steps that are missing.

23. a. Stop what you are doing or saying. **b.** Cool down by taking long, slow breaths.

24. c. Think about what is happening. **d.** Take action by walking away or by expressing your feelings calmly in "I" messages.

25. Role models show respect and compassion toward others. Name one specific thing you could say or do to make someone choose you as a role model.
Possible answers: visit people in care centers, volunteer in youth programs, help keep the classroom clean, welcome new students, discourage hurtful behavior, include everyone in activities, help younger brothers or sisters, listen to friends and family, respect rules

© Harcourt

Apply Skills 5 pts. each

18. Possible answers: You could express your feelings to the teaser in an "I" message, stand up for the boy, ask him to sit with you at lunch or walk home with you.

19. You can express your ideas and feelings in "I" messages and listen carefully so you understand each other's points of view. If you still cannot agree, you might negotiate a compromise—or even agree to do different sports.

Write About Health 5 pts.

20. Answers will vary, but students might write that young people who can't control their feelings may not have friends for long and probably have trouble getting along with their family members, too. Also, if they don't use self-control in expressing their feelings, others will become angry or annoyed and not do as they are asking.

Performance Assessment

Use the Chapter Project and the rubric provided on the Project Evaluation Sheet. See *Assessment Guide* pp. 18, 60, 71.

Portfolio Assessment

Have students select their best work from the following suggestions:
- Leveled Activities, p. 250
- Quick Activity, p. 253
- Write to Inform, p. 265
- Activities, p. 277

See *Assessment Guide* pp. 12–16.

CHAPTER 11

Families Together

Lesson	Pacing	Objectives	Reading Skills
Introduce the Chapter pp. 280–281		• Preview chapter concepts.	**Summarize** pp. 281, 340–341
1 **Families Meet Their Needs** pp. 282–286	3 class periods	• Describe the different types of families children live in. • Identify the roles of family members. • Explain how and why family members' roles change. • Define and describe extended families.	**Summarize** pp. 283, 286 • Compare and Contrast, p. 285 • Cause and Effect, p. 286
Building Good Character p. 287		• Recognize the importance of fairness in the family and in life.	
2 **Families Communicate** pp. 288–291	1 class period	• Explain why family members get along well when they communicate. • Describe the many different ways to communicate with family members. • Explain how communicating with your family helps you resist peer pressure.	**Summarize** p. 291 • Main Idea and Details, p. 289 • Sequence, p. 291
Life Skills pp. 292–293	1 class period	• Identify steps for good communication. • Practice solving communication problems.	
3 **Families Work Together** pp. 294–298	3 class periods	• Identify the values learned from the family and how they are taught. • Explain why cooperation is important in families. • Describe some family rules, and explain why they are important.	**Summarize** pp. 297, 298 • Main Idea and Details, p. 295 • Draw Conclusions, p. 298
Activities p. 299		• Extend chapter concepts.	
Chapter Review pp. 300–301	1 class period	• Assess chapter objectives.	

Vocabulary	Program Resources
	Music CD Teaching Resources, p. 43
traditions nuclear family single-parent family blended family extended family	Transparency 6 Activity Book, pp. 51–53
	Poster 3
	Transparency 6 Activity Book, pp. 51–52
	Activity Book, p. 54 Poster 7
values cooperate	Transparency 6 Activity Book, pp. 51–52, 55
	The Learning Site www.harcourtschool.com
	Assessment Guide, pp. 49–51

Interactive Transparencies available on CD-ROM.

Reading Skill

These reading skills are reinforced throughout this chapter and one skill is emphasized as the Focus Skill.

Summarize

- Draw Conclusions
- Identify Cause and Effect
- Identify Main Idea and Details
- Sequence
- Summarize

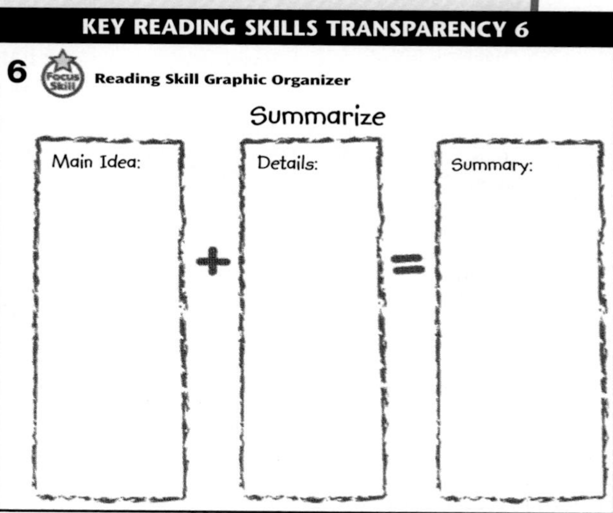
KEY READING SKILLS TRANSPARENCY 6
6
Reading Skill Graphic Organizer
Summarize
Main Idea:
Details:
Summary:

Life Skills

Life Skills are health-enhancing behaviors that can help students reduce risks to their health and safety.

Six Life Skills are reinforced throughout *Harcourt Health and Fitness*. The skill emphasized in this chapter is Communicate.

POSTER 7 COMMUNICATE
Communicate
LIFE SKILLS
The girl is calling 911 to get help in an emergency.
Steps for Communicating
1 Understand your audience.
2 Express your message in a clear, organized way.
3 Listen carefully, and answer any questions.
4 Gather feedback.
How well have YOU COMMUNICATED today?
POSTER 7

Building Good Character

Character education is an important aspect of health education. When children behave in ways that show good character, they promote the health and safety of themselves and others.

Six character traits are reinforced throughout *Harcourt Health and Fitness*. The trait emphasized in this chapter is Fairness.

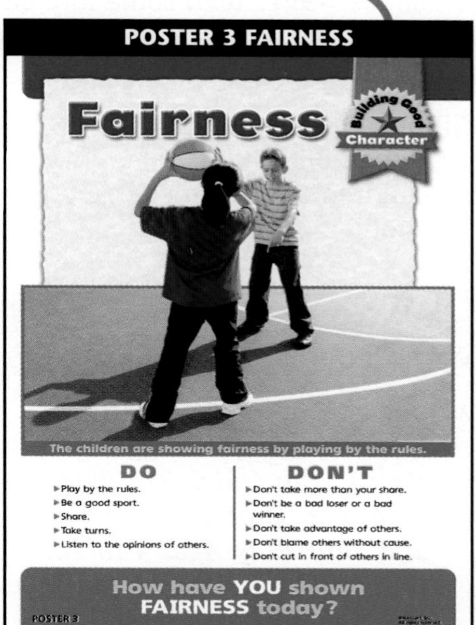
POSTER 3 FAIRNESS
Fairness
Building Good Character
The children are showing fairness by playing by the rules.
DO
Play by the rules.
Be a good sport.
Share.
Take turns.
Listen to the opinions of others.
DON'T
Don't take more than your share.
Don't be a bad loser or a bad winner.
Don't take advantage of others.
Don't blame others without cause.
Don't cut in front of others in line.
How have YOU shown FAIRNESS today?
POSTER 3

Resources

Coordinated School Health Program

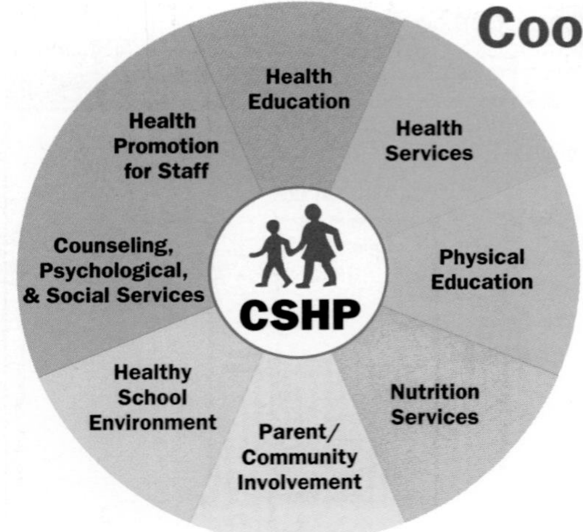

A Coordinated School Health Program endeavors to improve children's health and therefore their capacity to learn through the support of families, schools, and communities working together. The following information is provided to help classroom teachers be more aware of these resources.

Family/Community Involvement is one of the eight components of the Coordinated School Health Program. The **YMCA of the USA** offers support to parents with Building Strong Families summary, fact sheet, and parenting quiz. **www.ymca.net/**

Health Is Academic: A Guide to Coordinated School Health Programs, developed in collaboration with more than seventy national organizations and funded by the **CDC**, summarizes the concepts and the eight components of a Coordinated School Health Program. **www2.edc.org/MakingHealth Academic/**

The **American Red Cross** Homeland Security Advisory System lists recommendations for individuals, families, neighborhoods, schools, and businesses dealing with terrorism or unexpected events. Especially useful is instruction in how to help children cope with their response to disaster. **www.redcross.org/**

Other resources that support a Coordinated School Health Program:
- School-Home Connection
- Daily Physical Activity
- Daily Fitness Tips
- Activities: Home & Community
- Health Background: Webliography
- *Be Active! Resources for Physical Education*

Media Resources

Books for Students

Loredo, Betsy. ***Faraway Families***. Silver Moon Press, 1995. Tells how to keep distant relationships alive. EASY

Sanders, Pete, and Steve Myers. ***Divorce and Separation (What Do You Know About)***. Copper Beech Books, 1997. Text, some in comic book form, gives children insight. AVERAGE

Clifford, Eth. ***Family for Sale.*** Houghton Mifflin, 1996. Five children are left in charge of one another. ADVANCED

Books for Teachers and Families

Weinhaus, Evonne, and Karen Friedman. ***Stop Struggling with Your Child: Quick-Tip Parenting Solutions That Will Work for You and Your Kids Ages 4 to 12.*** HarperCollins, 1991. A practical and easy-to-implement guide.

Alexander, Shoshana. ***In Praise of Single Parents: Mothers and Fathers Embracing the Challenge.*** Houghton Mifflin, 1994. A look at the dynamic in the single-parent family.

Free and Inexpensive Materials

Sylvan Learning Center
Request their brochure *Seven Days of Activities for Family Learning Fun.*

U.S. Food and Drug Administration
Has consumer articles for families on topics of interest.

Federal Citizen Information Center
Ask for the poster "My History Is America's History" (#360K) on ways to find and preserve family history.

Mead Five-Star
Ask for "How to Have a Productive Teacher-Parent Conference" packet.

To access free and inexpensive resources on the Web, visit **www.harcourtschool.com/health/free**

Videos

When Your Mom and Dad Get Divorced. Sunburst Communications, 1992.

Everyday Etiquette. Rainbow Educational Media, 1996.

What's Right for Me: Making Good Decisions. Rainbow Educational Video, 1993.

These resources have been selected to meet a variety of individual needs. Please review all materials and websites prior to sharing them with students to ensure the content is appropriate for your class. Note that information, while correct at time of publication, is subject to change.

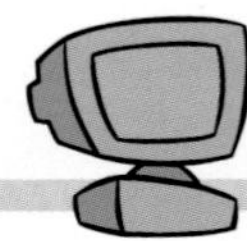

Visit **The Learning Site** for related links, activities, resources, and the health **Webliography.**

www.harcourtschool.com/health

Meeting Individual Needs

Below-Level

Tell students that SQ3R is a study strategy in which you survey the material, form questions, read, recite what was learned, and review information. As you name each step, have volunteers tell when it should be completed: before, during, or after reading.

Activities

- Draw a Picture, p. 284
- Family Caring Poster, p. 290
- Volunteers, p. 296

On-Level

If students are having a difficult time reading a selection, encourage them to continue reading until they get to the end. The meaning may become clearer when more information is available. Have them skim the selection before reading and reread as needed.

Activities

- Make a List, p. 284
- Peer Pressure, p. 290
- Helpers Wanted, p. 296

Challenge

To help students analyze content, have them make judgments on a health-related topic. Write scenarios on cards that could be considered right or wrong. Have students take turns pulling out a card, reading it aloud, and deciding if the action taken was, in their opinion, right or wrong.

Activities

- Write a Story, p. 284
- Acting Out Peer Pressure, p. 290
- Community Service Interview, p. 296

ESL/ELL

Reading Workshop

Provide students with graphic organizers to help them summarize ideas and concepts from the chapter. Model for students a possible main idea statement. Have students fill in the graphic organizer with three details to support that main idea.

Activities

- Language and Vocabulary, p. 289
- Comprehensible Input, p. 294
- Background and Experience, p. 295

Curriculum Integration

Use these topics to integrate health into your daily planning.

Integrated Language Arts/Reading Skills

- Who Am I?, p. 285
- Forms of Writing, p. 288
- More Ways to Communicate, p. 291

Math

- Time for Talking, p. 292

Physical Education

- Daily Fitness Tip, pp. 282, 288, 294
- Daily Physical Activity, p. 281

Social Studies

- Community Volunteer, p. 297

CHAPTER
11
Pages 280–301

CHAPTER SUMMARY

In this chapter, students

- ► learn that there are many types of families.
- ► find that family members' roles and responsibilities change over time.

Life Skills

Students learn about the importance of *communicating* with family members.

Building Good Character

Students learn about *fairness* and not taking advantage of other family members.

Consumer Health

Students learn to *make buying decisions* based on product comparisons.

Literature Springboard

Use the article "Family Ties to Your Health" to spark interest in the chapter topic. See the Read-Aloud Anthology on page RA-12 of this *Teacher Edition*.

Prereading Strategies

SCAN THE CHAPTER Have students preview the chapter content by scanning the titles, headings, pictures, tables, and graphs. Ask volunteers to speculate on what they will learn. Use their responses to determine their prior knowledge.

PREVIEW VOCABULARY Have students fold a sheet of paper in half lengthwise. In the left column, have them write definitions of the chapter vocabulary that they know. In the second column, they should define unfamiliar terms. Students may use dictionaries or the Glossary to find the definitions.

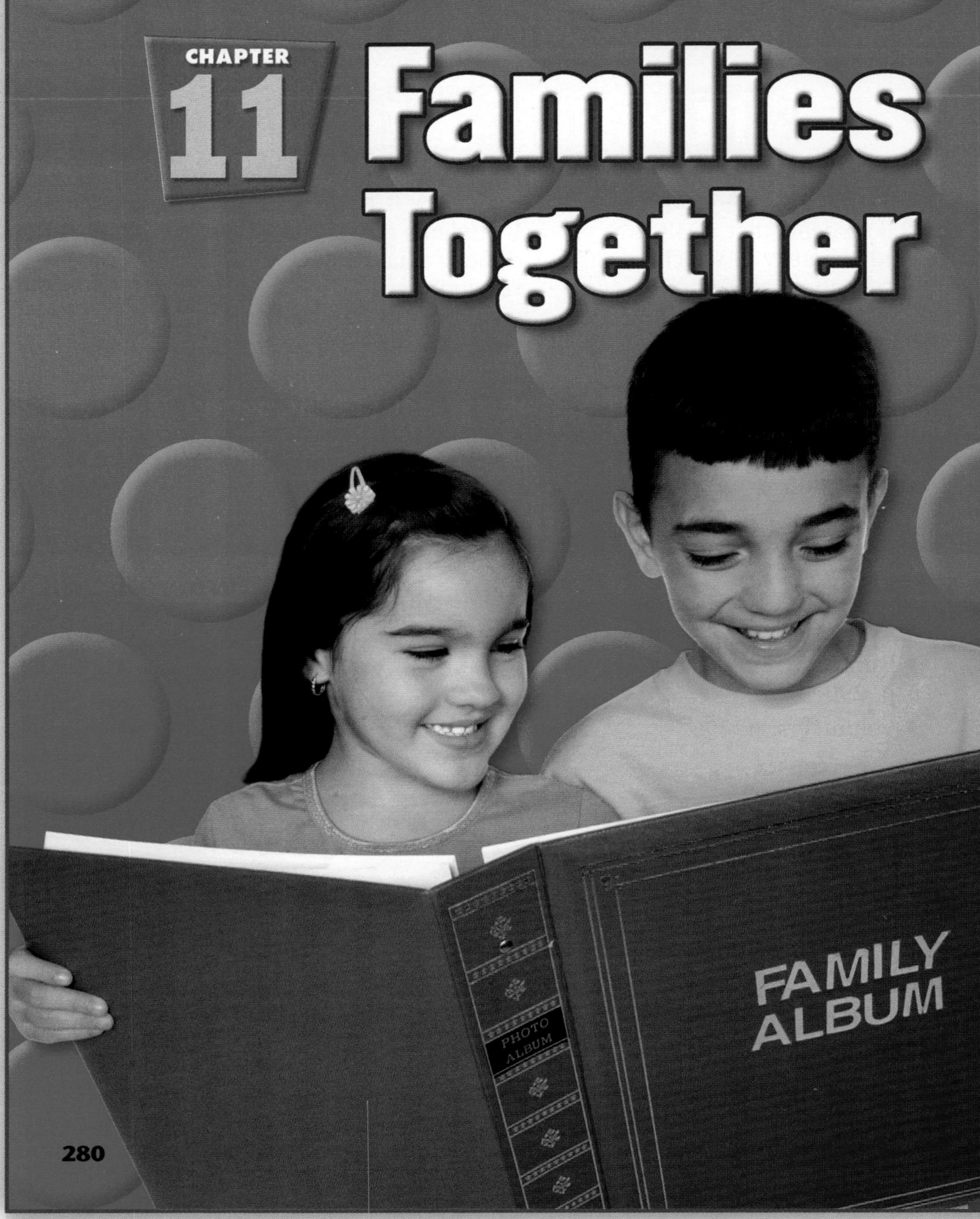

Reading Skill

SUMMARIZE To introduce or review this skill, have students use the Reading in Health Handbook, pp. 340–341. Teaching strategies and additional activities are also provided.

Students will have opportunities to practice and apply this skill throughout this chapter.

- Focus Skill Reading Mini-Lesson, p. 282
- Reading comprehension questions identified with the 
- *Activity Book* p. 53 (shown on p. 286)
- Lesson Summary and Review, pp. 286, 291, 298
- Chapter Review and Test Preparation, pp. 300–301

Reading Skill

SUMMARIZE A summary is a short statement that includes the main ideas and most important details in a passage. Use the Reading in Health Handbook on pages 340–341 and this graphic organizer to help you remember the main points as you read this chapter.

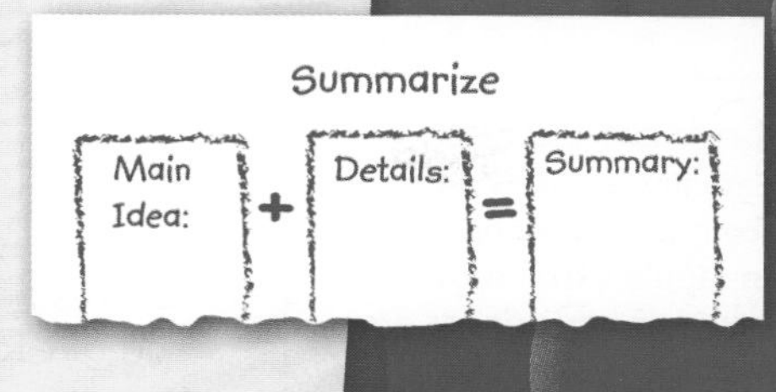

Health Graph

INTERPRET DATA Today many American adults are living in families with their own children, with children who are not related, without children, or with other relatives. Of 100 American families surveyed, how many were traditional married couples with their own children?

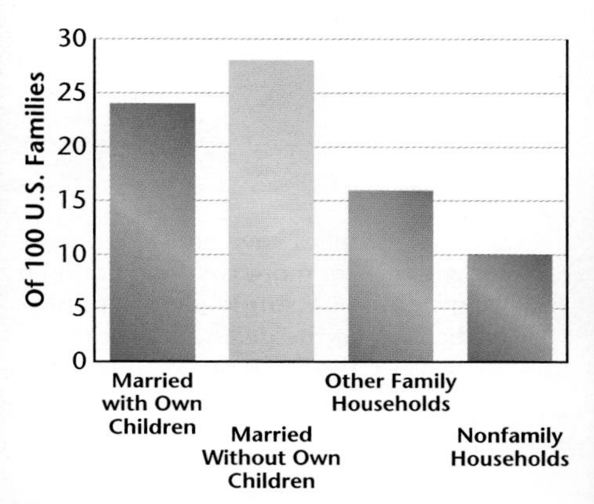

Daily Physical Activity

Find ways that you and your family can stay active for healthful living.

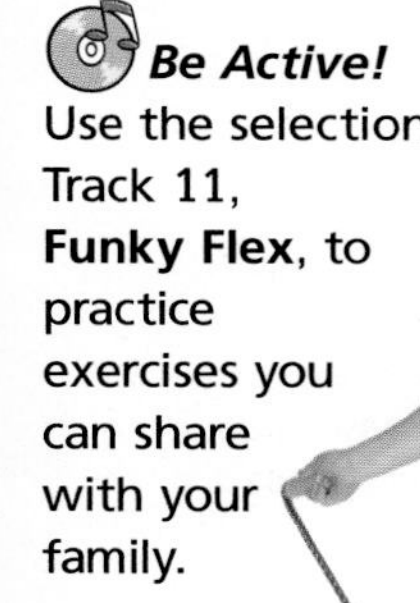

Be Active! Use the selection Track 11, **Funky Flex**, to practice exercises you can share with your family.

281

INTRODUCE THE CHAPTER

Health Graph

Interpret Data

Have students look at the graph and tell what information it contains. Invite volunteers to read each part of the graph (title, *x*-axis label, and *y*-axis label). Have students answer the Health Graph question. about 24 percent

What type of family was most common in America? married, without own children

What types of families do you think might be included in the Other category? Possible answer: families with adopted children, families with grandparents and grandchildren

Daily Physical Activity

Use *Be Active! Music for Daily Physical Activity* with the Instant Activity Cards to provide students with movement activities that can be done in limited space. Options for using these components are provided beginning on page TR2 in this *Teacher Edition.*

Chapter Project

What It Means to Be a Family (*Assessment Guide* p. 61)

ASSESS PRIOR KNOWLEDGE Use students' initial ideas for the project as a baseline assessment of their understanding of chapter concepts. Have students complete the project as they work through the chapter.

PERFORMANCE ASSESSMENT The project can be used for performance assessment. Use the Project Evaluation Sheet (rubric), *Assessment Guide* p. 72.

School-Home Connection

Distribute copies of the School-Home Connection (in English or Spanish). Have students take the page home to share with their families as you begin this chapter.

Follow Up Have volunteers share the results of their activities.

Supports the Coordinated School Health Program

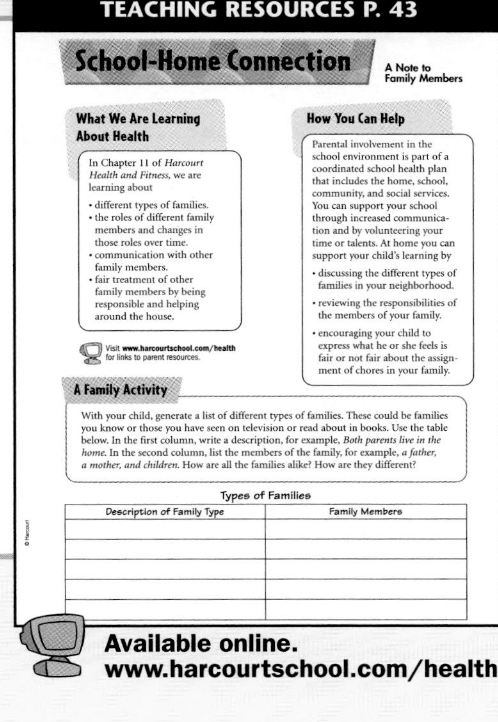

TEACHING RESOURCES P. 43

School-Home Connection

A Note to Family Members

What We Are Learning About Health

In Chapter 11 of *Harcourt Health and Fitness,* we are learning about

- different types of families.
- the roles of different family members and changes in those roles over time.
- communication with other family members.
- fair treatment of other family members by being responsible and helping around the house.

Visit **www.harcourtschool.com/health** for links to parent resources.

How You Can Help

Parental involvement in the school environment is part of a coordinated school health plan that includes the home, school, community, and social services. You can support your school through increased communication and by volunteering your time or talents. At home you can support your child's learning by

- discussing the different types of families in your neighborhood.
- reviewing the responsibilities of the members of your family.
- encouraging your child to express what he or she feels is fair or not fair about the assignment of chores in your family.

A Family Activity

With your child, generate a list of different types of families. These could be families you know or those you have seen on television or read about in books. Use the table below. In the first column, write a description, for example, *Both parents live in the home.* In the second column, list the members of the family, for example, *a father, a mother, and children.* How are all the families alike? How are they different?

Types of Families

Description of Family Type	Family Members

© Harcourt

Available online.
www.harcourtschool.com/health

LESSON 1
Pages 282–286

Objectives
- ► Describe the different types of families children live in.
- ► Identify the roles of family members.
- ► Explain how and why family members' roles change.
- ► Define and describe extended families.

When Minutes Count . . .
Assign the Quick Study, Lesson 1, Activity Book pp. 51–52 (shown on p. 283).

Program Resources
- ► Activity Book pp. 51–52, 53
- ► Transparency 6

Vocabulary
traditions p. 282,
nuclear family p. 282,
single-parent family p. 282,
blended family p. 283,
extended family p. 283

Daily Fitness Tip
Students are healthier and happier and do better in and out of school when they have strong families. They live healthful lives when they practice health-promoting behaviors, such as family walks, that they learn from their parents or other adults in the family.

For more guidelines about activities students can do, see *Be Active! Resources for Physical Education* p. 181.

1. MOTIVATE
Show students a variety of pictures of adults engaged in activities (reading, cooking, playing ball) with one or more nine-year-old children. Invite students to describe what's happening in each picture. Ask them who the adults might be. What relationship might the child and adult have if they are part of the same family? Encourage students to describe the different people who can be part of one family.

Families Meet Their Needs

Lesson Focus
Families are different from one another. It is in families that most people's basic needs are met.

Why Learn This?
Family life runs more smoothly when all family members find ways to respect and appreciate one another.

Vocabulary
traditions
nuclear family
single-parent family
blended family
extended family

Types of Families
Families can differ in many ways. Almost all families help meet the needs of their members. You get food, clothes, a place to sleep, and other things from your family. Family members take care of you and make sure you are safe. When you are afraid or sad, family members protect and help you. Most parents try hard to make a safe and loving home for their children.

Some families have **traditions** (trah•DIHSH•unz), or customs family members follow. Traditions are part of the way a family celebrates holidays and special occasions.

Some families have a mother, a father, and one or more children. This type of family is called a **nuclear family**.

Some families have only one parent with one or more children. Children may live in a **single-parent family** because of the death of a parent or because their parents are divorced.

282

Reading Skill

Mini-Lesson

SUMMARIZE Remind students that a summary is a brief statement that includes the main idea and important details in a text. Have them practice this skill by responding to the Focus Skill question on page 283. Have students draw and complete the graphic organizer as you model it on the transparency.

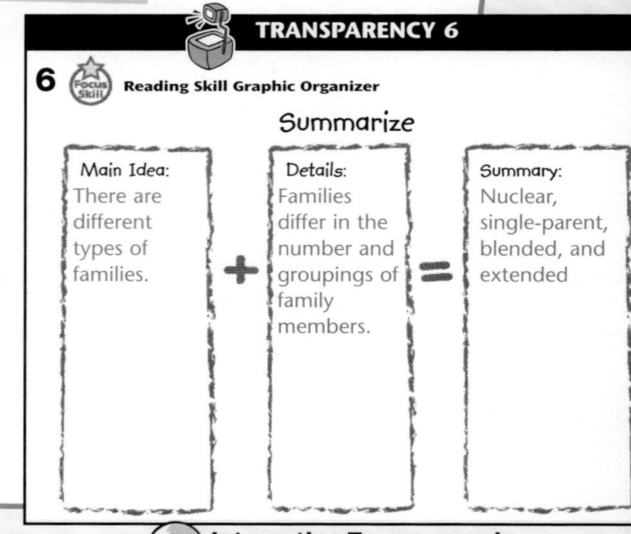

TRANSPARENCY 6

6 Reading Skill Graphic Organizer

Summarize

Main Idea:		Details:		Summary:
There are different types of families.	+	Families differ in the number and groupings of family members.	=	Nuclear, single-parent, blended, and extended

Interactive Transparencies available on CD-ROM.

Grandparents pass down traditions to their children and grandchildren. Traditions help keep family members close together.

A nuclear family includes two parents and their children. But some children do not grow up with both of their natural parents. Some children may grow up with only one parent, in a single-parent family.

Sometimes two single parents marry and form a blended family. Their children become part of the new family. The new parent is a stepparent, and the children become stepsisters or stepbrothers.

Other children live in extended families. These families may include other close relatives, such as grandparents, aunts, uncles, or cousins.

SUMMARIZE **What are the types of families?** nuclear, single-parent, blended, and extended

Did You Know?

Extended families may become more common as Americans live longer. Population projections for the year 2010 estimate that there will be about 131,000 Americans over the age of 100!

Quick Activity

Think About Families Look at the pictures on these pages. Make a table listing the ways these families are alike and different.

An **extended family** often has many members. Besides parents and children, there may be grandparents, cousins, uncles, and aunts.

When two single parents get married, they create a **blended family**. Each parent's child or children are now part of the blended family.

QUICK STUDY, ACTIVITY BOOK PP. 51–52

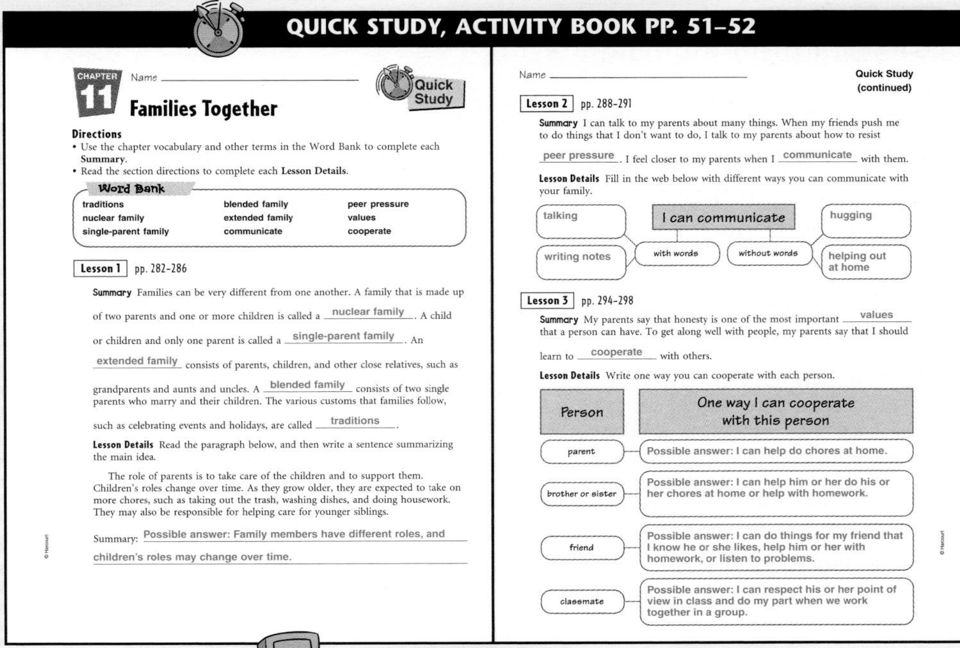

CHAPTER 11

Name ____________

Quick Study

Families Together

Directions

- Use the chapter vocabulary and other terms in the Word Bank to complete each **Summary**.
- Read the section directions to complete each **Lesson Details**.

Word Bank

traditions	blended family	peer pressure
nuclear family	extended family	values
single-parent family	communicate	cooperate

Lesson 1 pp. 282–286

Summary Families can be very different from one another. A family that is made up of two parents and one or more children is called a nuclear family. A child or children and only one parent is called a single-parent family. An extended family consists of parents, children, and other close relatives, such as grandparents and aunts and uncles. A blended family consists of two single parents who marry and their children. The various customs that families follow, such as celebrating events and holidays, are called traditions.

Lesson Details Read the paragraph below, and then write a sentence summarizing the main idea.

The role of parents is to take care of the children and to support them. Children's roles change over time. As they grow older, they are expected to take on more chores, such as taking out the trash, washing dishes, and doing housework. They may also be responsible for helping care for younger siblings.

Summary: Possible answer: Family members have different roles, and children's roles may change over time.

© Harcourt

Name ____________

Quick Study (continued)

Lesson 2 pp. 288–291

Summary I can talk to my parents about many things. When my friends push me to do things that I don't want to do, I talk to my parents about how to resist peer pressure. I feel closer to my parents when I communicate with them.

Lesson Details Fill in the web below with different ways you can communicate with your family.

I can communicate

with words: talking; writing notes

without words: hugging; helping out at home

Lesson 3 pp. 294–298

Summary My parents say that honesty is one of the most important values that a person can have. To get along well with people, my parents say that I should learn to cooperate with others.

Lesson Details Write one way you can cooperate with each person.

Person	One way I can cooperate with this person
parent	Possible answer: I can help do chores at home.
brother or sister	Possible answer: I can help him or her do his or her chores at home or help with homework.
friend	Possible answer: I can do things for my friend that I know he or she likes, help him or her with homework, or listen to problems.
classmate	Possible answer: I can respect his or her point of view in class and do my part when we work together in a group.

© Harcourt

Available online.
www.harcourtschool.com/health

2. TEACH

Interpret Visuals—Pictures

How are the pictured families the same? How are they different? Possible answer: All include some combination of adults and children. They differ in the number and identity of adults and the relationship of the adults to the children.

Quick Activity

Guide students to the idea that different kinds of families can serve the same functions for their members, including caring and support.

Content-Area Reading Support

Using Typographic Clues Direct students' attention to the words highlighted in yellow. Point out that, in most cases, what comes before in the sentence is a definition. Advise students to pay special attention to sentences that contain highlighted words because they usually give the meanings of the words.

Discuss

Critical Thinking **Why might children in a blended family have different last names?** Some may keep the last name of their natural father rather than take the stepfather's name.

Be sensitive to the fact that some students may have foster parents and that these students too are part of a family.

Health Background

Diverse Families The U.S. Census Bureau provides a great deal of statistical information about United States families, including living and housing conditions and financial status. These factors may affect the well-being of family members, although they do not necessarily determine it.

Source: *U.S. Bureau of the Census website*

For more background, visit the **Webliography** in Teacher Resources at **www.harcourtschool.com/health**
Keyword family life

TEACH *continued*

Interpret Visuals—Pictures

Have students look at the pictures on this page and describe what each shows. Invite volunteers to read the caption beneath each picture. Encourage students to talk about how a family changes when a new baby is born. Invite them to discuss why a new baby needs a lot of care and why caring for a new baby does not mean that parents are less interested in older children.

Discuss

Problem Solving What does saying that each family member has a role mean? How has your role in the family changed since you were little? Possible answer: A role is how you function, or act, in a family and what your responsibilities are. Students may describe having more freedom, more responsibilities, or more chores.

Critical Thinking How are showing respect and caring the same? Give examples. Possible answer: Both involve treating people well. An example is helping out at home without having to be told.

Activity

Caring Each student's paragraph should discuss at least one way of showing a family member that the student cares about him or her.

Discuss

Why is being a good listener when a member of your family talks a way of showing that you care? When you listen, you are showing that you think what he or she is saying is important. This shows that you think the family member is important, which shows that you care about him or her.

When your parents are busy, a grandparent may be able to help you. ▶

ACTIVITY

Building Good Character

Caring Emil's mother has had a baby and just returned home from the hospital. Write a paragraph describing ways Emil can help out and show that he cares.

The Roles of Family Members

All family members are important, including you. Each family member has a different role. A parent's main role is to support and take care of the children in the family. Your main role is to learn to be a responsible family member.

Family members' roles may change over time. When you were a baby, your family had to do everything for you. Now you are older and can do things to help the family. If there is a new baby in the family, you become an older brother or sister. You may then have to do chores or jobs to help out.

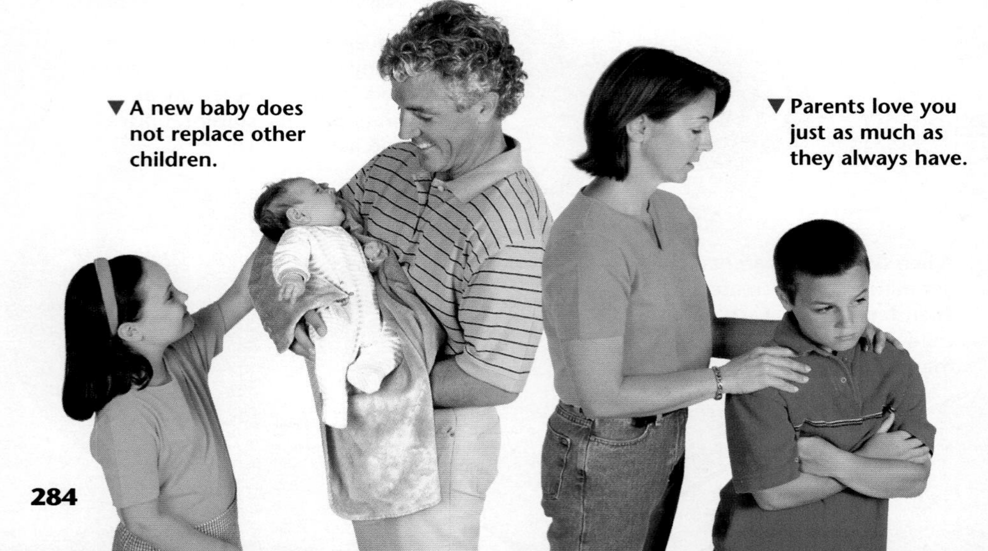

▼ A new baby does not replace other children.

▼ Parents love you just as much as they always have.

284

Meeting Individual Needs
Leveled Activities

BELOW-LEVEL Draw a Picture Have students draw a picture of one thing they do in their family—one role they play. The picture may show them doing homework, cleaning their room, or any other activity they do at home.

ON-LEVEL Make a List Have students list the things they can do to show that they respect and care for members of their family. Students may include things they do for one or more family members.

CHALLENGE Write a Story Have students write a story about the perfect older brother or sister. Their story should be written in the first person. It should describe how the perfect brother or sister, the main character, treats younger brothers or sisters, what the character does to help siblings, and how the character shows affection to them.

Members of a family also respect each other. When you respect family members, you value them for who they are. They value you, too.

Think about your family. What is special about each person in it? What roles does each person have? Do you help by taking out the trash? Does your older sister or brother help take care of a new baby?

Everyone's role in a family changes over time. Everyone gets older. Everyone has new things to do. Through it all, you and your family members can love, respect, and support one another in all you experience together.

COMPARE AND CONTRAST **What is your role in your family? How will it change as you get older? Make a chart to compare your role now with your role when you were younger.**

Health & Technology

Keeping in Touch It is sometimes difficult to keep a family together during outings. One way some families have found to keep in touch and to communicate is through the use of inexpensive shortwave radios. These pocket-size radios run on batteries and can act as a pager and as a walkie-talkie. Some of these devices have a range of up to 5 miles.

▼ Having fun together is one role everyone in a family can enjoy.

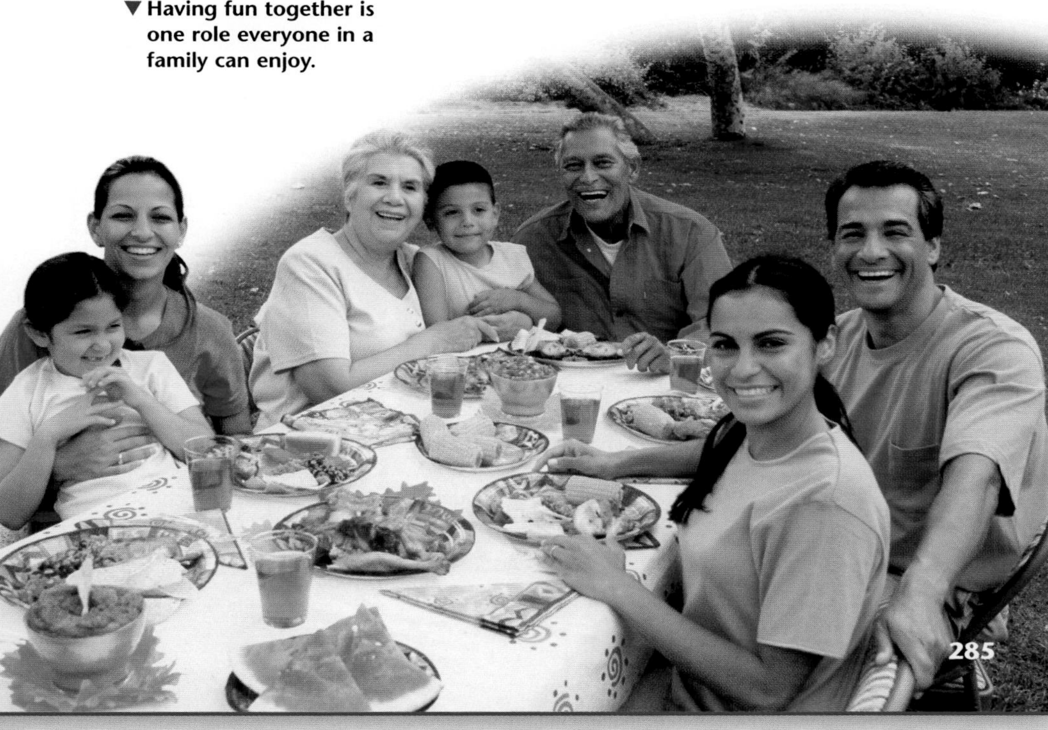

Discuss

Have students talk about their current roles in the family. Invite them to describe what they do and how they help out.

What is your role in your family now? How will it change as you get older?
Possible answer: caring for and helping siblings, doing chores; helping parents

Content-Area Reading Support

Using Paragraph Structure Direct attention to the first sentence in the second paragraph. Point out that this sentence states the topic of the paragraph: Everyone's role changes over time. The other sentences explain this topic sentence and give more details about it.

Urge students to pay particular attention to the first sentence of a paragraph because it may state the topic or the main idea of the paragraph. Point out that paragraphs in textbooks are often organized this way.

Language Arts

Who Am I? Write the identifications of family members (mother; brother, age 3; uncle, age 16; etc.) on separate index cards. Put the cards in a box. Invite a student to come to the front of the room, pick a card, and give clues about the person by describing the things he or she does in the family. The class should guess the role of the person in the family and the approximate age of the person.

Teacher Tip

Showing Sensitivity Children's roles in their families depend on many factors, including the family members with whom the children live and the family's socio-economic status. Accept student responses regarding their role now and what they think it will be in the future.

Interpret Visuals—Graphs

Tell students to use the graph title and labels to understand the graph topic. This graph shows the sizes of families with 5 or more people from the years 1970–2000.

3. WRAP UP

Lesson 1 Summary and Review

1. nuclear family; extended family; single-parent family; blended family; traditions
2. Possible answer: Most families have parents or other adults and children; people help and support each other; members respect and value one another for who they are.
3. Possible answer: Parent: take care of and support the family. Child: cared for by parents, helps out in the home. Older child: helps care for younger children.
4. Responses may include:

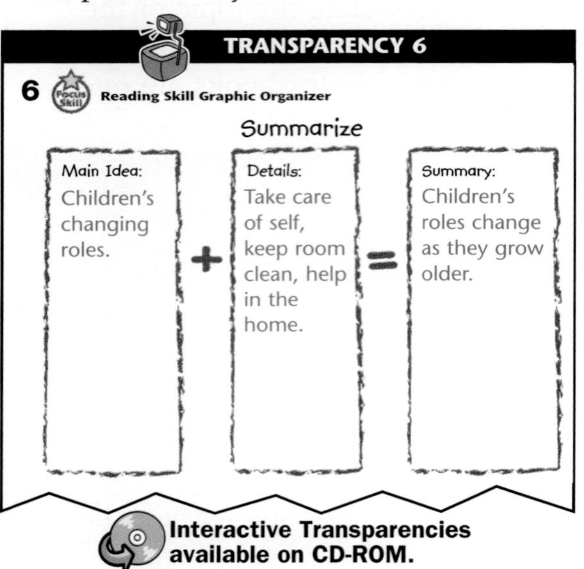

TRANSPARENCY 6
6
Reading Skill Graphic Organizer
Summarize
Main Idea:
Children's changing roles.
Details:
Take care of self, keep room clean, help in the home.
Summary:
Children's roles change as they grow older.

Interactive Transparencies available on CD-ROM.

5. Student responses may include increasing responsibility at each stage.

For **writing models** with examples, see *Teaching Resources* pp. 47–61. Rubrics are also provided.

When Minutes Count . . .

Quick Study Students can use *Activity Book* pages 51–52 (shown on p. 283) as they complete each lesson in this chapter.

Size of Households 1970 to 2000

Sampling of 100 Families: 0, 10, 20, 30

1970 1980 1990 2000

5 People or More

In what year was the number of families with five or more people the greatest?

Benefits of Extended Families

When you live in an extended family, you have grandparents or other adult relatives you can talk to. When you need encouragement and help with problems, they can help. Relatives can teach you things and tell you stories.

You may live with cousins who are close to your age. They can help with chores and be there to play with and share feelings with. Living in an extended family can be interesting and fun. Extended families can give you a lot of support.

CAUSE AND EFFECT **Make a list of reasons the roles of family members change. Write what the changes are.**

Lesson 1 Summary and Review

1. **Summarize with Vocabulary**
   Use vocabulary from the lesson to complete the statements.
   A _____ has a mother, father, and children. Some people live in an _____ with grandparents, aunts, or uncles. Others live with only one parent in a _____. Children who have stepparents live in a _____. No matter what kind of family you live in, you likely have _____ you follow, especially when you celebrate holidays.
2. **Critical Thinking** What do nearly all families have in common?
3. What roles do different family members have in a family?
4. **SUMMARIZE** Draw and complete this graphic organizer to show the roles a child has in a family over time.

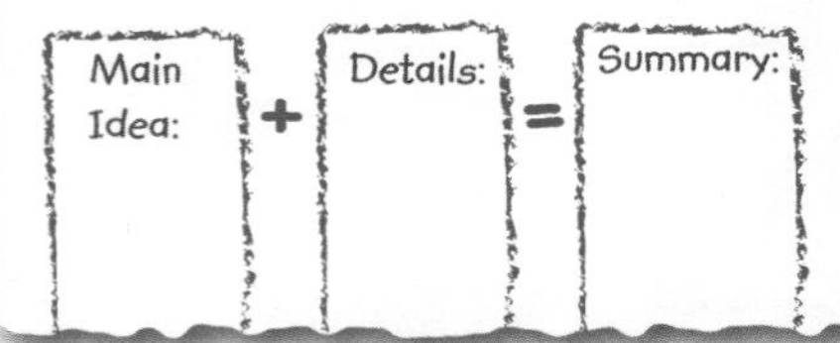

5. **Write to Inform—Description** 
   Think about how you will change over the years. What will you be like when you are older—in middle school, high school, and then college? Write how you think your role in your family will change at each new time in your life.

ACTIVITY BOOK P. 53

Name ______________

Reading Skill

Summarize

Families and Health

Your family can help you stay healthy in many ways. Parents or grandparents may tell you to brush your teeth every morning when you get up and every night before you go to bed. They may remind you to bathe or take a shower every day. When you do these things every day, you develop healthful habits. You will likely keep these habits your whole life.

The adults in your family may help keep you healthy in other ways. You may have a certain bedtime. Children often grumble about bedtimes. But going to bed on time helps keep you healthy. You may not know it, but getting enough sleep is very important for your health. Your body does not feel right—and it does not work right—when you're tired.

Parents and grandparents may help keep you healthy by having only healthful foods in the house. Junk foods usually have lots of fat and sugar. Fat and sugar are not good for your health. They tend to make you gain weight. Adults who care about their children's health keep healthful snacks in the house. They may stock up on fruits and vegetables—like carrots and celery—for you to snack on. The meals they cook for you don't have a lot of fat. When you get used to eating healthful foods as a child, you're likely to maintain a healthful diet when you grow up.

Getting along with family members also helps keep you healthy. When people get along, they're happier. They don't have stress. They can deal calmly with problems. Family members who get along help each other. Family members are healthier when they are calm and work well together.

Write two or three sentences that summarize the main points of this passage.

Possible answer: Adults in your family can help you practice and maintain healthful habits, such as keeping clean, getting enough sleep, and eating right. Getting along with family members also helps keep you healthy because you're calm and work well together.

© Harcourt

Available online. www.harcourtschool.com/health

Teacher Tip

Showing Sensitivity Try to obtain voluntary responses to discussion questions instead of calling on students. If students do not wish to speak about their families, do not press them to do so.

Fairness

Building Good Character

Not Taking Advantage of Others

Family members help one another in different ways. Children often help prepare meals, set the table, or wash the dishes after dinner.

When all family members are fair and help out cheerfully, everyone gets along. If family members try to avoid doing their share, arguments may start. A family member who doesn't help out is taking advantage of others in the family. He or she is not showing respect for other family members.

Sharing family responsibilities is fair to everyone. Here's how you can do your part.

- **Do your family chores cheerfully, knowing you are helping the people who care about you.**
- **Do your chores when they should be done, without having to be asked or reminded.**
- **If you see something that needs to be done, offer to do it. Don't hope someone else will do it instead.**
- **Don't avoid your chores by watching TV, playing video games, or going to a friend's house.**
- **If your brothers or sisters don't do their chores, don't fight with them. Explain to them that helping out shows respect for family members. Explain that avoiding or refusing to do their share takes advantage of others. Someone else will then have to do more than his or her share.**

Activity

Practice fairness by role-playing the following situation with your family. Your older brother is watching a show on TV instead of preparing dinner, which he is supposed to do. Your mom is due home soon. You know she'll be upset. What do you say to your brother? What can you do to help?

Using the Poster

Activity Suggest that students design and display a poster showing one or more ways that fairness makes family life easier and more enjoyable.

Display Poster 3 to remind students of ways to be fair to others. Students' posters can be displayed in the classroom, the school cafeteria, or other common areas.

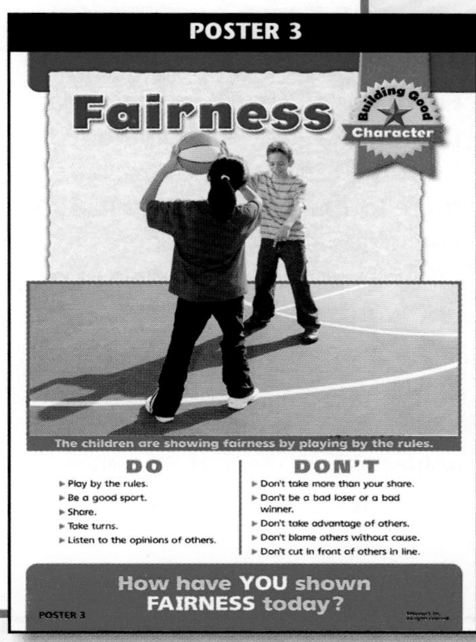

POSTER 3
Fairness
Building Good Character
The children are showing fairness by playing by the rules.
DO
Play by the rules.
Be a good sport.
Share.
Take turns.
Listen to the opinions of others.
DON'T
Don't take more than your share.
Don't be a bad loser or a bad winner.
Don't take advantage of others.
Don't blame others without cause.
Don't cut in front of others in line.
How have YOU shown FAIRNESS today?
POSTER 3

Building Good Character

Caring
Citizenship
Fairness
Respect
Responsibility
Trustworthiness

Objective

- Recognize the importance of fairness in the family and in life.

Program Resource

- Poster 3

BEFORE READING

Have students describe what it means to be fair. Invite them to describe situations in which they think fairness is important.

DISCUSS

Talk about why helping out in the family is fair to all family members. Invite students to tell how each point in the list is fair to other family members. **Why is avoiding doing your chores at home unfair to others in your family?** Others have to do them as well as their own.

ACTIVITY

Calmly remind your brother that he is supposed to make dinner. If he resists, tell him that Mom will be upset, and mention that making dinner will show respect for her.

Have students talk about why fairness is important in other situations.

- Your baby sister knocked over a vase of flowers. Do you pick it up or leave it for your parents to do?
- You brought snacks for each of your friends. One friend is late. Do you eat her snack or save it for her?
- Your partner did not do his part of the group project. What do you do?

LESSON 2
Pages 288–291

Objectives
- Explain why family members get along well when they communicate.
- Describe the many different ways to communicate with family members.
- Explain how communicating with your family helps you resist peer pressure.

When Minutes Count . . .
Assign the Quick Study, Lesson 2, Activity Book pp. 51–52 (shown on p. 283).

Program Resources
- Activity Book pp. 51–52
- Transparency 6
- Growth, Development, and Reproduction pp. 26–33

Daily Fitness Tip
Poor communication within a family can cause stress. Stress may lead to health problems, such as high blood pressure, as well as to social difficulties, such as having trouble getting along with others. Physical activity can help relieve stress. Getting the family involved in physical activities together can help reduce stress and allow family members to communicate. Family members who have little stress at home will generally live healthier lives.

For more about exercises that help with stress, see *Be Active! Resources for Physical Education* p. 157.

1. MOTIVATE
Remind students that there are ways to communicate without using words. Invite them to use gestures and expressions such as smiling and holding out the arms to show a friend that they are glad to see him or her.

Have students discuss how they feel when friends and family members talk to them. Encourage them to compare this to the way they feel when a friend or family member is cold and uncommunicative.

LESSON 2

Families Communicate

Lesson Focus
When family members communicate, they get along better and feel closer to one another.

Why Learn This?
Talking together helps family members understand one another and support one another when situations change.

Ways Families Communicate
When family members communicate, or talk with one another, they feel closer to one another.

Family members support one another. Try talking to your parents, brothers, and sisters about your feelings. Tell them about the good things that happen to you in school or with friends. Tell about things that make you sad or worried. Often, a family member can help you solve a problem.

For example, talk with your parents about your report card. Maybe you did not do as well as you had hoped in one subject. Your parents can work with you to help you do better.

Did You Know?
In one recent year, about 2.6 million children between the ages of 10 and 14 moved. Almost two-thirds of those moved within the same county.

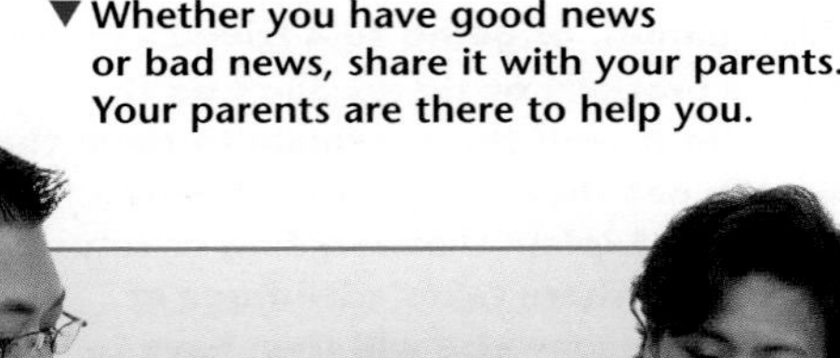

▼ Whether you have good news or bad news, share it with your parents. Your parents are there to help you.

288

Language Arts
Forms of Writing Explain that the form of a letter is different from the form of a note. A letter is more formal and has a salutation and a signature line. A note is informal and may include just a few words or phrases.

Have students write both a letter and a note telling a family member something. Invite volunteers to share their letters and notes with the class.

Teacher Tip
Personal, Emotional Issues
Some students may be thinking about very personal and emotional issues as they read this chapter. Discussions about communicating problems with parents or other adults should be kept general, unless students volunteer to talk about a personal issue.

When you share your problems and feelings with your parents, you are communicating with them. You are showing them that you love and trust them.

Show family members you appreciate them. Thanking a family member helps you make him or her feel appreciated.

Sometimes family members are very busy and have little time together. You can share your feelings or your news by writing notes or letters.

Actions are also a form of communication. Doing a favor for a family member shows that you care. The way you act toward others affects the way they act toward you. When you are nice to family members, you encourage them to be nice to you. That helps the whole family.

Quick Activity

Write a Letter Write a letter to someone in your family. In your letter, describe something special that has happened in school.

MAIN IDEA AND DETAILS Why is communication important in families? List some ways family members communicate.

It helps everyone feel closer; ways to communicate with family members: speak with them; actions, such as hugs; write to them (notes, letters).

2. TEACH

Interpret Visuals—Pictures

Have students look carefully at the picture on page 288.

What kind of news do you think the child is telling? How are the parents reacting to the news? The child is giving news he thinks is bad. The parents' reaction is supportive and understanding.

Content-Area Reading Support

Using Signal Words Direct students' attention to the beginning of the third paragraph on page 288. Explain that following the words *For example* are one or more examples of the subject being discussed. Invite students to use this phrase in the following: "I like to play games. For example, . . . "

Discuss

Problem Solving If your parent seems tired and grumpy after a hard day at work, what can you do to show that you care about him or her? Possible answer: offer a snack, make dinner, do a chore, hug him or her

Quick Activity

Letters should be friendly and describe a special school experience.

ESL/ELL Support

LANGUAGE AND VOCABULARY English spelling can be very confusing. Help students learn the difference between *form* and *forum*. Point out the word *form* in the last paragraph. Write it and the word *forum* on the board, and go over the definitions of both.

Beginning Have students write both words.

Intermediate Have students write sentences using each word.

Advanced Have students write a short story in which a person uses some form of communication as a forum for discussion.

Health Background

Parents and Work Parents of children under 18 comprise about 37 percent of the workforce. Most work full time and work an average of 36 minutes more per week than childless workers. Full-time worker parents now work six more 40-hour weeks per year than in the 1960s. When both parents work, they put in 3,450 hours a year at work, compared with 2,850 in 1965.

Source: *Employment Policy Foundation & Ohio State University website*

For more background, visit the **Webliography** in Teacher Resources at **www.harcourtschool.com/health**
Keyword family life

TEACH *continued*

Discuss

Help students understand peer pressure. Ask them to give examples of peer pressure they've experienced.

Critical Thinking Why are parents and other adults likely to have good advice about how to resist peer pressure? Possible answer: They've likely experienced it themselves.

Consumer Activity

Invite students to discuss times they've felt pressured by friends to buy things they don't want or need and can't afford. Suggest that they ask their parents or another trusted adult what to tell friends when they are pressuring them to buy something.

Critical Thinking How would you ask your parent to help you respond to a friend who wants you to spend money on something silly? Possible answer: "Mom, I want to tell my friend that I don't want to buy something, but I'm embarrassed and don't know how. What should I say?"

Problem Solving What could you say to a friend who asks you to buy something you don't want or can't afford? Possible answer: I want to spend the money on something more important to me.

Consumer Activity

Make Buying Decisions Sometimes your peers may pressure you into buying something you don't really need or want. How can you get advice from your family members that will help you resist peer pressure?

Family Relationships

In Chapter 8 you learned that *peer pressure* is the strong influence someone your own age can have on you. Peer pressure can sometimes be negative and hard to resist. One way to deal with peer pressure is to ask for advice from a parent, a grandparent, or another adult. He or she may have good advice about how you can resist peer pressure.

Sometimes what your friends want you to do may not be what your family thinks is right. As a family member, you need to consider your family's wishes and rules.

If you have a problem or are unsure about something, talk with your parents. They care about you and can give you good advice you can trust.

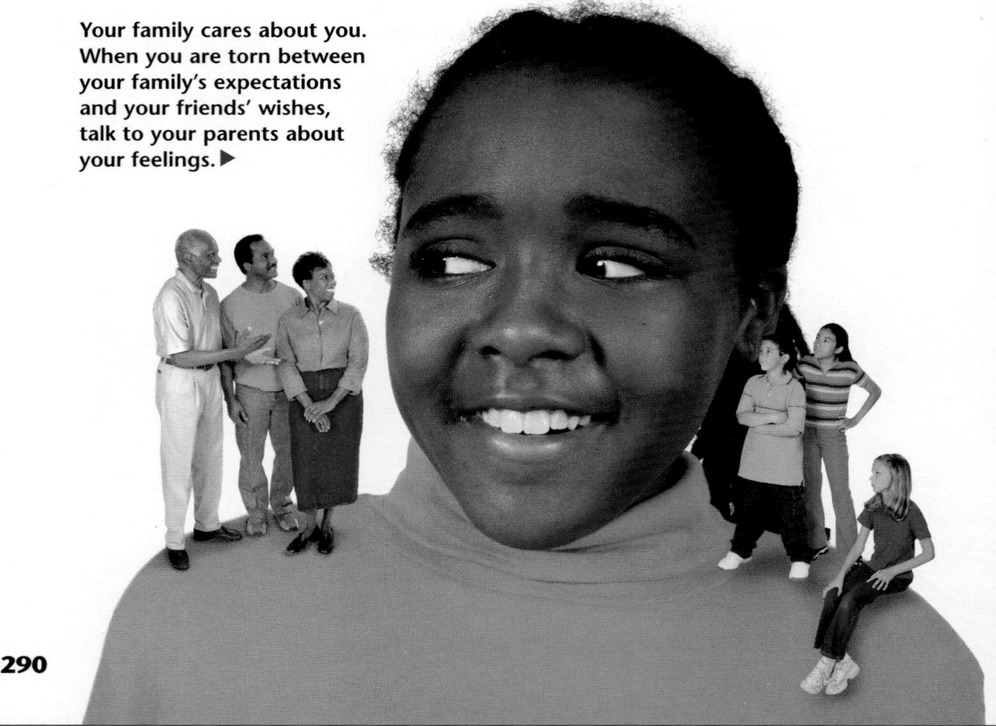

Your family cares about you. When you are torn between your family's expectations and your friends' wishes, talk to your parents about your feelings. ▶

290

Meeting Individual Needs
Leveled Activities

BELOW-LEVEL Family Caring Poster Have students create a poster or picture in which they illustrate a way to show family members that they care about them.

ON-LEVEL Peer Pressure Have students create a two-column list about peer pressure. In the first column, they list what they've been pressured to do by their peers. In the second column, they write how they resisted the pressure.

CHALLENGE Acting Out Peer Pressure Have students write a one-act play in which a child asks a parent how to deal with an incident of peer pressure. Students' plays should include setting, stage directions, and realistic dialogue. Students may enact their plays for the class.

What should you do when a family member does something that makes you angry? Take a deep breath. Try to relax and stay calm. Learning to control your anger can be very difficult, and it takes time.

Try talking or writing a note to the person. Communicating your feelings may help prevent an argument. Tell your family member how you feel. This shows that you trust him or her and want to get along.

If you keep cool and communicate honestly with family members, you'll settle conflicts more easily. Afterward, do a special favor for a member of your family to show that you care.

SEQUENCE **What steps would you take to resolve the conflict when a family member has made you angry? Give the steps in order.**

Ways Families Communicate

- **Express your feelings to family members.**
- **Show you care.**
- **Do something special.**
- **Write letters or notes.**
- **Plan activities together.**

Lesson 2 Summary and Review

1. **Summarize with Vocabulary** Use terms from this lesson to complete the statements.

   You should resist _____ when it may lead to do something you don't want to do. There are many ways to _____, including talking, writing notes, and doing things together.

2. **Critical Thinking** How can you show family members that you appreciate them?

3. What are three ways you can communicate your feelings to members of your family?

4. **SUMMARIZE** Draw and complete this graphic organizer to show ways being a good listener helps you improve communication among the members of your family.

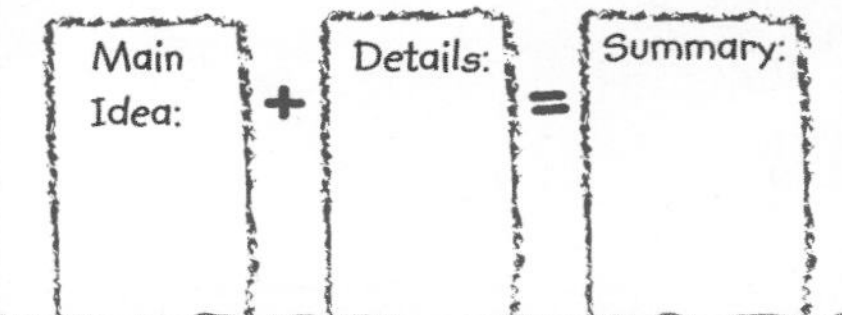

5. **Write to Inform—How-To** Write a paragraph to a younger sister or brother. Tell her or him what to do to practice controlling anger, both with friends and with family members.

First, I would relax to control my anger. Then, I would talk with the family member to communicate my feelings. I would explain how I felt, showing that I want to get along. Later, I might do a favor for that person to show that I care.

Teacher Tip

Child Abuse Lessons that provide strategies for teaching about child abuse, including sexual exploitation, are provided on pages TR30–TR33. Lessons are also provided in the optional component *Growth, Development, and Reproduction,* pp. 26–33. Use these lessons and components in compliance with state and local guidelines.

Language Arts

More Ways to Communicate Have students read the list of Ways Families Communicate on this page. Invite them to suggest other ways that family members can communicate. Write their suggestions on the board.

3. WRAP UP

Lesson 2 Summary and Review

1. peer pressure; communicate
2. thank the person; do a special favor; share your feelings
3. talk, leave notes or write letters, or use actions such as hugs
4. Responses may include:

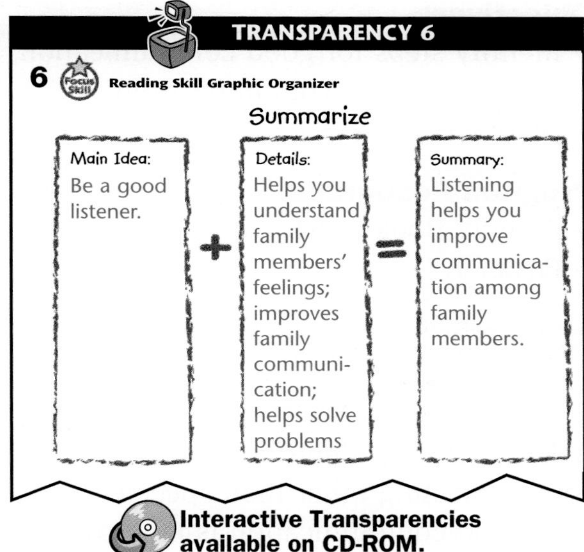

TRANSPARENCY 6
6
Focus Skill
Reading Skill Graphic Organizer
Summarize
Main Idea:
Be a good listener.
+
Details:
Helps you understand family members' feelings; improves family communication; helps solve problems
=
Summary:
Listening helps you improve communication among family members.
Interactive Transparencies available on CD-ROM.

5. The paragraph should suggest relaxing, taking a deep breath, talking calmly, and explaining feelings.

For **writing models** with examples, see *Teaching Resources* pp. 47–61. Rubrics are also provided.

When Minutes Count . . .

Quick Study Students can use *Activity Book* pages 51–52 (shown on p. 283) as they complete each lesson in this chapter.

Growth, Development, and Reproduction An optional lesson about the reproductive systems is provided in this supplement on pp. 26–33. Use this component in compliance with state and local guidelines.

Life Skills

Communicate
Make Responsible Decisions
Manage Stress
Refuse
Resolve Conflicts
Set Goals

Objectives

- Identify steps for good communication.
- Practice solving communication problems.

Program Resources

- Activity Book p. 54
- Poster 7

1. MOTIVATE

Ask students to identify ways of communicating other than speech. Ask why good communication is important in getting along with others. Explain that people get along better when they communicate well with one another. Invite students to discuss what happens when family members or friends don't share their feelings or discuss their problems.

2. TEACH

Have students read the introductory paragraph.

Step 1

Who is Katrina's audience? Why is it important to know your audience? Her audience is her family. The message needs to be targeted to the audience.

Step 2

Why is it important for Katrina to be clear about what the problem is? If she's clear, her family will understand the problem, and it will be easier to solve.

COMMUNICATE

With Your Family

Family members need to respect one another. Working on communication skills will help you get along with your family. Using the steps for **Communicating** will help you improve your skills.

Katrina and her new friend call each other every evening. Katrina's family has put a ten-minute limit on phone conversations. Katrina doesn't think this new rule is fair. What should she do?

1 Understand your audience.

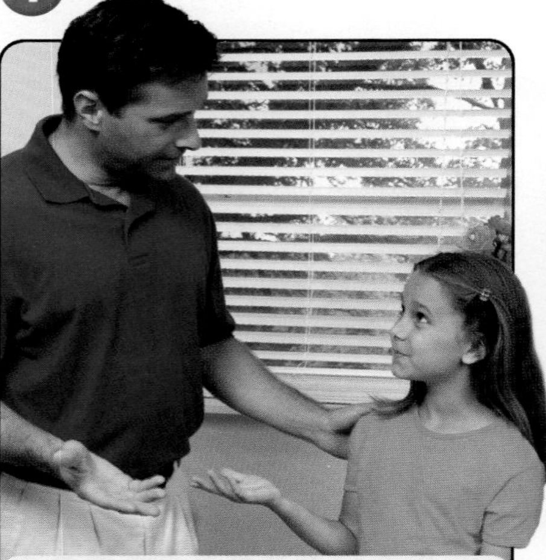

Katrina knows that she needs to talk to the whole family about the phone rules. She asks her dad to plan a family meeting.

2 Give a clear message.

Katrina tells her family that she and her new friend don't have enough time to talk at school. She explains that ten minutes isn't long enough to say everything she wants to say.

292

Math

Time for Talking Katrina and her brother each use the phone for 10 minutes every evening. Katrina's mother calls Katrina's grandmother and aunt every night and speaks to each of them for 15 minutes. Katrina's father calls Katrina's grandfather each night and speaks for 10 minutes. How many minutes does Katrina's family spend on the telephone each evening? 60 minutes, or 1 hour

ACTIVITY BOOK P. 54

Name ______________________

Life Skill
Communicate

Steps for Communicating

1. Understand your audience.
2. Give a clear message.
3. Listen carefully, and answer any questions.
4. Gather feedback.

Use the steps to help these students communicate with their families.

A. At 7:00 each evening, Jamie likes to watch his favorite TV program. His brother, who is one year older than Jamie, has just discovered a program on another channel that he wants to watch at 7:00. Lately, Jamie and his brother have been arguing over who gets to watch TV at 7:00.

- What should Jamie do to solve this problem?

Possible answer: Jamie should calmly talk to his brother to work out different days on which each can watch his program. If this doesn't work, Jamie may ask a parent to have a meeting at which a solution, involving switching days when each boy can watch the TV, is found.

B. Linda shares a room with her older sister, Maggie. Linda likes to keep her things in good order. Maggie's things are usually lying around all over the room. When Mom comes into the room, she gets angry about the mess. If Linda is there, Mom takes her anger out on Linda, telling her to clean up the room. Linda tries to tell Mom that the mess is not hers, that it's Maggie's. But her mother is often too angry to listen. "Just clean up this mess," her mother says, and walks out of the room. Linda thinks it's not fair that she is blamed for Maggie's mess.

- What should Linda do?

Possible answer: First, Linda should talk to Maggie about keeping the room neater. If that doesn't work, she should ask her mother for a quiet meeting to explain the situation. She may ask her mother to talk to Maggie to get her to keep the room neater.

© Harcourt

Available online.
www.harcourtschool.com/health

3 Listen carefully, and answer any questions.

"If the phone is always busy, we might miss important calls," Katrina's mom explains. "I need to use the phone to plan my activities, too," says her brother.

4 Gather feedback.

Katrina realizes that everyone else feels the rule is fair, so she agrees to the ten-minute limit. Then the family thinks of other ways Katrina can spend more time with her friend.

Problem Solving

Matt shares a room with his brother Dan. Sometimes Dan goes to play with friends and leaves the room in a mess. Matt finds it hard to do his homework when the room is a mess. He is really upset.

Use the steps for **Communicating** to help Matt solve his problem. What would you suggest Matt do to help Dan be more responsible?

Using the Poster

Activity Suggest that students use the communication steps shown in the poster to create a dialogue for any family situation or rule problem they want to write about. Students should illustrate the steps with pictures and use parts of the dialogue as captions below each picture.

Display students' posters in the classroom.

POSTER 7

Communicate

The girl is calling 911 to get help in an emergency.

Steps for Communicating

1. Understand your audience.
2. Express your message in a clear, organized way.
3. Listen carefully, and answer any questions.
4. Gather feedback.

How well have YOU COMMUNICATED today?

Step 3

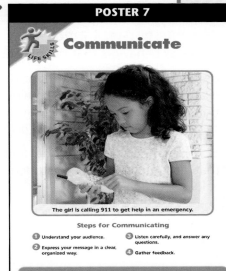

What is likely to happen if Katrina does not listen to her family? She'll get angry and not recognize other points of view. The problem won't be solved.

Do you think that Katrina's mother and brother gave her a reasonable response? Why? Possible answer: It was reasonable; they have a right to use the phone, too.

Building Good Character

Respect Ask students how Katrina's decision to talk to her whole family about the phone rules shows that she respects all family members. Possible answer: It shows that she understands that they have needs that she must honor, just as they should honor her needs.

Step 4

How did Katrina react to the feedback she got from her family? She understood and respected it.

How else could she spend more time with her friend? Possible answer: They could get together after school and over the weekend.

3. WRAP UP

Problem Solving

Ask students to describe steps in problem solving. Answers should reflect the steps for communicating with family members. Matt should ask Dan if he can speak with him. Matt should clearly explain the problem, listen to Dan's explanation, and think about it. Matt then might volunteer to help Dan keep the room clean. Or Matt might explain that he does his part to keep the room clean out of respect for Dan, so Dan should show him respect in return.

LESSON 3
Pages 294–298

Objectives
- ► Identify the values learned from the family and how they are taught.
- ► Explain why cooperation is important in families.
- ► Describe some family rules, and explain why they are important.

When Minutes Count . . .
Assign the Quick Study, Lesson 3, Activity Book pp. 51–52 (shown on p. 283).

Program Resources
- ► Activity Book pp. 51–52, 55
- ► Transparency 6

Vocabulary
values p. 294, **cooperate** p. 296

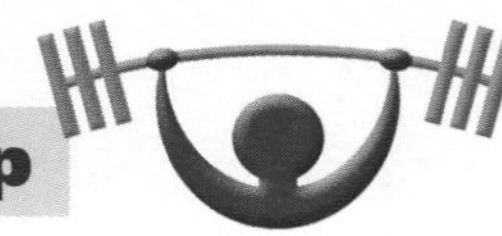

Daily Fitness Tip
Many of the values a child learns from his or her family involve developing healthful habits. It is from the family that most children learn habits of cleanliness, good hygiene, getting adequate sleep, and even the importance of exercise. When reinforced in the family, these values and habits help a child maintain good health throughout life.

For more about the value of exercise and health, see *Be Active! Resources for Physical Education* p. 151.

1. MOTIVATE
Ask students to identify similarities among healthful environments can be promoted in homes. Tell students that everyone has special talents, abilities, and characteristics. Family members often pass these special gifts on to others in the family. Invite volunteers to describe some things they have learned from members of their families—both special things and everyday things.

LESSON 3

Families Work Together

Lesson Focus
Family members learn important values when they cooperate and respect and care for each other.

Why Learn This?
What you learn from your family can help you with all your relationships.

Vocabulary
values
cooperate

How You Learn from Your Family
Family members care about you and teach you values (VAL•yooz). **Values** are strong beliefs about how people should behave and live.

Families pass down values from earlier generations (jen•er•AY•shunz), family members who came before. These include parents, grandparents, and great-grandparents.

Family members may teach you to be honest, kind, generous, and helpful. They may teach you to do things that help keep you safe and healthy. These values are shared by people everywhere.

When you are trustworthy, people know that you are honest and truthful.

When you treat people fairly, you show that you value them and that you know right from wrong.

A caring person understands other people and offers to help them whenever possible.

ESL/ELL Support
COMPREHENSIBLE INPUT Help students understand the concept of values as behaviors that people admire in others.

Beginning Provide pictures of people engaged in valued behavior, for example, petting an animal, helping an older person or a younger sibling, doing a chore at home. Have students say a word that describes the value shown, for example, *kindness*, *helping*.

Intermediate Have students look through magazines to find pictures that illustrate values. Have students describe the scene and the value or values shown.

Advanced Have students act out a skit that illustrates one value of their choice. They may improvise or write the dialogue they use in the skit.

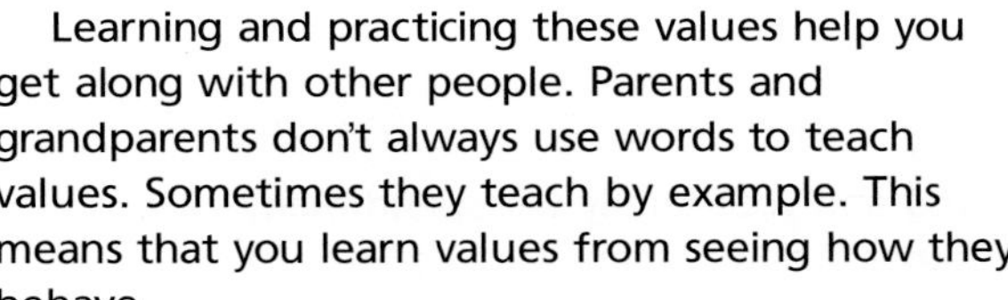

Helping people is one way of showing respect.

Everyone in a family should take some responsibility for helping out with family chores.

Being a good citizen means respecting your country.

Learning and practicing these values help you get along with other people. Parents and grandparents don't always use words to teach values. Sometimes they teach by example. This means that you learn values from seeing how they behave.

If your grandparents are always honest and fair, you will probably grow up to be that way. If your mother is always kind to others, you will learn the value of kindness. If your father works hard to do a job well, you could learn to take pride in doing your best.

Parents teach children to be responsible family members. Your family can teach you many important and helpful values.

MAIN IDEA AND DETAILS **What does it mean to teach by example? Describe some values that you can learn this way.**

ACTIVITY

Life Skills

Resolve Conflict

Suppose you and your family are planning to spend a day together. You disagree on what to do. What steps can you take to help your family choose an activity that satisfies everyone? For help, see the steps to Resolve Conflicts on pages 146–147.

To teach by example means teaching others to act a certain way by acting that way yourself. A parent who treats a child with kindness is teaching that child by example to be kind.

ESL/ELL Support

BACKGROUND AND EXPERIENCE Encourage students to share values that have been passed down from earlier generations.

Beginning Ask students if their parents or grandparents have talked to them about each of the values named in the pictures on these pages. Obtain a *yes* or *no* answer for each value.

Intermediate Ask students to name a value that has been passed down in the family and the family member from whom they learned the value.

Advanced Ask students to name a value that has come down through the family and tell a story about learning that value from a family member.

2. TEACH

Interpret Visuals—Pictures

Have students give examples from their own lives of each value pictured on this page.

Content-Area Reading Support

Using Typographic Clues Direct attention to the word highlighted in yellow on page 294. Point out that a definition follows the highlighted word. Advise students to pay attention to highlighted words because the meaning usually follows.

Activity

Resolve Conflicts Make a list of everyone's suggestions; add other activities; select an activity that all will enjoy. This shows that you want everyone to have a good time.

Discuss

Critical Thinking **What does it mean to teach by example? What values can you learn this way?** It means showing how to act by acting that way yourself, for example, being kind. **Why are many values passed from earlier generations still useful today?** Because they're about character. Good qualities never go out of date.

Health Background

Traditional Values Even though industrialization and globalization have affected human values, many people retain their traditional values. About 90 percent of respondents claimed strong values and taught their children obedience and respect. About 75 percent valued citizenship and respect for others. More than half thought trust was important, though some are increasingly careful about whom they trust.

Source: *World Values Survey (Univ. of Michigan)*

For more background, visit the **Webliography** in Teacher Resources at **www.harcourtschool.com/health** **Keyword** family life

TEACH *continued*

Interpret Visuals—Pictures

Have students describe how they think the family members feel as they work together on the project shown in the picture on this page.

In what ways can working with your family be fun? Possible answer: working on something that interests everyone, working willingly and with a sense of humor

Discuss

How does cooperating with your classmates make school more enjoyable? Possible answer: It makes things go smoothly, so you are relaxed and can enjoy things more.

Critical Thinking Are cooperation and dependability related? Can you have one without the other? Possible answer: The two are related; it is not possible to have one without the other.

Problem Solving What might you do if you wanted to help out in a community center but had no transportation to get there? Possible answers: Ask parents for a ride or for bus fare; carpool with other students' parents

In what ways can you help others in your community? How can you help on your own or with family members? Possible answer: volunteer at an after-school center or reading program, visit people at a senior center, or volunteer at an animal shelter

▲ Helping with projects is a way families cooperate and have fun.

Families can work together to help others in the community.▼

Personal Health Plan ▶

Real-Life Situation
Suppose you have to study for a test, practice for a school team game, and write a school report—all in two days.

Real-Life Plan
Write a step-by-step plan that describes how you would handle all this. Use the steps for Managing Stress on pages 10–11.

How Families Work Together

You and your family will spend many years together. It's important for everyone in the family to cooperate with each other. When you **cooperate** (koh•AHP•er•ayt) with others, you work with them and help them. For example, if you do your chores, you are cooperating with your family. You are also showing them that they can depend on you.

Families cooperate in many ways. You may work together on projects to make your home look better. Together, you may help others in your community. Even having fun together is a way of cooperating. Everyone has a good time when all family members try to get along.

Meeting Individual Needs
Leveled Activities

BELOW-LEVEL Volunteers Have students find pictures in magazines or newspapers of young people volunteering in the community.

ON-LEVEL Helpers Wanted Have students think of a place that needs volunteers. Have students create an ad that this organization might put in the paper to attract community volunteers. The ad should describe what the volunteers would do and tell why the work is important.

CHALLENGE Community Service Interview Have students find one community group that uses and needs volunteers, and conduct a phone interview with the volunteer coordinator. Students should prepare interview questions ahead of time, and then write up the interview as if it were an article in a local newspaper.

When you all cooperate, doing what needs to be done can be fun. ▼

▲ Playing together is another way a family can spend time together.

Quick Activity

Plan Family Fun Make a list of activities you and your family could do together. Include activities that you think each person in your family could do and would enjoy.

When you cooperate, you show family members you respect them. For example, when you ask your brother if you may borrow his bike, you are showing him respect.

Families that cooperate have less conflict and stress. So family members are happier and healthier. When a conflict arises, family members can talk it over and solve the problem more easily.

If you have a problem, share your feelings with your parents. They have lots of life experience and can help with your problem.

SUMMARIZE What are three ways family members can cooperate?

Three ways families can cooperate are by doing chores at home, doing home projects together, and helping together in the community.

Personal Health Plan

Plans should show the following:

- Student understands that tasks should be done in order.
- Student understands that tasks should be done one at a time and completed before going on to the next task.
- Student understands how much time each activity takes.
- Students may also request help with chores or for quiet time at home.

Discuss

How does making a good plan ahead of time help reduce stress? A good plan helps you to do tasks in an orderly way, making it more likely you'll get everything accomplished.

Quick Activity

Student lists should include activities that each family member would enjoy as well as activities that everyone is likely to enjoy together. Students should obtain input from family members and choose an activity all agree on.

Problem Solving **How would you let your family know how you're feeling and what you're doing? How would you explain how they can cooperate with you to help you?** Possible answer: Talk with them at a quiet time at home; be honest and unashamed about what you feel and need; understand that they probably feel good when you turn to them for help.

What are three ways family members can cooperate? Possible answer: Family members can cooperate by doing chores at home, working on projects together, and helping together in the community.

Social Studies

Community Volunteering Help students recognize that many people need some kind of help from the community at one time or another. Have students discuss how volunteering brings people in the community together the same way helping out at home brings family members closer. Discuss the relationship between helping out in the community and good citizenship. Have students brainstorm a list of community groups that use volunteers.

Teacher Tip

Community Services Discuss events that cause many people to need help from the community. Examples include natural disasters like floods, blizzards, tornadoes, and earthquakes. Even brief power outages can give rise to need. Be mindful of the sensitivities of students whose family members may rely on community services. Talking about such situations may make some students uncomfortable.

3. WRAP UP

Lesson 3 Summary and Review

1. values; generations; cooperate
2. Rules for healthful behavior get you into the habit of doing things that keep you healthy. You are likely to continue these habits your whole life.
3. When family members cooperate, they work together, so they're not fighting about who should do what. Cooperation means people respect and help each other, making life happier.
4. Responses may include:

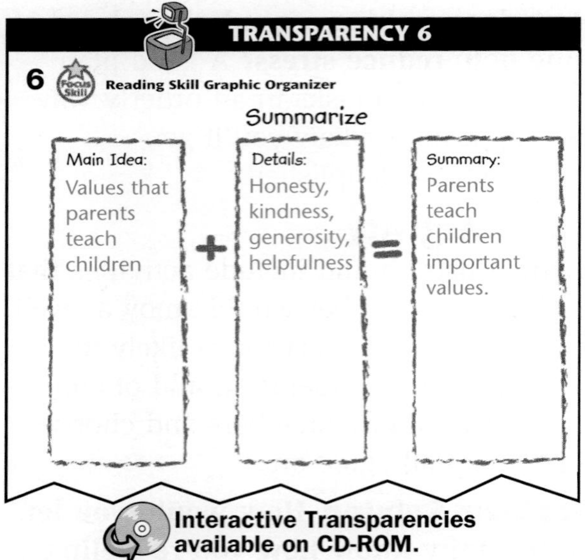
TRANSPARENCY 6

6 Reading Skill Graphic Organizer

Summarize

Main Idea:		Details:		Summary:
Values that parents teach children	+	Honesty, kindness, generosity, helpfulness	=	Parents teach children important values.

Interactive Transparencies available on CD-ROM.

5. Essays should name a value, explain why it is important, and provide examples of the value.

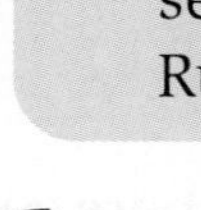

For **writing models** with examples, see *Teaching Resources* pp. 47–61. Rubrics are also provided.

When Minutes Count . . .

Quick Study Students can use *Activity Book* pages 51–52 (shown on p. 283) as they complete each lesson in this chapter.

Growth, Development, and Reproduction An optional lesson about the reproductive systems is provided in this supplement on pp. 44–49. Use this component in compliance with state and local guidelines.

Some rules to remember

Rules for health—Brush your teeth, bathe, get enough sleep, and eat healthful foods.

Rules for safety—Wear a bike helmet, do not stay out late, and let your parents know where you are.

Rules for cooperation—Help wash and dry the dishes, take out the trash, help with the laundry, and clean your room.

Why Rules Are Important

People sometimes groan when they hear the word *rules*. But rules are important in a family. Like values, they help people learn what's important and how to behave. They can also help keep people safe from harm or injury.

If everyone follows the rules, family members get along well together. Family life can be a more enjoyable experience.

DRAW CONCLUSIONS Why is family life happier when everyone follows the rules?

There is less conflict and fewer arguments about what should be done or not done or who should do what.

Lesson 3 Summary and Review

1. **Summarize with Vocabulary** Use vocabulary and other terms from this lesson to complete the statements.

   Parents often teach _____, such as respect, by example. They pass on values from people in earlier _____. Being able to _____ with others helps you work well with people.
2. Why might rules about healthful behavior at home lead a child to have good health habits throughout life?
3. **Critical Thinking** Why is there less conflict in a family in which everyone cooperates and works together?
4. **SUMMARIZE** Draw and complete this graphic organizer to show three values that parents or other adults teach children.

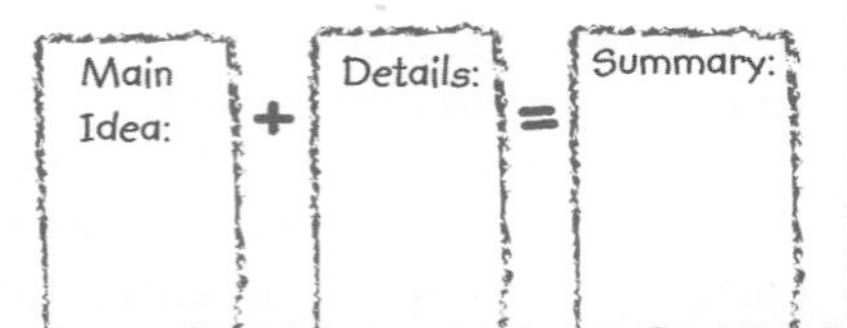

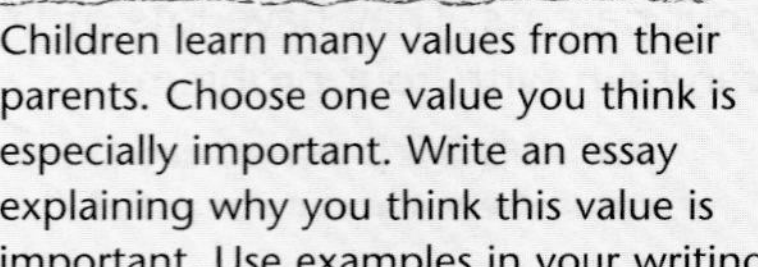

5. **Write to Inform—Explanation** Children learn many values from their parents. Choose one value you think is especially important. Write an essay explaining why you think this value is important. Use examples in your writing.

Cultural Connection

Rules Point out that families from different cultures often have different family rules. In some families, older children must care for younger children, sometimes missing school activities to do so. Girls and boys have different chores in some cultures. There are also different rules about going out with friends, about foods, and about other things.

ACTIVITY BOOK P. 55

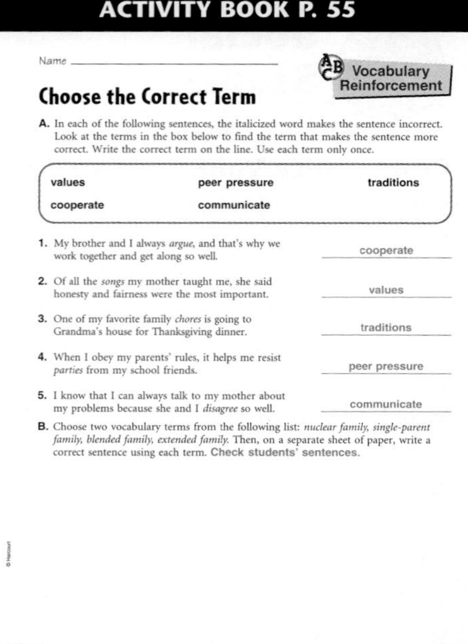
Name ____________

Vocabulary Reinforcement

Choose the Correct Term

A. In each of the following sentences, the italicized word makes the sentence incorrect. Look at the terms in the box below to find the term that makes the sentence more correct. Write the correct term on the line. Use each term only once.

values	peer pressure	traditions
cooperate	communicate	

1. My brother and I always *argue*, and that's why we work together and get along so well. cooperate
2. Of all the *songs* my mother taught me, she said honesty and fairness were the most important. values
3. One of my favorite family *chores* is going to Grandma's house for Thanksgiving dinner. traditions
4. When I obey my parents' rules, it helps me resist *parties* from my school friends. peer pressure
5. I know that I can always talk to my mother about my problems because she and I *disagree* so well. communicate

B. Choose two vocabulary terms from the following list: *nuclear family, single-parent family, blended family, extended family.* Then, on a separate sheet of paper, write a correct sentence using each term. Check students' sentences.

Available online. www.harcourtschool.com/health

ACTIVITIES

Art

Your Gift On your own, make a poster showing what you give to members of your family. It might be a love of shooting basketballs, patience, a sense of humor, or a talent in art. Think also of some of the ways that you are a help to other members of your family.

Language Arts

Family Traditions Look in the library for books about family traditions. Find out about how some of these traditions were started. Then write about one of the traditions, and share with the class what you learned.

Technology Project

Make an outline that lists important points about families from this chapter. Use a computer, if one is available, to make a presentation that includes your outline and pictures that show these important points. If you don't have a computer, make a colorful poster of your outline, with pictures.

For more activities, visit The Learning Site. www.harcourtschool.com/health

Home & Community

Communicating Make a bulletin board out of cork or cardboard to help family members communicate with one another. Decorate the bulletin board, and write a title above it, such as "Family Notes." Leave notepaper, a pencil, and tacks or tape near the bulletin board so family members can write and post messages to one another. With your parents' permission, attach the bulletin board to a wall in the kitchen or somewhere everyone can see and use it.

Career Link

Family Counselor At one time or another, every family has problems or conflicts. Sometimes families need someone to help them solve their problems. A family counselor is a professional who understands families and the problems they face. Suppose you are a family counselor. Write a paragraph explaining how you would advise family members on how to handle and resolve conflicts.

Career Link

Family Counselor Brainstorm with students the skills, training, and personality characteristics a family counselor needs. Have students prepare a list of questions they want to ask a family counselor about the training he or she needed and what he or she does. If your school has a guidance counselor, invite him or her to visit the class to be interviewed by the students. If an interview is not feasible, have students use library books or the Internet to research family counseling and family counselors.

The paragraph should focus on how students would counsel a family who had a problem. Students' paragraphs may or may not describe a specific problem.

For more information on health careers, visit the **Webliography** in Teacher Resources at **www.harcourtschool.com/health**
Keyword health careers

Activities

Art

Have students brainstorm a list of things—both material and nonmaterial—they give their families. Provide art materials for creating a poster. Invite student volunteers to talk about what they showed in their posters. Display posters in the classroom.

Language Arts

Discuss key words that can help students find books on the subject of family traditions. List key words on the board for students to copy and take to the library. The paper should describe one tradition and the family context (nationality) in which it is practiced.

Home & Community

Discuss where in the house all family members could see a bulletin board every day. Provide cardboard (from large cardboard boxes) for students who cannot purchase corkboards, as well as pencil, pad, and tacks or tape. Students may show their titled, decorated message centers to the class before taking them home.

Supports the Coordinated School Health Program

Technology Project

Review the outline form with students. If you have computers, show students how to indent and/or use the outline feature if there is one in the word-processing software. Students may draw their own pictures or find pictures in magazines to illustrate the important points about families they include in their outlines.

Chapter Review and Test Preparation

Pages 300–301

Reading Skill 5 pts. each

1. Possible answer: talking, hugging
2. Possible answer: caring, trustworthiness

Use Vocabulary 5 pts. each

3. E, values
4. B, peer pressure
5. F, blended family
6. A, traditions
7. C, cooperate
8. D, extended family

Check Understanding 5 pts. each

9. C, father hugging son
10. J, roles
11. D, You have more responsibilities.
12. G, Brush your teeth after meals.
13. A, communicate
14. G, a nuclear family

Think Critically 5 pts. each

15. You can conclude that younger children need more sleep in order to be healthy.
16. Possible answer: Cooperating involves showing respect, which makes conflict less likely. For example, you show respect for a family member when you do chores you have been asked to do.

Chapter Review and Test Preparation

Reading Skill

SUMMARIZE

Draw and then use this graphic organizer to answer questions 1 and 2.

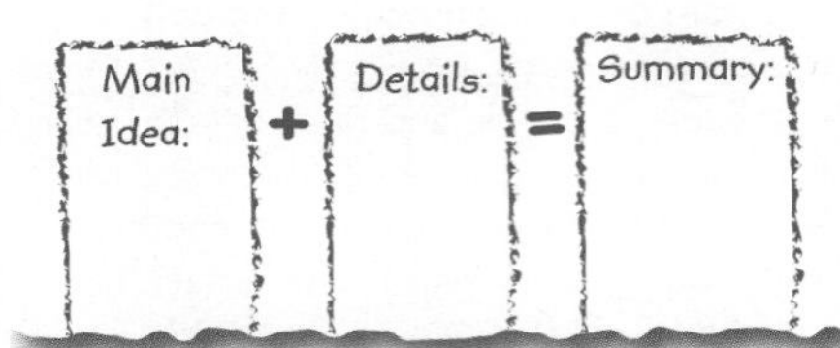

1 Write the main idea and details of how family members communicate.

2 Write values that make communicating with family members easy and useful.

Use Vocabulary

Match each term in Column B with its meaning in Column A.

Column A	Column B
3 Strong beliefs about how people should behave	**A** traditions
4 The influence of friends to get you to do things you don't want to do	**B** peer pressure
5 A family that forms when two single parents marry	**C** cooperate
6 Family customs	**D** extended family
7 To work with others	**E** values
8 A family of parents, children, and grandparents or other relatives	**F** blended family

Check Understanding

Choose the letter of the correct answer.

9 Which of the pictures below shows family members communicating well? (p. 289)

A

C

B

D

10 The things that family members do are known as their _____. (p. 284)

F needs
G traditions
H homes
J roles

11 As you grow older, how does your role in your family change? (p. 284)

A You no longer have to obey adults.
B You can boss around the younger children.
C You can stay up later at night.
D You have more responsibilities.

12 Which of the following is a rule that parents make to maintain their children's good health? (p. 298)

F Always say thank you.
G Brush your teeth after meals.
H Be a good listener.
J Remember family stories.

300

Formal Assessment

ASSESSMENT GUIDE P. 49

11 Name ______________ **Chapter Test**

Families Together

Write the letter of the best answer on the line at the left.

__A__ 1. You help and get along well with others when you _____ with them.
A cooperate **C** learn
B behave **D** have a good time

__J__ 2. Honesty and kindness are _____ that you learn from your family.
F rules **H** traditions
G chores **J** values

__B__ 3. A custom that a family follows for many generations is a _____.
A respect **C** healthy habit
B tradition **D** role

__H__ 4. No matter what kind of family you live in, everyone begins life with two _____.
F values **H** parents
G traditions **J** grandparents

__B__ 5. Children who live with only one parent live in a _____ family.
A nuclear **C** blended
B single-parent **D** step

__H__ 6. If you _____ problems to family members, they can help solve them.
F promise **H** communicate
G complain about **J** demand

__A__ 7. A child who lives in a family with a stepparent lives in a _____ family.
A blended **C** nuclear
B shared **D** working

__G__ 8. You can trust the advice you get from your _____.
F teammates **H** classmates
G parents **J** neighbors

© Harcourt

ASSESSMENT GUIDE P. 50

Name ______________

__D__ 9. When you say thank you to family members, it shows that you _____ them.
A help **C** share
B celebrate **D** appreciate

__F__ 10. Most families pass down values from grandparents to parents to children, so that each _____ learns them.
F generation **H** tradition
G peer **J** stepchild

Match each term in Column A with its meaning in Column B.

	Column A	Column B
__c__	11. peer pressure	**a** something you obey to stay healthy and to get along with your family
__d__	12. nuclear family	**b** sharing equally with your sister
__a__	13. rule	**c** strong pressure from friends
__e__	14. extended family	**d** a family in which children live with both natural parents
__b__	15. fairness	**e** a family in which parents and children live with other relatives

Write the letter of the best answer on the line at the left.

__C__ 16. Which of the following rules helps you stay healthy?
A Make your bed. **C** Brush your teeth.
B Do your homework. **D** Share your toys.

__F__ 17. When parents act the way they want you to act, how are they teaching you how to behave?
F by example **H** by rules
G by tradition **J** by punishing

__D__ 18. What is a child's main role in his or her family?
A to do chores
B to do favors
C to care for younger children
D to become a responsible family member

© Harcourt

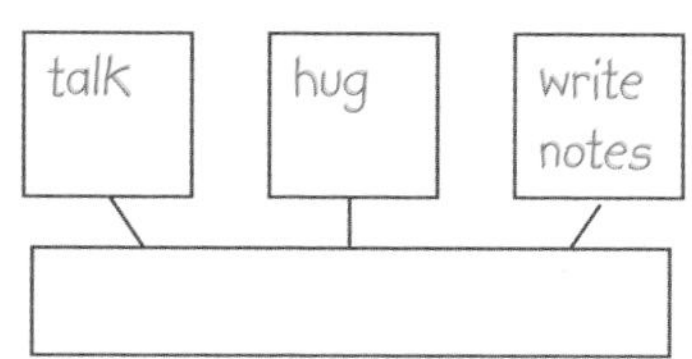

13 Which of the following words belongs in the empty box in the graphic organizer above? (pp. 288–289)

A communicate **C** responsible
B chores **D** proud

14 Two parents and their children are an example of _____. (pp. 282–283)

F an extended family
G a nuclear family
H a single-parent family
J a blended family

Think Critically

15 Getting enough sleep is important for good health. Young children must go to bed earlier than older children. What can you conclude about the need for healthful sleep at different ages?

16 How does cooperation help family members avoid conflict? Use one example in your answer.

17 If your mother had another baby, how would that change your role in your family? Give an example.

Apply Skills

18 **BUILDING GOOD CHARACTER**
Fairness You have just eaten a snack and put your dirty dishes in the sink. It's a family rule that everyone wash his or her dishes and not leave them in the sink. You have to study for an important test at school tomorrow, so you don't want to spend time washing the dishes you used. Anyway, your mother will probably wash them when she gets home from work. Should you wash your dishes, or should you leave them so you can study? Explain your decision.

19 **LIFE SKILLS**
Communicate Without asking your permission, your older sister took your CD player to a party. You are so angry, you don't know what to do. What is the best way to handle this situation? Whom should you tell about your feelings, and how should you describe the situation?

Write About Health

20 **Write to Inform—Explanation** Your parents said you could not go to a party on Friday night, even though they let your older brother go to weekend parties. You are very upset. Write a letter to a parent, explaining how you feel and asking if you can talk together about the situation.

ASSESSMENT GUIDE P. 51

Name ____________

G 19. When you ask your sister whether you can borrow something of hers before you take it, what are you showing her?

F that you are helpful
G that you respect her
H that you are afraid of her
J that she can use your things

C 20. What is a parent's main role in a family?

A to have children
B to make lots of rules
C to support and care for the children
D to make lots of money

In every family, family members sometimes do things that make each other angry or upset. What are three things you can do to control your anger?

21. Take a deep breath.

22. Try to relax and stay calm.

23. Control my anger by communicating my feelings.

Family members cooperate with each other when they do home projects together or when they help out together in the community. In the right-hand column, write about how you and your family might cooperate at home and in your community.

Home project my family and I can work on together	24. clean the house, paint the house, work in the garden, wash the car, do the shopping
How my family and I can help out in our community	25. volunteer at the library, in a hospital, in an after-school program, at a day care center, as tutors

© Harcourt

17. Possible answer: Because I would be older than the baby, I'd have more responsibilities. For example, I might have to help dress the baby or clean up my room by myself because my mother would no longer have the time.

Apply Skills 5 pts. each

18. Possible answer: I would wash them quickly and then study because it's not fair to leave them for my mother, who may also have things to do. I should follow the rule, but when my mother gets home I can explain the situation and ask if she minds doing my dishes just this one time while I study.

19. Possible answer: I would talk calmly with my older sister, telling her how I feel about what she did and asking that it not happen again. If that didn't resolve the problem, I'd ask for a family meeting to discuss it.

Write About Health 5 pts.

20. Students should maintain a calm, explanatory tone, giving reasons they think they should be allowed to attend a party. The letters should be reasonable, not shrill and accusatory.

Performance Assessment

Use the Chapter Project and the rubric provided on the Project Evaluation Sheet. See *Assessment Guide* pp. 18, 60, 72.

Portfolio Assessment

Have students select their best work from the following suggestions:

- Leveled Activities, p. 284
- Quick Activity, p. 289
- Write to Inform, p. 298
- Activities, p. 299

See *Assessment Guide* pp. 12–16.

CHAPTER 12

Living in a Healthful Community

Lesson	Pacing	Objectives	Reading Skills
Introduce the Chapter pp. 302–303		• Preview chapter concepts.	**Draw Conclusions** pp. 303, 330–331
1 **Enjoying a Healthful Environment** pp. 304–307	1 class period	• Identify clean air, land, and water as parts of a healthful environment. • Analyze factors that influence individual, family, and community health. • Describe healthful recreational activities.	**Draw Conclusions** pp. 305, 307 • Summarize, p. 307
2 **Protecting Your Community** pp. 308–310	1 class period	• Identify ways in which community workers promote healthful environments. • Identify a variety of community workers and their roles in promoting a healthful community. • Describe the jobs of emergency medical technicians and dispatchers.	**Draw Conclusions** p. 310 • Summarize, p. 308
Building Good Character p. 311		• Learn to be part of a community. • Keep your environment clean and safe.	
3 **Our Natural Resources** pp. 312–315	1 class period	• Define and identify natural resources as renewable or nonrenewable. • Identify ways that people use natural resources. • Explain how fossil fuels are used.	**Draw Conclusions** p. 315 • Compare and Contrast, p. 313
4 **Preventing Pollution** pp. 316–321	3 class periods	• Identify sources of air, water, and land pollution, and explain how these types of pollution affect human health. • Identify several ways to prevent air, water, and land pollution.	**Draw Conclusions** pp. 317, 321 • Cause and Effect, p. 319 • Main Idea and Details, p. 321
Life Skills pp. 322–323	1 class period	• Identify strategies to set goals. • Practice setting goals to conserve resources.	
5 **Ways to Practice Conservation** pp. 324–326	1 class period	• Define *conservation.* • Describe ways to conserve water, air, land, and other resources.	**Draw Conclusions** p. 326 • Compare and Contrast, p. 325 • Summarize, p. 326
Activities p. 327		• Extend chapter concepts.	
Chapter Review pp. 328–329	1 class period	• Assess chapter objectives.	

Vocabulary	Program Resources
	Music CD Teaching Resources, p. 47
environment	Transparency 2 Activity Book, pp. 56–58
graffiti	Transparency 2 Activity Book, pp. 56–57
	Poster 2
natural resources **renewable resources** **nonrenewable resources**	Transparency 2 Activity Book, pp. 56–57
pollution **solid waste**	Transparency 2 Activity Book, pp. 56–57
	Activity Book, p. 59 Poster 12
conservation	Transparency 2 Activity Book, pp. 56–57, 60
	The Learning Site www.harcourtschool.com
	Assessment Guide, pp. 52–54

Interactive Transparencies available on CD-ROM.

Reading Skill

These reading skills are reinforced throughout this chapter and one skill is emphasized as the Focus Skill.

- **Draw Conclusions**
- Compare and Contrast
- Identify Cause and Effect
- Identify Main Idea and Details
- Sequence
- Summarize

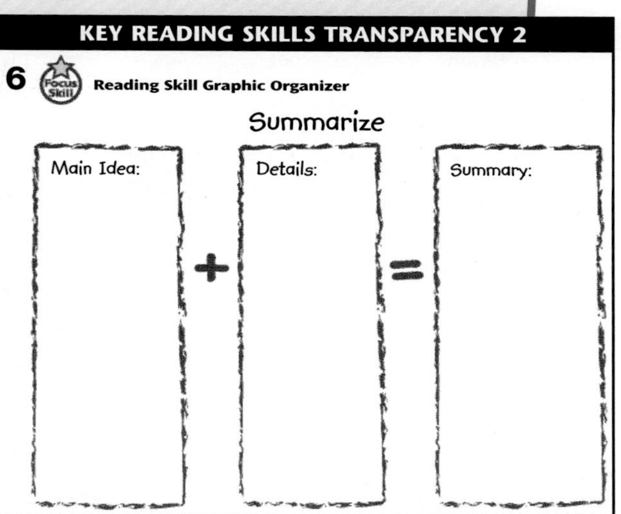
KEY READING SKILLS TRANSPARENCY 2
6
Reading Skill Graphic Organizer
Summarize
Main Idea:
+
Details:
=
Summary:

Life Skills

Life Skills are health-enhancing behaviors that can help students reduce risks to their health and safety.

Six Life Skills are reinforced throughout *Harcourt Health and Fitness*. The skill emphasized in this chapter is Set Goals.

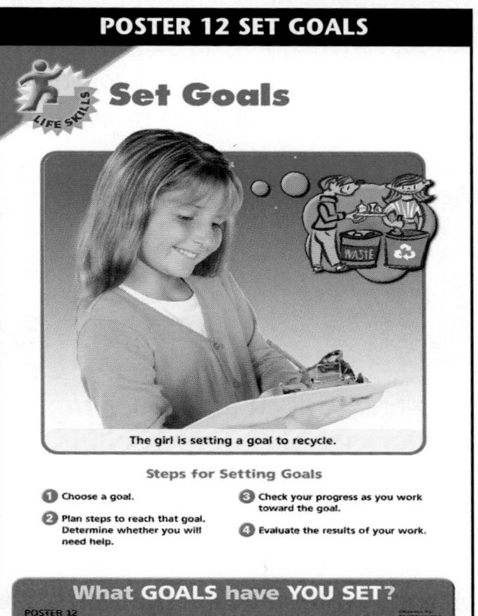
POSTER 12 SET GOALS
Set Goals
LIFE SKILLS
The girl is setting a goal to recycle.
Steps for Setting Goals
1 Choose a goal.
2 Plan steps to reach that goal. Determine whether you will need help.
3 Check your progress as you work toward the goal.
4 Evaluate the results of your work.
What GOALS have YOU SET?
POSTER 12

Building Good Character

Character education is an important aspect of health education. When children behave in ways that show good character, they promote the health and safety of themselves and others.

Six character traits listed below are reinforced throughout *Harcourt Health and Fitness*. The trait emphasized in this chapter is Citizenship.

POSTER 2 CITIZENSHIP
Citizenship
Building Good Character
The boys are showing good citizenship by following school rules.
DO
Take pride in your school, community, state, and country.
Obey laws and rules and respect authority.
Be a good neighbor.
Help keep your school and neighborhood safe and clean.
Cooperate with others.
Protect the environment.
DON'T
Don't break rules and laws.
Don't waste natural resources.
Don't damage public property or the property of others.
Don't litter. Don't hurt the environment in other ways.
How have YOU shown good CITIZENSHIP today?
POSTER 2

Resources

Coordinated School Health Program

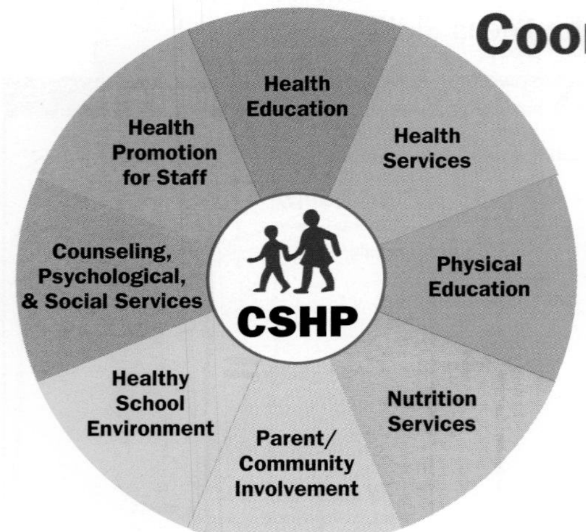

A Coordinated School Health Program endeavors to improve children's health and therefore their capacity to learn through the support of families, schools, and communities working together. The following information is provided to help classroom teachers be more aware of these resources.

The American Alliance for Health, Physical Education, Recreation, and Dance (**AAHPERD**) Jump Rope for Heart offers students, schools, and the community many benefits by engaging school-age children in community services while promoting the benefits of a heart-healthy lifestyle.
www.aahperd.org/
www.americanheart.org/

The National Institute of Environmental Health Services, a branch of the **National Institutes of Health**, offers *Your Environment Is Your Health Family Guide,* which identifies twenty easy steps to ensure personal environmental health. **www.health.nih.gov/**

Each year, more than 200,000 children are injured on America's playgrounds. To address the concern for playground safety, the **CDC** and the **University of Northern Iowa** established the National Program for Playground Safety (NPPS).
www.uni.edu/playground/tips/

Other resources that support a Coordinated School Health Program:

- School-Home Connection
- Daily Physical Activity
- Daily Fitness Tips
- Activities: Home & Community
- Health Background: Webliography
- *Be Active! Resources for Physical Education*

Media Resources

Books for Students

Showers, Paul. ***Where Does the Garbage Go?*** HarperCollins, 1994. Discusses wastes and recycling by using a classroom and a trip to a landfill. **EASY**

Markle, Sandra. ***After the Spill: The Exxon Valdez Disaster, Then and Now***. Walker and Company, 1999. Describes the oil spill and resulting damage. **AVERAGE**

Hooper, Meredith. ***The Drop in My Drink: The Story of Water on Our Planet***. Viking Children's Books, 1998. Explains conservation and the role of water on Earth. **ADVANCED**

Books for Teachers and Families

Nadakavukaren, Anne. ***Our Global Environment: A Health Perspective***. Waveland Press, 2000. Looks at environmental issues such as depletion of the ozone layer.

Liverman, Catharyn T., Carrie E. Ingalls, and Carolyn E. Fulco. ***Toxicology and Environmental Health Resources: The Role of the National Library of Medicine***. National Academy Press, 1997. Explains the public health impact of hazardous substances.

Free and Inexpensive Materials

World Wildlife Fund
Ask for the Action Kit which has tips on preserving Earth and wildlife.

Health Information Network
Will send free kits and brochures such as "Indoor Air Quality for Schools."

Federal Citizen Information Center
Request the pamphlet, *Catch the Spirit: A Student's Guide to Community Service* (#501K).

To access free and inexpensive resources on the Web, visit
www.harcourtschool.com/health/free

Videos

Down the Drain. 3-2-1 Contact, Children's Television Workshop, 1991.

Power Up: Energy in Our Environment. Rainbow Educational Media, 1992.

Clean Air—The Earth at Risk. Schlessinger Video Productions, 1993.

These resources have been selected to meet a variety of individual needs. Please review all materials and websites prior to sharing them with students to ensure the content is appropriate for your class. Note that information, while correct at time of publication, is subject to change.

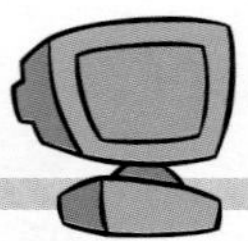

Visit **The Learning Site** for related links, activities, resources, and the health **Webliography.**

www.harcourtschool.com/health

Meeting Individual Needs

Below-Level

Have students sort vocabulary words into categories. Categories might be based on similarities or differences in letter or syllable patterns, word meanings, parts of speech, or ways words are used. You may want to extend the activity by including other similar words.

Activities

- Locate Recreational Areas, p. 306
- Make Posters, p. 310
- Costs, p. 315

On-Level

Using reference sources when reading can help students' understanding. Display resources, such as a dictionary or a computer. Have students identify a new word or idea in the chapter and write the meaning. Verify that meaning using one of the resources.

Activities

- Make a Brochure, p. 306
- Calculate Trash, p. 310
- The Dust Bowl, p. 315

Challenge

Have students explore their perspectives on a health-related topic, such as the importance of exercise. Have them write seven descriptive words, each on a puzzle piece, about the topic. They can then exchange puzzles with a partner, solve them, and compare ideas.

Activities

- Analyze Water Sources, p. 306
- Fire Safety Checklist, p. 310
- Compare Fossil Fuels, p. 315

ESL/ELL

Vocabulary Workshop

Have students use context to determine word meanings. Draw two columns on the board, one with vocabulary words and one with their definitions. Read a paragraph, pausing after each vocabulary word. Ask volunteers to draw a line connecting the word with its definition.

Activities

- Comprehensible Input, pp. 314, 318, 324

Curriculum Integration

Use these topics to integrate health into your daily planning.

Integrated Language Arts/Reading Skills

- Thank You, p. 308
- Polluted Picnic, p. 321
- Conservation Log, p. 322
- Water, Water Everywhere, p. 325

Math

- Trash Average, p. 317

Physical Education

- Daily Fitness Tip, pp. 304, 308, 312, 316, 324
- Daily Physical Activity, p. 303

Science

- Pulse Rate, p. 307
- Sick Soil, p. 313
- Mercury and Fish, p. 319

Social Studies

- Clean Water Act, p. 319

Art

- Trash Art, p. 320

CHAPTER 12

Pages 302–329

CHAPTER SUMMARY

In this chapter, students

- ► identify people who work to make a community a clean and healthful environment.
- ► describe air, water, and land pollution and how to prevent them.
- ► identify natural resources and how to conserve them.

Life Skills

Students learn how to *set goals* to conserve resources.

Building Good Character

Students show *citizenship* by helping make their community a clean and safe place to live.

Consumer Health

Students *access* valid health information.

Literature Springboard

Use the article "Packaging—Then and Now" to spark interest in the chapter topic. See the Read-Aloud Anthology on page RA-13 of this *Teacher Edition*.

Prereading Strategies

SCAN THE CHAPTER Have students preview the chapter content by scanning the titles, headings, pictures, tables, and graphs. Ask volunteers to speculate on what they will learn. Use their responses to determine their prior knowledge.

PREVIEW VOCABULARY As students preview the chapter vocabulary, have them write down terms that are unfamiliar. Have them use the Glossary to define unfamiliar words.

Words I Know	Words I've Seen or Heard	New Words

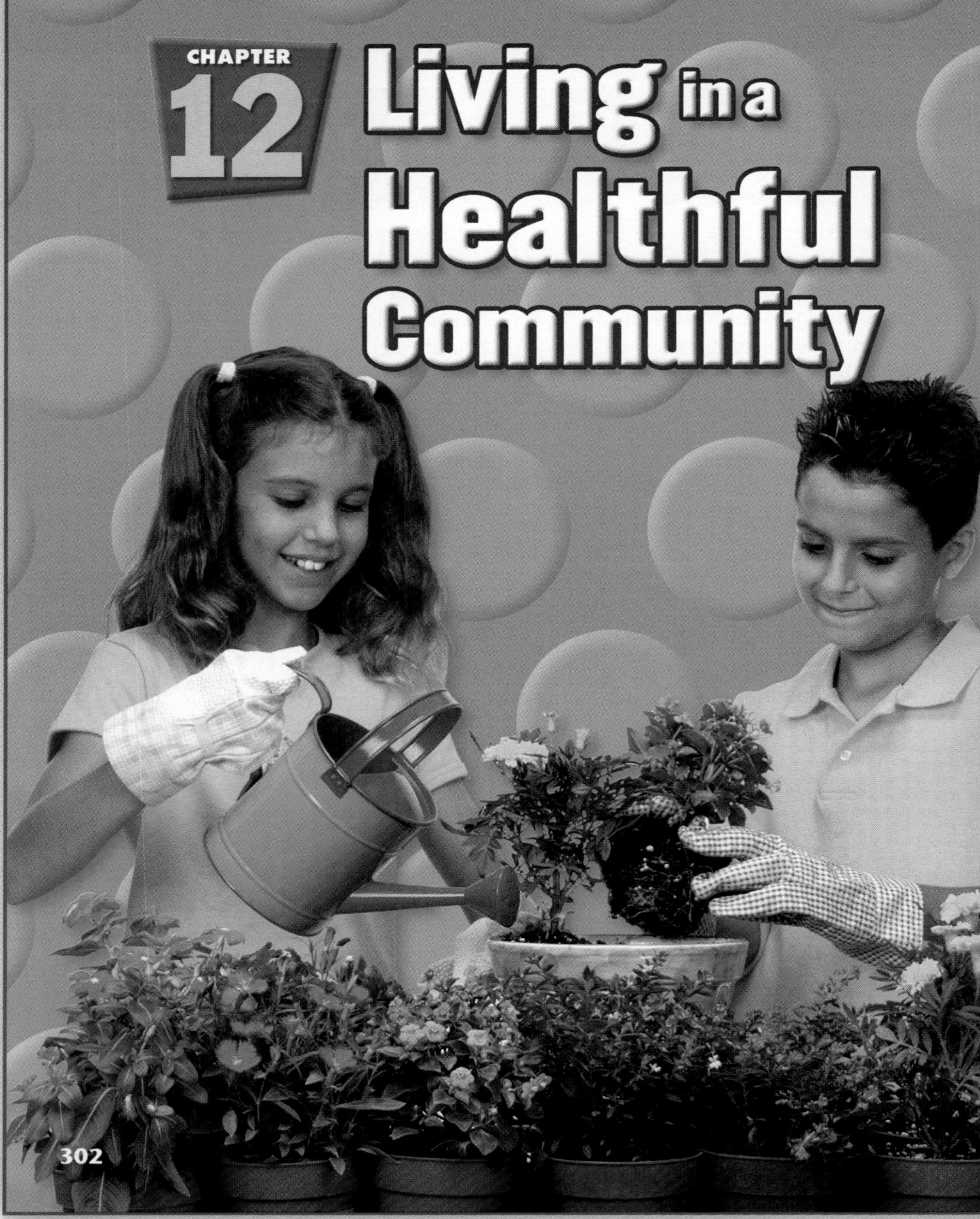

Reading Skill

DRAW CONCLUSIONS To introduce or review this skill, have students use the Reading in Health Handbook, pp. 332–333. Teaching strategies and additional activities are also provided.

Students will have opportunities to practice and apply this skill throughout this chapter.

- Focus Skill Reading Mini-Lesson, p. 304
- Reading comprehension questions identified with the 
- *Activity Book* p. 58 (shown on p. 307)
- Lesson Summary and Review, pp. 307, 310, 315, 321, 326
- Chapter Review and Test Preparation, pp. 328–329

Reading Skill

DRAW CONCLUSIONS Sometimes authors don't supply all the information. You have to use information from the passage plus what you already know to draw a conclusion. Use the Reading in Health Handbook on pages 332–333 and this graphic organizer to help you read the health facts in this chapter.

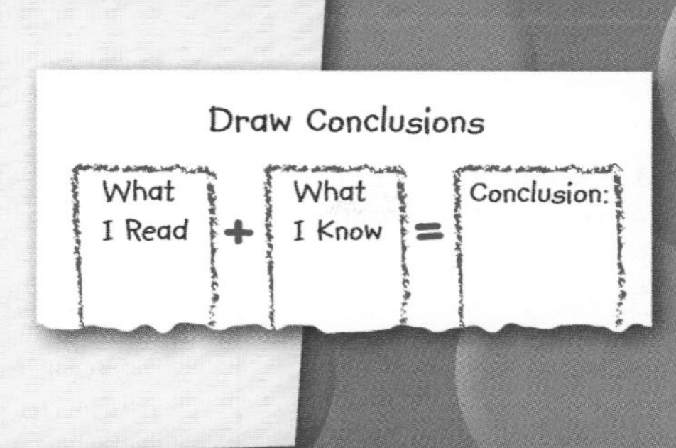

Health Graph

INTERPRET DATA Much lumber from trees is used in the United States. The circle graph shows softwood lumber use for a recent year. What were the top three uses for softwood lumber? What used the most softwood lumber in that year?

U.S. Softwood Lumber Consumption

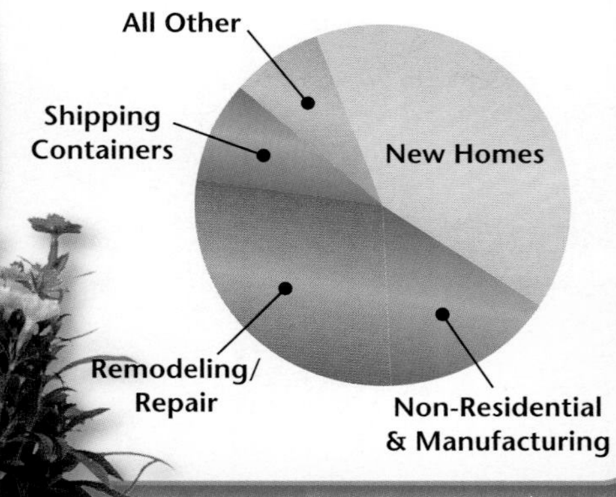

Daily Physical Activity

Live a healthful lifestyle. Exercise and be active in your community.

Be Active!

Use the selection Track 12, **Broadway Bound**, to share some exercise time with your classroom community.

303

INTRODUCE THE CHAPTER

Health Graph

Interpret Data

Have students examine the circle graph. Ask for volunteers to explain what information the graph is showing. The graph shows how softwood lumber was used and the relative popularity of each use in a recent year. Explain that softwood is wood that comes from coniferous trees (trees that have cones), like pines.

What were the top three uses for softwood lumber? The three most popular uses were building new homes, remodeling and repair of residences, and nonresidential and manufacturing uses.

Which product used the most softwood lumber that year? new homes

Daily Physical Activity

Use *Be Active! Music for Daily Physical Activity* with the Instant Activity Cards to provide students with movement activities that can be done in limited space. Options for using these components are provided beginning on page TR2 in this *Teacher Edition*.

Chapter Project

They Work to Keep You Healthy (*Assessment Guide* p. 61)

ASSESS PRIOR KNOWLEDGE Use students' initial ideas for the project as a baseline assessment of their understanding of chapter concepts. Have students complete the project as they work through the chapter.

PERFORMANCE ASSESSMENT The project can be used for performance assessment. Use the Project Evaluation Sheet (rubric), *Assessment Guide* p. 73.

School-Home Connection

Distribute copies of the School-Home Connection (in English or Spanish). Have students take the page home to share with their families as you begin this chapter.

Follow Up Have volunteers share the results of their activities.

Supports the Coordinated School Health Program

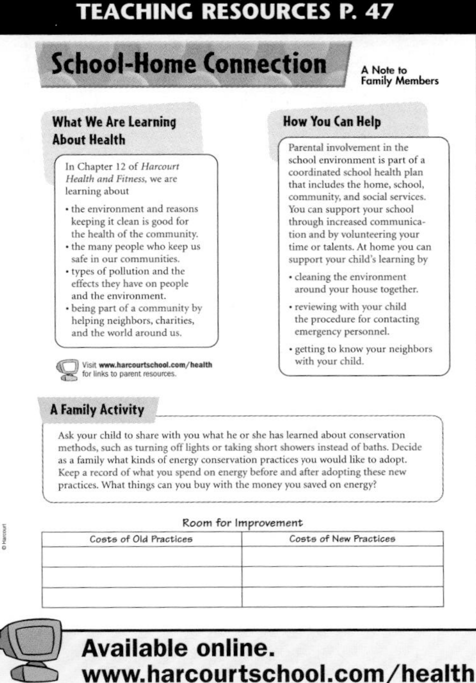

TEACHING RESOURCES P. 47

School-Home Connection

A Note to Family Members

What We Are Learning About Health

In Chapter 12 of *Harcourt Health and Fitness*, we are learning about

- the environment and reasons keeping it clean is good for the health of the community.
- the many people who keep us safe in our communities.
- types of pollution and the effects they have on people and the environment.
- being part of a community by helping neighbors, charities, and the world around us.

Visit **www.harcourtschool.com/health** for links to parent resources.

How You Can Help

Parental involvement in the school environment is part of a coordinated school health plan that includes the home, school, community, and social services. You can support your school through increased communication and by volunteering your time or talents. At home you can support your child's learning by

- cleaning the environment around your house together.
- reviewing with your child the procedure for contacting emergency personnel.
- getting to know your neighbors with your child.

A Family Activity

Ask your child to share with you what he or she has learned about conservation methods, such as turning off lights or taking short showers instead of baths. Decide as a family what kinds of energy conservation practices you would like to adopt. Keep a record of what you spend on energy before and after adopting these new practices. What things can you buy with the money you saved on energy?

Room for Improvement

Costs of Old Practices	Costs of New Practices

© Harcourt

Available online.
www.harcourtschool.com/health

LESSON 1
Pages 304–307

Objectives
- ► Identify clean air, land, and water as parts of a healthful environment.
- ► Analyze factors that influence individual, family, and community health.
- ► Describe healthful recreational activities.

When Minutes Count . . .
Assign the Quick Study, Lesson 1, Activity Book pp. 56–57 (shown on p. 305).

Program Resources
- ► Activity Book pp. 56–58
- ► Transparency 2

Vocabulary
environment p. 304

Daily Fitness Tip
Remind students that a healthful environment (with unpolluted air, water, and land) is good for mental health as well as physical health. Visiting a park, even a small one, with its cleaner and quieter environment, is a good way to manage stress.

1. MOTIVATE
Ask students to list four basic things they need to survive. Answers will likely include water, air, food, and shelter. Then ask them to list some things that are important to their daily life but not necessary to sustain life. Inform students that all of these items are part of their environment. Discuss what their lives would be like without these things. Ask: **If you were to design the perfect environment, what would it include?** Student responses will vary.

LESSON 1 Enjoying a Healthful Environment

Lesson Focus
A clean environment is important to your health.

Why Learn This?
You can use what you learn to enjoy your community in healthful ways.

Vocabulary
environment

A Healthful Environment
Your **environment** (en•VY•ruhn•muhnt) is made up of all the living and nonliving things that surround you. It includes plants, animals, air, water, soil, and even roads and buildings. A clean, healthful environment is important to your health. If your environment is dirty, you could become ill.

To stay healthy, people need to breathe clean air. Dirty air contains particles as well as harmful chemicals that can damage the lungs. Many people get asthma and other respiratory diseases from breathing dirty air.

304

Focus Skill Reading Skill

Mini-Lesson
DRAW CONCLUSIONS
Remind students that when you draw conclusions, you use the information that you learned from the passage, along with what you already know. Have them answer the Focus Skill question on page 305. Have them draw and complete the graphic organizer as you model it on the transparency.

TRANSPARENCY 2

2 Reading Skill Graphic Organizer

Draw Conclusions

What I Read	+	What I Know	=	Conclusion:
Dirty air can damage the lungs; dirty water can cause death; dirty land can lead to poisonous food and water.		Air, land, and water are part of our environment.		A person who lives in a dirty environment over a long period could become very ill or even die.

Interactive Transparencies available on CD-ROM.

Clean water is also extremely important for your health. People who drink water that has harmful chemicals or bacteria in it can become very ill and can even die.

Clean land, too, is important in many ways. We need it to grow healthful foods to feed ourselves and to feed animals. Plants that are grown on dirty land can become sick, unhealthful, or even poisonous. It is also important to keep land clean because most of our drinking water flows over the land or through the soil.

DRAW CONCLUSIONS What might happen to a person who lives in a dirty environment over a long period of time?
He or she could become very ill or even die.

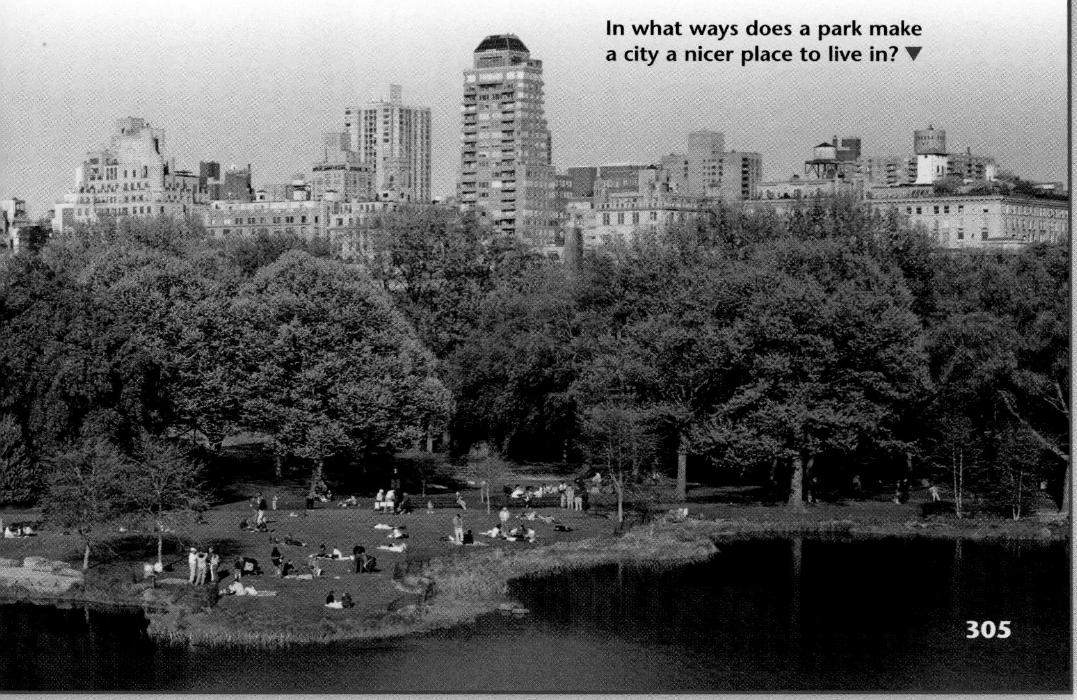

In what ways does a park make a city a nicer place to live in? ▼

QUICK STUDY, ACTIVITY BOOK PP. 56–57

CHAPTER 12 Name ________ Quick Study

Living in a Healthful Community

Directions
- Use lesson vocabulary and other words in the Word Bank to complete each **Summary**.
- Read the section directions to complete each **Lesson Details**.

Word Bank

air	environment	natural resources	pollution	land
clean	solid waste	nonrenewable resources	safe	water
conservation	healthful	renewable resources	graffiti	EMTs

Lesson 1 pp. 304-307

Summary All the living and nonliving things that surround you make up your environment. A healthful environment has clean air, water, and land.

Lesson Details Use pages 304–307 to give four examples of outdoor recreation.
Possible answers: softball, tennis, kickball, running track, hiking, gardening, biking, swinging, soccer

Lesson 2 pp. 308-310

Summary Custodians and other workers help keep a community healthy by keeping public areas clean and free of trash and graffiti. Police officers, firefighters, dispatchers, and EMTs keep a community safe and help people in an emergency.

Lesson 3 pp. 312-315

Summary Materials from nature that people use to meet their needs are called natural resources. Some resources, called renewable resources, can be replaced naturally. Resources that take a very long time to replace or cannot be replaced at all are called nonrenewable resources.

© Harcourt

Name ________ Quick Study (continued)

Lesson Details Use pp. 312–315 to complete the sentences. Possible answers:

1. Three natural resources are air, land, and water.
2. Two resources that will never run out are water and wind.
3. One nonrenewable resource is oil. It is considered nonrenewable because it takes millions of years to form underground.

Lesson 4 pp. 316-321

Summary Sometimes natural resources contain harmful materials such as smoke, chemicals, and solid waste. These materials are pollution.

Lesson Details Use pp. 316–321 to complete the sentences about pollution.
People can help reduce air pollution by walking, biking, and using public transportation. Water pollution can be reduced if people do not throw trash into water. People can reduce land pollution by recycling.

Lesson 5 pp. 324-326

Summary One way to keep the environment healthful is to conserve natural resources. Conservation is the careful use of resources.

Lesson Details Use pp. 324–326 to complete the graphic organizer about conservation.

Conservation of Natural Resources → Reduce, Reuse, Recycle → Water, Energy

© Harcourt

Available online.
www.harcourtschool.com/health

2. TEACH

Interpret Visuals—Pictures

Ask students to identify three living and three nonliving things that are found in the environment pictured on these pages. Living things might include the people, plants, organisms that live in the lake, or worms that live in the soil. Nonliving things might include rocks, air, water, and the land. **What things do you assume are in an environment like the one pictured here, even though you can't see them?** Students' responses may include air, organisms living under the water and earth, underground water, etc.

Discuss

Explain that animals, including humans, breathe in oxygen (O_2) and then exhale carbon dioxide (CO_2). Plants, on the other hand, use CO_2 and give off O_2. In high concentrations CO_2 is poisonous to animals. It is one of the pollutants given off by factories and vehicles when they burn things like oil and gas.

Critical Thinking What does this information tell you about plants and a healthful environment? Students may conclude that plants are important because they "clean" the air of excess poisonous CO_2.

Problem Solving What would happen to the air supply if there were suddenly no plants on earth? Since plants take in carbon dioxide and give off oxygen, the carbon dioxide content would increase while the oxygen content would decrease.

TEACH *continued*

Discuss

Aerobic exercise temporarily increases the body's heart rate and breathing rate. It is very beneficial to the heart and lungs. Fitness specialists recommend that healthy people spend at least 30 minutes per day doing some form of aerobic exercise.

What recreational activities are aerobic? soccer, bike riding, basketball, swimming, hiking

What recreational activities are not aerobic? fishing, stretching, watching a game

Critical Thinking Why can it be dangerous to engage in aerobic activities when the air quality is bad? When you exercise aerobically, you breathe more deeply, so you take in more pollutants.

Health Background

Air Pollution An air pollutant is any substance in the air that is a result of human activity and that causes damage to life or property. These pollutants also contribute to poor water quality. Airborne pollution can fall to the ground and end up in streams or lakes, affecting the water quality. Air pollutants can adversely affect health through the water by contaminating fish and making drinking water unsafe.

Source: *Environmental Protection Agency*

For more background, visit the **Webliography** in Teacher Resources at **www.harcourtschool.com/health**
Keyword community/environmental health

Did You Know?

In both rural and urban areas in the United States, the Rails-to-Trails Conservancy has built more than 1,200 recreation trails along old railroad tracks. This national organization is dedicated to creating a nationwide network of public trails. Thousands of people have contributed to the effort.

Healthful Community Activities

A healthful environment is important not just for your body. It is also important for your mental health. One way people enjoy a healthful environment is through outdoor *recreation* (rek•ree•AY•shuhn). Recreation is what you do to have fun or relax.

Cities and rural communities offer many forms of recreation. Many schools have playgrounds, softball fields, and basketball or tennis courts. A river, a lake, or a pond can be used for water sports such as swimming and fishing. Many people also enjoy other outdoor activities, such as gardening.

There are many good forms of recreation. ▶

306

Meeting Individual Needs
Leveled Activities

BELOW-LEVEL **Locate Recreational Areas** Ask students to find out what types of recreational areas exist in their community. Have them make maps to show where these recreational areas are.

ON-LEVEL **Make a Brochure** Have each student choose one recreational activity that he or she likes in the community and then make a brochure advertising that activity. Written descriptions and pictures should be included.

CHALLENGE **Analyze Water Sources** Have students find out where their community gets its drinking water. Then have them interview one of the workers at the facility to find out what happens to the water to get it ready to drink. Students should prepare visual presentations to share their findings.

Recreation areas can be added to a community. For example, railroad tracks no longer in use can be changed into trails for hiking and biking. Workers remove the old railroad tracks and change the land into a trail.

There are different kinds of rail-trails. In Boston, the Minuteman Trail takes people along a route that soldiers followed during the Revolutionary War. In Wisconsin, the Sugar Trail leads hikers through small towns and farms.

Some other kinds of trails are nature trails and exercise and fitness trails. Some trails go over water on boardwalks, while on still others, users need a canoe or boat.

SUMMARIZE What are some ways that communities can provide a healthful environment?

Lesson 1 Summary and Review

1 Summarize with Vocabulary

Use vocabulary and other terms from this lesson to complete the statements.

A healthful _____ is important to communities. Water, land, and air need to be _____ for people to have a healthful environment. In a healthful environment, many people enjoy outdoor _____, such as sports and gardening.

2 Explain what makes up an environment.

3 Critical Thinking Describe two of the recreation areas in your community. What makes these areas healthful?

4 Focus Skill DRAW CONCLUSIONS Draw and complete this graphic organizer to show the factors that create a healthful environment.

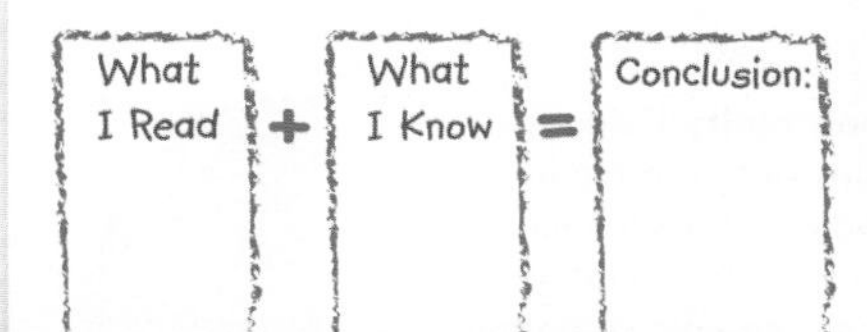

5 Write to Inform—Description

Describe the kind of environment you need in order to enjoy your favorite form of outdoor recreation.

Communities can provide opportunities for outdoor recreation, such as playing sports or gardening, and a clean environment for people to live in.

Science

Pulse Rate Explain to students how to take their pulses. Instruct them to place the index and middle fingers of one hand on the thumb side of the inner wrist of the other hand. Have them count the beats in a minute. This value is the resting pulse. Invite them to run in place for a minute or so and retake their pulses. Have students explain the increase in pulse rates. Check students' physical limitations before allowing them to exercise in class.

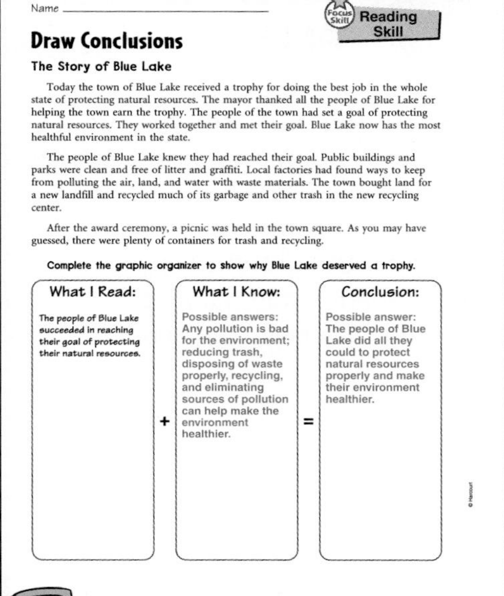

ACTIVITY BOOK P. 58

Name ______________________

Focus Skill Reading Skill

Draw Conclusions

The Story of Blue Lake

Today the town of Blue Lake received a trophy for doing the best job in the whole state of protecting natural resources. The mayor thanked all the people of Blue Lake for helping the town earn the trophy. The people of the town had set a goal of protecting natural resources. They worked together and met their goal. Blue Lake now has the most healthful environment in the state.

The people of Blue Lake knew they had reached their goal. Public buildings and parks were clean and free of litter and graffiti. Local factories had found ways to keep from polluting the air, land, and water with waste materials. The town bought land for a new landfill and recycled much of its garbage and other trash in the new recycling center.

After the award ceremony, a picnic was held in the town square. As you may have guessed, there were plenty of containers for trash and recycling.

Complete the graphic organizer to show why Blue Lake deserved a trophy.

What I Read:	+	What I Know:	=	Conclusion:
The people of Blue Lake succeeded in reaching their goal of protecting their natural resources.	+	Possible answers: Any pollution is bad for the environment; reducing trash, disposing of waste properly, recycling, and eliminating sources of pollution can help make the environment healthier.	=	Possible answer: The people of Blue Lake did all they could to protect natural resources properly and make their environment healthier.

© Harcourt

Available online. www.harcourtschool.com/health

3. WRAP UP

Lesson 1 Summary and Review

1. environment, clean, recreation
2. The environment includes all the living and nonliving things that surround you, including plants, animals, air, water, soil, roads, and buildings.
3. Possible answers are parks, hiking trails, lakes, basketball courts, and playgrounds. They provide areas in which to relax and exercise. The air might be cleaner there and it might be less noisy.
4. Responses may include:

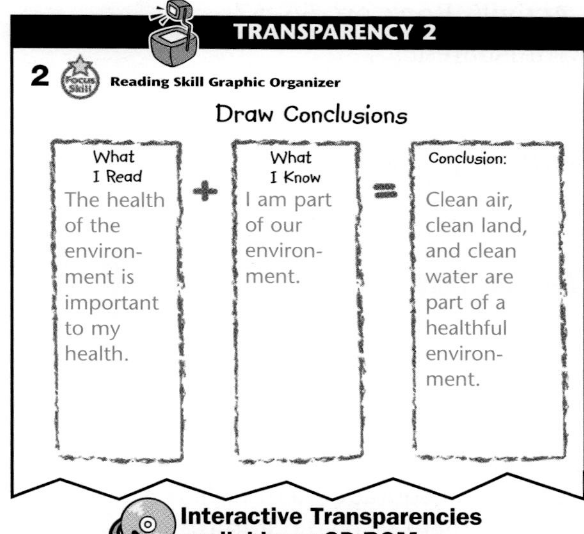

TRANSPARENCY 2
2 Focus Skill Reading Skill Graphic Organizer
Draw Conclusions
What I Read
The health of the environment is important to my health.
+
What I Know
I am part of our environment.
=
Conclusion:
Clean air, clean land, and clean water are part of a healthful environment.

5. Answers should include the favorite form of recreation and a description of the land, air, water, and/or structure needed for the activity.

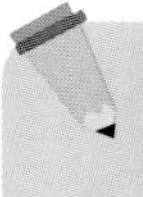

For **writing models** with examples, see *Teaching Resources* pp. 47–61. Rubrics are also provided.

When Minutes Count . . .

Quick Study Students can use *Activity Book* pages 56–57 (shown on p. 305) as they complete each lesson in this chapter.

LESSON 2

Pages 308–310

Objectives

- Identify ways in which community workers promote healthful environments.
- Identify a variety of community workers and their roles in promoting a healthful community.
- Describe the jobs of emergency medical technicians and dispatchers.

When Minutes Count . . .

Assign the Quick Study, Lesson 2, Activity Book pp. 56–57 (shown on p. 305).

Program Resources

- Activity Book pp. 56–57
- Transparency 2

Vocabulary

graffiti p. 308

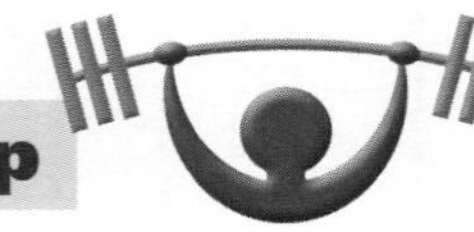

Daily Fitness Tip

Point out to students that keeping their environment clean and safe is important to their physical and mental health. Suggest that with adult supervision they get to know their neighbors. Encourage them to find ways to work with them to help out in their community. They could join a neighborhood association, or volunteer to help with cleanup projects. Raking leaves and picking up trash are good exercise and good for the community.

1. MOTIVATE

Have students list at least five occupations of persons who help make your school a healthful place. Answers might include cafeteria workers, who ensure the safety of food and cleanliness of the cafeteria; janitors, who clean the floors and bathrooms with disinfectants; and the school nurse, who helps keep the students' bodies healthy.

What would the school be like if no one did these jobs? Answers will vary.

LESSON 2

Protecting Your Community

Lesson Focus
Many people with different jobs work to keep your community clean and safe.

Why Learn This?
You can use what you learn to identify people who help take care of your community's health.

Vocabulary
graffiti

Keeping Your Community Clean

A community must be clean to protect the health of the people who live there. It takes many people to keep a community clean. For example, groundskeepers keep outside areas like parks clean and neat. They rake leaves and clean up trash and graffiti. **Graffiti** (gruh•FEET•ee) is writing or drawing made without permission on a public surface, such as a wall or a building.

Custodians and cleaners help keep inside areas clean by emptying trash cans, sweeping, and mopping floors. In hospitals, cleaners keep rooms, equipment, and supplies free from germs.

SUMMARIZE How are the jobs of custodians and cleaners important to the health of a community? They keep public areas clean and free of litter to prevent the spread of germs.

Quick Activity

Community Helpers Think of a community worker you have seen. List ways this person helps keep the community and your environment safe.

◄ Garbage collector

Custodian ►

308

Language Arts

Thank You Have students write a letter of appreciation to a school worker who helps keep the community safe or clean. Consider the groundskeepers, maintenance staff, janitors, cafeteria workers, and school nurse.

Keeping Your Community Safe

To be completely healthful, a community must be safe as well as clean. Many people work hard to keep your community safe. Police officers, for example, direct traffic, keep order, arrest criminals, and give first aid to accident victims.

Firefighters also help keep the community safe. They put out fires, rescue people, and perform first aid. They help prevent fires by giving people advice on how to keep their homes, schools, and workplaces safe.

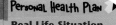

Personal Health Plan

Real-Life Situation
Suppose you were in an unsafe situation.
Real-Life Plan
Make a list, with addresses and phone numbers, of people you can contact if you come across an unsafe situation in your community.

▲ Firefighters

◀ The safety of a community depends on workers who respond to emergencies and help citizens stay safe.

Mounted police officers ▶

2. TEACH

Interpret Visuals—Pictures

Have students look at the pictures on these pages. Have them explain how each worker helps keep a community—both the people and their surroundings—clean and safe.

Discuss

Critical Thinking How does giving tickets to speeders enable police officers to help keep people safe? Speeding can cause crashes. Giving tickets to speeders may make drivers aware of the problem and discourage them from speeding in the future.

Quick Activity

Ask students to explain the importance of a community environmental health plan. Students' responses should focus on how the job impacts the health of both the community and the student's family. For example, the sentences accompanying a drawing of a garbage collector disposing of trash might say, "Garbage can attract rats and insects, which can spread disease. Garbage collectors protect the health of my family and my community by preventing the spread of disease."

Personal Health Plan

The list will vary, depending on the unsafe situation encountered. Possibilities include police, firefighters, EMTs, hospitals, and utility companies. Use this opportunity as a means to have students identify the importance of taking personal responsibility for maintaining a personal health plan for personal safety.

Teacher Tip

Stop, Drop, and Roll Review the three steps a person should follow if his or her clothes catch fire: STOP, DROP, and ROLL. First, STOP moving. DROP to the floor. Cover your face with your hands. With your hands still covering your face, ROLL back and forth until the fire is extinguished.

Activity

Communicate Help students recall the steps they need to take to communicate effectively. They should know the information that is needed.

3. WRAP UP

Lesson 2 Summary and Review

1. graffiti; dispatcher, firefighters, emergency medical technicians (or EMTs)
2. Possible answers: Clean: custodians, groundskeepers, cleaners in hospitals, and street sweepers; Safe: police officers, firefighters, emergency medical technicians, and dispatchers
3. People who work with food must be careful not to contaminate it.
4. Possible answers:

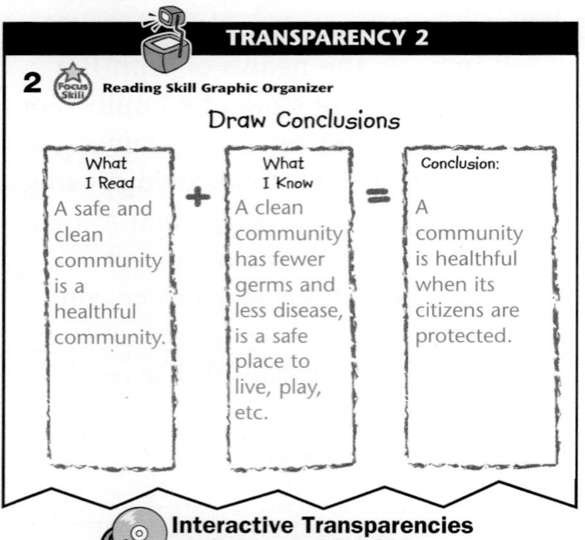

TRANSPARENCY 2
2 Focus Skill Reading Skill Graphic Organizer
Draw Conclusions
What I Read
A safe and clean community is a healthful community.
+
What I Know
A clean community has fewer germs and less disease, is a safe place to live, play, etc.
=
Conclusion:
A community is healthful when its citizens are protected.

Interactive Transparencies available on CD-ROM.

5. People would have to administer first aid and be responsible for getting themselves or others to a hospital. More people might die.

For **writing models** with examples, see *Teaching Resources* pp. 47–61. Rubrics are also provided.

When Minutes Count . . .

Quick Study Students can use *Activity Book* pages 56–57 (shown on p. 305) as they complete each lesson in this chapter.

ACTIVITY

Life Skills
Communicate
Imagine that you have an emergency and must call for help. Make a list of the information you will need to tell the dispatcher.

Emergency medical technicians (EMTs) are workers trained to handle serious injuries or sudden illnesses. EMTs give first aid at the scene of an accident and take care of patients on the way to a hospital.

If you call the police or fire station for help with an emergency, you are likely to talk to a *dispatcher*. Dispatchers tell safety workers like EMTs the information they need to find you.

DRAW CONCLUSIONS How does a dispatcher help save lives?

◀ **Dispatchers work together with police officers, firefighters, and EMTs to help citizens in an emergency.**

Dispatchers receive emergency calls and find out the location and the type of emergency. They notify the police, firefighters, or EMTs and send them to that location.

Lesson 2 Summary and Review

1. **Summarize with Vocabulary**
   Use vocabulary and other terms from this lesson to complete the statements.
   Writing or drawing on buildings is called _____. A _____ takes calls and directs police officers, _____, and _____ to provide help in emergencies.
2. Name five types of workers who help keep a community clean or safe.
3. **Critical Thinking** Why is it important to community health to practice cleanliness when preparing food in a school lunchroom?
4. **DRAW CONCLUSIONS** Draw and complete this graphic organizer to show the benefits of a safe and clean community.

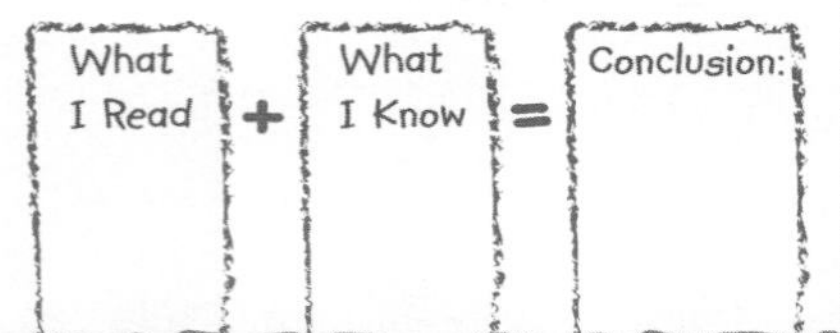

5. **Write to Inform—Description** 
   Describe what life might be like in a community that didn't have EMTs to help in emergencies. How would it be different from a community that does have EMTs?

310

Meeting Individual Needs
Leveled Activities

BELOW-LEVEL Make Posters Have students make posters that encourage people to dispose of trash properly.

ON-LEVEL Calculate Trash During a single National Beach Cleanup along one stretch of U.S. beaches, volunteers collected 641,994 plastic bags, 451,667 plastic bottles, 16,940 buckets, 249,202 plastic drinking straws, and 31,563 plastic toys. Have students find the total number of plastic items collected. 1,391,366 Then tell them that more than 41 million other pieces of plastic were also collected. Make it clear that these were only the plastic items. They don't include rubber, metal, paper, wood, cloth, and glass items. Students may wish to make posters as above.

CHALLENGE Fire Safety Checklist Have students make a checklist of potential fire hazards around homes. Then have them take the checklist home, asking their parents to help promote fire safety.

Citizenship

Building Good Character

Being a Good Neighbor

People in a community live and work together. They depend on one another to provide a clean and safe environment for everyone to enjoy. You can help, too! Here are some things you can do.

- **Volunteer to help out in your community. Organize a bake sale, and donate the proceeds to a local charity.**
- **Report unsafe or suspicious activity you see to your parents, teachers, or a police officer.**
- **Become involved. With adult supervision, work with some friends to clean up a local park or playground. Enjoy the clean and safe environment with a picnic afterward.**
- **Get to know your neighbors. Help a neighbor do yard work, take care of a pet, or clean the garage.**
- **Collect donations for a local shelter or Red Cross office.**
- **Become a *mentor*. A mentor is a positive role model to someone younger. As a mentor, or peer helper, you could help someone learn to read, for example.**

Activity

With your family, make a list of some useful things that could be done in your community. Choose one that you can do together. Plan how to do the task. When you have finished the task, write about how the experience helped make you a better neighbor.

1212

311

Building Good Character

Caring
Citizenship
Fairness
Respect
Responsibility
Trustworthiness

Objectives

- Learn to be part of a community.
- Keep your environment clean and safe.

Program Resource

- Poster 2

BEFORE READING

Brainstorm with students some ways to be a good citizen. Ask them to talk about role models of good citizenship in their own or others' neighborhoods. Discuss ways they might help keep their own community clean and safe. Encourage students to think about ways that they can become involved in their community.

DISCUSS

After students have read the page, ask if they can add any suggestions to the list. Write these suggestions on the board. Guide students in recognizing the activities for which they should have adult supervision or permission.

ACTIVITY

Help students get started with the activity by thinking of one or two suggestions as a class. Remind students that the purpose of the activity is not to solve all the problems but to think of ways to be more involved in keeping their community clean and safe.

Using the Poster

Activity Have students design their own posters about ways to make their community a clean and safe place to live.

Display The posters can be displayed in locations that are visible to all students, such as the school cafeteria, the school entrance, the auditorium, or other common areas.

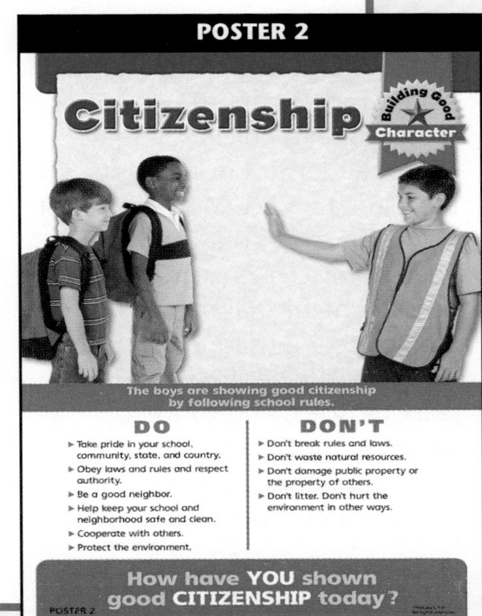
POSTER 2
Citizenship
Building Good Character
The boys are showing good citizenship by following school rules.
DO
Take pride in your school, community, state, and country.
Obey laws and rules and respect authority.
Be a good neighbor.
Help keep your school and neighborhood safe and clean.
Cooperate with others.
Protect the environment.
DON'T
Don't break rules and laws.
Don't waste natural resources.
Don't damage public property or the property of others.
Don't litter. Don't hurt the environment in other ways.
How have YOU shown good CITIZENSHIP today?

LESSON 3
Pages 312–315

Objectives
- ► Define and identify natural resources as renewable or nonrenewable.
- ► Identify ways that people use natural resources.
- ► Explain how fossil fuels are used.

When Minutes Count . . .
Assign the Quick Study, Lesson 3, Activity Book pp. 56–57 (shown on p. 305).

Program Resources
- ► Activity Book pp. 56–57
- ► Transparency 2

Vocabulary
natural resources p. 312,
renewable resources p. 313,
nonrenewable resources p. 313

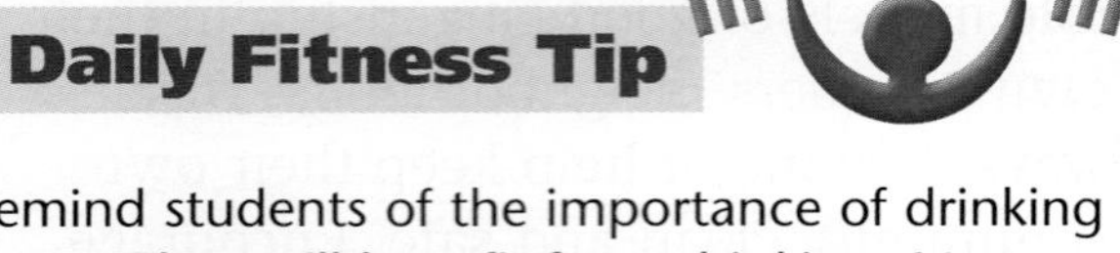
Daily Fitness Tip

Remind students of the importance of drinking water. They will benefit from drinking 64 ounces of water every day. They might freeze some water in plastic bottles the night before so it will stay cool all day, even in a hot car.

1. MOTIVATE

Ask students to think about how much they depend on the earth—even for one day's lunch. Challenge them to name all the natural resources used in providing their lunch today. Answers might include the plants used to make the bread; the plants or animals from which the lettuce, cheese, or meats on sandwiches came; the fruits or other vegetables; the trees for paper lunch bags; oil to make the plastic packaging and to power factories; and water used by plants, animals, and industry.

LESSON 3 Our Natural Resources

Lesson Focus
People use natural resources for energy, for food, and to make things.

Why Learn This?
You can use what you learn to help you understand where resources come from.

Vocabulary
natural resources
renewable resources
nonrenewable resources

Natural Resources

Everything that we use comes from the environment. Energy, building materials, clothing, food, and medicines are all made from natural resources. **Natural resources** (REE•sawr•suhz) are materials from nature that people use to meet their needs. Our natural resources include rocks, minerals, plants, animals, air, sunlight, water, and soil. Oil, metal, cotton, clay, and wind are also natural resources.

We must have some of these resources, such as air and water. Without them, we could not live. We could live without some other resources, such as coal and gas, but our lives would be very different.

The pictures on these pages show eight kinds of natural resources. Which of these resources are nonrenewable? Which are renewable? ▼

▲ Trees
▲ Air
▲ Animals

312

Teacher Tip

Plant Medicines In the United States, more than 40 percent of prescription medicines contain a chemical derived from plants. Of the estimated 250,000 species of plants on earth, only about 2 percent have been screened for possible medicinal benefits. Plant medicines are used to relax or stimulate the nervous system, to relax muscles, and to treat leukemia, heart ailments, glaucoma, pain, infections, and many other ailments.

Renewable resources are resources that can be replaced naturally. Trees, for example, are a renewable resource. When a tree is cut down, a new tree can be planted to grow in its place. Some renewable resources, such as water and wind, will never run out.

Other resources, however, take a very long time to replace or cannot be replaced at all. These are called **nonrenewable resources**. Oil is one of the most important nonrenewable resources. We use oil for energy. Oil is called a *fossil fuel* because it's made of the remains of tiny animals. Oil is found underground, and it takes millions of years to form. When we use oil, it's gone for good.

COMPARE AND CONTRAST How are renewable and nonrenewable resources alike and different?
Alike: Both are resources that people need. Different: Renewable resources can be replaced; nonrenewable resources can never be made again.

Did You Know?
The United States is the largest consumer of oil in the world. By 2100 the United States is expected to use more than 20 billion gallons of oil per day. That's about 70 gallons per person. This fuel is used to heat homes and run machinery and automobiles.

▲ Minerals
▲ Coal, oil, and gas
▲ Water
▼ Soil and crops

313

2. TEACH

Interpret Visuals—Pictures

Discuss the fact that some resources, such as water, are fixed in amount. When we deplete what is locally available in the ground or in reservoirs, we are dependent on the water cycle to replace what we've used. What we've polluted will eventually be cleaned through the water cycle, or we must clean it, which is costly. Certain resources are renewable in some cases and nonrenewable in others. For example, trees are renewable as long as the soil is healthy and some seeds remain. Nonrenewable resources can be replaced only over millions of years.

Discuss

Critical Thinking What is the difference between minerals in a geological sense and minerals in a nutrition sense? The minerals referred to in Chapter 3 are actually single elements. Most minerals in rocks are chemical compounds (made up of two or more elements). Calcium, for example, is a nutritional mineral, but it is not a geological mineral.

Help students understand the difference between oil from underground (a fossil fuel) and vegetable oil.

Teacher Tip

Dangers of Natural Gas
Natural gas (mostly methane) is an odorless and colorless fossil fuel used to power many household appliances. Safety Regulations require that mercaptan be added to the fuel to give it an odor so people can detect gas leaks. Many local gas companies give out samples of the odor so that consumers can recognize it. Tell students that if they smell natural gas, they should leave the area and report it immediately.

Science

Sick Soil To demonstrate how plants can absorb harmful materials from soil and water, have students cut the stem of a fresh white carnation and place the flower into a cup of water. Then have them add a few drops of red food coloring to represent harmful substances. The next day, students will see that the food coloring was absorbed by the flower through its stem and into its petals.

Health Background

Origins of Natural Gas Natural methane gas has three primary origins. *Biogenic* methane is the result of decomposition of organic materials by methane-producing microorganisms near the surface of the earth. (Such microorganisms also live in our own intestinal tracts.) *Abiogenic* methane originates when gases closer to the earth's core migrate upward and form methane deposits. *Thermogenic* methane is formed in a manner similar to that of oil. At very deep levels, where temperatures are higher, methane gas is found primarily, and less oil is found. Thermogenic natural gas provides 25 percent of the energy consumed in the United States.

Source: *Natural Gas Supply Association*

TEACH *continued*

Discuss

Problem Solving Think of natural resources and items made from natural resources that you use in your daily life. Make a list and then share it with the class. Students' responses should be specific, such as "I use a computer, parts of which are made from plastic, which comes from the fossil fuel oil, and parts of which are made from rocks and minerals."

Specific items will come from most of the following general ones:

Air is vital to nearly all living things.

Animals are used as food, and their hides or fur are sometimes used to make shoes, coats, and other clothing items.

Fossil fuels are used to provide energy to heat and cool homes and industries, to power various motor vehicles, and to manufacture many chemicals.

Land is used to grow crops and other plants; most of the **minerals** we use are mined from the land.

Plants are used as food sources, clothing, and other items.

Water is needed for drinking, cleaning, and hundreds of other human activities, and it is home to millions of living things.

Activity

Communicate Help students recall the steps for effective communication. They should understand the information the little sister would need (such as what a natural resource is and what items or benefits come from them) and give it at a level she'll understand. Then they should select two natural resources, such as fossil fuels and plants, and explain that they are sources of items in her room (such as a plastic camera and wooden furniture). Remind students that the little sister will respond best if they are not rude or condescending.

◀ Coal

▲ Coal is another fossil fuel resource that is nonrenewable. It is burned by energy plants to produce electricity.

▼ Energy plant

How People Use Resources

Many resources went into building your home and the things in it. Paper and wood come from trees. Metal comes from minerals in rocks. Glass is made from sand. Concrete, cement, and plaster are all made from rocks. Plastics are made from oil.

Some clothes are made from plant fibers such as cotton or from animal products such as wool. Other materials, like plastic, are made from oil. Your food comes from plants and animals, whose energy originally came from soil, water, and sunlight. The medicines and all the chemicals in your house come from plants, animals, rocks, or minerals.

ACTIVITY

Life Skills

Communicate

Suppose that your little sister says nothing in her room was ever part of the environment. Choose at least two natural resources, and explain to her how those resources were used to make things in her room.

314

ESL/ELL Support

COMPREHENSIBLE INPUT Help students understand the concepts of natural resources by drawing a circle containing the phrase *Natural Resources* in the center of a large sheet of kraft paper.

Beginning Have students glue pictures in circles that they connect to pictures of their primary source.

Intermediate Have students attach their pictures with a descriptive sentence ("Coins come from minerals in the earth.").

Advanced After they attach their pictures, have students write a paragraph that names some natural resources and products that come from them.

Natural resources are used to run your home. Electricity is made by burning coal or oil or by using sunlight, flowing water, wind, or heat from within the earth. The electricity runs through wires made of metals that come from rocks.

Your oven runs either on electricity or on gas, which comes from under ground. To heat your home, you might use oil, gas, wood, or electricity. Some homes are heated with corn-burning stoves.

DRAW CONCLUSIONS In what way is water an important natural resource?

Possible answers: People and animals need water to live. Plants, which give us food, building materials, and energy, also need water to live.

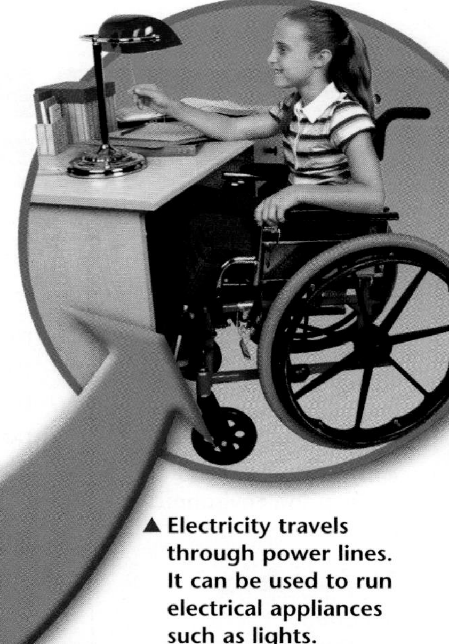

▲ **Electricity travels through power lines. It can be used to run electrical appliances such as lights.**

Lesson 3 Summary and Review

1. **Summarize with Vocabulary** Use vocabulary and other terms from this lesson to complete the statements.

   Materials from nature that people use are called _____. Plants are examples of _____ resources, which can be replaced. Coal and oil, which are _____ resources, are examples of _____ fuels.

2. Name five natural resources. Give an example of how people use each resource.

3. **Critical Thinking** In what ways is water a renewable resource? In what ways is it nonrenewable?

4. **DRAW CONCLUSIONS** Draw and complete this graphic organizer to show why people need to save natural resources.

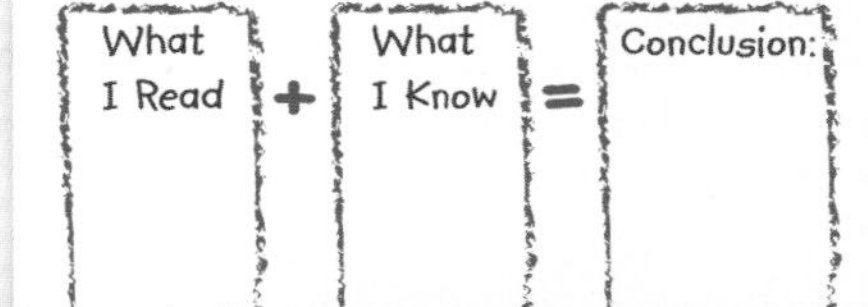

5. **Write to Express—Business Letter** Write a letter to your local power company to request information about your power supply. Ask what natural resources are used to produce electricity and where those resources come from.

315

Meeting Individual Needs
Leveled Activities

BELOW-LEVEL Solar Power Have students find examples of ways energy from the sun is used. Have them set up their examples in a display.

ON-LEVEL The Dust Bowl Have students find out how poor farming practices and drought in the 1930s led to the Dust Bowl. Have them find photographs of the southern plains prior to and during the Dust Bowl and share their findings with the class.

CHALLENGE Compare Fossil Fuels Have students find out how coal, oil, and natural gas form. Have them write a paragraph comparing the ways these sources of energy form.

3. WRAP UP

Lesson 3 Summary and Review

1. natural resources; renewable; nonrenewable; fossil
2. Possible answers for natural resources: water, air, land, minerals, plants and animals, and fossil fuels. Possible answers for uses: Water is used for drinking. People and animals need air to breathe. Land is used to grow crops. Plants and animals are used for food, shelter, and clothing. Minerals are used in manufacturing. Fossil fuels are used for energy and product manufacturing.
3. Renewable: you get fresh water when it rains; all the water we use goes back into the environment; Nonrenewable: water that is dirty is difficult to clean.
4. Examples may include:

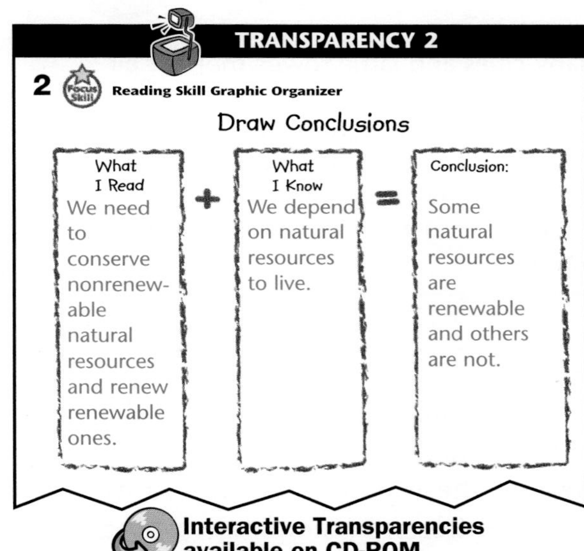

TRANSPARENCY 2

2 Reading Skill Graphic Organizer

Draw Conclusions

What I Read	+	What I Know	=	Conclusion:
We need to conserve nonrenewable natural resources and renew renewable ones.		We depend on natural resources to live.		Some natural resources are renewable and others are not.

Interactive Transparencies available on CD-ROM.

5. Letters should be in proper business letter format, courteous, and clear, with specific answerable questions.

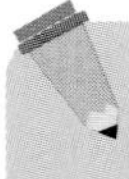

For **writing models** with examples, see *Teaching Resources* pp. 47–61. Rubrics are also provided.

When Minutes Count . . .

Quick Study Students can use *Activity Book* pages 56–57 (shown on p. 305) as they complete each lesson in this chapter.

LESSON 4

Pages 316–321

Objectives

- Identify sources of air, water, and land pollution, and explain how these types of pollution affect human health.
- Identify several ways to prevent air, water, and land pollution.

When Minutes Count . . .

Assign the Quick Study, Lesson 4, Activity Book pp. 56–57 (shown on p. 305).

Program Resources

- Activity Book pp. 56–57
- Transparency 2

Vocabulary

pollution p. 316, **solid waste** p. 317

Daily Fitness Tip

Many cities and large towns monitor air pollution on a daily basis. Stress to students that when smog or ozone alerts are issued, they should avoid being outdoors for extended periods of time. Suggest that they get exercise indoors, at a gym or recreation center, for example.

1. MOTIVATE

Have students compare the two pictures on these pages.

How do these pictures of the same city appear different? The picture on page 316 is cloudy and dirty while the picture of the city on page 317 appears clear and clean looking.

Explain to students that the picture on page 316 shows what the city looked like when its air was polluted with smog. The city has become a nicer looking and more healthful place for people to live and work through the use of air pollution controls.

LESSON 4

Preventing Pollution

Lesson Focus
People can protect natural resources by reducing pollution.

Why Learn This?
You can use what you learn to help protect the air, water, and land and to keep the environment healthful.

Vocabulary
pollution
solid waste

Preventing Air Pollution

People need clean air to stay healthy. But in many places, especially near cities and factories, the air is polluted. **Pollution** (puh•LOO•shuhn) is harmful material in the air, water, or land. Air pollution includes dust and smoke particles and gases such as ozone and carbon monoxide.

Air pollution can cause eye and skin irritation and breathing problems such as asthma. Air pollution can even contribute to serious diseases like heart disease and cancer. People who breathe polluted air get diseases such as colds and flu more often.

▼ Smog is a form of air pollution. Laws to reduce smog have made some cities more healthful places to live.

Myth and Fact

Myth: Air pollution affects only living things.
Fact: Chemicals in polluted air can eat away at many kinds of building materials. Buildings and sculptures made from limestone or marble are especially likely to suffer damage from air pollution.

316

Teacher Tip

Smoking Explain that cigarette smoke is a source of indoor air pollution. Tobacco smoke contains carcinogenic chemicals, which means that it can cause cancer. People who live with smokers have a greater risk of developing lung cancer and respiratory infections than people who live with nonsmokers.

Use the information in this lesson to discourage students from starting this addictive habit and from spending too much time in the presence of cigarette smoke.

If the energy plant where the electricity is made burns a fossil fuel to make the electricity, there is air pollution near the energy plant. Also, the use of energy to manufacture the appliance itself probably caused some air pollution.

A lot of air pollution comes from factories and energy plants. Many energy plants burn fossil fuels such as coal. The smoke and gas that are released pollute the air. Burning **solid waste** such as garbage and litter also releases harmful gases and particles into the air. One way industries reduce this kind of pollution is by installing "scrubbers" in smokestacks. Scrubbers take out many of the pollutants before they get into the air.

Cars and trucks are some of the worst polluters. Over the years, manufacturers have made cars and trucks that pollute less. However, it's still important to use cars only when necessary. You can reduce air pollution by walking, biking, and using public transportation.

Health & Technology

Biofilters Some industries are trying a new way to reduce air pollution. Biofilters are being used to filter polluted air by using microorganisms. These organisms feed on the pollutants, removing them from the air. Biofiltration can be used by small businesses such as paint shops and garages as well as by large factories.

Focus Skill **DRAW CONCLUSIONS** **How could using an electrical appliance in one place add to air pollution somewhere else?**

This gas/electric hybrid car uses less gas, so it does not pollute as much as most cars. ▶

2. TEACH

Content-Area Reading Support

Using Paragraph Structure Have students read the first sentence in the first paragraph on this page. Point out that the sentence gives the main idea of this paragraph. Explain that the sentences that follow explain why factories and energy plants cause so much pollution. Encourage students to pay attention to the first sentence of a paragraph.

Discuss

Have students take a deep breath and then exhale.

Critical Thinking **How is air filtered, or cleaned, when you breathe?** Students may wish to refer to the illustration on page 167. The mucus and cilia in the nose, and the mucus in the throat help trap dust, pollutants, and pollen from the air.

Point out that the nasal cavities and trachea remove many pollutants from the air before they get into the lungs. There are many other pollutants, however, that the human body cannot filter out.

Critical Thinking **What kinds of pollutants might be difficult for your body to filter out?** gases and tiny particles

Math

Trash Average Calculate the average amount of trash each person in a family generates each day. (1) collect all trash in a bag over several days; (2) weigh the bag; (3) calculate the weight of family trash per day by dividing the total weight by the number of days collected; (4) find the weight of trash per person per day by dividing step 3 by the number of people in the family. Then have students compare this to the national average of 4.4 pounds per day per person.

Health Background

Asthma Asthma is a disease of the lungs. People with asthma have difficulty breathing and often wheeze or cough when they breathe. Asthma interferes with the lungs' ability to remove carbon dioxide from the blood and replace it with oxygen. The airways become inflamed and narrowed. Pollen, dust, and air pollutants such as perfumes, cigarette smoke, and car exhaust can trigger asthma attacks.

Source: *American Academy of Allergy, Asthma & Immunology*

For more background, visit the **Webliography** in Teacher Resources at **www.harcourtschool.com/health**
Keyword diseases

TEACH *continued*

Interpret Visuals—Pictures

After students look at the illustrations on these pages, ask them to identify pollution sources that individuals have direct control over. Students may recognize that individuals who use pesticides, fertilizers, and motor oil are responsible, as are large factories, for these pollutants getting into our reservoirs and other water sources.

Consumer Activity

When researching bottled water, students should find out exactly where the water comes from, how it is treated (if at all), and what nutrients it contains. They should then compare it to the local tap water. In many cases, tap water and bottled water come from the same source.

When might bottled water be particularly useful? when the electricity goes out (during a blackout) and water pumps and treatment facilities might not work; when you visit another country and you're not sure if the water is safe for you; for convenience when exercising

Discuss

Explain that some manufacturing processes produce thermal, or heat, pollution. This pollution is the result of the disposal of very hot wastewater into nearby waterways. Thermal pollution raises the temperature of lakes, rivers, and streams.

Critical Thinking How could thermal pollution affect the environment? Hot wastewater dumped into waterways could make the water too hot for the plants and animals that live in the rivers and streams.

Consumer Activity

Accessing Valid Health Information Advertisers suggest that bottled water is more healthful than tap water. Is it true? Use library sources and the steps for accessing valid health information on pages 53–54 to help you find the answer.

Preventing Water Pollution

Polluted water is bad for living things. There are many sources of water pollution. Some factories dump chemicals into water. In some places, untreated sewage flows into the ocean. Sometimes, people dump trash in rivers, and boats spill fuel.

Many water pollutants begin on land. For example, many farms use chemicals to kill insects and fertilize the soil. Rainwater flows over the soil, picking up the chemicals and fertilizers. They become pollutants when they flow into streams, rivers, lakes, and oceans.

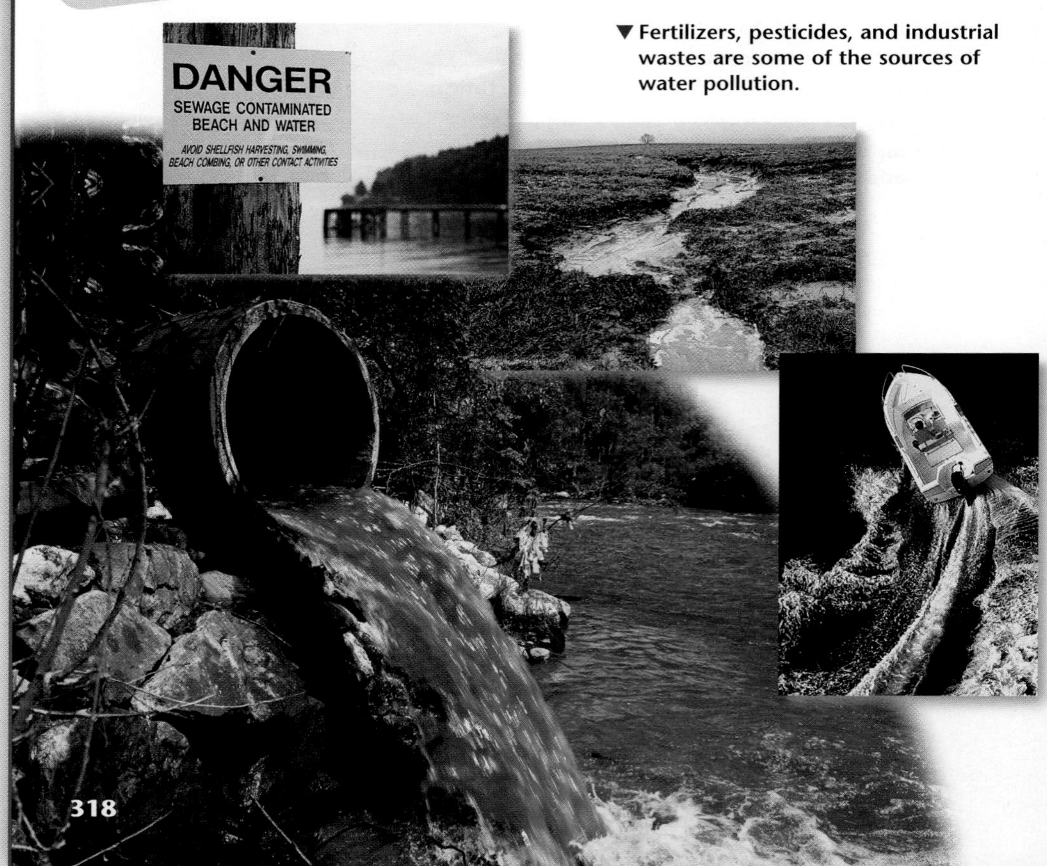

DANGER
SEWAGE CONTAMINATED BEACH AND WATER
AVOID SHELLFISH HARVESTING, SWIMMING, BEACH COMBING, OR OTHER CONTACT ACTIVITIES

▼ Fertilizers, pesticides, and industrial wastes are some of the sources of water pollution.

318

ESL/ELL Support

COMPREHENSIBLE INPUT While many students may have experience with pollution, the concept may be a difficult one to understand. Its effects may be easier to convey by drawing and writing.

Beginning Have students make a drawing of people dealing with air, land, and water pollution. For example, drawings may show a stick figure coughing while walking along a street where air is smoggy, swimming in obviously polluted water, or smelling garbage in the streets.

Intermediate Have students list places they go every week by car. Have them describe ways they could reduce air pollution by making changes to their weekly trips.

Advanced Have students discuss, and then write a paragraph about, what life would be like if there were no public sewer and trash services.

▲ The Cuyahoga River in Cleveland, Ohio, was once so polluted with trash and oil that it caught on fire. The fire made many people realize how important it was to clean up the nation's rivers. Today the Cuyahoga River is much cleaner.

Water pollution can be very dangerous. Water that is polluted with human waste carries pathogens that can make people very ill or even kill them. Swimming in water that is polluted with chemicals can hurt your skin. Drinking polluted water, or eating fish that have lived in it, can cause serious diseases of the liver, kidneys, and brain.

We can protect our water supply. The Environmental Protection Agency (EPA) controls water pollution. The United States government's Clean Water Act protects water supplies. You can help by not throwing trash into water.

CAUSE AND EFFECT **What might be the effects of pouring untreated sewage into a lake?** The sewage would pollute the lake water. People who swam in the water or drank the water could get very sick.

Quick Activity

Identify Water Pollutants Identify the kinds of water pollution shown on these pages. Choose one source of water pollution, and write about ways it can be controlled.

Quick Activity

Remind students that with the help of parents, they can express their concerns to local businesses that may be polluting. Remind them that—with their new knowledge—they can help prevent pollution from groundwater runoff by remembering, and respectfully reminding their family members, to safely dispose of pollutants such as motor oil and paints. They might contact their local sanitation department to find out which days or sites have been set aside for hazardous waste disposal.

Content-Area Reading Support

Using Abbreviations Direct students' attention to the letters *EPA* in parentheses. Ask a volunteer to explain what the letters stand for. Tell students that the letters in parentheses are the first letter of each word in **E**nvironmental **P**rotection **A**gency. Inform them that sometimes abbreviations are used in place of a full name in textbooks, but that usually the full name is used when it is first introduced. After its abbreviation is placed in parentheses, the abbreviation can be used from then on in place of the full name.

Science

Mercury and Fish Explain that mercury is a metal that occurs naturally in the environment. However, dangerously high levels of mercury occur when mercury is released into the atmosphere, primarily from burning household and industrial wastes, and from burning fossil fuels such as coal. Have students find out how fish can become contaminated with high levels of mercury and what sorts of health risks the fish pose to humans who eat them. Have students share their research.

Social Studies

Clean Water Act Have students research Ohio's Cuyahoga River fire of 1969 as well as the Clean Water Act. If they have classroom or home access to books with photos, or can access and print such photos on the Internet, they might present a photoessay of the river and the fire. Have them write a paragraph describing each image and the causes of the fire. They should write an accompanying summary of this disaster and the Clean Water Act of 1972.

Health Background

Mercury Matters The heavy metal mercury that pollutes water can be absorbed into the body by tissues and organs. It can cause cancer, badly harm unborn children, permanently damage the brain and kidneys, harm the lungs, stomach, and large intestine, and cause increased blood pressure and heart rate.

Source: *Environmental Protection Agency*

For more background, visit the **Webliography** in Teacher Resources at **www.harcourtschool.com/health** **Keyword** community/environmental health

TEACH *continued*

Discuss

After students have read these pages, assess their understanding of the relationship of land pollution to water pollution.

Critical Thinking How can land pollution affect drinking water? Poisonous chemicals and pollutants, like motor oil, fertilizers, pesticides, road salt, and paints, can leak into the ground or onto roadways, or can be disposed of improperly. Then rain can wash them into lakes and other water reservoirs, or they can soak into the ground and contaminate the groundwater, which is a major source of drinking water.

Critical Thinking How does a sanitary landfill help protect the land? A sanitary landfill has a plastic or clay liner that prevents harmful pollutants from seeping into the ground. Covering the trash with soil prevents the breeding of pests.

Activity

Responsibility—Guide students to recognize that Keona has a responsibility to protect the environment, even when no one is around to see her actions. Keona should carry the water bottle out of the woods. She can then either recycle it or dispose of it properly.

ACTIVITY

Building Good Character

Responsibility Keona has just finished drinking a bottle of water. There is no place to dispose of the plastic bottle because she is hiking in the woods. Name at least two ways Keona can show responsible behavior.

Preventing Land Pollution

Land pollution can harm your health and the environment. Littering is one kind of land pollution. Litter that is left in uncovered dumps can harm your health. Flies, mosquitoes, and rats that carry diseases often breed in dumps.

In many places, dumps are being replaced by sanitary landfills. In a *landfill*, trash is placed in a large pit that has a waterproof liner of plastic or clay. The trash is then covered with layers of soil. If the landfill is made properly, the waste won't harm the environment.

Poisonous chemicals and pollutants, like oil from cars, can be a problem. When it rains, chemicals on the road wash onto the land. They make the soil poisonous, which can kill plants and animals. These chemicals also get into the water supply.

◀ Salt makes an icy road safer to drive on. Since salt can harm plants and animals, many communities now use sand on icy roads.

▼ Litter that is not put in the proper place can cause disease.

320

Art

Trash Art Have students reuse bags or boxes to make trash containers for the car. They can color them or decorate them with wrapping paper, ribbon, and other scrap materials.

Teacher Tip

Take Responsibility Point out that many air pollutants smell bad to humans for good reason—they are poisonous. If something has a bad smell or makes you cough, for example, it is probably poisonous. Urge students to take action when something smells bad. Tell a parent, teacher, or public health authority such as a firefighter. Never assume that someone else has already reported a problem or that it will just go away on its own. Your report could save someone's life.

People can reduce land pollution by not dumping trash or garbage. Take empty paint cans, batteries, and cleaning supply containers to collection centers in your community that accept poisonous waste.

Recycling materials instead of throwing them away can also reduce land pollution. For example, metal cans can be used to make new cans. Plastic containers can be reused. Another thing you can do is use a fabric bag to carry things home from the store instead of getting a plastic or paper bag from the store.

MAIN IDEA AND DETAILS List three ways to reduce or prevent land pollution.

Possible answers: Replace dumps with sanitary landfills. Dispose of oil properly. Take measures to prevent oil spills. Pick up litter, and dispose of it properly. Use sand instead of salt for icy roads. Use reusable bags at the store.

▼ **Many states have Adopt-a-Highway programs. Businesses or groups adopt a section of a highway and then work to keep it free of litter.**

Lesson 4 Summary and Review

1. **Summarize with Vocabulary**
   Use vocabulary and other terms from this lesson to complete the statements.
   People need to protect air, land, and water from _____. Burning _____ pollutes the air. One way factories remove some pollutants from smoke is by using _____. To reduce land pollution, dumps are being replaced by _____.
2. Name one law that has helped reduce water pollution.
3. **Critical Thinking** What might happen if no one took responsibility for air pollution?
4. **DRAW CONCLUSIONS** Draw and complete this graphic organizer to show why people need to prevent pollution.

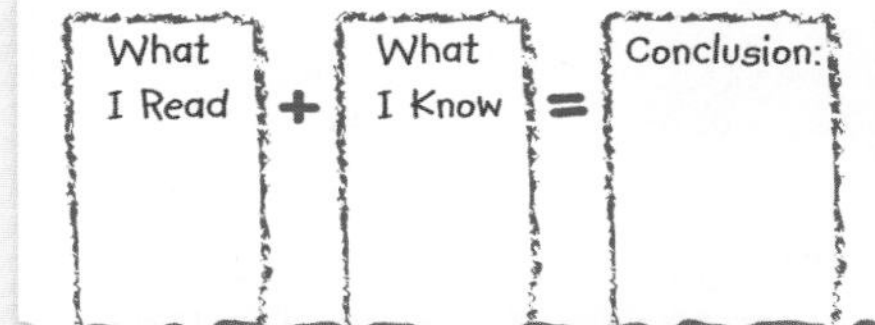

5. **Write to Inform—Explanation**
   Think of some rules that your school has, such as don't litter, keep the cafeteria clean, and so on. Write a paragraph explaining why these and other rules are important to your health and your classmates' health.

Language Arts

Polluted Picnic Have students imagine a picnic next to a polluted lake. Invite them to describe the scene and tell how it feels to look at and smell the pollution. Ask them to write a story about the "polluted picnic," including steps they take in the story to improve the situation for future picnics by the lake.

3. WRAP UP

Lesson 4 Summary and Review

1. pollution, solid waste, scrubbers, sanitary landfills
2. the Clean Water Act
3. Possible answers: The air would get more and more polluted. People would get sicker and sicker. More people would die from air pollution.
4. Responses may include:

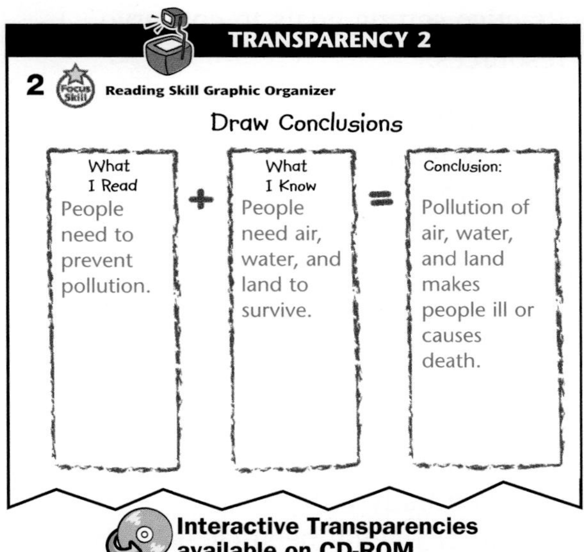

TRANSPARENCY 2
2 Reading Skill Graphic Organizer
Draw Conclusions
What I Read
People need to prevent pollution.
+
What I Know
People need air, water, and land to survive.
=
Conclusion:
Pollution of air, water, and land makes people ill or causes death.
Interactive Transparencies available on CD-ROM.

5. Answers should show an understanding of what pollution is, how it affects human health, and how it can be reduced or prevented.

For **writing models** with examples, see *Teaching Resources* pp. 47–61. Rubrics are also provided.

When Minutes Count . . .

Quick Study Students can use *Activity Book* pages 56–57 (shown on p. 305) as they complete each lesson in this chapter.

Life Skills

Communicate
Make Responsible Decisions
Manage Stress
Refuse
Resolve Conflicts
Set Goals

Objectives

- ► Identify strategies to set goals.
- ► Practice setting goals to conserve resources.

Program Resources

- ► Activity Book p. 59
- ► Poster 12

1. MOTIVATE

Tell students that on average, Americans use approximately 75 to 80 gallons of water per person per day. Much of this water eventually returns to the water supply after having been cleaned. Discuss with students what must be done to the water to make it usable.

2. TEACH

Direct students' attention to the photos of Jane and her family thinking about reducing the amount of water they consume.

Step 1

What is the first thing Jane must do? She must decide on a goal. Her goal is to reduce the amount of water she and her family use.

Step 2

What steps might Jane and her family take to save water? Possible answers: turn off the water while brushing teeth or shaving; take showers instead of baths; wash clothes and run the dishwasher only with full loads

Set Goals

To Save Resources

Think about the amount of resources you use every day. What are some ways your family can save some of these resources? Using the steps for **Setting Goals** can help you plan to save resources.

Jane knows that water is an important resource. She notices some ways water is wasted in her home. She talks about this with her parents. What should Jane do next?

1 Choose a goal.

Jane and her parents decide that their goal will be to reduce the amount of water wasted in their home.

2 List steps to meet the goal. Determine whether you will need any help.

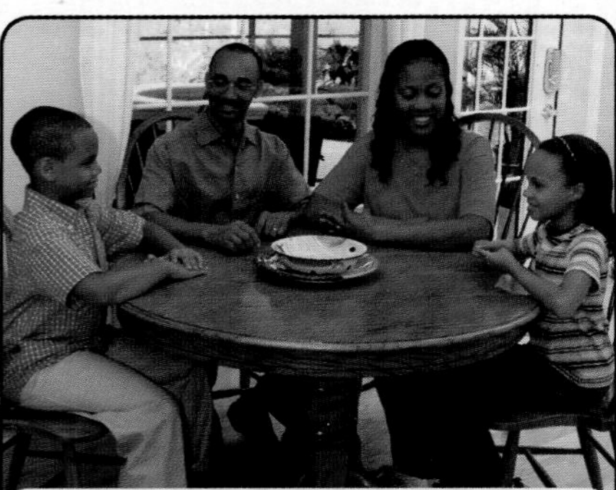

Jane discusses her goal and asks everyone to suggest ways to help reduce waste and save water.

Language Arts

Conservation Log Suggest to students that they keep an ongoing log in which they record their families' efforts to conserve resources. Have students set goals and discuss the goals with their families. However, be sensitive when assigning conservation projects. Some students' families may not want to participate in home recycling or energy conservation programs.

ACTIVITY BOOK P. 59

Name ____________________

Life Skill

Set Goals

Steps for Setting Goals

1. Choose a goal.
2. List steps to meet the goal. Determine whether you will need any help.
3. Check your progress as you work toward the goal.
4. Reflect on and evaluate your progress toward the goal.

Use the steps to help these students set goals.

A. Matt and his friends like to play basketball on the neighborhood court. One of the backboards is cracked, the baskets don't have nets, and grass is growing through cracks in the asphalt. Matt decides he wants to get the basketball court repaired.

- How can Matt get the help he needs to repair the basketball court?

Possible answer: Matt could talk to his parents about the condition of the court and his desire to repair it. Matt and his parents could contact other families and ask if they would be willing to volunteer time or materials to do the repairs. Finally, a date should be set for doing the work.

B. Kayla knows that she is careless about conserving energy. She usually forgets to turn off the lights or TV when she leaves the room. She often leaves her CD player on when she leaves for school.

- Use the steps for setting goals to help Kayla make a plan for saving energy.

Possible answer: Kayla should make a list of things she can do to save energy. She needs to find a way to remind herself to turn off lights, the TV, and the CD player. Kayla should keep a log of her activities and evaluate her progress after one week.

© Harcourt

Available online. www.harcourtschool.com/health

3 **Check your progress as you work toward the goal.**

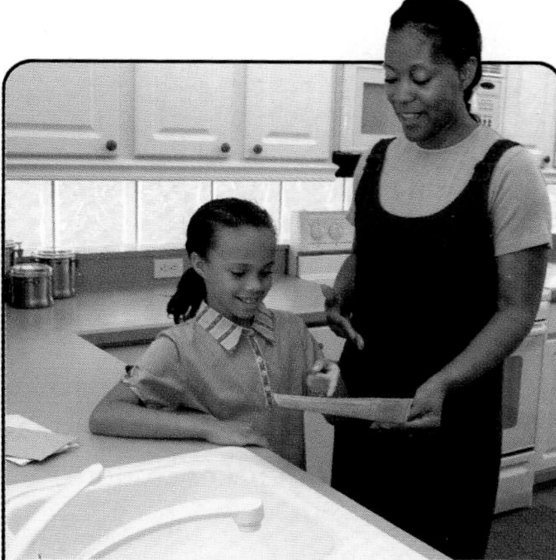

Jane and her mom check the water bill each month to see how much water the family is using. Jane records how much water is being saved.

4 **Reflect on and evaluate your progress toward the goal.**

Jane and her family discuss how many gallons of water they are saving. After a few months, her family finds that saving water is easy.

Problem Solving

Raoul hears on the news that the air in his city is becoming more polluted. Raoul knows that car exhaust causes air pollution. He notices that his family members drive the car a lot. They even drive to a store that is only two blocks away.

How might Raoul and his parents use the steps for **Setting Goals** to help them reduce air pollution? How does their effort demonstrate good citizenship?

Step 3

How did they monitor their progress? Jane's family checked the water bill each month to see how much water the family used.

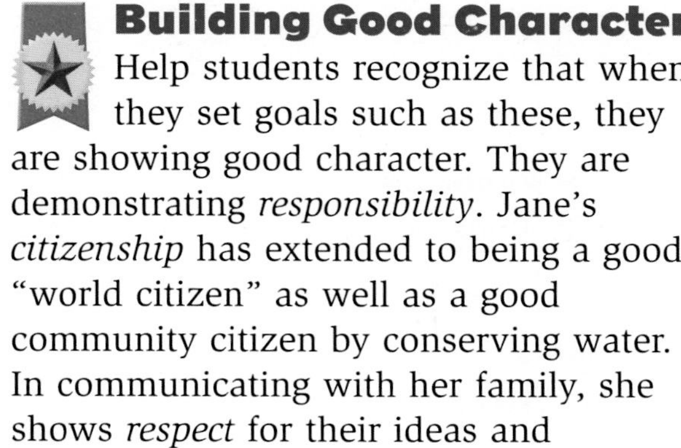

Building Good Character

Help students recognize that when they set goals such as these, they are showing good character. They are demonstrating *responsibility*. Jane's *citizenship* has extended to being a good "world citizen" as well as a good community citizen by conserving water. In communicating with her family, she shows *respect* for their ideas and viewpoints.

Critical Thinking **What would have happened if one of the faucets in Jane's house had been dripping?** Jane might have noticed that the water use was not going down as much as expected. Her family would have had to repair the drip to see the expected change in water use.

Step 4

How did Jane and her family evaluate their goals? Jane and her family compared the water use from month to month. They saw that the amount of water used was reduced.

3. WRAP UP

Problem Solving

Have students describe the importance of parental guidance and other trusted adults in goal setting. Their responses should reflect the steps for Setting Goals. Raoul and his parents should choose a goal (perhaps reducing the number of their car trips); list steps to meet that goal (combine trips from school with a trip to the library and walk to the store, for example); check their progress (see if they are using less gasoline); and evaluate their progress. (Do they feel they are getting more exercise? Are they spending less time in the car? Are they spending less on gas?)

Using the Poster

Activity Have students work in pairs to create a poster about setting a goal to conserve a particular resource.

Display The poster can be displayed in a location such as the cafeteria or an entrance to the school, to encourage all students to set goals.

POSTER 12
Set Goals
LIFE SKILLS
The girl is setting a goal to recycle.
Steps for Setting Goals
1 Choose a goal.
2 Plan steps to reach that goal. Determine whether you will need help.
3 Check your progress as you work toward the goal.
4 Evaluate the results of your work.
What GOALS have YOU SET?
POSTER 12

LESSON 5
Pages 324–326

Objectives
- Define *conservation*.
- Describe ways to conserve water, air, land, and other resources.

When Minutes Count . . .
Assign the Quick Study, Lesson 5, Activity Book pp. 56–57 (shown on p. 305).

Program Resources
- Activity Book pp. 56–57, 60
- Transparency 2

Vocabulary
conservation p. 324

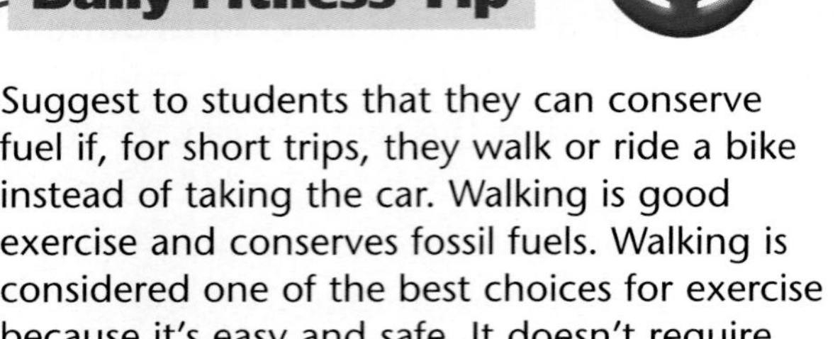

Daily Fitness Tip

Suggest to students that they can conserve fuel if, for short trips, they walk or ride a bike instead of taking the car. Walking is good exercise and conserves fossil fuels. Walking is considered one of the best choices for exercise because it's easy and safe. It doesn't require any training or special equipment, except for good shoes. Brisk walking can burn as many calories as running, but it's less likely to cause injuries.

For more on activity and fitness, see *Be Active! Resources for Physical Education* p. 161.

1. MOTIVATE

Optional Activity Materials: 2 baking pans, loose topsoil, sod with soil attached, hair dryer

Put some loose topsoil in one pan. In the other, put some sod with soil attached. Use a hair dryer and blow across each pan. Have students describe what happens.

What does this demonstration show? Soil covered by vegetation is protected from erosion by wind.

Critical Thinking What happens if topsoil is eroded by wind? The soil nutrients that help plants grow are lost, so plants and crops cannot grow well.

LESSON 5

Ways to Practice Conservation

Lesson Focus
Conserving resources such as water, air, and land is important to people's health.

Why Learn This?
You can use what you learn to practice conservation.

Vocabulary
conservation

Conservation Is Important

Clean air, water, and land are all part of a healthful environment. If not conserved, these resources and others will not last very long. **Conservation** (kahn•ser•VAY•shuhn) is the careful use of resources. Conservation makes resources last longer.

Conservation can help both renewable and nonrenewable resources last longer. For example, as long as people don't cut down trees faster than new ones grow, we should have forest resources. We can also conserve by using less of our resources such as fossil fuels and minerals. Recycling or reusing materials also reduces how much of our resources we use up.

Myth and Fact

Myth: Recycling aluminum cans saves only aluminum.

Fact: Recycling aluminum saves energy, too. The energy saved by recycling one aluminum can could run a television for three hours.

▼ Areas that protect animals and plants help conserve our natural resources.

ESL/ELL Support

COMPREHENSIBLE INPUT Review with students the meaning of *conservation* and the activities that help protect community resources and the environment.

Beginning Have students work in groups to pantomime different ways to conserve resources such as fossil fuels and water.

Intermediate Have students use construction paper and old magazines to make a poster showing several ways to conserve resources. Have them label their poster.

Advanced Have students make a list of the different ways people in their community conserve resources, such as through recycling. Have them share their work with the class.

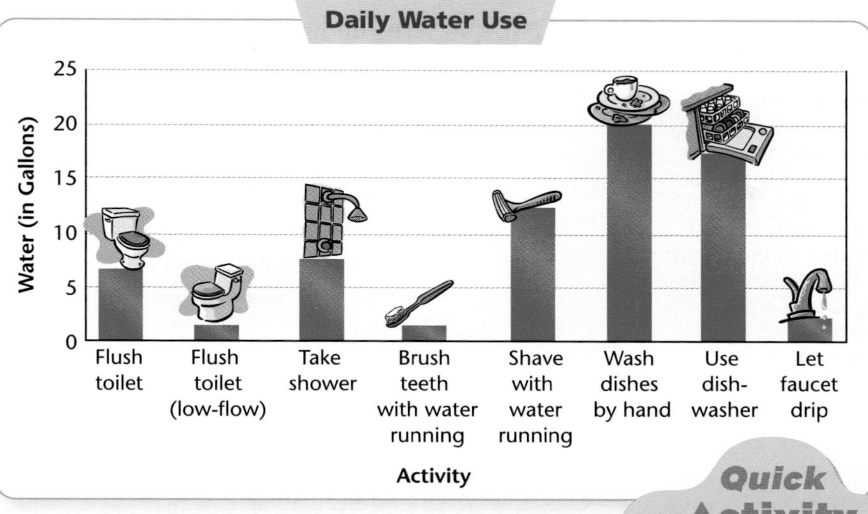

Quick Activity

Analyze Information Use the bar graph to estimate how much water a family of four uses each day for the activities listed. List ways this water use could be reduced.

We can conserve water in many ways. For example, turn off the faucet when brushing your teeth. Take showers instead of baths. A five-minute shower uses about one-half as much water as an average bath. If you live in a dry area, plant your garden with plants that need little water.

People can also conserve water by installing low-flow toilets and low-flow showerheads. One type of low-flow showerhead adds air to the water. It can cut the amount of water used by one-half. Low-flow aerators can also be installed on faucets in your home. They mix air with water. The air helps the flow of water feel strong even though it has been reduced.

COMPARE AND CONTRAST How are tree conservation and coal conservation alike and different?

You can conserve both by using less of them. You can grow more trees, but you can't grow more coal.

325

2. TEACH

Discuss

Students may find it hard to comprehend the idea of the need to conserve water. They might logically argue, "We can never use all the water. Water is cleaned and replenished in the water cycle." Acknowledge that we cannot deplete earth's total supply of water. Explain that, while water is purified through evaporation, that cycle doesn't purify the water at the same rate at which we pollute it. (Point out that, as rain falls through polluted air, it becomes polluted again.) To clean water artificially is time-consuming and costly. Also, if drought and overuse of water deplete a community's or an area's water supply, the water in that community or area may not be replenished for a long while. The water that evaporated may be held in the atmosphere in clouds that move on to rain in another area.

Interpret Visuals—Pictures

Explain that state and national parks are protected land areas. Have students read aloud the caption on page 324. Discuss with them some ways this land is protected. Students might answer that the land, animals, and plants are protected from human pollution and overuse.

Quick Activity

Before students attempt calculations, ask them to identify activities that waste water. Then have them answer the question about a family of four and list ways to conserve water. Flushing toilets and taking showers probably use the most water, since using the dishwasher will most likely occur once daily. To conserve water, they can fix dripping faucets, turn off water while brushing teeth or shaving, use low-flow toilets and showerheads, and use a dishwasher.

Teacher Tip

Conserve Water Tell students that every day millions of gallons of water are used to wash hotel sheets and towels that are used only once. In an effort to conserve water, some hotels are asking guests to hang their towels on a rack so they can be used the next day of their hotel stay.

Language Arts

Water, Water Everywhere Have students use construction paper and old magazines to make pamphlets to depict the ways in which we use water. Suggest that they write each pamphlet in the form of an ad, selling *water*, the wonderful commodity with so many uses.

Consumer Activity

Explain that many energy-efficient appliances cost more but they save money because they use less energy.

3. WRAP UP

Lesson 5 Summary and Review

1. Conservation, recycle
2. Possible answer: trees, sunlight, wind
3. When you burn less fossil fuel, you cause less air pollution. Using less oil also means there is less danger of polluting the land or water with the oil and its by-products.
4. Responses may include:

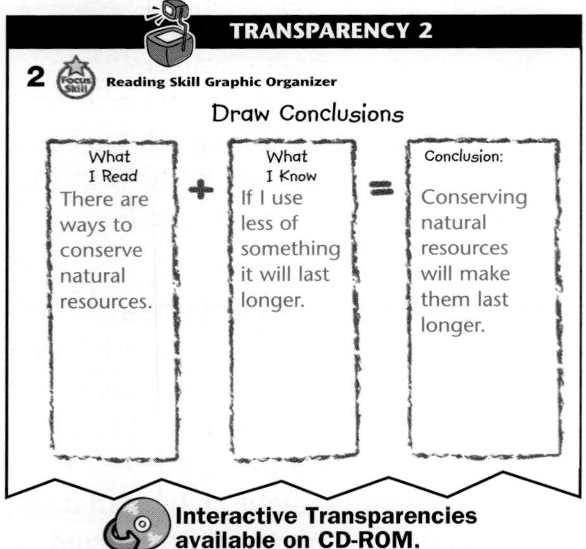

TRANSPARENCY 2
2 Reading Skill Graphic Organizer
Draw Conclusions
What I Read
There are ways to conserve natural resources.
+
What I Know
If I use less of something it will last longer.
=
Conclusion:
Conserving natural resources will make them last longer.

Interactive Transparencies available on CD-ROM.

5. The story should reflect good communication skills, steps in setting goals, and recognition of the concepts and vocabulary.

For **writing models** with examples, see *Teaching Resources* pp. 47–61. Rubrics are also provided.

Quick Study Students can use *Activity Book* pages 56–57 (shown on p. 305) as they complete each lesson in this chapter.

Consumer Activity

Energy Star Many electrical appliances are made to use less energy. The Energy Star program helps consumers choose efficient appliances. Products with the Energy Star label are sometimes cheaper than others because there is no sales tax on them.

▲ New energy-efficient light bulbs can save energy.

Other Ways to Conserve

The burning of fossil fuels produces most of the electricity used in the United States. Here are some ways your family can save fossil fuels.

- Replace regular (incandescent) light bulbs with fluorescent bulbs.
- Turn off lights when you leave a room for more than an hour.
- Put on sweaters instead of turning up the heat.
- Hang clothes to dry instead of using the dryer.
- Install ceiling fans to use instead of air conditioners.

SUMMARIZE What are two ways people can change their use of electricity to conserve resources?

Lesson 5 Summary and Review

1. **Summarize with Vocabulary**
   Use vocabulary and other terms from this lesson to complete the statements.
   _____ makes both renewable and nonrenewable resources last longer. When people _____ natural resources, they help the environment stay clean and they conserve resources.
2. Give two examples of renewable resources.
3. **Critical Thinking** Explain how conserving fossil fuels can also help conserve clean air, water, and land.
4. **DRAW CONCLUSIONS** Draw and complete this graphic organizer to show why people need to conserve resources.

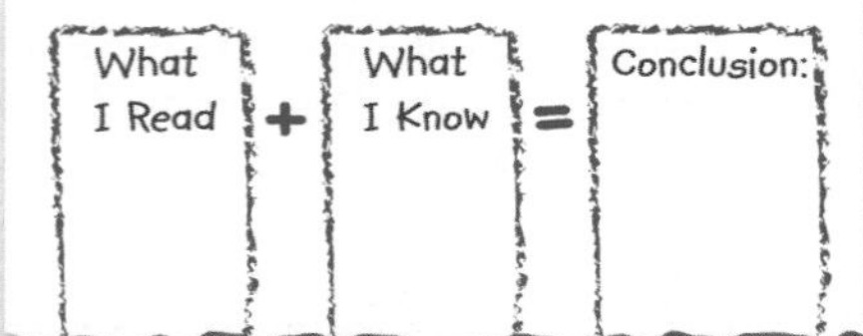

5. **Write to Entertain—Short Story** 
   Write a story about how a family works together to conserve a natural resource, such as water. Use words like *save*, *reduce*, *conserve*, and *resources*.

Possible answers: Turn off lights when not in a room, wear a sweater instead of turning up the heat, or use fluorescent bulbs.

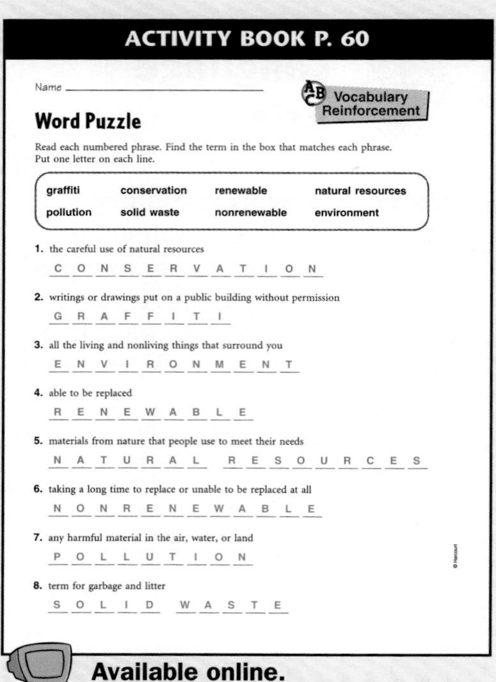

ACTIVITY BOOK P. 60

Name ____________

Vocabulary Reinforcement

Word Puzzle

Read each numbered phrase. Find the term in the box that matches each phrase. Put one letter on each line.

graffiti	conservation	renewable	natural resources
pollution	solid waste	nonrenewable	environment

1. the careful use of natural resources
   C O N S E R V A T I O N
2. writings or drawings put on a public building without permission
   G R A F F I T I
3. all the living and nonliving things that surround you
   E N V I R O N M E N T
4. able to be replaced
   R E N E W A B L E
5. materials from nature that people use to meet their needs
   N A T U R A L R E S O U R C E S
6. taking a long time to replace or unable to be replaced at all
   N O N R E N E W A B L E
7. any harmful material in the air, water, or land
   P O L L U T I O N
8. term for garbage and litter
   S O L I D W A S T E

Available online.
www.harcourtschool.com/health

ACTIVITIES

Science

Use It Again Recall that some resources can be replaced, while supplies of others are limited. Make lists of things you use at school and at home that are made from each of these two kinds of resources. Hint: Plastic products are made from oil, a fossil fuel. Make a plan for reusing some of them to conserve resources.

Physical Education

Physical Activities Find out what kinds of recreational activities are available in your community. Use the information to make a pamphlet to illustrate and map out where these activities take place. Invite others in your class to use the pamphlet to get ideas for recreational activities.

Technology Project

Use Internet resources to find the story about Greenville, and read it. Using your community's name, write a similar real or imaginary story of a successful pollution cleanup.

For more activities, visit The Learning Site. www.harcourtschool.com/health

Home & Community

Pollution Prevention Work as a team to make a pollution prevention chart with three columns labeled *Air, Land, Water.* Discuss how you can prevent each of these kinds of pollution. Write the ideas on the chart, and then display it.

Career Link

Conservationist A conservationist is a person who works to conserve natural resources, such as forests. Conservationists often work with government agencies and private groups to help pass laws to protect resources and to educate the public about conserving resources. Most conservationists have a college degree in science. Choose a natural resource that interests you. Research the role of conservationists in conserving that resource. How might things be different if there were no conservationists?

327

Career Link

Conservationist Discuss with students the variety of careers related to natural resources and conservation. Be sure students understand that conservationists are interested in a variety of environments, such as forests, watersheds, wetlands, oceans, rivers, farmlands, and deserts. Some specialize in birds, fish, insects, or mammals, or their habitats. Some focus on stone, minerals, or soil. If the topic is nature, you can most likely find a conservationist involved in saving some aspect of it.

For more information on health careers, visit the **Webliography** in Teacher Resources at **www.harcourtschool.com/health**
Keyword health careers

Activities

Science

In the United States, almost everything made of plastic is marked with a code for recycling. The code is molded into the plastic item. The symbol should be easily visible. Plastic items labeled with a 1 or a 2 are widely accepted for recycling. Encourage students to look at plastic items found at home and suggest ways for recycling these types of plastic.

Physical Education

Have students visit recreational areas in their community and make a list of recreational activities available to include in their pamphlet. Or students may wish to call the parks and recreation department to find out more about the types of recreation areas located in their neighborhood. Discuss the links between recreation and conservation—e.g., conserving trees makes places nicer for recreation; walking instead of driving conserves fossil fuels.

Home & Community

Suggest that students interview family members or neighbors for pollution-prevention ideas. Have students use these ideas to fill in their chart.

Supports the Coordinated School Health Program

Technology Project

Have students present their stories to the class. Afterward, guide students in a class discussion about cleaning up polluted areas in their community. Students may wish to share their stories with other classes.

Chapter Review and Test Preparation

Pages 328–329

Reading Skill 5 pts. each

1. clean land
2. Possible answers: People need to prevent pollution; people need to take care of their resources; people need to make a healthful environment.

Use Vocabulary 5 pts. each

3. E, dispatchers
4. A, emergency medical technicians
5. D, environment
6. F, natural resources
7. B, conservation

Check Understanding 5 pts. each

8. D, graffiti
9. J, oil
10. B, polluted
11. H, dumping waste into rivers and lakes
12. B, air
13. G, coal
14. D, turning old railroad tracks into trails
15. H, EMTs

Think Critically 5 pts. each

16. Possible answers: Leaving garbage, such as food that spoils, in the park can cause diseases in animals that eat the garbage; it can attract rodents and insects; it can make the area unattractive. It can also make the park unhealthful for other people who want to use it.
17. Possible answers: Since most drinking water comes from deep in the ground, clean water depends on clean land. Runoff from pesticides used on farmlands can pollute water.

Chapter Review and Test Preparation

Reading Skill

DRAW CONCLUSIONS

Draw and then use this graphic organizer to answer questions 1 and 2.

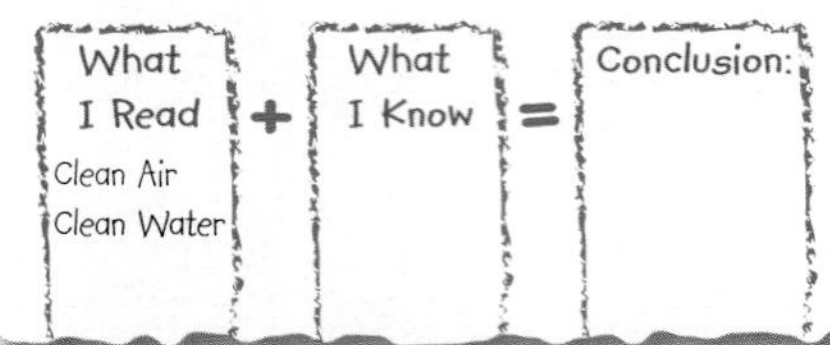

1 In the second box write another thing people need.

2 Draw a conclusion and write it in the third box.

Use Vocabulary

Match each term in Column B with its meaning in Column A.

Column A	Column B
3 People who call EMTs	**A** emergency medical technicians
4 Handle serious injuries or sudden illnesses	**B** conservation
5 Living and nonliving things that surround you	**C** environment
6 Natural materials people use	**D** dispatchers
7 Careful resource use	**E** resources

Check Understanding

Choose the letter of the correct answer.

8 Graffiti is a type of _____. (p.308)
A fossil fuel **C** music
B resource **D** pollution

9 Which is **NOT** solid waste? (p. 317)
F garbage **H** trash
G litter **J** oil

10 In an unhealthful environment, the air, water, and land are _____. (pp. 316, 318, 320)
A renewable **C** nonrenewable
B polluted **D** conserved

11 Which is **NOT** a cause of air pollution? (p. 317)

F

H

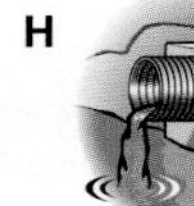

G

J

12 A scrubber is used to remove pollutants from _____. (p. 317)
A land **C** water
B smokestacks **D** landfills

328

Formal Assessment

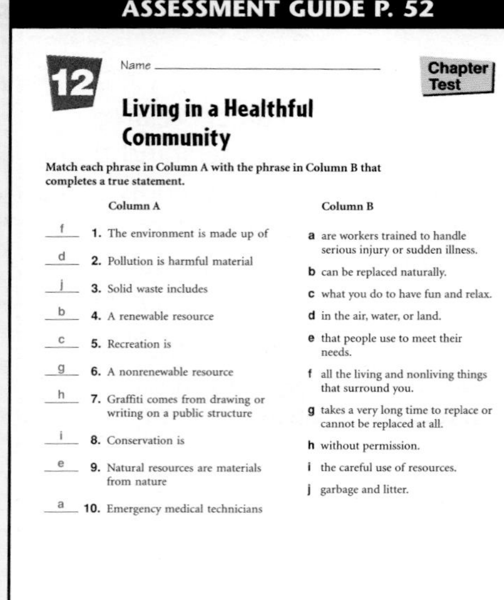

ASSESSMENT GUIDE P. 52

12 Name ________ Chapter Test

Living in a Healthful Community

Match each phrase in Column A with the phrase in Column B that completes a true statement.

	Column A	Column B
f	**1.** The environment is made up of	**a** are workers trained to handle serious injury or sudden illness.
d	**2.** Pollution is harmful material	**b** can be replaced naturally.
j	**3.** Solid waste includes	**c** what you do to have fun and relax.
b	**4.** A renewable resource	**d** in the air, water, or land.
c	**5.** Recreation is	**e** that people use to meet their needs.
g	**6.** A nonrenewable resource	**f** all the living and nonliving things that surround you.
h	**7.** Graffiti comes from drawing or writing on a public structure	**g** takes a very long time to replace or cannot be replaced at all.
i	**8.** Conservation is	**h** without permission.
e	**9.** Natural resources are materials from nature	**i** the careful use of resources.
a	**10.** Emergency medical technicians	**j** garbage and litter.

© Harcourt

ASSESSMENT GUIDE P. 53

Name ________

Write the letter of the best answer on the line at the left.

D **11.** You can get _____ diseases from breathing dirty air.
A environmental **C** resource
B renewable **D** respiratory

H **12.** Smog is a form of _____ pollution.
F renewable **H** air
G water **J** groundwater

C **13.** The _____ protects our water supply from pollution.
A EMT **C** EPA
B DNA **D** EKG

G **14.** Outdoor activities, such as gardening, are _____ for people.
F renewable **H** pollution
G recreation **J** resources

D **15.** Oil and gas are examples of _____ natural resources.
A renewable **C** pollution
B recreational **D** nonrenewable

F **16.** Plastic fabric is made from _____.
F oil **H** plant fibers
G coal **J** minerals

C **17.** Scrubbers in smokestacks help reduce air pollution by taking out many of the _____ before they get into the air.
A minerals **C** pollutants
B coal **D** natural resources

G **18.** The safety of a _____ relies on police officers and firefighters.
F mineral **H** pollutant
G community **J** resource

B **19.** _____ can help both renewable and nonrenewable resources last longer.
A Minerals **C** Pollutants
B Conservation **D** Recreation

F **20.** Renewable resources include _____.
F trees and water **H** coal and oil
G pollution and recreation **J** natural gas and copper

© Harcourt

Nonrenewable Resources

	oil	minerals

13 What nonrenewable fossil fuel is missing from the graphic organizer? (p. 313)
F sun **H** wind
G coal **J** rain

14 Recreation areas can be added to a community by _____. (p. 307)
A illegal dumping
B spreading organic fertilizer on fields
C picking up litter in the community
D turning old railroad tracks into trails

15 Dispatchers tell _____ where an emergency is and what kind of emergency it is. (p. 310)
F hospital nurses
G pollution technicians
H EMTs
J conservationists

Think Critically

16 Lisa and her friends had a picnic in the park. Lisa stayed to clean up, but her friends walked away. What could Lisa have said to her friends about why it's important to clean up their trash?

17 How is clean land related to clean water?

Apply Skills

18 **BUILDING GOOD CHARACTER**
Citizenship Mark lives across the street from Mrs. Lopez. She is retired and lives alone. She fell and broke her arm. What can Mark do to be a good neighbor to Mrs. Lopez?

19 **LIFE SKILLS**
Set Goals Mr. Carver notices that his electric bill is getting higher each month. He wants to lower his usage. What can Mr. Carver do to conserve electricity?

Write About Health

20 **Write to Inform—Description**
Describe what an ideal, healthful community would include.

329

Apply Skills 5 pts. each

18. Possible answers: Mark can go to the store for her or offer to help her with other chores around the house.

19. Possible answer: Mr. Carver can turn off lights, fans, and the TV in rooms he is not using. He can wear a sweater when it is cool instead of turning up the temperature.

Write About Health 5 pts.

20. Answers should include the descriptions and benefits of a healthful community that have been addressed in this chapter.

Performance Assessment

Use the Chapter Project and the rubric provided on the Project Evaluation Sheet. See *Assessment Guide* pp. 18, 61, 73.

Portfolio Assessment

Have students select their best work from the following suggestions:
- Leveled Activities, p. 306
- Quick Activity, p. 309
- Write to Inform, p. 315
- Activities, p. 327

See *Assessment Guide* pp. 12–16.

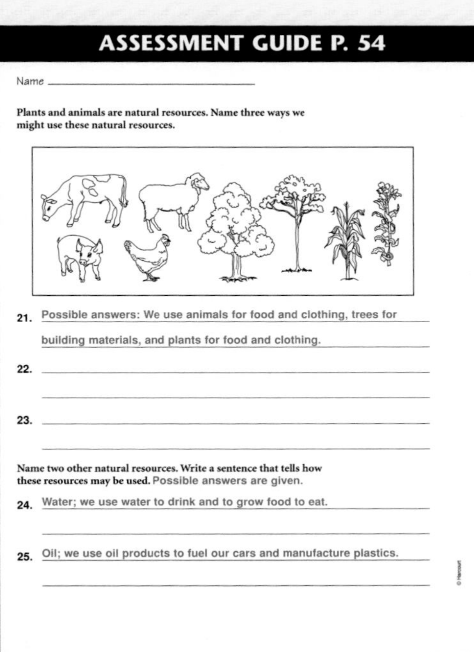

ASSESSMENT GUIDE P. 54

Name ______________________

Plants and animals are natural resources. Name three ways we might use these natural resources.

21. Possible answers: We use animals for food and clothing, trees for building materials, and plants for food and clothing.

22. ______________________

23. ______________________

Name two other natural resources. Write a sentence that tells how these resources may be used. Possible answers are given.

24. Water; we use water to drink and to grow food to eat.

25. Oil; we use oil products to fuel our cars and manufacture plastics.

© Harcourt

READING IN HEALTH HANDBOOK

Pages 330–331

Objective

► Compare and contrast information in expository text

1. TEACH/MODEL

Have students explain why it is helpful to compare and contrast text. to understand how things are alike and how they are different Point out the graphic organizer and discuss the Tips for Comparing and Contrasting. Have students read the paragraph in the example.

Read aloud the following model to help students see how to record in the graphic organizer information from the paragraph.

I know that my topic is Abby and Halley. Both girls are alike in that they both eat snacks every day. I will write that in the Alike column. I see the signal word *however* used to show what is different. Abby eats fruit and milk. She thinks eating right is important. Halley eats potato chips and soda and thinks eating right is not important. I will write that information in the Different column.

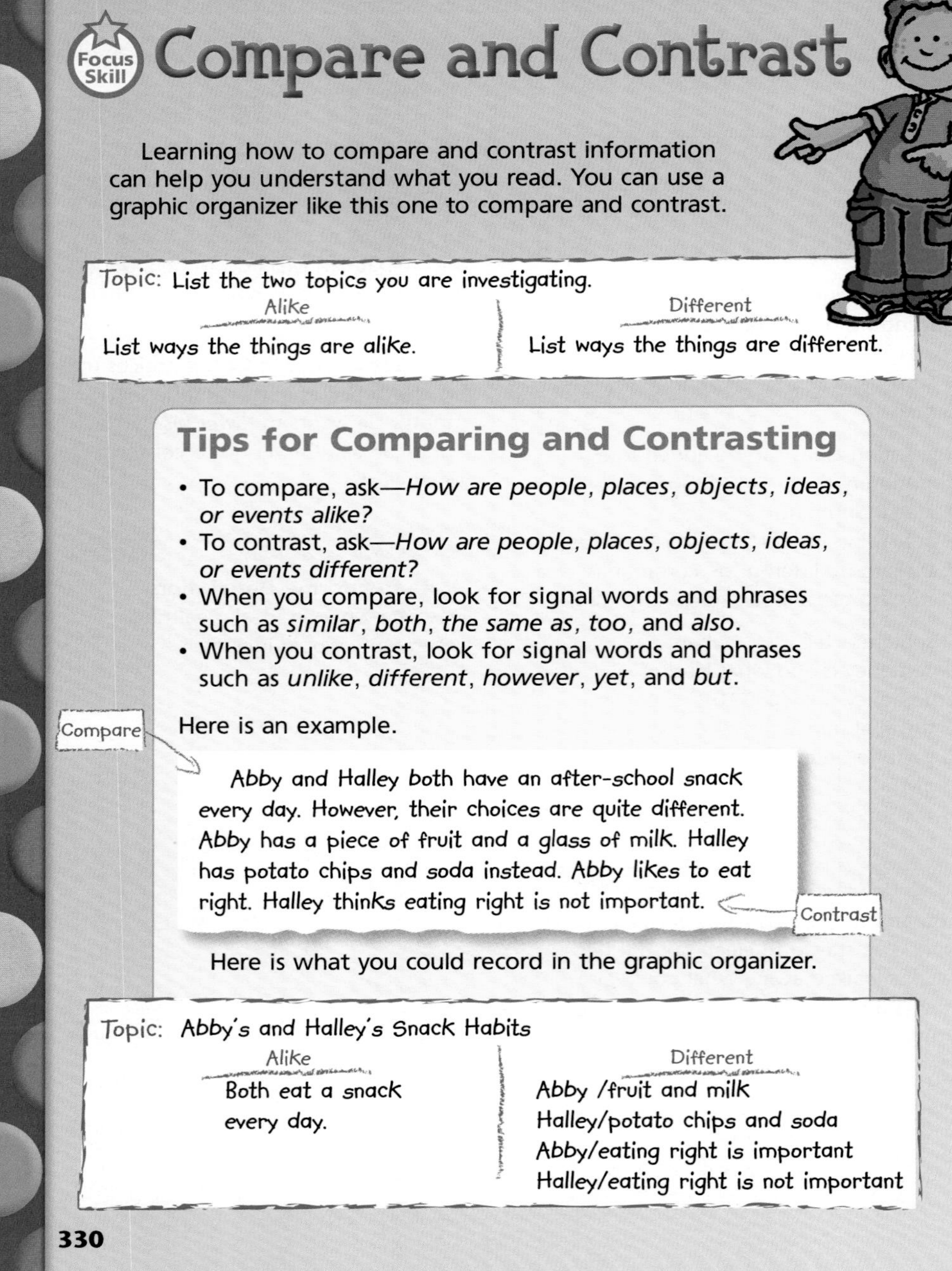

Focus Skill

Compare and Contrast

Learning how to compare and contrast information can help you understand what you read. You can use a graphic organizer like this one to compare and contrast.

Topic: List the two topics you are investigating.

Alike	Different
List ways the things are alike.	List ways the things are different.

Tips for Comparing and Contrasting

- To compare, ask—*How are people, places, objects, ideas, or events alike?*
- To contrast, ask—*How are people, places, objects, ideas, or events different?*
- When you compare, look for signal words and phrases such as *similar*, *both*, *the same as*, *too*, and *also*.
- When you contrast, look for signal words and phrases such as *unlike*, *different*, *however*, *yet*, and *but*.

Here is an example.

Compare

Abby and Halley both have an after-school snack every day. However, their choices are quite different. Abby has a piece of fruit and a glass of milk. Halley has potato chips and soda instead. Abby likes to eat right. Halley thinks eating right is not important.

Contrast

Here is what you could record in the graphic organizer.

Topic: Abby's and Halley's Snack Habits

Alike	Different
Both eat a snack every day.	Abby /fruit and milk Halley/potato chips and soda Abby/eating right is important Halley/eating right is not important

330

Skills in Context

COMPARE AND CONTRAST: Play a Compare and Contrast Game To compare, look for clues that tell how things are alike. To contrast, look for clues that tell how things are different. Make and play a compare-and-contrast game, using the text.

What You Need

- Index cards
- Writing tools

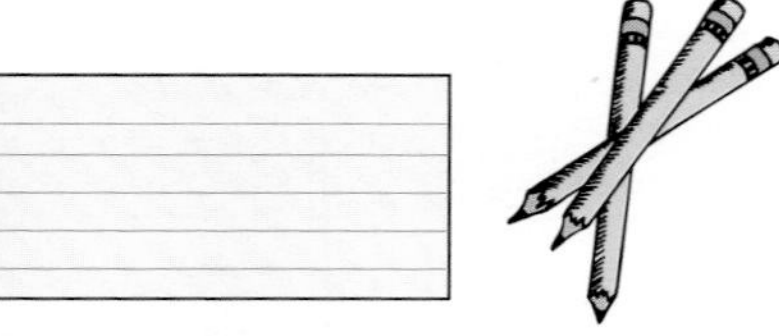

What To Do

1. Look in Chapter 3 to identify five sets of things that can be compared and contrasted.
2. For each set of things, use one card to write how the things are alike. use another card to write how the things are different. You should have five pairs of cards.
3. Play a matching game with a classmate. Each player takes turns turning over two cards at a time. Try to find something to compare and contrast about the items on the cards you turn over. If you are successful, keep the cards. If not, place the cards face down again. It is then the other player's turn.
4. The player with the most cards wins.

More About Compare and Contrast

Identifying how things are alike and how they are different can help readers understand ideas, events, people, and places. Use the graphic organizer from page 330 to sort the information given in the chart below.

Halley	likes to run	does not like apples	loves to eat hot dogs	enjoys soccer
Abby	loves to eat apples	enjoys soccer	likes to run	never eats hot dogs

Sometimes a paragraph compares and contrasts more than one topic. In the following paragraph, one topic being compared and contrasted is underlined. Find a second topic being compared and contrasted.

<u>Kurt and Barry both eat a healthful breakfast every morning. However, Kurt has milk and cereal, and Barry has eggs and juice.</u> Every day, Barry and Kurt leave for school at the same time. Barry rides his bike and gets there early. Kurt walks and gets there just before the bell rings.

Skill Practice

Read the following paragraph. Use the Tips for Comparing and Contrasting to answer the questions.

Justin and Amanda are both sick. Justin has an allergy to something in the air, unlike Amanda, who has pinkeye. Justin has itchy eyes. He sneezes many times a day. Amanda's eyes are itchy, too. Justin knows that he cannot pass his allergy to another person. Amanda, however, must be careful not to pass her pinkeye pathogens to anyone else.

1 What are two ways Justin and Amanda are alike?

2 What are two differences between their illnesses?

3 What are two signal words that helped you identify likenesses and differences in this paragraph?

2. PRACTICE

More About Comparing and Contrasting

Have students work in small groups to sort the information given on the chart.

Remind students that some paragraphs tell about ways a number of topics are alike and different. Read aloud the paragraph. Help students write the underlined information from the paragraph in a graphic organizer like the one used in the model. Have students identify the second topic being compared and contrasted. Organize that information in a second graphic organizer.

3. APPLY

Skill Practice

Have students use the Tips for Comparing and Contrasting to answer the questions.

1. Justin and Amanda are both sick, and both have itchy eyes.
2. Justin sneezes and has allergies. Amanda has pinkeye, which is contagious.
3. *Both* and *however* are signal words in this paragraph

Meeting Individual Needs
Leveled Activities

BELOW-LEVEL Have students find two objects in the classroom that are alike in some way but are not identical. Have each student make a list of three ways those two objects are alike and three ways those objects are different and then share observations with the class.

ON-LEVEL Give pairs of students a blank graphic organizer. Each partner identifies a different illness. Partners should use the graphic organizer to compare and contrast the two illnesses selected. Partners can share with the class the information from their completed graphic organizers.

CHALLENGE Give students blank graphic organizers. Have students use them to compare and contrast three illnesses they have chosen to research. Students should share with the class the information from their completed graphic organizers.

READING IN HEALTH HANDBOOK

Pages 332–333

Objective

► Use information from expository text to draw conclusions

1. TEACH/MODEL

Have students explain why it is helpful to draw conclusions about text. When not all of the information is given, readers must use text information and their own knowledge to understand what is written. Point out the graphic organizer, and discuss the Tips for Drawing Conclusions. Have students read the paragraph in the example.

Use the following to model aloud for students how to put information from the paragraph into the graphic organizer.

I read that Latrisha wanted to go for a bike ride but that it looked like it might rain. I wrote this in the What I Read box. I know that loud thunder usually signals a bad storm, so I wrote that in the What I Know box. For the Conclusion box, I figure out that Latrisha could not go for a bike ride.

Draw Conclusions

Draw conclusions by using information from the text and your own experience. This can help you understand what you read. You can use a graphic organizer like this one to help you draw conclusions.

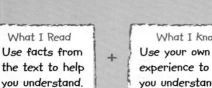

What I Read		What I Know		Conclusion:
Use facts from the text to help you understand.	+	Use your own experience to help you understand.	=	Combine facts and details in the text with prior knowledge or personal experience.

Tips for Drawing Conclusions

- To draw conclusions, ask—*What information do I need to think about?*
- Then ask—*What do I know from my own experience that could help me draw a conclusion?*
- Pay close attention to the information the author gives, as well as to your experience, to be sure the conclusion is valid, or makes sense.

Here is an example.

Latrisha wanted to go for a bike ride with her friends. Her mom was concerned about the dark storm clouds outside. A clap of thunder shook the room and Latrisha's mom shook her head. Latrisha picked up her book and went to her bedroom.

Story information

Your own experience

Here is what you could record in the graphic organizer.

What I Read		What I Know		Conclusion:
Latrisha wanted to go for a bike ride, but there were storm clouds outside.	+	Loud thunder usually signals a bad storm.	=	Latrisha could not go for a bike ride.

332

What You Need

- Chapter 6

Skills in Context

DRAW CONCLUSIONS: TWENTY-QUESTION CONCLUSIONS As you read, think about the details in the text and your own experience and knowledge. Then draw a conclusion from these things. You can play a game of Twenty Questions based on a subject found in Chapter 6.

What To Do

1. Form a group and choose one player to be the leader. The leader revisits Chapter 6 and chooses a person, place, thing, or event. The leader should not tell what he or she has chosen.
2. The other players take turns asking the leader yes or no questions. They should put together the clues they learn to draw a conclusion about what the leader has chosen.
3. The first player to guess correctly becomes the next leader.

More About Drawing Conclusions

Sensible conclusions based on your experience and the facts you read are valid. For example, suppose the paragraph on page 332 included a sentence that said the sun came out and Latrisha had a smile on her face. You could then draw a different conclusion about Latrisha's bike ride.

What I Read		What I Know		Conclusion:
It looked as if the bike ride would not happen, but the sun came out.	+	People smile when they are happy.	=	Since the sun came out and Latrisha was smiling, she must have gone for the bike ride.

Sometimes a paragraph might not contain enough information to draw a valid conclusion. Read the following paragraph. Think of one valid conclusion you could draw. Then, think of one conclusion that would be invalid.

> Allie knows that lightning usually hits the tallest object above ground. She decides to stay low to the ground. She wheels her bicycle into a nearby ditch and climbs in next to it. Then Allie looks up. She sees something she has never seen before.

Skill Practice

Read the following paragraph. Use the Tips for Drawing Conclusions to answer the questions.

> Paul could not wait to go swimming, fishing, and boating. As soon as he arrived at the lake, he ran down to the shore. Confused, he looked down at the water as he bent to pick up an old trash bag. Paul saw algae covering the water's surface. He ran back up to the house to talk to his mom.

1 What conclusion did you draw about Paul's trip to the lake?

2 What information did you use from your personal experience that helped you draw the conclusion?

3 What story information did you use to draw the conclusion?

Meeting Individual Needs
Leveled Activities

BELOW-LEVEL Ask students to recall a situation they felt was an emergency. Have them tell what made them feel that it was an emergency. As the situation went on, did they change their minds or draw different conclusions? Have students draw pictures to share their responses.

ON-LEVEL Give pairs of students a blank graphic organizer. Have partners identify a topic to explore from Chapter 12. Have students narrow the topic and draw a valid conclusion about something based on the given information. Have them share with the class the information from their completed graphic organizers.

CHALLENGE Have each student write examples of valid conclusions and invalid, or faulty, conclusions based on information in Chapter 12. Then have partners exchange papers and tell which conclusions are invalid and why.

2. PRACTICE

More About Drawing Conclusions

Have students compare the graphic organizer on page 332 with the one on this page. Lead students to see that a different conclusion has been drawn after the additional information is given.

Remind students that some paragraphs might not contain enough information to draw a valid conclusion. Read aloud the paragraph. Help students arrive at one valid conclusion. Allie stayed safe from the storm. Discuss with students other possible conclusions and why some may or may not be valid ones.

3. APPLY

Skill Practice

Have students use the Tips for Drawing Conclusions to answer the questions.

1. Paul did not go in the polluted water.
2. I don't like to see a nice recreation area become polluted, so I could tell that Paul was upset about the pollution.
3. Trash bags on the shore and algae covering the surface indicated possible polluted water.

READING IN HEALTH HANDBOOK

Pages 334–335

Objective

► Understand cause-and-effect relationships

1. TEACH/MODEL

Have students explain why it is helpful to understand cause-and-effect relationships. to understand how and why things happen Point out the graphic organizer and discuss the Tips for Identifying Cause and Effect. Have students read the paragraph in the example.

Read aloud the following model to help students see how to record in the graphic organizer information from the paragraph.

I know that Eddie roller-skated for 30 minutes. This must be the Cause of something, so I will write it in the Cause box. The signal word *because* is given and I read that Eddie's heart is beating faster. This is the effect, so I will write it in the Effect box.

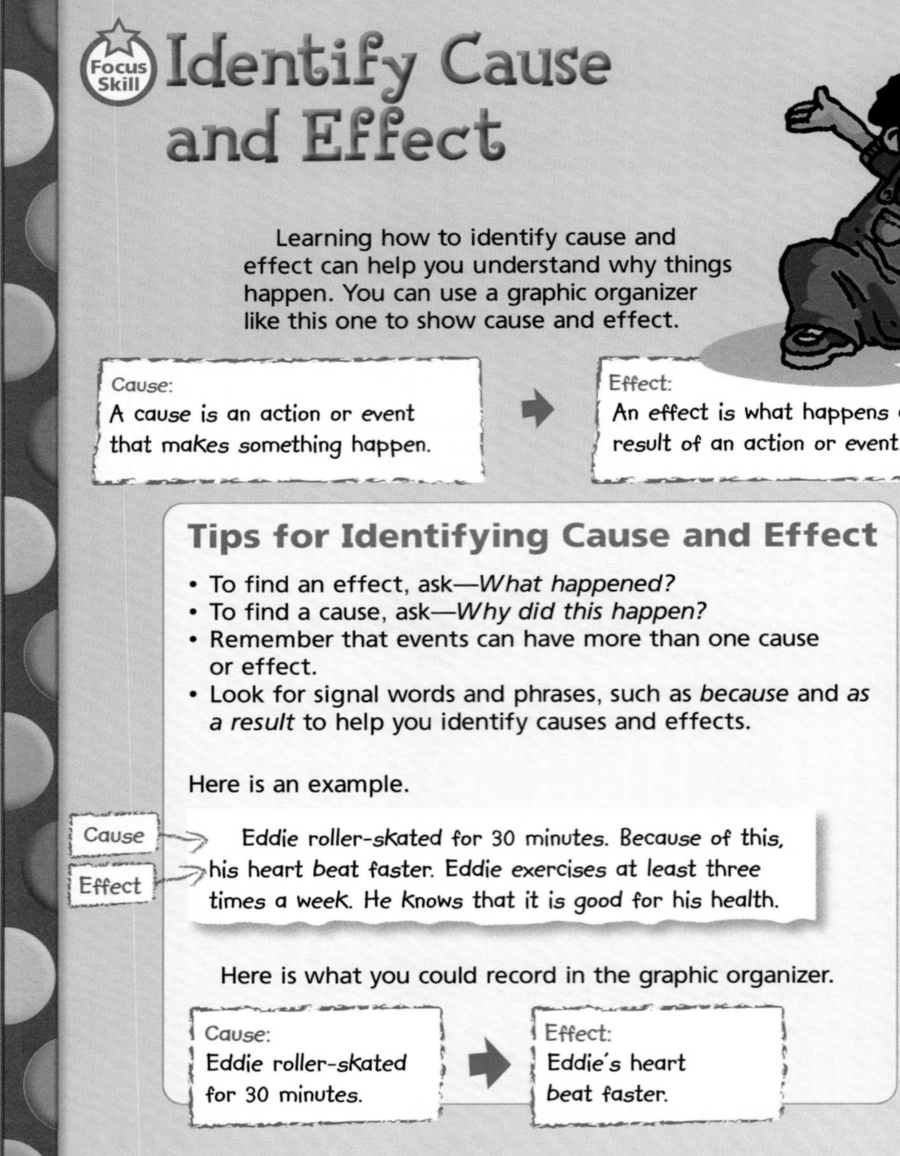

Focus Skill
Identify Cause and Effect
Learning how to identify cause and effect can help you understand why things happen. You can use a graphic organizer like this one to show cause and effect.
Cause:
A cause is an action or event that makes something happen.
Effect:
An effect is what happens as a result of an action or event.
Tips for Identifying Cause and Effect
• To find an effect, ask—What happened?
• To find a cause, ask—Why did this happen?
• Remember that events can have more than one cause or effect.
• Look for signal words and phrases, such as because and as a result to help you identify causes and effects.
Here is an example.
Cause
Effect
Eddie roller-skated for 30 minutes. Because of this, his heart beat faster. Eddie exercises at least three times a week. He knows that it is good for his health.
Here is what you could record in the graphic organizer.
Cause:
Eddie roller-skated for 30 minutes.
Effect:
Eddie's heart beat faster.
334

Skills in Context

CAUSE AND EFFECT: Play Cause-and-Effect Challenge Look through Chapter 9 to find examples of actions or events that cause things to happen. Then make a set of cause-and-effect cards to play a game with a partner.

What You Need

- Index cards
- Writing Tools

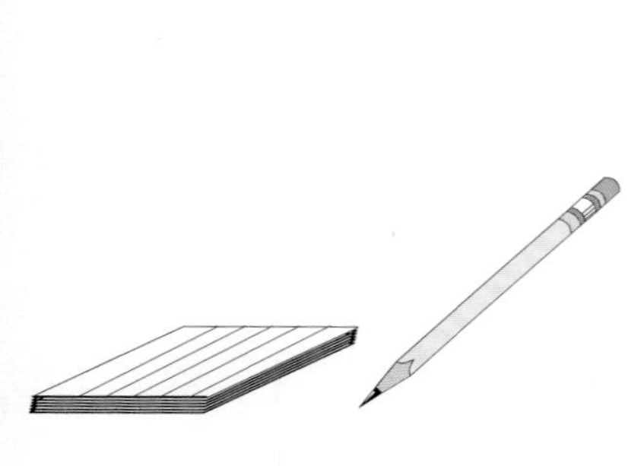

What To Do

1. Identify examples of actions or events from Chapter 9 that cause other things to happen. For each one, write the cause on one side of an index card and the effect on the other side.
2. Hold up one card so that your partner can read the cause side. Challenge your partner to name the effect.
3. Read the effect side of each of your partner's cards. Try to name the cause.
4. Work through the sets of cards until you and your partner have correctly named each cause and effect.

More About Cause and Effect

Events can have more than one cause or effect. For example, suppose the paragraph on page 334 included a sentence that said Eddie's lungs took in more air while he was roller-skating. You could then identify two effects of Eddie's roller-skating.

Cause: Eddie roller-skated for 30 minutes.

Effect: Eddie's heart beat faster.

Effect: Eddie's lungs took in more air.

Some paragraphs contain more than one cause and effect. In the following paragraph, one cause and its effect are underlined. Find a second cause and its effect.

The next day Eddie ran for 30 minutes after school. <u>Because he forgot to stretch first, he pulled a muscle in his leg.</u> Eddie's mom gave him first aid. As a result, Eddie's leg soon felt better. Eddie now understands the importance of stretching before exercising.

Skill Practice

Read the following paragraph. Use the Tips for Identifying Cause and Effect to help you answer the questions.

Sarah Smith's mom smokes two packs of cigarettes every day. Because of this, Mrs. Smith has bad breath. Her clothes smell like smoke. Even her hair smells like smoke. As a result of smoking, Mrs. Smith's teeth have turned yellow. Sarah wants her mom to stop smoking.

1 What has caused Mrs. Smith's teeth to turn yellow?

2 What are three other effects her smoking has caused?

3 What two signal phrases helped you identify the causes and effects in this paragraph?

Reading in Health Handbook

2. PRACTICE

More About Cause and Effect

Have students compare the graphic organizer on page 334 with the one on this page. Lead students to see that the Effect box now has two things listed instead of one.

Remind students that some paragraphs might have more than one cause and effect. Read aloud the paragraph. Have students identify the given cause and effect. cause: forgot to stretch; effect: pulled a muscle Have students identify the second cause and effect in the paragraph. Cause: Eddie's mom gave him first aid; Effect: Eddie's leg felt better.

3. APPLY

Skill Practice

Have students use the Tips for Identifying Cause and Effect to answer the questions.

1. Mrs. Smith smokes cigarettes.
2. She has bad breath. Her clothes and her hair smell bad.
3. *As a result* and *because* are signal words in this paragraph.

Reading in Health Handbook

Meeting Individual Needs
Leveled Activities

BELOW-LEVEL Have the class play a cause-and-effect game. The first player says a real or made-up event. Example: *I have a backache.* The next player expands the sentence by making up a cause for the event. Example: *because I have poor posture* The third player restates the cause as an event. Example: *I have poor posture.* The fourth player finishes the sentence with a new cause. Play continues until everyone has had a turn.

ON-LEVEL—Give pairs of students a blank graphic organizer. Have each student write a sentence that includes a cause and an effect. Have students use the graphic organizer to identify the causes and effects.

CHALLENGE—Have students draw a three- or four-panel comic strip that shows cause-and-effect relationships. They can find ideas for this activity in Chapter 4. Students should use speech balloons to show dialogue.

READING IN HEALTH HANDBOOK

Pages 336–337

Objective

► Recognize the main idea of a selection and identify the details that support it

1. TEACH/MODEL

Have students explain why it is helpful to identify the main idea and details of a selection. to know what a passage is mostly about Point out the graphic organizer, and discuss the Tips for Identifying Main Idea and Details. Have students read the paragraph in the example.

Read aloud the following model to help students see how to record in the graphic organizer information from the paragraph.

I read the entire paragraph and decide that it is mostly about skin being the largest organ on the body. I put this in the Main Idea box. The rest of the sentences give bits of information that support the main idea. One important detail is about the top layer of the skin. Another important detail is about the bottom layer of the skin. I write these in the boxes marked Details.

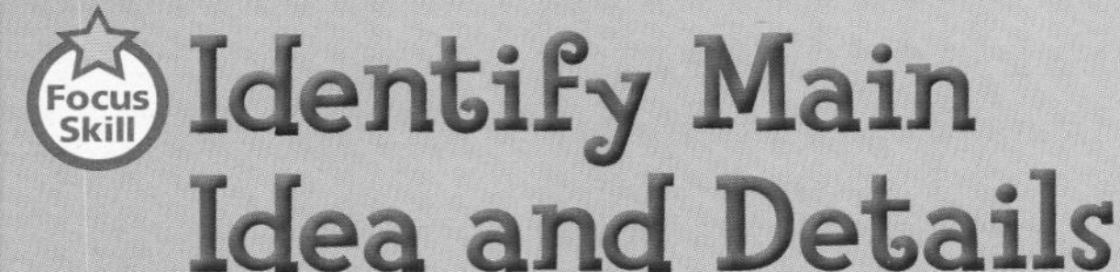

Identify Main Idea and Details

Being able to identify the main idea and details can help you understand what you read. You can use a graphic organizer like this one to show the main idea and details.

Main Idea: The most important idea of a paragraph, several paragraphs, or a selection

Detail: Information that tells more about the main idea	Detail: Information that tells more about the main idea	Detail: Information that tells more about the main idea

Tips for Identifying Main Idea and Details

- To find the main idea, ask—*What is this mostly about?*
- Remember that the main idea is not always stated in the first sentence.
- Look for details that answer questions such as *who*, *what*, *where*, *when*, *why*, and *how*.
- Use pictures as clues to help you figure out the main idea.

Here is an example.

Main Idea

Detail

Your skin is the largest organ of your body. It has two layers that enclose and protect the rest of your body. The epidermis is the top layer. It holds moisture in and keeps germs out. The dermis is the bottom layer. It contains blood vessels and nerve endings.

Here is what you could record in the graphic organizer.

Main Idea: Your skin is your body's largest organ.

Detail: Skin has two layers.	Detail: The first layer is the epidermis.	Detail: The second layer is the dermis.

336

Skills in Context

MAIN IDEA AND DETAILS: Banner of Details You can make your own main idea and details banner to help you retell parts of Chapter 2.

What You Need

- Long sheet of cloth or butcher paper
- Drawing materials
- Stick or pole

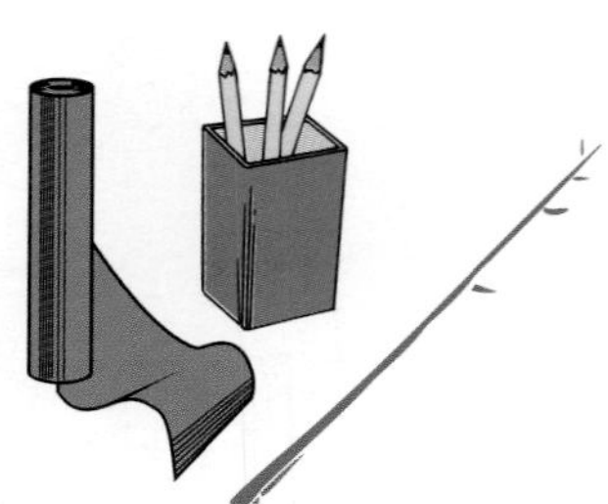

What To Do

1. Work with one or two classmates. Pick one passage from Chapter 2.
2. Together, decide what the main idea of the passage is. Write down details that answer the questions *who, what, where, when, why,* and *how.*
3. Design a banner that includes the main idea and the details of your passage. Make the main idea stand out. Decorate your banner with artwork.
4. Parade around the classroom with your banner. Then all the groups should gather and use their banners to retell their parts of the chapter.

More About Main Idea and Details

Sometimes the main idea is not at the beginning of a passage. If the main idea is not given, it can be understood from the details. Look below at the graphic organizer. What do you think the main idea is?

Main Idea: ?

Detail:	Detail:	Detail:
Sweat reaches the skin's surface through pores.	You sweat the most when you are hot.	Sweat changes from a liquid to a gas.

Sometimes a paragraph's main idea might contain details of different types. In this paragraph, identify whether the details give reasons, examples, facts, steps, or descriptions.

Wash your hands thoroughly to rid them of germs. First, be sure to use soap and warm water. Next, wash the skin on your knuckles and under your fingernails. Dirt tends to build up there. Finally, rinse your hands well and dry them.

Skill Practice

Read the following paragraph. Use the Tips for Identifying the Main Idea and Details to answer the questions.

We all have traits that make us special. Your physical traits determine the length of your toes. If you are a good artist with a kind heart, you can thank your mental and emotional traits. If your stomach feels queasy when you meet new people, your social traits are the reason. Your personal traits make you uniquely you!

1 What is the main idea of the paragraph?

2 What supporting details give more information about the main idea?

3 What details answer any of the questions—*who, what, where, when, why,* and *how*?

Reading in Health Handbook

Meeting Individual Needs
Leveled Activities

BELOW-LEVEL Have students copy a paragraph from Chapter 10, writing each sentence on an individual index card. Ask them to place the card with the main idea in the center of their desks and to place the cards with the details around it to form a web. Students tell a partner what the paragraph is mostly about.

ON-LEVEL Give pairs of students a blank graphic organizer. Have each partner tell a short story about skin care. Have partners use the graphic organizer to determine the main idea of each story and identify the important details. Partners can then share with the class the information from their completed graphic organizers.

CHALLENGE Give students blank graphic organizers. Have partners make up a story about a person who has an interesting personality. Tell students to include many extra details. Have partners use the graphic organizer to determine the story's main idea and the three most important details. Ask them to share the story with the class. Have the class tell the main idea of the story and the three most important details. Compare and discuss answers.

2. PRACTICE

More About Main Idea

Have students work in small groups to look at the information given on the graphic organizer. Discuss with students what is most likely the main idea given the set of details provided. Your body produces sweat.

Read aloud the paragraph. Help students identify and analyze the details to determine into which category each detail would fall. Reasons, facts, and descriptions are given.

3. APPLY

SKILL PRACTICE

Have students use the Tips for Identifying the Main Idea and Details to answer the questions.

1. We all have personal traits that make us special.
2. We have a variety of physical, mental, emotional, and social traits.
3. Who—everyone; what—traits that we have; why—because we are born with them

READING IN HEALTH HANDBOOK

Pages 338–339

Objective

► Understand that time-order words signal the sequence of events in text

1. TEACH/MODEL

Have students explain why it is helpful to pay attention to the sequence of events. Knowing the order in which things happen can help you understand what you read. Point out the graphic organizer and discuss the Tips for Understanding Sequence. Have students read the paragraph in the example.

Read aloud the following model to help students see how to record in the graphic organizer information from the paragraph.

I know that my topic is digestion. I read that the first thing that happens to the food is that it goes into the mouth and down the esophagus. I write that in the graphic organizer. I see from the signal word *next* that the second place the food goes is into the stomach and the small intestine. The last signal word *finally* tells me that the third thing is that the undigested waste goes into the large intestine. I write that in my graphic organizer.

Sequence

Paying attention to the sequence of events, or the order in which things happen, can help you understand what you read. You can use a graphic organizer like this one to show sequence.

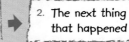

1. The first thing that happened →

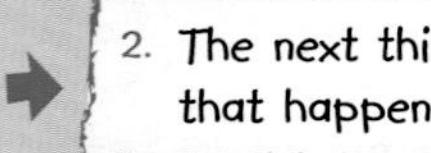

→ 3. The last thing that happened

Tips for Understanding Sequence

- Pay attention to the order in which events happen.
- Recall dates and times to help you understand the sequence.
- Look for signal words such as *first*, *next*, *then*, *last*, and *finally*.
- Sometimes it is helpful to add your own time-order words to help you understand sequence.

Here is an example.

Time-order word

What happens to the food you eat? First, food enters your body through your mouth and travels down the esophagus. Next, the food is broken down in your stomach, and the nutrients are absorbed in the small intestine. Finally, the undigested waste goes into your large intestine.

Here is what you could record in the graphic organizer.

1. Food goes into the mouth and down the esophagus. → 2. Food goes into the stomach and the small intestine. → 3. Undigested waste goes into the large intestine.

338

Skills in Context

SEQUENCE: Make a Sequence Chain Find a passage in Chapter 5 that is organized by the order in which things happen. Use the words *first, then, next,* and *finally* to make a sequence chain to tell what happens in the passage.

What To Do

1. Identify a passage in Chapter 5 that is organized by the order in which things happen.
2. Write each event on a separate strip, using a signal word to begin each sentence.
3. Use a paper punch to make two holes at the top and two holes at the bottom of each card. Tie the cards together with yarn so that they hang in order from top to bottom.
4. Use the sequence chain to retell this part of the text.

What You Need

- Writing tools
- Yarn
- Oaktag strips
- Paper punch

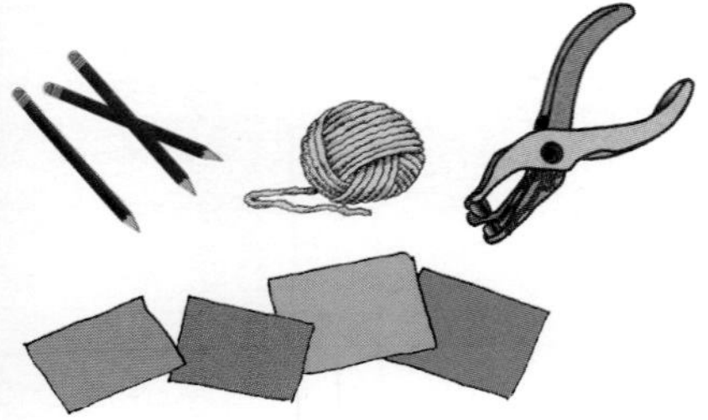

More About Sequence

Sometimes information is sequenced by dates. For example, on what date did you learn to walk? Kick a soccer ball? Play in your first soccer game? Use the graphic organizer to sequence some things that happened as your body was growing and changing.

1. I started walking on July 15, 1998. → 2. I first kicked a soccer ball on February 10, 1999. → 3. I played in my first soccer game on June 24, 2003.

When time-order words are not given, add your own words to help you understand the sequence. In the paragraph below, one time-order word has been included and underlined. How many more time-order words can you add to understand the paragraph's sequence?

Eating a cracker will start the process of digestion. First, your teeth will break the cracker into smaller parts. Your tongue will push the cracker around in your mouth. Saliva will begin to break down the nutrients in the cracker. Off it goes down the esophagus.

Skill Practice

Read the following paragraph. Use the Tips for Understanding Sequence to answer the questions.

When you call 911 in an emergency, first, tell the operator your name. Next, give the phone number and address from which you are calling. Then, tell the operator what the problem is. Last, give the operator a family member's name and phone number.

1 What is the first thing you should do when you call 911 in an emergency?

2 What might happen if you did not follow the right sequence or left out a step?

3 What four signal words helped you identify the sequence of instructions in this paragraph?

Reading in Health Handbook

2. PRACTICE

More About Sequence

Have students look at the events written in sequence on the graphic organizer. Give students a blank graphic organizer. Have them write events, in order, that are related to their bodies growing and changing.

Remind students that some paragraphs don't include time-order words. This can make it harder to understand an event's sequence. Read the paragraph aloud. The time-order word *first* is given. Students should find places to add the time-order words: *next, then,* and *finally*.

3. APPLY

SKILL PRACTICE

Have students use the Tips for Understanding Sequence to answer the questions.

1. Tell the operator your name.
2. If you left out a step when contacting 911, you would risk not having emergency help when it is needed.
3. *First, then, next,* and *last* are signal words in this paragraph.

Meeting Individual Needs
Leveled Activities

BELOW-LEVEL Write sentences from the text that detail the steps to take in an emergency. Write those steps on separate tagboard strips. Place them out of order on the chalk ledge. Have students rearrange the strips to show the correct order. Discuss how to determine the correct sequence by using time-order words as clues.

ON-LEVEL Have each student think of a favorite game and tell a partner how to play the game. Remind students to use signal words before each step of the directions. Have students write their directions on blank graphic organizers to share with the class.

CHALLENGE— Have students write fictitious stories about an emergency that occurred. Tell students to include time-order words as needed. Have them tell their stories into a tape recorder to play for the class. Ask students to raise both arms when they hear time-order words.

READING IN HEALTH HANDBOOK

Pages 340–341

Objective

► Identify the elements that make up a good summary

1. TEACH/MODEL

Have students explain why it is important to summarize a passage. to understand how to tell about the most important parts Point out the graphic organizer and discuss the Tips for Summarizing. Have students read the paragraph in the example.

Read aloud the following model to help students see how to record in the graphic organizer information from the paragraph.

I know that the main idea of the paragraph is that every member of a family has an important role. I write that in the Main Idea box. The paragraph includes details about children going to school and parents providing children with care and support. I write those in the box marked Details. Then I use my own words to write a summary statement about the paragraph in the Summary box.

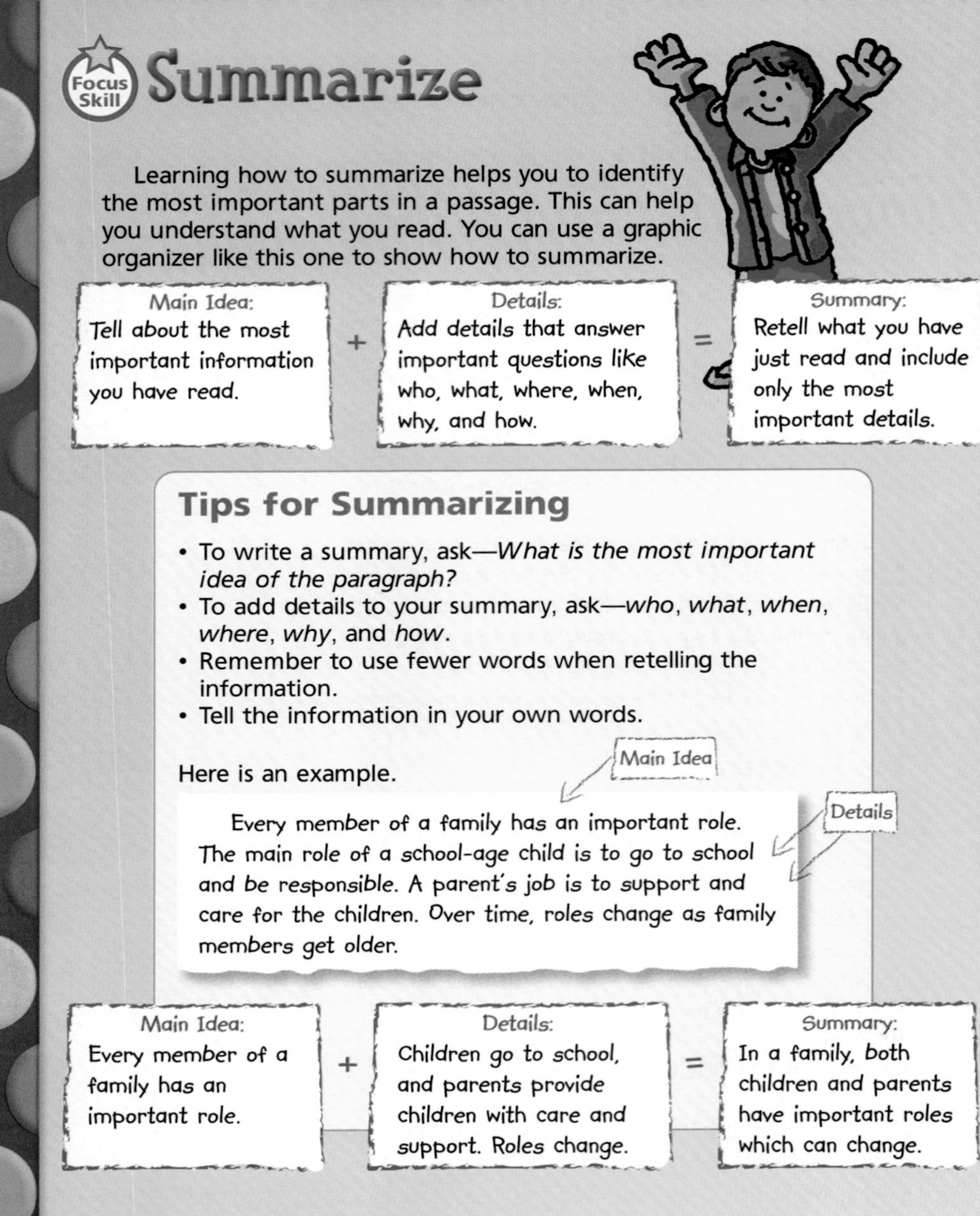

Summarize

Learning how to summarize helps you to identify the most important parts in a passage. This can help you understand what you read. You can use a graphic organizer like this one to show how to summarize.

Main Idea:		Details:		Summary:
Tell about the most important information you have read.	+	Add details that answer important questions like who, what, where, when, why, and how.	=	Retell what you have just read and include only the most important details.

Tips for Summarizing

- To write a summary, ask—*What is the most important idea of the paragraph?*
- To add details to your summary, ask—*who*, *what*, *when*, *where*, *why*, and *how*.
- Remember to use fewer words when retelling the information.
- Tell the information in your own words.

Here is an example.

Every member of a family has an important role. The main role of a school-age child is to go to school and be responsible. A parent's job is to support and care for the children. Over time, roles change as family members get older.

Main Idea:		Details:		Summary:
Every member of a family has an important role.	+	Children go to school, and parents provide children with care and support. Roles change.	=	In a family, both children and parents have important roles which can change.

340

Skills in Context

SUMMARY: Go on a Summary Hunt Summarize a passage to show that you understand it. How good are you at summarizing? Here is a fun way to find out.

What You Need

- Writing paper • Writing tools

What To Do

1. Work in a group of four.
2. Each group member picks a passage from Chapter 8 or 11 and writes a summary of it. Remember to put it in your own words.
3. Trade summaries with another group member. Try to identify the passage from the book that matches the summary on the paper you received.
4. When everyone has found his or her passage, discuss as a group details about the summaries that made it easy or difficult to find the passages.

More About Summarizing

Sometimes a paragraph has details that are not important enough to be included in a summary. For example, suppose the paragraph on page 340 included a sentence that told what it meant to be a responsible child. The graphic organizer would remain the same because that detail is not important to understanding the paragraph's main idea.

Main Idea:		Details:		Summary:
Every member of a family has an important role.	+	Children go to school, and parents provide children with care and support. Roles change.	=	In a family, both children and parents have important roles which can change.

Sometimes the main idea of a paragraph is not in the first sentence. In the following paragraph, two important details are underlined. What is the main idea?

> Ann's grandmother sews all her own clothes. <u>Ann's dad is an artist.</u> He loves drawing cartoons. <u>Ann's mom works every day in a restaurant.</u> She is an excellent cook. Ann respects every member of her family. Each person has a unique talent or skill.

Skill Practice

Read the following paragraph. Use the Tips for Summarizing to answer the questions.

> Susan Scott has a headache. When Susan's sister, Pam, gets a headache, Mr. Scott gives her a pain reliever. However, Mr. Scott does not let Susan take a pain reliever. He reminds Susan that she does not like the side effects. Instead, he has Susan lie down until she feels better.

1 If a friend asked you what this paragraph was about, what information would you include? What would you leave out?

2 What is the main idea of the paragraph?

3 What two details would you include in a summary of the paragraph?

2. PRACTICE

More About Summarizing

Remind students that a summary includes only the most important details of a passage. Direct attention to the graphic organizer. Discuss why the additional information given would not be included in the summary.

Often, the main idea of a paragraph is in the first sentence of the paragraph. However, it can be elsewhere in the paragraph. Read the paragraph aloud. Reread the underlined information aloud, and discuss what makes each sentence a detail. Have students identify the main idea of the paragraph. Encourage them to use their own words to write a summary.

3. APPLY

SKILL PRACTICE

Have students use the Tips for Summarizing to answer the questions.

1. When Susan has a headache, she rests instead of taking medicine.
2. Susan Scott has a headache.
3. Susan does not take medicine for headaches. She does not like the side effects. She lies down instead.

Meeting Individual Needs
Leveled Activities

BELOW-LEVEL Have students summarize an event that took place on the playground. Tell them to include the main thing that happened and the three most important details.

ON-LEVEL Have partners identify a passage from the text. Each student uses a graphic organizer to write a summary of the passage and then compares it to the partner's summary. Have students discuss the similarities and differences.

CHALLENGE Give students the following directions to plan and write stories using story wheels. Cut five circles out of paper, and attach a center arrow with a brass fastener. Divide each circle into eight parts. In the sections of the first circle, write descriptions of *who* the story is about. Fill the sections of the remaining circles with details of *when* the story takes place, *where* it happens, *what* happens at the beginning, and *what* happens at the end. Have students spin the wheels and write a story based on the selected details from the story wheels. Then have them write a story summary using a graphic organizer.

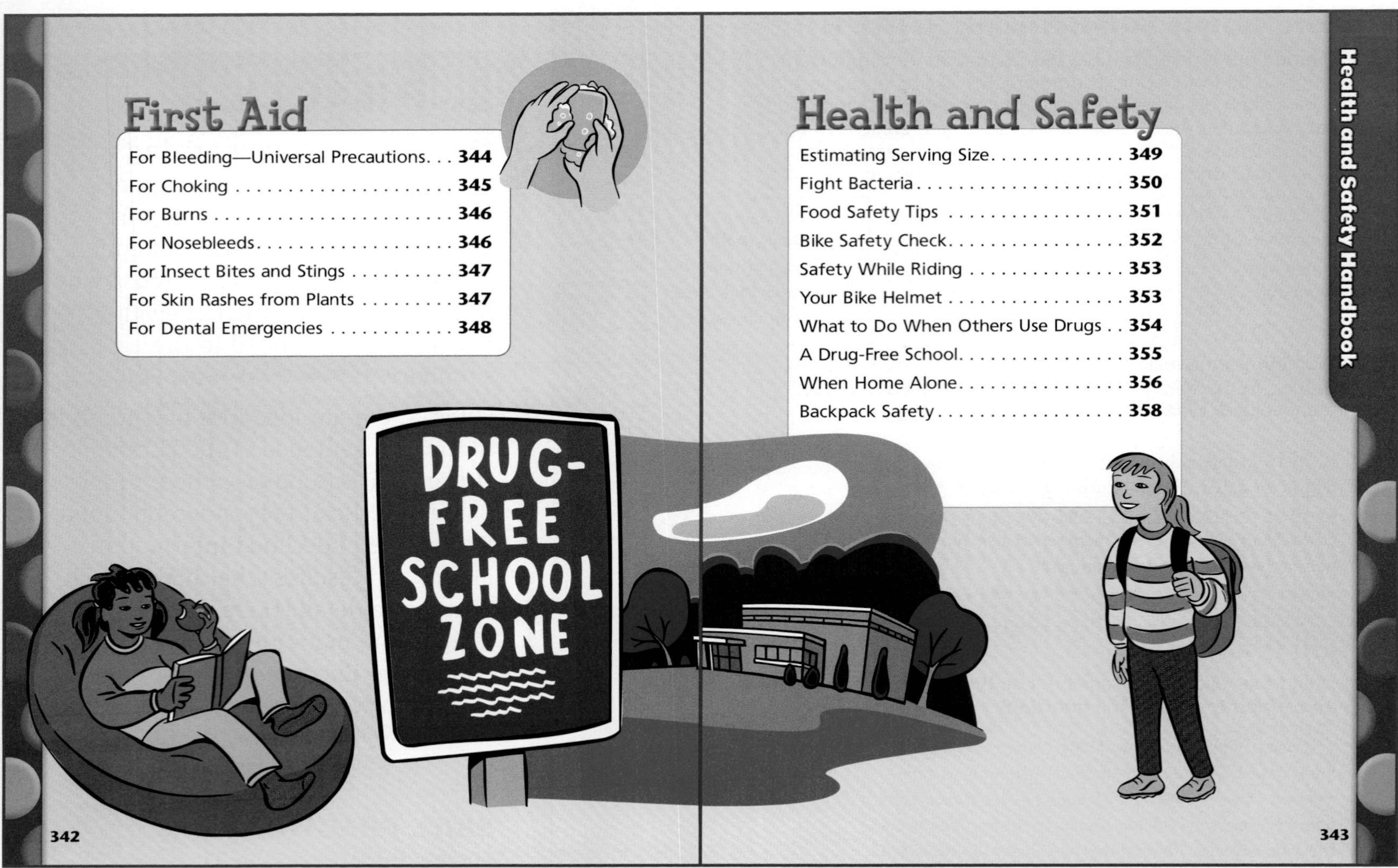

First Aid

Health and Safety

These pages are available in reproducible format in the *Teaching Resources* book.

USING THE HEALTH AND SAFETY HANDBOOK

This section of the Student Edition provides information that addresses important health concerns of children, such as nutrition, physical fitness, safety, and first aid. It is intended to supplement and extend the content of the Student Edition. **Copying masters of these pages are available in the *Teaching Resources*.**

In the Classroom

You can use these pages as stand-alone lessons. Discussion questions, activities, and additional background information are provided for you.

You may wish to make copies of these pages for children to refer to as you teach core lessons from the chapters in the Student Edition.

At Home

You may wish to send copies home so that children can discuss the topics with their families. These pages can also serve as a reference if children are completing health projects at home.

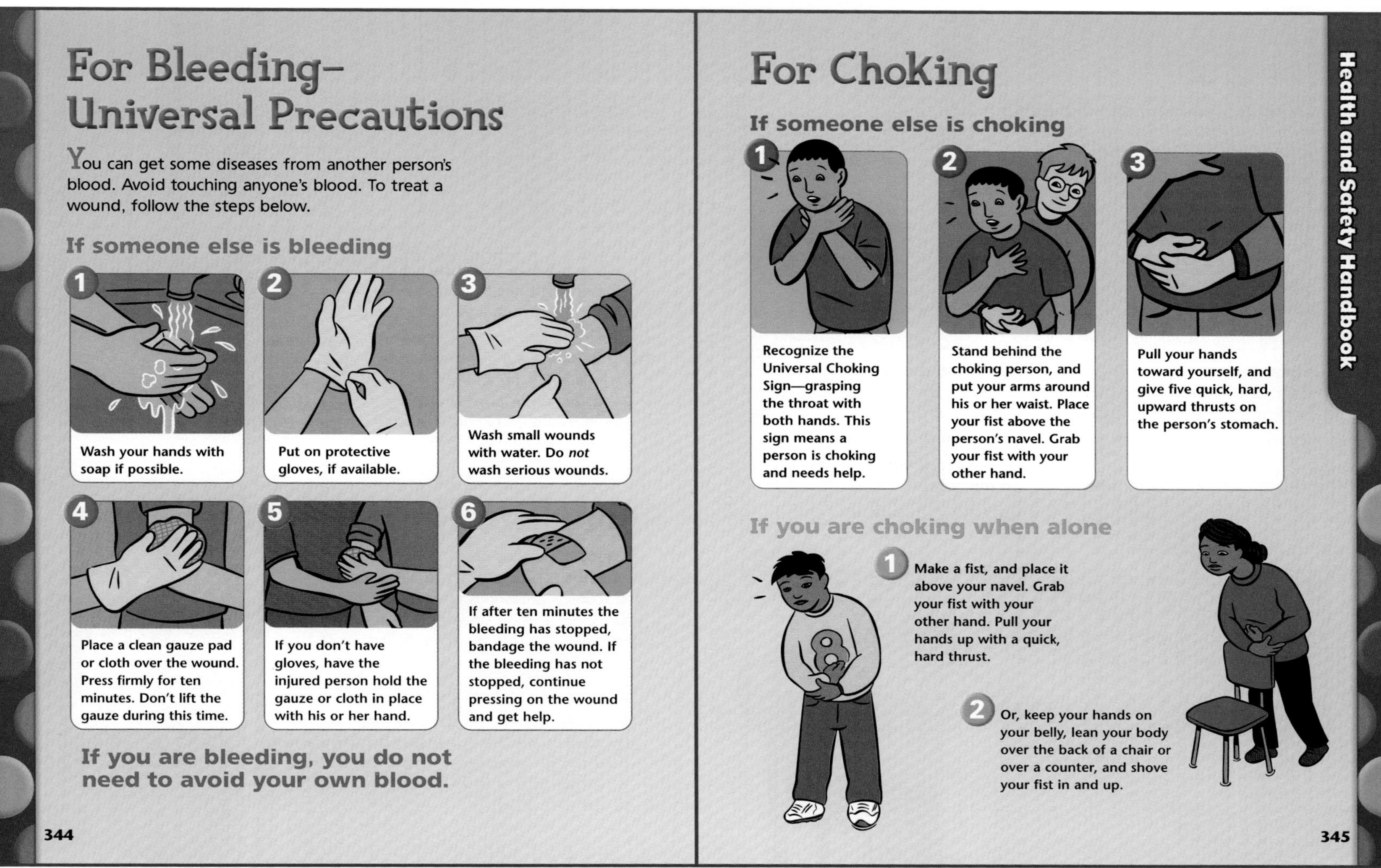

For Bleeding– Universal Precautions
You can get some diseases from another person's blood. Avoid touching anyone's blood. To treat a wound, follow the steps below.
If someone else is bleeding
1 Wash your hands with soap if possible.
2 Put on protective gloves, if available.
3 Wash small wounds with water. Do not wash serious wounds.
4 Place a clean gauze pad or cloth over the wound. Press firmly for ten minutes. Don't lift the gauze during this time.
5 If you don't have gloves, have the injured person hold the gauze or cloth in place with his or her hand.
6 If after ten minutes the bleeding has stopped, bandage the wound. If the bleeding has not stopped, continue pressing on the wound and get help.
If you are bleeding, you do not need to avoid your own blood.
344
For Choking
If someone else is choking
1 Recognize the Universal Choking Sign—grasping the throat with both hands. This sign means a person is choking and needs help.
2 Stand behind the choking person, and put your arms around his or her waist. Place your fist above the person's navel. Grab your fist with your other hand.
3 Pull your hands toward yourself, and give five quick, hard, upward thrusts on the person's stomach.
If you are choking when alone
1 Make a fist, and place it above your navel. Grab your fist with your other hand. Pull your hands up with a quick, hard thrust.
2 Or, keep your hands on your belly, lean your body over the back of a chair or over a counter, and shove your fist in and up.
345
Health and Safety Handbook

These pages are available in reproducible format in the *Teaching Resources* book.

HEALTH BACKGROUND

Unintentional Injuries are the leading cause of death in children from one to 21 years of age. For every childhood death caused by injury, there are many more hospitalizations and visits to the emergency room, private physicians, and school nurses. An even larger number of injuries are treated at home. Injuries are usually related to motor vehicle and bicycle accidents, drowning, fire, burns, poisoning, firearms, falls, suffocation, and choking. The level of risk to children depends on several factors, including socioeconomic status, gender, race, and age. Those at greater risk include younger children, poor children, males, and minorities. Level of risk is also closely related to a child's ability to recognize hazards and to respond to emergency situations. These records are maintained by the National Center for Health Statistics, CDC.

Discussion

Why is it important not to touch another person's blood? Serious communicable diseases, such as HIV and hepatitis B, can be spread by contact of blood with mucous membranes or broken skin.

What is the universal choking sign? grasping the throat with both hands

ACTIVITIES

Social Studies

American Red Cross Training Programs

The American Red Cross has been offering classes in first-aid techniques since 1909. Over the years the focus of these classes has shifted from first aid for use during disasters, epidemics, and wars to a variety of first-aid programs, such as standard first aid, community first aid and safety, and first aid for children. Encourage students to research and report on the history of the American Red Cross chapter in their region. They can also find out what courses are offered, when they're held, and how much they cost.

Art

Safety Calendars Have students make a calendar page for each month, with illustrations that show people practicing safety and giving first aid. Then have them write relevant safety tips on each page.

For Burns

- Minor burns are called first-degree burns and involve only the top layer of skin. The skin is red and dry, and the burn is painful.
- Second-degree burns cause deeper damage. The burns cause blisters, redness, swelling, and pain.
- Third-degree burns are the most serious. They damage all layers of the skin. The skin is usually white or charred black. The area may feel numb because nerve endings have been destroyed.

All burns need immediate first aid.

Minor Burns
- Run cool water over the burn or soak it for at least five minutes.
- Cover the burn with a clean dry bandage.
- Do *not* put lotion or ointment on the burn.

More Serious Burns
- Cover the burn with a cool, wet bandage or cloth.
- Do *not* break any blisters.
- Do *not* put lotion or ointment on the burn.
- Get help from an adult right away.

For Nosebleeds

- Sit down, and tilt your head forward. Pinch your nostrils together for at least ten minutes.
- You can also put a cloth-covered cold pack on the bridge of your nose.
- If your nose continues to bleed, get help from an adult.

346

For Insect Bites and Stings

- Always tell an adult about bites and stings.
- Scrape out the stinger with your fingernail.
- Wash the area with soap and water.
- A covered ice cube or cold pack will usually take away the pain from insect bites. A paste made from baking soda and water also helps.
- If the bite or sting is more serious and is on an arm or leg, keep the leg or arm dangling down. Apply a cold, wet cloth. Get help immediately.
- If you find a tick on your skin, remove it. Protect your fingers with a tissue or cloth to prevent contact with infectious tick fluids. If you must use your bare hands, wash them right away.
- If the tick has already bitten you, ask an adult to remove it. Using tweezers, an adult should grab the tick as close to your skin as possible and pull the tick out in one steady motion. Do not use petroleum jelly because it may cause the tick to struggle releasing its infectious fluids. Wash the bite site.

Health and Safety Handbook

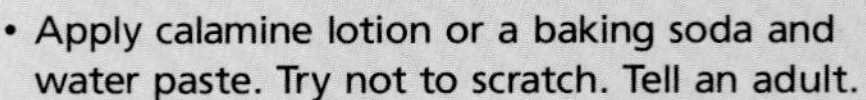

For Skin Rashes from Plants

Many poisonous plants have three leaves. Remember, "Leaves of three, let them be." If you touch a poisonous plant, wash the area and your hands. Put on clean clothes and wash the dirty ones. If a rash develops, follow these tips.

- Apply calamine lotion or a baking soda and water paste. Try not to scratch. Tell an adult.
- If you get blisters, do not pop them. If they burst, keep the area clean and dry. If your rash does not go away in two weeks, or if the rash is on your face or in your eyes, see your doctor.

347

These pages are available in reproducible format in the *Teaching Resources* book.

HEALTH BACKGROUND

Electric Shock is caused by electricity passing through the body. It can cause the heart to stop, and it can cause burns. Electricity passes easily through water, so water increases a person's chance of being shocked or even killed. Having wet skin, standing in a puddle, or touching water while using electricity provides a path for electricity to enter the body.

Discussion

Why is it important to keep harmful products in their original containers? If a harmful product is not in the right container, you won't know it is poisonous. In case of poisoning, you need to be able to tell the emergency operator or doctor the cause of the poisoning.

Tell what you would do to treat a mild burn. Use cool water to cool the burn; dry the area; loosely bandage the burn.

ACTIVITIES

Science

Identify Poisonous Plants Have groups of students research poison ivy, poison oak, poison sumac, and other common poisonous plants to find answers to questions such as the following: What do the plants look like? Where and when do they grow? How can you prevent a reaction to them? Is everyone allergic? After students have completed their research, have them transfer their accumulated data to posters. Display the posters in the school.

Math

Compare Prices for First-Aid Supplies Have partners make up a list of items for a first-aid kit. Then encourage students to call or visit several local stores to get prices for each item on their lists, including the quantity that can be bought for each price. Have them record prices in a chart and then use the chart to make comparisons to determine which store has the best overall prices.

For Dental Emergencies

You should know what to do if you have a dental emergency.

Broken Tooth

- Rinse your mouth with warm water. Wrap a cold pack with a cloth. Place it on the injured area. Save any parts of the broken tooth. Call your dentist immediately.

Knocked-Out Permanent Tooth

- Find the tooth and clean it carefully. Handle it by the top (crown), not the root. Put it back into the socket if you can. Hold it in place by biting on clean cloth. If the tooth cannot be put back in, place it in a cup with milk or water. See a dentist immediately. Time is very important in saving the tooth.

Bitten Tongue or Lip

- Apply pressure to the bleeding area with a cloth. Use a cold pack covered with a cloth to stop swelling. If the bleeding doesn't stop within 15 minutes, go to a hospital emergency room.

Food/Objects Caught Between Teeth

- Use dental floss to gently take out the object. Never use anything sharp to take out an object that is stuck between your teeth. If it cannot be removed, call your dentist.

Estimating Serving Size

Choosing a variety of foods is only half the story. You also need to choose the right amounts. The table below can help you estimate the number of servings you are eating of your favorite foods.

Estimating Serving Size

Food Group	Amount of Food in One Serving	Some Easy Ways to Estimate Serving Size
Bread, Cereal, Rice, and Pasta Group	$\frac{1}{2}$ cup cooked cereal, rice, or pasta 1 slice bread, $\frac{1}{2}$ medium bagel 1 cup ready-to-eat (dry) cereal	ice cream scoop
Vegetable Group	1 cup raw leafy vegetables $\frac{1}{2}$ cup other vegetables, cooked or chopped raw $\frac{1}{2}$ cup tomato sauce	about the size of a tennis ball
Fruit Group	1 medium apple, pear, or orange 1 medium banana $\frac{1}{2}$ cup chopped or cooked fruit 1 cup fresh fruit 4 oz cup fruit juice	about the size of a baseball
Milk, Yogurt, and Cheese Group	$1\frac{1}{2}$ oz natural cheese 8 oz yogurt 8 oz milk	about the size of three dominoes
Meat, Poultry, Fish, Dried Beans, Eggs, and Nuts Group	2–3 oz lean meat, chicken, or fish 2 tablespoons peanut butter $\frac{1}{2}$ cup cooked, dry beans	about the size of a computer mouse
Fats, Oils, and Sweets Group	1 teaspoon margarine or butter	about the size of the end of your thumb

These pages are available in reproducible format in the *Teaching Resources* book.

HEALTH BACKGROUND

Food and Your Teeth Some foods that one would least expect contain sugars or starches. Fruits, milk, bread, cereals and even vegetables are some examples. If you don't brush your teeth after eating, plaque bacteria use the sugar and starch to produce acids that attack the teeth for 20 minutes or more. These acids destroy the hard surface, or enamel, of the tooth. After a while, tooth decay occurs. The more often one eats and the longer foods remain in the mouth, the more damage occurs.

The key to choosing foods wisely is not to avoid these foods, but to think before you eat. Not only what you eat and how much you eat, but also when you eat can make a big difference in your dental health. Eat a balanced diet, learn to estimate serving size, and limit between-meal snacks.

Discussion

Why do the foods eaten during a meal cause less harm to your teeth than foods eaten as snacks? More saliva is released during a meal, which helps wash foods from the mouth thereby lessening the effects of acids.

Can both primary and permanent teeth be reimplanted? No. A baby tooth is not re-implanted as it is usually rejected during the healing process. A permanent tooth can be reimplanted if it is handled carefully after being knocked out and if a dentist is seen immediately.

ACTIVITIES

Language Arts

Bread Word Wall Explain to students that bread comes in many different forms, such as matzo, biscuits, and tortilla. Suggest students research kinds of bread that are typical of other countries. They can write the name of their "bread" and the country on a sticky note. Some students may want to find a picture of that bread to add to their note. Using a world map, students can place their notes on the country that shows the bread's origin.

Math

Make a Graph Suggest students work in groups using the Internet or library resources to research the number of teeth that different animals have. They can graph their findings to share with the rest of the class. For example, adult humans have 32 teeth and adult cats have 30 teeth.

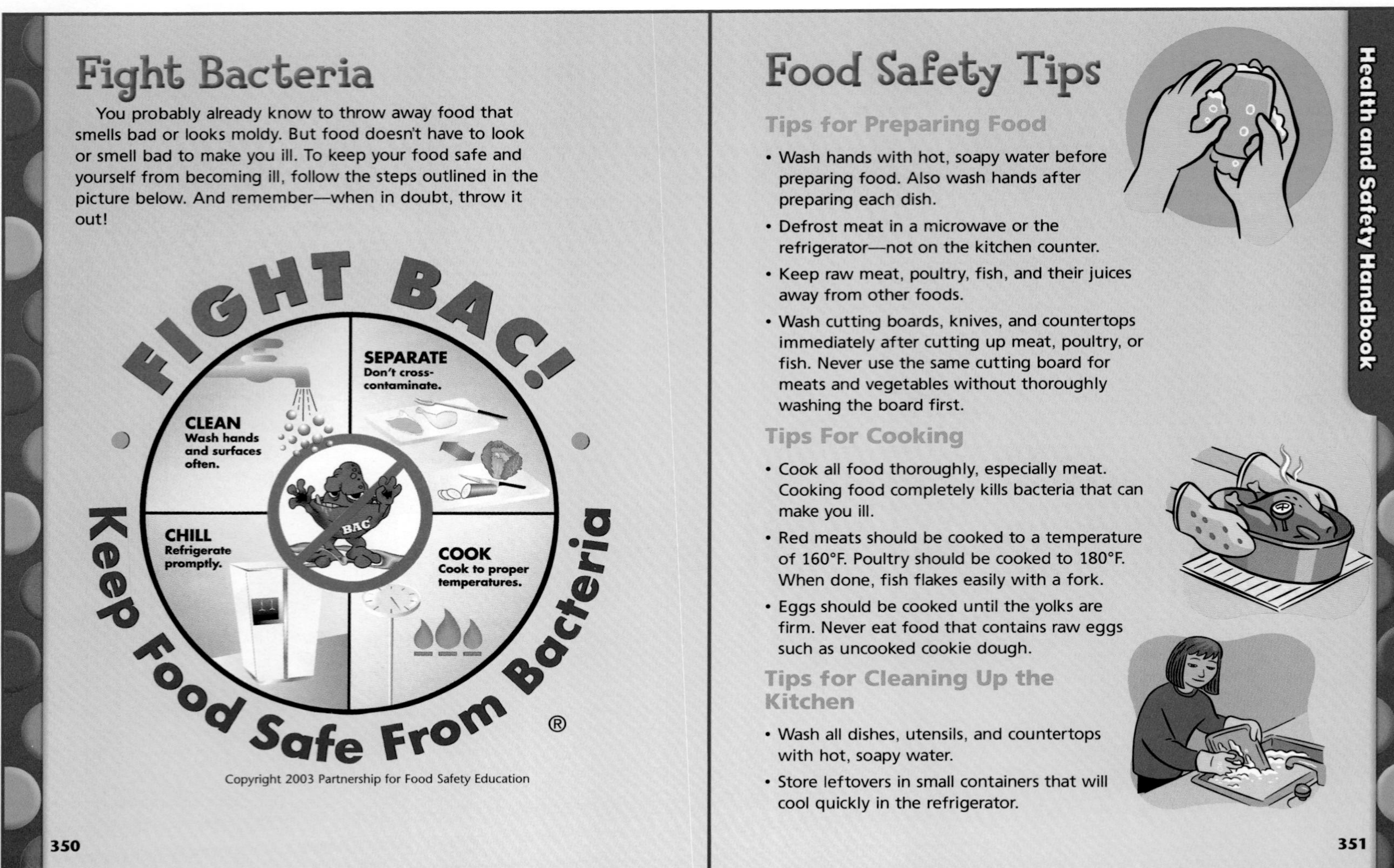

Fight Bacteria

You probably already know to throw away food that smells bad or looks moldy. But food doesn't have to look or smell bad to make you ill. To keep your food safe and yourself from becoming ill, follow the steps outlined in the picture below. And remember—when in doubt, throw it out!

FIGHT BAC!
SEPARATE
Don't cross-contaminate.
CLEAN
Wash hands and surfaces often.
CHILL
Refrigerate promptly.
COOK
Cook to proper temperatures.
BAC
Keep Food Safe From Bacteria ®

Copyright 2003 Partnership for Food Safety Education

350

Food Safety Tips

Tips for Preparing Food

- Wash hands with hot, soapy water before preparing food. Also wash hands after preparing each dish.
- Defrost meat in a microwave or the refrigerator—not on the kitchen counter.
- Keep raw meat, poultry, fish, and their juices away from other foods.
- Wash cutting boards, knives, and countertops immediately after cutting up meat, poultry, or fish. Never use the same cutting board for meats and vegetables without thoroughly washing the board first.

Tips For Cooking

- Cook all food thoroughly, especially meat. Cooking food completely kills bacteria that can make you ill.
- Red meats should be cooked to a temperature of 160°F. Poultry should be cooked to 180°F. When done, fish flakes easily with a fork.
- Eggs should be cooked until the yolks are firm. Never eat food that contains raw eggs such as uncooked cookie dough.

Tips for Cleaning Up the Kitchen

- Wash all dishes, utensils, and countertops with hot, soapy water.
- Store leftovers in small containers that will cool quickly in the refrigerator.

Health and Safety Handbook

351

These pages are available in reproducible format in the *Teaching Resources* book.

HEALTH BACKGROUND

Bacteria Items used for cleaning the kitchen can harbor germs. Tell students that kitchen sponges and dishcloths need to be kept very clean, allowed to dry between uses, and replaced or washed frequently. Otherwise, they can spread germs to kitchen dishes and surfaces, such as counters and tables.

Discussion

Many food safety rules concern keeping food at the proper temperature. Explain the reasons behind some of the rules. For example, here are explanations of two rules:

- Thawing food on the counter takes a long time; parts of the food reach room temperature long before all of the food is thawed. Germs grow quickly in the warm parts of the food.
- High temperatures kill germs. If food doesn't get hot enough while cooking, germs are not killed. Pink or red meat or poultry should be cooked until it is hot enough to kill all the germs that may be present.

What should you do if you think chicken is not cooked enough? Don't eat it. Tell an adult, and have it cooked more.

ACTIVITIES

Cultural

Dietary Customs Cultural, religious, and genetic factors influence dietary customs. For example many Jews and Muslims do not eat pork. Buddhists and Hindus may be strictly vegetarian. Many people of Asian, African, and Native American descent lack an enzyme necessary for digesting dairy products. Have students research and report on dietary customs of other cultures.

Science

Helpful Bacteria Certain kinds of helpful bacteria live in the intestines of human beings and other animals. These bacteria aid in digestion, help destroy harmful organisms, and also produce some vitamins needed by the body. Ask students to find out how some helpful bacteria are used to make food products such as yogurt, certain cheeses, and vinegar. Have students give short reports about their findings.

Bike Safety Check

A safe bike should be the right size for you.

- You should be able to rest your heel on the pedal when you sit on your bike with the pedal in the lowest position.
- When you are standing astride your bike with both feet flat on the ground, your body should be 2 inches (about 5 cm) above the bar that goes from the handlebar to the seat.

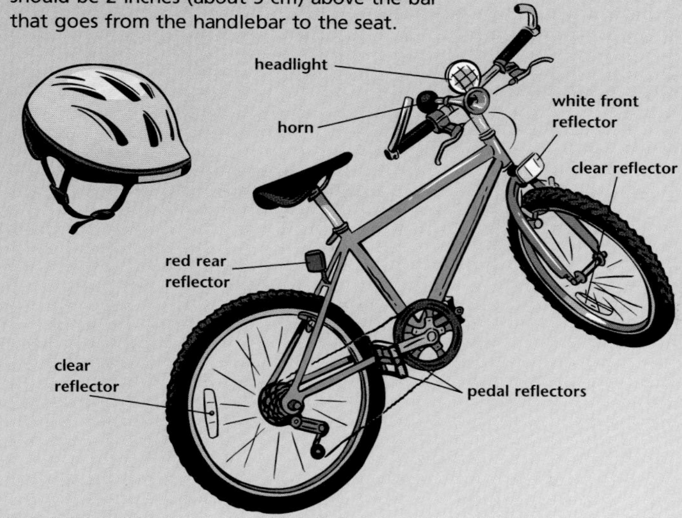

A bike should have all the safety equipment shown above. Does *your* bike pass the test?

Safety While Riding

Here are some tips for safe bicycle riding.

- Always wear your bike helmet, even for short distances.
- Check your bike every time you ride it. Is it in safe working condition?
- Ride in single file in the same direction as traffic. Never weave in and out of parked cars.
- Before you enter a street, **STOP**. **Look** left, right, and then left again. **Listen** for any traffic. **Think** before you go.
- Walk your bike across an intersection. **Look** left, right, and then left again. Wait for traffic to pass.
- Obey all traffic signs and signals.
- Do not ride your bike at night without an adult. If you do ride at night, be sure to wear light-colored clothing, use reflectors, and front and rear lights.

Your Bike Helmet

- About 500,000 children are involved in bike-related crashes every year. That's why it's important to always wear your bike helmet.
- Wear your helmet properly. It should lie flat on your head. The straps should be snug so it will stay in place if you fall.
- If you do fall and your helmet hits the ground, replace it—even if it doesn't look damaged. The inner foam lining may be crushed. It might not protect you if you fell again.

These pages are available in reproducible format in the *Teaching Resources* book.

HEALTH BACKGROUND

The Importance of Helmets Each year in the United States, hundreds of children are killed in bicycle-related accidents. Many children require emergency room treatment as a result of these injuries. Bicycles helmets are extremely effective in preventing brain and head injuries, making helmet use the most effective single way to reduce head injuries and deaths resulting from bicycle accidents.

Discussion

What should you be wearing on a bike ride? Possible answers: helmet; clothes that will not get caught on the pedals or in the chain; elbow and knee pads; light-or bright-colored clothing

What should you check on your bike before you go for a ride? Possible answers: check the air in the tires; see that the brakes work properly; make sure the bike has reflectors

ACTIVITIES

Art

Safe-Riding Park Diorama Have groups of students work together to design a park specifically for bicyclists, skateboarders, and in-line skaters. Suggest that students brainstorm ideas for their park designs, choose the best one, and then build a diorama of their final design. Encourage students to use a variety of materials in their dioramas.

Language Arts

Prepare Safety Demonstrations Have pairs of students compile a list of all the ways they can be safe when riding their bikes. Ask them to write a script that would allow them to present the information to a kindergarten or first-grade class. Encourage them to use props, especially examples of safety equipment.

What to Do When Others Use Drugs

You should make a personal commitment to not use alcohol, tobacco, or other drugs. But you may be around other students or adults who make unhealthful choices about drugs. Here is what you can do.

Know the Signs

Someone who has a problem with drugs may be sad or angry all the time, skip school or work, or forget events often.

Talk to a Trusted Adult

Do not keep someone's drug use a secret. Ask a trusted adult for help. You can also get support from adults to help you resist pressure to use drugs.

Where to get help
- Hospitals
- Alateen
- Alcoholics Anonymous
- Narcotics Anonymous
- Al-Anon
- Drug treatment centers

Be Supportive

If a person decides to stop using drugs, help them quit. Suggest healthful activities you can do together. Tell them you are happy they have quit.

Stay Healthy

Do not stay anywhere that drugs are being used. If you cannot leave, stay as far away from the drugs as possible.

354

A Drug-Free School

Many schools make rules and sponsor activities to encourage people to say *no* to drugs. This makes the schools a more healthful environment for everyone.

School Rules

Many schools decide to be drug free. They often have strict penalties for anyone found with drugs. For example, a person found with drugs may be expelled or suspended from school.

Positive Peer Pressure

Peer pressure can be bad or good. *Positive peer pressure* is the affect of people the same age encouraging each other to make healthful choices. For example, students may make posters or hold rallies to encourage others to choose not to use drugs.

355

These pages are available in reproducible format in the *Teaching Resources* book.

HEALTH BACKGROUND

Medicines and Drugs Explain to students how the development of medicines has helped people live longer, more comfortable lives. For example, before the discovery of vaccinations, many people lost their lives to infectious diseases like smallpox, polio, diphtheria, cholera, tetanus, and yellow fever. Penicillin and other antibiotics can cure some of these diseases and many others. Other medicines have been developed to treat chronic diseases such as diabetes, asthma, and heart disease. However, using drugs for purposes for which they were not intended, or using illegal drugs, such as marijuana, cocaine, or heroin, can be dangerous or can lead to dangerous behavior. People who abuse drugs can become addicted to them. Addiction can lead to serious illness or death.

Discussion

Why is tobacco smoke harmful? It contains nicotine, a highly addictive poison found in tobacco leaves; carbon monoxide, a poisonous gas; tar; and at least 60 other harmful substances.

Why is alcohol considered a drug? Where is it found? It is a substance, other than food, that causes changes in the way the body or mind works. It is found in beer, wine, and liquor.

ACTIVITIES

Art

Antidrug Campaign Have students design and create an antidrug campaign, using various media. Suggest they use positive peer pressure in their magazine ads, billboards, and bumper stickers. Students can display their media campaign during a drug-awareness program at school.

Science

Cigarette Tar Remind students that cigarettes contain tar, a sticky substance left by the smoke of certain burning substances. Suggest that, with an adult's help, they search for tar on barbeque grills, or chimneys, and take samples to observe and record its properties. Students can compare their findings with the rest of the class.

When Home Alone

Everyone stays home alone sometimes. When you stay home alone, it's important to know how to take care of yourself. Here are some easy rules to follow that will help keep you safe when you are home by yourself.

Do These Things

- Lock all the doors and windows. Be sure you know how to lock and unlock all the locks.
- If someone who is nasty or mean calls, hang up immediately. Tell an adult about the call when he or she gets home. Your parents may not want you to answer the phone at all.
- If you have an emergency, call 911. Be prepared to describe the problem and to give your full name, address, and telephone number. Follow all instructions given to you. Do not hang up the phone until you are told to do so.
- If you see anyone hanging around outside your home, call a neighbor or the police.
- If you see or smell smoke, go outside right away. If you live in an apartment, do not take the elevator. Go to a neighbor's house, and call 911 immediately.
- Entertain yourself. Time will pass more quickly if you are not bored. Work on a hobby, read a book or magazine, do your homework, or clean your room. Before you know it, an adult will be home.

356

Do Not Do These Things

- Do NOT use the stove, microwave, or oven unless an adult family member has given you permission, and you know how to use these appliances.
- Do NOT open the door for anyone you don't know or for anyone who is not supposed to be in your home.
- Do NOT talk to strangers on the telephone. Do not tell anyone that you are home alone. If the call is for an adult family member, say that he or she can't come to the phone right now and take a message.
- Do NOT have friends over unless you have permission from your parents or other adult family members.

A telephone with caller ID display can help you decide whether to answer the phone.

357

Health and Safety Handbook

These pages are available in reproducible format in the *Teaching Resources* book.

HEALTH BACKGROUND

Be Alert Children are aware of the need to be careful around strangers, but they may not know exactly what to do if confronted by a stranger. Inform children never to talk to a stranger, get into a car with a stranger, or accept a gift from a stranger. Tell children to yell loudly if they feel threatened or scared. Teach them to shout things like, "I don't know you!" and "Help! This isn't my dad!"

Discussion

Have students name trusted adults in their lives such as parents, guardians, grandparents, aunts, uncles, adult siblings, adult friends, religious leaders, teachers, principals, school nurses, and counselors.

What should you do if you are home alone and have an emergency? Call 911 or 0 (zero) for the operator.

What should you do if you are home alone and you see or smell smoke? Go outside right away; do not take the elevator if you live in an apartment; go to a neighbor's home and call 911 or the fire department immediately.

Why is it important that you know and follow safety rules? to avoid getting hurt

ACTIVITIES

Art/Language Arts

Draw Your Responsible Self Have students draw pictures of themselves taking responsibility for their own safety when home alone. Then have each student write a caption explaining his or her safety tip. Display students' drawings in the classroom.

Drama

Dramatic Reenactment Encourage partners to write a scene in which a stranger tries unsuccessfully to entice a child their age to open the door when he or she is home alone. Have students rehearse their scenes and present them to the class.

Health and Safety Handbook

Backpack Safety

Carrying a backpack that is too heavy can injure your back. Carrying one incorrectly also can hurt you.

Safe Weight

A full backpack should weigh no more than 10 to 15 percent of your body weight. Less is better. To find 10 percent, divide your body weight by 10. Here are some examples:

Your Weight (pounds)	Maximum Backpack Weight (pounds)
60	6
65	$6\frac{1}{2}$
70	7

This is the right way to carry a backpack.

Safe Use

- Use a pack with wide shoulder straps and a padded back.
- Lighten your load. Leave unnecessary items at home.
- Pack heavier items inside the pack so that they will be closest to your back.
- Always use both shoulder straps to carry the pack.
- Never wear a backpack while riding a bicycle. The weight makes it harder to stay balanced. Use the bicycle basket or saddlebags instead.

This is the wrong way to carry a backpack.

358

This page is available in reproducible format in the *Teaching Resources* book.

HEALTH BACKGROUND

Backpacks Children's backs are strong and flexible and can provide a logical way to carry a heavy load. However, children must be instructed to use backpacks safely. Heavy backpacks and those carried incorrectly, can alter the fluid-filled discs of the spine. That alteration can make the wearer susceptible to herniated or slipped discs and osteoarthritis later in life. According to the American Occupational Therapy Association backpacks are the cause of 7,000 annual emergency room visits nationwide.

Discussion

What are some things you should know about backpack safety?

- Buy the right size and keep it light.
- Pick up your backpack correctly (by bending at the knees), and always wear it correctly.
- Ask your school to consider buying two sets of textbooks—one for home and one for school.

What health concerns should you watch for if you carry a backpack? neck aches, headaches, low back pain, muscle spasms, achy and strained muscles, bad posture, and increased scoliosis complications.

ACTIVITIES

Language Arts

National School Backpack Awareness Day The American Occupational Therapy Association has declared September 25 as *National School Backpack Awareness Day*. Have students make posters outlining the do's and don'ts of backpack safety. Students can display their posters in the classroom and lunchroom.

Math

Compare Costs Have students use the Internet to research information about backpacks. (Review with students the rules for evaluating credible health websites.) Students should find the costs and features of several backpacks and make charts of their choices. Have them explain how they found their information and which backpack design offers the most features for the money.

Glossary

Numbers in parentheses indicate the pages on which the words are defined in context.

PRONUNCIATION RESPELLING KEY

Sound	As in	Phonetic Respelling	Sound	As in	Phonetic Respelling	Sound	As in	Phonetic Respelling
a	bat	(BAT)	eye	idea	(eye•DEE•uh)	th	thin	(THIN)
ah	lock	(LAHK)	i	bit	(BIT)	u	pull	(PUL)
air	rare	(RAIR)	ing	going	(GOH•ing)	uh	medal	(MED•uhl)
ar	argue	(AR•gyoo)	k	card	(KARD)		talent	(TAL•uhnt)
aw	law	(LAW)		kite	(KYT)		pencil	(PEN•suhl)
ay	face	(FAYS)	ngk	bank	(BANGK)		onion	(UHN•yuhn)
ch	chapel	(CHAP•uhl)	oh	over	(OH•ver)		playful	(play•fuhl)
e	test	(TEST)	oo	pool	(POOL)		dull	(DUHL)
	metric	(MEH•trik)	ow	out	(OWT)	y	yes	(YES)
ee	eat	(EET)	oy	foil	(FOYL)		ripe	(RYP)
	feet	(FEET)	s	cell	(SEL)	z	bags	(BAGZ)
	ski	(SKEE)		sit	(SIT)	zh	treasure	(TREZH•er)
er	paper	(PAY•per)	sh	sheep	(SHEEP)			
	fern	(FERN)	th	that	(THAT)			

abstinence (AB•stuh•nuhns)
Avoiding a behavior that can harm your health *(182)*

Activity Pyramid (ak•TIV•uh•tee PIR•uh•mid)
A guide to physical activity *(106)*

addiction (uh•DIK•shuhn)
A craving that makes a person keep using a drug even when he or she knows it is harmful *(195)*

advertising (AD•ver•tyz•ing)
A way businesses give people information about their products *(48)*

aerobic exercise (air•OH•bik EK•ser•syz)
Physical activity that makes your heart and lungs work harder, improving the health of your cardiovascular system *(100)*

air bag (AIR BAG)
In a car, van, or truck, a bag that inflates during a collision to protect the people in the front seat *(144)*

alcohol (AL•kuh•hawl)
A drug found in beer, wine, and liquor *(224)*

alcoholism (AL•kuh•hawl•iz•uhm)
A disease in which people cannot control their use of alcohol *(229)*

allergy (AL•er•jee)
A noncommunicable disease in which a person's body reacts to a certain substance *(176)*

anaerobic exercise (an•air•OH•bik EK•ser•syz)
Physical activity that makes your muscles stronger and bigger *(100)*

antibodies (AN•tih•bahd•eez)
Chemicals the body makes to fight disease *(167)*

arteries (AR•ter•eez)
Blood vessels that carry blood away from the heart *(22)*

arthritis (ar•THRYT•is)
A noncommunicable disease in which the body's joints become damaged and are painful *(179)*

asthma (AZ•muh)
A noncommunicable disease of the respiratory system; it causes breathing problems *(177)*

bacteria (bak•TIR•ee•uh)
One-celled living things; most are harmless, but some can cause disease *(162)*

balanced diet (BAL•uhnst DY•uht)
A diet made up of healthful amounts of foods from each of the food groups *(69)*

basic needs (BAY•sik NEEDZ)
The physical, mental, emotional, and social needs that all people have *(252)*

blended family (BLEND•uhd FAM•uh•lee)
A family that is formed when two single parents with children marry *(283)*

brain (BRAYN)
The organ that controls the nervous system *(12)*

bronchi (BRAHNG•ky)
The two tubes that carry air from the trachea to the lungs *(20)*

bully (BUL•ee)
A person who hurts or frightens others, especially those who are smaller, weaker, different, or alone *(149)*

caffeine (ka•FEEN)
A drug found in coffee, tea, chocolate, and certain soft drinks *(196)*

cancer (KAN•ser)
A disease in which body cells that are not normal grow out of control *(175)*

capillaries (KAP•uh•lair•eez)
The tiny blood vessels that deliver blood to the tissues *(22)*

carbohydrates (kar•boh•HY•drayts)
The starches and sugars that are the body's main source of energy *(60)*

cavity (KAV•ih•tee)
A hole in a tooth *(36)*

cell (SEL)
The smallest working part of the body *(4)*

cocaine (koh•KAYN)
A powerful drug made from the leaves of the coca plant *(202)*

communicable disease (kuh•MYOO•nih•kuh•buhl dih•ZEEZ)
An illness that can spread from person to person *(158)*

compassion (kuhm•PASH•uhn)
An understanding of the needs and feelings of others *(268)*

compromise (KAHM•pruh•myz)
A solution in which each side in a conflict gives up part of what it wants *(263)*

conflict (KAHN•flikt)
A disagreement between people who have different needs or wishes *(262)*

conflict resolution (KAHN•flikt reh•zuh•LOO•shuhn)
The resolving of a problem between people *(262)*

conservation (kahn•ser•VAY•shuhn)
The careful use of resources to make them last longer *(324)*

consumer (kuhn•SOOM•er)
A person who buys a product *(48)*

cooperate (koh•AHP•er•ayt)
To work helpfully with others *(296)*

dermis (DER•muhs)
The thick bottom layer of skin; it contains blood vessels and nerves *(33)*

diabetes (dy•uh•BEET•eez)
A noncommunicable disease in which the body stops making insulin and so cannot use sugar properly *(178)*

diaphragm (DY•uh•fram)
The muscle beneath your lungs that helps move air into and out of the lungs *(21)*

disease (dih•ZEEZ)
A condition that damages or weakens part of the body *(158)*

dose (DOHS)
The amount of medicine you should take each time you use it *(191)*

drug (DRUHG)
A substance other than food that changes the way the body works *(188)*

drug dependence (DRUHG dih•PEN•duhns)
The need to take a drug just to feel normal *(201)*

emergency (ee•MER•juhn•see)
A situation in which help is needed right away *(116)*

environment (en•VY•ruhn•muhnt)
All of the living and nonliving things that surround you, including plants, animals, air, water, soil, buildings, and roads *(304)*

epidermis (ep•uh•DER•mis)
The top layer of the skin *(32)*

esophagus (ih•SAHF•uh•guhs)
A tubelike organ that pushes food from your mouth to your stomach *(16)*

expiration date (eks•puh•RAY•shuhn DAYT)
A date on a medicine container that tells you when the medicine will no longer be safe to take *(192)*

extended family (ek•STEN•duhd FAM•uh•lee)
A family that includes more than just parents and children; it may include grandparents or other relatives *(283)*

family emergency plan (FAM•uh•lee ee•MER•juhn•see PLAN)
Steps your family takes to stay safe during an emergency *(118)*

fats (FATS)
Nutrients that give your body more energy than any other kind of nutrient *(61)*

flood (FLUHD)
An overflow of water onto normally dry land *(139)*

food guide pyramid (FOOD GYD PIR•uh•mid)
A diagram that helps people choose foods for a healthful diet *(69)*

food poisoning (FOOD POY•zuhn•ing)
An illness caused by eating food that contains germs *(84)*

fungi (FUN•jy)
Simple living things, such as molds, yeasts, and mushrooms; some fungi can cause disease *(163)*

gang (GANG)
A group of people who use and sell drugs, carry weapons, and use violence to commit crimes *(150)*

goal (GOHL)
Something you are willing to work for *(255)*

graffiti (gruh•FEET•ee)
Writing or drawing done on public or private propery without permission *(308)*

habit (HAB•it)
Something you do so often that you don't even think about it *(72)*

hazard (HAZ•erd)
An object or condition that makes a place unsafe *(122)*

heart (HART)
The organ that pumps blood through the body *(22)*

hurricane (HER•ih•kayn)
A storm that forms over an ocean; it has strong winds and heavy rain, and it can cause flooding *(139)*

illegal drug (ih•LEE•guhl DRUHG)
A drug that is not a medicine and that is against the law to sell, buy, have, or use *(200)*

immune system (ih•MYOON SIS•tuhm)
The body system that fights off disease *(166)*

immunity (ih•MYOO•nih•tee)
The body's ability to fight off pathogens *(167)*

infection (in•FEK•shuhn)
The growth of pathogens in the body *(163)*

ingredients (in•GREE•dee•uhnts)
All the things used to make a food, medicine, health-care product, or household product *(81)*

inhalants (in•HAYL•uhnts)
Substances that have fumes some people use as drugs *(197)*

intoxicated (in•TAHKS•ih•kayt•uhd)
A condition in which a person is strongly affected by too much alcohol *(228)*

large intestine (LARJ in•TES•tuhn)
The last organ of the digestive system; it removes water to form solid waste *(17)*

lens (LENZ)
In the eye, the clear, curved part that bends light to form an image on the back of the eye *(42)*

lifeguard (LYF•gard)
A person who is trained to rescue people who are in danger of drowning *(128)*

lightning (LYT•ning)
A large release of electricity between clouds and the ground; it can injure or kill people, cause fires, and damage property *(139)*

lungs (LUHNGZ)
Organs that allow oxygen from the air to pass into your body *(21)*

marijuana (mair•uh•WAH•nuh)
An illegal drug made from the hemp plant *(200)*

medicine (MED•uh•suhn)
A drug used to treat or cure a health problem *(188)*

minerals (MIN•er•uhlz)
Nutrients that help your body grow and work and are not made by living things *(62)*

muscle (MUHS•uhl)
An organ that contracts and relaxes to produce movement *(25)*

muscular system (MUHS•kyoo•ler SIS•tuhm)
The body system that allows your body to move *(25)*

natural resources (NACH•er•uhl REE•sawrs•uhz)
Materials from nature that people use to meet their needs; they include rocks, minerals, plants, animals, air, sunlight, water, and soil *(312)*

negotiate (nih•GOH•shee•ayt)
To work together to resolve a conflict *(263)*

nerves (NERVZ)
Bundles of fibers that carry messages *(12)*

nervous system (NERV•uhs SIS•tuhm)
The body system that coordinates all of the body's activities *(12)*

nicotine (NIK•uh•teen)
A very addictive chemical in tobacco; it speeds up the nervous system *(219)*

noncommunicable disease (nahn•kuh•MYOO•nih•kuh•buhl dih•ZEEZ)
An illness that does not spread from person to person *(159)*

nonrenewable resources (nahn-rih•NOO•uh•buhl REE•sawrs•uhz)
Resources that take a very long time to replace or that cannot be replaced at all *(313)*

nuclear family (NOO•klee•er FAM•uh•lee)
A family consisting of a mother, father, and one or more children *(282)*

nucleus (NOO•klee•uhs)
The control center of a cell *(6)*

nutrients (NOO•tree•uhnts)
Substances the body can use *(18)*

nutritious (noo•TRISH•uhs)
Having value as a food *(80)*

organs (AWR•guhnz)
Groups of tissues that work together to perform a certain job *(7)*

over-the-counter medicines (OH•ver•thuh•kown•ter MED•uh•suhnz)
Medicines that can be bought without a prescription *(191)*

pathogens (PATH•uh•juhnz)
Organisms, such as bacteria or viruses, that cause communicable diseases *(162)*

peer pressure (PIR PRESH•er)
The strong influence people your own age can have on you *(207)*

plaque (PLAK)
A sticky film that forms on your teeth *(36)*

pollution (puh•LOO•shuhn)
Harmful materials that make the air, water, and land unsafe *(316)*

posture (PAHS•cher)
The position of the body in standing or sitting *(92)*

prescription (prih•SKRIP•shuhn)
A doctor's order for medicine *(190)*

prescription medicine (prih•SKRIP•shun MED•uh•suhn)
Medicine that only an adult can buy and then only with a doctor's order *(190)*

privacy (PRY•vuh•see)
Time by yourself *(254)*

proteins (PROH•teenz)
A kind of nutrient that gives you energy and helps build and repair your cells *(61)*

pupil (PYOO•puhl)
In the eye, the opening though which light enters *(42)*

renewable resources (rih•NOO•uh•buhl REE•sawrs•uhz)
Resources that can be replaced by nature—for example, trees *(313)*

resistance (rih•ZIS•tuhns)
The body's natural ability to fight off disease *(180)*

rest (REST)
Quiet time to relax and give your heart, muscles, and mind a chance to slow down *(102)*

retina (RET•uh•nuh)
In the eye, the part on which an image forms; the image is carried by nerve signals to the brain *(42)*

role model (ROHL•mahd•uhl)
A person who sets a good example *(272)*

self-concept (self•KAHN•sept)
The way you think about yourself *(248)*

self-confidence (self•KAHN•fih•duhns)
A good feeling you have about what you are able to do *(248)*

366

self-control (self•kuhn•TROHL)
Your ability to express your feelings responsibly *(258)*

self-respect (self•rih•SPEKT)
The feeling that you have about yourself when you like yourself and are proud of what you do *(206)*

serving (SER•ving)
The measured amount of a food a person should eat at one time *(69)*

side effects (SYD ih•FEKTS)
Unwanted changes a medicine may cause in the body *(189)*

single-parent family (SING•guhl PAIR•uhnt FAM•uh•lee)
A family made up of one parent and his or her children *(282)*

skeletal system (SKEL•uh•tuhl SIS•tuhm)
The body system made up of all your bones; it supports your body, protects your organs, and allows you to move *(24)*

skull (SKUHL)
The bones of your head that protect your brain *(24)*

small intestine (SMAWL in•TES•tuhn)
A tubelike organ just below the stomach; nutrients are absorbed into the body through its walls *(16)*

solid waste (SAHL•id WAYST)
Garbage and litter *(317)*

spine (SPYN)
The backbone; it is made up of small bones that protect your spinal cord *(24)*

stomach (STUHM•uhk)
The organ that mixes digestive juices with food *(16)*

system (SIS•tuhm)
A group of organs that work together *(7)*

tar (TAR)
A dark, sticky material that coats the lungs and air passages of smokers *(219)*

tissue (TISH•oo)
A group of cells of the same kind that work together to do a job *(7)*

tornado (tawr•NAY•doh)
A violent windstorm that spins in a funnel shape *(139)*

trachea (TRAY•kee•uh)
The tube that carries air to the bronchi; the air then passes into the lungs *(20)*

Glossary

367

traditions (truh•DISH•uhnz)
Customs that family members follow *(282)*

trait (TRAYT)
A characteristic, or quality, that a person has *(4)*

vaccine (vak•SEEN)
A medicine that can prevent a certain disease *(170)*

values (VAL•yooz)
Strong beliefs about how people should behave and live *(294)*

veins (VAYNZ)
Blood vessels that carry blood back to the heart *(22)*

virus (VY•ruhs)
The smallest kind of pathogen *(162)*

vitamins (VY•tuh•minz)
Nutrients that help your body do certain jobs and are made by living things *(62)*

water (WAW•ter)
A nutrient necessary for life; it helps your body break down foods and carry nutrients to your cells *(63)*

weapon (WEP•uhn)
An object that can be used to kill, injure, or threaten someone *(151)*

368

Index

Boldfaced numbers refer to illustrations.

B

D

E

Index

CREDITS

Cover Design: Bill Smith Studio

Photographs:

KEY: (t) top, (b) bottom, (l) left, (r) right, (c) center, (bg) background, (fg) foreground

Cover Photographer: Brian Fraunfelter

5 (t) Getty Images; 7 (t) G.W. Willis, M.D./Visuals Unlimited; 7 (tc) Science Vu/Visuals Unlimited; 7 (bc) Dr. Mary Notter/Phototake; 7 (b) Fred Hossler/Visuals Unlimited; 13 (tl) Chris Lowe/Index Stock Imagery; 13 (tc) Tim Davis/Photo Researchers; 13 (cl) Mark Richards/PhotoEdit; 13 (cr) Index Stock Imagery; 13 (bl) Myrleen Ferguson Cate/PhotoEdit; 13 (bc) David Young-Wolff/PhotoEdit; 22 Frank Siteman/Mira.com; 23 Dennis Kunkel/Phototake; 27 Warren Morgan/Corbis; 37 (t) E.R. Degginger/Color-Pic; 37 (b) Science Photo Library/Photo Researchers; 39 Royalty-Free/Corbis; 52 Stephen Simpson/Getty Images; 55 Tom Stewart/Corbis; 60 David Brooks/Corbis; 64 (l) Christie's Images; 64 (r) The Art Archive/Musee Bouilhet-Christofle Paris/Dagli Orti; 70 (tr) Michael Newman/PhotoEdit; 87 Jeff Zaruba/Corbis; 88 (tl) Michael Pohuski/FoodPix; 88 (br) Jim Scherer Photography/StockFood; 99 Craig Hammell/Corbis; 100 (l) Jeffry W. Myers/Corbis; 100 (r) Diaphor Agency/Index Stock Imagery; 106 (tl) Richard Hutchings/Corbis; 106 (cr) Ty Allison/Getty Images; 106 (bc) Michael Newman/PhotoEdit; 106 (br) Tom & Dee Ann McCarthy/Corbis; 108 (l) Tony Freeman/PhotoEdit; 108 (r) David Young-Wolff/PhotoEdit; 109 (b) Bill O'Connor/Peter Arnold, Inc.; 109 (inset) David Young-Wolff/PhotoEdit; 112 (tr) Tom & Dee Ann McCarthy/Corbis; 112 (br) Richard Hutchings/Corbis; 117 (tl) David R. Frazier; 117 (tr) Tony Freeman/PhotoEdit; 117 (b) Pat LaCroix/Getty Images; 129 Robert Harding Picture Library/Alamy Images; 130 Mark E. Gibson Photography; 131 PA1 Harry C. Craft, III/U.S. Coast Guard Digital; 137 (t) Roy Morsch/ Bruce Coleman, Inc.; 137 (c) Jeri Gleiter/Getty Images; 137 (b) E.R. Degginger/Color-Pic; 139 (l) Charles A. Doswell, III/Visuals Unlimited; 139 (r) Marc Epstein/Visuals Unlimited; 139 (b) Aaron Horowitz/Corbis; 143 (r) Myrleen Ferguson Cate/PhotoEdit; 153 Andrea Booher/FEMA ; 160 Dennis MacDonald/PhotoEdit; 162 (inset) Dr. Dennis Kunkel/Visuals Unlimited; 162 (l) Bettmann/Corbis; 163 (tl) Network Productions/Index Stock Imagery; 163 (tr) Gopal Murti/Phototake; 163 (cr) Dr. David Phillips/Visuals Unlimited; 163 (br) Dr. Dennis Kunkel/Visuals Unlimited; 164 Custom Medical Stock Photo; 165 (inset) Science VU/CDC/Visuals Unlimited; 165 George H.H. Huey/Corbis; 166 Dennis Kunkel/Phototake; 169 (tr) Chris Lowe/Phototake; 169 (br) Spencer Grant/PhotoEdit; 170 Tony Freeman/PhotoEdit; 174 (inset) Lester Lefkowitz/Corbis; 174 (l) Brand X/Creatas Royalty Free Stock Resources; 176 (inset) BIOS (Klein/Hubert)/Peter Arnold, Inc.; 180 (l) Creatas Royalty Free Stock Resources; 180 (r) David Young-Wolff/PhotoEdit; 183 Creatas Royalty Free Stock Resources; 185 (tl) Custom Medical Stock Photos; 185 (tr) Chris Lowe/Phototake; 185 (bl) Science VU/CDC/Visuals Unlimited; 185 (br) BIOS (Klein/Hubert)/Peter Arnold, Inc.; 188 (l) Rob and Ann Simpson/Visuals Unlimited; 195 Mark E. Gibson Photography; 200 (l) D. Lyons/Bruce Coleman, Inc.; 200 (r) Bob Child/AP/Wide World Photos; 201 (t) Andrew Lichtenstein/The Image Works; 201 (b) Royalty-Free/Corbis; 202 (l) Ivan Polunin/Bruce Coleman, Inc.; 202 (c) Mick Rock/Bruce Coleman, Inc.; 202 (r) brt Photo/Mira.com; 204 Royalty-free/Corbis; 206 (t) Tony Freeman/PhotoEdit; 207 (t) Tony Freeman/PhotoEdit; 207 (b) Bob Daemmrich Photography; 213 Bob Daemmrich Photography; 218 (r) Michael Newman/PhotoEdit; 219 (t) Phototake; 219 (b) Clark Overton/Phototake; 223 Dennis MacDonald/PhotoEdit; 228 (t) Tom Carter/PhotoEdit; 241 (b) Custom Medical Stock Photos; 243 Tony Freeman/PhotoEdit; 249 (t) Jonathan Nourok/PhotoEdit; 249 (b) Lawrence Migdale; 250 (r) Tom & Dee Ann McCarthy/Corbis; 254 (b) Larry Dale Gordon/Getty Images; 256 (l) Lucidio Studio/Corbis; 256 (r) Amos Morgan/Getty Images; 257 (l), (r) Getty Images; 258 (t) Jim Cummins/Getty Images; 260 Tom & Dee Ann McCarthy/Corbis; 264 (bg) Getty Images; 264 (t) Russell Burden/Index Stock Imagery; 269 Omni-Photo Communications/Index Stock Imagery; 270 (t) Lawrence Migdale; 282 (l), (r) Creatas Royalty Free Stock Resources; 283 (l) SW Productions/Brand X Pictures; 283 (r) Creatas Royalty Free Stock Resources; 285 Ronnie Kaufman/Corbis; 296 (l) Ariel Skelley/Corbis; 296 (r) SW Productions/Brand X Pictures; 297 (l) Royalty-free/Corbis; 297 (r) Creatas Royalty Free Stock Resources; 304 (b) Greg Probst/Panoramic Images/NGS Images.com; 306 (cl) Andre Gallant/Getty Images; 306 (cr) Syracuse Newspapers/John Berry/The Image Works; 306 (bl) Jack Affleck/Superstock; 306 (br) Renee Lynn/Photo Researchers; 307 (t) Fred Bruemmer/Peter Arnold, Inc.; 307 (b) Jim Olive/Peter Arnold, Inc.; 308 (l) Karl Weatherly/Corbis; 308 (r) Mark E. Gibson Photography; 309 (t) Royalty-Free/Corbis; 309 (b) Laima Druskis/Photo Researchers; 310 Ted Horowitz/Corbis; 312 (l) Jeff Greenberg/Peter Arnold, Inc.; 312 (c) Matt Meadows/Peter Arnold, Inc.; 312 (r) Paul A. Souders/Corbis; 312 (bg) Harvey Lloyd/Peter Arnold, Inc.; 313 (l) David R. Frazier/Photo Researchers; 313 (c) Scott Barrow, Inc.; 313 (r) Bill Ross/Corbis; 314 (t) V.C.L./Getty Images; 314 (b) Grapes.Michaud/Photo Researchers; 316 (b) Robert Landau/Corbis; 316 (inset) Judyth Olatt; Ecoscene/Corbis; 317 (b) Bill Ross/Corbis; 318 (bl) Michael St. Maur Sheil/Corbis; 318 (br) P. Plisson/Explorer/Photo Researchers; 318 (tl) Jeff Greenberg/Photo Researchers; 318 (tr) Garry D. McMichael/Photo Researchers; 319 (inset) The Cleveland Digital Library; 319 (r) Mark E. Gibson Photography; 320 (b) Michael P. Gadomski/Photo Researchers; 320 (t) Mark Joseph/Getty Images; 321 Bob Daemmrich Photography; 324 Mark E. Gibson Photography; 327 Tim Thompson/Getty Images.

All other photos © Harcourt School Publishers. Harcourt photos provided by the Harcourt Index, Harcourt IPR, and Harcourt photographers; Weronica Ankarorn, Victoria Bowen, Eric Camden, Annette Coolidge, Doug Dukane, Ken Kinzie, Brian Minnich, and Steve Williams.

Illustrations:

Lisa Blackshear, x, xi, xii, xiii, 10, 11, 48-49, 76, 77, 84-85, 93, 104, 105, 122-123, 126, 127, 128, 136-137, 142-143, 146, 147, 152, 172, 173, 198, 220, 221, 232, 234, 235, 252-253, 266, 267, 275, 282-283, 294, 295; David Brooks, ix, 330, 332, 334, 336, 338, 340; Denny Butts, 118, 119; Jean Calder, iv, 12, 17, 18, 21, 22, 24-25; Mark Collins, 56, 132, 154, 244, 278, 300, 328; Mike Dammer, vi, 87, 118; John Karapelou, vii, 6, 7, 13, 28, 33, 37, 43, 44, 167, 171, 184, 203, 222, 227; Ed Shems, 62, 86, 176, 196, 212, 224, 229, 231, 240, 241, 299, 325; Martin Shovel, 12, 16, 24, 27, 37, 38, 44, 55, 63, 92, 99, 111, 120, 124, 131, 140, 153, 167, 168, 177, 183, 213, 243, 257, 265, 269, 277, 288, 324, 327; Carl Wiens, ix, 342, 343, 344, 345, 346, 347, 348, 349, 350, 351, 352, 353, 354, 355, 356, 357, 358.

Read-Aloud Anthology

Read-Aloud Anthology

CONTENTS

Mark's Fingers

by Mary O'Neill

I like my fingers.
They grip a ball,
Turn a page,
Break a fall,
Help whistle
A call.
Shake hands
And shoot
Rubber bands.
When candy is offered
They take enough.
They fill my pockets
With wonderful stuff,
And they always tell me
Smooth from rough.
They follow rivers
On a map,
They double over
When I rap,
They smack together
When I clap.
They button buttons,
Tie shoelaces,
Open doors to
Brand-new places.
They shape and float
My paper ships,
Fasten papers to
Paper clips,
And carry ice cream
To my lips. . . .

Using the Selection

Read aloud "Mark's Fingers" as students listen. Reread the poem slowly and encourage students to pantomime actions to go with the words. Then ask which actions that they can do now are things they could not have done when they were in kindergarten. (Students may mention whistling, shooting rubber bands, snapping their fingers, buttoning buttons, and tying shoelaces.) Explain that developing coordination is part of the growth process. In this chapter students will learn about families and about growth and development.

A Pig Is Never Blamed

by Babette Deutsch

A pig is never blamed in case
he forgets to wash his face.
No dirty suds are on his soap,
because with soap he does not cope.
He never has to clean the tub
after he has had a scrub,
for whatever mess he makes,
a bath is what he never takes.
But then, what is a pool to him?
Poor pig, he never learns to swim.
And all the goodies he can cram
down his gullet turn to ham.
It's mean:
keeping clean.
You hardly want to, till you're very big.
But it's worse to be a pig.

Using the Selection

Ask students to explain what they already know about why keeping clean is important. Ask them to name times when it is especially important to wash their hands and whether they have ever felt annoyed when they have to stop doing something they are enjoying to take a bath. Then invite students to listen to a poem about a creature who never has to worry about keeping clean.

Using the Selection

Read aloud "Greedy Mable." Reread the poem as students listen to name the things Mable ate. Have volunteers write the names of the foods on the board. Then help children preview Chapter 3 by looking at the picture of the Food Guide Pyramid on page 68. Invite them to study the pyramid and draw conclusions about the kinds of foods that would help Mable solve her problem.

Greedy Mable

by Georgie Adams

Greedy Mable
at the table
ate as much as
she was able.

Pies and pastries
cold or hot.
Greedy Mable
ate the lot.

Chili, chicken
fish in batter...
Wider Mable grew
and fatter.

Till at last
her mother said,
'Mable, it is
time for bed."

But when upon
the bed she sat,
Greedy Mable's
bed fell flat.

It really couldn't
stand the weight
from all that
Greedy Mable ate.

Said Greedy Mable
on her heels,
'I'll eat a little
LESS at meals!"

Making Fitness a Family Affair

Excerpt from Current Health 1®The Weekly Reader Corporation, December 2002

Have you ever thought about asking your parents for some advice, but couldn't seem to find the right time to ask them? Do you wish your family were closer, like some of the families on TV? Have you ever thought about adding a little bit of exercise to your day but didn't know how to start?

How about improving your family relationships and exercising at the same time? Here are some stories from regular families and how they combined the two.

Joshua's Story

My birthday is in September. All I wanted was a dog. My parents didn't like the idea because they thought I'd forget to take care of him. So before my parents would agree to a dog, they made rules. I would have to feed him, bathe him, and walk him every day. Of course, I agreed to do anything to get a dog. For my birthday, we went to the pound where I picked out a young Labrador retriever.

At first, it was easy to walk him every day. Then one day I got the flu. I couldn't walk him for about a week. My mom started to walk Rudy. When I started to feel better, my mom still wanted to keep walking the dog because she liked the exercise. So we started to walk together each morning and evening. Soon my sister and dad started to walk with us too. We have some great talks while we are walking.

Using the Selection

There are many ways to get fit. Exercising with your family is one way to get healthy and get connected at the same time. Read this excerpt to students. Then ask them to think of other ways they might use exercise as a family group event.

Joy's Story

My mom has been a runner for several years. I didn't like running, but last summer, my mom woke us all up at 8:00 a.m., before it got real hot, and made us jog or walk around the track at the high school. There are six kids in my family, so my mom thought that the best way to get us all exercising at the same time was at a track. She like being able to see all of us. My little brothers can ride their bikes around the track so that they can keep up with us. At first I thought my mom was a drill sergeant, but then she started to invite friends to come with us. We would all walk and jog, and the time would go so fast. Now I'm even thinking of going out for track this spring.

What Will You Do?

There are so many things you can do to fit a little exercise into your day. The families that you just read about didn't think they had time, but they made exercising a priority. They all felt better about themselves because of it. They noticed they were sick less often, they were sleeping better, and they felt they had shaped up. These are great reasons for you to get started exercising with your family.

I Need My Knees, but No More, Please

by Stan Lee Werlin

I am very displeased
to discover that knees
can be banged up and bruised
with incredible ease.

They're so bony and bumpy,
lamentably lumpy,
and sorer than sore
when I crash on the floor
or dance without looking
right into the door—
I'm just glad that I haven't got four!

Using the Selection

Read aloud "I Need My Knees, but No More, Please" and invite students to tell about times when they have had similar problems. Ask students to describe the circumstances that caused their injury and to suggest ways they can prevent the same kind of injury in the future.

Defusing Difficult Situations

Excerpt from Current Health 1® The Weekly Reader Corporation, January 2003

It Happens to Everyone

Everyone gets into conflicts. The reason for this is that "we all see things differently," say experts at the University of Illinois.

There is always at least one loser when people deal with conflict by fighting, yelling, ignoring, or running away. It is wise to run away if someone threatens or tries to hurt you, but most problems are best solved when both parties cooperate.

Coping With Conflict

How would you deal with these conflicts? Choose the answer that best describes what you would actually do.

1. Your brother loses your favorite CD. You:
   a. scream at him.
   b. break his CD player.
   c. calmly tell him you are angry and ask him to replace the CD.
2. Your best friend ignores you at lunchtime. You:
   a. tell her she's mean and hateful.
   b. tell everyone at school she's mean and hateful.
   c. tell her that you feel hurt when she ignores you and ask her why she did it.
3. Your dad calls you a slob when you spill milk on the floor. You:
   a. tell him he's a bigger slob.
   b. tell him you're sorry you're a slob.
   c. explain that his remark makes you feel worthless and stupid, say that spilling the milk was an accident, and offer to clean up the mess.

Using the Selection

Read the excerpt to students. Then list on the board the three helpful words to resolve conflicts: firm, fair, and friendly. Lead a discussion on why resolving conflicts peacefully helps improve one's self esteem.

For more information on conflict resolution, check out the "Out On A Limb" website at www.urbanext.uiuc.edu/conflict

Answers: If you chose a and b answers, you are not really solving these conflicts. If you chose c answers, you are doing a great job of getting along in difficult situations.

Help Yourself, Help the World

Experts at the Teachers College at Columbia University in New York use three words to sum up the best way to resolve conflicts: firm, fair, and friendly. Be firm about the need to solve the problem. Be sure the solution is fair to both people. And be friendly rather than hostile.

Once you're skilled at solving conflicts, you are likely to see your self-esteem improve. You will feel better about yourself because you are not letting people push you around. When you feel better about yourself, your family, friends, and community benefit since you become a more pleasant person.

No Measles, No Mumps for Me

by Paul Showers

I like to hear my grandmother tell stories. I like the stories about when she was a little girl. My grandmother was sick a lot when she was little.

First she got whooping cough. She coughed all day and all night. Sometimes she had trouble catching her breath. She had to go to bed and stay there.

Grandmother got over whooping cough. Later she got the mumps. Her face swelled up on both sides. It hurt her to chew and swallow. Pickles hurt her the most. She couldn't eat them at all.

Grandmother got over the mumps. Later she got the measles. She had a fever and a runny nose. There were red spots all over her body. She had to go to bed with the measles, too.

I'm glad I didn't live in those days. Children got whooping cough, measles, and mumps. They got rubella, polio, tetanus, and diphtheria. Some children got very sick. Some even died.

I've never had whooping cough or mumps or measles or polio or any of the rest. And I never will, either. Because I've had shots, and sometimes special drops.

When you get the shots, or the drops, you are helping your body to keep well.

Using the Selection

Ask students to describe childhood diseases they have heard older relatives or friends mention that children today do not worry about catching. (Students may mention diseases such as polio, measles, and mumps.) Read aloud "No Measles, No Mumps for Me." After students listen to the selection, encourage them to predict how advances in medicine may change life for children of the future and then retell the story as if one of their grandchildren were telling it about them.

Using the Selection

Ask students to tell about the kinds of medicines their families give them when they are ill. Discuss different forms medicines can take, such as pills or capsules, liquid, inhalers, sprays, and rub-on creams. Explain that some medicines are made from natural substances, such as plants, and some are made in a laboratory. But long before medical technology was developed, people knew how to use medicines to cure illnesses.

How Medicine Came

Cherokee**, **Southeast
Selection from (The Circle of Thanks: Native American Poems and Songs of Thanksgiving)

Long ago,
the animals and the birds,
the fish and insects and plants
could all talk.
They lived with the people
in peace and friendship.

Then the people invented
bows and blowguns and spears.
They began to kill
the animals and birds and fish
for their flesh and their skins.
The animals then joined together.
They invented diseases
to weaken the people.

The plants remained friendly
to the people.
Each tree and shrub and herb agreed
to offer a cure for each new disease.
Each said, "When I am called upon,
I shall help the humans in their need."

So it is that the plants gave us medicine.
So it is that we must be thankful to them.

Where There's SMOKE *by Janet Munsil*

On the very last night of the year, Daisy's parents always get dressed up really fancy and go cha-cha dancing at the Topaz Ballroom. When they get home very late at night, Daisy's mom wakes her up with a lipsticky kiss.

"Happy New Year, Daisy. We've made New Year's resolutions! That's a promise you make to yourself that you want to keep all year. I resolve to learn to play a musical instrument this year!"

"Now, what do you resolve to do?"

Daisy and her dad looked at each other for a long time.

Daisy nibbled her nails. Her dad smoked a cigarette.

They pretended they didn't hear the question.

Daisy thought about it. And she chomped. And she thought. And she chomped.

Think, chomp, think, chomp, think, chompchompchomp.

And then she said, "I resolve to pick up my toys."

"That's a good one, but is there anything else?" asked her mum.

"I resolve to turn off the lights when I leave the room."

"Maybe a bad habit you'd like to break?" asked her dad.

"I resolve not to punch my friends in the nose."

"That's a good one," said her mom, "but isn't there one other thing that you'd like to stop doing?"

"I don't think so," chomped Daisy. Chompchompchomp.

"Well, maybe just one. I'll stop biting my nails. I will not bite my nails ever again. Now, what's your resolution, Dad?"

"Not to eat a whole lemon meringue pie before dinner?" suggested Dad.

"I can think of one for you," said Daisy. "It's something that makes the house smoky and your clothes smelly and our eyes sting-y and it makes you cough all night and all morning long."

"But I've tried to stop smoking lots of times and I can't," whined Dad.

"I'll help you," said Daisy, "and you'll help me. Starting tomorrow."

"It's a deal," said Dad.

Daisy chomped all night, since it was her last chance. Her dad puffed so much he set off the smoke detector.

Daisy woke up the next morning to the sound of her mum playing the trumpet.

SQEEeekeeSQREEkeeSQREEKEESQEEeeEEeEEe!

Her dad was wearing a deep-sea diver's helmet to keep th.e noise down.

"Good morning, Daisy," he said. "Ready to stop biting your nails?"

"Yes. Ready to stop puffing?"

"Yes. But all the noise from mum's resolution is making me nervous. I'm going to go for a walk. Bye."

"All this noise makes me nervous," said Daisy. "I'm going to play outside. Bye."

Daisy didn't REALLY want to play outside. There was something else she wanted to do. Something she hadn't done for a long time. She wanted to bite her nails, really-really badly. But she also didn't want to bite them, because she'd made a deal with her dad. She decided to go to her treehouse. That way, if she started to chomp by accident, nobody would see.

She went outside.

She looked all around.

She made sure nobody was following her.

She climbed up to her treehouse.

She peeked over the ledge. . .

"DAD!" said Daisy.

"Daisy!" said Dad.

"WHAT ARE YOU DOING HERE?"

"I'm having trouble with my resolution," said Dad.

"Me too," said Daisy. "I want to stop biting my nails like crazy, but I don't know how."

"I want to stop smoking, but I don't know how."

"We need to think of some ways to help each other out," said Daisy.

So they went up to Daisy's room and thought and listened to Mom practicing the tuba. And they made a plan.

Daisy gave her dad some chewing gum and a bubble pipe so he could chew and blow bubbles instead of puff. Daisy's dad helped put bandages on all her fingers so she wouldn't chomp. And he shared his gum.

Everything worked for a little while, but sooner or later, Daisy and her dad would catch each other in the treehouse. And they'd sit there, and sigh, and listen to mom play the drums.

So Daisy and her dad did things together to keep their minds off chomping and puffing.

They baked cookies.

They did jigsaws.

Where There's SMOKE *continued*

They made spice racks.

They did fingerpainting.

They built things out of frozen treat sticks. They built things out of spaghetti.

They built things out of macaroni and cheese.

They built things out of the cookies that burned.

Daisy and her dad learned how to knit.

They knit teacosies, 100 pairs of socks, 60 hats, 59 mittens, 30 pairs of long underwear, two scarves that were a thousand meters long, and a muffler for the car. They knit mom a cover for her tuba, even though it was now on its way to the attic.

"Well, we've done it, Daisy," said her dad. "We've been so busy with our hobbies that we forgot all about our bad habits! Now I think I'll go for a little walk. Bye."

"Wait!" said Daisy, who had heard that one before.

"I'll go too." And they went to the corner store together.

"We have certainly been good at keeping our resolutions!" said Mom.

"I'll call Grandma right now and ask her to take us to the symphony! Oh, and thank you very much for the tuba cover, but I have decided to play the electric guitar instead."

Grandma came right over. "WOW!" she said. "I can't believe it! NO smoking? No chomping? Quick, everybody in the taxi!" she yelled. "We're going to the symphony orchestra!"

Not once in the whole concert did Daisy bite her nails.

Not once did her dad cough or look in his pocket for his cigarettes.

Using the Selection

Write New Year's Resolution on the board and help students define resolution. Invite volunteers to tell about resolutions they have made or would like to make.
Help children recognize that keeping a resolution to stop doing something they do all the time, or to break a habit, is much more difficult.

My Puppy

by Aileen Fisher

It's funny
my puppy
knows just how I feel.

When I'm happy
he's yappy
and squirms like an eel.

When I'm grumpy
he's slumpy
and stays at my heel.

It's funny
my puppy
knows such a great deal.

Using the Selection

This selection can be used to begin a discussion about different feelings and different ways people show their feelings. Have students look at the pictures on page 256 and 257 and name the feelings they think the children in the pictures are expressing.

Family Ties to Your Health

Excerpt from Current Health 1®The Weekly Reader Corporation, December 2002

Gotta Move!

Parents and other family members are role models for many things. Their words and actions tell kids what is important. For instance, some parents play tennis, jog, or work out. Their kids learn to value exercise.

But active parents don't automatically produce active kids. The key is fun. Kids need to like what they do, and parents can help by planning fun activities. These might include relay races, soccer, bowling, or planting a garden. Neighborhood kids can join in too.

Happy Mealtime

Experts say family meals lead to happier, healthier kids. Dinner talk also helps families connect. And kids quickly catch on to etiquette (ET-uh-kit; good manners).

Good Cheer

Family members influence each other's emotional health. Do you talk problems over with a family member?

Kids with a healthy self-image usually come from cooperative families. Family members cheer each other up. They do this with hugs, advice, sincere praise, and their ability to listen.

Connections

No matter whether the family is large or small, everyone needs close connections with it. People need to trust and take pride in each other. And one-on-one time with parents, grandparents, or a favorite uncle or aunt can make those connections stronger.

Using the Selection

Modern families are busy. The kids go to school and many parents work. Read the selection to students. Then suggest they brainstorm at least two family activities for categories such as chores, meals, and exercise.

Getting Along with Granny

Grandparents play important roles—roles that have gotten harder. More divorces mean more blended families. More grandparents spend extra time with both their grandkids and their step grandkids.

How Healthy Is Your Tree?

Your family also influences the diseases you may get. Your lifestyle influences your health too. Your family history will help you map out a personal prevention plan.

Safe at Home

It's easy to tell which families have safety smarts. They use seatbelts every time they ride in a car. They wear special helmets and pads for sports. They know the basics of fire safety. They are prepared for emergencies and have plans that every family member knows about. They are aware of safety in a wide range of areas, from food handling to first aid.

Game's Over

Most kids learn that their families influence them a lot. But the top winners are kids who do two things. They look over their family influences. Then they keep the good things and trade in the not-so-good ones. You can do the same. It's a smart way to improve your health!

Packaging–Then and Now

Philip E. Bishop, Ph.D

These days, nearly everything comes in a disposable package. Packaging preserves and protects a product. We shouldn't take modern packaging for granted. After all, it took inventors a long time to come up with the ordinary cardboard box. But today packaging threatens to bury us under mounds of plastic and paper trash.

In the Early Days

Before there was packaging as we know it today, or even as people knew it thousands of years ago, there were very few ways to keep or store food. Food was usually eaten where and when it was found or shortly after that. If people needed a container, they would use what was provided by nature, such as gourds, shells, or leaves. A bit later people began to weave fabrics. They would wrap foods in the fabrics. People would also weave baskets out of reeds and grasses so they could store extra food.

Everything in Pots and Barrels

In ancient Egypt and Greece, clay vases and jars were the containers of choice. Some jars were as tall as an adult. The jars were used to store and transport nearly everything, from olive oil to wine.

The trouble with clay jars, of course, was that they broke. Eventually the fragile clay containers were replaced with wooden barrels, first made by the ancient inhabitants of France. Barrels have been used for packaging for nearly 2,000 years.

Bags and Boxes: The Triumph of Paper

Your great-grandparents probably bought sugar from their grocer's wooden barrel. But selling food from a barrel did have its drawbacks. Rats and flies could easily contaminate products stored in barrels.

By the late 1800s, packaging was being taken over by paper. Manufacturers were catching on to the cardboard box, but storing empty boxes took up a lot of space. In 1890 a machine was invented to crease the cardboard boxes so that they could be easily stored until they were needed. It was a packaging revolution!

Waxed cardboard boxes were good for keeping products such as salt dry. But cardboard packaging didn't work for some things, such as candy. The candies absorbed the taste of the glue used to make the boxes and tasted awful! The candy manufacturer decided to wrap the candies in tinfoil. This kept the candy tasting good, and children could recycle the foil by selling it to a tinsmith.

The Perils of Packaging

Modern packaging has been a great success, but it has caused some problems. What do we do with all that disposable packaging? Fast-food restaurants wrap individual food portions. Manufacturers ship products all over the world packed in foam "peanuts," sheets of plastic "bubbles," or other materials. Some scientists warn that this type of throwaway packaging is dangerous for the environment. In response, some companies now use peanuts made from starch that dissolve when they get wet. Other companies are recycling foam peanuts by using them as housing insulation. Most communities offer recycling programs for bottles, cans, cardboard boxes, and paper products. These are all helping, but they have not made much of a dent in the world's piles of discarded packaging.

Consumers around the world seem to love the convenience of boxed hamburgers and the look of flashy soft-drink cans. For centuries this type of better packaging has been a part of economic progress. Whether this progress continues may depend on how environmentally responsible manufacturers and consumers are willing to be.

Teacher Reference Section

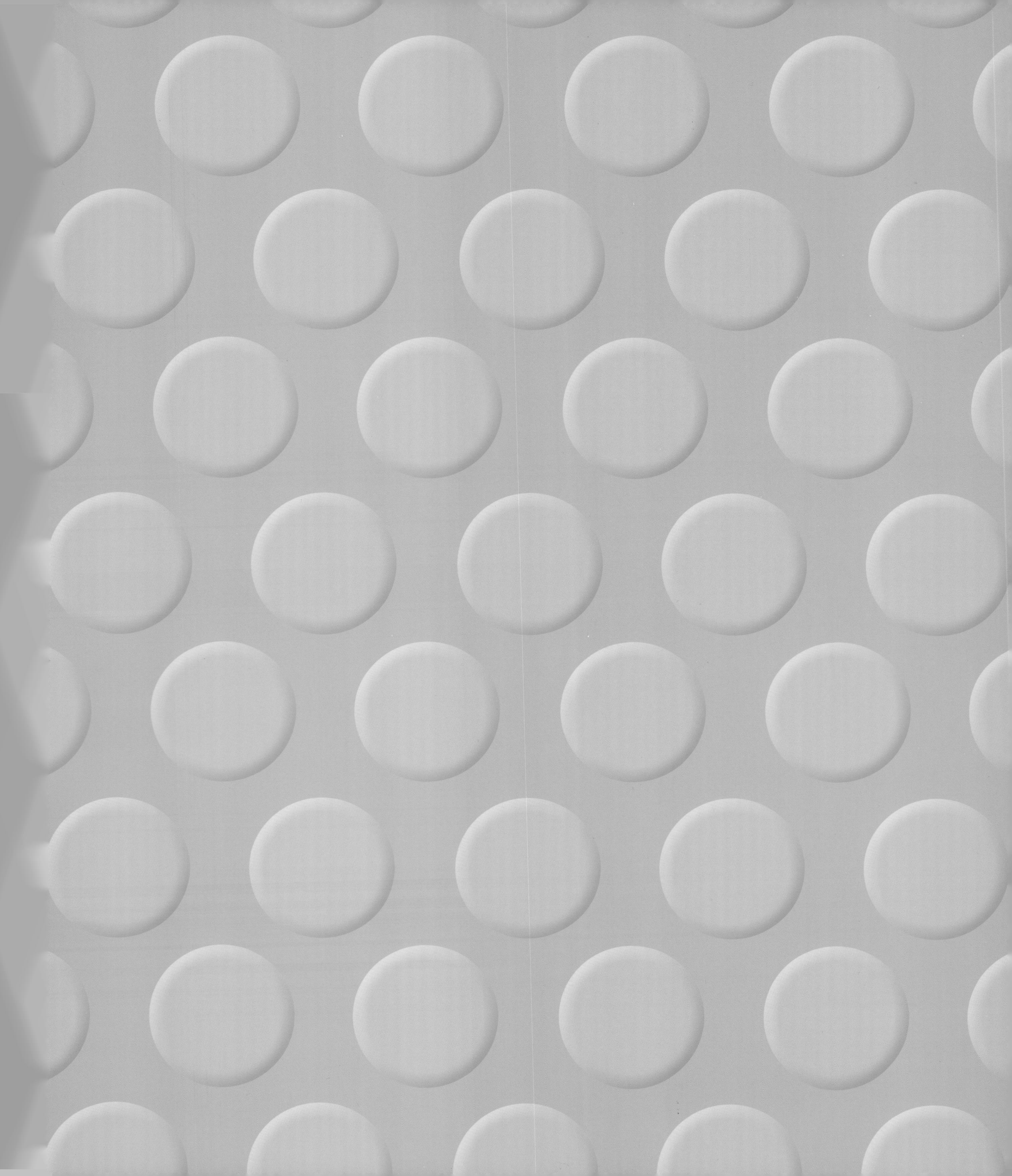

Teacher Reference

RESOURCES FOR DAILY PHYSICAL ACTIVITY

Be Active! Music for Daily Physical Activity

Health professionals and health and physical educators recommend that all people add activity to their daily routines. The selections on this CD are designed for classroom and physical educators to use in helping students to be active. The music is high-energy in engaging styles. Timed musical changes can be used to alternate intervals of aerobic activities with intervals of activities to build strength and flexibility. Tracks can be repeated or combined for longer workouts.

Be Active! Music Descriptions

1. **Saucy Salsa** Fun music with a Latin flavor (:30 on, :15 off)
2. **Get on Board** A familiar American railroad tune (continuous music)
3. **Late for Supper** A traditional Appalachian folk tune (continuous music)
4. **Jam and Jive** Music that swings (1:00 on, :15 off)
5. **Flexercise** Familiar Top 40 sounds (varying timing)
6. **Muscle Mambo** Caribbean dance style (:30 on, :15 off)
7. **Movin' and Groovin'** Rhythm is king. (varying tempos, moods)
8. **Jumping and Pumping** High-energy club dance (:30 fast, :30 slow)
9. **Hop to It** A familiar children's song (continuous music)
10. **Super Stress Buster** Mellow, melodic music (continuous music)
11. **Funky Flex** A strong bass beat for moving and stretching (continuous music)
12. **Broadway Bound** A famous Gershwin tune (continuous music)

Instant Activity Cards

Instant Activity Cards are graphic cues to guide physical activity. The cards illustrate exercises. Sets of four cards are preselected for use with each chapter. Display the cards one at a time to lead students through a simple routine. You are also free to select any other cards you like from those provided. You can build a longer routine for daily use and teach it to your students.

Using Instant Activity Cards

Modifying Activities for the Classroom Specific modifications are given for individual cards. Obviously, hoops and jump ropes cannot be used inside a small classroom. Students can pantomime these exercises, for example, by rocking their hips for plastic hoop movements. Some stretches can be done while standing with support from a desk or chair. Some strength exercises can be done while seated.

Activity Routines Each routine should follow the same, basic structure: warm up, work out, and cool down. Begin with low-intensity aerobic exercise followed by stretching. Then move to higher intensity aerobic exercise or a mix of aerobic, strength, and flexibility exercises. End with a cool down of low-intensity aerobic activity and stretching.

CHAPTER 1

Suggested Music: Be Active! Music for Daily Physical Activity, Track 1, Saucy Salsa

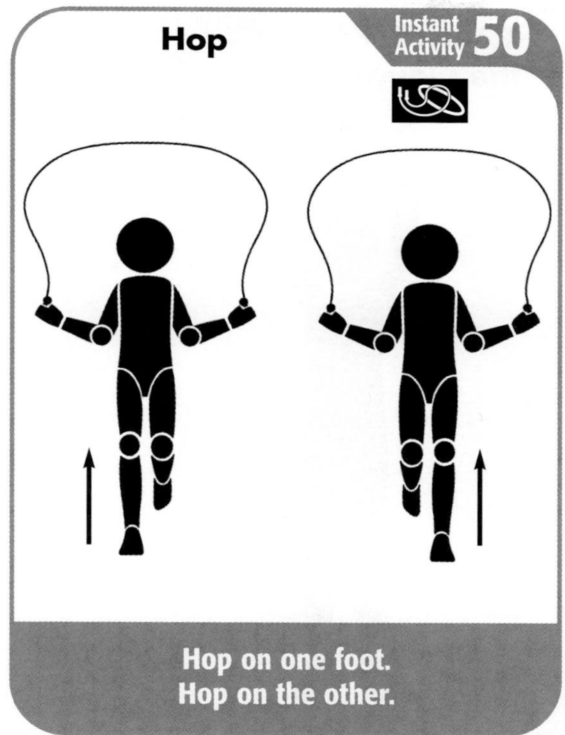

Hop Students can pantomime jump rope movements for this skill. Signal students when to change hopping feet.

Side Stretch

Power Knee Lift Any low, stable object can be used as a step.

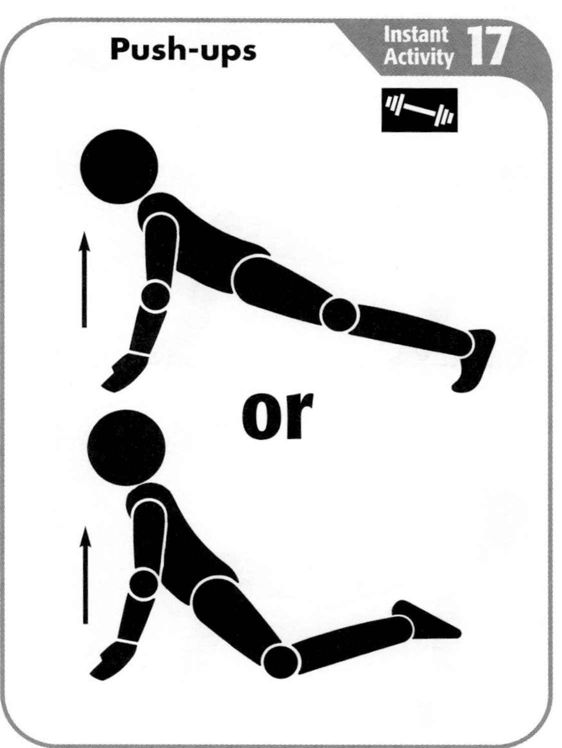

Push-up To avoid floor dirt, students can place their hands on a book or use a chair or shelf that is immobile.

Harcourt

CHAPTER 2

Suggested Music: Be Active! Music for Daily Physical Activity, Track 2, Get on Board

Cardio Combo

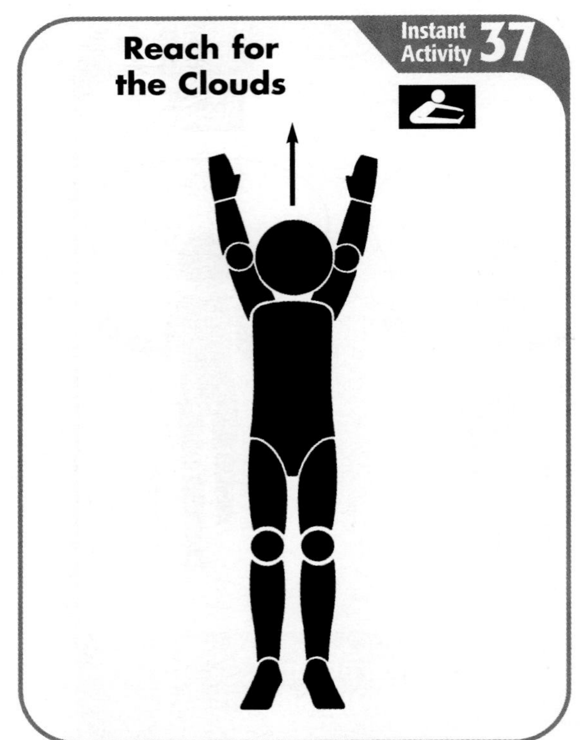

Reach for the Clouds

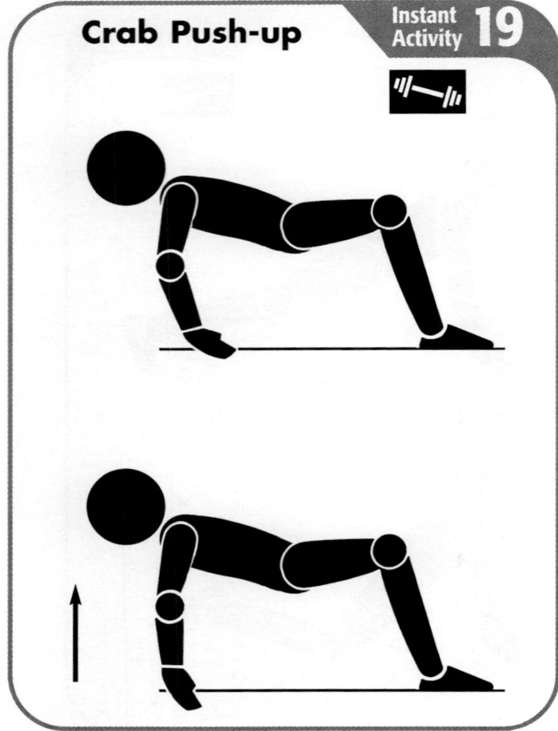

Crab Push-up Students can do a similar exercise while seated by lifting themselves off their chairs.

Straddle
Instant Activity 52
Spread your legs on one jump.
Bring them together on the next.

Straddle Students can pantomime jump rope movements for this skill. Be sure students have enough lateral space to move their legs.

Harcourt

CHAPTER 3

Suggested Music: Be Active! Music for Daily Physical Activity, Track 3, Late for Supper

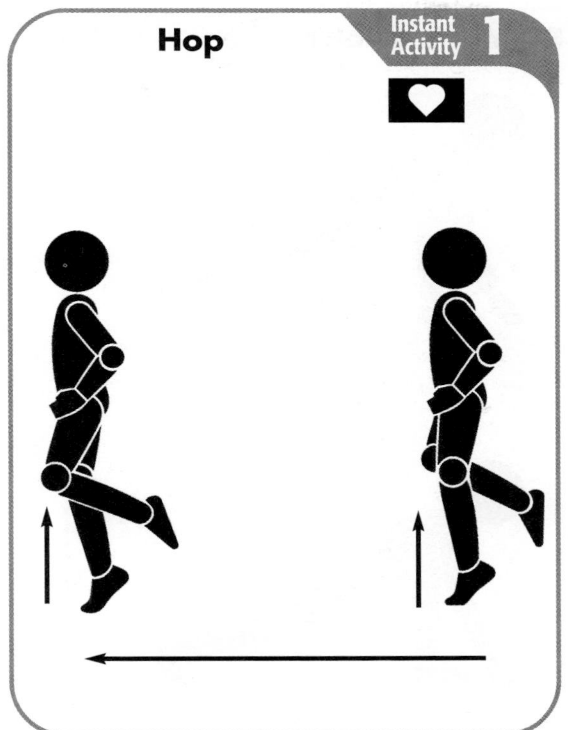

Hop Students can hold a desk or chair back for balance while they hop. Signal students when to change feet.

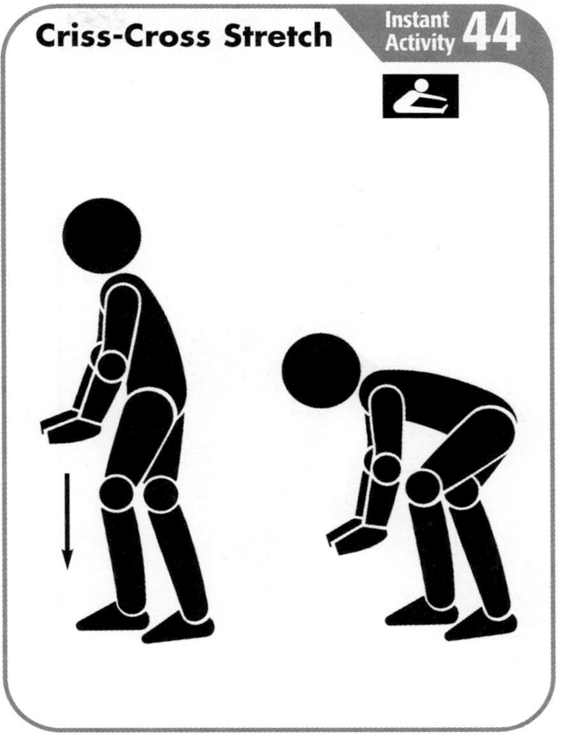

Criss-Cross Stretch Be sure that students do not lock their knees.

Overhead Press For increased benefit, students can hold and lift any object, such as a textbook.

Skier Students can pantomime jump rope movements for this skill. Be sure that students have enough lateral space to move safely.

Harcourt

CHAPTER 4

Suggested Music: Be Active! Music for Daily Physical Activity, Track 4, Jam and Jive

Run Have students run in place.

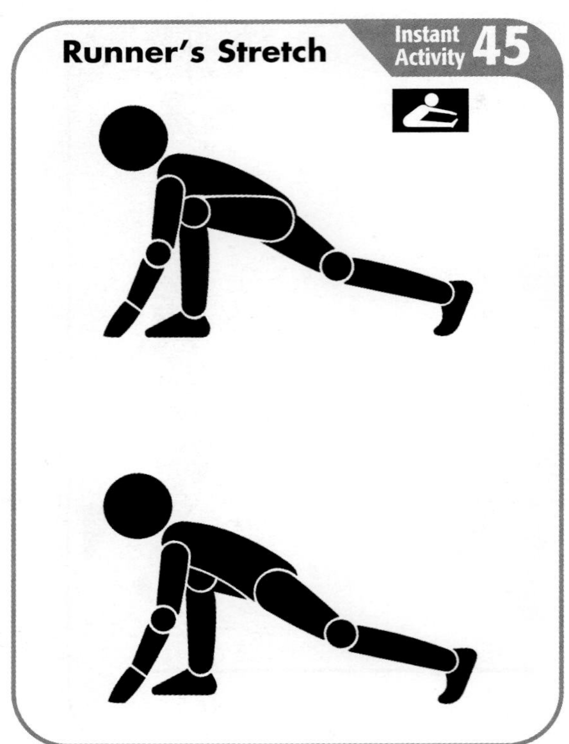

Runner's Stretch If floor dirt is a concern, students need not touch the floor for an effective stretch.

Biceps Curl To add challenge, students can hold objects of similar weight in each hand, for example notebooks or textbooks.

Criss-Cross Jump Students can pantomime jump rope movements for this skill. It is also known as a matador or matador cross.

Harcourt

CHAPTER 5

Suggested Music: Be Active! Music for Daily Physical Activity, Track 5, Flexercise

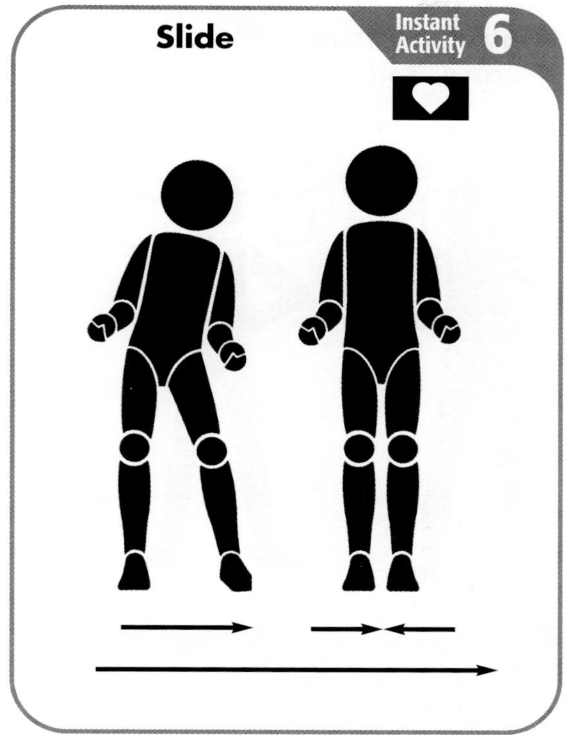

Slide Have students move back and forth rather than continuously in one direction.

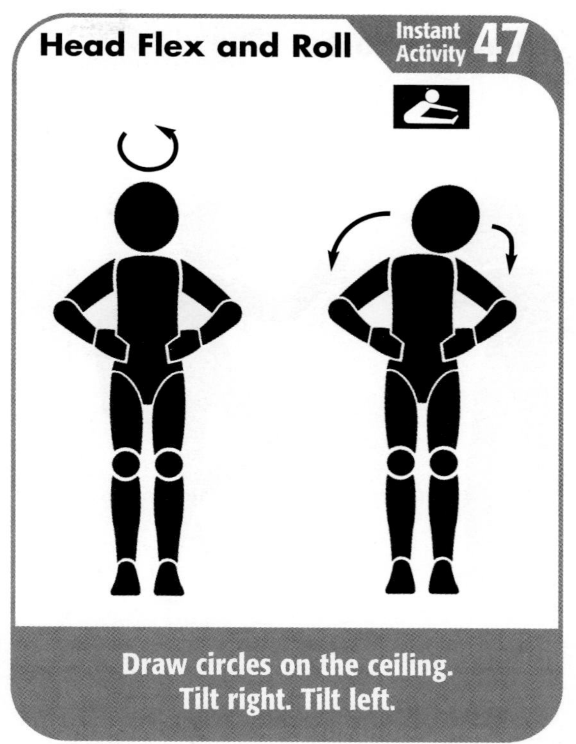

Head Flex

Arm Circle Be sure students have enough room to avoid hitting desks, chairs, and other students.

Hip Hoop Students can pantomime the plastic hoop movements for this skill. For the most benefit, encourage students to make large hip motions.

Harcourt

CHAPTER 6

Suggested Music: Be Active! Music for Daily Physical Activity, Track 6, Muscle Mambo

Dance to Music Students are free to follow the music. Encourage them to use all the space around them by bending low and reaching high.

Shoulder Shrug and Roll

Instant Activity 48

Shoulders up and down
Draw circles.

Shoulder Shrug and Roll

Lunge

Knee Hoop Students can pantomime plastic hoop movements for this skill. Be sure that students use vigorous knee movements.

Harcourt

CHAPTER 7

Suggested Music: Be Active! Music for Daily Physical Activity, Track 7, Movin' and Groovin'

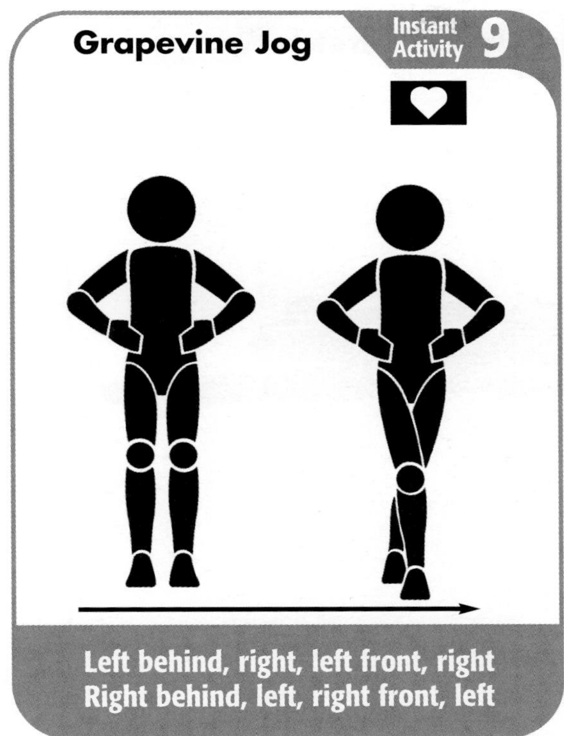

Grapevine Jog
Instant Activity 9
Left behind, right, left front, right
Right behind, left, right front, left

Grapevine Jog Students can grapevine back and forth rather than continuously in one direction.

Hamstring Stretch This exercise can be done while seated.

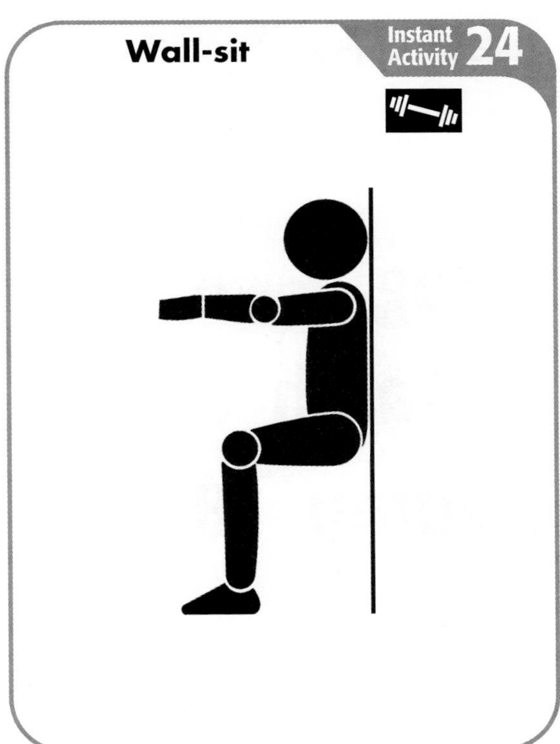

Wall-Sit Students can use any stable object for support. Students can do this activity in pairs.

Ankle-hop
Instant Activity 60
Turn hoop on one ankle.
Hop on the other foot.

Ankle-Hop Students can pantomime plastic hoop movements for this skill.

Harcourt

CHAPTER 8

Suggested Music: Be Active! Music for Daily Physical Activity, Track 8, Jumping and Pumping

Jumping Jack

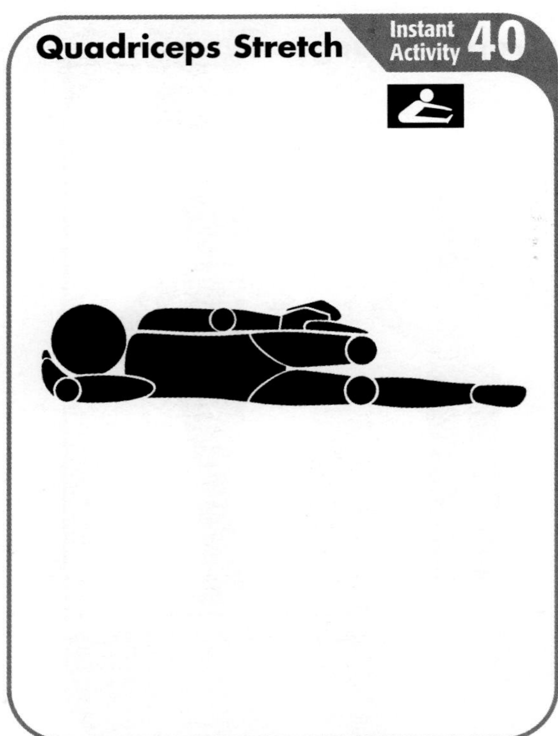

Quadriceps Stretch Students can do this stretch while standing. They can hold a chair back or desk for balance.

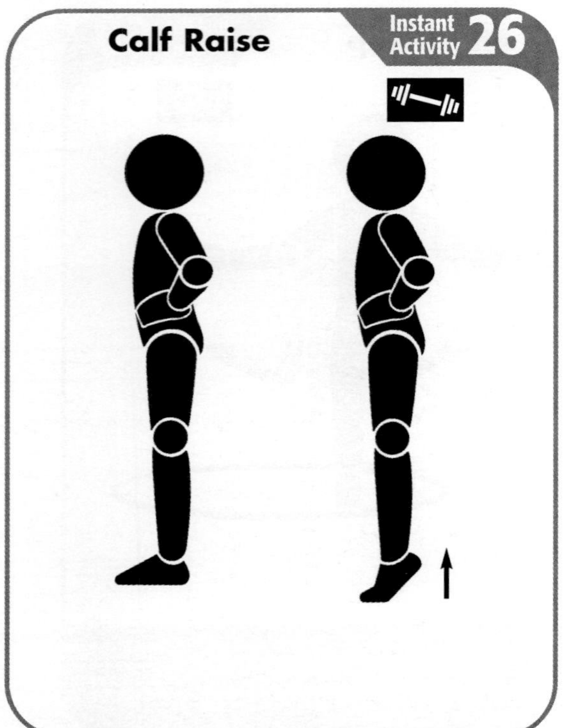

Calf Raise Younger students may have problems with balance. They can hold a chair back or desk for balance.

Cardio Combo

Harcourt

CHAPTER 9

Suggested Music: Be Active! Music for Daily Physical Activity, Track 9, Hop to It

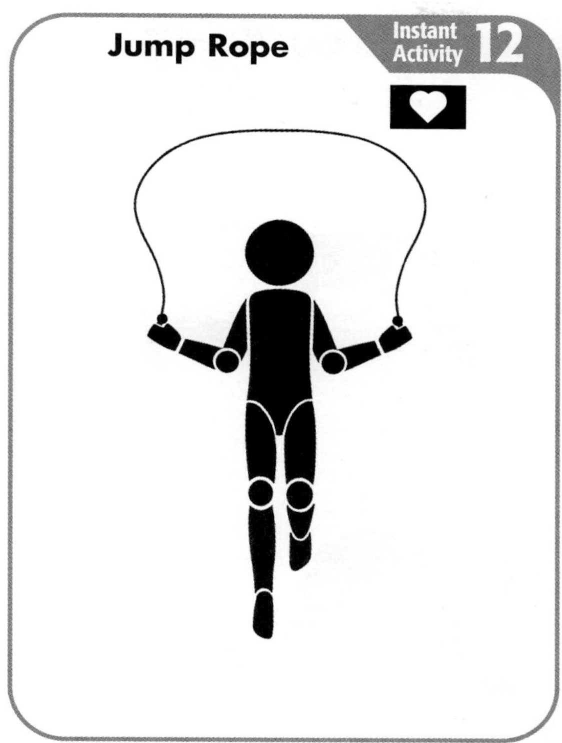

Jump Rope Students can pantomime jump rope movements for this skill.

Calf Stretch Students need not touch the floor; they can do the stretch standing and use any stable object for support.

Bear Walk Students can move forward and backward in rhythm rather than walking continuously in one direction.

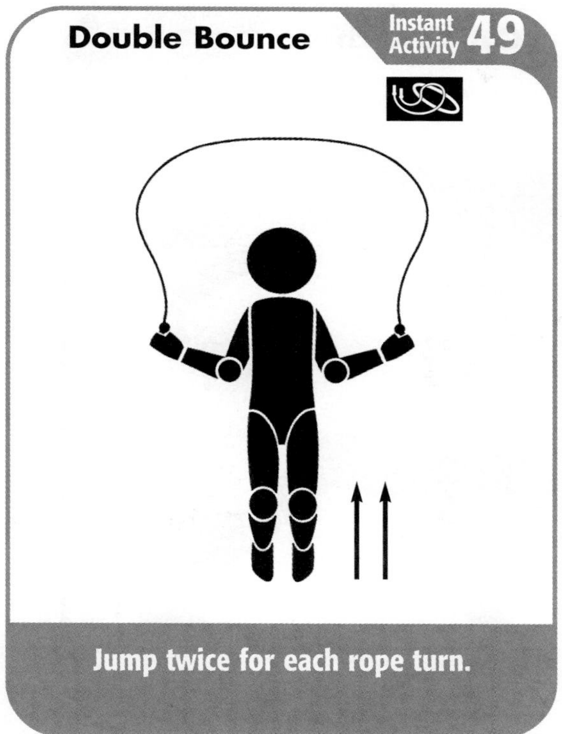

Double Bounce Students can pantomime jump rope movements for this skill.

Harcourt

CHAPTER 10

Suggested Music: Be Active! Music for Daily Physical Activity, Track 10, Super Stress Buster

Bell Jump

Stretch Like a Cat

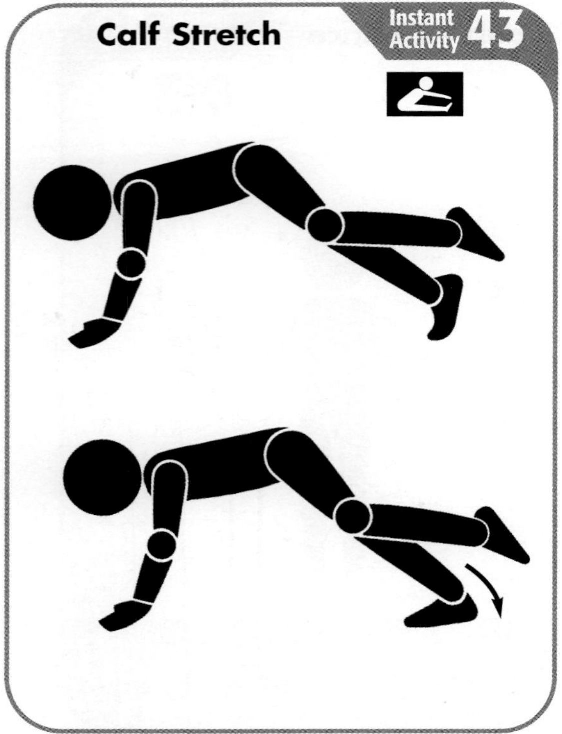

Calf Stretch Students need not touch the floor; they can use any stable object for support.

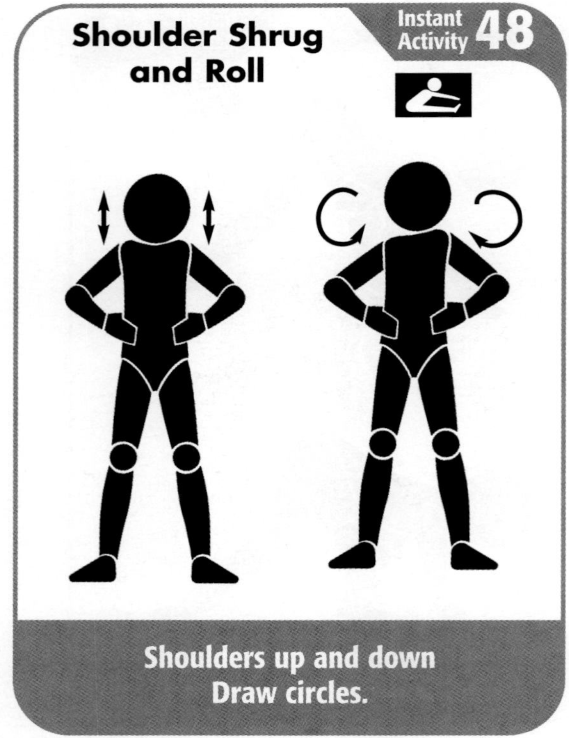

Shoulder Shrug and Roll

Harcourt

CHAPTER 11

Suggested Music: Be Active! Music for Daily Physical Activity, Track 11, Funky Flex

Punch and Kick

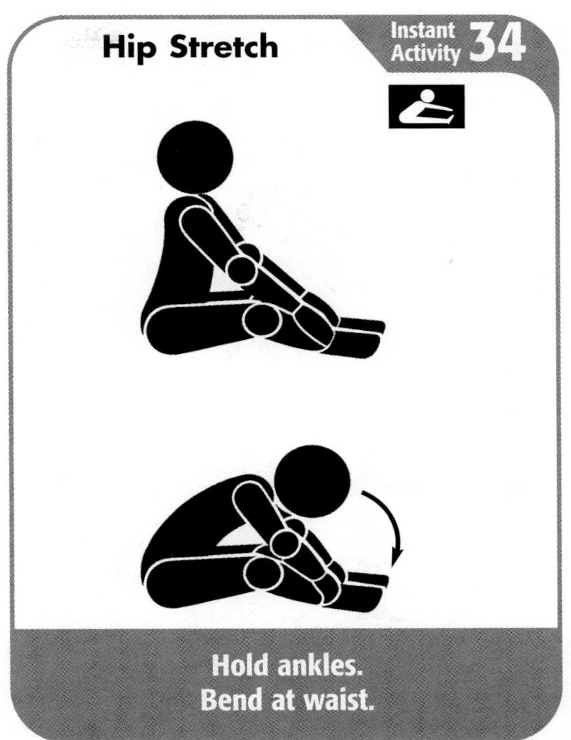

Hip Stretch This stretch can be done while seated by crossing one ankle on the opposite thigh and bending at the waist.

Martial Arts Kick Be sure that students have adequate space for safety. Younger students can hold onto a desk or chair back for balance.

Lunge

Harcourt

CHAPTER 12

Suggested Music: Be Active! Music for Daily Physical Activity, Track 12, Broadway Bound

Four-square Hop Students can hop around the four sides of a book, desk, or chair.

Runner's Stretch

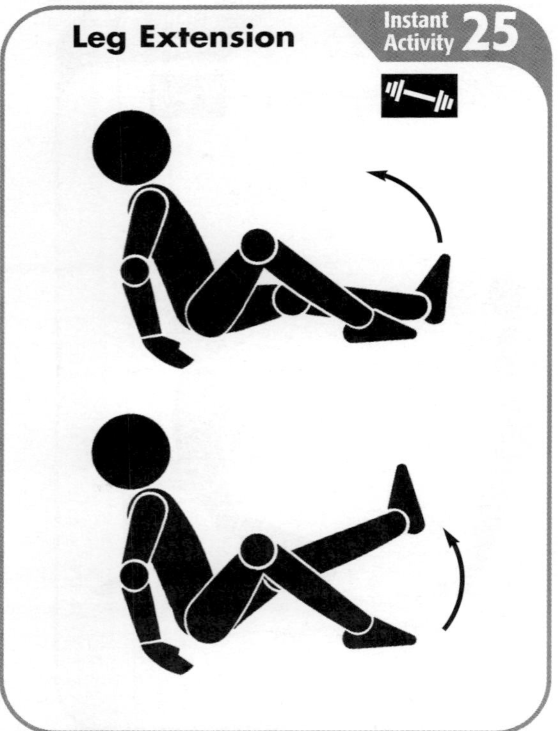

Leg Extension Students can also do this exercise while seated.

Bicycle Students can also do this exercise while seated. Have them sit back in their chairs and hold the chair edges for support.

Harcourt

EXTRA ACTIVITY CARDS

Handwalk

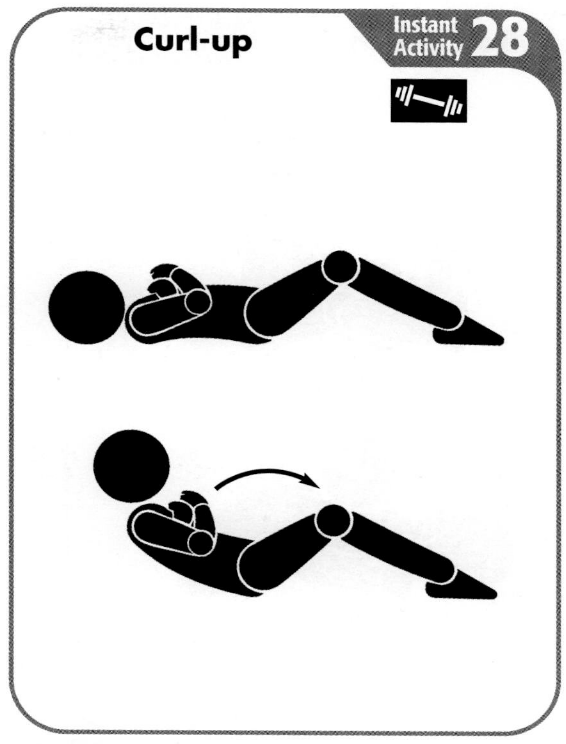

Curl-up

Twist and Crunch

Seal Walk

Harcourt

EXTRA ACTIVITY CARDS (CONT'D)

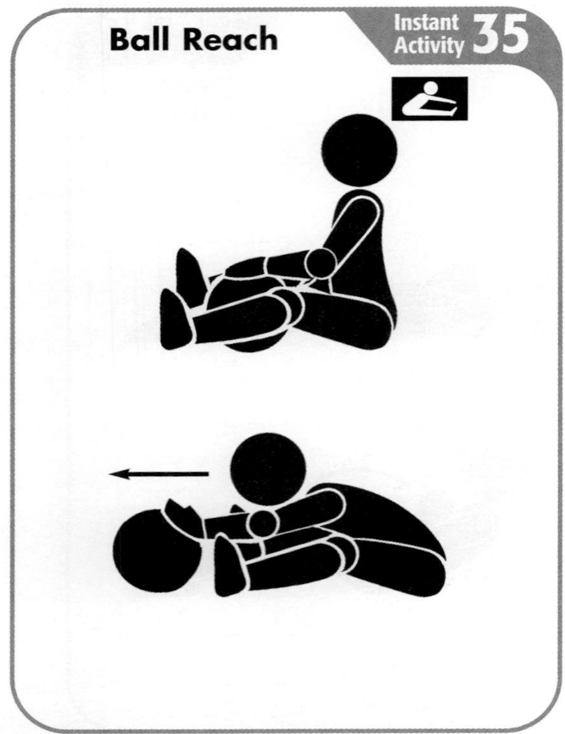

Ball Reach

Push and Pull
Instant Activity 36
Hook hands.
Slow and smooth

Push and Pull

Leg Stretch

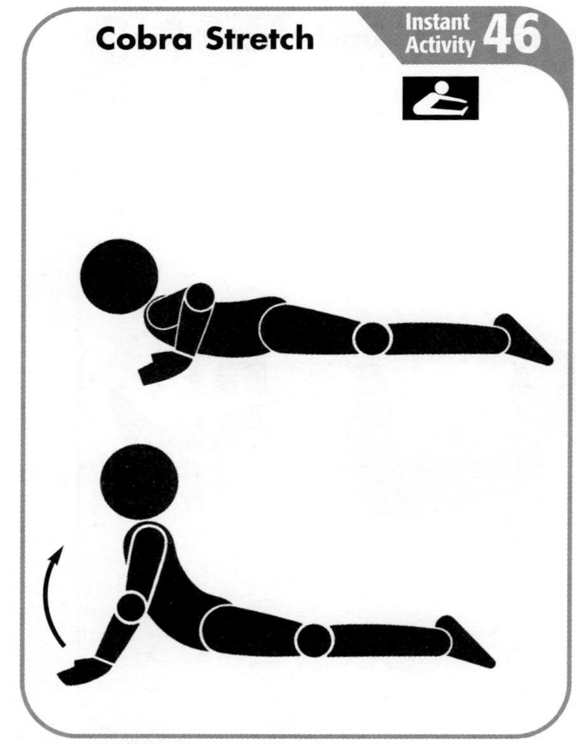

Cobra Stretch

Harcourt

EXTRA ACTIVITY CARDS (CONT'D)

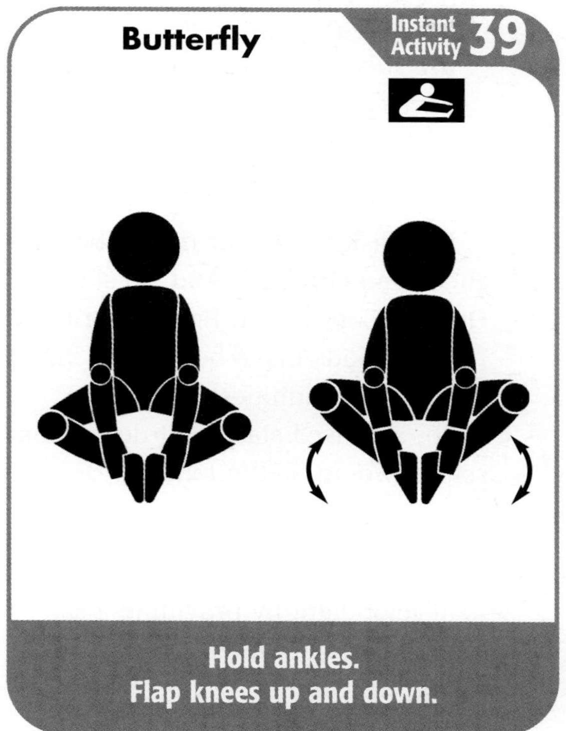

Butterfly
Hold ankles.
Flap knees up and down.

Arms
Instant Activity 61
Turn the hoop on one arm.
Switch to the other.

Arms

Elevator
Instant Activity 62
Move the hoop up and down.

Elevator

360° Spin
Spin your body
all the way around.

Harcourt

HELPING STUDENTS SUCCEED THROUGH COORDINATED SCHOOL HEALTH

by Thomas M. Fleming, Ph.D.

Most of us, whether we are teachers or parents, want the same things for our children. We want them to be successful. We want them to develop intellectually, do well in school, and make good grades. We want our children to be able to express their emotions constructively and to cope successfully with the demands of daily life. We want them to have healthy social lives by developing quality relationships with friends, family, and teachers. We want our children to be happy, and we want this for *all* children, not just our own.

If this positive growth and development is to happen for all children, then the historical role and mission of schools must change—and change is coming. It was once believed that the home, with help and support from community agencies and religious organizations, could prepare the child for the adult world. As adolescent health issues and societal problems in general have escalated during the past twenty years and as dropout rates have increased, school policymakers have begun to rethink the mission of a school. Effective schools see the link between health status and student success and have begun to play a more prominent role in addressing the health needs of their students. If we expect all children to succeed, schools must help them overcome the problems that interfere with learning, such as unsafe environments, drug abuse, family problems, and untreated health problems.

What Is the Mission of a School?

For many people, the following statement describes a school's mission:

> The mission of a school is to promote academic achievement and the intellectual development of students.

This statement, while correct, is incomplete. It is incomplete because to accomplish the mission of helping children develop intellectually, education must occur in an environment that is conducive to learning—in a place where children feel safe, secure, and cared for. Why is a safe, secure, and healthful environment so important for learning to take place? It is important because research indicates that young people do better in school and are less involved in risky behavior when the school atmosphere is caring.

> *When adolescents feel cared for by people at their school and feel like a part of the school, they are less likely to use substances, engage in violence, or initiate sexual activity at an earlier age."* (National Longitudinal Study of Adolescent Health; *Journal of School Health,* April 2002)

Less risky behavior means better health and more successful students. And, as stated by the Centers for Disease Control and Prevention (CDC) in Atlanta, Georgia "Healthy kids make better students. Better students make healthy communities."

So, a revised statement describing the mission of a school would be the following:

> The mission of a school is to educate students and assist in their intellectual, emotional, physical, and social development by providing a safe, secure, and caring school environment within which learning and student success can best occur.

What Are the Goals of Coordinated School Health?

There is little doubt that a well-supported approach to coordinated school health (CSH) can be instrumental in helping a school fulfill its mission. One of the more obvious goals of a CSH program is to improve the health status of school-age children. But this should not be the only goal. Quality CSH can certainly improve specific health behaviors and outcomes—such as improved dietary and physical activity patterns—but it can also include the goals of helping young people experience academic, emotional, and social success.

In terms of academic success, children who are chronically ill, abused, hungry, depressed, or troubled will have a difficult time functioning well in the classroom, no matter how good the school. These health problems are barriers to learning and will persist unless an intervention is introduced through the school or community. In an era of high-stakes testing and accountability, the academic expectations are the same for all students, regardless of health considerations. A good school health program that reduces barriers to learning will help level the playing field in the arena of high-stakes testing.

What Are the Components of Coordinated School Health?

The Division of Adolescent and School Health (DASH) within the CDC has promoted an eight-component model since the early 1980s. But CSH can be effective with fewer components. For example, Texas has recently mandated a four-component model that all elementary schools in the state are to implement. Regardless of the number of components, the CSH model is a framework that enables communities to collaborate with schools in such a way that the physical, mental, and social well-being of students is enhanced. Many individuals, from both the school and the community, are involved in a coordinated model by working together to improve the school environment and, in so doing, to provide students with opportunities to improve their health status and their chances for success.

The CDC Coordinated School Health Model has eight components:

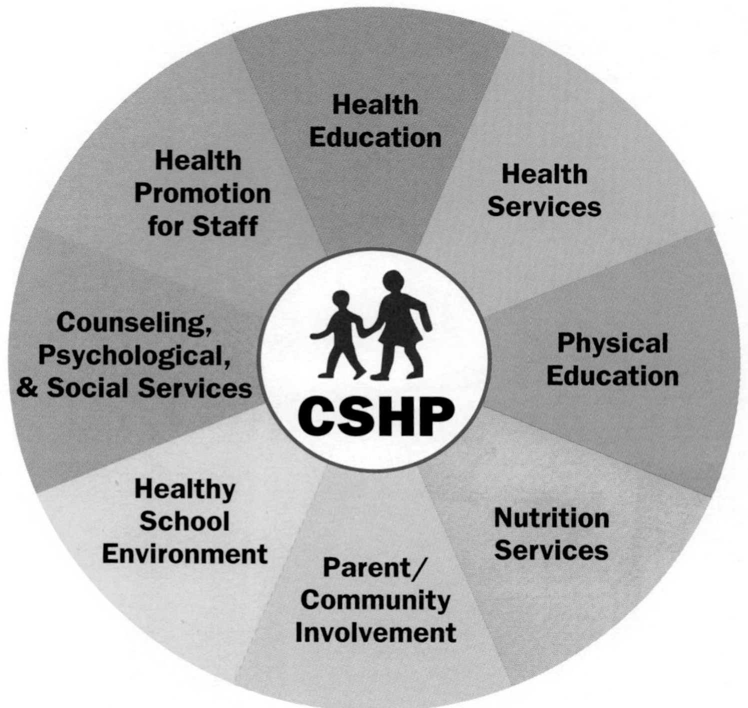

The Texas model has four components:

- Health Education
- Physical Education
- Nutrition/Cafeteria Services
- Family/Community Involvement

Few school districts in this country currently have a quality CSH model in place. One reason is that implementing such a model means developing alliances and collaborative associations within communities. That not only takes work but also runs counter to the role of schools in the minds of many school policymakers. However, the concept of coordinating program components within schools and communities has gained public support and momentum in recent years. Momentum grows as the public becomes more aware of the staggering health-care costs of preventable illnesses. Tobacco-related health problems and the current obesity epidemic alone should serve as indicators of the need for CSH.

In most school districts in this country, for many different reasons, school health has been limited to curricular interventions that have been, at best, fragmented. A few select individuals have delivered the health promotion message to students, regardless of the health topic. These individuals include the classroom teacher, the physical education teacher, or the school nurse. There has been little concentrated effort to coordinate school health services, health education, nutrition/cafeteria services, physical education, and family/community initiatives so that they resemble a coordinated model.

What Does Coordinated School Health Look Like?

A good way to understand coordinated school health is to depict school health programs that are uncoordinated. The January 1999 issue of *Phi Delta Kappan* featured a report on CSH programs. The following examples of an uncoordinated approach to student health are taken from that article:

> In the uncoordinated school health program, while teachers are busy explaining the food pyramid to students, the cafeteria manager may be planning a lunch of pizza and french fries, and the school business manager may be counting the proceeds from the soft drink and candy machines. Nobody asks the custodian or the secretary, both of whom probably know more about what the troubled kids are up to than anyone else in the building, to share their observations about kids.

> The health education curriculum presents information about the dangers of smoking, but school policy allows students to smoke on the school grounds. A depressed, pregnant, drug-using teenager in Maryland saw three counselors each week—a suicide prevention counselor, a parenting counselor, and a drug abuse counselor—and none of them talked to the others. All the while, the student missed so many classes that she flunked the semester and dropped out when her baby was born.

To begin to dismantle these unproductive approaches to school health programming, communities and schools need to understand the importance of school health promotion—not only to assist in preventing disease but to enhance the school climate and further ensuring the opportunities for student success. All of us who are interested in schools and children must understand the central theme of CSH. That is, the problems associated with adolescent health are more effectively overcome from multiple directions rather than by singular components working in isolation from each other.

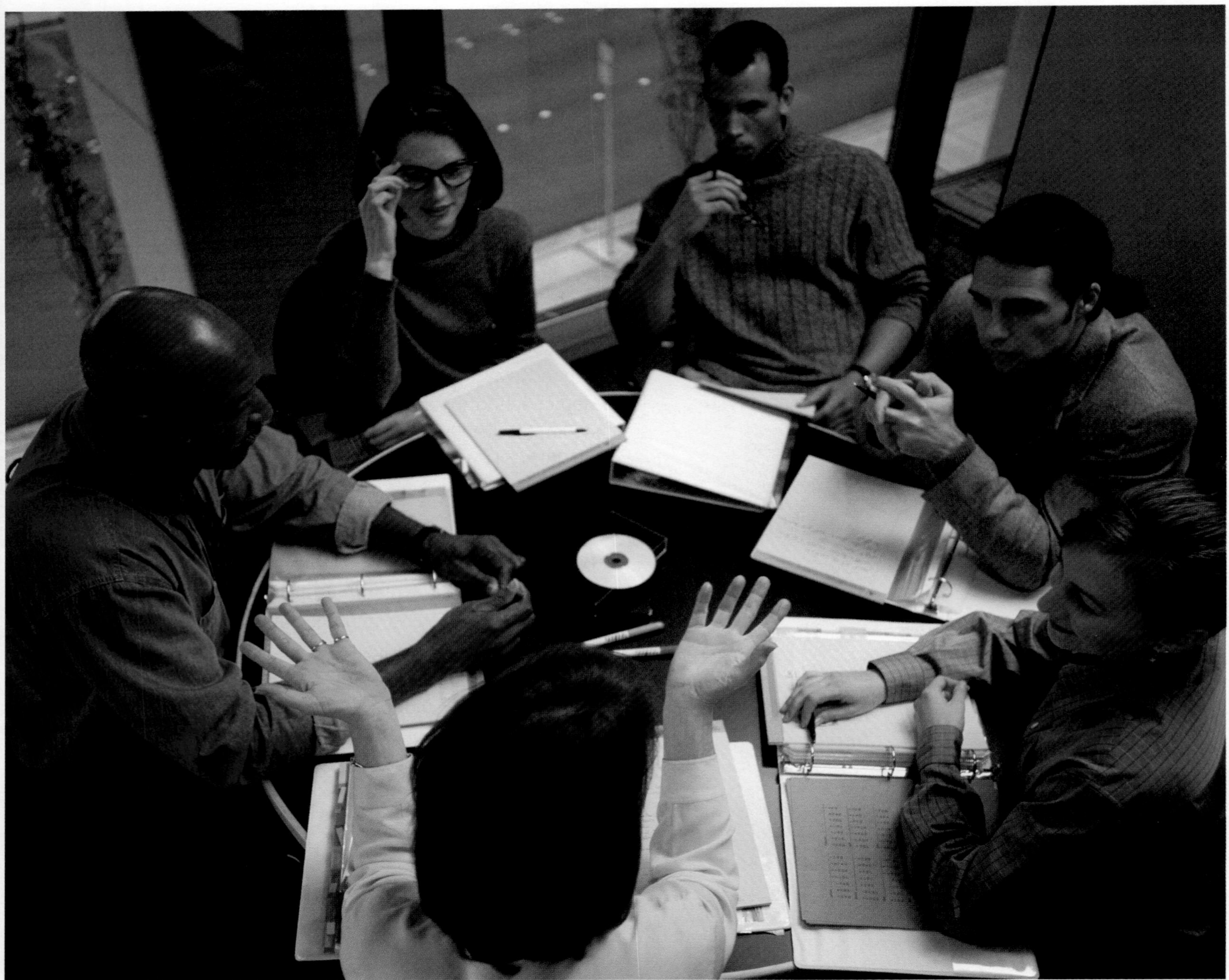

How Can You Get Started with Coordinated School Health?

As a classroom teacher, you can help promote a coordinated approach to school health on your campus. Here are some things you can do:

- Become a CSH "champion," or advocate, in your school, district, or community.
- Determine if your district has a school health advisory council in place—a representative school/community group that provides input to the local school board regarding school health issues. Such a representative group can recommend school health strategies that are consistent with local needs and values, including CSH.
- Seek the support of the principal and other interested stakeholders, such as the school nurse, physical education teachers, classroom teachers, nutrition services personnel, and community organizations.
- Obtain material about how to establish CSH, such as the School Health Starter Kit from the CDC.
- Consider a commercial product with a reduced number of program components as a first step. Excellent commercial programs, such as the Coordinated Approach to Children's Health (CATCH) or The Great Body Shop, can provide training and materials.

CSH is a vehicle for bringing families, communities, and schools together to work toward the common goal of enriching the lives of schoolchildren. CSH is not just about student health. It's also about making schools safer and more caring. It's about making schools better places to learn. CSH is not just about kids. It's about all of us.♥

HOW *HARCOURT HEALTH AND FITNESS* SUPPORTS COORDINATED SCHOOL HEALTH

The development of knowledge and skills alone is not enough to ensure that children achieve health literacy. A collaborative approach that coordinates the efforts of the families, schools, and the community is the most effective way to promote health literacy for all children.

A Coordinated School Health Program involves eight components that work together to develop and reinforce health knowledge, skills, attitudes, and behaviors. Each of these eight components is vital to the overall goal of promoting health literacy. The components are most effective when they are planned and implemented in a consistent and supportive manner.

- The program provides a comprehensive approach to teaching health, with content that addresses all the major strands of health.
- Where appropriate, the program suggests resources that teachers and other school personnel may consult for making the links to all components of CSH. See the Resources page for each chapter in the Teacher Editions. See also the References for Coordinated School Health in the *Teaching Resources* book.
- The content and teaching strategies address the physical, emotional, and social needs of children.
- ***Harcourt Health and Fitness*** goes beyond the teaching of health content by focusing on healthful skills and behaviors. For example, the Life Skills and Building Good Character features teach life-enhancing behaviors that will contribute to a lifetime of good health.

- Together with ***Be Active! Resources for Physical Education***, the program provides a comprehensive and coordinated approach to teaching physical education.
- Specific features of the ***Harcourt Health and Fitness Teacher Editions*** that support CSH include the following:

 **School-Home Connection**

 **Daily Physical Activity**

 **Daily Fitness Tip**

 **Activities for Home and Community**

 **Health Background: Webliography**

INJURY PREVENTION IS A PARTNERSHIP

Jan Marie Ozias, Ph.D., R.N.

Why are injury prevention and control of concern to schools?

- Injuries are the leading killer of children and youth in the United States and a major cause of hospital care and long-term disability. Of the 22 million injuries to children that occur yearly in the United States, it is estimated that 10 to 25 percent occur in and around schools and school events.
- Schools are not only where students learn about safety practices but also where students spend many hours daily. The community expects schools to teach students knowledge and skills for safe, responsible lifestyles. Parents want to trust that school buildings, the ways to and from schools, and school activities are safe—all the time.
- Schools are work sites for many adults in every community. The people who staff schools need protection from unnecessary risks and need to take responsibility for injury prevention practices.

Why don't we use the term *accidents* anymore?

The U.S. Centers for Disease Control and Prevention analyzed "accidents" using the concept of epidemiology (the study of diseases that affect people) and determined that most accidents are not random occurrences. They are predictable and preventable.

Let us examine a fatal car collision caused by a teenage driver who was drinking, showing off, and driving on a rain-slick road without using a safety belt. None of these factors is a random occurrence, that is, a true accident.

The event and the injuries that resulted follow a predictable pattern. Epidemiology examines the relationship among three elements:

- **Host**—a person who could become ill or injured due to his or her own resistance, skills, or state of mind
- **Agent**—a direct cause of illness, such as a virus, or of harm, such as a car
- **Environment**—such as rules, weather conditions, and cleanliness

If we can alter any one of the three epidemiological elements, we can break the chain of events that lead to a high risk of illness or harm. For example, immunizing a child breaks the chain of events leading to disease if the child is later exposed to a virus. Here is a home safety example:

Host: Curious 5-year-old child
Agent: Cigarette lighter
Environment: unsupervised garage with flammable materials

Changing any of the three elements breaks the link between the host and the agent. If you teach young students the skill of self-discipline and the risks of fire, add adult supervision to the environment, or keep lighters out of reach, no fire!

In order to help students and staff identify what can and cannot be controlled, we use *unintended injury* to refer to burns, crashes, and falls. (These were previously called *accidents.*) We distinguish unintended injuries from deliberate or intended injuries, injuries caused by violence, assault, and self-harm.

Do children think injuries are preventable?

Children can tell us about injury prevention—they know it's not just about "accidents" or "kids being kids." In a study of 12 elementary schools, students were asked about their playground injuries. Almost a third of the injured students thought they could have prevented their injuries. When they were asked how, the most common replies were not going so fast, watching, being more careful, not fighting, and avoiding the situation. About half the same injured students thought someone else or something in the environment had influenced the injury. The most frequent reasons were *actions of another student* or *an object*, such as a rock or playground equipment. Developmentally, students can learn to use their senses to recognize hazards like these, connect them to unsafe situations, and then act to prevent injuries.

What do we know about students' injuries?

Detailed reports about student injuries come from the National Pediatric Trauma Registry study of school–age children (5- to 18-year-olds) seen in 74 emergency rooms over an eight year period. Here are some results from that study:

- More injuries (49 percent) occurred in recreational areas than in any other school area.
- Falls were the most common cause of injury (46 percent), followed by sports activities (30 percent).
- Assaults or intended injury caused 10 percent of the injuries
- Students with disabilities were more likely to be hurt; 17 percent of the injured students already had a disability or chronic illness.
- Forty-six percent of the injuries occurred among 10- to 14-year-olds.
- Almost 40 percent of the cases involved head injuries.

Do schools handle injuries properly?

The same hospital emergency room study also found that 16 percent of the children received no or inadequate first aid; they were sent home rather than sent to receive care. How prepared is your school to handle injuries? Does it have a registered nurse and staff trained in first aid? Who fills in for the nurse if he or she is unavailable?

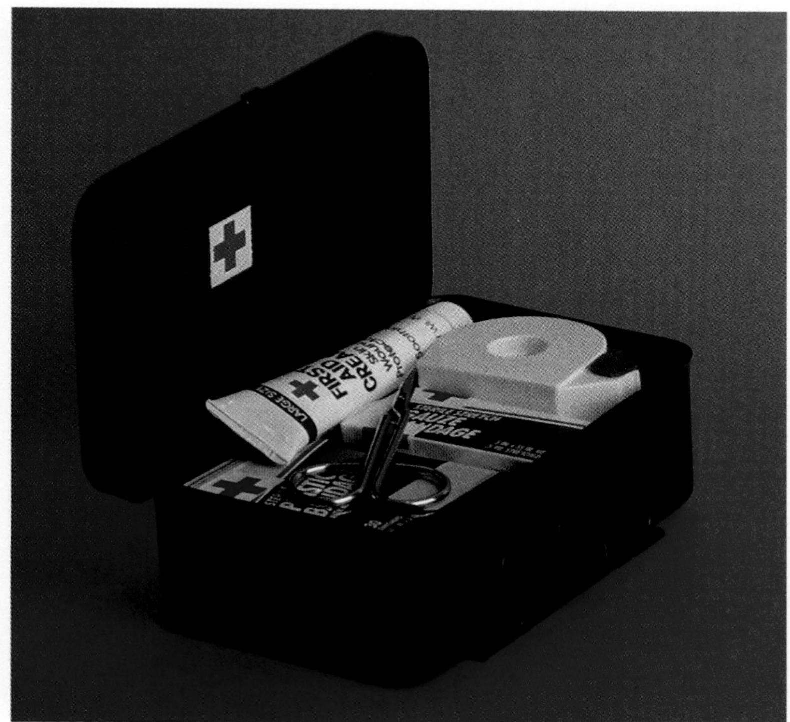

Where do violence and abuse fit in injury prevention?

Assault injuries to students seen in emergency rooms included beatings (more than 50 percent of the assaults), stabbings (14 percent), gunshot wounds (10 percent), or being deliberately hit by an object. Although violence receives much more media attention and causes staff to worry, most of the students injured at school—in a ratio of 9 to 1—are injured unintentionally. Regardless, conflict resolution as a life skill can reduce aggression and intended injuries, especially when it is taught in elementary school and applied in the home, community, and workplace.

Student violence prevention in elementary schools begins with recognizing and stopping bullying. Programs must include prevention but also intervene with students who bully and, separately, the victims and parents. Adults must create a caring social climate that does not ignore or tolerate bullying. Two evaluated programs are: *Bullying Prevention Program: Blueprints for violence prevention* (Boulder, CO) and *Bully-proofing your elementary school* (Longmont, CO: Sopris West).

"Stranger danger" addresses community concerns for children when they are unsupervised. Many children also may be at risk in the presence of a neighbor, a family acquaintance, on the Internet, or even a relative. Teachers should work with approved school resources to include opportunities for students to learn how to handle uncomfortable situations involving touch, secrets, or pressure by an older person to do something that children feel is wrong or unsafe.

Are school buses safe?

While much attention is being given to installing safety belts in school buses—primarily to reinforce the habit of using them in cars and to prevent disruptive behavior—school buses are quite safe. Considering the number of passenger miles they travel, school buses are 37 times safer than cars. Even so, an average of seven children die annually in school transportation-related crashes. Another 19 students die getting on or off a bus, or are hit by a bus or a passing vehicle. Half of these pedestrians are children between the ages of five and seven!

What needs to happen in schools?

In addition to quality student instruction, the Centers for Disease Control and Prevention (2001) recommends that schools

- establish a safety council that includes parents and students as part of a school health program advisory committee. The safety council would identify and correct safety hazards and establish safety policies.
- develop reporting methods so that school staff can analyze unintended and intended injuries and target the most common or most serious situations and develop better prevention strategies.
- develop and implement emergency plans to properly assess, manage and refer injured students.

What are safety education priorities for elementary grades?

Among elementary-school children, common unintended injuries are related to the following:

- traffic
- bicycles
- water
- playgrounds
- fire
- personal trauma (falls, cuts)

Appropriate education goals for elementary grades are to develop in students **habits** of safety that will guide **behaviors** and prepare students for the risk-taking years of middle school. We must convey more than just knowledge of safety risks and rules, we must focus on habits and behaviors (what to do) and skills (how to perform the *behaviors*). *Positive* role models at school and at home, guided practice, and social reinforcement of emerging skills are appropriate strategies to build these habits and behaviors.♥

NUTRITION BEHAVIORS FOR CHILDREN

Carl A. Stockton, Ph.D.

As I think about promoting positive dietary behaviors in children, I have to look at my fourth-grade daughter's current eating habits. Her eating practices are being molded at this early stage in her life. Children learn at a young age what kinds of food adults around them eat. In trying to teach her about positive nutritional choices, I find myself selecting healthful foods for her, such as green beans, apples, oranges, and other fruits and vegetables, that are part of my own diet. Nutritional eating practices are learned behaviors, and it is important that we start molding these behaviors early in a child's life.

Poor Health Habits

Our society has been extremely negligent in promoting positive eating behaviors in our children. Many studies have shown that poor diets and lack of physical activity together account for more than 300,000 premature deaths among adults each year. These poor health habits begin in our children. According to the U.S. Centers for Disease Control and Prevention, the percentage of children who are overweight has more than doubled in the past 20 years, and more than 9 million children (15 percent) are seriously overweight. Studies have shown that obese children are more likely to become obese adults. As adults, they are at increased risk for many premature diseases.

Eating habits of children and young people in the United States are poor. Children make poor nutritional choices that put them at risk for health problems. Contrary to common misconceptions, children do not instinctively select the nutrients that they need for proper growth and development. If I allowed my daughter to select food instinctively, she would have a diet of candy, soda, and cookies—hardly a healthful diet.

Another common misconception is that children can handle a poor diet when they are young because they will burn off the Calories; this is a dangerous misconception. Although it is true that children are able to metabolize the extra Calories because of increased activity, the poor eating habits they develop in childhood will continue into adulthood and can be detrimental. Establishing good nutritional habits during childhood is critical because changing poor eating behaviors in adulthood is difficult. Think about your own nutritional habits. I challenge you to choose one nutritional habit that you would like to change and to spend one week trying to change that habit. You can probably guess that trying to change the habit would be difficult. Now consider that if you had developed a more positive eating pattern as a child, you would most likely not need to make this behavior change as an adult.

Poor Diets

Children would get the proper amount of nutrients if they could only learn proper eating habits. Contrary to common beliefs, children do not need vitamin and mineral supplements. Unless there is a medical reason for vitamin and mineral supplements, children receive all the nutrients they need through a balanced diet. Taking vitamin pills only seems to be an easy solution for making up the nutrients missed in a child's dietary intake.

On another note, did you know that pound per pound children need to consume more water than do adults? Children lose a greater percent of water through evaporation than adults. Therefore, children need to consume more water per pound of body weight than adults need to consume.

Even though adults have shown some improvement in their dietary patterns, our children's eating habits remain poor. According to the U.S. Department of Health and Human Services, more than 84 percent of children eat too much fat. Children on average consume about 40 percent of their calories from fat. Children are not consuming enough fruits and vegetables in their diet. The National Cancer Institute recommends that children consume five servings of fruits and vegetables per day. Only 20 percent of our children actually meet this recommendation. Did you know that 51 percent of our children eat less than one serving of fruit a day? Furthermore, fried potatoes account for a large proportion of the vegetables eaten by children.

Did you know that one in five students skips breakfast on a regular basis? Several research studies have found that not eating breakfast can affect children's intellectual performance in school. Even moderate malnutrition can have a long-term effect on how well a child performs in school. Several studies have reported that undernourished children become sick, miss school, and score lower on tests than do children who receive the proper amount of nourishment. Therefore, it is important for children to eat properly and not skip meals.

Promoting Good Nutrition

What can we do as teachers to encourage our students to become better eaters? The opportunity to promote better eating habits is in front of us. We have a captive audience

to whom to promote good nutrition and also positive health behaviors. We as teachers need to develop a comprehensive scope and sequence for nutrition education. It is important to keep reinforcing positive eating behaviors at every grade level. Nutrition education involves more than just educating students about healthful eating. We need to help children learn skills, not just facts about nutrition. The USDA's *Nutrition and Your Health: Dietary Guidelines For Americans, 2000* is a good source for learning diet and lifestyle skills. In this document, you can find healthful activities and practices that students can actually put into practice.

Give children repeated opportunities to practice healthful eating. Practicing a positive health behavior enough times will usually make that behavior the norm for children, not the exception. Teaching children about nutrition is no different from teaching children math skills. If we want our children to excel in mathematics, we give them multiple opportunities to practice math problems. The same holds true for developing positive eating practices. Practice, practice, practice!

Practicing Good Nutrition

What types of activities can teachers do to promote positive nutritional practices in children? First of all, request healthful snacks for class parties. This will create a positive atmosphere for eating these kinds of foods. Give students many chances to taste foods low in fat, sodium, and added sugar and foods high in vitamins, minerals, and fiber. Also teach children how to make healthful choices in the school cafeteria or when packing their lunches. This promotes positive behaviors and keeps children involved in learning about nutrition. Emphasize the positive aspects of healthful eating rather than the harmful effects of unhealthful eating.

Finally, make nutrition education activities fun. Be creative with your activities, and try to show your students that learning can be fun. Nutrition education curricula resources exist and are readily available, often for free. Many nutrition-based materials can be obtained from volunteer agencies and governmental offices. Use them!

I would be remiss if I failed to mention the use of computers and technology in the classroom. If you are fortunate enough to have computers in your classroom, integrate the use of these learning tools with nutrition education. Surf the nutrition information highway, search CD-ROMs, and experience nutrition multimedia along with your students. Who knows, even your own nutritional habits may improve!♥

BECOMING PHYSICALLY ACTIVE

Charlie Gibbons, Ed.D.

Children have always enjoyed the opportunity to play outdoors and rarely refuse to take advantage of an opportunity to run and have fun. However, in recent years not as many children are outdoors playing. Some studies have shown that children are less active and that childhood obesity is on the rise. How true is this? Are children in the United States becoming less active and more overweight? If they are, what are the influencing factors?

Physical activity and fitness have become such a national health concern that several national documents from the U.S. Department of Health and Human Services have emphasized the importance of physical activity and fitness. *Healthy People 2010* has established objectives aimed at increasing the proportion of adolescents who spend at least 50 percent of school physical education class time being physically active. *Physical Activity and Health: A Report of the Surgeon General* emphasizes that regular participation in moderate physical activity is an essential component of a healthy lifestyle.

How physically active are children and adolescents?

Numerous national studies (First and Second National Children and Youth Fitness Study, The President's Council on Physical Fitness and Sports School Population Fitness Study, Youth Fitness Behavior Surveillance System, and *Healthy People 2010*) have been conducted to determine the physical activity levels of children and adolescents in the United States. The general finding is that children and youth in the United States are less active and physically fit than is recommended for optimal protection against future chronic diseases.

In addition to studies conducted on fitness levels of children and adolescents, a number of studies have been conducted to determine the prevalence of childhood obesity in the United States. The general finding is that children and youth are getting more overweight.

Why are children and adolescents less physically active and fit?

If children and adolescents are less active and are becoming more overweight, there must be some influencing factors. Researchers have emphasized the influencing role of television watching on sedentary (inactive) behavior and obesity. Television watching is a popular childhood leisure activity. The majority of children spend more time watching television than they spend in school. During television watching, physical activity ceases and metabolism slows down. As television watching increases among children and adolescents, physical activity decreases. As physical activity decreases among children and adolescents, obesity increases. According to the U.S. Centers for Disease Control and Prevention (CDC), the percentage of young people who are overweight has more than doubled in the past 30 years, and the number of deaths due to inactivity and poor diet is at least 300,000 a year for all ages.

In recent years there also has been an explosion in the use of computers, computer games, and video games by children and adolescents. These advances in technology also may help to promote sedentary behavior among children and adolescents and to increase the likelihood of obesity and the development of chronic diseases.

Television is a very powerful medium that has a pervasive influence on the health knowledge, attitudes, and behavior of children, adolescents, and adults. Researchers have suggested another avenue in which television watching influences obesity. Television watching may influence obesity among children and adolescents by increasing the number of nutritional messages to which they are exposed. Much too often foods in commercials and the foods shown in television programs are high in Calories and low in nutritional value.

What health problems are associated with inactivity?

Researchers have found obesity in childhood and adolescence to be associated with developmental risk factors for cardiovascular diseases, hypertension, high blood cholesterol, and diabetes. These problems become more pronounced in adulthood. Obese children are at an increased risk of obesity as adults. Recent studies have shown that the problems of obesity and physical inactivity among young adults are increasing at alarming rates. As the prevalence of adult obesity increases, morbidity and mortality increase.

At the same time, children and adolescents today are being bombarded with societal messages that emphasize thinness. These social pressures for thinness increase the health risk for overweight youth suffering from eating disorders.

What are the benefits of regular physical activity?

According to the *Report of the Surgeon General*, regular physical activity that is performed on an almost daily basis reduces the risk of developing or dying from some of the leading causes of illness and death in the United States.

Children should learn the importance of warm-up activities, which prepare the body for physical activity and prevent injuries, and of cool-down activities, which allow for continual blood return from the lower extremities of the body to prevent blood from pooling in the legs.

How can teachers help?

It is important to remember that children and adolescents are less likely to engage in physical activity and will choose inactivity if they are not enjoying the physical activity. A healthy level of physical activity requires regular participation in activities that increase energy expenditure above resting levels. An active child participates in physical education classes, plays sports, performs regular household chores, spends recreational time outdoors, and regularly travels by foot, bicycle, or roller blades. Opportunities for physical activity should be fun, increase confidence in participation in physical activity, and involve friends and peers. Positive role models for physical activity include parents and teachers.

If children and adolescents are supposed to be able to carry out only everyday tasks with vigor and alertness and without undue fatigue, then for too many of them there is no need for physical activity because their everyday tasks do not require much energy. With the increase in television watching, computer use, and playing computer and video games, more and more children and adolescents are engaging in more sedentary practices. The lack of participation in physical activity by the youth of the United States is a national concern. It is imperative that this concern be addressed by the families, schools, and communities in the United States.

As a teacher, you can help alleviate this problem with your students by modeling a physically active lifestyle, helping them understand the importance of being physically active, and encouraging them to participate every day in physical activity that they enjoy. ♥

Regular physical activity improves health in the following ways:

- It reduces the risk of dying prematurely from heart disease.
- It reduces the risk of developing high blood pressure.
- It reduces feelings of depression and anxiety.
- It helps control weight.
- It reduces the risk of developing diabetes.
- It helps build and maintain healthy bones, muscles, and joints.
- It promotes psychological well-being.
- It helps alleviate stress.

What is physical activity and fitness?

Have you ever gone for a walk? Have you ever done any gardening? If your answer is yes for these activities, or for any activities of this energy level or higher, you have been involved in physical activity. And if you have engaged in these types of activities for at least 30 minutes per day, you have been improving your fitness. You have been engaging in physical activity that will help ensure Calories are expended and health benefits will be conferred.

Children and adolescents should engage in

- aerobic activities that will help improve and maintain the cardio-respiratory system,
- physically challenging activities that will improve and maintain the muscular system, and
- stretching activities that will improve and maintain flexibility and help prevent injuries.

THE NEW FACE OF PHYSICAL EDUCATION

by Lisa Bunting, M.Ed.

Do you remember push-ups and pull-ups, running endless laps to "get in shape," or standing in rows to do military-style calisthenics? How about waiting your turn to run a relay race to see who was the fastest in the class? Perhaps you experienced the stress of watching your peers pick teams to play a competitive game. Your class may have played elimination games like dodge ball. Or you may have participated in athletic games such as basketball, flag football, and softball, designed to parallel college sports. Most of us remember these activities because they represented our school experience in physical education.

The old-style traditional P.E. class focused on competition, winning and losing, and keeping score. This approach to P.E. often featured military-style exercises and drills and tests that were supposedly designed to prepare students to become better athletes. Typically, the instruction showcased a few students who were athletic and already fit, while others sat around and cheered for them. The emphasis in the "old P.E." was on athletic proficiency, sports development, and athletic fitness. Few pieces of equipment were available to students. Sometimes students were punished for mistakes and misconduct in class by being made to run or perform push-ups. Often there were no individual student learning goals based on interest and ability levels, just group goals based on athletics.

By the mid 1990s, studies found that an alarming number of children and adults were overweight and inactive. Research such as that referred to in the 1996 *Surgeon General's Report on Physical Activity and Health* supported the health benefits of regular exercise and physical activity. Educational reformers suggested that new standards and objectives should be written for physical education. The goal of physical education changed from developing athletes and athletic fitness to helping young people become active, now and for the rest of their lives. "New P.E." was born.

The new approach to physical education represents a new philosophy of teaching, as well as a revised curriculum. It is a rethinking of major goals and objectives and signals a shift in focus from physical fitness outcomes toward physical activity goals. New P.E. is centered on standards and objectives, and it features a variety of activities in which all young people are active and successful. Activities are designed to be developmentally appropriate, and instruction meets the needs of all students, especially those who are not athletically gifted. There is an emphasis on competency in many movement forms and proficiency in a few. There is a focus on health-related fitness, rather than athletic fitness, and on the acquisition of knowledge and skills for a lifetime of physical activity.

A P.E. class in a contemporary gym looks vastly different from the classes in gyms of twenty years ago. There is a flurry of activity as students work individually, with partners, and in small groups. Many pieces of equipment are used during the same lesson. For example, during a volleying lesson, students may choose to use foam balls, balloons, beach balls or volleyballs. The variety of equipment and activity choices leads to success in a fun-filled environment. Students remain engaged and active during most of the class time. The teacher facilitates the lesson by integrating warm-up activities, fitness, skills, and social objectives, as well as a cool-down.

Traditional concepts such as the teaching of gross motor skills will always be a part of physical education. But the addition of instruction in health-related activities and a focus on staying active now and in the future reflect a more contemporary model. This new model of physical activity instruction provides students with knowledge and skills to live a healthy, active life now and is essential in meeting the challenges of the national obesity epidemic.♥

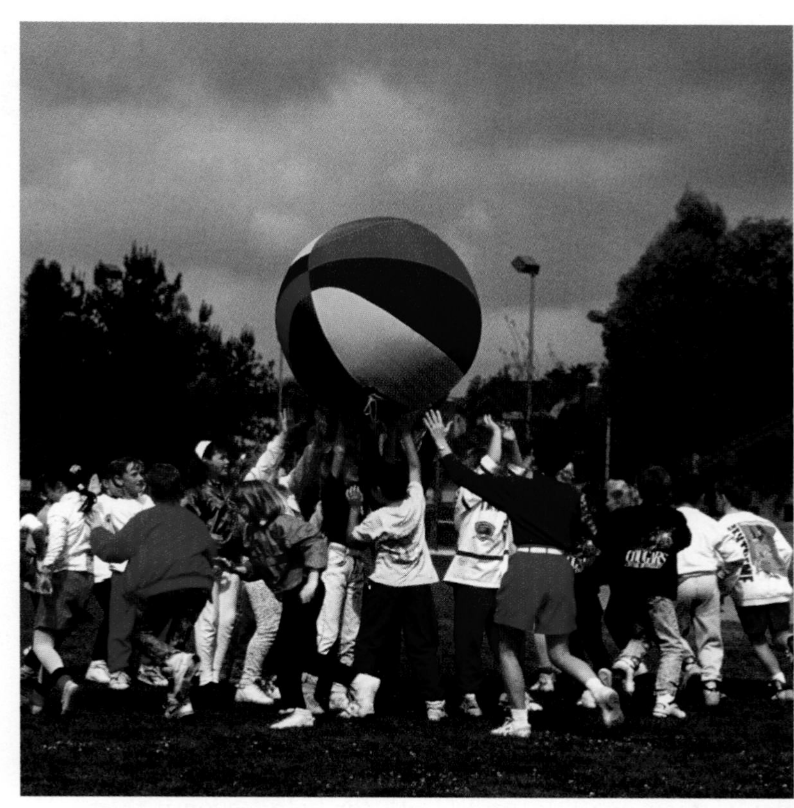

Be Active! Resources for Physical Education provides instructional strategies, games, and activities and a variety of resources designed to meet the needs of contemporary physical education. This program can also be used with *Harcourt Health and Fitness.* The chart shows a correlation of the two programs.

Harcourt Health and Fitness Correlated to *Be Active! Resources for Physical Education*

***Harcourt Health and Fitness* Chapters**	***Be Active! Resources for Physical Education* Lessons**
1 Body Systems at Work	55, 59, 61, 67, 69
2 Personal Health	58, 63
3 Food and Your Health	57, 62, 68
4 Fitness and Activity	1–53, 56, 59–61, 63–66, 72–76, 84–87
5 Safe at Home	73–74, 77–83
6 Safe Away from Home	74, 79–81
7 Guarding Against Disease	53–60, 62–65, 68–71
8 Medicines, Drugs, and Your Health	71
9 Harmful Effects of Tobacco and Alcohol	70–71
10 Your Needs and Feelings	72–76, 82–83, 88–90
11 Families Together	88–90
12 Living in a Healthful Community	54, 76, 79, 81

STRATEGIES FOR TEACHING ABOUT CHILD ABUSE, INCLUDING SEXUAL EXPLOITATION

All children have a right to be raised in a safe, nurturing, and loving environment. They should understand that saying *no* to abuse of any sort is their personal right and an appropriate response. Children should know that a support network of trusted adults is present to help them understand, confront, and deal with abusive situations. Most importantly, children should be made aware that it is never too late to ask for help.

In some families it can be difficult to discuss sexual abuse and exploitation—the subject is still considered too private to acknowledge or discuss. Fortunately, more communities and schools, with the help of news and entertainment media, are confronting and dealing with incidences of sexual abuse. The consistent message is that it is never acceptable for an adult to use a child for sexual purposes. Learning communication skills and refusal skills empowers more children to recognize sexual abuse, to resist it when possible, and to ask for help—even if they have to ask more than one person.

The lessons on the following pages can be used to help children learn to identify, report, and resist abuse or sexual exploitation. They can also help children explain the impact of neglect and abuse. Be sure to consult your school administation and/or guidance services if you need support or additional resources to discuss these topics with children.

Background

Child abuse and neglect is defined as any act or failure to act on the part of a parent or caregiver that results in death, serious physical or emotional harm, or sexual abuse or exploitation or that presents an imminent risk of serious harm. Child abuse and neglect are defined in both federal and state legislation. The **Federal Child Abuse Prevention and Treatment Act,** as amended in 1996 (CAPTA P. L. 104-235) provides the foundation upon which state definitions are based. For example, the California Child Abuse Reporting Law, like laws in other states, provides the legal basis for action to protect children and allow intervention by public agencies if a child is maltreated. The state of Texas mandates that anyone "having cause to believe that a child's physical or mental health or welfare has been or may be adversely affected by abuse or neglect" *must* report the case immediately to a state or local law enforcement agency or to the Texas Department of Protective and Regulatory Services. Reporting suspected child abuse to any other person or agency will *not* satisfy the reporter's obligation under this law.

The Federal Child Abuse Prevention and Treatment Act identifies four major types of maltreatment: physical abuse, child neglect, sexual abuse, and emotional abuse.

- **Physical abuse** is infliction of physical injury as the result of punching, beating, kicking, biting, burning, shaking, or otherwise harming a child.
- **Child neglect** is failure to provide for a child's basic needs. Neglect can be physical, educational, or emotional. It includes withholding of medically indicated treatment.
- **Sexual abuse** is fondling a child's genitals, intercourse, incest, rape, sodomy, exhibitionism, and commercial exploitation through prostitution or the production of pornographic materials. *Child* is defined as a person under the age of 18. **Sexual abuse is a serious criminal offense and must be handled within state guidelines.**
- **Emotional abuse** (psychological/verbal abuse, mental injury) is an act or failure to act on the part of parents or other caregivers that has caused or could cause serious behavioral, cognitive, emotional, or mental disorders.

People who *must* report child abuse are referred to as mandated reporters. Although these people vary from state to state, they usually include physicians, dentists, police, school counselors, and teachers. Those persons legally mandated to report suspected child abuse have immunity from criminal or civil liability for reporting as required. Mandated reporters should always keep in mind that their responsibility is only to report suspected abuse, not investigate it.

It is, however, the moral responsibility of *every* adult to ensure children's safety, prevent problems before they occur, and resolve problems that do happen before they become crises. If a child becomes a victim, the physical or emotional scars can last a lifetime if not treated.

What Are the Signs of Possible Abuse?

- Nervousness around adults
- Aggression toward adults or other children
- Inability to stay awake or to concentrate for extended periods
- Sudden dramatic changes in personality or activities
- Unnatural interest in sex
- Frequent or unexplained bruises or injuries
- Inconsistent explanations of injury
- Low self-esteem
- Poor hygiene

When Should I Report What I've Observed?

If you suspect that a child has been abused, you can ask the child an open-ended question, such as "How did you get hurt?" to elicit more information. Asking the parent or guardian open-ended questions may also aid your decision. You should also listen to what children say as they speak directly to you or to a friend and to what they may say indirectly through play, schoolwork, or their reaction to books they read. However, reporters should always be aware that children's disclosures are rarely direct and complete. Often they are tentative and only "hint" at what's going on, such as, "I don't want to go home" or "I don't like my stepdad any more." Many times the child will use this approach to "test the waters" to see how the non-offending family member or adult will react to the disclosure.

The bottom line, however, is that if you seriously suspect abuse or neglect because of the presence of two or more indicators and the absence of an adequate explanation, you have an obligation to report it.

Where Should I Report Suspected Abuse?

If you suspect that a child is victimized, follow any school/district procedures and policies. If you believe that the child is in immediate and serious danger and policies for reporting abuse are not apparent or a response is not evident, contact the police or your county department of human services. The **Childhelp National Child Abuse Hotline at 1-800-A-CHILD** will also provide assistance and help you determine whether abuse has indeed occurred.

The following agencies provide detailed and specific information for dealing with child abuse. To locate each site online, use an Internet search engine to search for the agency's name or visit the **National Clearinghouse on Child Abuse and Neglect Information,** a national resource for those seeking information on the prevention, identification, and treatment of child abuse and neglect.

National Agencies/Organizations

American Professional Society on the Abuse of Children
Provides professional education, publications, and legislative updates to ensure that everyone affected by child maltreatment receives the best possible professional response.

CDC—National Center for Injury Prevention and Control
Defines child maltreatment; cites occurrence and consequences, groups at risk, risk factors, and references.

Child Abuse Prevention Network
Provides tools for professionals to identify, investigate, treat, and prevent all forms of child abuse and neglect.

United States Department of Health and Human Services: Center for Mental Health Services Knowledge Exchange Network
Provides access to searchable databases on child welfare.

State Agencies/Departments

California Institute on Human Services: Child Abuse Training & Technical Assistance Centers
Explains the California Child Abuse Reporting Law, the reporting mandate, responsibilities and protection, and ways to identify evidence of child abuse.

Georgia Department of Human Resources: Child Care and Parent Services Section
The child abuse and neglect statutes for the state of Georgia require mandated reporters to report injuries "inflicted by non-accidental means."

Indiana Family & Social Services Administration: Division of Family & Children Bureau of Child Development
Indiana state statutes define child abuse "acts or omissions" as the standard for reporting child abuse and neglect. The state maintains a hotline for reporting abuse in the state: 800-800-5556.

Minnesota Department of Human Services
Provides information on child abuse and neglect as defined by Minnesota law. To report suspected child abuse or neglect, contact your county social service agency or the police.

Missouri Department of Social Services
The local Division of Family Services office is available to discuss concerns and can advise on whether or not to call the hotline. The DFS maintains a 24-hour hotline at 800-392-3738.

Ohio Department of Job and Family Services: Bureau of Child Care Services
Ohio state statutes define mandatory reporters as those professionals in health care, mental health, social work, and education/child care.

Pennsylvania Department of Public Welfare: Office of Children, Youth, and Families
The Pennsylvania state statutes on child abuse require mandated reporters to report suspected child abuse and neglect as a "recent act or failure to act." The state maintains a hotline for reporting abuse: 877-4PA-KIDS.

South Carolina Department of Health and Human Services: Child Care and Development Services
State statutes define maltreatment as physical or sexual abuse or exploitation, neglect, emotional/mental injury, and abandonment.

Texas Department of Protective and Regulatory Services
Provides information on child protective services and on all aspects of child abuse and neglect as defined by Texas law.

Lesson 1 Defining Sexual Abuse

Objectives: to identify the characteristics of sexual abuse; to have students explain the impact of abuse

Any contact with a child could be considered sexual. It is the intent of the person making the contact that defines the act. The victim knows or can "feel" the difference between hugging and fondling or tender and passionate kissing.

"Good touching," "bad touching," and "secret touching" are three examples that help clarify what is or is not against the law. Any kind of secret touching is against the law.

Good touching is when a child does something he or she is suppose to, like helping a grandparent, and the grandparent then hugs the child. Bad touching is when siblings fight and one child gets injured. Secret touching is any time anyone (man, boy, woman, or girl) wants to touch a child, or wants the child to touch him or her, anywhere that does not seem right to the child or that would be covered with the underclothes or swimming suit of the person being touched.

Lead students in a discussion about good touches, bad touches, and secret touches. Reinforce the idea that the areas covered by the underclothes or bathing suit are the areas that are inappropriate for other people to touch or photograph except in some clinical situations.

Sexual abuse may also include any unwanted conversation or action that is designed to stimulate the abuser. Point out that if someone starts to talk about things that make children uncomfortable or starts to make suggestions that do not seem right, children should leave the place and inform a trusted adult about what happened. If children do not get help from one source, they should continue to seek help until they get it.

You may wish to tell children that if they know or think that they have been sexually abused at any time in their life, they need to tell a trusted adult. Sexual abuse can leave someone with confused and hurtful feelings. The abuse can have a long-lasting negative impact on a person's life. It can also cause suffering among family members. It is important to seek help. Emphasize the three steps toward avoiding sexual abuse: identifying the support network, using refusal skills, and avoiding unsafe situations. These are developed in the following lessons.

Lesson 2 Identifying Your Support Network

Objective: to identify ways to seek assistance from a trusted adult if concerned, abused, or threatened, including how to overcome fear of telling

Discuss the term *trusted adult* with children. Explain that sometimes their parents or guardians may not be nearby when they need help. Such "trusted adults" should be individuals well known to the child and *may* include grandparents, teachers, counselors, nurses, doctors, firefighters, police officers, and neighbors.

Suggest that children think about people who might be able to help them in difficult situations. Have them create a chart with two columns. The first column should have the heading "Family Members, Friends, and Others I Know and Can Trust." The second column should have the heading "Community Members I Can Trust." Instruct children to fill in the first section by writing the names of family members, teachers, and other trusted adults. (Younger children can draw their responses.)

Ask children to work as a group to fill in the second column. Encourage them to name aloud the people they put on the list. After children have listed the members of the support network, ask:

- **What is a support network?** a group of trusted adults who can help you in difficult situations
- **Why is it important to have a support network?** to know that there is someone you can go to if you have a problem; for security
- **What should you do if you go to a member of your support network but don't get help?** Children may have a variety of answers, but emphasize that they should not give up. If children do not say this themselves, tell them, "If one support person can't or won't help, keep asking people until someone does help." You may want to emphasize that feeling safe is a basic right of every person.

Lesson 3 Using Refusal Skills

Objectives: to identify ways to seek assistance if worried, abused, or threatened; to develop and use communication skills to tell others when touching is unwanted

Refusal skills are an important part of staying safe. Discuss the fact that the commnunication skills children can use to say *no* to tobacco, alcohol, and drugs can also be used to combat sexual abuse. Acknowledge that it is more difficult for children to say *no* to an adult or authority figure than to a peer. When refusal skills are directed at adults, not only should the refusal be forceful, but children should remove themselves from the situation as quickly as possible. They should report the situation to a person within their support network as soon as they can. Remind children of these important points to remember:

- **You are a special person. You have the right to feel safe.**
- **No adult, not even a family member, has the right to touch you in ways that make you feel uncomfortable.**
- **When any person asks you to do anything that makes you feel unsafe or uncomfortable, you can say "No!" or "Stop!" loudly and firmly. You do not have to be polite. Get help from a trusted adult.**

Then refer children back to the lessons in the student edition on refusal skills and communication skills. Reread the text, and discuss any of the skills that may be unclear to children. Have them role-play situations in which they are approached by a stranger and asked to go somewhere with him or her. Remind children to refuse the stranger in a firm manner. Then have them make up their own refusal situations to share with the class.

Lesson 4 Avoiding Unsafe Situations

Objective: to recognize and avoid situations that can increase the risk of abuse

Children may think that most child sexual abuse is by strangers. However, relatives and other people who children know well are responsible for more than 80 percent of all abuse that occurs.

To address this misconception, emphasize that no one, including close friends and people in children's families, has the right to touch or relate to children in ways that make them feel uncomfortable. If children find themselves in such a situation, they should leave and tell someone they trust what happened. Stress that there are signs that suggest something is wrong, such as a person's use of threats, bribery, or secrecy.

Reinforce the rules for personal safety by organizing children into groups and holding a "safety bee." Before the safety bee, write on index cards different situations that involve risk. Read each situation to the groups. Ask them to identify the risk and the steps they could take to be safer. Encourage the groups to think about the situation and to check the safety lists they created in Lesson 2 before answering. After two or three rounds, ask them to make up similar situations and write them on index cards. Suggest possible scenarios such as these:

- **When you are alone with your uncle, he talks about things that make you feel uncomfortable.**
- **A family member wants you to go somewhere alone with him or her and insists that you not tell anyone about it.**

Program Organization

Content Areas	Pre-Kindergarten	Kindergarten	Grade 1	Grade 2
Human Body; Growth and Development	**1** Good Health **2** My Body	**1** Growing Inside and Out	**1** You Are Growing	**1** Your Growing Body
Consumer/ Personal Health	**3** Caring for My Skin **4** Staying Clean **5** Caring for My Teeth	**2** Staying Healthy **3** Caring For Your Teeth	**2** Taking Care of Your Body **3** Your Teeth	**2** Caring for Your Body **3** Caring for Your Teeth
Nutrition	**6** Food for Energy **7** Choosing Foods	**4** Food for Health	**4** Wonderful Food	**4** Food for Fitness
Physical Activity and Fitness	**8** Exercise **9** Rest	**5** Being Active	**5** Keeping Active	**5** Keeping Fit and Active
Injury Prevention	**10** Safety at Home **11** Fire Safety **12** Safety Away from Home **13** Safety with Strangers	**6** Home and Travel Safety **7** Safety While Playing	**6** Being Safe **7** Avoiding Danger	**6** Avoiding Danger **7** Staying Safe
Disease Prevention and Control	**14** Staying Well	**8** Staying Well	**8** Staying Well	**8** Staying Well
Drug Use Prevention	**15** Taking Medicine **16** Say No to Drugs	**9** Medicines Help—Drugs Hurt	**9** About Medicines and Drugs	**9** Medicines and Drugs
Emotional, Intellectual, and Social Health	**17** My Feelings **18** Friends	**10** All About Feelings	**10** You Have Feelings	**10** Your Feelings
Family Life	**19** My Family and Me	**11** Family Life	**11** Your Family	**11** Your Family
Community and Environmental Health	**20** My Community	**12** A Healthy Community	**12** A Healthful Neighborhood	**12** Caring for Your Neighborhood

Grade 3	Grade 4	Grade 5	Grade 6
1 Your Amazing Body	**1** Body Systems at Work	**1** A Growing and Changing Body	**1** Growth and Development
2 Taking Care of Yourself	**2** Personal Health	**2** Being a Wise Health Consumer	**2** Personal and Consumer Health
3 Food for a Healthy Body	**3** Food and Your Health	**3** Foods for Good Nutrition	**3** Preparing Healthful Foods
4 Activity for a Healthy Body	**4** Fitness and Activity	**4** Keeping Fit and Active	**4** Keeping Active
5 Keeping Safe **6** Emergency Safety	**5** Safe at Home **6** Safe Away from Home	**5** Planning for Safety **6** Preventing Violence	**5** Staying Safe Every Day **6** Emergencies and First Aid
7 Preventing Disease	**7** Guarding Against Disease	**7** Learning About Disease	**7** Controlling Disease
8 Medicines and Other Drugs **9** Avoiding Tobacco and Alcohol	**8** Medicines, Drugs, and Your Health **9** Harmful Effects of Tobacco and Alcohol	**8** Legal and Illegal Drugs **9** About Tobacco and Alcohol	**8** Drugs and Health **9** Tobacco and Alcohol
10 About Yourself and Others	**10** Your Needs and Feelings	**10** Dealing with Feelings	**10** Setting Goals
11 Your Family and You	**11** Families Together	**11** Supporting Your Family	**11** Family and Responsibility
12 Health in the Community	**12** Living in a Healthful Community	**12** Working Toward a Healthful Community	**12** Community Health

Human Body, Growth, and Development

Grade 3

- Identify the parts and functions of the skeletal, muscular, and nervous systems. (1-1)
- List ways to keep these systems healthy. (1-1)
- Explain the interrelationships of body systems. (1-1)
- Describe the parts and functions of the respiratory and digestive systems. (1-2)
- Identify health behaviors related to keeping these systems healthy. (1-2)
- Explain the interrelationships of body systems. (1-2)
- List and explain the stages of growth and development. (1-3)
- Describe physical and mental changes that occur during the stages of growth. (1-3)
- Identify ways to show respect for adults. (1-BGC)
- Describe how the body changes as one grows. (1-4)
- Understand that individuals grow at different rates. (1-4)
- Identify steps for communicating. (1-LS)
- Use communication skills to express concerns. (1-LS)
- Identify healthful habits. (1-5)
- Identify ways to seek assistance if touched in a manner that hurts or feels uncomfortable. (1-5)

Grade 4

- Explain how inherited and acquired traits make an individual unique. (1-1)
- Describe how the body is organized from cells to body systems. (1-1)
- Compare growth from infancy to adulthood. (1-1)
- Identify steps to manage stress.
- Use stress management skills to deal with stress in a healthful way. (1-LS)
- Explain the functions of the brain and nervous system. (1-2)
- Describe behaviors that keep the nervous system healthy. (1-2)
- Identify ways to show respect for others by accepting individual differences. (1-BGC)
- Identify the parts and functions of the digestive system. (1-3)
- Describe behaviors that keep the digestive system healthy. (1-3)
- Identify the parts and functions of the respiratory and circulatory systems. (1-4)
- Describe healthful behaviors to take care of the respiratory and circulatory systems. (1-4)
- Explain the functions of the skeletal and muscular systems. (1-5)
- Describe behaviors that keep the skeletal and muscular systems healthy. (1-5)

Grade 5

- Identify the basic structure of the human body. (1-1)
- Explain the functions of the body transport organs and systems. (1-1)
- Recognize how personal habits affect the health of body systems. (1-1)
- Identify the three body systems that coordinate body movements. (1-2)
- Explain ways to keep body coordination systems healthy. (1-2)
- Learn about heredity and environmental influences on growth. (1-3)
- Identify major hormones of the endocrine system. (1-3)
- Examine some functions of hormones. (1-3)
- Describe how growth occurs. (1-3)
- Describe the growth stages form the prenatal stage to older adulthood. (1-4)
- Learn about changes that occur during puberty. (1-4)
- Identify ways to build a good reputation by showing trustworthiness. (1-BGC)
- Learn about the physical, mental, and emotional changes accompanying the growth spurt during puberty. (1-5)
- Compare and contrast concrete thinking and abstract thinking. (1-5)
- Explain problem-solving choices to handle problems of adolescence. (1-5)
- Identify the steps for conflict resolution. (1-LS)
- Use the steps to resolve a conflict. (1-LS)
- Explain how exercise and good nutrition help growing bodies. (1-6)
- Describe how sleep, rest, and hygiene affect growth. (1-6)

Grade 6

- Describe the different parts and functions of body systems. (1-1)
- Analyze the relationships among body systems. (1-1)
- Identify healthful behaviors to care for body systems. (1-1)
- Describe major events in human development from fertilization to birth. (1-2)
- Explain how growth occurs. (1-2)
- Describe how traits are inherited. (1-2)
- Demonstrate ways to show respect and consideration to people who are different from you. (1-BGC)
- Describe changes in male and female anatomy and physiology during puberty. (1-3)
- Analyze the role of hormones as they relate to growth and development. (1-3)
- Identify the varying emotions that adolescents experience and ways to deal with them. (1-4)
- Describe how relationships change during adolescence and healthy ways to communicate with family, friends, and others. (1-4)
- Identify effective communication skills. (1-LS)
- Use communication skills to express feelings. (1-LS)
- Analyze healthful and unhealthful behaviors during adolescence. (1-5)
- Explain the importance of regular physical activity. (1-5)

Consumer/Personal Health

Grade 3

- Explain how and why to keep skin clean. (2-1)
- Explain how and why to protect skin and eyes from the sun. (2-1)
- Explain how plaque can lead to cavities and loss of teeth. (2-2)
- Describe and demonstrate how to brush and floss correctly. (2-2)
- Explain how to protect teeth from injury. (2-2)
- Identify ways to show self-respect and respect for others through good grooming. (2-BGC)
- Describe problems that can affect the ears. (2-3)
- Describe how to protect and care for the ears, eyes, and nose. (2-3)
- Identify the importance of information on a health-care product label. (2-4)
- Explain how to choose a health-care product wisely. (2-4)
- Identify the steps for goal setting. (2-LS)
- Use the goal-setting steps to make a healthful choice when buying a health-care product. (2-LS)
- Identify the ways ads get your attention and persuade you to buy products. (2-5)
- Explain where to get good information about health-care products. (2-5)

Grade 4

- Describe the function and structure of skin. Explain how to take care of skin, including the use of sunscreen. (2-1)
- Demonstrate the ability to identify personal health needs. (2-1)
- Describe tooth and gum problems and explain how to prevent them. (2-2)
- Describe and demonstrate how to brush and floss correctly. (2-2)
- Identify and explain the causes of common vision and hearing problems. (2-3)
- Describe and demonstrate how to take good care of eyes and ears. (2-3)
- Identify communication skills. (2-LS)
- Use communication skills to make one's health needs known. (2-LS)
- Describe how advertisements can be analyzed to choose products that best meet your needs. (2-4)
- Explain how the usefulness and value of health products and services can be determined by comparison. (2-4)
- Explain the importance of refusal skills that are helpful in resisting negative peer pressure and media influences. (2-4)
- Recognize the importance of trustworthiness and truthfulness with family members about personal care. (2-BGC)
- Identify factual sources, including media and technology, for obtaining health information. (2-5)
- Describe a variety of ways to convey accurate health information and ideas. (2-5)

Grade 5

- Explain why it's important to keep your skin, hair, and nails healthy. (2-1)
- Explain how changes in hormone levels can affect personal health habits. (2-1)
- Identify ways to develop self-confidence. (2-BGC)
- Identify the structure and function of teeth. (2-2)
- Explain how to keep teeth and gums healthy. (2-2)
- Identify dental problems. (2-2)
- Identify parts of the eye and the ear and explain how the parts of each function. (2-3)
- Describe how to take good care of your eyes and ears. (2-3)
- Identify steps to communicate. (2-LS)
- Use the communicating steps to solve problems. (2-LS)
- Explain the importance of choosing health-care products wisely. (2-4)
- Identify and evaluate sources of health information. (2-4)
- Demonstrate how to use labels to make wise product choices. (2-4)

Grade 6

- Describe the structure of the skin. (2-1)
- Explain how to take good care of skin, hair, and nails. (2-1)
- Describe the importance of protection from the sun. (2-1)
- Identify the importance of making wise choices for hair and skin products. (2-2)
- Describe and demonstrate how to use labels to make wise product decisions. (2-2)
- Identify steps for making decisions. (2-LS)
- Use the decision-making steps to make choices about health-care products. (2-LS)
- Identify the importance of caring for teeth and gums. (2-3)
- Describe and demonstrate ways to prevent tooth decay and gum disease. (2-3)
- Describe the structure and function of the eyes and ears. (2-4)
- Explain how and why to take good care of the eyes and ears. (2-4)
- Recognize the importance of fairness by not taking advantage of others. (2-BGC)
- Describe the importance of correct body position for computer use. (2-5)
- Identify ways to avoid injuries when using technology products. (2-5)
- Identify sources of reliable health information. (2-6)
- Determine criteria for evaluating health websites. (2-6)

Nutrition

Grade 3

- Identify food sources. (3-1)
- Identify food sources of nutrients. (3-1)
- Identify types of nutrients. (3-1)
- Explain how food choices affect health. (3-1)
- Explain strategies for making a personal health plan as a commitment to a healthful diet. (3-2)
- Describe food combinations in a balanced diet, such as that set out in the USDA Food Guide Pyramid. (3-2)
- Learn how to make decisions affecting health by choosing healthful foods and snacks guided by the USDA Food Guide Pyramid. (3-3)
- Identify ways to show responsibility in making health decisions about lunch. (3-BGC)
- Learn how to make wise choices when shopping for food. (3-4)
- Gather data to make informed health choices. (3-4)
- Identify and practice steps to make responsible decisions about healthful food choices. (3-LS)
- Learn how to handle and store foods to keep them safe to eat. (3-5)

Grade 4

- Identify the six major nutrients, their sources, and their functions in the body. (3-1)
- Explain why mealtimes are important. (3-1)
- Identify ways to show self-respect and respect for others during meals. (3-BGC)
- Identify the food groups and explain why they are important. (3-2)
- Explain what a balanced diet is and why it is important. (3-2)
- Use nutrition information from a food guide pyramid to make healthful food choices. (3-3)
- Demonstrate healthful eating practices by making healthful food choices. (3-3)
- Identify the steps for decision-making. (3-LS)
- Use the decision-making steps to make healthful food choices. (3-LS)
- Learn how to make wise choices when shopping for food. (3-4)
- Gather data to make informed health choices. (3-4)
- Learn how to read and compare food labels. (3-4)
- Describe how food poisoning occurs. (3-5)
- Explain how to handle food safely to prevent food poisoning. (3-5)

Grade 5

- Identify the six basic nutrients. (3-1)
- Describe how the basic nutrients give the body energy. (3-1)
- Explain how to use the USDA Food Guide Pyramid to help plan a balanced diet. (3-2)
- Identify the food groups used in the USDA Food Guide Pyramid. (3-2)
- Understand the size of a serving. (3-2)
- Understand the importance of portion control when deciding on the number and size of servings. (3-3)
- Describe the importance between calories and energy balance. (3-3)
- Explain how family, friends, and culture affect food choices. (3-4)
- Explain how health, the seasons, emotions, and knowledge about foods may affect food choices. (3-4)
- Learn how practicing self-control helps you choose healthful foods. (3-BGC)
- Explain how to use food labels to evaluate the nutrition of foods. (3-5)
- Describe the influences of advertising on food choices. (3-5)
- Identify decision-making steps. (3-LS)
- Use decision-making steps to make healthful food choices. (3-LS)
- Explain how germs get into food and what they do to it. (3-6)
- Describe how to store and prepare food safely. (3-6)

Grade 6

- Identify six types of nutrients important to health. (3-1)
- Describe the role of each type of nutrient in the body. (3-1)
- Explain how the Food Guide Pyramid helps people obtain a balanced diet. (3-2)
- Describe a healthful vegetarian diet. (3-2)
- Identify healthful foods from Mexico, Asia, and the Mediterranean. (3-3)
- Explain how foods from different parts of the world can provide a healthful and balanced diet. (3-3)
- Recognize that good health depends on making food choices that satisfy nutritional needs. (3-4)
- Identify the steps for making responsible food choices. (3-BGC)
- Explain the importance of making healthful food choices. (3-5)
- Explain how to select healthful foods in supermarkets and restaurants. (3-5)
- Identify steps for decision making.
- Use the decision-making steps to make healthful food choices. (3-LS)
- Describe how to store and prepare foods safely. (3-6)
- Identify spices used to enhance food flavors. (3-6)

Physical Activity and Fitness

Grade 3	Grade 4	Grade 5	Grade 6
• Understand how to improve fitness. (4-1) • Understand how exercise increases strength, flexibility, and endurance. (4-1) • Understand the importance of fitness for overall wellness. (4-1) • Identify ways to show fairness to others during sports and games. (4-BGC) • Describe how to take personal responsibility for preventing injury. (4-2) • Explain the need for obeying safety rules at home, school, work, and play. (4-2) • Identify the steps for decision-making. (4-LS) • Use the decision-making steps to make safe choices. (4-LS) • Describe the importance of taking personal responsibility for preventing accidental injuries. (4-LS) • Explain individual needs for relaxation and sleep. (4-3) • Demonstrate the ability to set a personal health goal. (4-3)	• Describe how good posture can improve wellness and self-image. (4-1) • Demonstrate good posture while sitting, standing, and moving. (4-1) • Recognize the importance of fairness by being a good listener. (4-BGC) • Explain the benefits of regular physical activity. (4-2) • Describe the differences between aerobic and anaerobic exercise. (4-2) • Describe the importance of sleep and rest to overall fitness and a proper balance of sleep, rest, and activity. (4-2) • Identify goal-setting steps. (4-LS) • Practice goal setting for fitness. (4-LS) • Describe how to use the Activity Pyramid to improve physical fitness. (4-3) • Describe the importance of developing a personal health plan for fitness. (4-3) • Identify safety gear necessary for injury prevention. (4-3)	• List three reasons sleep, food choices, and physical activity are important to a healthful lifestyle. (4-1) • Define *physical activity*, and give examples of its benefits and barriers. (4-1) • Identify ways to demonstrate fairness during a competitive game. (4-BGC) • List three ways exercise helps the respiratory and circulatory systems. (4-2) • Apply the Activity Pyramid when planning physical activities. (4-2) • Identify the four steps in goal setting. (4-LS) • Apply the goal-setting model to set up plans for a healthful lifestyle. (4-LS) • List the three issues that should be addressed to exercise safely. (4-3) • List three kinds of exercise and give an example of each. (4-3)	• Examine the components of physical fitness. (4-1) • Comprehend concepts related to health promotion and disease prevention. (4-1) • Learn how to use the Activity Pyramid to improve physical fitness. (4-1) • Understand the importance of good posture. (4-1) • Identify goal-setting steps. (4-LS) • Practice goal setting for fitness. (4-LS) • Describe the importance of different types of exercise. (4-2) • Develop a personal exercise and fitness program. (4-2) • Recognize the importance of respect by being a good sport. (4-BGC) • Describe safety rules and how to play and exercise safely. (4-3) • Identify safety equipment necessary for injury prevention. (4-3)

Injury Prevention

Grade 3	Grade 4	Grade 5	Grade 6
• Explain why obeying safety rules at school and around vehicles is important. (5-1) • Describe the importance of taking personal responsibility for reducing hazards and avoiding unsafe situations. (5-1) • Recognize the importance of responsibility for one's own safety at school. (5-BGC) • Describe how to stay safe around strangers, bullies, and weapons. (5-2) • Explain how to ask for help from a trusted adult when needed. (5-2) • Identify steps to resolve conflicts. (5-LS) • Use negotiation to handle conflicts with friends. (5-LS) • Explain how to prevent injuries when participating in activities such as bicycling, skating, skateboarding, or scootering. (5-3) • Describe how to be safe around vehicles. (5-3) • Make a home fire escape plan. (6-1) • List safety rules for preventing poisoning. (6-1) • Explain the need for obeying safety rules. (6-BGC) • List safety rules for using electricity and household products. (6-2) • Identify kitchen safety rules. (6-2) • Describe first aid for cuts, insect stings, and choking. (6-2) • Use communication skills to get help in an emergency. (6-LS) • Identify safety rules in case of disasters. (6-3) • Recognize emergencies and practice appropriate behaviors. (6-3)	• Recognize an emergency and know how to respond. (5-1) • Explain how to develop a family emergency plan. (5-1) • Describe ways to demonstrate good citizenship during an emergency or practice drill. (5-BGC) • Identify strategies for preventing injuries in the home. (5-2) • Develop a fire safety plan. (5-2) • Identify the steps for decision-making. (5-LS) • Use the decision-making steps to staying safe. (5-LS) • Identify safety rules for swimming, diving, and boating. (5-3) • Describe how to respond to a water emergency. (5-3) • Identify strategies for avoiding injuries when camping and hiking, and during cold and hot weather. (6-1) • Describe appropriate responses during weather emergencies. (6-1) • Describe ways to show responsibility during outdoor activities by being a positive role model. (6-BGC) • Identify personal behaviors to prevent injuries when skating, skateboarding, biking, and riding in a motor vehicle. (6-2) • Discuss the use of safety gear and equipment to avoid injuries when traveling. (6-2) • Identify steps for resolving conflicts. (6-LS) • Apply conflict-resolution skills to handle conflicts with friends. (6-LS) • Identify strategies for avoiding deliberate injuries. (6-3) • Develop and use skills to avoid, resolve, and cope with conflicts. (6-3)	• Recognize and reduce the hazards that lead to unexpected injuries. (5-1) • Explain how to respond to emergency situations. (5-1) • Practice first aid for injuries. (5-1) • Identify steps for making responsible decisions. (5-LS) • Use the decision-making steps to make healthful decisions about safety. (5-LS) • Practice safety at play and in motor vehicles. (5-2) • Analyze safety equipment. (5-2) • Identify ways to show compassion for injured persons. (5-BGC) • Explain how to prevent home fires. (5-3) • Recognize fire hazards in the home. (5-3) • Describe how to survive a home fire. (5-3) • Identify acts of violence. (6-1) • Describe ways to avoid violence. (6-1) • Describe effective listening skills used in being fair. (6-BGC) • Explain strategies for avoiding violence, gangs, and weapons. (6-2) • Identify alternatives to joining a gang. (6-2) • Identify skills used to resolve conflicts. (6-LS) • Apply skills to resolve conflicts before conflicts become violent. (6-LS) • Demonstrate strategies for avoiding violence on the street and at school. (6-3) • Describe safe ways to respond to a terrorist attack. (6-3)	• Describe the potential hazards in and around the home and how to prevent injury from them. (5-1) • Identify safety concerns in the kitchen. (5-1) • Identify common household hazards. (5-2) • Explain safe baby-sitting practices. (5-2) • Recognize the importance of fairness by playing by the rules. (5-BGC) • Explain swimming and boating safety rules. (5-3) • Describe how to respond to a water emergency. (5-3) • Identify steps for conflict resolution. (5-LS) • Use conflict resolution to resolve conflicts that could lead to violence. (5-LS) • Describe the danger of gangs and how to avoid conflicts with them. (5-4) • Identify ways to stay safe in violent situations. (5-4) • Explain how the media affect violent behavior. (5-4) • Explain how to prepare for emergency situations. (6-1) • Describe how to respond to emergency situations in order to reduce risks. (6-1) • Identify steps for effective communication. (6-LS) • Practice communication skills for handling emergencies. (6-LS) • Describe first-aid treatment for common injuries. (6-2) • Identify ways to show responsibility when responding to an emergency situation. (6-BGC) • Identify life-threatening injuries. (6-3) • Describe first aid for medical emergencies. (6-3)

Disease Prevention and Control

Grade 3	Grade 4	Grade 5	Grade 6
• Recognize symptoms of common illnesses. (7-1) • Identify health behaviors that prevent the spread of disease. (7-1) • Explain what a disability is and discuss how to treat a person with a disability. (7-1) • Identify some pathogens that cause some communicable diseases. (7-2) • Identify health behaviors that prevent the spread of disease and behaviors that cause the transmission of disease. (7-2) • Explain some of the body's defense systems in preventing and fighting disease. (7-3) • Identify health behaviors that prevent the spread of disease. (7-3) • Communicate with parents about health problems. (7-3) • Identify and share feelings in appropriate ways. (7-LS) • Practice ways to reduce stress. (7-LS) • Demonstrate the ability to locate health information from parents and family members, the school, and the community. (7-4) • Explain actions to take when illness occurs, such as informing parents or other trusted adults. (7-4) • Apply concepts to show concern for people who are hurt or ill. (7-BGC) • Identify healthful food choices. (7-5) • Explore activities that promote fitness and health. (7-5) • Describe the harmful effects of tobacco on health and explain why people should abstain. (7-5)	• Understand what disease is, and how it affects the body. (7-1) • Distinguish between communicable and noncommunicable diseases. (7-1) • Learn to be more caring by identifying ways to help those who are ill. (7-BGC) • Understand that diseases are caused by pathogens. (7-2) • Distinguish among viruses, bacteria, and fungi as different types of pathogens. (7-2) • Identify ways that pathogens can be spread. (7-2) • Describe the immune system's function as a defense against pathogens. (7-3) • Identify ways of helping the body defend itself against disease. (7-3) • Learn to identify situations that are stressful. (7-LS) • Use the steps to manage stress to help lead a more healthful life. (7-LS) • Identify noncommunicable diseases and their symptoms. (7-4) • Understand how noncommunicable diseases can be managed. (7-4) • Identify healthful lifestyle choices that help prevent illness. (7-5) • Understand how resistance, managing stress, and abstinence from tobacco help prevent disease. (7-5)	• Identify the two types of disease. (7-1) • Explain how lifestyle choices affect the risk of contracting some diseases. (7-1) • Develop respect for people with disabilities. (7-1) • Identify four kinds of pathogens that can cause communicable diseases. (7-2) • Learn how to protect yourself form these pathogens. (7-2) • Understand how the body defends itself form disease by blocking and destroying pathogens. (7-3) • Understand how vaccines and antibiotics can fight disease. (7-3) • Understand the importance of seeking treatment from health-care professionals. (7-4) • Learn the role and importance of immunizations. (7-4) • Identify steps to manage stress. (7-LS) • Practice steps to manage stress to keep your body healthy. (7-LS) • Identify the causes and symptoms of noncommunicable diseases. (7-5) • Understand the difference between chronic and acute diseases. (7-5) • Learn how to take responsibility for your own health. (7-BGC) • Learn how to make healthful choices to reduce your risk of disease. (7-6) • Understand the importance of eating well, exercising, and avoiding tobbaco. (7-6)	• Describe three types of health risk factors. (7-1) • Give examples of behaviors that promote health and prevent disease. (7-1) • Demonstrate ways to communicate with and have consideration for others. (7-1) • List steps for managing stress. (7-LS) • Apply steps for managing stress to promote health and prevent disease. (7-LS) • Distinguish among bacteria, viruses, fungi, and protozoa. (7-2) • Describe various modes of disease transmission. (7-2) • Explain the benefits of abstinence in sexual activity to prevent STDs. (7-2) • Identify the body's defenses against disease. (7-3) • Explain how you can develop immunity to a disease. (7-3) • Assess the role of antibiotics in fighting disease. (7-3) • Classify diseases as communicable or noncommunicable. (7-4) • Compare healthy cell growth to cell growth in the disease process. (7-4) • List noncommunicable diseases and prevention and treatment techniques. (7-4) • Demonstrate care and concern toward ill persons in the family, the school, and the community. (7-BGC) • Describe how to prevent the spread of communicable disease. (7-5) • Explain how practicing positive health behaviors can reduce the risk of disease. (7-5) • Describe the impact of tobacco use on personal health. (7-5)

Drug Use Prevention

Grade 3

- Explain what drugs are. (8-1)
- Distinguish between drugs that help the body and drugs that harm the body. (8-1)
- Distinguish between over-the-counter and prescription medicines. (8-1)
- Explain what caffeine is and what it does to the body. (8-1)
- Understand that medicines can be helpful only when used correctly. (8-2)
- Know rules for using medicines safely. (8-2)
- Recognize the importance of trustworthiness when reporting dangerous situations. (8-BGC)
- List the dangerous physical effects of using inhalants, marijuana, or cocaine, and tell why these drugs should be avoided. (8-3)
- Describe how to avoid breathing inhalants. (8-3)
- Identify refusal skills. (8-LS)
- Use refusal skills to say *no* to drug use. (8-LS)
- Emphasize the importance of saying *no* to drugs. (8-4)
- Learn various ways to say *no* to drugs. (8-4)
- Identify people who can help you refuse drugs. (8-4)
- Identify the effects of tobacco on the body. (9-1)
- Describe the hazards of environmental tobacco smoke. (9-1)
- Identify ways to be trustworthy in situations concerning tobacco and alcohol. (9-BGC)
- Describe some effects of alcohol on the body and on behavior. (9-2)
- Identify safety risks associated with alcohol use. (9-2)

Grade 4

- Recognize that medicines are drugs that help the body. (8-1)
- Distinguish between prescription and over-the-counter medicines. (8-1)
- Recognize that medicines are drugs that help the body. (8-2)
- Distinguish between prescription and over-the-counter medicines. (8-2)
- Identify skills needed to refuse OTC medicines. (8-LS)
- Use refusal skills to say *no* to over-the-counter medicines. (8-LS)
- Recognize the dangerous effects of marijuana and cocaine. (8-3)
- Recognize that cocaine use can lead to immediate addiction. (8-3)
- Demonstrate responsibility by recognizing the importance of practicing self-control. (8-BGC)
- Explain why saying *no* to drugs is a healthful decision. (8-4)
- Demonstrate how to say *no* to illegal drugs. (8-4)
- Recognize the warning signs of drug use. (8-5)
- Identify people and organizations that can help with drug recovery. (8-5)
- Describe tobacco products and the harm they cause to the body. (9-1)
- Explain why some young people begin smoking and why stopping is difficult. (9-1)
- Describe alcohol and the harm it causes to body systems and behavior. (9-2)
- Identify some effects of problem drinking. (9-2)

Grade 5

- Recognize the warning signs of drug use. (8-1)
- Identify people and organizations that can help with drug recovery. (8-1)
- Discuss how to use medicines safely. (8-2)
- Interpret a medicine label. (8-2)
- Distinguish between medicine misuse and medicine abuse. (8-2)
- Explain how the use of illegal drugs can harm the body. (8-3)
- Describe crack and cocaine and analyze their short-term and long-term effects on the body. (8-3)
- Describe marijuana and inhalants and analyze their short-term and long-term effects on the body. (8-3)
- Identify ways to be trustworthy about not using drugs. (8-BGC)
- Describe the negative consequences of illegal drug use. (8-4)
- Analyze how illegal drug use can interfere with activities and goals. (8-4)
- Explain strategies for saying *no* to illegal drug use. (8-4)
- Identify refusal skills. (8-LS)
- Use refusal skills to stay drug-free. (8-LS)
- Recognize when someone needs help refusing or getting off drugs. (8-5)
- Describe methods for getting help about illegal drug use. (8-5)
- Name three harmful substances in tobacco smoke. (9-1)
- Describe the harmful effects of tobacco use on parts of the body. (9-1)

Grade 6

- Explain that medicines are drugs that can help you stay healthy when used safely and properly. (8-1)
- Distinguish between prescription and over-the-counter medicines. (8-1)
- Analyze the choices and consequences related to the abuse of drugs. (8-2)
- Describe drug dependency and addiction, and relate the impact of these on a person's ability to achieve goals. (8-2)
- Describe the impact of risky behaviors on personal and family health. (8-2)
- Recognize that following laws about drug use is central to good citizenship. (8-BGC)
- Analyze the use and abuse of prescription and nonprescription drugs. (8-3)
- Identify the choices and consequences related to the abuse of stimulants and depressants. (8-3)
- Describe the harmful effects of steroid use. (8-3)
- Describe the dangers of using marijuana, illegal narcotics, inhalants, cocaine, crack, and hallucinogens. (8-4)
- Identify steps for refusing. (8-LS)
- Use refusal steps to say *no* to drug use. (8-LS)
- Describe the immediate and long-term effects of using drugs. (8-5)
- Identify strategies you can use for avoiding drugs. (8-5)
- Name three harmful substances in tobacco smoke. (9-1)
- Identify parts of the body that are affected by tobacco use. (9-1)

Drug Use Prevention (continued)

Grade 3

- Identify skills needed to refuse. (9-LS)
- Use refusal skills to say *no* to alcohol and tobacco. (9-LS)
- Explain reasons for refusing alcohol and tobacco and demonstrate ways to refuse alcohol and tobacco. (9-3)
- Describe laws regarding the use and packaging of alcohol and tobacco products. (9-3)

Grade 4

- Demonstrate strategies for refusing the use of alcohol and tobacco. (9-3)
- Discuss ways to resist peer pressure to use alcohol and tobacco. (9-3)
- Identify ways to say *no.* (9-LS)
- Practice ways to refuse alcohol and tobacco. (9-LS)
- List warning signs of alcohol and tobacco use. (9-4)
- Name sources of help for alcohol or tobacco users. (9-4)
- Identify ways to show trustworthiness by reporting dangerous situations. (9-BGC)

Grade 5

- Identify reasons people use tobacco. (9-1)
- Explain what blood alcohol level is and what it measures. (9-2)
- Describe how alcohol affects health, abilities, and body functions. (9-2)
- Explain what alcoholism is and who might suffer from it. (9-2)
- Identify ways to be a good citizen by showing respect for authority. (9-BGC)
- List reasons for choosing not to use alcohol or tobacco. (9-3)
- Develop strategies for dealing with peer pressure. (9-3)
- Analyze advertisements for alcohol and tobacco products. (9-3)
- Identify ways to say *no.* (9-LS)
- Use refusal skills to say *no* to alcohol and tobacco. (9-LS)
- Identify the warning signs of a problem with alcohol. (9-4)
- Explain why people who are addicted to alcohol or tobacco need help to stop using these drugs. (9-4)
- Identify sources of support available to people who want to stop using alcohol or tobacco. (9-4)

Grade 6

- Describe the effects of tobacco use on parts of the body. (9-1)
- Define environmental tobacco smoke (ETS).
- List three dangers of using smokeless tobacco. (9-2)
- Explain why it is difficult for an addicted person to stop using tobacco. (9-2)
- Identify ways to be trustworthy when talking about problems. (9-BGC)
- Describe the effects of alcohol on a person who drinks it. (9-3)
- Explain blood alcohol level (BAL) and its relation to the amount of alcohol a person drinks. (9-3)
- List four ways that drinking alcohol can affect a person's safety. (9-3)
- Describe the effects of peer pressure. (9-4)
- Analyze advertisements for tobacco and alcohol products. (9-4)
- Practice strategies for refusing offers of alcohol or tobacco products. (9-4)
- Identify ways of refusing. (9-LS)
- Apply refusal strategies to situations in which alcohol or tobacco are offered. (9-LS)
- Identify places where a person with alcoholism can get help. (9-5)
- Identify people who could help a young person with an alcohol problem. (9-5)
- Describe three kinds of recovery programs. (9-5)

Emotional, Intellectual, and Social Health

Grade 3

- Understand that each person is unique and worthwhile. (10-1)
- Recognize the importance of respecting and taking care of oneself. (10-1)
- Learn ways to control uncomfortable feelings and express them in healthy, responsible ways. (10-1)
- Identify effective strategies for coping with fear, stress, anger, and grief. (10-2)
- Know when to seek help with these emotions from a parent or other trusted adult. (10-2)
- Identify ways to manage stress. (10-LS)
- Apply stress-management skills to situations at school. (10-LS)
- Describe ways to have healthful relationships with family members and friends. (10-3)
- Understand the difference between positive and negative peer pressure and know how to stand up to peer pressure that is not helpful or positive. (10-3)

Grade 4

- Identify personality traits, and differentiate between those that can and cannot be changed. (10-1)
- Describe how a good attitude and a positive self-concept contribute to self-confidence and high self-esteem. (10-1)
- Identify the four basic physical needs. (10-2)
- Identify examples of basic emotional, mental, and social needs. (10-2)
- Recognize how setting goals helps people meet their needs. (10-2)
- Recognize the importance of expressing feelings in safe ways. (10-3)
- Learn to identify feelings such as grief, stress, and anger. (10-3)
- List and apply effective steps for anger management. (10-3)
- Describe self-control strategies for expressing feelings. (10-3)
- Recognize shared interests, goals, and values as factors in friendship. (10-4)
- Identify and practice effective strategies for resolving conflicts by using negotiation and compromise. (10-4)
- Describe characteristics needed to be a responsible friend and family member. (10-4)

Grade 5

- Recognize that each person shapes his or her own self-concept. (10-1)
- Realize that a positive self-concept helps a person make healthful decisions. (10-1)
- Distinguish between needs and wants. (10-2)
- Identify practical strategies for setting and achieving short-term and long-term goals. (10-2)
- Identify sources of help in setting and working toward goals. (10-2)
- Identify strategies for making and keeping friends. (10-3)
- Explain how to deal with peer pressure. (10-3)
- Practice communication skills. (10-3)
- Distinguish between healthy and unhealthy relationships. (10-3)
- Recognize the importance of respecting individual differences, including speech problems. (10-BGC)
- Identify three ways in which people communicate their feelings. (10-4)
- Explain and practice effective strategies for stress management. (10-4)

Grade 6

- Identify elements that contribute to a strong self-concept. (10-1)
- Explain the importance of being aware of personal strengths and weaknesses. (10-1)
- Explain the differences between long-term goals and short-term goals. (10-2)
- Identify steps for setting goals. (10-2)
- Explain how having goals can help you make wise decisions. (10-2)
- Explain the meaning and importance of self-control. (10-3)
- Describe strategies for coping with anger, stress, and grief. (10-3)
- Know when to ask for help in dealing with unpleasant feelings. (10-3)
- Identify ways to manage stress. (10-LS)
- Apply stress management skills to situations at school. (10-LS)
- Recognize that lasting friendships depend on shared interests and values. (10-4)
- Understand the positive and negative aspects of peer pressure. (10-4)

Emotional, Intellectual, and Social Health (continued)

Grade 3	Grade 4	Grade 5	Grade 6
• Know how to resolve conflicts in a way that everyone involved can accept. (10-3) • Recognize how to be a good friend by caring. (10-BGC) • Understand that effective communication includes both speaking and listening. (10-4) • Recognizing the importance of being kind, apologizing, and forgiving others for their mistakes. (10-4)	• Identify skills to resolve conflicts. (10-LS) • Apply conflict resolution skills to conflicts at school. (10-LS) • Explain the steps in conflict resolution. (10-LS) • Explain the importance of respecting differences in people. (10-5) • Describe how people can work together to help others. (10-5) • Learn ways to make a difference as a role model. (10-5) • Recognize the importance of caring by being a good friend. (10-BGC) • Describe the qualities of a good friend. (10-BGC) • Describe how peer pressure works and how you can effectively respond to it. (10-6) • Explain how a strong self-concept can help you avoid the influences of negative peer pressure. (10-6) • Demonstrate refusal and negotiation skills to enhance health. (10-6)	• Identify steps to cope with and manage stress. (10-LS) • Use the stress management skills to deal with stress. (10-LS) • Learn effective strategies for resolving conflicts. (10-5) • Explain the importance of respecting differences. (10-5) • Analyze respectful ways of communicating with others. (10-5) • Define boredom, anger, loneliness, grief, and shyness, and identify possible sources of these feelings. (10-6) • Learn effective strategies for coping with uncomfortable feelings. (10-6)	• Recognize the importance of trustworthiness by being a dependable friend. (10-BGC) • Describe skills that people can use to work collaboratively. (10-5) • Analyze ways students can make a difference in their communities. (10-5) • Emphasize the role of brainstorming in mediation and conflict resolution. (10-6) • Summarize how to resolve a conflict in a way that all parties can accept. (10-6)

Family Life

Grade 3	Grade 4	Grade 5	Grade 6
• Describe different kinds of families and the basic needs that families have and try to meet. (11-1) • Describe ways family members can work and play together. (11-1) • Describe respectful communication among family members. (11-1) • Recognize the importance of fairness by not taking advantage of others. (11-BGC) • Describe some major changes that can affect family members. (11-2) • Describe strategies for coping with changes in the family. (11-2) • Use "I" messages to communicate feelings. (11-LS) • Use listening and negotiating skills to help resolve conflicts. (11-LS) • Identify strategies for resolving conflicts. (11-LS) • Define roles and responsibilities in the context of a family. (11-3) • Name ways family members can help each other when changes occur. (11-3)	• Describe the different types of families children live in. (11-1) • Identify the roles of family members. (11-1) • Explain how and why family members' roles change. (11-1) • Define and describe extended families. (11-1) • Recognize the importance of fairness in the family and in life. (11-BGC) • Explain why family members get along well when they communicate. (11-2) • Describe the many different ways to communicate with family members. (11-2) • Explain how communicating with your family helps you resist peer pressure. (11-2) • Identify steps for good communication. (11-LS) • Practice solving communication problems. (11-LS) • Identify the values learned from the family and how they are taught. (11-3) • Explain why cooperation is important in families. (11-3) • Describe some family rules, and explain why they are important. (11-3)	• Identify some kinds of changes that families experience. (11-1) • Describe how children's responsibilities change as they mature. (11-1) • Recognize the importance of caring by supporting and forgiving family members. (11-BGC) • Describe ways to communicate effectively with family members. (11-2) • Identify causes of conflicts in the family and ways to resolve them. (11-2) • Explain what to do if something bad happens in the family. (11-2) • Identify the steps used to communicate effectively. (11-LS) • Use communication to solve problems. (11-LS) • Explain why the family should be the focal point for seeking health advice and promoting good health. (11-3) • Recognize the importance of developing a family health plan. (11-3)	• Identify the skills of a responsible family member. (11-1) • Identify the skill of self-discipline. (11-1) • Identify and practice caring behaviors with family members. (11-BGC) • Recognize the importance of communication, cooperation, and compromise in a family. (11-2) • Identify strategies for resolving conflicts. (11-2) • Identify and practice strategies for resolving conflicts. (11-LS) • Identify some changes that affect families. (11-3) • Describe ways in which family members might respond to changes. (11-3) • Identify times a family may need help form someone. (11-3)

Community and Environmental Health

Grade 3	Grade 4	Grade 5	Grade 6
• Identify the various places and people one can go to for health care. (12-1) • Distinguish between different healthcare facilities. (12-1) • Define and identify pollution, noise pollution, and air pollution. (12-2) • Describe how to protect yourself and the environment from pollution. (12-2) • Identify ways to build citizenship by taking pride in your school. (12-BGC) • Identify sources of water pollution. (12-3) • Describe the steps in the treatment of sewage. (12-3) • Identify ways that individuals can prevent water pollution. (12-3) • Identify ways to improve the community environment. (12-LS) • Use the steps for setting goals to successfully complete a community improvement project. (12-LS) • Describe how littering affects the environment and the community. (12-4) • Explain how to protect the environment by reducing, reusing, and recycling. (12-4)	• Identify clean air, land, and water as parts of a healthful environment. (12-1) • Analyze factors that influence individual, family, and community health. (12-1) • Describe healthful recreational activities. (12-1) • Identify ways in which community workers promote healthful environments. (12-2) • Identify a variety of community workers and their roles in promoting a healthful community. (12-2) • Describe the jobs of emergency medical technicians and dispatchers. (12-2) • Learn to be part of a community. (12-BGC) • Keep your environment clean and safe. (12-BGC) • Define and identify natural resources as renewable or nonrenewable. (12-3) • Identify ways that people use natural resources. (12-3) • Explain how fossil fuels are used. (12-3) • Identify sources of air, water, and land pollution, and explain how these types of pollution affect human health. (12-4) • Identify several ways to prevent air, water, and land pollution. (12-4) • Identify strategies to set goals. (12-LS) • Practice setting goals to conserve resources. (12-LS) • Define conservation. (12-5) • Describe ways to conserve water, air, land, and other resources. (12-5)	• Identify programs that promote community health. (12-1) • Identify private groups as sources of health information. (12-1) • Find our about roles of the World Health Organization and local health agencies in disease prevention. (12-1) • Explain the role of health agencies involved in community health. (12-2) • Identify sources of assistance in the event of an emergency. (12-3) • List some causes of forest fires and explosions. (12-3) • Demonstrate ways to help support positive family interactions. (12-3) • Participate in community efforts to address local issues. (12-BGC) • Identify environmental factor that affect community health. (12-4) • Analyze how environmental and personal health are related. (12-4) • Identify environmental protection programs that promote community health, such as recycling and waste disposal. (12-4) • Describe how a safe school leads to a healthful community. (12-LS) • Identify ways in which communication skills enhance goal achievement. (12-LS) • Identify methods of accessing valid health information. (12-5) • Cite ways of knowing if health information, products, and services are valid and reliable. (12-5) • Identify programs that promote community health through consumer protection. (12-5)	• Describe natural disasters and their effects. (12-1) • Identify groups and agencies that respond to natural disasters. (12-1) • Describe response procedures to natural disasters. (12-1) • Identify ways to prepare for emergencies such as earthquakes and severe weather. (12-2) • Learn how to prepare a disaster kit. (12-2) • Identify agencies that are responsible for food safety. (12-3) • Understand the procedures that ensure water quality. (12-3) • Understand how solid wastes are disposed of and can be used to enhance a community. (12-3) • Identify and describe energy resources. (12-4) • Identify water resources and their uses. (12-4) • Understand how to conserve energy and water resources and why conservation is important. (12-4) • Identify ways to maintain or improve a healthful school environment. (12-BGC) • Describe the effects of air pollution on human health. (12-5) • Identify the effects of acid rain, water pollution, and toxic wastes. (12-5) • Use strategies for setting goals to solve environmental problems. (12-LS) • Identify and give example of the Three R's. (12-6) • Identify the causes of noise pollution. (12-6) • Understand what you can do to protect the environment. (12-6)

Using *Harcourt Health and Fitness* with *Collections* and *Trophies*

Harcourt Health and Fitness Chapter	Reading Skill	
	***Collections*, Grade 4 (A Harcourt Reading Program)**	***Trophies*, Grade 4 (A Harcourt Reading Program)**
1 Body Systems at Work	**Sequencing**	
	The Seven Children, T273, T278, T280, T287, *Nights of the Pufflings,* T358, *The Cricket in Times Square,* T608, *Blue Willow,* T1114, T1120, T1129, *I Have Heard of a Land,* T1228, *Two Lands, One Heart,* T1310	*Lou Gehrig,* 102J, 109, 113, *Nights of the Pufflings,* 206I, 210, 212, 214, 228-229, *How to Babysit an Orangutan,* 252I, 258, 260, 270-271, *Look to the North,* 372I, 380, 384, 396-397, *Fire!,* 502J, 507, 509, *Blue Willow,* 568J, 575, 581
2 Personal Health	**Main Idea and Details**	
	Kid's Invention Book: T752–T753, T756, T759, T762, T764, T774- T775, *The Case of Pablo's Nose*: T801, *In the Days of King Adobe*: T837, *Fire*: T991	*The Kid's Invention Book*: 400I, 404, 410, 412, 420-421, *In the Days of King Adobe*: 438I, 442, 444, 452-453, A *Very Important Day*: 543D, 694
3 Food and Your Health	**Compare/Contrast**	
	Donovan's Word Jar, T76, *Lou Gehrig,* T170, *Stealing Home,* T558, T560, T566, *Red Writing Hood,* T878, *Fire!,* T984, *House, House,* T1078, *I Have Heard of a Land,* T1220, T1234, *The Down and Up Fall,* T1390	*Stealing Home,* 300I, 302, 306, 308, 314, 324–325, *Two Lands, One Heart,* 350I, 356, 358, 362, 370–371, *One Grain of Rice,* 472I, 478, 482, 484, 498–499
4 Fitness and Activity	**Cause and Effect**	
	The Gardener, T24, T36, *Charlotte's Web,* T394, T400, *Look to the North,* T646, T648, T656, *Fire!,* T984, T988, T990	*The Baker's Neighbor,* 150I, 154, 156, 158, 166, 172, 173, *The Garden of Happiness,* 230I, 232, 236, 238, 240, 250–251, *Look to the North,* 397B
5 Safe at Home	**Sequencing**	
	The Seven Children, T273, T278, T280, T287, *Nights of the Pufflings,* T358, *The Cricket in Times Square,* T608, *Blue Willow,* T1114, T1120, T1129, *I Have Heard of a Land,* T1228, *Two Lands, One Heart,* T1310	*Lou Gehrig,* 102J, 109, 113, *Nights of the Pufflings,* 206I, 210, 212, 214, 228–229, *How to Babysit an Orangutan,* 252I, 258, 260, 270–271, *Look to the North,* 372I, 380, 384, 396–397, *Fire!,* 502J, 507, 509, *Blue Willow,* 568J, 575, 581
6 Safe Away from Home	**Draw Conclusions**	
	The Garden of Happiness, T312, T314, T316, *Charlotte's Web,* T400, T406, *How to Babysit an Orangutan,* T450, T452, *Stealing Home,* T556, T568, *House, House,* T1068, T1070, T1072	*Sarah, Plain and Tall,* 274I, 276, 278, 280, 282, 284, 298–299, *The Cricket in Times Square,* 326I, 328, 332, 334, 348–349, *Red Writing Hood,* 471B

Correlations

Harcourt Health and Fitness Chapter	Reading Skill	
	***Collections*, Grade 4 (A Harcourt Reading Program)**	***Trophies*, Grade 4 (A Harcourt Reading Program)**
7 Guarding Against Disease	**Compare/Contrast**	
	Donovan's Word Jar, T76, *Lou Gehrig,* T170, *Stealing Home,* T558, T560, T566, *Red Writing Hood,* T878, *Fire!,* T984, *House, House,* T1078, *I Have Heard of a Land,* T1220, T1234, *The Down and Up Fall,* T1390	*Stealing Home,* 300I, 302, 306, 308, 314, 324–325, *Two Lands, One Heart,* 350I, 356, 358, 362, 370–371, *One Grain of Rice,* 472I, 478, 482, 484, 498–499
8 Medicines, Drugs, and Your Health	**Summarize**	
	The Seven Children, T273, T278, T280, T287, *Nights of the Pufflings,* T358, *The Cricket in Times Square,* T608, *Blue Willow,* T1114, T1120, T1129, *I Have Heard of a Land,* T1228, *Two Lands, One Heart,* T1310	*Lou Gehrig,* 102J, 109, 113, *Nights of the Pufflings,* 206I, 210, 212, 214, 228–229, *How to Babysit an Orangutan,* 252I, 258, 260, 270–271, *Look to the North,* 372I, 380, 384, 396–397, *Fire!,* 502J, 507, 509, *Blue Willow,* 568J, 575, 581
9 Harmful Effects of Tobacco and Alcohol	**Cause and Effect**	
	The Gardener, T24, T36, *Charlotte's Web,* T394, T400, *Look to the North,* T646, T648, T656, *Fire!,* T984, T988, T990	*The Baker's Neighbor,* 150I, 154, 156, 158, 166, 172, 173, *The Garden of Happiness,* 230I, 232, 236, 238, 240, 250–251, *Look to the North,* 397B
10 Your Needs and Feelings	**Main Idea and Details**	
	Kid's Invention Book: T752–T753, T756, T759, T762, T764, T774– T775, *The Case of Pablo's Nose*: T801, *In the Days of King Adobe*: T837, *Fire*: T991	*The Kid's Invention Book*: 400I, 404, 410, 412, 420–421, *In the Days of King Adobe*: 438I, 442, 444, 452–453, A *Very Important Day*: 543D, 694
11 Families Together	**Summarize**	
	The Seven Children, T273, T278, T280, T287, *Nights of the Pufflings,* T358, *The Cricket in Times Square,* T608, *Blue Willow,* T1114, T1120, T1129, *I Have Heard of a Land,* T1228, *Two Lands, One Heart,* T1310	*Lou Gehrig,* 102J, 109, 113, *Nights of the Pufflings,* 206I, 210, 212, 214, 228–229, *How to Babysit an Orangutan,* 252I, 258, 260, 270–271, *Look to the North,* 372I, 380, 384, 396–397, *Fire!,* 502J, 507, 509, *Blue Willow,* 568J, 575, 581
12 Living in a Healthful Community	**Draw Conclusions**	
	The Garden of Happiness, T312, T314, T316, *Charlotte's Web,* T400, T406, *How to Babysit an Orangutan,* T450, T452, *Stealing Home,* T556, T568, *House, House,* T1068, T1070, T1072	*Sarah, Plain and Tall,* 274I, 276, 278, 280, 282, 284, 298–299, *The Cricket in Times Square,* 326I, 328, 332, 334, 348–349, *Red Writing Hood,* 471B

National Health Education Standards

HEALTH EDUCATION STANDARD 1:

Students will comprehend concepts related to health promotion and disease prevention.

Rationale Basic to health education is a foundation of knowledge about the interrelationship of behavior and health, interactions within the human body, and the prevention of diseases and other health problems. Experiencing physical, mental, emotional and social changes as one grows and develops provides a self-contained "learning laboratory." Comprehension of health-promotion strategies and disease prevention concepts enables students to become health-literate, self-directed learners which establishes a foundation for leading healthy and productive lives.

PERFORMANCE INDICATORS:
As a result of health instruction in Grades K–4, students will:

	Indicator	Grade	Pages
1	describe relationships between personal health behaviors and individual well being.	Grade K:	12, 14, 22–29, 48–55, 74–85, 92–103, 164–169
		Grade 1:	26–29, 43–59, 102–127, 130–141, 164–181, 205
		Grade 2:	9, 15, 16, 17, 25–28, 32–33, 34–35, 42–43, 64–85, 88–103
		Grade 3:	30–55, 86–102, 126–140, 164–166, 216–231
		Grade 4:	32-57, 92–110, 136–152, 248–276, 282–298
2	identify indicators of mental, emotional, social and physical health during childhood.	Grade K:	14, 15, 23, 24, 25, 29, 75, 76, 77, 79, 81, 82, 83, 84, 85, 92, 93, 94, 95, 96, 97, 99, 100, 101, 157
		Grade 1:	28, 29, 31, 35, 37, 49, 52–53, 55, 74–75, 87, 90, 92–93, 96, 99, 103, 109, 112, 116, 134–135, 147, 150–151, 155, 178-179, 192–193, 211, 213, 214–215, 230–231
		Grade 2:	27, 36–37, 42, 56–57, 94–95, 131–133, 139, 218–229
		Grade 3:	22-23, 116–117, 156–157, 206–207, 231, 233–236, 250–251, 272–273
		Grade 4:	10–11, 33, 39, 40, 46–47, 49, 53, 76–77, 104–105, 123, 126–127, 129, 137, 139, 146–147, 149, 150, 172–173, 198, 199, 234–235, 250, 253, 257, 261, 266–267, 271, 275, 284, 289, 290, 292–293, 296, 297, 322–333
3	describe the basic structure and functions of the human body systems.	Grade K:	2, 8, 10, 11, 22, 23, 24, 25, 27, 36, 39, 64, 65, 111
		Grade 1:	10–17
		Grade 2:	6–17
		Grade 3:	4–13
		Grade 4:	2–27
4	describe how the family influences personal health.	Grade K:	75, 85, 117, 152–157
		Grade 1:	167–168
		Grade 2:	36–37, 45, 58–59, 103, 129, 132–133, 139–141, 148–151, 161, 212–213, 215–216, 230–231, 232–233, 234–235, 245
		Grade 3:	242–254
		Grade 4:	107, 116, 118–125, 141, 282–298
5	describe how physical, social and emotional environments influence personal health.	Grade K:	74–85, 95–103, 110–117, 152–157
		Grade 1:	42–59, 130–141, 282–298
		Grade 2:	25–26, 27–31, 188–207
		Grade 3:	86–102, 164–165, 216–236
		Grade 4:	32–57, 158–182, 248–276, 282–298
6	identify common health problems of children.	Grade K:	110–117
		Grade 1:	42–59, 146–149
		Grade 2:	28–31, 34–35, 146–163
		Grade 3:	34–39, 78–80, 146–166
		Grade 4:	32–57, 158–182

PERFORMANCE INDICATORS: As a result of health instruction in Grades K–4, students will:		
7	identify health problems that should be detected and treated early.	**Grade K:** 110–117 **Grade 1:** 42–59, 146–159 **Grade 2:** 28–31, 146–163 **Grade 3:** 34–39, 146–166 **Grade 4:** 158–182
8	explain how childhood injuries and illnesses can be prevented or treated.	**Grade K:** 10, 12, 14, 22–29, 48–55, 74–85, 95–103, 110–117, 124–127 **Grade 1:** 26–29, 130–141, 146–159 **Grade 2:** 9, 17, 25–26, 28–31, 33, 124–143, 146–153 **Grade 3:** 34–39, 106–119, 126–140, 146–166 **Grade 4:** 114–133, 136–152, 158–182
As a result of health instruction in Grades 5–8, students will:		
1	explain the relationship between positive health behaviors and the prevention of injury, illness, disease and premature death.	**Grade 5:** 38–67, 72–106, 110–121, 138–166, 188–222, 228–237, 289–316, 324–331, 345–368 **Grade 6:** 4–36, 41–74, 118–140, 144–172, 176–200, 204–241, 246–251, 294–295, 332–333, 334–349
2	describe the interrelationship of mental, emotional, social and physical health during adolescence.	**Grade 5:** 2–34, 38–51, 73, 92–94 **Grade 6:** 20–36, 41–74
3	explain how health is influenced by the interaction of body systems.	**Grade 5:** 2–34, 38–51, 73, 118–121 **Grade 6:** 4–11, 20–25, 204–241
4	describe how family and peers influence the health of adolescents.	**Grade 5:** 30–31, 58–59, 124–125, 160–161, 230–231, 292–293, 298–303, 321–340, 354–358 **Grade 6:** 32–33, 135, 178–181, 294–295, 328–333
5	analyze how environment and personal health are interrelated.	**Grade 5:** 90, 323, 345–368, 376–397 **Grade 6:** 41, 46–47, 376–397
6	describe ways to reduce risks related to adolescent health problems.	**Grade 5:** 38–43, 58–59, 92–94, 110–132, 138–166, 188–222, 306–311 **Grade 6:** 126–127, 138–166, 214–216, 345–368
7	explain how appropriate health care can prevent premature death and disability.	**Grade 5:** 126–127, 138–166, 214–216, 345–368 **Grade 6:** 118–140, 144–172, 176–200, 298–301, 386–397
8	describe how lifestyle, pathogens, family history and other risk factors are related to the cause or prevention of disease and other health problems.	**Grade 5:** 41, 46, 50, 53, 54, 56, 58–59, 93–94, 188–222, 259–284, 306–311, 345–368 **Grade 6:** 41, 46–47, 144–172, 204–241, 278–303, 322–327, 354–358

HEALTH EDUCATION STANDARD 2:

Students will demonstrate the ability to access valid health information and health-promoting products and services.

Rationale Accessing valid health information and health-promoting products and services is important in the prevention, early detection, and treatment of most health problems. Critical thinking involves the ability to identify valid health information and to analyze, select, and access health-promoting services and products. Applying skills of information analysis, organization, comparison, synthesis and evaluation to health issues provides a foundation for individuals to move toward becoming health literate and responsible, productive citizens.

PERFORMANCE INDICATORS:

As a result of health instruction in Grades K–4, students will:

1	**identify characteristics of valid health information and health-promoting products and services.**	**Grade K:** 124–131 **Grade 1:** 25, 30–35, 164–169 **Grade 2:** 38–41 **Grade 3:** 46–49, 50–54, 72–75 **Grade 4:** 8, 108
2	**demonstrate the ability to locate resources from home, school and community that provide valid health information.**	**Grade K:** 37, 74–85, 124–131, 164–169 **Grade 1:** 25, 30–35 **Grade 2:** 38–41, 228–245 **Grade 3:** 46–49, 50–54, 64–75, 95, 97, 242–254, 260–263 **Grade 4:** 8, 114–133, 190–192
3	**explain how media influences the selection of health information, products and services.**	**Grade K:** No correlation **Grade 1:** 25, 30–35 **Grade 2:** 38–41 **Grade 3:** 46–49, 50–55, 108 **Grade 4:** 48–50, 52–55
4	**demonstrate the ability to locate school and community health helpers.**	**Grade K:** 74–85, 117, 124–131, 164–169 **Grade 1:** 34, 56–57 **Grade 2:** 150–151, 155–156, 228–245 **Grade 3:** 150, 153, 223, 260–263 **Grade 4:** 48–55, 114–133

As a result of health instruction in Grades 5–8, students will:

1	**analyze the validity of health information, products, and services.**	**Grade 5:** 11, 33, 38–67, 91, 96–99, 230–231, 234–235, 282–284, 345–368 **Grade 6:** 48–59, 70–74, 226–227, 246–251, 296–297
2	**demonstrate the ability to utilize resources from home, school, and community that provide valid health information.**	**Grade 5:** 33, 38–67, 91, 230–231, 234–235, 282–284, 321–340, 345–368 **Grade 6:** 70–74, 174–200, 222–226, 246–251, 385
3	**analyze how media influences the selection of health information and products.**	**Grade 5:** 11, 38–67, 91, 96–99, 278–279, 296–297 **Grade 6:** 2, 25, 48–53, 62, 70, 74, 136, 139, 250, 294, 296, 304, 333
4	**demonstrate the ability to locate health products and services.**	**Grade 5:** 33, 38–67, 91, 96–99, 234–235, 282–284, 345–368 **Grade 6:** 48–59, 70–74, 222–226, 246–251, 304–306
5	**compare the costs and validity of health products.**	**Grade 5:** 33, 38–67, 91, 96–99, 234–235, 282–284, 345–368 **Grade 6:** 48–59, 70–74, 222–226, 246–251, 304–306

	As a result of health instruction in Grades 5–8, students will:	
6	**describe situations requiring professional health services.**	**Grade 5:** 41, 50–51, 53, 56, 188–222 **Grade 6:** 176–200, 210–211, 302–303, 334–335

HEALTH EDUCATION STANDARD 3:

Students will demonstrate the ability to practice health-enhancing behaviors and reduce health risks.

Rationale Research confirms that many diseases and injuries can be prevented by reducing harmful and risk taking behaviors. More importantly, recognizing and practicing health enhancing behaviors can contribute to a positive quality of life. Strategies used to maintain and improve positive health behaviors will utilize knowledge and skills that help students become critical thinkers and problem solvers. By accepting responsibility for personal health, students will have a foundation for living a healthy, productive life.

	PERFORMANCE INDICATORS: As a result of health instruction in Grades K–4, students will:	
1	**identify responsible health behaviors.**	**Grade K:** 10, 12, 14, 22–29, 48–55, 74–85, 95–103, 110–117, 124–127 **Grade 1:** 24, 32, 37, 42, 47, 84, 87, 104, 123, 125, 135, 137, 141, 149, 153, 157, 159, 196–197, 204, 212, 215, 235 **Grade 2:** 2, 15, 16, 17, 25–26, 27–31, 33–35, 41, 42–63, 64–85, 88–103, 126–127, 128–129, 130–131, 134–137, 138–191, 230–231 **Grade 3:** 24–25, 30–57, 60–81, 86–102, 164–165, 282–298 **Grade 4:** 32-57, 92–110, 114–133, 135–152, 198–199, 248–276
2	**identify personal health needs.**	**Grade K:** 22–29, 48–55, 124–127 **Grade 1:** 26–29, 42–59, 130–141 **Grade 2:** 15, 16, 25–27, 33, 42–43, 48–63, 64–85, 88–103 **Grade 3:** 24–25, 30–57, 60–81, 86–102, 106–119, 164–165 **Grade 4:** 32-59, 92–110, 248–276
3	**compare behaviors that are safe to those that are risky or harmful.**	**Grade K:** 10, 12, 14, 22–29, 36–39, 48–55, 95–103, 128–131, 152–157 **Grade 1:** 26–29, 42–59, 104–127, 130–141, 164–181 **Grade 2:** 9, 17, 25–27, 28–31, 48–63, 124–143, 166–185 **Grade 3:** 33, 39, 106–119, 126–140, 196–270 **Grade 4:** 32-57, 114–133, 136–152, 194–197, 188–215, 218–242
4	**demonstrate strategies to improve or maintain personal health.**	**Grade K:** 10, 12, 14, 22–29, 36–39, 48–55, 95–103, 124–127 **Grade 1:** 26–29, 42–59, 104–127, 130–141, 188–202 **Grade 2:** 15, 16, 25–27, 28–31, 33, 41, 42–43, 48–63, 64–85, 88–103 **Grade 3:** 30–57, 86–102, 106–119, 164–166 **Grade 4:** 32–57, 92–110, 248–276
5	**develop injury prevention and management strategies for personal health.**	**Grade K:** 10, 12, 14, 36–39, 74–85, 95–103, 104–127, 130–141 **Grade 1:** 42–59 **Grade 2:** 9, 17, 25–27, 33, 124–143 **Grade 3:** 106–119, 126–140 **Grade 4:** 92–110, 114–133, 136–152
6	**demonstrate ways to avoid and reduce threatening situations.**	**Grade K:** 10, 12, 14, 22–29, 36–39, 48–55, 74–85, 94–103, 128–131, 152–157 **Grade 1:** 26–29, 42–59, 104–127, 130–141, 164–181 **Grade 2:** 9, 17, 25–27, 28–31, 48–63, 124–143, 166–185 **Grade 3:** 33, 39, 106–119, 126–140, 196–270 **Grade 4:** 32–57, 114–133, 136–152, 194–215, 218–242

	PERFORMANCE INDICATORS: As a result of health instruction in Grades K–4, students will:	
7	apply skills to manage stress.	**Grade K:** 28–29, 152–157 **Grade 1:** 90–93, 122–123, 192–193 **Grade 2:** 92, 132, 172, 198, 217, 223 **Grade 3:** 112–113, 116–117, 222–227 **Grade 4:** 146–147
	As a result of health instruction in Grades 5–8, students will:	
1	explain the importance of assuming responsibility for personal health behaviors.	**Grade 5:** 22, 30–31, 72–106, 110–132, 219, 274–277, 327–331, 334–340 **Grade 6:** 4–36, 41–74, 118–140, 176–200, 346, 349, 374
2	analyze a personal health assessment to determine health strengths and risks.	**Grade 5:** 234–244, 332–333, 345–368 **Grade 6:** 41, 46–47, 118–140
3	distinguish between safe and risky or harmful behaviors in relationships.	**Grade 5:** 84–85, 91–92, 102, 170–184, 259–284, 332–333, 345–368 **Grade 6:** 41, 46–47, 250–252, 350–355
4	demonstrate strategies to improve or maintain personal and family health.	**Grade 5:** 28, 100–101, 124–125, 294–296, 354–365 **Grade 6:** 41–74, 118–140, 311–319
5	develop injury prevention and management strategies for personal and family health.	**Grade 5:** 126–127, 259–284 **Grade 6:** 118–140, 144–172, 176–200, 246–251, 386–397
6	demonstrate ways to avoid and reduce threatening situations.	**Grade 5:** 170–184, 332–333 **Grade 6:** 166–172
7	demonstrate strategies to manage stress.	**Grade 5:** 92, 170–184, 210–211, 304–311, 332–333 **Grade 6:** 166–172, 212–213, 238–239, 322–327, 354–358

HEALTH EDUCATION STANDARD 4:

Students will analyze the influence of culture, media, technology and other factors on health.

Rationale Health is influenced by a variety of factors that co-exist within society. These include the cultural context as well as media and technology. A critical thinker and problem solver is able to analyze, evaluate and interpret the influence of these factors on health. The health literate, responsible and productive citizen draws upon the contributions of culture, media, technology and other factors to strengthen individual, family and community health.

PERFORMANCE INDICATORS: As a result of health instruction in Grades K–4, students will:		
1	**describe how culture influences personal health behaviors.**	**Grade K:** 49, 63 **Grade 1:** 20, 96, 117 **Grade 2:** 70, 102, 135, 178, 193, 215 **Grade 3:** 39 **Grade 4:** 16, 34, 268–269
2	**explain how media influences thoughts, feelings, and health behaviors.**	**Grade K:** 124–131 **Grade 1:** 25, 30–35, 164–169 **Grade 2:** 38–41 **Grade 3:** 46–49, 50–54, 72–75 **Grade 4:** 8, 108
3	**describe ways technology can influence personal health.**	**Grade K:** No correlation **Grade 1:** 5, 28, 33, 45, 90, 139, 148, 154, 208 **Grade 2:** 58–59, 240–243 **Grade 3:** 27, 55, 81, 103, 121, 141, 167, 211, 237, 255, 279 **Grade 4:** 27, 55, 87, 95, 111, 131, 153, 183, 213, 243, 277, 299, 327
4	**explain how information from school and family influences health.**	**Grade K:** 37, 117, 164–169 **Grade 1:** 164–181, 204–217 **Grade 2:** 98, 188–203 **Grade 3:** 46–49, 222–223, 228–229, 242–254 **Grade 4:** 8, 114–133, 282–298
As a result of health instruction in Grades 5–8, students will:		
1	**describe the influence of cultural beliefs on health behaviors and the use of health services.**	**Grade 5:** 20, 21, 51, 88–91, 272 **Grade 6:** 19
2	**analyze how messages from media and other sources influence health behaviors.**	**Grade 5:** 11, 38–67, 91, 96–99, 278–279, 296–297 **Grade 6:** 2, 25, 48–53, 62, 70, 74, 136, 139, 250, 294, 296, 304, 333
3	**analyze the influence of technology on personal and family health.**	**Grade 5:** 6, 35, 65, 97, 107, 133, 162, 167, 185, 223, 255, 285, 317, 341 **Grade 6:** 66–69, 113
4	**analyze how information from peers influences health.**	**Grade 5:** 175, 178, 181, 292–293, 298–305, 312–313 **Grade 6:** 19, 65, 159, 252–254, 328–333

HEALTH EDUCATION STANDARD 5:

Students will demonstrate the ability to use interpersonal communication skills to enhance health.

Rationale Personal, family, and community health are enhanced through effective communication. A responsible individual will use verbal and non-verbal skills in developing and maintaining healthy personal relationships. Ability to organize and to convey information, beliefs, opinions, and feelings are skills which strengthen interactions and can reduce or avoid conflict. When communicating, individuals who are health literate, demonstrate care, consideration, and respect of self and others.

PERFORMANCE INDICATORS:
As a result of health instruction in Grades K–4, students will:

	Indicator	Grade	Pages
1	**distinguish between verbal and non-verbal communication.**	**Grade K:**	75, 111, 141, 155
		Grade 1:	7, 11, 15, 17, 33, 40, 51, 57, 58, 60, 61, 65, 73, 77, 79, 80, 87, 91, 97, 99, 101, 103, 116, 133, 137, 139, 142, 149, 155, 157, 159, 163, 169, 171, 173, 175, 177, 180, 183, 187, 195, 199, 200, 207, 209, 213, 219, 225, 229, 233, 234, 237
		Grade 2:	29, 31, 35, 41, 42, 50, 55, 59, 63, 93, 99, 101, 102, 105, 120, 127, 131, 137, 141, 145, 149, 155, 159, 161, 162, 165, 217, 224, 227, 231, 235, 247
		Grade 3:	29, 31, 35, 41, 42, 55, 59, 63, 93, 99, 101, 102, 105, 127, 131, 137, 141, 145, 149, 155, 159, 161, 162, 165, 217, 219, 224, 227, 231, 235, 247
		Grade 4:	9, 14, 19, 23, 29, 35, 41, 45, 50, 54, 57, 64, 71, 75, 83, 86, 89, 96, 110, 113, 120, 125, 130, 133, 140, 145, 152, 155, 160, 165, 171, 179, 182, 185, 193, 197, 204, 209, 215, 223, 229, 233, 238, 242, 245, 251, 255, 259, 265, 272, 276, 279, 286, 291, 298, 307, 310, 315, 321, 326, 329
2	**describe characteristics needed to be a responsible friend and family member.**	**Grade K:**	29, 62–63, 74–77, 82–85, 94–95, 96–103, 117, 152–157
		Grade 1:	24, 32, 37, 42, 47, 84, 87, 104, 123, 125, 135, 137, 141, 149, 153, 157, 159, 196–197, 204, 212, 215, 235
		Grade 2:	98, 188–203, 210–225
		Grade 3:	17, 51, 222–223, 228–229, 242–254
		Grade 4:	46–47, 141, 205, 260–265, 273, 282–298
3	**demonstrate healthy ways to express needs, wants, and feelings.**	**Grade K:**	9, 11, 12, 13, 15, 23, 24, 25, 26, 27, 28, 29, 36, 37, 38, 39, 40, 41, 49, 51, 52, 53, 55, 62, 63, 64, 66, 67, 74, 75, 76, 77, 83, 84, 85, 94, 97, 98, 101, 103, 110, 113, 115, 117, 124, 125, 126, 128, 129, 130, 131, 152, 153, 154, 155, 156, 157, 164, 165, 166, 167, 168, 169
		Grade 1:	7, 9, 11, 13, 17, 20, 23, 29, 33, 35, 38, 41, 47, 51, 55, 57, 58, 59, 61, 64, 65, 68, 69, 72, 73, 75, 77, 79, 80, 83, 87, 91, 92, 93, 97, 99, 100, 101, 103, 105, 107, 109, 111, 112, 116, 119, 121, 122, 123, 125, 133, 135, 137, 139, 140, 141, 145, 151, 153, 157, 159, 160, 163, 169, 171, 173, 175, 177, 179, 180, 181, 183, 187, 188, 191, 193, 195, 199, 200, 201, 203, 207, 209, 211, 213, 215, 217, 223, 225, 227, 229, 231, 233, 234, 235, 237
		Grade 2:	98, 188–203
		Grade 3:	22–23, 116–117, 156–157, 206–207, 231, 233–236, 250–251, 272–273
		Grade 4:	8, 15, 18, 21, 22, 34, 40, 44, 49, 51, 53, 146–148, 198–199, 205, 260–265, 282–298
4	**demonstrate ways to communicate care, consideration, and respect of self and others.**	**Grade K:**	29, 62–63, 74–77, 82–85, 94–95, 96–103, 117, 152–157
		Grade 1:	24, 32, 37, 42, 47, 84, 87, 104, 123, 125, 135, 137, 141, 149, 153, 157, 159, 196–197, 204, 212, 215, 235
		Grade 2:	29, 39, 61, 103, 132–133, 150–151, 188–203, 214–217
		Grade 3:	22–23, 116–117, 156–157, 206–207, 231, 233–236, 250–251, 272–273
		Grade 4:	141, 146–148, 260–265, 282–298

PERFORMANCE INDICATORS: As a result of health instruction in Grades K–4, students will:		
5	demonstrate attentive listening skills to build and maintain healthy relationships.	**Grade K:** 14, 15, 23, 24, 25, 29, 75, 76, 77, 79, 81, 82, 83, 84, 85, 92, 93, 94, 95, 96, 97, 99, 100, 101, 157 **Grade 1:** 28, 29, 31, 35, 37, 49, 52–53, 55, 74–75, 87, 90, 92–93, 96, 99, 103, 109, 112, 116, 134–135, 147, 150–151, 155, 178–179, 192–193, 211, 213, 214–215, 230–231 **Grade 2:** 36–37, 42, 56–57, 94–95, 131–133, 139, 218–219 **Grade 3:** 22–23, 116–117, 156–157, 206–207, 231, 233–236, 250–251, 272–273 **Grade 4:** 10–11, 33, 39, 40, 46–47, 49, 53, 76–77, 104–105, 123, 126–127, 129, 137, 139, 146–147, 149, 150, 172–173, 198, 199, 234–235, 250, 253, 257, 261, 266–267, 271, 275, 284, 289, 290, 292–293, 296, 297, 322–333
6	demonstrate refusal skills to enhance health.	**Grade K:** 74–85, 94–95, 128–131 **Grade 1:** 35, 122–125, 130–141, 164–165, 172–179 **Grade 2:** 129, 166–185 **Grade 3:** 128, 206–210 **Grade 4:** 141, 149–150, 198–199, 206–209, 234–235, 276
7	differentiate between negative and positive behaviors used in conflict situations.	**Grade K:** 14, 15, 23, 24, 25, 29, 75, 76, 77, 79, 81, 82, 83, 84, 85, 92, 93, 94, 95, 96, 97, 99, 100, 101, 157 **Grade 1:** 28, 29, 31, 35, 37, 49, 52–53, 55, 74–75, 87, 90, 92–93, 96, 99, 103, 109, 112, 116, 134–135, 147, 150–151, 155, 178–179, 192–193, 211, 213, 214–215, 230–231 **Grade 2:** 27, 36–37, 42, 56–57, 94–95, 131–133, 139, 218–229 **Grade 3:** 22–23, 116–117, 156–157, 206–207, 231, 233–236, 250–251, 272–273 **Grade 4:** 10–11, 33, 39, 40, 46–47, 49, 53, 76–77, 104–105, 123, 126–127, 129, 137, 139, 146–147, 149, 150, 172–173, 198, 199, 234–235, 250, 253, 257, 261, 266–267, 271, 275, 284, 289, 290, 292–293, 296, 297, 322–333
8	demonstrate non-violent strategies to resolve conflicts.	**Grade K:** 14, 15, 23, 24, 25, 29, 75, 76, 77, 79, 81, 82, 83, 84, 85, 92, 93, 94, 95, 96, 97, 99, 100, 101, 157 **Grade 1:** 28, 29, 31, 35, 37, 49, 52–53, 55, 74–75, 87, 90, 92–93, 96, 99, 103, 109, 112, 116, 134–135, 147, 150–151, 155, 178–179, 192–193, 211, 213, 214–215, 230–231 **Grade 2:** 27, 36–37, 42, 56–57, 94–95, 131–133, 139, 218–229 **Grade 3:** 22–23, 116–117, 156–157, 206–207, 231, 233–236, 250–251, 272–273 **Grade 4:** 10–11, 33, 39, 40, 46–47, 49, 53, 76–77, 104–105, 123, 126–127, 129, 137, 139, 146–147, 149, 150, 172–173, 198, 199, 234–235, 250, 253, 257, 261, 266–267, 271, 275, 284, 289, 290, 292–293, 296, 297, 322–333
As a result of health instruction in Grades 5–8, students will:		
1	demonstrate effective verbal and non-verbal communication skills to enhance health.	**Grade 5:** 11, 21, 27, 44, 88, 92, 95, 96, 98, 145, 205, 233, 252–255, 272, 307 **Grade 6:** 19, 27, 36, 47, 53, 59, 69, 74, 125, 134, 140, 151, 158, 165, 172, 183, 192, 200, 256, 272, 283, 293, 299, 306, 315, 325, 338, 351, 358
2	describe how the behavior of family and peers affects interpersonal communication.	**Grade 5:** 30–31, 58–59, 175, 180–182, 230, 252–253, 273, 321–340 **Grade 6:** 30–31, 52, 54–55, 65, 135, 159, 176–200, 294–295, 334–349
3	demonstrate healthy ways to express needs, wants and feelings.	**Grade 5:** 30–31, 58–59, 206–207, 230, 328–331 **Grade 6:** 28–33, 159, 176–200, 320–327
4	demonstrate ways to communicate care, consideration, and respect of self and others.	**Grade 5:** 30–31, 58–59, 175, 230, 252–254, 273, 328–331 **Grade 6:** 19, 65, 135, 159, 184–185, 273–274, 332–333, 352–353

As a result of health instruction in Grades 5–8, students will:		
5	**demonstrate communication skills to build and maintain healthy relationships.**	**Grade 5:** 30–31, 58–59, 175, 206–207, 230, 273, 328–331 **Grade 6:** 19, 32–33, 65, 273–274, 304–306, 332–333, 352–353
6	**demonstrate refusal and negotiation skills to enhance health.**	**Grade 5:** 176–177, 246–251, 274–277, 332–333 **Grade 6:** 165–172, 252–256, 268–272
7	**analyze the possible causes of conflict among youth in schools and communities.**	**Grade 5:** 30–31, 178–179, 332–333 **Grade 6:** 166–172, 350–353
8	**demonstrate strategies to manage conflict in healthy ways.**	**Grade 5:** 30–31, 176–177, 332–333 **Grade 6:** 166–172, 350–353

HEALTH EDUCATION STANDARD 6:

Students will demonstrate the ability to use goal-setting and decision-making skills to enhance health.

Rationale Decision making and goal setting are essential lifelong skills needed in order to implement and sustain health-enhancing behaviors. These skills make it possible for individuals to transfer health knowledge into healthy lifestyles. When applied to health issues, decision-making and goal-setting skills will enable individuals to collaborate with others to improve the quality of life in their families, schools and communities.

PERFORMANCE INDICATORS: As a result of health instruction in Grades K–4, students will:		
1	**demonstrate the ability to apply a decision-making process to health issues and problems.**	**Grade K:** 10, 12, 14, 92 **Grade 1:** 42–59, 107, 124, 146–159, 164–181 **Grade 2:** 18–19, 25, 41–43, 53, 56–57, 73, 92 **Grade 3:** 23, 41, 50, 51, 91, 109, 117, 123, 251, 253 **Grade 4:** 104–105, 114–133, 141, 248–276
2	**explain when to ask for assistance in making health-related decisions and setting health goals.**	**Grade K:** 26–27, 37, 74–85, 117, 124–127 **Grade 1:** 7, 23, 38, 41, 59, 73, 83, 93, 100, 109, 125, 137, 145, 151, 163, 171, 183, 193, 209, 211, 223, 231, 237 **Grade 2:** 59, 61, 169–170 **Grade 3:** 27, 243, 249, 254 **Grade 4:** 141
3	**predict outcomes of positive health decisions.**	**Grade K:** 10, 12, 14, 22–29, 48–55, 74–85, 95–103, 110–117, 124–127 **Grade 1:** 24, 32, 37, 42, 47, 84, 87, 104, 123, 125, 135, 137, 141, 149, 153, 157, 159, 196–197, 204, 212, 215, 235 **Grade 2:** 2, 15, 16, 17, 25–26, 27–31, 33–35, 41, 42–63, 64–85, 88–103, 126–127, 128–129, 130–131, 134–137, 138–191, 230–231 **Grade 3:** 24–25, 30–57, 60–81, 86–102, 164–165, 282–298 **Grade 4:** 32–57, 92–110, 114–133, 135–152, 198–199, 248–276
4	**set a personal health goal and track progress toward its achievement.**	**Grade K:** 10, 12, 14, 92 **Grade 1:** 42–59, 107, 124, 146–159, 164–181 **Grade 2:** 18–19, 25, 41–43, 53, 56–57, 73, 92 **Grade 3:** 23, 41, 50, 51, 91, 109, 117, 123, 251, 253 **Grade 4:** 104–105, 114–133, 141, 248–276

Education Resource Center
University of Delaware
Newark, DE 19716-2940

	As a result of health instruction in Grades 5–8, students will:	
1	**demonstrate the ability to apply a decision-making process to health issues and problems individually and collaboratively.**	**Grade 5:** 30–31, 38–67, 188–222, 321–340, 345–368 **Grade 6:** 204–241, 273–274, 287, 302–303, 307, 334–335, 352–358, 386–397
2	**analyze how health-related decisions are influenced by individuals, family, and community values.**	**Grade 5:** 30–31, 38–67, 188–222, 321–340, 345–368 **Grade 6:** 204–241, 273–274, 287, 302–303, 307, 334–335, 352–358, 386–397
3	**predict how decisions regarding health behaviors have consequences for self and others.**	**Grade 5:** 30–31, 38–67, 188–222, 321–340, 345–368 **Grade 6:** 204–241, 273–274, 287, 302–303, 307, 334–335, 352–358, 386–397
4	**apply strategies and skills needed to attain personal health goals.**	**Grade 5:** 28, 100–101, 124–125, 294–296, 354–365 **Grade 6:** 41–74, 118–140, 311–319
5	**describe how personal health goals are influenced by changing information, abilities, priorities, and responsibilities.**	**Grade 5:** 28, 100–101, 124–125, 294–296, 354–365 **Grade 6:** 41–74, 118–140, 311–319
6	**develop a plan that addresses personal strengths, needs, and health risks.**	**Grade 5:** 28, 100–101, 124–125, 294–296, 354–365 **Grade 6:** 41–74, 118–140, 311–319

HEALTH EDUCATION STANDARD 7:

Students will demonstrate the ability to advocate for personal, family and community health.

Rationale Quality of life is dependent on an environment that protects and promotes the health of individuals, families, and communities. Responsible citizens, who are health literate, are characterized by advocating and communicating for positive health in their communities. A variety of health advocacy skills are critical to these activities.

	PERFORMANCE INDICATORS: As a result of health instruction in Grades K–4, students will:	
1	**describe a variety of methods to convey accurate health information and ideas.**	**Grade K:** 8, 12, 14, 22, 26, 40, 48, 50, 62, 64, 65, 66, 76, 78, 80, 82, 84, 92, 94, 96, 98, 100, 102, 110, 112, 114, 116, 124, 126, 128, 130, 152, 154, 156, 164, 166, 168 **Grade 1:** 7, 9, 11, 13, 17, 20, 23, 29, 33, 35, 38, 41, 47, 51, 55, 57, 58, 59, 61, 64, 65, 68, 69, 72, 73, 75, 77, 79, 80, 83, 87, 91, 92, 93, 97, 99, 100, 101, 103, 105, 107, 109, 111, 112, 116, 119, 121, 122, 123, 125, 133, 135, 137, 139, 140, 141, 145, 151, 153, 157, 159, 160, 163, 169, 171, 173, 175, 177, 179, 180, 181, 183, 187, 188, 191, 193, 195, 199, 200, 201, 203, 207, 209, 211, 213, 215, 217, 223, 225, 227, 229, 231, 233, 234, 235, 237 **Grade 2:** 9, 98, 180–203, 228–245 **Grade 3:** 22–23, 116–117, 156–157, 206–207, 231, 233–236, 250–251, 272–273 **Grade 4:** 8, 15, 18, 21, 22, 34, 40, 44, 49, 51, 53, 146–148, 198–199, 205, 260–265, 282–298

PERFORMANCE INDICATORS: As a result of health instruction in Grades K–4, students will:		
2	express information and opinions about health issues.	**Grade K:** 79, 83, 85, 153, 157 **Grade 1:** 164–181, 184–201, 204–218 **Grade 2:** 35, 42, 44, 55, 59, 60, 63, 93, 99, 101, 105, 127, 129, 131, 137, 141, 145, 149, 155, 159, 161, 165, 213, 217, 223, 227, 231, 237, 243, 247 **Grade 3:** 5, 7, 13, 16, 18, 21, 26, 33, 35, 37, 39, 40, 42, 45, 46, 49, 53, 54, 61, 63, 67, 70, 74, 75, 90, 95, 97, 102, 110, 114, 115, 120, 128, 133, 138, 140, 147, 151, 155, 162, 166, 199, 200, 205, 210, 221, 223, 225, 232, 236, 242, 244, 247, 249, 254, 263, 271, 276, 277, 278 **Grade 4:** 9, 14, 19, 23, 26, 35, 41, 45, 50, 54, 64, 67, 75, 83, 84, 86, 94, 96, 103, 125, 130, 140, 145, 152, 160, 165, 171, 179, 182, 189, 193, 195, 197, 201, 204, 207, 209, 210, 212, 223, 229, 233, 236, 238, 242, 251, 253, 255, 259, 265, 272, 276, 283, 286, 291, 297, 298, 307, 308, 310, 315, 321, 326
3	identify community agencies that advocate for healthy individuals, families, and communities.	**Grade K:** 39, 74–85, 164–169, 222–236 **Grade 1:** 114, 119, 126, 131, 220–235 **Grade 2:** 232–235 **Grade 3:** 64–67, 137–138, 210–211, 260–263, 279 **Grade 4:** 52–55, 117–118, 131, 144, 153, 271, 277, 304–327
4	demonstrate the ability to influence and support others in making positive health choices.	**Grade K:** 14, 15, 23, 24, 25, 29, 75, 76, 77, 79, 81, 82, 83, 84, 85, 92, 93, 94, 95, 96, 97, 99, 100, 101, 152–157, 164–169, 220–235 **Grade 1:** 28, 29, 31, 35, 37, 42–59, 74–75, 87, 90, 92–93, 96, 99, 103, 104–127, 134–135, 147, 150–151, 155, 178–179, 192–193, 211, 213, 214–215, 230–231 **Grade 2:** 9, 10, 15, 17, 25, 27, 36–37, 41, 42, 56–57, 94–95, 131–133, 139, 188–203, 218–245 **Grade 3:** 22–23, 89–91, 95, 116–117, 156–157, 163, 206–207, 231, 233–236, 250–251, 260–279 **Grade 4:** 10–11, 33, 39, 40, 46–47, 49, 53, 76–77, 97, 104–105, 123, 126–127, 129, 137, 139, 141, 146–147, 149, 150, 172–173, 198, 199, 234–235, 250, 253, 257, 261, 266–267, 271, 275, 284, 289, 290, 292–293, 296, 297, 322–333
As a result of health instruction in Grades 5–8, students will:		
1	analyze various communication methods to accurately express health information and ideas.	**Grade 5:** 11, 38–67, 91, 96–99, 296–297 **Grade 6:** 2, 25, 48–53, 62, 70, 74, 136, 139, 250, 294, 296, 304, 333
2	express information and opinions about health issues.	**Grade 5:** 29, 33, 39, 42, 46, 48, 51, 57, 61, 66, 83, 96, 111, 116, 130, 133, 153, 195, 218, 240 **Grade 6:** 32–33, 294–295, 302–303, 334–335, 386–397
3	identify barriers to effective communication of information, ideas, feelings, and opinions about health issues.	**Grade 5:** 15, 25, 27, 30–31, 58–59, 100–101, 114, 124–125, 140–143, 147, 158–159, 160–163, 171–175, 176–179, 180–181, 183, 210–211, 240, 248, 250, 251, 264, 276, 277, 281, 307, 308, 309, 311, 314–316, 334–335, 348, 357, 361, 362–363, 364–365 **Grade 6:** 8, 10, 16, 32–33, 45, 46, 49, 54–55, 67, 73, 126–127, 149, 150, 153, 155, 166–167, 170, 179, 181, 184–185, 189, 191, 210, 213, 230, 237, 268–269, 295, 300–301, 326–327, 336–337, 345, 352–353, 355, 366, 368, 372, 378, 382, 393
4	demonstrate the ability to influence and support others in making positive health choices.	**Grade 5:** 265, 273, 275, 280–281, 324–326, 332–333 **Grade 6:** 32–33, 302–306, 352–353
5	demonstrate the ability to work cooperatively when advocating for healthy individuals, families, and schools.	**Grade 5:** 90, 323, 345–368, 376–397 **Grade 6:** 41, 46–47, 376–397